HANDBOOK OF SPECTROSCOPY

Handbook of Spectroscopy

Volume I

Editor

J. W. Robinson
Department of Chemistry
Louisiana State University
Baton Rouge, La

published by:

CRC PRESS

18901 Cranwood Parkway, Cleveland, Ohio 44128

HANDBOOK OF SPECTROSCOPY
VOLUME I

International Standard Book Number (ISBN)

Complete Set 0-87819-333-2
Volume I 0-87819-331-6

Library of Congress Catalog Card Number 73-77524

THE EDITOR

J. W. Robinson, B.Sc., Ph.D., is Professor of Chemistry and Chairman of the Analytical Division at Louisiana State University, Baton Rouge, La., U.S.

Dr. Robinson earned his degrees at the University of Birmingham in England (B.Sc., 1949, and Ph.D., 1952). He obtained his American citizenship in 1965.

Dr. Robinson has authored more than 100 publications and has recently written two books, *Undergraduate Instrumental Analysis* and *Atomic Absorption Spectroscopy.* He is Editor of *Spectroscopy Letters* and *Environmental Letters.* He is a former Chairman of the National Society of Applied Spectroscopy and is currently Chairman of both the Gordon Conference and the Louisiana State University International Symposium on Analytical Chemistry. Dr. Robinson is also Director of the Saul Gordon Workshop on Atomic Absorption Spectroscopy.

CONTRIBUTORS
for VOLUMES I AND II

David A. Allison, Ph.D.
Department of Chemistry
University of Alberta
Edmonton, Alberta, Canada

Juanita H. Allison, Ph.D.
Department of Chemistry
University of Alberta
Edmonton, Alberta, Canada

Stanley S. Ballard, Ph.D.
Department of Physics
University of Florida
Gainesville, Florida

Eugene P. Bertin, Ph.D.
RCA/David Sarnoff Research Center
Princeton, New Jersey

Norman S. Bhacca, Ph.D.
Department of Chemistry
Louisiana State University
Baton Rouge, Louisiana

L. S. Birks, M.S.
Head, X-Ray Optics Branch
Naval Research Laboratory
Washington, D. C.

J. S. Browder, Ph.D.
Department of Physics
Jacksonville University
Jacksonville, Florida

Dennis B. Brown, Ph.D.
X-Ray Optics Branch
Naval Research Laboratory
Washington, D. C.

Alex Burr, Ph.D.
Physics Department
New Mexico State University
Las Cruces, New Mexico

L. R. P. Butler, Ph.D.
Head, Applied Spectroscopy Division
National Physical Research Laboratory
Council for Scientific and Industrial Research
Pretoria, South Africa

Horacio A. Farach, Ph.D.
Department of Physics and Astronomy
University of South Carolina
Columbia, South Carolina

R. W. Fink, Ph.D.
Department of Chemistry
Georgia Institute of Technology
Atlanta, Georgia

A. G. Gaydon, D.Sc., F.R.S.
Imperial College
London, England

John V. Gilfrich, B.S.
X-Ray Optics Branch
Naval Research Laboratory
Washington, D. C.

Jeanette G. Grasselli, M.S.
The Standard Oil Company (Ohio)
Research and Engineering Department
Cleveland, Ohio

N. J. Harrick, Ph.D.
Harrick Scientific Corporation
Ossining, New York

H. G. C. Human, Ph.D.
Applied Spectroscopy Division
National Physical Research Laboratory
Council for Scientific and Industrial Research
Pretoria, South Africa

R. O. Kagel, Ph.D.
Dow Corning Corporation
Midland, Michigan

Francis W. Karasek, Ph.D.
Department of Chemistry
University of Waterloo
Waterloo, Ontario, Canada

Richard A. Nyquist, B.S.
The Dow Chemical Company
Midland, Michigan

Charles P. Poole, Jr., Ph.D.
Department of Physics and Astronomy
University of South Carolina
Columbia, South Carolina

P. Venugopala Rao, Ph.D.
Department of Physics
Emory University
Atlanta, Georgia

A. E. Sandstrom, Ph.D.
Royal University of Uppsala
Uppsala, Sweden

R. H. Scott, Ph.D.
Applied Spectroscopy Division
National Physical Research Laboratory
Council for Scientific and Industrial Research
Pretoria, South Africa

Professor Kai Siegbahn
Institute of Physics
Uppsala University
Uppsala, Sweden

R. K. Skogerboe, Ph.D.
Department of Chemistry
Colorado State University
Fort Collins, Colorado

A. Lee Smith, Ph.D.
Dow Corning Corporation
Midland, Michigan

R. E. Smith, Ph.D.
Imperial College
London, England

William J. Veigele, Ph.D.
Kaman Sciences Corporation
Colorado Springs, Colorado

J. B. Willis, D.Sc., Ph.D.
Division of Chemical Physics
Commonwealth Scientific and Industrial Research Organization
P. O. Box 160
Clayton, Victoria, Australia 3168

PREFACE

The principal objective of this handbook is to provide a readily accessible source of information on the major fields of spectroscopy. Specifically, these fields are NMR, IR, Raman, UV (absorption and fluorescence), ESCA, X-ray (absorption diffraction fluorescence), mass spectrometry, atomic absorption, flame photometry, emission spectrography, and flame spectroscopy.

Because of the considerable quantity of information amassed on these spectroscopic fields, it was necessary to publish the Handbook in two volumes. An attempt was made to select the related subject matter for each volume for ease of use, but it is felt that these are companion volumes.

The book will provide some theoretical information, but is mostly dedicated to providing a reference for the spectroscopic data available on the most important materials in the particular field.

The handbook will be of maximum value to the practicing spectroscopist. Many scientists are experts in one or two fields of spectroscopy, but relative novices in other similar fields. This handbook will be invaluable to people wishing to get information about these other fields.

It will be of particular use to analytical, organic, inorganic chemists or spectroscopists wishing to identify materials or compounds. The book will indicate to him which techniques may provide him with useful information and what kind of information those will provide him and will not provide him. In short, it will be a companion to those spectroscopists who have need to broaden their horizons into the major fields discussed.

Because of space limitations, the Handbook will not provide a complete reference service in all fields, but it will provide the most important information available, thereby providing a reference in breadth.

J. W. Robinson
Louisiana State University

TABLE OF CONTENTS, VOLUME 1

TABLE OF CONTENTS, VOLUME 2

Section A

X-Ray Spectroscopy

X-RAY SPECTROSCOPY

L. S. Birks, Naval Research Laboratory

I. CHARACTERISTIC X-RAY EMISSION LINES

Alex Burr, New Mexico State University

The following table contains the wavelength, precision of measurement, and energy of the most useful characteristic x-ray lines for each element. In the table the first column lists the element, the characteristic line, and the atomic levels involved in the production of the x-ray photon. The middle columns give the wavelength (in Å* units) and the precision of measurement in the form of the probable error in the last digit. The last column gives the energy of the line in kiloelectron volts.

The Å* wavelength unit is the unit of the x-ray wavelength scale in which all the more precise x-ray wavelengths are measured. It was designed to be as close to the angstrom unit as possible. The Å* wavelength unit is completely defined by Bearden,[1] and some comments on the x-ray wavelength scale in general are given by Thomsen and Burr.[2] Later advances[3] in the measurement of atomic constants have shown that the Å* unit is 20 ppm smaller than the angstrom unit. Thus, for almost all the lines listed in the following table, no error will be created if Å* is read as angstrom. However, in those rare cases where the utmost precision is required, the differences must be considered.

The precision with which a quantity can be measured is often as important as the measurement itself. The table has been constructed with strict attention to the number of significant figures recorded. The number in the column after the wavelength represents the probable error assigned to the last digit of the wavelength. A rough idea, good for most purposes, of the precision of the energy reported can be obtained from the number of significant figures in the energy. If a better estimate of precision is required, it can be obtained from the wavelength error. In the case of a few lines with a wavelength precision of the order of 10 ppm, it must be remembered that the uncertainty of the conversion factor between Å* units and keV is about 10 ppm and must be added to the uncertainty in the wavelength measurement. Again, this last complication will be of interest only to those who need the utmost accuracy.

The primary source of this table is an article by Bearden[4] which reported the most probable value of every measured characteristic x-ray line based on a critical review of all known measurements of that line. An extensive report[5] lists each measurement which was considered in this review and discusses in considerable detail the process followed in arriving at the results. In a few cases, notably the Mα and Mβ lines of the lanthanides,[6] values measured after the above mentioned study had been completed are given here.

TABLE 1

Wavelength, Probable Error in Last Digit of Wavelength, and Energy of Some Characteristic Emission Lines

Line	Wavelength Å*	P.E. in Last Wavelength Digit	Energy keV
3 Lithium			
$K\bar{\alpha}$ KL	228.0	1	0.0543
4 Beryllium			
$K\bar{\alpha}$ KL	114.0	1	0.1085
5 Boron			
$K\bar{\alpha}$ KL	67.6	3	0.1833
6 Carbon			
$K\bar{\alpha}$ KL	44.7	3	0.277
7 Nitrogen			
$K\bar{\alpha}$ KL	31.6	4	0.3924
8 Oxygen			
$K\bar{\alpha}$ KL	23.62	3	0.5249
9 Fluorine			
$K\bar{\alpha}$ $KL_{2,3}$	18.32	2	0.6768
10 Neon			
$K\bar{\alpha}$ $KL_{2,3}$	14.610	3	0.8486
$K\beta$ KM	14.452	5	0.8579
11 Sodium			
$K\bar{\alpha}$ $KL_{2,3}$	11.9101	9	1.0410
$K\beta$ KM	11.575	2	1.0711
12 Magnesium			
$K\bar{\alpha}$ $KL_{2,3}$	9.8900	2	1.25360
$K\beta$ KM	9.521	2	1.3022
13 Aluminum			
$K\alpha_2$ KL_2	8.34173	9	1.48627
$K\alpha_1$ KL_3	8.33934	9	1.48670
$K\beta$ KM	7.960	2	1.5574
14 Silicon			
$K\alpha_2$ KL_2	7.12791	9	1.73938
$K\alpha_1$ KL_3	7.12542	9	1.73998
$K\beta$ KM	6.753	1	1.8359
15 Phosphorus			
$K\alpha_2$ KL_2	6.160	1	2.0127
$K\alpha_1$ KL_3	6.157	1	2.0137
$K\beta$ KM	5.796	2	2.1390
16 Sulfur			
$K\alpha_2$ KL_2	5.37496	8	2.30664
$K\alpha_1$ KL_3	5.37216	7	2.30784
$K\beta_1$ KM	5.0316	2	2.4640

TABLE 1 (continued)

Wavelength, Probable Error in Last Digit of Wavelength, and Energy of Some Characteristic Emission Lines

Line	Wavelength Å*	P. E. in Last Wavelength Digit	Energy keV
17 Chlorine			
$K\alpha_2$ KL_2	4.7307	1	2.62078
$K\alpha_1$ KL_3	4.7278	1	2.62239
$K\beta$ KM	4.4034	3	2.8156
$L\eta$ L_2M_1	67.33	9	0.1841
$L\ell$ L_3M_1	67.90	9	0.1826
18 Argon			
$K\alpha_2$ KL_2	4.19474	5	2.95563
$K\alpha_1$ KL_3	4.19180	5	2.95770
$K\beta_{1,3}$ $KM_{2,3}$	3.8860	2	3.1905
$L\eta$ L_2M_1	55.9	1	0.2217
$L\ell$ L_3M_1	56.3	1	0.2201
19 Potassium			
$K\alpha_2$ KL_2	3.7445	2	3.3111
$K\alpha_1$ KL_3	3.7414	2	3.3138
$K\beta_{1,3}$ $KM_{2,3}$	3.4539	2	3.5896
$L\eta$ L_2M_1	47.24	2	0.2625
$L\ell$ L_3M_1	47.74	1	0.25971
20 Calcium			
$K\alpha_2$ KL_2	3.36166	3	3.68809
$K\alpha_1$ KL_3	3.35839	3	3.69168
$K\beta_{1,3}$ $KM_{2,3}$	3.0897	2	4.0127
$L\eta$ L_2M_1	40.46	2	0.3064
$L\ell$ L_3M_1	40.96	2	0.3027
$L\bar{a}$ $L_3M_{4,5}$	36.33	2	0.3413
21 Scandium			
$K\alpha_2$ KL_2	3.0342	1	4.0861
$K\alpha_1$ KL_3	3.0309	1	4.0906
$K\beta_{1,3}$ $KM_{2,3}$	2.7796	2	4.4605
$L\eta$ L_2M_1	35.13	2	0.3529
$L\beta_1$ L_2M_4	31.02	2	0.3996
$L\ell$ L_3M_1	35.59	3	0.3483
$L\bar{a}$ $L_3M_{4,5}$	31.35	3	0.3954
22 Titanium			
$K\alpha_2$ KL_2	2.75216	2	4.50486
$K\alpha_1$ KL_3	2.74851	2	4.51084
$K\beta_{1,3}$ $KM_{2,3}$	2.51391	2	4.93181
$L\eta$ L_2M_1	30.89	3	0.4013
$L\beta_1$ L_2M_4	27.05	2	0.4584
$L\ell$ L_3M_1	31.36	2	0.3953
$L\bar{a}$ $L_3M_{4,5}$	27.42	2	0.4522
23 Vanadium			
$K\alpha_2$ KL_2	2.50738	2	4.94464
$K\alpha_1$ KL_3	2.50356	2	4.95220
$K\beta_{1,3}$ $KM_{2,3}$	2.28440	2	5.42729
$L\eta$ L_2M_1	27.34	3	0.4535
$L\beta_1$ L_2M_4	23.88	4	0.5192
$L\ell$ L_3M_1	27.77	1	0.4465
$L\bar{a}$ $L_3M_{4,5}$	24.25	3	0.5113

TABLE 1 (continued)

Wavelength, Probable Error in Last Digit of Wavelength, and Energy of Some Characteristic Emission Lines

Line	Wavelength Å*	P. E. in Last Wavelength Digit	Energy keV
24 Chromium			
$K\alpha_2$ KL_2	2.293606	3	5.40551
$K\alpha_1$ KL_3	2.28970	2	5.41472
$K\beta_{1,3}$ $KM_{2,3}$	2.08487	2	5.94671
$L\eta$ L_2M_1	24.30	3	0.5102
$L\beta_1$ L_2M_4	21.27	1	0.5828
$L\ell$ L_3M_1	24.78	1	0.5003
$L\bar{a}$ $L_3M_{4,5}$	21.64	3	0.5728
25 Manganese			
$K\alpha_2$ KL_2	2.10578	2	5.88765
$K\alpha_1$ KL_3	2.101820	9	5.89875
$K\beta_{1,3}$ $KM_{2,3}$	1.91021	2	6.49045
$L\eta$ L_2M_1	21.85	2	0.5675
$L\beta_1$ L_2M_4	19.11	2	0.6488
$L\ell$ L_3M_1	22.29	1	0.5563
$L\bar{a}$ $L_3M_{4,5}$	19.45	1	0.6374
26 Iron			
$K\alpha_2$ KL_2	1.939980	9	6.39084
$K\alpha_1$ KL_3	1.936042	9	6.40384
$K\beta_{1,3}$ $KM_{2,3}$	1.75661	2	7.05798
$L\eta$ L_2M_1	19.75	4	0.628
$L\beta_1$ L_2M_4	17.26	1	0.7185
$L\ell$ L_3M_1	20.15	1	0.6152
$L\bar{a}$ $L_3M_{4,5}$	17.59	2	0.7050
27 Cobalt			
$K\alpha_2$ KL_2	1.792850	9	6.91530
$K\alpha_1$ KL_3	1.788965	9	6.93032
$K\beta_{1,3}$ $KM_{2,3}$	1.62079	2	7.64943
$L\eta$ L_2M_1	17.87	3	0.694
$L\beta_1$ L_2M_4	15.666	8	0.7914
$L\ell$ L_3M_1	18.292	8	0.6778
$L\bar{a}$ $L_3M_{4,5}$	15.972	6	0.7762
28 Nickel			
$K\alpha_2$ KL_2	1.661747	8	7.46089
$K\alpha_1$ KL_3	1.657910	8	7.47815
$K\beta_{1,3}$ $KM_{2,3}$	1.500135	8	8.26466
$L\eta$ L_2M_1	16.27	3	0.762
$L\beta_1$ L_2M_4	14.271	6	0.8688
$L\ell$ L_3M_1	16.693	9	0.7427
$L\bar{a}$ $L_3M_{4,5}$	14.561	3	0.8515
29 Copper			
$K\alpha_2$ KL_2	1.544390	2	8.02783
$K\alpha_1$ KL_3	1.540562	2	8.04778
$K\beta_{1,3}$ $KM_{2,3}$	1.392218	9	8.90529
$L\eta$ L_2M_1	14.90	2	0.832
$L\beta_1$ L_2M_4	13.053	3	0.9498
$L\ell$ L_3M_1	15.286	9	0.8111
$L\bar{a}$ $L_3M_{4,5}$	13.336	3	0.9297

TABLE 1 (continued)

Wavelength, Probable Error in Last Digit of Wavelength, and Energy of Some Characteristic Emission Lines

Line	Wavelength Å*	P. E. in Last Wavelength Digit	Energy keV
30 Zinc			
$K\alpha_2$ KL_2	1.439000	8	8.61578
$K\alpha_1$ KL_3	1.435155	7	8.63886
$K\beta_{1,3}$ $KM_{2,3}$	1.29525	2	9.5720
$L\eta$ L_2M_1	13.68	2	0.906
$L\beta_1$ L_2M_4	11.983	3	1.0347
$L\ell$ L_3M_1	14.02	2	0.884
$L\bar{\alpha}$ $L_3M_{4,5}$	12.254	3	1.0117
31 Gallium			
$K\alpha_2$ KL_2	1.34399	1	9.22482
$K\alpha_1$ KL_3	1.340083	9	9.25174
$K\beta_3$ KM_2	1.20835	5	10.2603
$K\beta_1$ KM_3	1.20789	2	10.2642
$L\eta$ L_2M_1	12.597	2	0.9842
$L\beta_1$ L_2M_4	11.023	2	1.1248
$L\ell$ L_3M_1	12.953	2	0.9572
$L\bar{\alpha}$ $L_3M_{4,5}$	11.292	1	1.09792
32 Germanium			
$K\alpha_2$ KL_2	1.258011	9	9.85532
$K\alpha_1$ KL_3	1.254054	9	9.88642
$K\beta_3$ KM_2	1.12936	9	10.9780
$K\beta_1$ KM_3	1.12894	2	10.9821
$L\eta$ L_2M_1	11.609	2	1.0680
$L\beta_1$ L_2M_4	10.175	1	1.2185
$L\ell$ L_3M_1	11.965	4	1.0362
$L\bar{\alpha}$ $L_3M_{4,5}$	10.4361	8	1.18800
33 Arsenic			
$K\alpha_2$ KL_2	1.17987	1	10.50799
$K\alpha_1$ KL_3	1.17588	1	10.54372
$K\beta_3$ KM_2	1.05783	5	11.7203
$K\beta_1$ KM_3	1.05730	2	11.7262
$L\eta$ L_2M_1	10.734	1	1.1550
$L\beta_1$ L_2M_4	9.4141	8	1.3170
$L\ell$ L_3M_1	11.072	1	1.1198
$L\bar{\alpha}$ $L_3M_{4,5}$	9.6709	8	1.2820
34 Selenium			
$K\alpha_2$ KL_2	1.10882	2	11.1814
$K\alpha_1$ KL_3	1.10477	2	11.2224
$K\beta_3$ KM_2	0.99268	5	12 4896
$K\beta_1$ KM_3	0.99218	3	12.4959
$L\eta$ L_2M_1	9.962	1	1.2446
$L\beta_1$ L_2M_4	8.7358	5	1.41923
$L\ell$ L_3M_1	10.294	1	1.2044
$L\bar{\alpha}$ $L_3M_{4,5}$	8.9900	5	1.37910
35 Bromine			
$K\alpha_2$ KL_2	1.04382	2	11.8776
$K\alpha_1$ KL_3	1.03974	2	11.9242
$K\beta_3$ KM_2	0.93327	5	13.2845

TABLE 1 (continued)

Wavelength, Probable Error in Last Digit of Wavelength, and Energy of Some Characteristic Emission Lines

Line	Wavelength Å*	P. E. in Last Wavelength Digit	Energy keV
$K\beta_1$ KM_3	0.93279	2	13.2914
$L\eta$ L_2M_1	9.255	1	1.3396
$L\beta_1$ L_2M_4	8.1251	5	1.52590
$L\ell$ L_3M_1	9.585	1	1.2935
$L\bar{a}$ $L_3M_{4,5}$	8.3746	5	1.48043
36 Krypton			
$K\alpha_2$ KL_2	0.9841	1	12.598
$K\alpha_1$ KL_3	0.9801	1	12.649
$K\beta_3$ KM_2	0.8790	1	14.104
$K\beta_1$ KM_3	0.8785	1	14.112
$L\beta_1$ L_2M_4	7.576	3	1.6366
$L\bar{a}$ $L_3M_{4,5}$	7.817	3	1.5860
37 Rubidium			
$K\alpha_2$ KL_2	0.92969	1	13.3358
$K\alpha_1$ KL_3	0.925553	9	13.3953
$K\beta_3$ KM_2	0.82921	3	14.9517
$K\beta_1$ KM_3	0.82868	2	14.9613
$L\eta$ L_2M_1	8.0415	4	1.54177
$L\beta_1$ L_2M_4	7.0759	3	1.75217
$L\ell$ L_3M_1	8.3636	4	1.48238
$L\alpha_2$ L_3M_4	7.3251	3	1.69256
$L\alpha_1$ L_3M_5	7.3183	2	1.69413
38 Strontium			
$K\alpha_2$ KL_2	0.87943	1	14.0979
$K\alpha_1$ KL_3	0.87526	1	14.1650
$K\beta_3$ KM_2	0.78345	3	15.8249
$K\beta_1$ KM_3	0.78292	2	15.8357
$L\eta$ L_2M_1	7.5171	3	1.64933
$L\beta_1$ L_2M_4	6.6239	3	1.87172
$L\ell$ L_3M_1	7.8362	3	1.58215
$L\alpha_2$ L_3M_4	6.8697	3	1.80474
$L\alpha_1$ L_3M_5	6.8628	2	1.80656
39 Yttrium			
$K\alpha_2$ KL_2	0.83305	1	14.8829
$K\alpha_1$ KL_3	0.82884	1	14.9584
$K\beta_3$ KM_2	0.74126	3	16.7258
$K\beta_1$ KM_3	0.74072	2	16.7378
$L\eta$ L_1M_1	7.0406	3	1.76095
$L\beta_1$ L_3M_4	6.2120	3	1.99584
$L\ell$ L_3M_1	7.3563	3	1.68536
$L\alpha_2$ L_3M_4	6.4558	3	1.92047
$L\alpha_1$ L_3M_5	6.4488	2	1.92256
40 Zirconium			
$K\alpha_2$ KL_2	0.79015	1	15.6909
$K\alpha_1$ KL_3	0.78593	1	15.7751
$K\beta_3$ KM_2	0.70228	4	17.654
$K\beta_1$ KM_3	0.70173	3	17.6678

TABLE 1 (continued)

Wavelength, Probable Error in Last Digit of Wavelength, and Energy of Some Characteristic Emission Lines

Line	Wavelength Å*	P. E. in Last Wavelength Digit	Energy keV
$L\eta$ L_1M_1	6.6069	3	1.87654
$L\beta_1$ L_3M_4	5.8360	3	2.1244
$L\ell$ L_3M_1	6.9185	3	1.79201
$L\alpha_2$ L_3M_4	6.0778	3	2.0399
$L\alpha_1$ L_3M_5	6.0705	2	2.04236
$L\beta_{2,15}$ $L_3N_{4,5}$	5.5863	3	2.2194
41 Niobium			
$K\alpha_2$ KL_2	0.75044	1	16.5210
$K\alpha_1$ KL_3	0.74620	1	16.6151
$K\beta_3$ KM_2	0.66634	3	18.6063
$K\beta_1$ KM_3	0.66576	2	18.6225
$L\eta$ L_2M_1	6.2109	3	1.99620
$L\beta_1$ L_2M_4	5.4923	3	2.2574
$L\ell$ L_3M_1	6.5176	3	1.90225
$L\alpha_2$ L_3M_4	5.7319	3	2.1630
$L\alpha_1$ L_3M_5	5.7243	2	2.16589
$L\beta_{2,15}$ $L_3N_{4,5}$	5.2379	3	2.3670
42 Molybdenum			
$K\alpha_2$ KL_2	0.713590	6	17.3743
$K\alpha_1$ KL_3	0.709300	1	17.47934
$K\beta_3$ KM_2	0.632872	9	19.5903
$K\beta_1$ KM_3	0.632288	9	19.6083
$L\eta$ L_2M_1	5.8475	3	2.1202
$L\beta_1$ L_2M_4	5.17708	8	2.39481
$L\ell$ L_3M_1	6.1508	3	2.01568
$L\alpha_2$ L_3M_4	5.41437	8	2.28985
$L\alpha_1$ L_3M_5	5.40655	8	2.29316
$L\beta_{2,15}$ $L_3N_{4,5}$	4.9232	2	2.5183
43 Technetium			
$K\alpha_2$ KL_2	0.67932	3	18.2508
$K\alpha_1$ KL_3	0.67502	3	18.3671
$K\beta_3$ KM_2	0.60188	4	20.599
$K\beta_1$ KM_3	0.60130	4	20.619
$L\beta_1$ L_2M_4	4.8873	8	2.5368
$L\alpha_1$ L_3M_5	5.1148	3	2.4240
44 Ruthenium			
$K\alpha_2$ KL_2	0.647408	5	19.1504
$K\alpha_1$ KL_3	0.643083	4	19.2792
$K\beta_3$ KM_2	0.573067	4	21.6346
$K\beta_1$ KM_3	0.572482	4	21.6568
$L\eta$ L_2M_1	5.2050	2	2.38197
$L\beta_1$ L_2M_4	4.62058	3	2.68323
$L\ell$ L_3M_1	5.5035	3	2.2528
$L\alpha_2$ L_3M_4	4.85381	7	2.54431
$L\alpha_1$ L_3M_5	4.84575	5	2.55855
$L\beta_{2,15}$ $L_3N_{4,5}$	4.3718	2	2.8360

TABLE 1 (continued)

Wavelength, Probable Error in Last Digit of Wavelength, and Energy of Some Characteristic Emission Lines

Line	Wavelength Å*	P. E. in Last Wavelength Digit	Energy keV
45 Rhodium			
$K\alpha_2$ KL_2	0.617630	4	20.0737
$K\alpha_1$ KL_3	0.613279	4	20.2161
$K\beta_3$ KM_2	0.546200	4	22.6989
$K\beta_1$ KM_3	0.545605	4	22.7236
$L\eta$ L_2M_1	4.9217	2	2.5191
$L\beta_1$ L_2M_4	4.37414	4	2.83441
$L\ell$ L_3M_1	5.2169	3	2.3765
$L\alpha_2$ L_3M_4	4.60545	9	2.69205
$L\alpha_1$ L_3M_5	4.59743	9	2.69674
$L\beta_{2,15}$ $L_3N_{4,5}$	4.1310	2	3.0013
46 Palladium			
$K\alpha_2$ KL_2	0.589821	3	21.0201
$K\alpha_1$ KL_3	0.585448	3	21.1771
$K\beta_3$ KM_2	0.521123	4	23.7911
$K\beta_1$ KM_3	0.520520	4	23.8187
$L\eta$ L_2M_1	4.6605	2	2.6603
$L\beta_1$ L_2M_4	4.14622	5	2.99022
$L\ell$ L_3M_1	4.9525	3	2.5034
$L\alpha_2$ L_3M_4	4.37588	7	2.83329
$L\alpha_1$ L_3M_5	4.36767	5	2.83861
$L\beta_{2,15}$ $L_3N_{4,5}$	3.90887	4	3.17179
47 Silver			
$K\alpha_2$ KL_2	0.563798	4	21.9903
$K\alpha_1$ KL_3	0.5594075	6	22.16292
$K\beta_3$ KM_2	0.497685	4	24.9115
$K\beta_1$ KM_3	0.497069	4	24.9424
$L\eta$ L_2M_1	4.4183	2	2.8061
$L\beta_1$ L_2M_4	3.93473	3	3.15094
$L\ell$ L_3M_1	4.7076	2	2.6337
$L\alpha_2$ L_3M_4	4.16294	5	2.97821
$L\alpha_1$ L_3M_5	4.15443	3	2.98431
$L\beta_{2,15}$ $L_3N_{4,5}$	3.70335	3	3.34781
48 Cadmium			
$K\alpha_2$ KL_2	0.539422	3	22.9841
$K\alpha_1$ KL_3	0.535010	3	23.1736
$K\beta_3$ KM_2	0.475730	5	26.0612
$K\beta_1$ KM_3	0.475105	6	26.0955
$L\eta$ L_2M_1	4.19315	9	2.95675
$L\beta_1$ L_2M_4	3.73823	4	3.31657
$L\ell$ L_3M_1	4.48014	9	2.76735
$L\alpha_2$ L_3M_4	3.96496	6	3.12691
$L\alpha_1$ L_3M_5	3.95635	4	3.13373
$L\beta_{2,15}$ $L_3N_{4,5}$	3.51408	4	3.52812
49 Indium			
$K\alpha_2$ KL_2	0.516544	3	24.0020
$K\alpha_1$ KL_3	0.512113	3	24.2097

TABLE 1 (continued)

Wavelength, Probable Error in Last Digit of Wavelength, and Energy of Some Characteristic Emission Lines

Line	Wavelength Å*	P. E. in Last Wavelength Digit	Energy keV
$K\beta_3$ KM_2	0.455181	4	27.2377
$K\beta_1$ KM_3	0.454545	4	27.2759
$L\eta$ L_2M_1	3.98327	9	3.11254
$L\beta_1$ L_2M_4	3.55531	4	3.48721
$L\ell$ L_3M_1	4.26873	9	2.90440
$L\alpha_2$ L_3M_4	3.78073	6	3.27929
$L\alpha_1$ L_3M_5	3.77192	4	3.28694
$L\beta_{2,15}$ $L_3N_{4,5}$	3.33838	3	3.71381
50 Tin			
$K\alpha_2$ KL_2	0.495053	3	25.0440
$K\alpha_1$ KL_3	0.490599	3	25.2713
$K\beta_3$ KM_2	0.435877	5	28.4440
$K\beta_1$ KM_3	0.435236	5	28.4860
$L\eta$ L_2M_1	3.78876	9	3.27234
$L\beta_1$ L_2M_4	3.38487	3	3.66280
$L\ell$ L_3M_1	4.07165	9	3.04499
$L\alpha_2$ L_3M_4	3.60891	4	3.43542
$L\alpha_1$ L_3M_5	3.59994	3	3.44398
$L\beta_{2,15}$ $L_3N_{4,5}$	3.17505	3	3.90486
51 Antimony			
$K\alpha_2$ KL_2	0.474827	3	26.1108
$K\alpha_1$ KL_3	0.470354	3	26.3591
$K\beta_3$ KM_2	0.417737	4	29.6792
$K\beta_1$ KM_3	0.417085	3	29.7256
$L\eta$ L_2M_1	3.60765	9	3.43661
$L\beta_1$ L_2M_4	3.22567	4	3.84357
$L\ell$ L_3M_1	3.88826	9	3.18860
$L\alpha_2$ L_3M_4	3.44840	6	3.59532
$L\alpha_1$ L_3M_5	3.43941	4	3.60472
$L\beta_{2,15}$ $L_3N_{4,5}$	3.02335	3	4.10078
52 Tellurium			
$K\alpha_2$ KL_2	0.455784	3	27.2017
$K\alpha_1$ KL_3	0.451295	3	27.4723
$K\beta_3$ KM_2	0.400659	4	30.9443
$K\beta_1$ KM_3	0.399995	5	30.9957
$L\eta$ L_2M_1	3.43832	9	3.60586
$L\beta_1$ L_2M_4	3.07677	6	4.02958
$L\ell$ L_3M_1	3.71696	9	3.33555
$L\alpha_2$ L_3M_4	3.29846	9	3.7588
$L\alpha_1$ L_3M_5	3.28920	6	3.76933
$L\beta_{2,15}$ $L_3N_{4,5}$	2.88217	8	4.3017
53 Iodine			
$K\alpha_2$ KL_2	0.437829	7	28.3172
$K\alpha_1$ KL_3	0.433318	5	28.6120
$K\beta_3$ KM_2	0.384564	4	32.2394
$K\beta_1$ KM_3	0.383905	4	32.2947
$L\eta$ L_2M_1	3.27979	9	3.7801
$L\beta_1$ L_2M_4	2.93744	6	4.22072
$L\ell$ L_3M_1	3.55754	9	3.48502

TABLE 1 (continued)

Wavelength, Probable Error in Last Digit of Wavelength, and Energy of Some Characteristic Emission Lines

Line	Wavelength Å*	P. E. in Last Wavelength Digit	Energy keV
$L\alpha_2$ L_3M_4	3.15791	6	3.92604
$L\alpha_1$ L_3M_5	3.14860	6	3.93765
$L\beta_{2,15}$ $L_3N_{4,5}$	2.75053	8	4.5075
54 Xenon			
$K\alpha_2$ KL_2	0.42087	2	29.458
$K\alpha_1$ KL_3	0.41634	2	29.779
$K\beta_3$ KM_2	0.36941	2	33.562
$K\beta_1$ KM_3	0.36872	2	33.624
$L\alpha_1$ L_3M_5	3.0166	2	4.1099
55 Cesium			
$K\alpha_2$ KL_2	0.404835	4	30.6251
$K\alpha_1$ KL_3	0.400290	4	30.9728
$K\beta_3$ KM_2	0.355050	4	34.9194
$K\beta_1$ KM_3	0.354364	7	34.9869
$L\eta$ L_2M_1	2.9932	2	4.1421
$L\beta_1$ L_2M_4	2.6837	2	4.6198
$L\ell$ L_3M_1	3.2670	2	3.7950
$L\alpha_2$ L_3M_4	2.9020	2	4.2722
$L\alpha_1$ L_3M_5	2.8924	2	4.2865
$L\beta_{2,15}$ $L_3N_{4,5}$	2.5118	2	4.9359
56 Barium			
$K\alpha_2$ KL_2	0.389668	5	31.8171
$K\alpha_1$ KL_3	0.385111	4	32.1936
$K\beta_3$ KM_2	0.341507	4	36.3040
$K\beta_1$ KM_3	0.340811	3	36.3782
$L\eta$ L_2M_1	2.8627	3	4.3309
$L\beta_1$ L_2M_4	2.56821	5	4.82753
$L\ell$ L_3M_1	3.1355	2	3.9541
$L\alpha_2$ L_3M_4	2.78553	5	4.45090
$L\alpha_1$ L_3M_5	2.77595	5	4.46626
$L\beta_{2,15}$ $L_3N_{4,5}$	2.40435	6	5.1565
57 Lanthanum			
$K\alpha_2$ KL_2	0.375313	2	33.0341
$K\alpha_1$ KL_3	0.370737	2	33.4418
$K\beta_3$ KM_2	0.328686	4	37.7202
$K\beta_1$ KM_3	0.327983	3	37.8010
$L\eta$ L_2M_1	2.740	3	4.525
$L\beta_1$ L_2M_4	2.45891	5	5.0421
$L\ell$ L_3M_1	3.006	3	4.124
$L\alpha_2$ L_3M_4	2.67533	5	4.63423
$L\alpha_1$ L_3M_5	2.66570	5	4.65097
$L\beta_{2,15}$ $L_3N_{4,5}$	2.3030	3	5.3835
$M\beta$ M_4N_6	14.573	5	0.8508
$M\bar{\alpha}$ $M_5N_{6,7}$	14.859	5	0.8344
58 Cerium			
$K\alpha_2$ KL_2	0.361683	2	34.2789
$K\alpha_1$ KL_3	0.357092	2	34.7197
$K\beta_3$ KM_2	0.316520	4	39.1701

TABLE 1 (continued)

Wavelength, Probable Error in Last Digit of Wavelength, and Energy of Some Characteristic Emission Lines

Line	Wavelength Å*	P. E. in Last Wavelength Digit	Energy keV
$K\beta_1$ KM_3	0.315816	2	39.2573
$L\eta$ L_2M_1	2.6203	4	4.7315
$L\beta_1$ L_2M_4	2.3561	3	5.2622
$L\ell$ L_3M_1	2.8917	4	4.2875
$L\alpha_2$ L_3M_4	2.5706	3	4.8230
$L\alpha_1$ L_3M_5	2.5615	2	4.8402
$L\beta_{2,15}$ $L_3N_{4,5}$	2.2087	2	5.6134
$M\beta$ M_4N_6	13.786	5	0.8993
$M\bar{\alpha}$ $M_5N_{6,7}$	14.078	5	0.8807
59 Praseodymium			
$K\alpha_2$ KL_2	0.348749	2	35.5502
$K\alpha_1$ KL_3	0.344140	2	36.0263
$K\beta_3$ KM_2	0.304975	5	40.6529
$K\beta_1$ KM_3	0.304261	4	40.7482
$L\eta$ L_2M_1	2.512	3	4.935
$L\beta_1$ L_2M_4	2.2588	3	5.4889
$L\ell$ L_3M_1	2.7841	4	4.4532
$L\alpha_2$ L_3M_4	2.4729	3	5.0135
$L\alpha_1$ L_3M_5	2.4630	2	5.0337
$L\beta_{2,15}$ $L_3N_{4,5}$	2.1194	4	5.850
$M\beta$ M_4N_6	13.056	5	0.9496
$M\bar{\alpha}$ $M_5N_{6,7}$	13.339	5	0.9295
60 Neodymium			
$K\alpha_2$ KL_2	0.336472	2	36.8474
$K\alpha_1$ KL_3	0.331846	2	37.3610
$K\beta_3$ KM_2	0.294027	3	42.1665
$K\beta_1$ KM_3	0.293299	2	42.2713
$L\eta$ L_2M_1	2.4094	4	5.1457
$L\beta_1$ L_2M_4	2.1669	2	5.7216
$L\ell$ L_3M_1	2.6760	4	4.6330
$L\alpha_2$ L_3M_4	2.3807	3	5.2077
$L\alpha_1$ L_3M_5	2.3704	2	5.2304
$L\beta_{2,15}$ $L_3N_{4,5}$	2.0360	3	6.0894
$M\beta$ M_4N_6	12.399	5	0.9999
$M\bar{\alpha}$ $M_5N_{6,7}$	12.667	5	0.9788
61 Promethium			
$K\alpha_2$ KL_2	0.324803	4	38.1712
$K\alpha_1$ KL_3	0.320160	4	38.7247
$K\beta_3$ KM_2	0.28363	4	43.713
$K\beta_1$ KM_3	0.28290	3	43.826
$L\beta_1$ L_2M_4	2.0797	4	5.961
$L\alpha_2$ L_3M_4	2.2926	4	5.4078
$L\alpha_1$ L_3M_5	2.2822	3	5.4325
$L\beta_{2,15}$ $L_3N_{4,5}$	1.9559	6	6.339
62 Samarium			
$K\alpha_2$ KL_2	0.313698	2	39.5224
$K\alpha_1$ KL_3	0.309040	2	40.1181
$K\beta_3$ KM_2	0.27376	2	45.289
$K\beta_1$ KM_3	0.27301	2	45.413

TABLE 1 (continued)

Wavelength, Probable Error in Last Digit of Wavelength, and Energy of Some Characteristic Emission Lines

Line	Wavelength Å*	P. E. in Last Wavelength Digit	Energy keV
$L\eta$ L_2M_1	2.21824	3	5.5892
$L\beta_1$ L_2M_4	1.99806	3	6.2051
$L\ell$ L_3M_1	2.4823	4	4.9945
$L\alpha_2$ L_3M_4	2.21062	3	5.6084
$L\alpha_1$ L_3M_5	2.1998	2	5.6361
$L\beta_{2,15}$ $L_3N_{4,5}$	1.88221	3	6.5870
$M\beta$ M_4N_6	11.249	5	1.1022
$M\bar{\alpha}$ $M_5N_{6,7}$	11.485	5	1.0795
63 Europium			
$K\alpha_2$ KL_2	0.303118	2	40.9019
$K\alpha_1$ KL_3	0.298446	2	41.5422
$K\beta_3$ KM_2	0.264332	5	46.9036
$K\beta_1$ KM_3	0.263577	5	47.0379
$L\eta$ L_2M_1	2.1315	2	5.8166
$L\beta_1$ L_2M_4	1.9203	2	6.4564
$L\ell$ L_3M_1	2.3948	2	5.1772
$L\alpha_2$ L_3M_4	2.1315	2	5.8166
$L\alpha_1$ L_3M_5	2.1209	2	5.8457
$L\beta_{2,15}$ $L_3N_{4,5}$	1.8118	2	6.8432
$M\beta$ M_4N_6	10.736	5	1.1548
$M\bar{\alpha}$ $M_5N_{6,7}$	10.955	5	1.1317
64 Gadolinium			
$K\alpha_2$ KL_2	0.293038	2	42.3089
$K\alpha_1$ KL_3	0.288353	2	42.9962
$K\beta_3$ KM_2	0.25534	2	48.555
$K\beta_1$ KM_3	0.25460	2	48.697
$L\eta$ L_2M_1	2.0494	1	6.0495
$L\beta_1$ L_2M_4	1.8468	2	6.7132
$L\ell$ L_3M_1	2.3122	2	5.3621
$L\alpha_2$ L_3M_4	2.0578	2	6.0250
$L\alpha_1$ L_3M_5	2.0468	2	6.0572
$L\beta_{2,15}$ $L_3N_{4,5}$	1.7455	2	7.1028
$M\beta$ M_4N_6	10.249	5	1.2097
$M\bar{\alpha}$ $M_5N_{6,7}$	10.469	5	1.1843
65 Terbium			
$K\alpha_2$ KL_2	0.283423	2	43.7441
$K\alpha_1$ KL_3	0.278724	2	44.4816
$K\beta_3$ KM_2	0.24683	2	50.229
$K\beta_1$ KM_3	0.24608	2	50.382
$L\eta$ L_2M_1	1.9730	2	6.2839
$L\beta_1$ L_2M_4	1.7768	3	6.978
$L\ell$ L_3M_1	2.2352	2	5.5467
$L\alpha_2$ L_3M_4	1.9875	2	6.2380
$L\alpha_1$ L_2M_5	1.9765	2	6.2728
$L\beta_{2,15}$ $L_3N_{4,5}$	1.6830	2	7.3667
$M\beta$ M_4N_6	9.787	5	1.2668
$M\bar{\alpha}$ $M_5N_{6,7}$	10.014	5	1.2381
66 Dysprosium			
$K\alpha_2$ KL_2	0.274247	2	45.2078

TABLE 1 (continued)

Wavelength, Probable Error in Last Digit of Wavelength, and Energy of Some Characteristic Emission Lines

Line	Wavelength Å*	P. E. in Last Wavelength Digit	Energy keV
$K\alpha_1$ KL_3	0.269533	2	45.9984
$K\beta_3$ KM_2	0.23862	2	51.957
$K\beta_1$ KM_3	0.23788	2	52.119
$L\eta$ L_2M_1	1.89743	7	6.5342
$L\beta_1$ L_2M_4	1.71062	7	7.2477
$L\ell$ L_3M_1	2.15877	7	5.7431
$L\alpha_2$ L_3M_4	1.91991	3	6.4577
$L\alpha_1$ L_2M_5	1.90881	3	6.4952
$L\beta_{2,15}$ $L_3N_{4,5}$	1.62369	7	7.6357
$M\beta$ M_4N_6	9.359	5	1.3247
$M\bar{\alpha}$ $M_5N_{6,7}$	9.589	5	1.2930
67 Holmium			
$K\alpha_2$ KL_2	0.265486	2	46.6997
$K\alpha_1$ KL_3	0.260756	2	47.5467
$K\beta_3$ KM_2	0.23083	2	53.711
$K\beta_1$ KM_3	0.23012	2	53.877
$L\eta$ L_2M_1	1.8264	2	6.7883
$L\beta_1$ L_2M_4	1.6475	2	7.5253
$L\ell$ L_3M_1	2.0860	2	5.9434
$L\alpha_2$ L_3M_4	1.8561	2	6.6795
$L\alpha_1$ L_3M_5	1.8450	2	6.7198
$L\beta_{2,15}$ $L_3N_{4,5}$	1.5671	2	7.911
$M\beta$ M_4N_6	8.959	5	1.3839
$M\bar{\alpha}$ $M_5N_{6,7}$	9.193	5	1.3486
68 Erbium			
$K\alpha_2$ KL_2	0.257110	2	48.2211
$K\alpha_1$ KL_3	0.252365	2	49.1277
$K\beta_3$ KM_2	0.22341	2	55.494
$K\beta_1$ KM_3	0.22266	2	55.681
$L\eta$ L_2M_1	1.7566	1	7.0579
$L\beta_1$ L_2M_4	1.5873	1	7.8109
$L\ell$ L_3M_1	2.015	1	6.152
$L\alpha_2$ L_3M_4	1.7955	2	6.9050
$L\alpha_1$ L_3M_5	1.78425	9	6.9487
$L\beta_{2,15}$ $L_3N_{4,5}$	1.51399	9	8.1890
$M\beta$ M_4N_6	8.584	5	1.4443
$M\bar{\alpha}$ $M_5N_{6,7}$	8.822	5	1.4054
69 Thulium			
$K\alpha_2$ KL_2	0.249095	2	49.7726
$K\alpha_1$ KL_3	0.244338	2	50.7416
$K\beta_3$ KM_2	0.21636	2	57.304
$K\beta_1$ KM_3	0.21556	2	57.517
$L\eta$ L_2M_1	1.6963	2	7.3088
$L\beta_1$ L_2M_4	1.5304	2	8.101
$L\ell$ L_3M_1	1.9550	2	6.3419
$L\alpha_2$ L_3M_4	1.7381	2	7.1331
$L\alpha_1$ L_3M_5	1.7268	2	7.1799
$L\beta_{2,15}$ $L_3N_{4,5}$	1.4640	2	8.468
$M\beta$ M_4N_6	8.238	5	1.5050
$M\bar{\alpha}$ $M_5N_{6,7}$	8.475	5	1.4629

TABLE 1 (continued)

Wavelength, Probable Error in Last Digit of Wavelength, and Energy of Some Characteristic Emission Lines

Line	Wavelength Å*	P. E. in Last Wavelength Digit	Energy keV
70 Ytterbium			
$K\alpha_2$ KL_2	0.241424	2	51.3540
$K\alpha_1$ KL_3	0.236655	2	52.3889
$K\beta_3$ KM_2	0.2096	1	59.14
$K\beta_1$ KM_3	0.20884	8	59.37
$L\eta$ L_2M_1	1.63560	5	7.5802
$L\beta_1$ L_2M_4	1.47565	5	8.4018
$L\ell$ L_3M_1	1.89415	5	6.5455
$L\alpha_2$ L_3M_4	1.68285	5	7.3673
$L\alpha_1$ L_3M_5	1.67189	4	7.4156
$L\beta_{2,15}$ $L_3N_{4,5}$	1.41550	5	8.7588
$M\beta$ M_4N_6	7.912	5	1.5670
$M\bar{\alpha}$ $M_5N_{6,7}$	8.141	5	1.5229
71 Lutetium			
$K\alpha_2$ KL_2	0.234081	2	52.9650
$K\alpha_1$ KL_3	0.229298	2	54.0698
$K\beta_3$ KM_2	0.20309	4	61.05
$K\beta_1$ KM_3	0.20231	3	61.283
$L\eta$ L_2M_1	1.5779	1	7.8575
$L\beta_1$ L_2M_4	1.42359	3	8.7090
$L\ell$ L_3M_1	1.8360	1	6.7528
$L\alpha_2$ L_3M_4	1.63029	5	7.6049
$L\alpha_1$ L_3M_4	1.61951	3	7.6555
$L\beta_{15}$ L_3N_4	1.3715	1	9.0395
$L\beta_2$ L_3N_5	1.37012	3	9.0489
$M\beta$ M_4N_6	7.601	2	1.6312
$M\bar{\alpha}$ $M_5N_{6,7}$	7.840	2	1.5813
72 Hafnium			
$K\alpha_2$ KL_2	0.227024	3	54.6114
$K\alpha_1$ KL_3	0.222227	3	55.7902
$K\beta_3$ KM_2	0.19686	4	62.98
$K\beta_1$ KM_3	0.19607	3	63.234
$L\eta$ L_2M_1	1.52325	5	8.1393
$L\beta_1$ L_2M_4	1.37410	5	9.0227
$L\ell$ L_3M_1	1.78145	5	6.9596
$L\alpha_2$ L_3M_4	1.58046	5	7.8446
$L\alpha_1$ L_3M_4	1.56958	5	7.8990
$L\beta_{15}$ L_3N_4	1.32783	5	9.3371
$L\beta_2$ L_3N_5	1.32639	5	9.3473
$M\beta$ M_4N_6	7.303	1	1.6976
$M\bar{\alpha}$ $M_5N_{6,7}$	7.539	1	1.6446
73 Tantalum			
$K\alpha_2$ KL_2	0.220305	8	56.277
$K\alpha_1$ KL_3	0.215497	4	57.532
$K\beta_3$ KM_2	0.190890	2	64.9488
$K\beta_1$ KM_3	0.190089	4	65.223
$L\eta$ L_2M_1	1.47106	5	8.4280
$L\beta_1$ L_2M_4	1.32698	3	9.3431
$L\ell$ L_3M_1	1.72841	5	7.1731
$L\alpha_2$ L_3M_4	1.53293	2	8.0879

TABLE 1 (continued)

Wavelength, Probable Error in Last Digit of Wavelength, and Energy of Some Characteristic Emission Lines

Line	Wavelength Å*	P. E. in Last Wavelength Digit	Energy keV
$L\alpha_1$ L_3M_5	1.52197	2	8.1461
$L\beta_{15}$ L_3N_4	1.28619	5	9.6394
$L\beta_2$ L_3N_5	1.28454	2	9.6518
$M\beta$ M_4N_6	7.023	1	1.7655
$M\bar{\alpha}$ $M_5N_{6,7}$	7.252	1	1.7096
74 Tungsten			
$K\alpha_2$ KL_2	0.213828	2	57.9817
$K\alpha_1$ KL_3	0.2090100	Std	59.31824
$K\beta_3$ KM_2	0.185181	2	66.9514
$K\beta_1$ KM_3	0.184374	2	67.2443
$L\eta$ L_2M_1	1.42110	3	8.7243
$L\beta_1$ L_2M_4	1.281809	9	9.67235
$L\ell$ L_3M_1	1.6782	1	7.3878
$L\alpha_2$ L_3M_4	1.48743	2	8.3352
$L\alpha_1$ L_3M_5	1.47639	2	8.3976
$L\beta_{15}$ L_3N_4	1.24631	3	9.9478
$L\beta_2$ L_3N_5	1.24460	3	9.9615
$M\beta$ M_4N_6	6.757	1	1.8349
$M\alpha_2$ M_5N_6	6.992	2	1.7731
$M\alpha_1$ M_5N_7	6.983	1	1.7754
75 Rhenium			
$K\alpha_2$ KL_2	0.207611	1	59.7179
$K\alpha_1$ KL_3	0.202781	2	61.1403
$K\beta_3$ KM_2	0.179697	3	68.994
$K\beta_1$ KM_3	0.178880	3	69.310
$L\eta$ L_2M_1	1.37342	5	9.0272
$L\beta_1$ L_2M_4	1.23858	2	10.0100
$L\ell$ L_3M_1	1.63056	5	7.6036
$L\alpha_2$ L_3M_4	1.44396	5	8.5862
$L\alpha_1$ L_3M_5	1.43290	4	8.6525
$L\beta_{15}$ L_3N_4	1.20819	5	10.2617
$L\beta_2$ L_3N_5	1.20660	4	10.2752
$M\beta$ M_4N_6	6.504	1	1.9061
$M\bar{\alpha}$ $M_5N_{6,7}$	6.729	1	1.8425
76 Osmium			
$K\alpha_2$ KL_2	0.201639	2	61.4867
$K\alpha_1$ KL_3	0.196794	2	63.0005
$K\beta_3$ KM_2	0.174431	3	71.077
$K\beta_1$ KM_3	0.173611	3	71.413
$L\eta$ L_2M_1	1.32785	7	9.3370
$L\beta_1$ L_2M_4	1.19727	7	10.3553
$L\ell$ L_3M_1	1.58498	7	7.8222
$L\alpha_2$ L_3M_4	1.40234	5	8.8410
$L\alpha_1$ L_3M_5	1.39121	5	8.9117
$L\beta_{15}$ L_3N_4	1.17167	5	10.5816
$L\beta_2$ L_3N_5	1.16979	8	10.5985
$M\beta$ M_4N_6	6.267	1	1.9783
$M\bar{\alpha}$ $M_5N_{6,7}$	6.490	1	1.9102

TABLE 1 (continued)

Wavelength, Probable Error in Last Digit of Wavelength, and Energy of Some Characteristic Emission Lines

Line	Wavelength Å*	P. E. in Last Wavelength Digit	Energy keV
77 Iridium			
$K\alpha_2$ KL_2	0.195904	2	63.2867
$K\alpha_1$ KL_3	0.191047	2	64.8956
$K\beta_3$ KM_2	0.169367	2	73.2027
$K\beta_1$ KM_3	0.168542	2	73.5608
$L\eta$ L_2M_1	1.28448	3	9.6522
$L\beta_1$ L_2M_4	1.15781	3	10.7083
$L\ell$ L_3M_1	1.54094	3	8.0458
$L\alpha_2$ L_3M_4	1.36250	5	9.0995
$L\alpha_1$ L_3M_5	1.35128	3	9.1751
$L\beta_{15}$ L_3N_4	1.13707	3	10.9036
$L\beta_2$ L_3N_5	1.13532	3	10.9203
$M\beta$ M_4N_6	6.038	1	2.0535
$M\alpha_2$ M_5N_6	6.275	3	1.9758
$M\alpha_1$ M_5N_7	6.262	1	1.9799
78 Platinum			
$K\alpha_2$ KL_2	0.190381	4	65.122
$K\alpha_1$ KL_3	0.185511	4	66.832
$K\beta_3$ KM_2	0.164501	3	75.368
$K\beta_1$ KM_3	0.163675	3	75.748
$L\eta$ L_2M_1	1.2429	2	9.975
$L\beta_1$ L_2M_4	1.11990	2	11.0707
$L\ell$ L_3M_1	1.4995	2	8.268
$L\alpha_2$ L_3M_4	1.32432	2	9.3618
$L\alpha_1$ L_3M_5	1.31304	3	9.4423
$L\beta_2$ L_3N_5	1.10200	3	11.2505
$M\beta$ M_4N_6	5.828	1	2.1273
$M\alpha_2$ M_5N_6	6.058	3	2.047
$M\alpha_1$ M_5N_7	6.047	1	2.0505
79 Gold			
$K\alpha_2$ KL_2	0.185075	2	66.9895
$K\alpha_1$ KL_3	0.180195	2	68.8037
$K\beta_3$ KM_2	0.159810	2	77.580
$K\beta_1$ KM_3	0.158982	3	77.984
$L\eta$ L_2M_1	1.20273	3	10.3083
$L\beta_1$ L_2M_4	1.08353	3	11.4423
$L\ell$ L_3M_1	1.45964	9	8.4939
$L\alpha_2$ L_3M_4	1.28772	3	9.6280
$L\alpha_1$ L_3M_5	1.27640	3	9.7133
$L\beta_{15}$ L_3N_4	1.07188	5	11.5667
$L\beta_2$ L_3N_5	1.07022	3	11.5847
$M\beta$ M_4N_6	5.624	1	2.2046
$M\alpha_2$ M_5N_6	5.854	3	2.118
$M\alpha_1$ M_5N_7	5.840	1	2.1229
80 Mercury			
$K\alpha_2$ KL_2	0.179958	3	68.895
$K\alpha_1$ KL_3	0.175068	3	70.819
$K\beta_3$ KM_2	0.155321	3	79.822
$K\beta_1$ KM_3	0.154487	3	80.253
$L\eta$ L_2M_1	1.1640	1	10.6512

TABLE 1 (continued)

Wavelength, Probable Error in Last Digit of Wavelength, and Energy of Some Characteristic Emission Lines

Line	Wavelength Å*	P. E. in Last Wavelength Digit	Energy keV
$L\beta_1$ L_2M_4	1.04863	5	11.8226
$L\ell$ L_3M_1	1.4216	1	8.7210
$L\alpha_2$ L_3M_4	1.25264	7	9.8976
$L\alpha_1$ L_3M_5	1.24120	5	9.9888
$L\beta_{15}$ L_3N_4	1.04151	7	11.9040
$L\beta_2$ L_3N_5	1.03975	7	11.9241
$M\beta$ M_4N_6	5.4318	9	2.2825
$M\alpha_1$ M_5N_7	5.6476	9	2.1953
81 Thallium			
$K\alpha_2$ KL_2	0.175036	2	70.8319
$K\alpha_1$ KL_3	0.170136	2	72.8715
$K\beta_3$ KM_2	0.150980	6	82.118
$K\beta_1$ KM_3	0.150142	5	82.576
$L\eta$ L_2M_1	1.12769	3	10.9943
$L\beta_1$ L_2M_4	1.01513	4	12.2133
$L\ell$ L_3M_1	1.38477	3	8.9532
$L\alpha_2$ L_3M_4	1.21875	3	10.1728
$L\alpha_1$ L_3M_5	1.20739	4	10.2685
$L\beta_{15}$ L_3N_4	1.01201	3	12.2510
$L\beta_2$ L_3N_5	1.01031	3	12.2715
$M\beta$ M_4N_6	5.249	1	2.3621
$M\alpha_2$ M_5N_6	5.472	2	2.2656
$M\alpha_1$ M_5N_7	5.460	1	2.2706
82 Lead			
$K\alpha_2$ KL_2	0.170294	2	72.8042
$K\alpha_1$ KL_3	0.165376	2	74.9694
$K\beta_3$ KM_2	0.146810	4	84.450
$K\beta_1$ KM_3	0.145970	6	84.936
$L\eta$ L_2M_1	1.09241	7	11.3493
$L\beta_1$ L_2M_4	0.98291	3	12.6137
$L\ell$ L_3M_1	1.34990	7	9.1845
$L\alpha_2$ L_3M_4	1.18648	5	10.4495
$L\alpha_1$ L_3M_5	1.17501	2	10.5515
$L\beta_{15}$ L_3N_4	0.98389	7	12.6011
$L\beta_2$ L_3N_5	0.98221	7	12.6226
$M\beta$ M_4N_6	5.076	1	2.4427
$M\alpha_2$ M_5N_6	5.299	2	2.3397
$M\alpha_1$ M_5N_7	5.286	1	2.3455
83 Bismuth			
$K\alpha_2$ KL_2	0.165717	2	74.8148
$K\alpha_1$ KL_3	0.160789	2	77.1079
$K\beta_3$ KM_2	0.142779	7	86.834
$K\beta_1$ KM_3	0.141948	3	87.343
$L\eta$ L_2M_1	1.05856	3	11.7122
$L\beta_1$ L_2M_4	0.951978	9	13.0235
$L\ell$ L_3M_1	1.31610	7	9.4204
$L\alpha_2$ L_3M_4	1.15536	1	10.73091
$L\alpha_1$ L_3M_5	1.14386	2	10.8388
$L\beta_{15}$ L_3N_4	0.95702	5	12.9549
$L\beta_2$ L_3N_5	0.95518	4	12.9799
$M\beta$ M_4N_6	4.909	1	2.5255

TABLE 1 (continued)

Wavelength, Probable Error in Last Digit of Wavelength, and Energy of Some Characteristic Emission Lines

Line	Wavelength Å*	P. E. in Last Wavelength Digit	Energy keV
$M\alpha_2$ M_5N_6	5.130	2	2.4170
$M\alpha_1$ M_5N_7	5.118	1	2.4226
84 Polonium			
$K\alpha_2$ KL_2	0.16130	1	76.862
$K\alpha_1$ KL_3	0.15636	1	79.290
$K\beta_3$ KM_2	0.13892	2	89.25
$K\beta_1$ KM_3	0.13807	2	89.80
$L\beta_1$ L_2M_4	0.9220	2	13.447
$L\ell$ L_3M_1	1.2829	5	9.664
$L\alpha_2$ L_3M_4	1.12548	5	11.0158
$L\alpha_1$ L_3M_5	1.11386	4	11.1308
$L\beta_{15}$ L_3N_4	0.9312	2	13.314
$L\beta_2$ L_3N_5	0.92937	5	13.3404
85 Astatine			
$K\alpha_2$ KL_2	0.15705	2	78.95
$K\alpha_1$ KL_3	0.15210	2	81.52
$K\beta_3$ KM_2	0.13517	4	91.72
$K\beta_1$ KM_3	0.13432	4	92.30
$L\beta_1$ L_2M_4	0.89349	9	13.876
$L\alpha_2$ L_3M_4	1.09671	5	11.3048
$L\alpha_1$ L_3M_5	1.08500	5	11.4268
86 Radon			
$K\alpha_2$ KL_2	0.15294	3	81.07
$K\alpha_1$ KL_3	0.14798	3	83.78
$K\beta_3$ KM_2	0.13155	5	94.24
$K\beta_1$ KM_3	0.13069	5	94.87
$L\beta_1$ L_2M_4	0.86605	9	14.316
$L\alpha_2$ L_3M_4	1.06899	5	11.5979
$L\alpha_1$ L_3M_5	1.05723	5	11.7270
87 Francium			
$K\alpha_2$ KL_2	0.14896	3	83.23
$K\alpha_1$ KL_3	0.14399	3	86.10
$K\beta_3$ KM_2	0.12807	5	96.81
$K\beta_1$ KM_3	0.12719	5	97.47
$L\beta_1$ L_2M_4	0.83940	9	14.770
$L\alpha_2$ L_3M_4	1.04230	5	11.8950
$L\alpha_1$ L_3M_5	1.03049	5	12.0313
$L\beta_2$ L_3N_5	0.858	2	14.45
88 Radium			
$K\alpha_2$ KL_2	0.14512	2	85.43
$K\alpha_1$ KL_3	0.14014	2	88.47
$K\beta_3$ KM_2	0.12469	3	99.43
$K\beta_1$ KM_3	0.12382	3	100.13
$L\eta$ L_2M_1	0.90742	5	13.6630
$L\beta_1$ L_2M_4	0.81375	5	15.2358
$L\ell$ L_3M_1	1.16719	5	10.6222
$L\alpha_2$ L_3M_4	1.01656	5	12.1962
$L\alpha_1$ L_3M_5	1.00473	5	12.3397
$L\beta_{15}$ L_3N_4	0.83722	5	14.8086
$L\beta_2$ L_3N_5	0.83537	5	14.8414

TABLE 1 (continued)

Wavelength, Probable Error in Last Digit of Wavelength, and Energy of Some Characteristic Emission Lines

Line	Wavelength Å*	P. E. in Last Wavelength Digit	Energy keV
89 Actinium			
$K\alpha_2$ KL_2	0.14141	2	87.67
$K\alpha_1$ KL_3	0.136417	8	90.884
$K\beta_3$ KM_2	0.12143	2	102.10
$K\beta_1$ KM_3	0.12055	2	102.85
$L\beta_1$ L_2M_4	0.78903	9	15.713
$L\alpha_2$ L_3M_4	0.99178	5	12.5008
$L\alpha_1$ L_3M_5	0.97993	5	12.6520
90 Thorium			
$K\alpha_2$ KL_2	0.137829	2	89.953
$K\alpha_1$ KL_3	0.132813	2	93.350
$K\beta_3$ KM_2	0.118268	3	104.831
$K\beta_1$ KM_3	0.117396	9	105.609
$L\eta$ L_2M_1	0.85446	4	14.5099
$L\beta_1$ L_2M_4	0.765210	9	16.2022
$L\ell$ L_3M_1	1.11508	4	11.1186
$L\alpha_2$ L_3M_4	0.96788	2	12.8096
$L\alpha_1$ L_3M_5	0.95600	3	12.9687
$L\beta_{15}$ L_3N_4	0.79539	5	15.5875
$L\beta_2$ L_3N_5	0.79354	3	15.6237
$M\beta$ M_4N_6	3.941	1	3.1458
$M\alpha_2$ M_5N_6	4.151	2	2.987
$M\alpha_1$ M_5N_7	4.1381	9	2.9961
91 Protactinium			
$K\alpha_2$ KL_2	0.134343	9	92.287
$K\alpha_1$ KL_3	0.129325	3	95.868
$K\beta_3$ KM_2	0.11523	2	107.60
$K\beta_1$ KM_3	0.114345	8	108.427
$L\eta$ L_2M_1	0.8295	1	14.946
$L\beta_1$ L_2M_4	0.74232	5	16.702
$L\ell$ L_3M_1	1.0908	1	11.366
$L\alpha_2$ L_3M_4	0.94482	5	13.1222
$L\alpha_1$ L_3M_5	0.93284	5	13.2907
$L\beta_2$ L_3N_5	0.7737	1	16.024
$M\beta$ M_4N_6	3.827	1	3.2397
$M\alpha_2$ M_5N_6	4.035	3	3.072
$M\alpha_1$ M_5N_7	4.022	1	3.0823
92 Uranium			
$K\alpha_2$ KL_2	0.130968	4	94.665
$K\alpha_1$ KL_3	0.125947	3	98.439
$K\beta_3$ KM_2	0.112296	4	110.406
$K\beta_1$ KM_3	0.111394	5	111.300
$L\eta$ L_2M_1	0.80509	2	15.3997
$L\beta_1$ L_2M_4	0.719984	8	17.2200
$L\ell$ L_3M_1	1.06712	2	11.6183
$L\alpha_2$ L_3M_4	0.922558	9	13.4388
$L\alpha_1$ L_3M_5	0.910639	9	13.6147
$L\beta_{15}$ L_3N_4	0.756642	9	16.3857
$L\beta_2$ L_3N_5	0.754681	9	16.4283
$M\beta$ M_4N_6	3.716	1	3.3367

TABLE 1 (continued)

Wavelength, Probable Error in Last Digit of Wavelength, and Energy of Some Characteristic Emission Lines

Line	Wavelength Å*	P. E. in Last Wavelength Digit	Energy keV
$M\alpha_2$ M_5N_6	3.924	1	3.1595
$M\alpha_1$ M_5N_7	3.910	1	3.1708
93 Neptunium			
$L\eta$ L_2M_1	0.7809	2	15.876
$L\beta_1$ L_2M_4	0.698478	9	17.7502
$L\ell$ L_3M_1	1.0428	6	11.890
$L\alpha_2$ L_3M_4	0.901045	9	13.7597
$L\alpha_1$ L_3M_5	0.889128	9	13.9441
$L\beta_2$ L_3N_5	0.736230	9	16.8400
94 Plutonium			
$L\eta$ L_2M_1	0.7591	1	16.333
$L\beta_1$ L_2M_4	0.67772	2	18.2937
$L\ell$ L_3M_1	1.0226	1	12.124
$L\alpha_2$ L_3M_4	0.88028	2	14.0842
$L\alpha_1$ L_3M_5	0.86830	2	14.2786
$L\beta_{15}$ L_3N_4	0.7205	1	17.208
$L\beta_2$ L_3N_5	0.71851	2	17.2553
95 Americium			
$L\beta_1$ L_2M_4	0.657655	9	18.8520
$L\ell$ L_3M_1	1.0012	6	12.384
$L\alpha_2$ L_3M_4	0.860266	9	14.4119
$L\alpha_1$ L_3M_5	0.848187	9	14.6172
$L\beta_{15}$ L_3N_4	0.70341	2	17.6258
$L\beta_2$ L_3N_5	0.701390	9	17.6765

REFERENCES

1. **Bearden, J. A.,** *Phys. Rev.,* 137, 455, 1965.
2. **Thomsen, J. S. and Burr, A. F.,** *Am. J. Phys.,* 36, 803, 1968.
3. **Taylor, B. N., Parker, W. H., and Langenbern, D. N.,** *The Fundamental Constants and Quantum Electrodynamics,* Academic Press, New York, 1969.
4. **Bearden, J. A.,** *Rev. Mod. Phys.,* 39, 78, 1967.
5. **Bearden, J. A. and collaborators,** X-Ray Wavelengths, NYO-10586, Natl. Tech. Inf. Service, Springfield, Va., 1964.
6. **Fischer, D. W. and Baun, W. L.,** *J. Appl. Phys.,* 38, 4830, 1967.

II. CHARACTERISTIC X-RAY ABSORPTION EDGES

Alex Burr, New Mexico State University

The following table contains the available information on five selected x-ray absorption edges for each element. Under each edge, the wavelength in angstroms is first given, followed by the energy of the edge in kiloelectron volts. Some idea of the precision of the measurement can be obtained because care was taken that in each case only figures with some significance were recorded.

The main source of data for the table was a report[1] by Bearden and collaborators on x-ray wavelengths with a few measurements of heavy elements added. That report in turn was based on an earlier and more detailed work by Matthews.[2] These reports should be consulted if more details are desired as to just how these numbers were obtained.

It is very difficult to measure precisely an absorption edge; the chemical composition affects the results as do the thickness and the uniformity of the sample. It is rare to find agreement within reported errors between different investigators. Indirect methods of calculating absorption limits using emission line data often give values differing significantly from experimental ones. Nevertheless, these data can be helpful for indicating the spectral region where absorption effects should be found, for suggesting material for β line filters, and for aiding in the design of balanced Ross filters.

However, except when a rough estimate will do, these figures should not be used for determining binding energies or for predicting the energies of characteristic x-ray lines. For these purposes one should use binding energy tables[3] or energy level difference tables,[4] where information from many sources other than absorption edges is combined to give the best results.

Further information about absorption edges and absorption coefficients can be obtained from a series of reports[5] by McMaster et al.

TABLE 2

X-Ray Absorption Edges

	K		L_1		L_2		L_3		M_4		M_5	
Z	Å	keV	Å	keV	Å	keV	Å	keV	Å	keV	Å	keV
3 Li	226.5	0.05475										
4 Be	111.0	0.112										
6 C	43.68	0.28384										
7 N	30.99	0.4000										
8 O	23.32	0.5317										
10 Nl	14.3018	0.866889										
11 Na	11.569	1.07167				405.0	0.0306	(unresolved)				
12 Mg	9.5122	1.30339	197.3	0.06284	249.3	0.04973	250.7	0.04945				
13 Al	7.94813	1.559878	142.5	0.08701		170.4	0.07278	(unresolved)				
14 Si	6.738	1.8400				123.0	0.1006	(unresolved)				
15 P	5.784	2.1435				94	0.123	(unresolved)				
16 S	5.0185	2.47048										
17 Cl	4.3971	2.81960										
18 A	3.87090	3.20290										
19 K	3.4365	3.6078				42.1	0.2946	(unresolved)				
20 Ca	3.0703	4.0381			35.13	0.3529	35.49	0.34931				
21 Sc	2.762	4.489										
22 Ti	2.49734	4.96452				27.29	0.4544	(unresolved)				
23 V	2.2691	5.4639										
24 Cr	2.07020	5.9888	16.7	0.741	17.9	0.691	20.7	0.598				
25 Mn	1.89643	6.5376										
26 Fe	1.74346	7.11120			17.202	0.7208	17.525	0.7074				
27 Co	1.60815	7.70954			15.618	0.7938	15.915	0.7790				
28 Ni	1.48807	8.33165			14.242	0.8706	14.525	0.8536				
29 Cu	1.38059	8.9803			13.014	0.95268	13.288	0.93306				
30 Zn	1.2834	9.6607	13.06	0.9495	11.862	1.04523	12.131	1.02201				
31 Ga	1.1958	10.3682	9.517	1.3028	10.828	1.1450	11.100	1.1169				
32 Ge	1.11658	11.1036	8.773	1.4132	9.924	1.2494	10.187	1.2170				
33 As	1.0450	11.865	8.107	1.5293	9.125	1.3587	9.367	1.3235				
34 Se	0.97974	12.6545	7.503	1.6525	8.407	1.4747	8.646	1.4340			227.8	0.05443
35 Br	0.9204	13.470	6.959	1.781	7.753	1.599	7.984	1.5530				

TABLE 2 (continued)

X-Ray Absorption Edges

Z	K Å	K keV	L_1 Å	L_1 keV	L_2 Å	L_2 keV	L_3 Å	L_3 keV	M_4 Å	M_4 keV	M_5 Å	M_5 keV
36 Kr	0.86552	14.3244	6.47	1.915	7.168	1.7297	7.392	1.6772				
37 Rb	0.81554	15.2023	6.008	2.063	6.644	1.8661	6.862	1.8067				
38 Sr	0.76973	16.107	5.592	2.217	6.173	2.0085	6.387	1.9411				
39 Y	0.72766	17.038	5.217	2.377	5.756	2.1540	5.962	2.0794				
40 Zr	0.68883	17.9989	4.879	2.541	5.378	2.3053	5.579	2.2225				
41 Nb	0.65298	18.9869	4.575	2.710	5.031	2.4641	5.230	2.3706				
42 Mo	0.61978	20.0039	4.304	2.881	4.719	2.6274	4.913	2.5234				
43 Te	0.58906	21.0473	4.058	3.055	4.436	2.7948	4.630	2.6780				
44 Ru	0.56051	22.1193	3.835	3.233	4.180	2.9663	4.369	2.8377				
45 Rh	0.53395	23.2198	3.629	3.417	3.9425	3.1448	4.1299	3.0021				
46 Pd	0.50920	24.348	3.4369	3.607	3.7228	3.33031	3.9074	3.17298				
47 Ag	0.48589	25.5165	3.2564	3.8072	3.5164	3.5258	3.6999	3.35096				
48 Cd	0.46407	26.7159	3.0849	4.0190	3.3257	3.7280	3.5047	3.5376		28.13		0.4408 (unresolved)
49 In	0.44371	27.9420	2.9260	4.2373	3.1473	3.9393	3.3237	3.7302				
50 Sn	0.42467	29.1947	2.7769	4.4648	2.9823	4.1573	3.1557	3.9288		24.28		0.511 (unresolved)
51 Sb	0.40668	30.4860	2.6388	4.6984	2.8294	4.3819	3.0003	4.1323				
52 Te	0.38974	31.3114	2.5099	4.9397	2.6879	4.6126	2.8555	4.3418				
53 I	0.37381	33.1665	2.3880	5.192	2.5542	4.8540	2.7196	4.5587		19.66		0.631 (unresolved)
54 Xe	0.3584	34.59	2.2737	5.4528	2.4292	5.1037	2.5926	4.7822				
55 Cs	0.34451	35.987	2.1673	5.721	2.3139	5.3581	2.4740	5.0113				
56 Ba	0.33104	37.452	2.0678	5.996	2.2048	5.6233	2.3629	5.2470	15.56	0.7967	15.89	0.7801
57 La	0.31844	38.934	1.9780	6.268	2.1053	5.889	2.261	5.484				
58 Ce	0.30648	40.453	1.8934	6.548	2.0124	6.161	2.166	5.723				
59 Pr	0.29518	42.002	1.8141	6.834	1.9255	6.439	2.0791	5.963	13.122	0.9448	13.394	0.9257
60 Nd	0.28453	43.574	1.7390	7.1294	1.8440	6.7234	1.9967	6.2092	12.459	0.9951	12.737	0.9734
61 Pm	0.27431	45.198	1.6674	7.436	1.7676	7.014	1.9191	6.4605				
62 Sm	0.26464	46.849	1.6002	7.7478	1.6953	7.3132	1.8457	6.7172	11.288	1.0983	11.552	1.0732
63 Eu	0.25553	48.519	1.5381	8.0607	1.6271	7.6199	1.7761	6.9806	10.711	1.1575	11.013	1.1258
64 Gd	0.24681	50.233	1.4784	8.3864	1.5632	7.9310	1.7117	7.2430				
65 Tb	0.23841	52.002	1.4223	8.7167	1.5023	8.2527	1.6497	7.5153				

TABLE 2 (continued)

X-Ray Absorption Edges

Z	K		L₁		L₂		L₃		M₄		M₅	
	Å	keV	Å	keV	Å	keV	Å	keV	Å	keV	Å	keV
66 Dy	0.23048	53.793	1.3692	9.0548	1.4445	8.5830	1.5916	7.7897				
67 Ho	0.22291	55.619	1.3190	9.3994	1.3905	8.9164	1.5368	8.0676				
68 Er	0.21567	57.487	1.2706	9.7574	1.3386	9.2622	1.4835	8.3575	8.601	1.4415	8.847	1.4013
69 Tm	0.20880	59.38	1.2250	10.1206	1.2892	9.6171	1.4334	8.6496			8.487	1.4609
70 Yb	0.20224	61.30	1.1818	10.4904	1.2428	9.9761	1.3862	8.9441				
71 Lu	0.19585	63.31	1.1402	10.8740	1.1985	10.3448	1.3405	9.2490				
72 Hf	0.18982	65.31	1.0997	11.274	1.1548	10.7362	1.2972	9.5577				
73 Ta	0.18394	67.403	1.0613	11.682	1.1137	11.132	1.2553	9.8766	6.87	1.804	7.11	1.743
74 W	0.17837	69.508	1.02467	12.0996	1.0745	11.538	1.2155	10.1999	6.59	1.880	6.83	1.814
75 Re	0.17302	71.658	0.9894	12.530	1.0371	11.954	1.1773	10.5306	6.33	1.958	6.560	1.890
76 Os	0.16787	73.856	0.9558	12.972	1.0014	12.381	1.1408	10.8683	6.073	2.042	6.30	1.967
77 Ir	0.16292	76.101	0.9236	13.423	0.9671	12.820	1.1058	11.212	5.83	2.126	6.05	2.048
78 Pt	0.15818	78.381	0.8931	13.883	0.93414	13.2723	1.0723	11.562	5.59	2.217	5.81	2.133
79 Au	0.153593	80.720	0.86376	14.3537	0.90259	13.7361	1.04000	11.9212	5.374	2.307	5.584	2.220
80 Hg	0.14918	83.109	0.8353	14.842	0.8722	14.215	1.0091	12.286	5.157	2.404	5.36	2.313
81 Tl	0.14495	85.533	0.8081	15.343	0.8434	14.699	0.9793	12.660	4.952	2.504	5.153	2.406
82 Pb	0.140880	88.005	0.78196	15.855	0.81538	15.2053	0.95073	13.0406	4.757	2.606	4.955	2.502
83 Bi	0.13694	90.534	0.7571	16.376	0.7887	15.719	0.9234	13.426	4.572	2.711	4.764	2.603
88 Ra			0.6445	19.236	0.6707	18.486	0.8028	15.444				
90 Th	0.11307	109.646	0.6059	20.464	0.6299	19.683	0.7607	16.299	3.557	3.485	3.729	3.325
91 Pa			0.5868	21.128	0.6102	20.319	0.7409	16.733	3.436	3.608	3.618	3.436
92 U	0.10723	115.62	0.5695	21.771	0.5919	20.945	0.7223	17.165	3.333	3.720	3.497	3.545
93 Np							0.70419	17.606				
94 Pu			0.5365	23.109	0.5572	22.253	0.6875	18.053				
95 Am							0.61002	18.054				

REFERENCES

1. **Bearden, J. A. and collaborators,** X-Ray Wavelengths, NYO-10586, Natl. Tech. Inf. Service, Springfield, Va., 1964.
2. **Matthews, G.,** Master's essay, Johns Hopkins University, Baltimore, Md., 1964.
3. **Bearden, J. A. and Burr, A. F.,** *Rev. Mod. Phys.,* 39, 125, 1967.
4. **Bearden, J. A. and Burr, A. F.,** Atomic Energy Levels, NYO-2543-1, Natl. Tech. Inf. Service, Springfield, Va., 1965.
5. **McMaster, W. and collaborators,** UCRL-50174, Natl. Tech. Inf. Service, Springfield, Va.

III. MASS ATTENUATION AND ABSORPTION CROSS SECTIONS FOR 94 ELEMENTS; 0.1 keV to 1 MeV

William J. Veigele, Kaman Sciences Corporation

When x and gamma rays, in the energy range from 0.1 keV to 1 MeV, traverse matter they are attenuated primarily by photoelectric absorption, incoherent scattering, and coherent scattering. The probabilities of these interactions occurring per unit depth of penetration are called cross sections, and the total attenuation cross section μ is related to those for the mechanisms above by

$$\mu = \tau + \sigma_I + \sigma_C. \quad (1)$$

Incoherent scattering collisions may be divided into scattering and absorption components such that

$$\sigma_I = \sigma_s + \sigma_a. \quad (2)$$

Attenuation follows the exponential law

$$I = I_o \exp[-(\mu/\rho)\rho x], \quad (3)$$

where I and I_o are intensities at a depth x and at the surface, ρ is the density, and (μ/ρ) is defined as the mass attenuation coefficient. It is given here in cm^2/g.

Table 3 lists values of τ/ρ, σ_c/ρ, σ_I/ρ, σ_a/ρ, and μ/ρ for 94 elements from 0.1 keV to 1 MeV. Entries such as 1.93 + 4 are read 1.93 x 10^4 cm^2/g. Energies include absorption edge (K, L, . . .) and fluorescence (L_3–K) energies. At some low energies data were obtained by calculation slightly above and below subshell absorption edges. At higher energies data are given at all edges.

Data were taken from: Veigele, W. J., Briggs, E., Bates, L., Henry, E. M., and Bracewell, B., DNA 2433F, Vol. I and II, Kaman Sciences Corporation, Colorado Springs, Colorado, 31 July 1971; Henry, E. M., Bates, C. L., and Veigele, W. J., *Phys. Rev.*, 6, 2131, 1972; and Veigele, W. J., *Atomic Data*, 5, 51, 1973.

TABLE 3

Mass Attenuation and Absorption Cross Sections for 94 Elements; 0.1 keV to 1 MeV

Hydrogen **Z = 1**

Energy (keV)	τ/ρ (cm^2/g)	σ_c/ρ (cm^2/g)	σ_I/ρ (cm^2/g)	σ_a/ρ (cm^2/g)	μ/ρ (cm^2/g)
0.1	1.16+4	3.97–1	6.52–4	1.73–7	1.16+4
0.12	6.55+3	3.96–1	8.94–4	2.86–7	6.55+3
0.13	5.10+3	3.96–1	1.04–3	3.61–7	5.10+3
0.15	3.26+3	3.96–1	1.35–3	5.47–7	3.26+3
0.17	2.21+3	3.96–1	1.72–3	7.93–7	2.21+3
0.2	1.32+3	3.95–1	2.34–3	1.27–6	1.32+3
0.25	6.39+2	3.94–1	3.61–3	2.45–6	6.39+2
0.3	3.61+2	3.92–1	5.16–3	4.21–6	3.61+2
0.35	2.17+2	3.90–1	6.95–3	6.63–6	2.17+2
0.4	1.39+2	3.88–1	9.03–3	9.83–6	1.39+2
0.45	9.61+1	3.86–1	1.14–2	1.40–5	9.65+1
0.5	6.76+1	3.83–1	1.40–2	1.90–5	6.80+1
0.55	4.85+1	3.81–1	1.67–2	2.51–5	4.89+1
0.6	3.67+1	3.78–1	1.98–2	3.22–5	3.71+1
0.65	2.92+1	3.74–1	2.30–2	4.06–5	2.96+1
0.7	2.29+1	3.71–1	2.65–2	5.04–5	2.33+1
0.75	1.78+1	3.67–1	3.02–2	6.15–5	1.82+1
0.8	1.41+1	3.63–1	3.41–2	7.38–5	1.45+1
0.85	1.18+1	3.59–1	3.80–2	8.73–5	1.22+1

TABLE 3 (continued)

Energy (keV)	τ/ρ (cm²/g)	σ_c/ρ (cm²/g)	σ_I/ρ (cm²/g)	σ_a/ρ (cm²/g)	μ/ρ (cm²/g)
0.9	9.86+0	3.55−1	4.21−2	1.02−4	1.03+1
0.95	8.02+0	3.51−1	4.64−2	1.18−4	8.41+0
1.0	6.50+0	3.46−1	5.08−2	1.36−4	6.90+0
1.2	3.71+0	3.28−1	6.93−2	2.22−4	4.11+0
1.5	1.75+0	2.97−1	9.90−2	3.91−4	2.15+0
1.7	1.15+0	2.77−1	1.19−1	5.29−4	1.54+0
2.0	6.62−1	2.47−1	1.48−1	7.64−4	1.06+0
2.5	3.11−1	2.02−1	1.92−1	1.21−3	7.06−1
3.0	1.67−1	1.65−1	2.28−1	1.67−3	5.61−1
3.5	9.90−2	1.36−1	2.57−1	2.14−3	4.91−1
4.0	6.28−2	1.13−1	2.79−1	2.60−3	4.54−1
5.0	2.93−2	8.07−2	3.09−1	3.45−3	4.19−1
6.0	1.57−2	6.02−2	3.28−1	4.25−3	4.04−1
7.0	9.25−3	4.64−2	3.40−1	5.01−3	3.96−1
8.0	5.85−3	3.69−2	3.48−1	5.74−3	3.91−1
9.0	3.90−3	3.00−2	3.54−1	6.44−3	3.88−1
10.0	2.72−3	2.48−2	3.58−1	7.12−3	3.85−1
12.0	1.45−3	1.78−2	3.62−1	8.45−3	3.81−1
15.0	6.71−4	1.17−2	3.64−1	1.03−2	3.76−1
17.0	4.36−4	9.24−3	3.64−1	1.16−2	3.73−1
20.0	2.48−4	6.76−3	3.62−1	1.33−2	3.69−1
25.0	1.15−4	4.38−3	3.58−1	1.60−2	3.63−1
30.0	6.10−5	3.06−3	3.54−1	1.86−2	3.57−1
35.0	3.57−5	2.26−3	3.49−1	2.09−2	3.51−1
40.0	2.25−5	1.73−3	3.44−1	2.31−2	3.46−1
50.0	1.03−5	1.11−3	3.34−1	2.71−2	3.35−1
60.0	5.49−6	7.74−4	3.25−1	3.05−2	3.26−1
70.0	3.21−6	5.69−4	3.17−1	3.35−2	3.17−1
80.0	2.02−6	4.36−4	3.09−1	3.62−2	3.09−1
90.0	1.34−6	3.44−4	3.01−1	3.85−2	3.01−1
100.0	9.27−7	2.79−4	2.94−1	4.06−2	2.94−1
120.0	4.91−7	1.94−4	2.81−1	4.41−2	2.82−1
150.0	2.25−7	1.24−4	2.65−1	4.81−2	2.65−1
170.0	1.46−7	9.67−5	2.55−1	5.02−2	2.55−1
200.0	8.26−8	6.99−5	2.43−1	5.25−2	2.43−1
250.0	3.79−8	4.48−5	2.25−1	5.52−2	2.25−1
300.0	2.01−8	3.11−5	2.11−1	5.69−2	2.11−1
350.0	1.17−8	2.28−5	1.99−1	5.80−2	1.99−1
400.0	7.36−9	1.75−5	1.89−1	5.86−2	1.89−1
500.0	3.38−9	1.12−5	1.73−1	5.90−2	1.73−1
600.0	1.79−9	7.75−6	1.60−1	5.87−2	1.60−1
700.0	1.05−9	5.71−6	1.49−1	5.81−2	1.49−1
800.0	6.56−0	4.36−6	1.40−1	5.74−2	1.40−1
900.0	4.35−0	3.46−6	1.33−1	5.65−2	1.33−1
1,000.0	3.02−0	2.79−6	1.26−1	5.55−2	1.26−1
Helium		**Z = 2**			
0.1	5.40+4	4.00−1	1.28−4	3.28−8	5.40+4
0.15	1.89+4	4.00−1	2.49−4	9.97−8	1.89+4
0.2	8.61+3	3.99−1	4.52−4	2.47−7	8.61+3
0.3	2.70+3	3.98−1	1.02−3	8.42−7	2.70+3

TABLE 3 (continued)

Energy (keV)	τ/ρ (cm²/g)	σ_c/ρ (cm²/g)	σ_I/ρ (cm²/g)	σ_a/ρ (cm²/g)	μ/ρ (cm²/g)
0.4	1.13+3	3.97−1	1.81−3	1.98−6	1.13+3
0.5	5.70+2	3.95−1	2.83−3	3.86−6	5.70+2
0.6	3.18+2	3.92−1	4.04−3	6.62−6	3.18+2
0.7	1.94+2	3.89−1	5.48−3	1.05−5	1.95+2
0.8	1.25+2	3.86−1	7.12−3	1.55−5	1.26+2
0.9	8.48+1	3.82−1	8.88−3	2.17−5	8.52+1
1.0	6.09+1	3.78−1	1.09−2	2.94−5	6.13+1
1.2	3.43+1	3.70−1	1.52−2	4.92−5	3.47+1
1.5	1.65+1	3.54−1	2.28−2	9.17−5	1.69+1
1.7	1.09+1	3.43−1	2.83−2	1.29−4	1.13+1
2.0	6.39+0	3.25−1	3.71−2	1.97−4	6.76+0
2.5	3.05+0	2.94−1	5.25−2	3.44−4	3.40+0
3.0	1.66+0	2.63−1	6.76−2	5.22−4	2.00+0
3.5	9.95−1	2.33−1	8.19−2	7.26−4	1.31+0
4.0	6.37−1	2.07−1	9.47−2	9.44−4	9.38−1
5.0	3.01−1	1.62−1	1.16−1	1.39−3	5.79−1
6.0	1.63−1	1.29−1	1.32−1	1.84−3	4.23−1
7.0	9.69−2	1.04−1	1.43−1	2.28−3	3.44−1
8.0	6.17−2	8.47−2	1.52−1	2.69−3	2.98−1
9.0	4.14−2	7.05−2	1.58−1	3.08−3	2.70−1
10.0	2.90−2	5.94−2	1.63−1	3.46−3	2.52−1
12.0	1.56−2	4.38−2	1.69−1	4.17−3	2.29−1
15.0	7.29−3	2.98−2	1.74−1	5.15−3	2.11−1
17.0	4.76−3	2.38−2	1.76−1	5.78−3	2.05−1
20.0	2.73−3	1.77−2	1.77−1	6.67−3	1.98−1
25.0	1.27−3	1.17−2	1.77−1	8.06−3	1.90−1
30.0	6.82−4	8.25−3	1.76−1	9.35−3	1.84−1
35.0	4.02−4	6.13−3	1.74−1	1.05−2	1.80−1
40.0	2.54−4	4.73−3	1.72−1	1.16−2	1.77−1
50.0	1.18−4	3.05−3	1.67−1	1.36−2	1.71−1
60.0	6.32−5	2.13−3	1.63−1	1.54−2	1.65−1
70.0	3.72−5	1.57−3	1.59−1	1.69−2	1.61−1
80.0	2.35−5	1.21−3	1.55−1	1.82−2	1.56−1
90.0	1.57−5	9.53−4	1.51−1	1.94−2	1.52−1
100.0	1.09−5	7.74−4	1.48−1	2.05−2	1.49−1
120.0	5.83−6	5.38−4	1.42−1	2.22−2	1.42−1
150.0	2.71−6	3.44−4	1.33−1	2.42−2	1.34−1
170.0	1.76−6	2.68−4	1.29−1	2.53−2	1.29−1
200.0	1.01−6	1.94−4	1.22−1	2.65−2	1.22−1
250.0	4.69−7	1.24−4	1.13−1	2.78−2	1.14−1
300.0	2.51−7	8.63−5	1.06−1	2.87−2	1.06−1
350.0	1.48−7	6.34−5	1.00−1	2.92−2	1.00−1
400.0	9.39−8	4.85−5	9.53−2	2.95−2	9.53−2
500.0	4.38−8	3.11−5	8.70−2	2.97−2	8.70−2
600.0	2.35−8	2.16−5	8.05−2	2.96−2	8.05−2
700.0	1.39−8	1.59−5	7.52−2	2.93−2	7.52−2
800.0	8.85−9	1.21−5	7.07−2	2.89−2	7.07−2
900.0	5.94−9	9.61−6	6.69−2	2.84−2	6.69−2
1,000.0	4.15−9	7.74−6	6.35−2	2.80−2	6.36−2

TABLE 3 (continued)

Energy (keV)	τ/ρ (cm^2/g)	σ_c/ρ (cm^2/g)	σ_I/ρ (cm^2/g)	σ_a/ρ (cm^2/g)	μ/ρ (cm^2/g)
Lithium	**Z = 3**				
0.1	1.20+5	5.18−1	5.90−4	1.56−7	1.20+5
0.15	4.55+4	5.16−1	1.21−3	4.86−7	4.55+4
0.2	2.20+4	5.13−1	2.07−3	1.12−6	2.20+4
0.3	7.49+3	5.06−1	4.45−3	3.62−6	7.49+3
0.4	3.36+3	4.96−1	7.56−3	8.16−6	3.36+3
0.5	1.78+3	4.84−1	1.12−2	1.51−5	1.78+3
0.6	1.05+3	4.71−1	1.52−2	2.43−5	1.05+3
0.7	6.68+2	4.56−1	1.93−2	3.57−5	6.68+2
0.8	4.49+2	4.41−1	2.34−2	4.89−5	4.49+2
0.9	3.15+2	4.26−1	2.74−2	6.39−5	3.15+2
1.0	2.28+2	4.11−1	3.12−2	7.98−5	2.29+2
1.2	1.32+2	3.81−1	3.80−2	1.14−4	1.32+2
1.5	6.49+1	3.42−1	4.62−2	1.68−4	6.52+1
1.7	4.35+1	3.20−1	5.05−2	2.05−4	4.38+1
2.0	2.58+1	2.92−1	5.60−2	2.61−4	2.61+1
2.5	1.25+1	2.58−1	6.35−2	3.61−4	1.29+1
3.0	6.94+0	2.32−1	7.03−2	4.73−4	7.24+0
3.5	4.20+0	2.11−1	7.67−2	5.99−4	4.49+0
4.0	2.71+0	1.94−1	8.28−2	7.38−4	2.99+0
5.0	1.30+0	1.64−1	9.41−2	1.05−3	1.56+0
6.0	7.14−1	1.39−1	1.04−1	1.38−3	9.57−1
7.0	4.29−1	1.18−1	1.13−1	1.74−3	6.60−1
8.0	2.75−1	1.01−1	1.20−1	2.09−3	4.97−1
9.0	1.86−1	8.68−2	1.26−1	2.45−3	3.99−1
10.0	1.31−1	7.50−2	1.31−1	2.79−3	3.37−1
12.0	7.12−2	5.73−2	1.38−1	3.44−3	2.67−1
15.0	3.37−2	4.03−2	1.44−1	4.35−3	2.18−1
17.0	2.21−2	3.28−2	1.47−1	4.91−3	2.02−1
20.0	1.28−2	2.49−2	1.49−1	5.71−3	1.87−1
25.0	6.03−3	1.68−2	1.50−1	6.94−3	1.73−1
30.0	3.26−3	1.21−2	1.50−1	8.06−3	1.65−1
35.0	1.93−3	9.07−3	1.49−1	9.10−3	1.60−1
40.0	1.23−3	7.06−3	1.47−1	1.01−2	1.55−1
50.0	5.77−4	4.61−3	1.44−1	1.18−2	1.49−1
60.0	3.10−4	3.24−3	1.40−1	1.33−2	1.44−1
70.0	1.84−4	2.40−3	1.37−1	1.46−2	1.40−1
80.0	1.17−4	1.84−3	1.34−1	1.58−2	1.36−1
90.0	7.81−5	1.46−3	1.31−1	1.68−2	1.32−1
100.0	5.46−5	1.19−3	1.28−1	1.77−2	1.29−1
120.0	2.93−5	8.27−4	1.22−1	1.92−2	1.23−1
150.0	1.37−5	5.30−4	1.15−1	2.10−2	1.16−1
170.0	8.97−6	4.14−4	1.11−1	2.19−2	1.12−1
200.0	5.16−6	2.99−4	1.06−1	2.29−2	1.06−1
250.0	2.41−6	1.91−4	9.81−2	2.41−2	9.82−2
300.0	1.30−6	1.33−4	9.19−2	2.48−2	9.21−2
350.0	7.70−7	9.78−5	8.68−2	2.53−2	8.69−2
400.0	4.89−7	7.49−5	8.24−2	2.55−2	8.25−2
500.0	2.30−7	4.80−5	7.53−2	2.57−2	7.53−2
600.0	1.24−7	3.33−5	6.96−2	2.56−2	6.97−2
700.0	7.38−8	2.45−5	6.50−2	2.53−2	6.51−2
800.0	4.70−8	1.87−5	6.12−2	2.50−2	6.12−2

TABLE 3 (continued)

Energy (keV)	τ/ρ (cm^2/g)	σ_c/ρ (cm^2/g)	σ_I/ρ (cm^2/g)	σ_a/ρ (cm^2/g)	μ/ρ (cm^2/g)
900.0	3.16–8	1.48–5	5.79–2	2.46–2	5.79–2
1,000.0	2.22–8	1.20–5	5.50–2	2.42–2	5.50–2

Beryllium Z = 4

Energy (keV)	τ/ρ (cm^2/g)	σ_c/ρ (cm^2/g)	σ_I/ρ (cm^2/g)	σ_a/ρ (cm^2/g)	μ/ρ (cm^2/g)
0.1	8.05+3	7.10–1	4.07–4	1.09–7	8.05+3
0.1103 K	6.43+3	7.09–1	4.84–4	1.43–7	6.43+3
0.1117	1.57+5	7.09–1	4.95–4	1.48–7	1.57+5
0.15	8.47+4	7.08–1	8.56–4	3.48–7	8.47+4
0.2	4.48+4	7.05–1	1.49–3	8.09–7	4.48+4
0.3	1.63+4	6.98–1	3.27–3	2.67–6	1.63+4
0.4	7.75+3	6.88–1	5.67–3	6.16–6	7.75+3
0.5	4.19+3	6.76–1	8.63–3	1.17–5	4.20+3
0.6	2.54+3	6.62–1	1.20–2	1.95–5	2.54+3
0.7	1.66+3	6.46–1	1.58–2	2.96–5	1.66+3
0.8	1.12+3	6.28–1	1.98–2	4.22–5	1.12+3
0.9	7.91+2	6.10–1	2.39–2	5.71–5	7.92+2
1.0	5.92+2	5.91–1	2.81–2	7.39–5	5.93+2
1.2	3.57–2	5.52–1	3.64–2	1.14–4	3.58+2
1.5	1.80+2	4.95–1	4.77–2	1.82–4	1.81+2
1.7	1.23+2	4.59–1	5.44–2	2.31–4	1.23+2
2.0	7.40+1	4.10–1	6.27–2	3.06–4	7.44+1
2.5	3.68+1	3.45–1	7.31–2	4.29–4	3.72+1
3.0	2.07+1	2.97–1	8.05–2	5.50–4	2.11+1
3.5	1.27+1	2.61–1	8.63–2	6.73–4	1.30+1
4.0	8.26+0	2.33–1	9.12–2	8.00–4	8.59+0
5.0	4.03+0	1.93–1	9.95–2	1.07–3	4.32+0
6.0	2.23+0	1.65–1	1.07–1	1.37–3	2.50+0
7.0	1.35+0	1.44–1	1.13–1	1.68–3	1.61+0
8.0	8.73–1	1.26–1	1.19–1	2.01–3	1.12+0
9.0	5.93–1	1.11–1	1.24–1	2.35–3	8.28–1
10.0	4.20–1	9.77–2	1.29–1	2.69–3	6.46–1
12.0	2.30–1	7.72–2	1.36–1	3.36–3	4.43–1
15.0	1.10–1	5.61–2	1.43–1	4.31–3	3.09–1
17.0	7.23–2	4.62–2	1.46–1	4.92–3	2.65–1
20.0	4.20–2	3.56–2	1.49–1	5.77–3	2.27–1
25.0	1.99–2	2.45–2	1.51–1	7.06–3	1.96–1
30.0	1.08–2	1.78–2	1.51–1	8.23–3	1.80–1
35.0	6.43–3	1.35–2	1.51–1	9.31–3	1.71–1
40.0	4.10–3	1.06–2	1.50–1	1.03–2	1.64–1
50.0	1.93–3	7.02–3	1.47–1	1.21–2	1.56–1
60.0	1.04–3	4.97–3	1.43–1	1.36–2	1.49–1
70.0	6.19–4	3.69–3	1.40–1	1.50–2	1.44–1
80.0	3.94–4	2.85–3	1.37–1	1.62–2	1.40–1
90.0	2.65–4	2.27–3	1.34–1	1.72–2	1.36–1
100.0	1.85–4	1.84–3	1.31–1	1.82–2	1.33–1
120.0	1.00–4	1.29–3	1.25–1	1.97–2	1.27–1
150.0	4.70–5	8.28–4	1.18–1	2.15–2	1.19–1
170.0	3.08–5	6.46–4	1.14–1	2.24–2	1.15–1
200.0	1.78–5	4.67–4	1.08–1	2.35–2	1.09–1
250.0	8.38–6	3.00–4	1.01–1	2.47–2	1.01–1
300.0	4.54–6	2.08–4	9.44–2	2.55–2	9.46–2

TABLE 3 (continued)

Energy (keV)	τ/ρ (cm²/g)	σ_c/ρ (cm²/g)	σ_I/ρ (cm²/g)	σ_a/ρ (cm²/g)	μ/ρ (cm²/g)
350.0	2.70−6	1.53−4	8.91−2	2.59−2	8.92−2
400.0	1.73−6	1.17−4	8.46−2	2.62−2	8.47−2
500.0	8.20−7	7.50−5	7.73−2	2.64−2	7.73−2
600.0	4.47−7	5.21−5	7.14−2	2.63−2	7.15−2
700.0	2.68−7	3.83−5	6.67−2	2.60−2	6.68−2
800.0	1.72−7	2.93−5	6.28−2	2.57−2	6.28−2
900.0	1.17−7	2.32−5	5.94−2	2.53−2	5.94−2
1,000.0	8.26−8	1.88−5	5.64−2	2.48−2	5.65−2

Boron Z = 5

Energy (keV)	τ/ρ (cm²/g)	σ_c/ρ (cm²/g)	σ_I/ρ (cm²/g)	σ_a/ρ (cm²/g)	μ/ρ (cm²/g)
0.1	1.49+4	9.24−1	2.68−4	7.09−8	1.49+4
0.15	6.17+3	9.23−1	5.48−4	2.21−7	6.17+3
0.1873 K	3.66+3	9.21−1	8.36−4	4.24−7	3.67+3
0.1887 K	8.20+4	9.21−1	8.48−4	4.33−7	8.20+4
0.2	6.68+4	9.20−1	9.46−4	5.12−7	6.68+4
0.3	2.88+4	9.14−1	2.08−3	1.70−6	2.88+4
0.4	1.42+4	9.04−1	3.63−3	3.96−6	1.42+4
0.5	7.98+3	8.92−1	5.59−3	7.60−6	7.98+3
0.6	4.91+3	8.78−1	7.89−3	1.28−5	4.91+3
0.7	3.24+3	8.62−1	1.05−2	1.99−5	3.24+3
0.8	2.24+3	8.44−1	1.34−2	2.89−5	2.24+3
0.9	1.61+3	8.25−1	1.65−2	3.98−5	1.61+3
1.0	1.19+3	8.04−1	1.97−2	5.26−5	1.19+3
1.2	7.37+2	7.62−1	2.65−2	8.43−5	7.38+2
1.5	3.77+2	6.94−1	3.70−2	1.45−4	3.78+2
1.7	2.58+2	6.50−1	4.38−2	1.92−4	2.59+2
2.0	1.57+2	5.87−1	5.34−2	2.71−4	1.58+2
2.5	7.93+1	4.95−1	6.71−2	4.14−4	7.98+1
3.0	4.50+1	4.21−1	7.77−2	5.59−4	4.55+1
3.5	2.78+1	3.63−1	8.61−2	7.05−4	2.83+1
4.0	1.83+1	3.18−1	9.27−2	8.49−4	1.87+1
5.0	9.04+0	2.54−1	1.03−1	1.14−3	9.40+0
6.0	5.06+0	2.11−1	1.10−1	1.43−3	5.38+0
7.0	3.09+0	1.80−1	1.16−1	1.73−3	3.39+0
8.0	2.01+0	1.57−1	1.22−1	2.05−3	2.29+0
9.0	1.38+0	1.39−1	1.26−1	2.37−3	1.64+0
10.0	9.78−1	1.23−1	1.30−1	2.70−3	1.23+0
12.0	5.41−1	9.92−2	1.37−1	3.37−3	7.78−1
15.0	2.61−1	7.39−2	1.45−1	4.35−3	4.80−1
17.0	1.73−1	6.16−2	1.48−1	4.99−3	3.83−1
20.0	1.02−1	4.80−2	1.52−1	5.89−3	3.01−1
25.0	4.86−2	3.35−2	1.55−1	7.26−3	2.37−1
30.0	2.66−2	2.46−2	1.56−1	8.52−3	2.07−1
35.0	1.59−2	1.88−2	1.55−1	9.65−3	1.90−1
40.0	1.02−2	1.49−2	1.55−1	1.07−2	1.80−1
50.0	4.86−3	9.92−3	1.52−1	1.26−2	1.67−1
60.0	2.64−3	7.06−3	1.49−1	1.42−2	1.58−1
70.0	1.58−3	5.28−3	1.46−1	1.56−2	1.52−1
80.0	1.01−3	4.09−3	1.42−1	1.69−2	1.47−1
90.0	6.81−4	3.25−3	1.39−1	1.80−2	1.43−1
100.0	4.79−4	2.65−3	1.36−1	1.89−2	1.39−1
120.0	2.60−4	1.86−3	1.30−1	2.06−2	1.33−1
150.0	1.23−4	1.20−3	1.23−1	2.24−2	1.24−1
170.0	8.08−5	9.35−4	1.19−1	2.34−2	1.20−1

TABLE 3 (continued)

Energy (keV)	τ/ρ (cm^2/g)	σ_c/ρ (cm^2/g)	σ_I/ρ (cm^2/g)	σ_a/ρ (cm^2/g)	μ/ρ (cm^2/g)
200.0	4.69–5	6.77–4	1.13–1	2.45–2	1.14–1
250.0	2.22–5	4.35–4	1.05–1	2.58–2	1.05–1
300.0	1.21–5	3.02–4	9.83–2	2.65–2	9.87–2
350.0	7.23–6	2.22–4	9.28–2	2.70–2	9.30–2
400.0	4.63–6	1.70–4	8.81–2	2.73–2	8.83–2
500.0	2.20–6	1.09–4	8.05–2	2.75–2	8.06–2
600.0	1.20–6	7.57–5	7.45–2	2.74–2	7.45–2
700.0	7.23–7	5.57–5	6.95–2	2.71–2	6.96–2
800.0	4.65–7	4.26–5	6.54–2	2.67–2	6.55–2
900.0	3.15–7	3.37–5	6.19–2	2.63–2	6.19–2
1,000.0	2.23–7	2.73–5	5.88–2	2.59–2	5.88–2

Carbon **Z = 6**

Energy (keV)	τ/ρ (cm^2/g)	σ_c/ρ (cm^2/g)	σ_I/ρ (cm^2/g)	σ_a/ρ (cm^2/g)	μ/ρ (cm^2/g)
0.1	2.65+4	1.20+0	1.92–4	5.06–8	2.65+4
0.15	1.08+4	1.20+0	3.92–4	1.58–7	1.08+4
0.2	5.58+3	1.20+0	6.83–4	3.71–7	5.58+3
0.2831 K	2.53+3	1.19+0	1.35–3	1.04–6	2.53+3
0.2845 K	4.90+4	1.19+0	1.36–3	1.06–6	4.90+4
0.3	4.20+4	1.19+0	1.51–3	1.24–6	4.20+4
0.4	2.29+4	1.18+0	2.65–3	2.89–6	2.29+4
0.5	1.34+4	1.17+0	4.11–3	5.59–6	1.34+4
0.6	8.44+3	1.15+0	5.83–3	9.50–6	8.44+3
0.7	5.64+3	1.14+0	7.82–3	1.49–5	5.64+3
0.8	3.95+3	1.12+0	1.01–2	2.18–5	3.95+3
0.9	2.87+3	1.10+0	1.24–2	3.02–5	2.87+3
1.0	2.15+3	1.08+0	1.50–2	4.04–5	2.15+3
1.2	1.32+3	1.03+0	2.06–2	6.60–5	1.32+3
1.5	6.92+2	9.60–1	2.96–2	1.18–4	6.93+2
1.7	4.80+2	9.09–1	3.59–2	1.60–4	4.81+2
2.0	2.96+2	8.33–1	4.52–2	2.34–4	2.97+2
2.5	1.52+2	7.16–1	5.97–2	3.79–4	1.53+2
3.0	8.74+1	6.16–1	7.23–2	5.38–4	8.81+1
3.5	5.46+1	5.31–1	8.30–2	7.05–4	5.52+1
4.0	3.62+1	4.63–1	9.19–2	8.74–4	3.67+1
5.0	1.81+1	3.63–1	1.05–1	1.21–3	1.86+1
6.0	1.02+1	2.95–1	1.15–1	1.54–3	1.06+1
7.0	6.29+0	2.47–1	1.22–1	1.86–3	6.66+0
8.0	4.12+0	2.12–1	1.28–1	2.19–3	4.46+0
9.0	2.83+0	1.85–1	1.33–4	2.53–3	3.15+0
10.0	2.02+0	1.63–1	1.37–1	2.87–3	2.32+0
12.0	1.13+0	1.31–1	1.45–1	3.55–3	1.40+0
15.0	5.48–1	9.86–2	1.52–1	4.59–3	7.99–1
17.0	3.65–1	8.29–2	1.56–1	5.26–3	6.05–1
20.0	2.15–1	6.53–2	1.60–1	6.24–3	4.41–1
25.0	1.04–1	4.60–2	1.64–1	7.75–3	3.14–1
30.0	5.71–2	3.40–2	1.66–1	9.12–3	2.57–1
35.0	3.44–2	2.61–2	1.66–1	1.04–2	2.27–1
40.0	2.22–2	2.07–2	1.65–1	1.15–2	2.08–1
50.0	1.06–2	1.39–2	1.63–1	1.36–2	1.88–1
60.0	5.81–3	9.95–3	1.60–1	1.53–2	1.76–1
70.0	3.49–3	7.46–3	1.56–1	1.69–2	1.67–1
80.0	2.24–3	5.80–3	1.53–1	1.82–2	1.61–1
90.0	1.52–3	4.63–3	1.50–1	1.94–2	1.56–1

TABLE 3 (continued)

Energy (keV)	τ/ρ (cm²/g)	σ_c/ρ (cm²/g)	σ_I/ρ (cm²/g)	σ_a/ρ (cm²/g)	μ/ρ (cm²/g)
100.0	1.07–3	3.78–3	1.47–1	2.04–2	1.51–1
120.0	5.85–4	2.65–3	1.41–1	2.22–2	1.44–1
150.0	2.80–4	1.71–3	1.33–1	2.42–2	1.35–1
170.0	1.85–4	1.34–3	1.28–1	2.53–2	1.30–1
200.0	1.08–4	9.71–4	1.22–1	2.65–2	1.23–1
250.0	5.19–5	6.24–4	1.13–1	2.78–2	1.14–1
300.0	2.86–5	4.34–4	1.06–1	2.87–2	1.07–1
350.0	1.72–5	3.19–4	1.00–1	2.92–2	1.01–1
400.0	1.12–5	2.45–4	9.52–2	2.95–2	9.54–2
500.0	5.40–6	1.57–4	8.69–2	2.97–2	8.70–2
600.0	3.00–6	1.09–4	8.04–2	2.96–2	8.05–2
700.0	1.82–6	8.00–5	7.51–2	2.93–2	7.52–2
800.0	1.19–6	6.12–5	7.06–2	2.89–2	7.07–2
900.0	8.17–7	4.84–5	6.68–2	2.84–2	6.69–2
1,000.0	5.84–7	3.92–5	6.35–2	2.80–2	6.36–2

Nitrogen **Z = 7**

Energy (keV)	τ/ρ (cm²/g)	σ_c/ρ (cm²/g)	σ_I/ρ (cm²/g)	σ_a/ρ (cm²/g)	μ/ρ (cm²/g)
0.1	4.45+4	1.40+0	1.34–4	3.60–8	4.45+4
0.15	1.76+4	1.40+0	2.85–4	1.16–7	1.76+4
0.2	9.02+3	1.40+0	4.95–4	2.69–7	9.02+3
0.3	3.41+3	1.39+0	1.10–3	8.95–7	3.42+3
0.4	1.70+3	1.38+0	1.92–3	2.10–6	1.70+3
0.4009 K	1.69+3	1.38+0	1.93–3	2.11–6	1.69+3
0.4023	2.98+4	1.38+0	1.95–3	2.13–6	2.98+4
0.5	1.90+4	1.37+0	2.98–3	4.06–6	1.90+4
0.6	1.22+4	1.36+0	4.25–3	6.93–6	1.22+4
0.7	8.32+3	1.34+0	5.72–3	1.09–5	8.32+3
0.8	5.90+3	1.33+0	7.39–3	1.60–5	5.90+3
0.9	4.33+3	1.31+0	9.17–3	2.23–5	4.33+3
1.0	3.27+3	1.29+0	1.11–2	3.00–5	3.27+3
1.2	2.08+3	1.25+0	1.54–2	4.95–5	2.08+3
1.5	1.10+3	1.17+0	2.25–2	8.97–5	1.10+3
1.7	7.67+2	1.12+0	2.75–2	1.24–4	7.68+2
2.0	4.78+2	1.05+0	3.53–2	1.85–4	4.79+2
2.5	2.48+2	9.17–1	4.81–2	3.09–4	2.49+2
3.0	1.44+2	8.01–1	5.99–2	4.54–4	1.45+2
3.5	9.05+1	6.99–1	7.07–2	6.14–4	9.13+1
4.0	6.04+1	6.12–1	8.02–2	7.83–4	6.11+1
5.0	3.05+1	4.80–1	9.55–2	1.13–3	3.11+1
6.0	1.74+1	3.87–1	1.07–1	1.47–3	1.79+1
7.0	1.08+1	3.20–1	1.16–1	1.82–3	1.12+1
8.0	7.08+0	2.70–1	1.23–1	2.16–3	7.48+0
9.0	4.89+0	2.33–1	1.28–1	2.49–3	5.25+0
10.0	3.51+0	2.04–1	1.33–1	2.83–3	3.84+0
12.0	1.96+0	1.62–1	1.41–1	3.50–3	2.27+0
15.0	9.63–1	1.21–1	1.49–1	4.50–3	1.23+0
17.0	6.44–1	1.02–1	1.53–1	5.16–3	8.99–1
20.0	3.81–1	8.09–2	1.57–1	6.13–3	6.19–1
25.0	1.85–1	5.74–2	1.61–1	7.64–3	4.04–1
30.0	1.02–1	4.27–2	1.64–1	9.03–3	3.08–1
35.0	6.17–2	3.29–2	1.64–1	1.03–2	2.59–1
40.0	3.99–2	2.61–2	1.64–1	1.15–2	2.30–1

TABLE 3 (continued)

Energy (keV)	τ/ρ (cm^2/g)	σ_c/ρ (cm^2/g)	σ_I/ρ (cm^2/g)	σ_a/ρ (cm^2/g)	μ/ρ (cm^2/g)
50.0	1.92−2	1.76−2	1.62−1	1.35−2	1.99−1
60.0	1.05−2	1.26−2	1.59−1	1.53−2	1.82−1
70.0	6.32−3	9.50−3	1.56−1	1.68−2	1.72−1
80.0	4.07−3	7.39−3	1.53−1	1.82−2	1.64−1
90.0	2.76−3	5.91−3	1.49−1	1.94−2	1.58−1
100.0	1.94−3	4.84−3	1.46−1	2.04−2	1.53−1
120.0	1.06−3	3.40−3	1.40−1	2.22−2	1.45−1
150.0	5.09−4	2.20−3	1.33−1	2.42−2	1.35−1
170.0	3.36−4	1.72−3	1.28−1	2.53−2	1.30−1
200.0	1.96−4	1.25−3	1.22−1	2.65−2	1.23−1
250.0	9.41−5	8.04−4	1.13−1	2.78−2	1.14−1
300.0	5.16−5	5.59−4	1.06−1	2.87−2	1.07−1
350.0	3.11−5	4.12−4	1.00−1	2.92−2	1.01−1
400.0	2.01−5	3.16−4	9.52−2	2.95−2	9.55−2
500.0	9.67−6	2.02−4	8.69−2	2.97−2	8.72−2
600.0	5.34−6	1.40−4	8.04−2	2.96−2	8.06−2
700.0	3.23−6	1.03−4	7.51−2	2.93−2	7.52−2
800.0	2.10−6	7.89−5	7.07−2	2.89−2	7.08−2
900.0	1.44−6	6.26−5	6.69−2	2.84−2	6.69−2
1,000.0	1.02−6	5.05−5	6.35−2	2.80−2	6.36−2

Oxygen **Z = 8**

Energy (keV)	τ/ρ (cm^2/g)	σ_c/ρ (cm^2/g)	σ_I/ρ (cm^2/g)	σ_a/ρ (cm^2/g)	μ/ρ (cm^2/g)
0.1	6.23+4	1.60+0	1.07−4	2.80−8	6.23+4
0.15	2.56+4	1.60+0	2.16−4	8.70−8	2.56+4
0.2	1.32+4	1.60+0	3.76−4	2.04−7	1.32+4
0.3	5.01+3	1.59+0	8.31−4	6.79−7	5.01+3
0.4	2.48+3	1.59+0	1.46−3	1.60−6	2.49+3
0.5	1.44+3	1.58+0	2.27−3	3.10−6	1.44+3
0.5313 K	1.23+3	1.57+0	2.56−3	3.71−6	1.23+3
0.5327	1.90+4	1.57+0	2.57−3	3.74−6	1.90+4
0.6	1.60+4	1.56+0	3.24−2	5.30−6	1.60+4
0.7	1.09+4	1.55+0	4.38−3	8.35−6	1.09+4
0.8	7.94+3	1.54+0	5.68−3	1.24−5	7.94+3
0.9	5.89+3	1.52+0	7.07−3	1.73−5	5.89+3
1.0	4.50+3	1.50+0	8.62−3	2.33−5	4.50+3
1.2	2.91+3	1.46+0	1.20−2	3.88−5	2.91+3
1.5	1.57+3	1.39+0	1.78−2	7.15−5	1.57+3
1.7	1.11+3	1.34+0	2.20−2	9.95−5	1.11+3
2.0	6.98+2	1.26+0	2.86−2	1.51−4	7.00+2
2.5	3.68+2	1.13+0	4.00−2	2.60−4	3.69+2
3.0	2.16+2	1.00+0	5.10−2	3.92−4	2.17+2
3.5	1.37+2	8.86−1	6.15−2	5.43−4	1.38+2
4.0	9.21+1	7.84−1	7.11−2	7.07−4	9.30+1
5.0	4.71+1	6.21−1	8.73−2	1.05−3	4.78+1
6.0	2.70+1	5.01−1	1.00−1	1.41−3	2.76+1
7.0	1.68+1	4.12−1	1.10−1	1.77−3	1.73+1
8.0	1.11+1	3.47−1	1.18−1	2.12−3	1.16+1
9.0	7.71+0	2.97−1	1.24−1	2.46−3	8.13+0
10.0	5.55+0	2.58−1	1.30−1	2.80−3	5.94+0
12.0	3.13+0	2.02−1	1.37−1	3.46−3	3.47+0
15.0	1.54+0	1.49−1	1.46−1	4.45−3	1.84+0
17.0	1.03+0	1.26−1	1.50−1	5.09−3	1.31+0
20.0	6.14−1	9.95−2	1.54−1	6.05−3	8.68−1

TABLE 3 (continued)

Energy (keV)	τ/ρ (cm^2/g)	σ_c/ρ (cm^2/g)	σ_I/ρ (cm^2/g)	σ_a/ρ (cm^2/g)	μ/ρ (cm^2/g)
25.0	2.99–1	7.09–2	1.59–1	7.55–3	5.29–1
30.0	1.66–1	5.28–2	1.62–1	8.96–3	3.80–1
35.0	1.00–1	4.08–2	1.63–1	1.02–2	3.04–1
40.0	6.49–2	3.25–2	1.63–1	1.14–2	2.60–1
50.0	3.13–2	2.19–2	1.61–1	1.35–2	2.14–1
60.0	1.72–2	1.58–2	1.58–1	1.53–2	1.91–1
70.0	1.04–2	1.19–2	1.55–1	1.68–2	1.78–1
80.0	6.69–3	9.26–3	1.52–1	1.82–2	1.68–1
90.0	4.54–3	7.41–3	1.49–1	1.94–2	1.61–1
100.0	3.21–3	6.08–3	1.46–1	2.04–2	1.55–1
120.0	1.76–3	4.28–3	1.40–1	2.22–2	1.46–1
150.0	8.45–4	2.78–3	1.32–1	2.42–2	1.36–1
170.0	5.60–4	2.17–3	1.28–1	2.53–2	1.31–1
200.0	3.29–4	1.58–3	1.22–1	2.65–2	1.24–1
250.0	1.58–4	1.02–3	1.13–1	2.78–2	1.14–1
300.0	8.73–5	7.07–4	1.06–1	2.87–2	1.07–1
350.0	5.28–5	5.21–4	1.00–1	2.92–2	1.01–1
400.0	3.42–5	3.99–4	9.52–2	2.95–2	9.56–2
500.0	1.66–5	2.56–4	8.70–2	2.97–2	8.72–2
600.0	9.26–6	1.78–4	8.05–2	2.96–2	8.07–2
700.0	5.66–6	1.31–4	7.52–2	2.93–2	7.53–2
800.0	3.70–6	9.99–5	7.07–2	2.89–2	7.08–2
900.0	2.55–6	7.92–5	6.69–2	2.85–2	6.70–2
1,000.0	1.83–6	6.40–5	6.36–2	2.80–2	6.37–2

Fluorine **Z = 9**

Energy (keV)	τ/ρ (cm^2/g)	σ_c/ρ (cm^2/g)	σ_I/ρ (cm^2/g)	σ_a/ρ (cm^2/g)	μ/ρ (cm^2/g)
0.1	8.64+4	1.71+0	7.20–5	1.96–8	8.64+4
0.15	3.61+4	1.71+0	1.59–4	6.53–8	3.61+4
0.2	1.87+4	1.70+0	2.79–4	1.52–7	1.87+4
0.3	7.05+3	1.70+0	6.20–4	5.08–7	7.06+3
0.4	3.45+3	1.69+0	1.09–3	1.19–6	3.45+3
0.5	1.97+3	1.68+0	1.70–3	2.32–6	1.97+3
0.6	1.23+3	1.67+0	2.43–3	3.97–6	1.24+3
0.6847 K	8.77+2	1.66+0	3.15–3	5.87–6	8.79+2
0.6861 K	1.22+4	1.66+0	3.16–3	5.91–6	1.22+4
0.7	1.25+4	1.66+0	3.29–3	6.28–6	1.25+4
0.8	9.74+3	1.65+0	4.28–3	9.32–6	9.74+3
0.9	7.26+3	1.63+0	5.33–3	1.30–5	7.26+3
1.0	5.61+3	1.62+0	6.51–3	1.77–5	5.62+3
1.2	3.74+3	1.58+0	9.12–3	2.95–5	3.74+3
1.5	2.03+3	1.52+0	1.37–2	5.50–5	2.04+3
1.7	1.44+3	1.47+0	1.70–2	7.71–5	1.44+3
2.0	9.13+2	1.40+0	2.23–2	1.18–4	9.14+2
2.5	4.84+2	1.27+0	3.17–2	2.08–4	4.86+2
3.0	2.86+2	1.15+0	4.11–2	3.19–4	2.87+2
3.5	1.83+2	1.03+0	5.04–2	4.50–4	1.84+2
4.0	1.23+2	9.20–1	5.92–2	5.96–4	1.24+2
5.0	6.35+1	7.39–1	7.47–2	9.15–4	6.43+1
6.0	3.67+1	6.00–1	8.76–2	1.26–3	3.74+1
7.0	2.30+1	4.95–1	9.80–2	1.60–3	2.36+1
8.0	1.53+1	4.16–1	1.06–1	1.94–3	1.58+1
9.0	1.06+1	3.55–1	1.13–1	2.28–3	1.11+1

TABLE 3 (continued)

Energy (keV)	τ/ρ (cm²/g)	σ_c/ρ (cm²/g)	σ_I/ρ (cm²/g)	σ_a/ρ (cm²/g)	μ/ρ (cm²/g)
10.0	7.68+0	3.07−1	1.19−1	2.60−3	8.11+0
12.0	4.36+0	2.39−1	1.27−1	3.24−3	4.72+0
15.0	2.17+0	1.74−1	1.35−1	4.17−3	2.48+0
17.0	1.46+0	1.46−1	1.39−1	4.77−3	1.74+0
20.0	8.72−1	1.15−1	1.44−1	5.66−3	1.13+0
25.0	4.28−1	8.20−2	1.49−1	7.08−3	6.59−1
30.0	2.39−1	6.12−2	1.51−1	8.40−3	4.51−1
35.0	1.45−1	4.74−2	1.52−1	9.63−3	3.45−1
40.0	9.45−2	3.78−2	1.53−1	1.08−2	2.85−1
50.0	4.59−2	2.55−2	1.52−1	1.27−2	2.23−1
60.0	2.54−2	1.84−2	1.49−1	1.44−2	1.93−1
70.0	1.54−2	1.38−2	1.47−1	1.59−2	1.76−1
80.0	9.95−3	1.08−2	1.44−1	1.72−2	1.64−1
90.0	6.77−3	8.66−3	1.41−1	1.84−2	1.56−1
100.0	4.80−3	7.10−3	1.38−1	1.94−2	1.50−1
120.0	2.65−3	5.01−3	1.33−1	2.10−2	1.40−1
150.0	1.28−3	3.26−3	1.25−1	2.30−2	1.30−1
170.0	8.49−4	2.55−3	1.21−1	2.39−2	1.24−1
200.0	5.00−4	1.85−3	1.15−1	2.51−2	1.18−1
250.0	2.41−4	1.19−3	1.07−1	2.64−2	1.09−1
300.0	1.33−4	8.32−4	1.01−1	2.72−2	1.01−1
350.0	8.09−5	6.12−4	9.49−2	2.77−2	9.56−2
400.0	5.25−5	4.69−4	9.02−2	2.80−2	9.07−2
500.0	2.56−5	3.01−4	8.24−2	2.82−2	8.27−2
600.0	1.42−5	2.09−4	7.62−2	2.80−2	7.65−2
700.0	8.69−6	1.54−4	7.12−2	2.78−2	7.14−2
800.0	5.67−6	1.18−4	6.70−2	2.74−2	6.71−2
900.0	3.90−6	9.31−5	6.34−2	2.70−2	6.35−2
1,000.0	2.80−6	7.52−5	6.02−2	2.65−2	6.03−2

Neon **Z = 10**

Energy (keV)	τ/ρ (cm²/g)	σ_c/ρ (cm²/g)	σ_I/ρ (cm²/g)	σ_a/ρ (cm²/g)	μ/ρ (cm²/g)
0.1	1.23+5	1.98+0	6.35−5	1.71−8	1.23+5
0.12	8.69+4	1.98+0	8.88−5	2.88−8	8.69+4
0.15	5.44+4	1.98+0	1.36−4	5.55−8	5.44+4
0.2	2.85+4	1.98+0	2.37−4	1.29−7	2.86+4
0.25	1.69+4	1.98+0	3.66−4	2.50−7	1.69+4
0.3	1.08+4	1.98+0	5.25−4	4.29−7	1.08+4
0.4	5.28+3	1.97+0	9.25−4	1.01−6	5.28+3
0.5	2.99+3	1.96+0	1.44−3	1.97−6	2.99+3
0.6	1.87+3	1.95+0	2.06−3	3.37−6	1.87+3
0.7	1.25+3	1.94+0	2.79−3	5.33−6	1.25+3
0.8	8.75+2	1.93+0	3.63−3	7.92−6	8.77+2
0.8662 K	7.08+2	1.92+0	4.23−3	9.95−6	7.10+2
0.8676	9.05+3	1.92+0	4.24−3	1.00−5	9.06+3
0.88	9.66+3	1.92+0	4.35−3	1.04−5	9.67+3
0.9	9.61+3	1.91+0	4.54−3	1.11−5	9.61+3
1.0	7.66+3	1.90+0	5.55−3	1.51−5	7.66+3
1.2	4.94+3	1.86+0	7.80−3	2.53−5	4.95+3
1.5	2.74+3	1.80+0	1.18−2	4.74−5	2.74+3
1.7	1.95+3	1.76+0	1.47−2	6.68−5	1.95+3
2.0	1.25+3	1.68+0	1.94−2	1.03−4	1.25+3

TABLE 3 (continued)

Energy (keV)	τ/ρ (cm²/g)	σ_c/ρ (cm²/g)	σ_I/ρ (cm²/g)	σ_a/ρ (cm²/g)	μ/ρ (cm²/g)
2.5	6.74+2	1.55+0	2.78−2	1.83−4	6.75+2
3.0	4.03+2	1.41+0	3.66−2	2.86−4	4.04+2
3.5	2.59+2	1.28+0	4.54−2	4.08−4	2.60+2
4.0	1.76+2	1.16+0	5.38−3	5.47−4	1.77+2
5.0	9.15+1	9.47−1	6.94−2	8.60−4	9.25+1
6.0	5.33+1	7.77−1	8.29−2	1.21−3	5.41+1
7.0	3.35+1	6.45−1	9.43−2	1.57−3	3.43+1
8.0	2.24+1	5.42−1	1.04−1	1.93−3	2.31+1
9.0	1.57+1	4.63−1	1.12−1	2.29−3	1.62+1
10.0	1.13+1	4.00−1	1.18−1	2.64−3	1.19+1
12.0	6.47+0	3.09−1	1.28−1	3.32−3	6.91+0
15.0	3.23+0	2.24−1	1.38−1	4.30−3	3.60+0
17.0	2.19+0	1.86−1	1.42−1	4.93−3	2.51+0
20.0	1.31+0	1.46−1	1.47−1	5.85−3	1.60+0
25.0	6.47−1	1.04−1	1.53−1	7.33−3	9.04−1
30.0	3.62−1	7.77−2	1.56−1	8.71−3	5.95−1
35.0	2.21−1	6.02−2	1.58−1	1.00−2	4.39−1
40.0	1.44−1	4.80−2	1.58−1	1.12−2	3.50−1
50.0	7.01−2	3.25−2	1.57−1	1.33−2	2.60−1
60.0	3.89−2	2.34−2	1.55−1	1.51−2	2.17−1
70.0	2.36−2	1.76−2	1.53−1	1.66−2	1.94−1
80.0	1.53−2	1.38−2	1.50−1	1.80−2	1.79−1
90.0	1.04−2	1.10−2	1.47−1	1.92−2	1.68−1
100.0	7.42−3	9.05−3	1.44−1	2.02−2	1.60−1
120.0	4.10−3	6.40−3	1.38−1	2.20−2	1.49−1
150.0	1.98−3	4.16−3	1.31−1	2.40−2	1.37−1
170.0	1.32−3	3.26−3	1.26−1	2.50−2	1.31−1
200.0	7.80−4	2.37−3	1.20−1	2.62−2	1.24−1
250.0	3.78−4	1.53−3	1.12−1	2.76−2	1.14−1
300.0	2.10−4	1.07−3	1.05−1	2.84−2	1.06−1
350.0	1.28−4	7.84−4	9.92−2	2.90−2	1.00−1
400.0	8.32−5	6.02−4	9.43−2	2.93−2	9.49−2
500.0	4.07−5	3.86−4	8.61−2	2.95−2	8.66−2
600.0	2.28−5	2.68−4	7.97−2	2.93−2	8.00−2
700.0	1.40−5	1.97−4	7.44−2	2.90−2	7.47−2
800.0	9.18−6	1.51−4	7.00−2	2.86−2	7.02−2
900.0	6.34−6	1.19−4	6.63−2	2.82−2	6.64−2
1,000.0	4.57−6	9.64−5	6.30−2	2.77−2	6.31−2

Sodium **Z = 11**

0.1	1.24+5	2.10+0	2.34−4	6.22−8	1.24+5
0.15	6.04+4	2.10+0	4.82−4	1.95−7	6.04+4
0.2	3.35+4	2.10+0	8.25−4	4.46−7	3.35+4
0.3	1.34+4	2.09+0	1.77−3	1.44−6	1.34+4
0.4	6.75+3	2.07+0	3.01−3	3.25−6	6.76+3
0.5	3.87+3	2.05+0	4.47−3	6.00−6	3.87+3
0.6	2.45+3	2.03+0	6.07−3	9.70−6	2.45+3
0.7	1.63+3	2.00+0	7.73−3	1.43−5	1.64+3
0.8	1.16+3	1.98+0	9.40−3	1.97−5	1.16+3
0.9	8.48+2	1.95+0	1.11−2	2.59−5	8.50+2
1.0	6.42+2	1.92+0	1.27−2	3.26−5	6.44+2

TABLE 3 (continued)

Energy (keV)	τ/ρ (cm^2/g)	σ_c/ρ (cm^2/g)	σ_I/ρ (cm^2/g)	σ_a/ρ (cm^2/g)	μ/ρ (cm^2/g)
1.072 K	5.52+2	1.90+0	1.38−2	3.77−5	5.54+2
1.072	8.22+3	1.90+0	1.38−2	3.77−5	8.22+3
1.2	6.13+3	1.86+0	1.58−2	4.78−5	6.13+3
1.5	3.40+3	1.77+0	1.99−2	7.41−5	3.41+3
1.7	2.43+3	1.72+0	2.26−2	9.42−5	2.44+3
2.0	1.57+3	1.64+0	2.65−2	1.29−4	1.57+3
2.5	8.46+2	1.52+0	3.30−2	1.99−4	8.47+2
3.0	5.07+2	1.40+0	3.96−2	2.87−4	5.08+2
3.5	3.27+2	1.29+0	4.64−2	3.92−4	3.29+2
4.0	2.23+2	1.18+0	5.30−2	5.11−4	2.24+2
5.0	1.17+2	9.93−1	6.58−2	7.87−4	1.18+2
6.0	6.83+1	8.32−1	7.74−2	1.10−3	6.92+1
7.0	4.32+1	7.00−1	8.77−2	1.43−3	4.40+1
8.0	2.90+1	5.94−1	9.65−2	1.78−3	2.97+1
9.0	2.03+1	5.10−1	1.04−1	2.13−3	2.09+1
10.0	1.48+1	4.42−1	1.10−1	2.47−3	1.53+1
12.0	8.46+0	3.42−1	1.20−1	3.14−3	8.93+0
15.0	4.26+0	2.48−1	1.30−1	4.09−3	4.64+0
17.0	2.89+0	2.06−1	1.35−1	4.70−3	3.23+0
20.0	1.74+0	1.62−1	1.40−1	5.59−3	2.04+0
25.0	8.64−1	1.15−1	1.46−1	7.01−3	1.13+0
30.0	4.86−1	8.63−2	1.49−1	8.34−3	7.21−1
35.0	2.98−1	6.71−2	1.51−1	9.58−3	5.16−1
40.0	1.95−1	5.36−2	1.51−1	1.07−2	4.00−1
50.0	9.56−2	3.64−2	1.51−1	1.28−2	2.83−1
60.0	5.33−2	2.62−2	1.49−1	1.45−2	2.29−1
70.0	3.25−2	1.98−2	1.47−1	1.60−2	1.99−1
80.0	2.11−2	1.55−2	1.44−1	1.74−2	1.81−1
90.0	1.45−2	1.24−2	1.41−1	1.85−2	1.68−1
100.0	1.03−2	1.02−2	1.39−1	1.95−2	1.59−1
120.0	5.72−3	7.21−3	1.33−1	2.12−2	1.46−1
150.0	2.78−3	4.70−3	1.26−1	2.32−2	1.34−1
170.0	1.86−3	3.69−3	1.22−1	2.42−2	1.27−1
200.0	1.10−3	2.68−3	1.16−1	2.53−2	1.20−1
250.0	5.35−4	1.73−3	1.08−1	2.66−2	1.10−1
300.0	2.98−4	1.21−3	1.01−1	2.75−2	1.03−1
350.0	1.81−4	8.89−4	9.58−2	2.80−2	9.69−2
400.0	1.18−4	6.82−4	9.10−2	2.82−2	9.18−2
500.0	5.80−5	4.37−4	8.32−2	2.84−2	8.37−2
600.0	3.25−5	3.04−4	7.70−2	2.83−2	7.73−2
700.0	1.99−5	2.23−4	7.19−2	2.80−2	7.21−2
800.0	1.31−5	1.71−4	6.76−2	2.77−2	6.78−2
900.0	9.03−6	1.35−4	6.40−2	2.72−2	6.42−2
1,000.0	6.49−6	1.09−4	6.08−2	2.68−2	6.09−2

Magnesium **Z = 12**

0.1	1.48+5	2.37+0	2.46−4	6.53−8	1.48+5
0.15	7.88+4	2.36+0	5.09−4	2.06−7	7.88+4
0.2	4.49+4	2.36+0	8.79−4	4.76−7	4.49+4
0.3	1.83+4	2.35+0	1.92−3	1.56−6	1.83+4
0.4	9.32+3	2.33+0	3.30−3	3.57−6	9.33+3
0.5	5.37+3	2.31+0	4.98−3	6.72−6	5.37+3
0.6	3.42+3	2.28+0	6.88−3	1.11−5	3.42+3

TABLE 3 (continued)

Energy (keV)	τ/ρ (cm²/g)	σ_c/ρ (cm²/g)	σ_I/ρ (cm²/g)	σ_a/ρ (cm²/g)	μ/ρ (cm²/g)
0.7	2.29+3	2.25+0	8.93−3	1.67−5	2.29+3
0.8	1.64+3	2.21+0	1.11−2	2.35−5	1.64+3
0.9	1.19+3	2.18+0	1.33−2	3.14−5	1.19+3
1.0	9.04+2	2.14+0	1.54−2	4.03−5	9.06+2
1.2	5.66+2	2.07+0	1.96−2	6.07−5	5.68+2
1.305	4.45+2	2.02+0	2.16−2	7.19−5	4.47+2
1.305_K	6.10+3	2.02+0	2.16−2	7.19−5	6.11+3
1.5	4.26+3	1.95+0	2.53−2	9.53−5	4.27+3
1.7	3.07+3	1.88+0	2.86−2	1.20−4	3.08+3
2.0	2.00+3	1.78+0	3.31−2	1.61−4	2.00+3
2.5	1.09+3	1.63+0	3.96−2	2.35−4	1.09+3
3.0	6.61+2	1.50+0	4.57−2	3.22−4	6.62+2
3.5	4.30+2	1.38+0	5.16−2	4.22−4	4.31+2
4.0	2.94+2	1.28+0	5.74−2	5.35−4	2.96+2
5.0	1.55+2	1.09+0.	6.87−2	7.96−4	1.56+2
6.0	9.13+1	9.28−1	7.91−2	1.10−3	9.23+1
7.0	5.80+1	7.93−1	8.86−2	1.42−3	5.89+1
8.0	3.90+1	6.80−1	9.72−2	1.77−3	3.98+1
9.0	2.74+1	5.87−1	1.05−1	2.12−3	2.81+1
10.0	2.00+1	5.12−1	1.11−1	2.47−3	2.06+1
12.0	1.15+1	3.98−1	1.21−1	3.17−3	1.20+1
15.0	5.80+0	2.89−1	1.32−1	4.16−3	6.22+0
17.0	3.94+0	2.40−1	1.37−1	4.80−3	4.32+0
20.0	2.38+0	1.88−1	1.43−1	5.71−3	2.71+0
25.0	1.18+0	1.34−1	1.48−1	7.17−3	1.47+0
30.0	6.67−1	1.01−1	1.52−1	8.53−3	9.20−1
35.0	4.10−1	7.86−2	1.54−1	9.81−3	6.42−1
40.0	2.68−1	6.29−2	1.55−1	1.10−2	4.86−1
50.0	1.32−1	4.28−2	1.55−1	1.31−2	3.29−1
60.0	7.35−2	3.10−2	1.53−1	1.49−2	2.58−1
70.0	4.49−2	2.34−2	1.51−1	1.65−2	2.19−1
80.0	2.92−2	1.83−2	1.48−1	1.79−2	1.96−1
90.0	2.00−2	1.47−2	1.45−1	1.91−2	1.80−1
100.0	1.43−2	1.21−2	1.43−1	2.01−2	1.69−1
120.0	7.94−3	8.56−3	1.37−1	2.19−2	1.54−1
150.0	3.88−3	5.58−3	1.30−1	2.39−2	1.39−1
170.0	2.59−3	4.38−3	1.26−1	2.49−2	1.33−1
200.0	1.54−3	3.19−3	1.20−1	2.61−2	1.24−1
250.0	7.55−4	2.06−3	1.11−1	2.75−2	1.14−1
300.0	4.22−4	1.44−3	1.05−1	2.83−2	1.06−1
350.0	2.58−4	1.06−3	9.88−2	2.88−2	1.00−1
400.0	1.69−4	8.13−4	9.39−2	2.91−2	9.49−2
500.0	8.38−5	5.21−4	8.58−2	2.93−2	8.64−2
600.0	4.73−5	3.63−4	7.94−2	2.92−2	7.98−2
700.0	2.93−5	2.67−4	7.42−2	2.89−2	7.45−2
800.0	1.93−5	2.04−4	6.98−2	2.85−2	7.00−2
900.0	1.35−5	1.61−4	6.60−2	2.81−2	6.62−2
1,000.0	9.74−6	1.31−4	6.27−2	2.76−2	6.29−2

Aluminum **Z = 13**

0.1	1.20+5	2.50+0	2.18−4	5.78−8	1.20+5
0.117_{L_I}	1.11+5	2.50+0	2.85−4	8.87−8	1.11+5

TABLE 3 (continued)

Energy (keV)	τ/ρ (cm² /g)	σ_c/ρ (cm² /g)	σ_I/ρ (cm² /g)	σ_a/ρ (cm² /g)	μ/ρ (cm² /g)
0.1184	1.22+5	2.50+0	2.91–4	9.16–8	1.22+5
0.15	8.81+4	2.50+0	4.48–4	1.81–7	8.81+4
0.2	5.24+4	2.50+0	7.71–4	4.17–7	5.24+4
0.3	2.22+4	2.48+0	1.68–3	1.37–6	2.23+4
0.4	1.15+4	2.46+0	2.91–3	3.15–6	1.15+4
0.5	6.71+3	2.44+0	4.42–3	5.97–6	6.71+3
0.6	4.28+3	2.40+0	6.14–3	9.92–6	4.29+3
0.7	2.90+3	2.37+0	8.04–3	1.51–5	2.90+3
0.8	2.06+3	2.33+0	1.01–2	2.15–5	2.06+3
0.9	1.52+3	2.29+0	1.22–2	2.90–5	1.53+3
1.0	1.15+3	2.25+0	1.43–2	3.77–5	1.16+3
1.2	7.20+2	2.17+0	1.86–2	5.82–5	7.22+2
1.5	3.91+2	2.04+0	2.48–2	9.48–5	3.93+2
1.56_K	3.51+2	2.01+0	2.59–2	1.03–4	3.53+2
1.56^K	4.48+3	2.01+0	2.59–2	1.03–4	4.48+3
1.7	3.60+3	1.96+0	2.86–2	1.22–4	3.60+3
2.0	2.37+3	1.84+0	3.37–2	1.67–3	2.37+3
2.5	1.32+3	1.67+0	4.11–2	2.48–4	1.32+3
3.0	8.06+2	1.52+0	4.74–2	3.36–4	8.07+2
3.5	5.28+2	1.40+0	5.30–2	4.33–4	5.29+2
4.0	3.64+2	1.30+0	5.82–2	5.38–4	3.66+2
5.0	1.94+2	1.12+0	6.81–2	7.79–4	1.95+2
6.0	1.15+2	9.64–1	7.72–2	1.05–3	1.16+2
7.0	7.34+1	8.34–1	8.56–2	1.35–3	7.44+1
8.0	4.96+1	7.23–1	9.33–2	1.67–3	5.04+1
9.0	3.50+1	6.30–1	1.00–1	2.01–3	3.57+1
10.0	2.55+1	5.52–1	1.06–1	2.35–3	2.62+1
12.0	1.47+1	4.32–1	1.16–1	3.02–3	1.53+1
15.0	7.47+0	3.15–1	1.27–1	4.00–3	7.91+0
17.0	5.09+0	2.62–1	1.32–1	4.63–3	5.48+0
20.0	3.08+0	2.05–1	1.37–1	5.53–3	3.42+0
25.0	1.54+0	1.46–1	1.43–1	6.94–3	1.82+0
30.0	8.66–1	1.10–1	1.47–1	8.27–3	1.12+0
35.0	5.32–1	8.59–2	1.49–1	9.51–3	7.67–1
40.0	3.49–1	6.89–2	1.50–1	1.07–2	5.67–1
50.0	1.71–1	4.71–2	1.50–1	1.28–2	3.69–1
60.0	9.58–2	3.41–2	1.49–1	1.45–2	2.79–1
70.0	5.85–2	2.58–2	1.46–1	1.61–2	2.31–1
80.0	3.81–2	2.02–2	1.44–1	1.74–2	2.02–1
90.0	2.61–2	1.62–2	1.41–1	1.86–2	1.84–1
100.0	1.86–2	1.33–2	1.39–1	1.96–2	1.71–1
120.0	1.04–2	9.47–3	1.34–1	2.14–2	1.54–1
150.0	5.08–3	6.18–3	1.27–1	2.33–2	1.38–1
170.0	3.40–3	4.86–3	1.22–1	2.43–2	1.31–1
200.0	2.02–3	3.54–3	1.17–1	2.55–2	1.22–1
250.0	9.95–4	2.29–3	1.09–1	2.68–2	1.12–1
300.0	5.58–4	1.60–3	1.02–1	2.77–2	1.04–1
350.0	3.43–4	1.18–3	9.64–2	2.81–2	9.79–2
400.0	2.25–4	9.03–4	9.16–2	2.84–2	9.27–2
500.0	1.12–4	5.80–4	8.37–2	2.86–2	8.44–2
600.0	6.38–5	4.03–4	7.75–2	2.85–2	7.79–2
700.0	3.97–5	2.96–4	7.24–2	2.82–2	7.27–2
800.0	2.64–5	2.27–4	6.81–2	2.79–2	6.83–2

TABLE 3 (continued)

Energy (keV)	τ/ρ (cm^2/g)	σ_c/ρ (cm^2/g)	σ_I/ρ (cm^2/g)	σ_a/ρ (cm^2/g)	μ/ρ (cm^2/g)
900.0	1.85−5	1.79−4	6.44−2	2.74−2	6.46−2
1,000.0	1.35−5	1.45−4	6.12−2	2.70−2	6.14−2

Silicon **Z = 14**

Energy (keV)	τ/ρ (cm^2/g)	σ_c/ρ (cm^2/g)	σ_I/ρ (cm^2/g)	σ_a/ρ (cm^2/g)	μ/ρ (cm^2/g)
0.1	5.70+4	2.79+0	1.88−4	4.99−8	5.70+4
0.12	1.03+5	2.79+0	2.57−4	8.20−8	1.03+5
0.14	9.68+4	2.79+0	3.41−4	1.28−7	9.68+4
0.148 L_I	9.13+4	2.79+0	3.78−4	1.50−7	9.13+4
0.1494	1.01+5	2.79+0	3.84−4	1.55−7	1.01+5
0.15	1.00+5	2.79+0	3.87−4	1.56−7	1.00+5
0.17	8.40+4	2.79+0	4.93−4	2.27−7	8.40+4
0.18	7.69+4	2.79+0	5.49−4	2.68−7	7.69+4
0.2	6.43+4	2.78+0	6.70−4	3.63−7	6.43+4
0.24	4.52+4	2.78+0	9.53−4	6.21−7	4.52+4
0.3	2.82+4	2.77+0	1.47−3	1.20−6	2.82+4
0.4	1.48+4	2.75+0	2.55−3	2.78−6	1.48+4
0.5	8.71+3	2.72+0	3.90−3	5.30−6	8.71+3
0.6	5.58+3	2.69+0	5.47−3	8.88−6	5.59+3
0.7	3.80+3	2.65+0	7.23−3	1.36−5	3.80+3
0.8	2.71+3	2.61+0	9.15−3	1.96−5	2.71+3
0.9	2.00+3	2.57+0	1.11−2	2.68−5	2.00+3
1.0	1.52+3	2.53+0	1.32−2	3.51−5	1.53+3
1.2	9.69+2	2.43+0	1.75−2	5.53−5	9.72+2
1.5	5.31+2	2.29+0	2.40−2	9.29−5	5.33+2
1.7	3.78+2	2.19+0	2.81−2	1.22−4	3.80+2
1.839 K	3.06+2	2.12+0	3.08−2	1.44−4	3.08+2
1.839	3.74+3	2.12+0	3.08−2	1.44−4	3.74+3
2.0	3.00+3	2.05+0	3.39−2	1.71−4	3.00+3
2.5	1.66+3	1.84+0	4.24−2	2.61−4	1.66+3
3.0	1.01+3	1.67+0	4.96−2	3.58−4	1.01+3
3.5	6.61+2	1.53+0	5.59−2	4.62−4	6.63+2
4.0	4.56+2	1.41+0	6.14−2	5.72−4	4.57+2
5.0	2.43+2	1.21+0	7.13−2	8.14−4	2.44+2
6.0	1.44+2	1.05+0	8.00−2	1.09−3	1.45+2
7.0	9.18+1	9.18−1	8.81−2	1.38−3	9.28+1
8.0	6.21+1	8.04−1	9.54−2	1.70−3	6.30+1
9.0	4.39+1	7.06−1	1.02−1	2.03−3	4.46+1
10.0	3.21+1	6.22−1	1.08−1	2.37−3	3.28+1
12.0	1.86+1	4.91−1	1.18−1	3.06−3	1.92+1
15.0	9.45+0	3.60−1	1.29−1	4.07−3	9.93+0
17.0	6.45+0	2.99−1	1.35−1	4.73−3	6.88+0
20.0	3.92+0	2.35−1	1.41−1	5.66−3	4.29+0
25.0	1.96+0	1.67−1	1.47−1	7.13−3	2.28+0
30.0	1.11+0	1.26−1	1.51−1	8.50−3	1.39+0
35.0	6.87−1	9.85−2	1.53−1	9.78−3	9.39−1
40.0	4.52−1	7.92−2	1.54−1	1.10−2	6.85−1
50.0	2.24−1	5.43−2	1.54−1	1.31−2	4.32−1
60.0	1.26−1	3.95−2	1.53−1	1.50−2	3.18−1
70.0	7.71−2	2.99−2	1.51−1	1.66−2	2.58−1
80.0	5.05−2	2.34−2	1.49−1	1.80−2	2.22−1

TABLE 3 (continued)

Energy (keV)	τ/ρ (cm^2/g)	σ_c/ρ (cm^2/g)	σ_I/ρ (cm^2/g)	σ_a/ρ (cm^2/g)	μ/ρ (cm^2/g)
90.0	3.47−2	1.88−2	1.46−1	1.92−2	1.99−1
100.0	2.48−2	1.55−2	1.43−1	2.03−2	1.84−1
120.0	1.39−2	1.10−2	1.38−1	2.21−2	1.63−1
150.0	6.84−3	7.19−3	1.31−1	2.41−2	1.45−1
170.0	4.60−3	5.65−3	1.27−1	2.52−2	1.37−1
200.0	2.75−3	4.12−3	1.21−1	2.64−2	1.28−1
250.0	1.36−3	2.67−3	1.12−1	2.77−2	1.16−1
300.0	7.64−4	1.86−3	1.05−1	2.86−2	1.08−1
350.0	4.70−4	1.37−3	9.97−2	2.91−2	1.02−1
400.0	3.10−4	1.05−3	9.47−2	2.94−2	9.61−2
500.0	1.55−4	6.77−4	8.66−2	2.96−2	8.74−2
600.0	8.80−5	4.70−4	8.01−2	2.95−2	8.07−2
700.0	5.48−5	3.46−4	7.49−2	2.92−2	7.53−2
800.0	3.64−5	2.65−4	7.04−2	2.88−2	7.07−2
900.0	2.55−5	2.09−4	6.66−2	2.84−2	6.69−2
1,000.0	1.85−5	1.70−4	6.33−2	2.79−2	6.35−2
Phosphorus	**Z = 15**				
0.1	1.01+4	2.91+0	1.54−4	4.10−8	1.01+4
0.12	7.69+3	2.90+0	2.12−4	6.77−8	7.69+3
0.1315 $L_{II,III}$	6.63+3	2.90+0	2.50−4	8.82−8	6.63+3
0.1329	5.35+4	2.90+0	2.55−4	9.09−8	5.35+4
0.14	1.01+5	2.90+0	2.81−4	1.06−7	1.01+5
0.15	8.87+4	2.90+0	3.19−4	1.29−7	8.87+4
0.17	8.14+4	2.90+0	4.06−4	1.86−7	8.14+4
0.18	7.68+4	2.90+0	4.51−4	2.20−7	7.68+4
0.1886 L_I	7.16+4	2.90+0	4.92−4	2.51−7	7.19+4
0.19	7.96+4	2.90+0	4.99−4	2.56−7	7.96+4
0.2	7.36+4	2.90+0	5.49−4	2.97−7	7.36+4
0.24	5.41+4	2.89+0	7.81−4	5.09−7	5.41+4
0.3	3.43+4	2.88+0	1.20−3	9.82−7	3.43+4
0.4	1.81+4	2.86+0	2.10−3	2.28−6	1.81+4
0.5	1.07+4	2.84+0	3.22−3	4.37−6	1.07+4
0.6	6.87+3	2.81+0	4.53−3	7.37−6	6.87+3
0.7	4.68+3	2.78+0	6.02−3	1.14−5	4.68+3
0.8	3.34+3	2.74+0	7.66−3	1.65−5	3.34+3
0.9	2.47+3	2.70+0	9.38−3	2.26−5	2.47+3
1.0	1.88+3	2.65+0	1.12−2	2.98−5	1.88+3
1.2	1.18+3	2.56+0	1.50−2	4.76−5	1.19+3
1.5	6.52+2	2.41+0	2.09−2	8.15−5	6.55+2
1.7	4.67+2	2.31+0	2.47−2	1.08−4	4.69+2
2.0	3.02+2	2.16+0	3.03−2	1.54−4	3.04+2
2.146 K	2.50+2	2.09+0	3.28−2	1.78−4	2.52+2
2.146	2.84+3	2.09+0	3.28−2	1.78−4	2.84+3
2.5	1.90+3	1.94+0	3.89−2	2.42−4	1.90+3
3.0	1.17+3	1.75+0	4.64−2	3.40−4	1.17+3
3.5	7.69+2	1.58+0	5.31−2	4.46−4	7.71+2
4.0	5.33+2	1.45+0	5.89−2	5.57−4	5.34+2
5.0	2.86+2	1.24+0	6.89−2	7.95−4	2.87+2
6.0	1.71+2	1.08+0	7.73−2	1.05−3	1.72+2
7.0	1.10+2	9.45−1	8.49−2	1.33−3	1.11+2

TABLE 3 (continued)

Energy (keV)	τ/ρ (cm^2/g)	σ_c/ρ (cm^2/g)	σ_I/ρ (cm^2/g)	σ_a/ρ (cm^2/g)	μ/ρ (cm^2/g)
8.0	7.45+1	8.33−1	9.17−2	1.63−3	7.54+1
9.0	5.28+1	7.37−1	9.78−2	1.94−3	5.37+1
10.0	3.88+1	6.54−1	1.03−1	2.26−3	3.95+1
12.0	2.26+1	5.21−1	1.13−1	2.92−3	2.32+1
15.0	1.16+1	3.83−1	1.24−1	3.90−3	1.21+1
17.0	7.93+0	3.30−1	1.29−1	4.53−3	8.38+0
20.0	4.84+0	2.51−1	1.35−1	5.45−3	5.23+0
25.0	2.44+0	1.79−1	1.41−1	6.87−3	2.76+0
30.0	1.39+0	1.35−1	1.45−1	8.20−3	1.67+0
35.0	8.63−1	1.05−1	1.47−1	9.45−3	1.12+0
40.0	5.69−1	8.49−2	1.48−1	1.06−2	8.02−1
50.0	2.83−1	5.84−2	1.49−1	1.27−2	4.90−1
60.0	1.60−1	4.25−2	1.48−1	1.45−2	3.50−1
70.0	9.82−2	3.23−2	1.46−1	1.61−2	2.76−1
80.0	6.44−2	2.53−2	1.44−1	1.75−2	2.34−1
90.0	4.44−2	2.04−2	1.41−1	1.86−2	2.06−1
100.0	3.18−2	1.68−2	1.39−1	1.97−2	1.87−1
120.0	1.78−2	1.19−2	1.34−1	2.14−2	1.64−1
150.0	8.79−3	7.79−3	1.27−1	2.34−2	1.44−1
170.0	5.91−3	6.13−3	1.23−1	2.44−2	1.35−1
200.0	3.53−3	4.47−3	1.17−1	2.56−2	1.25−1
250.0	1.74−3	2.90−3	1.09−1	2.69−2	1.14−1
300.0	9.82−4	2.02−3	1.02−1	2.78−2	1.05−1
350.0	6.04−4	1.49−3	9.68−2	2.83−2	9.89−2
400.0	3.98−4	1.15−3	9.20−2	2.86−2	9.35−2
500.0	1.98−4	7.36−4	8.41−2	2.88−2	8.50−2
600.0	1.12−4	5.12−4	7.78−2	2.87−2	7.85−2
700.0	6.98−5	3.77−4	7.27−2	2.84−2	7.32−2
800.0	4.63−5	2.89−4	6.84−2	2.80−2	6.88−2
900.0	3.23−5	2.28−4	6.47−2	2.76−2	6.50−2
1,000.0	2.34−5	1.85−4	6.15−2	2.71−2	6.18−2

Sulfur Z = 16

Energy (keV)	τ/ρ (cm^2/g)	σ_c/ρ (cm^2/g)	σ_I/ρ (cm^2/g)	σ_a/ρ (cm^2/g)	μ/ρ (cm^2/g)
0.1	1.40+4	3.19+0	1.33−4	3.55−8	1.40+4
0.12	1.10+4	3.19+0	1.84−4	5.90−8	1.10+4
0.14	8.76+3	3.19+0	2.45−4	9.23−8	8.77+3
0.15	7.84+3	3.19+0	2.78−4	1.13−7	7.85+3
0.1641 $L_{II,III}$	6.74+3	3.19+0	3.31−4	1.47−7	6.74+3
0.1655 $L_{II,III}$	4.96+4	3.19+0	3.37−4	1.51−7	4.96+4
0.17	1.00+5	3.19+0	3.54−4	1.63−7	1.00+5
0.18	8.39+4	3.19+0	3.94−4	1.92−7	8.39+4
0.2	7.16+4	3.19+0	4.80−4	2.60−7	7.16+4
0.2285 L_I	6.02+4	3.18+0	6.22−4	3.86−7	6.02+4
0.2299 L_I	6.66+4	3.18+0	6.30−4	3.93−7	6.66+4
0.24	6.23+4	3.18+0	6.84−4	4.46−7	6.23+4
0.3	4.16+4	3.17+0	1.06−3	8.63−7	4.16+4
0.4	2.23+4	3.15+0	1.85−3	2.01−6	2.23+4
0.5	1.33+4	3.13+0	2.85−3	3.87−6	1.33+4
0.6	8.60+3	3.10+0	4.03−3	6.56−6	8.61+3
0.7	5.89+3	3.07+0	5.38−3	1.02−5	5.89+3

TABLE 3 (continued)

Energy (keV)	τ/ρ (cm^2/g)	σ_c/ρ (cm^2/g)	σ_I/ρ (cm^2/g)	σ_a/ρ (cm^2/g)	μ/ρ (cm^2/g)
0.8	4.21+3	3.03+0	6.89−3	1.49−5	4.22+3
0.9	3.12+3	2.99+0	8.48−3	2.05−5	3.13+3
1.0	2.38+3	2.94+0	1.02−2	2.73−5	2.39+3
1.2	1.51+3	2.85+0	1.38−2	4.41−5	1.51+3
1.5	8.32+2	2.69+0	1.96−2	7.72−5	8.34+2
1.7	5.95+2	2.58+0	2.35−2	1.04−4	5.97+2
2.0	3.85+2	2.42+0	2.93−2	1.50−4	3.88+2
2.472_K	2.19+2	2.18+0	3.78−2	2.36−4	2.21+2
2.472	2.36+3	2.18+0	3.78−2	2.36−4	2.36+3
2.5	2.29+3	2.17+0	3.83−2	2.41−4	2.29+3
3.0	1.41+3	1.95+0	4.64−2	3.44−4	1.42+3
3.5	9.35+2	1.76+0	5.37−2	4.57−4	9.37+2
4.0	6.50+2	1.60+0	6.01−2	5.75−4	6.52+2
5.0	3.50+2	1.36+0	7.08−2	8.24−4	3.52+2
6.0	2.10+2	1.17+0	7.96−2	1.09−3	2.11+2
7.0	1.35+2	1.03+0	8.72−2	1.37−3	1.37+2
8.0	9.22+1	9.12−1	9.39−2	1.67−3	9.33+1
9.0	6.56+1	8.11−1	9.99−2	1.98−3	6.65+1
10.0	4.82+1	7.23−1	1.05−1	2.30−3	4.90+1
12.0	2.82+1	5.81−1	1.15−1	2.96−3	2.89+1
15.0	1.45+1	4.31−1	1.26−1	3.96−3	1.51+1
17.0	9.96+0	3.60−1	1.31−1	4.61−3	1.04+1
20.0	6.09+0	2.83−1	1.38−1	5.56−3	6.51+0
25.0	3.09+0	2.02−1	1.44−1	7.03−3	3.43+0
30.0	1.76+0	1.52−1	1.48−1	8.40−3	2.06+0
35.0	1.10+0	1.19−1	1.51−1	9.68−3	1.37+0
40.0	7.24−1	9.59−2	1.52−1	1.09−2	9.72−1
50.0	3.61−1	6.62−2	1.53−1	1.30−2	5.80−1
60.0	2.04−1	4.83−2	1.52−1	1.49−2	4.04−1
70.0	1.26−1	3.67−2	1.50−1	1.65−2	3.13−1
80.0	8.28−2	2.88−2	1.48−1	1.80−2	2.59−1
90.0	5.71−2	2.32−2	1.45−1	1.92−2	2.26−1
100.0	4.10−2	1.91−2	1.43−1	2.03−2	2.03−1
120.0	2.31−2	1.36−2	1.38−1	2.21−2	1.74−1
150.0	1.14−2	8.90−3	1.31−1	2.41−2	1.51−1
170.0	7.69−3	7.00−3	1.26−1	2.52−2	1.41−1
200.0	4.61−3	5.11−3	1.21−1	2.64−2	1.30−1
250.0	2.28−3	3.32−3	1.12−1	2.78−2	1.18−1
300.0	1.29−3	2.32−3	1.05−1	2.86−2	1.09−1
350.0	7.96−4	1.71−3	9.97−2	2.92−2	1.02−1
400.0	5.25−4	1.31−3	9.47−2	2.95−2	9.66−2
500.0	2.63−4	8.43−4	8.66−2	2.97−2	8.77−2
600.0	1.50−4	5.87−4	8.02−2	2.95−2	8.09−2
700.0	9.32−5	4.32−4	7.49−2	2.92−2	7.55−2
800.0	6.20−5	3.31−4	7.05−2	2.89−2	7.09−2
900.0	4.34−5	2.61−4	6.67−2	2.84−2	6.70−2
1,000.0	3.15−5	2.12−4	6.34−2	2.79−2	6.36−2

Chlorine **Z = 17**

0.1	1.73+4	3.26+0	1.13−4	2.98−8	1.73+4
0.12	1.40+4	3.26+0	1.53−4	4.86−8	1.40+4

TABLE 3 (continued)

Energy (keV)	τ/ρ (cm^2/g)	σ_c/ρ (cm^2/g)	σ_I/ρ (cm^2/g)	σ_a/ρ (cm^2/g)	μ/ρ (cm^2/g)
0.14	1.14+4	3.26+0	2.02−4	7.57−8	1.14+4
0.15	1.03+4	3.26+0	2.29−4	9.23−8	1.03+4
0.17	8.42+3	3.26+0	2.92−4	1.34−7	8.42+3
0.18	7.64+3	3.26+0	3.25−4	1.58−7	7.65+3
0.1998 $L_{II,III}$	6.38+3	3.25+0	3.96−4	2.14−7	6.38+3
0.2012	4.09+4	3.25+0	4.01−4	2.19−7	4.09+4
0.22	6.76+4	3.25+0	4.77−4	2.85−7	6.76+4
0.24	5.78+4	3.25+0	5.65−4	3.68−7	5.78+4
0.2695 L_I	4.85+4	3.25+0	7.09−4	5.19−7	4.85+4
0.2709	5.35+5	3.25+0	7.16−4	5.27−7	5.35+4
0.3	4.52+4	3.24+0	8.73−4	7.13−7	4.52+4
0.4	2.52+4	3.22+0	1.53−3	1.67−6	2.52+4
0.5	1.52+4	3.20+0	2.37−3	3.22−6	1.52+4
0.6	9.87+3	3.18+0	3.36−3	5.47−6	9.87+3
0.7	6.79+3	3.14+0	4.50−3	8.55−6	6.79+3
0.8	4.87+3	3.11+0	5.79−3	1.25−5	4.88+3
0.9	3.62+3	3.07+0	7.16−3	1.74−5	3.63+3
1.0	2.77+3	3.03+0	8.63−3	2.32−5	2.77+3
1.2	1.77+3	2.94+0	1.18−2	3.79−5	1.77+3
1.5	9.77+2	2.79+0	1.70−2	6.74−5	9.80+2
1.7	7.01+2	2.69+0	2.06−2	9.17−5	7.03+2
2.0	4.55+2	2.53+0	2.59−2	1.35−4	4.58+2
2.5	2.52+2	2.27+0	3.46−2	2.20−4	2.54+2
2.822 K	1.82+2	2.11+0	3.97−2	2.82−4	1.85+2
2.822	1.85+3	2.11+0	3.97−2	2.82−4	1.86+3
3.0	1.58+3	2.04+0	4.26−2	3.19−4	1.58+3
3.5	1.05+3	1.83+0	4.98−2	4.28−4	1.05+3
4.0	7.30+2	1.66+0	5.63−2	5.45−4	7.32+2
5.0	3.96+2	1.40+0	6.71−2	7.90−4	3.98+2
6.0	2.38+2	1.20+0	7.59−2	1.05−3	2.40+2
7.0	1.54+2	1.05+0	8.32−2	1.32−3	1.55+2
8.0	1.05+2	9.29−1	8.96−2	1.60−3	1.06+2
9.0	7.51+1	8.28−1	9.53−2	1.89−3	7.60+1
10.0	5.53+1	7.42−1	1.00−1	2.19−3	5.62+1
12.0	3.25+1	6.01−1	1.09−1	2.81−3	3.32+1
15.0	1.68+1	4.50−1	1.20−1	3.76−3	1.74+1
17.0	1.16+1	3.77−1	1.25−1	4.38−3	1.21+1
20.0	7.09+0	2.96−1	1.31−1	5.29−3	7.52+0
25.0	3.60+0	2.11−1	1.38−1	6.71−3	3.95+0
30.0	2.07+0	1.59−1	1.41−1	8.03−3	2.37+0
35.0	1.29+0	1.25−1	1.44−1	9.26−3	1.55+0
40.0	8.52−1	1.01−1	1.45−1	1.04−2	1.10+0
50.0	4.27−1	6.95−2	1.46−1	1.25−2	6.42−1
60.0	2.42−1	5.09−2	1.45−1	1.43−2	4.38−1
70.0	1.49−1	3.87−2	1.43−1	1.59−2	3.32−1
80.0	9.83−2	3.04−2	1.41−1	1.72−2	2.70−1
90.0	6.80−2	2.45−2	1.39−1	1.84−2	2.32−1
100.0	4.88−2	2.02−2	1.37−1	1.95−2	2.06−1
120.0	2.75−2	1.44−2	1.32−1	2.12−2	1.74−1
150.0	1.37−2	9.42−3	1.25−1	2.32−2	1.48−1

TABLE 3 (continued)

Energy (keV)	τ/ρ (cm^2/g)	σ_c/ρ (cm^2/g)	σ_I/ρ (cm^2/g)	σ_a/ρ (cm^2/g)	μ/ρ (cm^2/g)
170.0	9.22–3	7.42–3	1.21–1	2.42–2	1.38–1
200.0	5.53–3	5.42–3	1.16–1	2.54–2	1.27–1
250.0	2.75–3	3.52–3	1.08–1	2.67–2	1.14–1
300.0	1.55–3	2.46–3	1.01–1	2.75–2	1.05–1
350.0	9.61–4	1.82–3	9.58–2	2.80–2	9.85–2
400.0	6.35–4	1.39–3	9.10–2	2.83–2	9.30–2
500.0	3.18–4	8.96–4	8.32–2	2.85–2	8.44–2
600.0	1.82–4	6.24–4	7.70–2	2.84–2	7.78–2
700.0	1.13–4	4.59–4	7.20–2	2.81–2	7.26–2
800.0	7.55–5	3.51–4	6.77–2	2.77–2	6.82–2
900.0	5.29–5	2.78–4	6.41–2	2.73–2	6.44–2
1,000.0	3.85–5	2.25–4	6.09–2	2.68–2	6.12–2

Argon **Z = 18**

Energy (keV)	τ/ρ (cm^2/g)	σ_c/ρ (cm^2/g)	σ_I/ρ (cm^2/g)	σ_a/ρ (cm^2/g)	μ/ρ (cm^2/g)
0.1	1.98+4	3.25+0	8.97–5	2.38–8	1.98+4
0.13	1.50+4	3.24+0	1.43–4	4.97–8	1.51+4
0.15	1.25+4	3.24+0	1.86–4	7.53–8	1.25+4
0.2	8.01+3	3.24+0	3.23–4	1.75–7	8.01+3
0.21	7.37+3	3.24+0	3.55–4	2.02–7	7.37+3
0.2452 $L_{II,III}$	5.56+3	3.24+0	4.80–4	3.20–7	5.57+3
0.2466	3.17+4	3.24+0	4.86–4	3.26–7	3.17+4
0.25	7.80+4	3.24+0	4.99–4	3.39–7	7.80+4
0.28	4.96+4	3.23+0	6.22–4	4.74–7	4.96+4
0.3	4.45+4	3.23+0	7.12–4	5.82–7	4.45+4
0.3193 L_I	3.96+4	3.23+0	8.05–4	7.00–7	3.96+4
0.3207	4.35+4	3.23+0	8.12–4	7.09–7	4.35+4
0.4	2.86+4	3.21+0	1.25–3	1.36–6	2.86+4
0.5	1.74+4	3.19+0	1.94–3	2.64–6	1.74+4
0.6	1.13+4	3.17+0	2.75–3	4.49–6	1.13+4
0.7	7.76+3	3.14+0	3.70–3	7.03–6	7.77+3
0.8	5.58+3	3.11+0	4.77–3	1.03–5	5.58+3
0.9	4.15+3	3.08+0	5.91–3	1.44–5	4.15+3
1.0	3.17+3	3.04+0	7.15–3	1.93–5	3.17+3
1.2	2.01+3	2.96+0	9.84–3	3.16–5	2.02+3
1.5	1.11+3	2.82+0	1.43–2	5.68–5	1.11+3
1.7	7.91+2	2.72+0	1.74–2	7.79–5	7.94+2
2.0	5.11+2	2.57+0	2.21–2	1.15–4	5.14+2
2.5	2.81+2	2.32+0	2.99–2	1.92–4	2.83+2
3.0	1.72+2	2.08+0	3.73–2	2.81–4	1.74+2
3.203 K	1.44+2	1.99+0	4.00–2	3.21–4	1.46+2
3.203	1.48+3	1.99+0	4.00–2	3.21–4	1.48+3
3.5	1.17+3	1.87+0	4.41–2	3.83–4	1.17+3
4.0	8.16+2	1.69+0	5.03–2	4.92–4	8.18+2
5.0	4.43+2	1.41+0	6.10–2	7.27–4	4.45+2
6.0	2.67+2	1.21+0	6.98–2	9.74–4	2.68+2
7.0	1.73+2	1.05+0	7.70–2	1.23–3	1.74+2
8.0	1.18+2	9.27–1	8.31–2	1.49–3	1.19+2
9.0	8.42+1	8.27–1	8.85–2	1.76–3	8.51+1
10.0	6.21+1	7.42–1	9.32–2	2.04–3	6.29+1
12.0	3.65+1	6.05–1	1.01–1	2.61–3	3.72+1
15.0	1.89+1	4.56–1	1.11–1	3.49–3	1.94+1

TABLE 3 (continued)

Energy (keV)	τ/ρ (cm^2/g)	σ_c/ρ (cm^2/g)	σ_I/ρ (cm^2/g)	σ_a/ρ (cm^2/g)	μ/ρ (cm^2/g)
17.0	1.30+1	3.83–1	1.16–1	4.07–3	1.35+1
20.0	7.99+0	3.03–1	1.22–1	4.93–3	8.41+0
25.0	4.07+0	2.16–1	1.28–1	6.26–3	4.41+0
30.0	2.34+0	1.63–1	1.32–1	7.50–3	2.63+0
35.0	1.46+0	1.27–1	1.34–1	8.66–3	1.72+0
40.0	9.66–1	1.03–1	1.36–1	9.73–3	1.20+0
50.0	4.85–1	7.11–2	1.36–1	1.17–2	6.92–1
60.0	2.75–1	5.21–2	1.36–1	1.34–2	4.63–1
70.0	1.70–1	3.97–2	1.34–1	1.49–2	3.44–1
80.0	1.12–1	3.13–2	1.32–1	1.61–2	2.76–1
90.0	7.77–2	2.52–2	1.30–1	1.73–2	2.33–1
100.0	5.59–2	2.08–2	1.28–1	1.83–2	2.05–1
120.0	3.16–2	1.48–2	1.24–1	1.99–2	1.70–1
150.0	1.57–2	9.71–3	1.18–1	2.18–2	1.43–1
170.0	1.06–2	7.65–3	1.14–1	2.27–2	1.32–1
200.0	6.39–3	5.59–3	1.09–1	2.38–2	1.21–1
250.0	3.18–3	3.63–3	1.01–1	2.51–2	1.08–1
300.0	1.81–3	2.54–3	9.51–2	2.58–2	9.95–2
350.0	1.12–3	1.88–3	9.00–2	2.63–2	9.30–2
400.0	7.40–4	1.44–3	8.55–2	2.66–2	8.77–2
500.0	3.72–4	9.27–4	7.82–2	2.68–2	7.95–2
600.0	2.13–4	6.45–4	7.24–2	2.67–2	7.32–2
700.0	1.33–4	4.75–4	6.76–2	2.64–2	6.82–2
800.0	8.90–5	3.64–4	6.36–2	2.61–2	6.41–2
900.0	6.24–5	2.88–4	6.02–2	2.56–2	6.06–2
1,000.0	4.55–5	2.33–4	5.72–2	2.52–2	5.75–2

Potassium **Z = 19**

Energy (keV)	τ/ρ (cm^2/g)	σ_c/ρ (cm^2/g)	σ_I/ρ (cm^2/g)	σ_a/ρ (cm^2/g)	μ/ρ (cm^2/g)
0.1	2.17+4	3.69+0	2.40–4	6.35–8	2.17+4
0.15	1.46+4	3.69+0	4.91–4	1.98–7	1.46+4
0.2	9.76+3	3.68+0	8.42–4	4.55–7	9.76+3
0.2938 $L_{II,III}$	5.08+3	3.66+0	1.73–3	1.37–6	5.08+3
0.298	7.95+4	3.66+0	1.78–3	1.43–6	7.95+4
0.3	6.54+4	3.66+0	1.80–3	1.46–6	6.54+4
0.32	4.65+4	3.65+0	2.02–3	1.75–6	4.65+4
0.35	3.90+4	3.64+0	2.38–3	2.25–6	3.90+4
0.3764 L_I	3.35+4	3.63+0	2.71–3	2.75–6	3.35+4
0.3778	3.71+4	3.63+0	2.73–3	2.78–6	3.71+4
0.4	3.41+4	3.63+0	3.02–3	3.25–6	3.41+4
0.5	2.12+4	3.59+0	4.44–3	5.93–6	2.12+4
0.6	1.39+4	3.55+0	5.96–3	9.47–6	1.40+4
0.7	9.68+3	3.50+0	7.51–3	1.38–5	9.69+3
0.8	6.99+3	3.45+0	9.07–3	1.89–5	6.99+3
0.9	5.21+3	3.40+0	1.06–2	2.47–5	5.21+3
1.0	4.00+3	3.35+0	1.22–2	3.12–5	4.00+3
1.2	2.56+3	3.24+0	1.52–2	4.60–5	2.57+3
1.5	1.41+3	3.08+0	1.96–2	7.35–5	1.42+3
1.7	1.01+3	2.97+0	2.26–2	9.55–5	1.02+3
2.0	6.58+2	2.81+0	2.71–2	1.34–4	6.61+2
2.5	3.63+2	2.56+0	3.46–2	2.12–4	3.66+2
3.0	2.24+2	2.33+0	4.17–2	3.05–4	2.26+2

TABLE 3 (continued)

Energy (keV)	τ/ρ (cm^2/g)	σ_c/ρ (cm^2/g)	σ_I/ρ (cm^2/g)	σ_a/ρ (cm^2/g)	μ/ρ (cm^2/g)
3.5	1.48+2	2.11+0	4.85−2	4.10−4	1.51+2
3.607 $_K$	1.37+2	2.06+0	4.98−2	4.34−4	1.39+2
3.607	1.29+3	2.06+0	4.98−2	4.34−4	1.29+3
4.0	9.80+2	1.92+0	5.48−2	5.25−4	9.82+2
5.0	5.37+2	1.60+0	6.58−2	7.75−4	5.38+2
6.0	3.25+2	1.36+0	7.51−2	1.04−3	3.27+2
7.0	2.12+2	1.18+0	8.29−2	1.32−3	2.13+2
8.0	1.45+2	1.04+0	8.95−2	1.60−3	1.47+2
9.0	1.04+2	9.31−1	9.52−2	1.89−3	1.05+2
10.0	7.70+1	8.37−1	1.00−1	2.19−3	7.80+1
12.0	4.55+1	6.87−1	1.09−1	2.79−3	4.63+1
15.0	2.37+1	5.23−1	1.19−1	3.72−3	2.44+1
17.0	1.64+1	4.41−1	1.24−1	4.35−3	1.70+1
20.0	1.01+1	3.49−1	1.30−1	5.26−3	1.06+1
25.0	5.20+0	2.50−1	1.37−1	6.70−3	5.58+0
30.0	3.00+0	1.88−1	1.41−1	8.04−3	3.33+0
35.0	1.88+0	1.47−1	1.44−1	9.29−3	2.17+0
40.0	1.25+0	1.19−1	1.45−1	1.05−2	1.51+0
50.0	6.30−1	8.25−2	1.46−1	1.26−2	8.59−1
60.0	3.59−1	6.06−2	1.46−1	1.44−2	5.65−1
70.0	2.23−1	4.63−2	1.44−1	1.60−2	4.14−1
80.0	1.47−1	3.64−2	1.42−1	1.74−2	3.26−1
90.0	1.02−1	2.94−2	1.40−1	1.86−2	2.72−1
100.0	7.37−2	2.43−2	1.38−1	1.97−2	2.36−1
120.0	4.18−2	1.73−2	1.33−1	2.15−2	1.92−1
150.0	2.08−2	1.14−2	1.27−1	2.35−2	1.59−1
170.0	1.41−2	8.96−3	1.23−1	2.45−2	1.46−1
200.0	8.50−3	6.55−3	1.17−1	2.57−2	1.32−1
250.0	4.24−3	4.26−3	1.09−1	2.70−2	1.18−1
300.0	2.41−3	2.98−3	1.03−1	2.79−2	1.08−1
350.0	1.49−3	2.20−3	9.70−2	2.84−2	1.01−1
400.0	9.89−4	1.69−3	9.22−2	2.87−2	9.48−2
500.0	4.98−4	1.09−3	8.43−2	2.89−2	8.59−2
600.0	2.85−4	7.57−4	7.80−2	2.88−2	7.91−2
700.0	1.78−4	5.57−4	7.29−2	2.85−2	7.37−2
800.0	1.19−4	4.27−4	6.86−2	2.81−2	6.92−2
900.0	8.32−5	3.38−4	6.49−2	2.77−2	6.54−2
1,000.0	6.06−5	2.74−4	6.17−2	2.72−2	6.21−2

Calcium Z = 20

Energy (keV)	τ/ρ (cm^2/g)	σ_c/ρ (cm^2/g)	σ_I/ρ (cm^2/g)	σ_a/ρ (cm^2/g)	μ/ρ (cm^2/g)
0.1	2.34+4	3.99+0	2.68−4	7.13−8	2.34+4
0.15	1.65+4	3.98+0	5.54−4	2.24−7	1.65+4
0.2	1.14+4	3.98+0	9.52−4	5.15−7	1.14+4
0.3	5.89+3	3.95+0	2.05−3	1.67−6	5.89+3
0.3469 $L_{II,III}$	4.50+3	3.94+0	2.69−3	2.53−6	4.51+3
0.3483	3.69+4	3.93+0	2.71−3	2.55−6	3.69+4
0.35	3.91+4	3.93+0	2.74−3	2.59−6	3.91+4
0.37	3.86+4	3.93+0	3.03−3	3.03−6	3.86+4
0.4	3.37+4	3.91+0	3.50−3	3.78−6	3.37+4
0.4371 L_I	2.78+4	3.90+0	4.11−3	4.84−6	2.78+4
0.4385	3.17+4	3.90+0	4.13−3	4.88−6	3.17+4
0.5	2.41+4	3.87+0	5.21−3	6.99−6	2.41+4

TABLE 3 (continued)

Energy (keV)	τ/ρ (cm^2/g)	σ_c/ρ (cm^2/g)	σ_I/ρ (cm^2/g)	σ_a/ρ (cm^2/g)	μ/ρ (cm^2/g)
0.6	1.62+4	3.82+0	7.08−3	1.13−5	1.62+4
0.7	1.13+4	3.77+0	9.03−3	1.67−5	1.13+4
0.8	8.20+3	3.71+0	1.10−2	2.31−5	8.20+3
0.9	6.12+3	3.64+0	1.30−2	3.05−5	6.13+3
1.0	4.74+3	3.58+0	1.49−2	3.85−5	4.74+3
1.2	2.98+3	3.45+0	1.86−2	5.66−5	2.99+3
1.5	1.68+3	3.26+0	2.35−2	8.76−5	1.68+3
2.0	7.83+2	2.96+0	3.10−2	1.51−4	7.86+2
2.5	4.37+2	2.70+0	3.81−2	2.29−4	4.40+2
3.0	2.69+2	2.46+0	4.49−2	3.21−4	2.71+2
3.5	1.78+2	2.24+0	5.13−2	4.25−4	1.80+2
4.0	1.25+2	2.05+0	5.73−2	5.39−4	1.27+2
4.038_K	1.22+2	2.03+0	5.77−2	5.48−4	1.24+2
4.038	1.11+3	2.03+0	5.77−2	5.48−4	1.11+3
5.0	6.27+2	1.72+0	6.80−2	7.91−4	6.29+2
6.0	3.82+2	1.47+0	7.73−2	1.06−3	3.84+2
7.0	2.50+2	1.27+0	8.52−2	1.35−3	2.51+2
8.0	1.72+2	1.12+0	9.19−2	1.64−3	1.73+2
9.0	1.24+2	9.96−1	9.77−2	1.94−3	1.25+2
10.0	9.16+1	8.96−1	1.03−1	2.24−3	9.26+1
12.0	5.43+1	7.38−1	1.11−1	2.85−3	5.51+1
15.0	2.84+1	5.67−1	1.21−1	3.79−3	2.91+1
17.0	1.97+1	4.81−1	1.26−1	4.43−3	2.03+1
20.0	1.22+1	3.82−1	1.33−1	5.36−3	1.27+1
25.0	6.24+0	2.74−1	1.40−1	6.84−3	6.66+0
30.0	3.60+0	2.06−1	1.44−1	8.22−3	3.96+0
35.0	2.26+0	1.62−1	1.47−1	9.50−3	2.57+0
40.0	1.50+0	1.31−1	1.49−1	1.07−2	1.78+0
50.0	7.59−1	9.07−2	1.50−1	1.28−2	1.00−0
60.0	4.33−1	6.67−2	1.49−1	1.47−2	6.49−1
70.0	2.69−1	5.11−2	1.48−1	1.64−2	4.68−1
80.0	1.78−1	4.03−2	1.46−1	1.78−2	3.64−1
90.0	1.24−1	3.25−2	1.44−1	1.91−2	3.00−1
100.0	8.90−2	2.69−2	1.41−1	2.02−2	2.57−1
120.0	5.05−2	1.92−2	1.37−1	2.20−2	2.06−1
150.0	2.53−2	1.26−2	1.30−1	2.41−2	1.68−1
170.0	1.71−2	9.94−3	1.26−1	2.51−2	1.53−1
200.0	1.03−2	7.28−3	1.20−1	2.64−2	1.38−1
250.0	5.18−3	4.73−3	1.12−1	2.78−2	1.22−1
300.0	2.95−3	3.31−3	1.05−1	2.86−2	1.12−1
350.0	1.83−3	2.45−3	9.95−2	2.92−2	1.04−1
400.0	1.22−3	1.88−3	9.46−2	2.95−2	9.77−2
500.0	6.16−4	1.21−3	8.65−2	2.97−2	8.84−2
600.0	3.54−4	8.44−4	8.01−2	2.95−2	8.13−2
700.0	2.23−4	6.21−4	7.49−2	2.92−2	7.57−2
800.0	1.49−4	4.76−4	7.05−2	2.89−2	7.11−2
900.0	1.05−4	3.77−4	6.67−2	2.84−2	6.72−2
1,000.0	7.70−5	3.05−4	6.34−2	2.79−2	6.37−2

Scandium **Z = 21**

0.1	2.65+4	3.92+0	2.24−4	5.94−8	2.65+4

TABLE 3 (continued)

Energy (keV)	τ/ρ (cm^2/g)	σ_c/ρ (cm^2/g)	σ_I/ρ (cm^2/g)	σ_a/ρ (cm^2/g)	μ/ρ (cm^2/g)
0.15	1.81+4	3.92+0	4.61−4	1.86−7	1.81+4
0.2	1.24+4	3.91+0	7.91−4	4.28−7	1.24+4
0.3	6.43+3	3.89+0	1.71−3	1.39−6	6.43+3
0.4	3.76+3	3.86+0	2.92−3	3.16−6	3.77+3
0.403 $L_{II,III}$	3.71+3	3.85+0	2.96−3	3.23−6	3.71+3
0.4044	2.63+4	3.85+0	2.98−3	3.26−6	2.63+4
0.42	3.24+4	3.85+0	3.20−3	3.63−6	3.24+4
0.45	2.81+4	3.84+0	3.63−3	4.42−6	2.81+4
0.48	2.44+4	3.82+0	4.08−3	5.27−6	2.44+4
0.4997 L_I	2.23+4	3.82+0	4.38−3	5.89−6	2.23+4
0.5011	2.56+4	3.82+0	4.40−3	5.93−6	2.56+4
0.56	2.01+4	3.79+0	5.33−3	8.01−6	2.01+4
0.6	1.73+4	3.77+0	6.00−3	9.63−6	1.73+4
0.7	1.22+4	3.72+0	7.71−3	1.43−5	1.22+4
0.8	8.87+3	3.67+0	9.47−3	2.00−5	8.87+3
0.9	6.65+3	3.61+0	1.13−2	2.65−5	6.65+3
1.0	5.12+3	3.55+0	1.30−2	3.37−5	5.12+3
1.2	3.24+3	3.43+0	1.64−2	5.02−5	3.24+3
1.5	1.83+3	3.24+0	2.10−2	7.88−5	1.83+3
2.0	8.55+2	2.95+0	2.80−2	1.37−4	8.58+2
2.5	4.78+2	2.69+0	3.45−2	2.08−4	4.81+2
3.0	2.94+2	2.45+0	4.07−2	2.92−4	2.96+2
3.5	1.95+2	2.24+0	4.66−2	3.87−4	1.97+2
4.0	1.36+2	2.05+0	5.21−2	4.92−4	1.38+2
4.493 K	9.98+1	1.88+0	5.72−2	6.02−4	1.02+2
4.493	8.78+2	1.88+0	5.72−2	6.02−4	8.80+2
5.0	6.62+2	1.72+0	6.21−2	7.23−4	6.64+2
6.0	4.06+2	1.47+0	7.08−2	9.77−4	4.07+2
7.0	2.66+2	1.27+0	7.83−2	1.25−3	2.68+2
8.0	1.84+2	1.11+0	8.48−2	1.52−3	1.85+2
9.0	1.33+2	9.85−1	9.03−2	1.80−3	1.34+2
10.0	9.85+1	8.84−1	9.51−2	2.08−3	9.95+1
12.0	5.86+1	7.28−1	1.03−1	2.65−3	5.94+1
15.0	3.08+1	5.62−1	1.12−1	3.52−3	3.14+1
17.0	2.14+1	4.78−1	1.17−1	4.11−3	2.19+1
20.0	1.32+1	3.82−1	1.23−1	4.98−3	1.37+1
25.0	6.81+0	2.74−1	1.30−1	6.36−3	7.22+0
30.0	3.94+0	2.07−1	1.34−1	7.65−3	4.28+0
35.0	2.47+0	1.62−1	1.37−1	8.86−3	2.77+0
40.0	1.65+0	1.31−1	1.38−1	9.97−3	1.92+0
50.0	8.34−1	9.09−2	1.39−1	1.20−2	1.06+0
60.0	4.77−1	6.70−2	1.39−1	1.37−2	6.83−1
70.0	2.96−1	5.13−2	1.38−1	1.53−2	4.86−1
80.0	1.96−1	4.05−2	1.36−1	1.66−2	3.73−1
90.0	1.36−1	3.28−2	1.34−1	1.78−2	3.03−1
100.0	9.84−2	2.71−2	1.32−1	1.89−2	2.57−1
120.0	5.59−2	1.94−2	1.28−1	2.06−2	2.03−1
150.0	2.80−2	1.27−2	1.21−1	2.25−2	1.62−1
170.0	1.90−2	1.00−2	1.18−1	2.35−2	1.47−1
200.0	1.15−2	7.35−3	1.12−1	2.47−2	1.31−1
250.0	5.76−3	4.78−3	1.05−1	2.60−2	1.15−1
300.0	3.29−3	3.35−3	9.85−2	2.68−2	1.05−1

TABLE 3 (continued)

Energy (keV)	τ/ρ (cm²/g)	σ_c/ρ (cm²/g)	σ_I/ρ (cm²/g)	σ_a/ρ (cm²/g)	μ/ρ (cm²/g)
350.0	2.05–3	2.48–3	9.31–2	2.73–2	9.77–2
400.0	1.36–3	1.91–3	8.85–2	2.76–2	9.18–2
500.0	6.92–4	1.23–3	8.10–2	2.78–2	8.29–2
600.0	4.00–4	8.55–4	7.50–2	2.77–2	7.63–2
700.0	2.52–4	6.29–4	7.01–2	2.74–2	7.10–2
800.0	1.69–4	4.82–4	6.60–2	2.70–2	6.66–2
900.0	1.20–4	3.82–4	6.24–2	2.66–2	6.29–2
1,000.0	8.79–5	3.09–4	5.93–2	2.61–2	5.97–2

Titanium Z = 22

Energy (keV)	τ/ρ (cm²/g)	σ_c/ρ (cm²/g)	σ_I/ρ (cm²/g)	σ_a/ρ (cm²/g)	μ/ρ (cm²/g)
0.1	2.94+4	4.04+0	1.98–4	5.25–8	2.94+4
0.15	1.95+4	4.04+0	4.06–4	1.64–7	1.95+4
0.2	1.33+4	4.03+0	6.95–4	3.76–7	1.33+4
0.3	6.99+3	4.01+0	1.50–3	1.22–6	6.99+3
0.4	4.13+3	3.98+0	2.58–3	2.79–6	4.13+3
0.45	3.28+3	3.96+0	3.21–3	3.91–6	3.29+3
0.4568 $L_{II,III}$	3.19+3	3.96+0	3.30–3	4.08–6	3.19+3
0.4582	2.01+4	3.96+0	3.32–3	4.11–6	2.01+4
0.48	2.64+4	3.95+0	3.61–3	4.67–6	2.64+4
0.5	2.42+4	3.94+0	3.88–3	5.23–6	2.42+4
0.56	1.88+4	3.92+0	4.74–3	7.13–6	1.88+4
0.563 L_I	1.86+4	3.92+0	4.78–3	7.23–6	1.86+4
0.5644	2.15+4	3.92+0	4.80–3	7.28–6	2.15+4
0.6	1.87+4	3.90+0	5.34–3	8.59–6	1.87+4
0.7	1.33+4	3.85+0	6.90–3	1.29–5	1.33+4
0.8	9.75+3	3.80+0	8.53–3	1.80–5	9.75+3
0.9	7.36+3	3.74+0	1.02–2	2.41–5	7.37+3
1.0	5.69+3	3.69+0	1.18–2	3.08–5	5.69+3
1.2	3.61+3	3.57+0	1.50–2	4.63–5	3.62+3
1.5	2.05+3	3.38+0	1.95–2	7.35–5	2.06+3
2.0	9.64+2	3.09+0	2.62–2	1.29–4	9.67+2
2.5	5.45+2	2.82+0	3.25–2	1.97–4	5.48+2
3.0	3.34+2	2.58+0	3.84–2	2.77–4	3.36+2
3.5	2.20+2	2.35+0	4.41–2	3.68–4	2.23+2
4.0	1.54+2	2.15+0	4.95–2	4.69–4	1.56+2
4.966 K	8.59+1	1.82+0	5.89–2	6.84–4	8.78+1
4.966	7.28+2	1.82+0	5.89–2	6.84–4	7.30+2
5.0	7.16+2	1.81+0	5.92–2	6.92–4	7.17+2
6.0	4.44+2	1.54+0	6.78–2	9.39–4	4.46+2
7.0	2.95+2	1.33+0	7.53–2	1.20–3	2.96+2
8.0	2.05+2	1.16+0	8.18–2	1.47–3	2.07+2
9.0	1.49+2	1.03+0	8.74–2	1.75–3	1.50+2
10.0	1.11+2	9.20–1	9.22–2	2.03–3	1.12+2
12.0	6.65+1	7.56–1	1.00–1	2.59–3	6.73+1
15.0	3.51+1	5.84–1	1.09–1	3.44–3	3.58+1
17.0	2.44+1	4.99–1	1.14–1	4.01–3	2.51+1
20.0	1.52+1	4.00–1	1.20–1	4.86–3	1.57+1
25.0	7.85+0	2.88–1	1.27–1	6.22–3	8.26+0
30.0	4.55+0	2.17–1	1.31–1	7.49–3	4.90+0
35.0	2.86+0	1.70–1	1.34–1	8.67–3	3.16+0
40.0	1.90+0	1.38–1	1.35–1	9.77–3	2.18+0
50.0	9.62–1	9.55–2	1.37–1	1.18–2	1.19+0

TABLE 3 (continued)

Energy (keV)	τ/ρ (cm^2/g)	σ_c/ρ (cm^2/g)	σ_I/ρ (cm^2/g)	σ_a/ρ (cm^2/g)	μ/ρ (cm^2/g)
60.0	5.49–1	7.04–2	1.36–1	1.35–2	7.56–1
70.0	3.41–1	5.40–2	1.35–1	1.50–2	5.30–1
80.0	2.26–1	4.27–2	1.33–1	1.63–2	4.02–1
90.0	1.57–1	3.46–2	1.32–1	1.75–2	3.23–1
100.0	1.13–1	2.86–2	1.30–1	1.85–2	2.71–1
120.0	6.42–2	2.04–2	1.25–1	2.02–2	2.10–1
150.0	3.21–2	1.35–2	1.19–1	2.22–2	1.65–1
170.0	2.18–2	1.06–2	1.15–1	2.31–2	1.48–1
200.0	1.32–2	7.78–3	1.10–1	2.43–2	1.31–1
250.0	6.61–3	5.06–3	1.03–1	2.55–2	1.15–1
300.0	3.78–3	3.55–3	9.68–2	2.63–2	1.04–1
350.0	2.36–3	2.63–3	9.15–2	2.68–2	9.65–2
400.0	1.57–3	2.02–3	8.70–2	2.71–2	9.06–2
500.0	8.03–4	1.30–3	7.96–2	2.73–2	8.17–2
600.0	4.66–4	9.07–4	7.37–2	2.72–2	7.51–2
700.0	2.96–4	6.67–4	6.89–2	2.69–2	6.99–2
800.0	2.00–4	5.11–4	6.48–2	2.66–2	6.56–2
900.0	1.42–4	4.05–4	6.14–2	2.61–2	6.19–2
1,000.0	1.05–4	3.28–4	5.83–2	2.57–2	5.87–2

Vanadium **Z = 23**

Energy (keV)	τ/ρ (cm^2/g)	σ_c/ρ (cm^2/g)	σ_I/ρ (cm^2/g)	σ_a/ρ (cm^2/g)	μ/ρ (cm^2/g)
0.1	3.30+4	4.15+0	1.74–4	4.62–8	3.30+4
0.15	2.14+4	4.15+0	3.58–4	1.44–7	2.14+4
0.2	1.45+4	4.14+0	6.14–4	3.32–7	1.45+4
0.3	7.63+3	4.12+0	1.33–3	1.08–6	7.64+3
0.4	4.53+3	4.10+0	2.29–3	2.48–6	4.54+3
0.45	3.61+3	4.08+0	2.86–3	3.48–6	3.61+3
0.48	3.18+3	4.07+0	3.21–3	4.16–6	3.18+3
0.5	2.92+3	4.06+0	3.45–3	4.66–6	2.93+3
0.5147 $L_{II,III}$	2.76+3	4.06+0	3.64–3	5.05–6	2.76+3
0.5161	1.56+4	4.06+0	3.65–3	5.09–6	1.56+4
0.56	2.05+4	4.04+0	4.22–3	6.37–6	2.05+4
0.6	1.77+4	4.02+0	4.77–3	7.68–6	1.77+4
0.6275 L_I	1.59+4	4.01+0	5.15–3	8.66–6	1.59+4
0.6289	1.84+4	4.01+0	5.17–3	8.71–6	1.84+4
0.7	1.44+4	3.98+0	6.19–3	1.16–5	1.44+4
0.8	1.06+4	3.93+0	7.68–3	1.63–5	1.06+4
0.9	8.08+3	3.87+0	9.20–3	2.18–5	8.09+3
1.0	6.27+3	3.82+0	1.07–2	2.80–5	6.28+3
1.2	4.00+3	3.70+0	1.37–2	4.25–5	4.01+3
1.5	2.28+3	3.52+0	1.80–2	6.81–5	2.28+3
2.0	1.08+3	3.23+0	2.44–2	1.20–4	1.08+3
2.5	6.02+2	2.95+0	3.03–2	1.84–4	6.05+2
3.0	3.67+2	2.70+0	3.60–2	2.60–4	3.70+2
3.5	2.42+2	2.48+0	4.15–2	3.47–4	2.45+2
4.0	1.69+2	2.27+0	4.67–2	4.43–4	1.71+2
5.0	9.23+1	1.91+0	5.61–2	6.58–4	9.43+1
5.465 K	7.26+1	1.77+0	6.01–2	7.66–4	7.44+1
5.465	6.29+2	1.77+0	6.01–2	7.66–4	6.31+2
6.0	4.91+2	1.63+0	6.45–2	8.96–4	4.93+2
7.0	3.25+2	1.40+0	7.19–2	1.15–3	3.27+2
8.0	2.26+2	1.22+0	7.84–2	1.42–3	2.27+2

TABLE 3 (continued)

Energy (keV)	τ/ρ (cm^2/g)	σ_c/ρ (cm^2/g)	σ_I/ρ (cm^2/g)	σ_a/ρ (cm^2/g)	μ/ρ (cm^2/g)
9.0	1.64+2	1.08+0	8.40–2	1.69–3	1.65+2
10.0	1.22+2	9.61–1	8.90–2	1.97–3	1.23+2
12.0	7.32+1	7.87–1	9.71–2	2.52–3	7.41+1
15.0	3.87+1	6.08–1	1.06–1	3.35–3	3.94+1
17.0	2.70+1	5.20–1	1.11–1	3.91–3	2.76+1
20.0	1.68+1	4.18–1	1.17–1	4.74–3	1.73+1
25.0	8.71+0	3.02–1	1.24–1	6.07–3	9.13+0
30.0	5.06+0	2.28–1	1.28–1	7.33–3	5.42+0
35.0	3.19+0	1.79–1	1.31–1	8.49–3	3.50+0
40.0	2.13+0	1.44–1	1.32–1	9.57–3	2.41+0
50.0	1.08+0	1.00–1	1.34–1	1.15–2	1.32+0
60.0	6.21–1	7.39–2	1.33–1	1.32–2	8.28–1
70.0	3.87–1	5.68–2	1.32–1	1.47–2	5.76–1
80.0	2.57–1	4.49–2	1.31–1	1.60–2	4.33–1
90.0	1.79–1	3.64–2	1.29–1	1.72–2	3.44–1
100.0	1.29–1	3.01–2	1.27–1	1.82–2	2.86–1
120.0	7.37–2	2.16–2	1.23–1	1.99–2	2.18–1
150.0	3.71–2	1.42–2	1.17–1	2.18–2	1.68–1
170.0	2.52–2	1.12–2	1.13–1	2.27–2	1.50–1
200.0	1.53–2	8.22–3	1.08–1	2.38–2	1.32–1
250.0	7.71–3	5.35–3	1.01–1	2.51–2	1.14–1
300.0	4.41–3	3.75–3	9.51–2	2.59–2	1.03–1
350.0	2.76–3	2.78–3	8.99–2	2.64–2	9.55–2
400.0	1.84–3	2.14–3	8.55–2	2.66–2	8.95–2
500.0	9.41–4	1.38–3	7.82–2	2.68–2	8.05–2
600.0	5.46–4	9.59–4	7.25–2	2.67–2	7.40–2
700.0	3.46–4	7.06–4	6.77–2	2.65–2	6.88–2
800.0	2.34–4	5.41–4	6.37–2	2.61–2	6.45–2
900.0	1.66–4	4.28–4	6.03–2	2.57–2	6.09–2
1,000.0	1.22–4	3.47–4	5.73–2	2.53–2	5.78–2

Chromium **Z = 24**

Energy (keV)	τ/ρ (cm^2/g)	σ_c/ρ (cm^2/g)	σ_I/ρ (cm^2/g)	σ_a/ρ (cm^2/g)	μ/ρ (cm^2/g)
0.1	4.37+4	4.43+0	1.35–4	3.56–8	4.37+4
0.15	2.70+4	4.43+0	2.75–4	1.11–7	2.70+4
0.2	1.78+4	4.42+0	4.75–4	2.57–7	1.78+4
0.3	9.10+3	4.40+0	1.03–3	8.42–7	9.10+3
0.4	5.31+3	4.38+0	1.78–3	1.93–6	5.32+3
0.5	3.41+3	4.35+0	2.70–3	3.64–6	3.42+3
0.5769 $L_{II,III}$	2.53+3	4.33+0	3.48–3	5.40–6	2.53+3
0.5783	1.76+4	4.32+0	3.50–3	5.44–6	1.76+4
0.59	2.11+4	4.32+0	3.62–3	5.75–6	2.11+4
0.6	2.14+4	4.32+0	3.73–3	6.02–6	2.14+4
0.67	1.61+4	4.29+0	4.51–3	8.10–6	1.61+4
0.6939 L_I	1.48+4	4.28+0	4.79–3	8.89–6	1.48+4
0.6953	1.68+4	4.28+0	4.81–3	8.94–6	1.68+4
0.7	1.67+4	4.28+0	4.86–3	9.10–6	1.67+4
0.75	1.42+4	4.26+0	5.46–3	1.09–5	1.42+4
0.8	1.23+4	4.23+0	6.06–3	1.29–5	1.23+4
0.9	9.37+3	4.19+0	7.31–3	1.74–5	9.38+3
1.0	7.29+3	4.14+0	8.57–3	2.25–5	7.29+3
1.2	4.65+3	4.03+0	1.11–2	3.47–5	4.66+3
1.5	2.65+3	3.86+0	1.49–2	5.73–5	2.65+3

TABLE 3 (continued)

Energy (keV)	τ/ρ (cm^2/g)	σ_c/ρ (cm^2/g)	σ_I/ρ (cm^2/g)	σ_a/ρ (cm^2/g)	μ/ρ (cm^2/g)
2.0	1.26+3	3.57+0	2.11–2	1.06–4	1.26+3
2.5	7.03+2	3.28+0	2.71–2	1.68–4	7.06+2
3.0	4.30+2	3.01+0	3.29–2	2.42–4	4.33+2
3.5	2.84+2	2.76+0	3.84–2	3.27–4	2.87+2
4.0	1.99+2	2.53+0	4.37–2	4.22–4	2.01+2
5.0	1.09+2	2.13+0	5.34–2	6.35–4	1.11+2
5.989_K	6.70+1	1.81+0	6.21–2	8.72–4	6.89+1
5.989	5.71+2	1.81+0	6.21–2	8.72–4	5.73+2
6.0	5.68+2	1.81+0	6.22–2	8.75–4	5.70+2
7.0	3.76+2	1.55+0	6.99–2	1.13–3	3.78+2
8.0	2.62+2	1.35+0	7.69–2	1.41–3	2.64+2
9.0	1.90+2	1.18+0	8.29–2	1.69–3	1.91+2
10.0	1.42+2	1.05+0	8.82–2	1.97–3	1.43+2
12.0	8.52+1	8.60–1	9.70–2	2.54–3	8.62+1
15.0	4.52+1	6.62–1	1.07–1	3.39–3	4.60+1
17.0	3.15+1	5.67–1	1.12–1	3.96–3	3.22+1
20.0	1.97+1	4.56–1	1.18–1	4.81–3	2.02+1
25.0	1.02+1	3.31–1	1.25–1	6.17–3	1.07+1
30.0	5.94+0	2.49–1	1.30–1	7.45–3	6.32+0
35.0	3.74+0	1.95–1	1.33–1	8.65–3	4.07+0
40.0	2.51+0	1.58–1	1.35–1	9.75–3	2.80+0
50.0	1.28+0	1.09–1	1.36–1	1.17–2	1.52+0
60.0	7.32–1	8.07–2	1.36–1	1.35–2	9.49–1
70.0	4.57–1	6.20–2	1.35–1	1.50–2	6.54–1
80.0	3.03–1	4.91–2	1.33–1	1.63–2	4.86–1
90.0	2.11–1	3.98–2	1.31–1	1.75–2	3.83–1
100.0	1.53–1	3.30–2	1.29–1	1.86–2	3.15–1
120.0	8.73–2	2.36–2	1.25–1	2.03–2	2.36–1
150.0	4.40–2	1.56–2	1.20–1	2.22–2	1.79–1
170.0	2.99–2	1.23–2	1.16–1	2.32–2	1.58–1
200.0	1.82–2	9.01–3	1.11–1	2.44–2	1.38–1
250.0	9.18–3	5.87–3	1.03–1	2.57–2	1.18–1
300.0	5.27–3	4.12–3	9.71–2	2.65–2	1.07–1
350.0	3.30–3	3.05–3	9.19–2	2.70–2	9.82–2
400.0	2.20–3	2.35–3	8.74–2	2.72–2	9.19–2
500.0	1.13–3	1.51–3	8.00–2	2.74–2	8.26–2
600.0	6.57–4	1.05–3	7.41–2	2.73–2	7.58–2
700.0	4.17–4	7.76–4	6.92–2	2.70–2	7.04–2
800.0	2.82–4	5.95–4	6.51–2	2.67–2	6.60–2
900.0	2.00–4	4.71–4	6.16–2	2.63–2	6.23–2
1,000.0	1.48–4	3.81–4	5.86–2	2.58–2	5.91–2

Manganese **Z = 25**

Energy (keV)	τ/ρ (cm^2/g)	σ_c/ρ (cm^2/g)	σ_I/ρ (cm^2/g)	σ_a/ρ (cm^2/g)	μ/ρ (cm^2/g)
0.1	4.51+4	4.55+0	1.41–4	3.76–8	4.51+4
0.15	2.87+4	4.55+0	2.93–4	1.18–7	2.87+4
0.2	1.91+4	4.54+0	5.06–4	2.74–7	1.91+4
0.3	9.86+3	4.52+0	1.10–3	9.00–7	9.87+3
0.4	5.82+3	4.50+0	1.91–3	2.07–6	5.83+3
0.5	3.76+3	4.47+0	2.89–3	3.91–6	3.76+3
0.59	2.67+3	4.43+0	3.89–3	6.19–6	2.68+3
0.6	2.58+3	4.43+0	4.01–3	6.48–6	2.58+3
$0.6433_{L_{II,III}}$	2.23+3	4.41+0	4.53–3	7.83–6	2.23+3
0.6447	1.03+4	4.41+0	4.55–3	7.87–6	1.03+4

TABLE 3 (continued)

Energy (keV)	τ/ρ (cm^2/g)	σ_c/ρ (cm^2/g)	σ_I/ρ (cm^2/g)	σ_a/ρ (cm^2/g)	μ/ρ (cm^2/g)
0.67	1.72+4	4.40+0	4.86−3	8.73−6	1.72+4
0.7	1.56+4	4.39+0	5.24−3	9.82−6	1.56+4
0.75	1.32+4	4.36+0	5.89−3	1.18−5	1.32+4
0.7683 L_I	1.25+4	4.35+0	6.12−3	1.26−5	1.25+4
0.7697	1.45+4	4.35+0	6.14−3	1.26−5	1.45+4
0.8	1.31+4	4.34+0	6.55−3	1.39−5	1.31+4
0.9	1.00+4	4.29+0	7.89−3	1.88−5	1.00+4
1.0	7.84+3	4.24+0	9.26−3	2.43−5	7.84+3
1.2	5.05+3	4.12+0	1.20−2	3.74−5	5.06+3
1.5	2.90+3	3.94+0	1.59−2	6.08−5	2.91+3
2.0	1.39+3	3.64+0	2.19−2	1.09−4	1.39+3
2.5	7.86+2	3.35+0	2.75−2	1.68−4	7.90+2
3.0	4.81+2	3.09+0	3.29−2	2.39−4	4.84+2
3.5	3.17+2	2.84+0	3.80−2	3.20−4	3.20+2
4.0	2.21+2	2.61+0	4.29−2	4.10−4	2.24+2
5.0	1.21+2	2.21+0	5.21−2	6.14−4	1.23+2
6.0	7.40+1	1.88+0	6.03−2	8.44−4	7.60+1
6.539 K	5.87+1	1.73+0	6.44−2	9.78−4	6.05+1
6.539	4.87+2	1.73+0	6.44−2	9.78−4	4.88+2
7.0	4.06+2	1.62+0	6.78−2	1.09−3	4.07+2
8.0	2.83+2	1.41+0	7.44−2	1.36−3	2.85+2
9.0	2.05+2	1.24+0	8.04−2	1.63−3	2.07+2
10.0	1.54+2	1.10+0	8.56−2	1.91−3	1.55+2
12.0	9.25+1	8.93−1	9.43−2	2.48−3	9.35+1
15.0	4.92+1	6.87−1	1.04−1	3.32−3	5.00+1
17.0	3.44+1	5.88−1	1.09−1	3.88−3	3.51+1
20.0	2.15+1	4.75−1	1.15−1	4.71−3	2.21+1
25.0	1.12+1	3.45−1	1.23−1	6.05−3	1.17+1
30.0	6.55+0	2.61−1	1.27−1	7.31−3	6.94+0
35.0	4.14+0	2.05−1	1.30−1	8.49−3	4.48+0
40.0	2.78+0	1.65−1	1.32−1	9.58−3	3.07+0
50.0	1.42+0	1.14−1	1.34−1	1.15−2	1.67+0
60.0	8.18−1	8.45−2	1.33−1	1.33−2	1.04+0
70.0	5.12−1	6.50−2	1.33−1	1.48−2	7.09−1
80.0	3.41−1	5.15−2	1.31−1	1.61−2	5.23−1
90.0	2.38−1	4.18−2	1.29−1	1.73−2	4.09−1
100.0	1.73−1	3.46−2	1.27−1	1.83−2	3.34−1
120.0	9.88−2	2.48−2	1.23−1	2.00−2	2.47−1
150.0	4.99−2	1.64−2	1.18−1	2.19−2	1.84−1
170.0	3.40−2	1.29−2	1.14−1	2.29−2	1.61−1
200.0	2.07−2	9.48−3	1.09−1	2.40−2	1.39−1
250.0	1.05−2	6.18−3	1.02−1	2.53−2	1.19−1
300.0	6.04−3	4.34−3	9.57−2	2.61−2	1.06−1
350.0	3.79−3	3.21−3	9.05−2	2.66−2	9.76−2
400.0	2.54−3	2.47−3	8.61−2	2.69−2	9.11−2
500.0	1.30−3	1.59−3	7.88−2	2.70−2	8.17−2
600.0	7.57−4	1.11−3	7.30−2	2.69−2	7.49−2
700.0	4.81−4	8.18−4	6.82−2	2.67−2	6.95−2
800.0	3.25−4	6.27−4	6.42−2	2.63−2	6.52−2
900.0	2.31−4	4.96−4	6.08−2	2.59−2	6.15−2
1,000.0	1.71−4	4.02−4	5.78−2	2.55−2	5.83−2

TABLE 3 (continued)

Energy (keV)	τ/ρ (cm²/g)	σ_c/ρ (cm²/g)	σ_I/ρ (cm²/g)	σ_a/ρ (cm²/g)	μ/ρ (cm²/g)
Iron	**Z = 26**				
0.1	5.21+4	4.84+0	1.31–4	3.51–8	5.21+4
0.15	3.34+4	4.84+0	2.75–4	1.11–7	3.34+4
0.2	2.24+4	4.83+0	4.74–4	2.57–7	2.24+4
0.3	1.15+4	4.82+0	1.03–3	8.42–7	1.15+4
0.4	6.73+3	4.79+0	1.79–3	1.94–6	6.74+3
0.5	4.35+3	4.76+0	2.72–3	3.67–6	4.35+3
0.59	3.08+3	4.73+0	3.66–3	5.83–6	3.08+3
0.6	2.97+3	4.72+0	3.78–3	6.10–6	2.97+3
0.67	2.35+3	4.69+0	4.58–3	8.24–6	2.35+3
0.7	2.14+3	4.68+0	4.94–3	9.28–6	2.14+3
0.7117 $L_{II,III}$	2.07+3	4.68+0	5.09–3	9.70–6	2.07+3
0.7131	8.80+3	4.67+0	5.10–3	9.75–6	8.80+3
0.75	1.50+4	4.66+0	5.56–3	1.12–5	1.50+4
0.8	1.30+4	4.63+0	6.19–3	1.32–5	1.30+4
0.8454 L_I	1.13+4	4.61+0	6.78–3	1.52–5	1.13+4
0.8468	1.31+4	4.61+0	6.79–3	1.53–5	1.31+4
0.9	1.13+4	4.58+0	7.49–3	1.79–5	1.13+4
1.0	8.85+3	4.53+0	8.80–3	2.32–5	8.86+3
1.2	5.74+3	4.42+0	1.15–2	3.58–5	5.74+3
1.5	3.31+3	4.24+0	1.53–2	5.87–5	3.31+3
2.0	1.59+3	3.93+0	2.13–2	1.06–4	1.59+3
2.5	9.10+2	3.63+0	2.68–2	1.65–4	9.14+2
3.0	5.56+2	3.35+0	3.22–2	2.34–4	5.59+2
3.5	3.66+2	3.09+0	3.73–2	3.15–4	3.69+2
4.0	2.55+2	2.85+0	4.23–2	4.05–4	2.58+2
5.0	1.39+2	2.42+0	5.15–2	6.09–4	1.42+2
6.0	8.51+1	2.07+0	5.99–2	8.41–4	8.72+1
7.0	5.60+1	1.78+0	6.74–2	1.09–3	5.79+1
7.112 K	5.37+1	1.75+0	6.82–2	1.12–3	5.55+1
7.112	4.35+2	1.75+0	6.82–2	1.12–3	4.37+2
8.0	3.18+2	1.54+0	7.43–2	1.36–3	3.20+2
9.0	2.32+2	1.35+0	8.04–2	1.64–3	2.33+2
10.0	1.74+2	1.20+0	8.58–2	1.92–3	1.76+2
12.0	1.06+2	9.72–1	9.49–2	2.50–3	1.07+2
15.0	5.65+1	7.45–1	1.05–1	3.36–3	5.74+1
17.0	3.96+1	6.38–1	1.10–1	3.94–3	4.04+1
20.0	2.49+1	5.15–1	1.17–1	4.78–3	2.55+1
25.0	1.30+1	3.76–1	1.24–1	6.15–3	1.35+1
30.0	7.62+0	2.84–1	1.29–1	7.44–3	8.03+0
35.0	4.82+0	2.23–1	1.32–1	8.97–3	5.18+0
40.0	3.24+0	1.80–1	1.34–1	9.77–3	3.56+0
50.0	1.66+0	1.25–1	1.36–1	1.18–2	1.92+0
60.0	9.56–1	9.19–2	1.36–1	1.35–2	1.18+0
70.0	5.99–1	7.07–2	1.35–1	1.51–2	8.05–1
80.0	3.99–1	5.61–2	1.34–1	1.64–2	5.89–1
90.0	2.78–1	4.55–2	1.32–1	1.76–2	4.56–1
100.0	2.02–1	3.77–2	1.30–1	1.87–2	3.70–1
120.0	1.15–1	2.71–2	1.26–1	2.04–2	2.69–1
150.0	5.84–2	1.79–2	1.20–1	2.24–2	1.96–1
170.0	3.98–2	1.41–2	1.16–1	2.34–2	1.70–1

TABLE 3 (continued)

Energy (keV)	τ/ρ (cm^2/g)	σ_c/ρ (cm^2/g)	σ_I/ρ (cm^2/g)	σ_a/ρ (cm^2/g)	μ/ρ (cm^2/g)
200.0	2.42–2	1.04–2	1.11–1	2.46–2	1.46–1
250.0	1.23–2	6.75–3	1.04–1	2.59–2	1.23–1
300.0	7.06–3	4.74–3	9.79–2	2.67–2	1.10–1
350.0	4.43–3	3.51–3	9.26–2	2.72–2	1.01–1
400.0	2.97–3	2.71–3	8.81–2	2.75–2	9.37–2
500.0	1.52–3	1.74–3	8.06–2	2.77–2	8.39–2
600.0	8.89–4	1.22–3	7.47–2	2.76–2	7.68–2
700.0	5.66–4	8.96–4	6.98–2	2.73–2	7.12–2
800.0	3.84–4	6.87–4	6.57–2	2.69–2	6.68–2
900.0	2.73–4	5.44–4	6.22–2	2.65–2	6.30–2
1,000.0	2.02–4	4.40–4	5.91–2	2.61–2	5.97–2

Cobalt **Z = 27**

0.1 M_I	5.18+4	4.95+0	1.20–4	3.19–8	5.18–4
0.1014	5.48+4	4.95+0	1.23–4	3.31–8	5.48+4
0.15	3.64+4	4.94+0	2.47–4	9.99–8	3.64+4
0.2	2.46+4	4.94+0	4.27–4	2.31–7	2.46+4
0.3	1.27+4	4.92+0	9.34–4	7.61–7	1.27+4
0.4	7.45+3	4.90+0	1.62–3	1.76–6	7.45+3
0.5	4.79+3	4.87+0	2.46–3	3.33–6	4.79+3
0.6	3.27+3	4.84+0	3.43–3	5.55–6	3.27+3
0.7	2.36+3	4.80+0	4.50–3	8.46–6	2.36+3
0.7829 $L_{II,III}$	1.85+3	4.76+0	5.45–3	1.14–5	1.85+3
0.7843	7.16+3	4.76+0	5.47–3	1.15–5	7.16+3
0.79	1.10+4	4.76+0	5.53–3	1.17–5	1.10+4
0.8	1.34+4	4.75+0	5.65–3	1.21–5	1.34+4
0.85	1.22+4	4.73+0	6.24–3	1.41–5	1.22+4
0.9	1.06+4	4.70+0	6.84–3	1.64–5	1.06+4
0.9249 L_I	9.89+3	4.69+0	7.15–3	1.75–5	9.89+3
0.9263	1.15+4	4.69+0	7.16–3	1.76–5	1.15+4
1.0	9.52+3	4.65+0	8.07–3	2.13–5	9.52+3
1.2	6.19+3	4.54+0	1.06–2	3.30–5	6.20+3
1.5	3.59+3	4.37+0	1.42–2	5.46–5	3.59+3
2.0	1.73+3	4.06+0	1.99–2	9.95–5	1.74+3
2.5	1.00+3	3.77+0	2.52–2	1.55–4	1.00+3
3.0	6.11+2	3.49+0	3.03–2	2.21–4	6.15+2
3.5	4.03+2	3.22+0	3.52–2	2.98–4	4.06+2
4.0	2.81+2	2.98+0	4.00–2	3.85–4	2.84+2
5.0	1.54+2	2.54+0	4.90–2	5.81–4	1.56+2
6.0	9.40+1	2.17+0	5.71–2	8.05–4	9.62+1
7.0	6.20+1	1.87+0	6.45–2	1.05–3	6.39+1
7.709 K	4.78+1	1.69+0	6.94–2	1.23–3	4.95+1
7.709	3.93+2	1.69+0	6.94–2	1.23–3	3.95+2
8.0	3.56+2	1.63+0	7.13–2	1.31–3	3.57+2
9.0	2.58+2	1.43+0	7.73–2	1.58–3	2.60+2
10.0	1.94+2	1.26+0	8.27–2	1.86–3	1.95+2
12.0	1.17+2	1.02+0	9.18–2	2.43–3	1.18+2
15.0	6.22+1	7.77–1	1.02–1	3.28–3	6.31+1
17.0	4.36+1	6.65–1	1.07–1	3.84–3	4.43+1
20.0	2.73+1	5.38–1	1.14–1	4.67–3	2.79+1
25.0	1.42+1	3.93–1	1.21–1	6.02–3	1.48+1
30.0	8.33+0	2.97–1	1.26–1	7.29–3	8.76+0

TABLE 3 (continued)

Energy (keV)	τ/ρ (cm²/g)	σ_c/ρ (cm²/g)	σ_I/ρ (cm²/g)	σ_a/ρ (cm²/g)	μ/ρ (cm²/g)
35.0	5.28+0	2.33−1	1.30−1	8.48−3	5.64+0
40.0	3.55+0	1.88−1	1.32−1	9.59−3	3.87+0
50.0	1.82+0	1.30−1	1.33−1	1.16−2	2.08+0
60.0	1.05+0	9.61−2	1.33−1	1.33−2	1.28+0
70.0	6.58−1	7.39−2	1.33−1	1.48−2	8.64−1
80.0	4.39−1	5.86−2	1.31−1	1.61−2	6.28−1
90.0	3.07−1	4.76−2	1.30−1	1.73−2	4.84−1
100.0	2.23−1	3.95−2	1.28−1	1.84−2	3.90−1
120.0	1.28−1	2.83−2	1.24−1	2.01−2	2.80−1
150.0	6.49−2	1.87−2	1.18−1	2.20−2	2.02−1
170.0	4.43−2	1.48−2	1.15−1	2.30−2	1.74−1
200.0	2.71−2	1.09−2	1.10−1	2.42−2	1.47−1
250.0	1.38−2	7.08−3	1.02−1	2.55−2	1.23−1
300.0	7.97−3	4.98−3	9.63−2	2.63−2	1.09−1
350.0	5.02−3	3.69−3	9.11−2	2.67−2	9.98−2
400.0	3.37−3	2.84−3	8.66−2	2.70−2	9.28−2
500.0	1.74−3	1.83−3	7.93−2	2.72−2	8.29−2
600.0	1.02−3	1.28−3	7.35−2	2.71−2	7.58−2
700.0	6.52−4	9.42−4	6.87−2	2.68−2	7.03−2
800.0	4.44−4	7.22−4	6.46−2	2.65−2	6.58−2
900.0	3.17−4	5.72−4	6.12−2	2.61−2	6.21−2
1,000.0	2.35−4	4.63−4	5.81−2	2.56−2	5.88−2
Nickel	**Z = 28**				
0.1	5.90+4	5.34+0	1.13−4	3.02−8	5.90+4
0.1111 M_I	5.34+4	5.34+0	1.36−4	4.05−8	5.34+4
0.1125	5.63+4	5.34+0	1.39−4	4.19−8	5.63+4
0.15	4.26+4	5.34+0	2.37−4	9.58−8	4.26+4
0.2	2.88+4	5.33+0	4.09−4	2.22−7	2.88+4
0.3	1.49+4	5.32+0	8.96−4	7.30−7	1.49+4
0.4	8.72+3	5.29+0	1.55−3	1.69−6	8.72+3
0.5	5.68+3	5.26+0	2.37−3	3.21−6	5.69+3
0.6	3.91+3	5.23+0	3.31−3	5.35−6	3.91+3
0.7	2.73+3	5.19+0	4.35−3	8.18−6	2.74+3
0.8	2.10+3	5.14+0	5.47−3	1.17−5	2.10+3
0.8597 $L_{II,III}$	1.73+3	5.12+0	6.16−3	1.41−5	1.73+3
0.8611	6.25+3	5.12+0	6.18−3	1.42−5	6.25+3
0.9	1.22+4	5.10+0	6.64−3	1.59−5	1.22+4
1.0	9.48+3	5.04+0	7.84−3	2.07−5	9.49+3
1.0073 L_I	9.31+3	5.04+0	7.92−3	2.11−5	9.31+3
1.0087	1.08+4	5.04+0	7.94−3	2.12−5	1.08+4
1.2	7.10+3	4.93+0	1.03−2	3.23−5	7.11+3
1.5	4.12+3	4.75+0	1.39−2	5.37−5	4.12+3
2.0	2.00+3	4.44+0	1.96−2	9.86−5	2.00+3
2.5	1.16+3	4.13+0	2.50−2	1.54−4	1.16+3
3.0	7.05+2	3.83+0	3.01−2	2.21−4	7.09+2
3.5	4.64+2	3.55+0	3.51−2	2.98−4	4.68+2
4.0	3.23+2	3.29+0	4.00−2	3.85−4	3.27+2
5.0	1.77+2	2.82+0	4.91−2	5.85−4	1.79+2
6.0	1.08+2	2.42+0	5.75−2	8.12−4	1.10+2
7.0	7.09+1	2.08+0	6.51−2	1.06−3	7.30+1
8.0	4.94+1	1.81+0	7.21−2	1.33−3	5.12+1

Energy (keV)	τ/ρ (cm^2/g)	σ_c/ρ (cm^2/g)	σ_I/ρ (cm^2/g)	σ_a/ρ (cm^2/g)	μ/ρ (cm^2/g)
8.333_K	4.42+1	1.73+0	7.42−2	1.42−3	4.60+1
8.333	3.41+2	1.73+0	7.42−2	1.42−3	3.43+2
9.0	2.79+2	1.59+0	7.84−2	1.61−3	2.81+2
10.0	2.11+2	1.40+0	8.40−2	1.90−3	2.13+2
12.0	1.29+2	1.13+0	9.37−2	2.49−3	1.31+2
15.0	7.02+1	8.59−1	1.05−1	3.37−3	7.11+1
17.0	4.95+1	7.33−1	1.10−1	3.96−3	5.03+1
20.0	3.13+1	5.93−1	1.17−1	4.83−3	3.20+1
25.0	1.65+1	4.33−1	1.25−1	6.22−3	1.71+1
30.0	9.72+0	3.29−1	1.30−1	7.55−3	1.02+1
35.0	6.18+0	2.58−1	1.34−1	8.79−3	6.58+0
40.0	4.17+0	2.08−1	1.36−1	9.95−3	4.51+0
50.0	2.14+0	1.44−1	1.38−1	1.20−2	2.42+0
60.0	1.24+0	1.06−1	1.38−1	1.38−2	1.48+0
70.0	7.78−1	8.16−2	1.38−1	1.54−2	9.97−1
80.0	5.19−1	6.47−2	1.36−1	1.68−2	7.20−1
90.0	3.63−1	5.26−2	1.34−1	1.80−2	5.50−1
100.0	2.63−1	4.36−2	1.33−1	1.91−2	4.40−1
120.0	1.51−1	3.14−2	1.29−1	2.09−2	3.11−1
150.0	7.66−2	2.07−2	1.23−1	2.29−2	2.20−1
170.0	5.23−2	1.64−2	1.19−1	2.39−2	1.88−1
200.0	3.19−2	1.20−2	1.14−1	2.51−2	1.58−1
250.0	1.62−2	7.85−3	1.06−1	2.65−2	1.31−1
300.0	9.38−3	5.52−3	1.00−1	2.73−2	1.15−1
350.0	5.91−3	4.09−3	9.48−2	2.78−2	1.05−1
400.0	3.97−3	3.15−3	9.01−2	2.81−2	9.73−2
500.0	2.05−3	2.03−3	8.25−2	2.83−2	8.66−2
600.0	1.21−3	1.42−3	7.65−2	2.82−2	7.91−2
700.0	7.72−4	1.04−3	7.15−2	2.79−2	7.33−2
800.0	5.27−4	8.01−4	6.73−2	2.76−2	6.86−2
900.0	3.77−4	6.34−4	6.37−2	2.71−2	6.47−2
1,000.0	2.81−4	5.14−4	6.05−2	2.67−2	6.13−2

Copper **Z = 29**

Energy (keV)	τ/ρ (cm^2/g)	σ_c/ρ (cm^2/g)	σ_I/ρ (cm^2/g)	σ_a/ρ (cm^2/g)	μ/ρ (cm^2/g)
0.1	6.44+4	5.30+0	8.46−5	2.25−8	6.44+4
0.1191_{M_I}	5.26+4	5.29+0	1.14−4	3.64−8	5.27+4
0.1205	5.47+4	5.29+0	1.17−4	3.76−8	5.48+4
0.15	4.75+4	5.29+0	1.76−4	7.10−8	4.75+4
0.2	3.10+4	5.29+0	3.04−4	1.65−7	3.10+4
0.3	1.62+4	5.28+0	6.67−4	5.44−7	1.62+4
0.4	9.44+3	5.26+0	1.16−3	1.26−6	9.45+3
0.5	6.46+3	5.23+0	1.77−3	2.40−6	6.47+3
0.6	4.33+3	5.20+0	2.47−3	4.00−6	4.33+3
0.7	2.86+3	5.17+0	3.26−3	6.14−6	2.86+3
0.8	2.39+3	5.13+0	4.12−3	8.82−6	2.40+3
0.9	1.61+3	5.09+0	5.01−3	1.20−5	1.61+3
$0.937_{L_{II,III}}$	1.55+3	5.08+0	5.35−3	1.33−5	1.55+3
0.9384	6.68+3	5.08+0	5.37−3	1.34−5	6.68+3
0.96	1.12+4	5.07+0	5.57−3	1.42−5	1.12+4
1.0	1.05+4	5.05+0	5.95−3	1.58−5	1.05+4
1.0963_{L_I}	8.08+3	5.00+0	6.86−3	1.99−5	8.08+3
1.0977	9.20+3	5.00+0	6.87−3	1.99−5	9.21+3

TABLE 3 (continued)

Energy (keV)	τ/ρ (cm²/g)	σ_c/ρ (cm²/g)	σ_I/ρ (cm²/g)	σ_a/ρ (cm²/g)	μ/ρ (cm²/g)
1.2	7.62+3	4.96+0	7.89–3	2.49–5	7.62+3
1.5	4.37+3	4.80+0	1.09–2	4.24–5	4.38+3
2.0	2.14+3	4.52+0	1.60–2	8.14–5	2.14+3
2.5	1.20+3	4.23+0	2.10–2	1.32–4	1.21+3
3.0	7.33+2	3.94+0	2.60–2	1.94–4	7.37+2
3.5	4.98+2	3.67+0	3.08–2	2.66–4	5.02+2
4.0	3.47+2	3.40+0	3.54–2	3.47–4	3.51+2
5.0	1.90+2	2.91+0	4.41–2	5.31–4	1.93+2
6.0	1.16+2	2.50+0	5.20–2	7.42–4	1.18+2
7.0	7.64+1	2.16+0	5.93–2	9.76–4	7.86+1
8.0	5.32+1	1.87+0	6.61–2	1.23–3	5.52+1
8.979_K	3.89+1	1.65+0	7.21–2	1.49–3	4.07+1
8.979	2.96+2	1.65+0	7.21–2	1.49–3	2.97+2
9.0	2.94+2	1.64+0	7.22–2	1.49–3	2.96+2
10.0	2.23+2	1.45+0	7.77–2	1.77–3	2.24+2
12.0	1.36+2	1.16+0	8.73–2	2.34–3	1.38+2
15.0	7.41+1	8.80–1	9.81–2	3.18–3	7.51+1
17.0	5.23+1	7.49–1	1.04–1	3.75–3	5.32+1
20.0	3.31+1	6.05–1	1.11–1	4.58–3	3.38+1
25.0	1.75+1	4.42–1	1.18–1	5.92–3	1.81+1
30.0	1.03+1	3.36–1	1.24–1	7.19–3	1.08+1
35.0	6.57+0	2.63–1	1.27–1	8.38–3	6.96+0
40.0	4.43+0	2.12–1	1.30–1	9.49–3	4.77+0
50.0	2.28+0	1.47–1	1.32–1	1.15–2	2.56+0
60.0	1.32+0	1.08–1	1.32–1	1.32–2	1.56+0
70.0	8.31–1	8.30–2	1.31–1	1.47–2	1.05+0
80.0	5.55–1	6.59–2	1.30–1	1.60–2	7.51–1
90.0	3.89–1	5.36–2	1.28–1	1.72–2	5.71–1
100.0	2.82–1	4.44–2	1.27–1	1.82–2	4.53–1
120.0	1.62–1	3.19–2	1.23–1	2.00–2	3.17–1
150.0	8.24–2	2.11–2	1.17–1	2.19–2	2.21–1
170.0	5.64–2	1.67–2	1.14–1	2.29–2	1.87–1
200.0	3.44–2	1.23–2	1.09–1	2.40–2	1.56–1
250.0	1.76–2	8.00–3	1.02–1	2.53–2	1.27–1
300.0	1.02–2	5.63–3	9.57–2	2.62–2	1.11–1
350.0	6.41–3	4.17–3	9.07–2	2.66–2	1.01–1
400.0	4.31–3	3.22–3	8.62–2	2.69–2	9.37–2
500.0	2.23–3	2.07–3	7.89–2	2.71–2	8.33–2
600.0	1.31–3	1.45–3	7.31–2	2.70–2	7.59–2
700.0	8.42–4	1.07–3	6.84–2	2.67–2	7.03–2
800.0	5.75–4	8.18–4	6.44–2	2.64–2	6.58–2
900.0	4.12–4	6.47–4	6.09–2	2.60–2	6.20–2
1,000.0	3.07–4	5.24–4	5.79–2	2.55–2	5.87–2

Zinc **Z = 30**

0.1	6.77+4	5.51+0	9.27–5	2.47–8	6.77+4
0.1352_{M_I}	5.20+4	5.51+0	1.60–4	5.80–8	5.20+4
0.1366	5.46+4	5.51+0	1.63–4	5.98–8	5.46+4
0.15	4.99+4	5.50+0	1.94–4	7.86–8	5.00+4
0.2	3.54+4	5.50+0	3.37–4	1.83–7	3.54+4
0.3	1.88+4	5.49+0	7.39–4	6.03–7	1.88+4
0.4	1.11+4	5.47+0	1.29–3	1.40–6	1.11+4

TABLE 3 (continued)

Energy (keV)	τ/ρ (cm^2/g)	σ_c/ρ (cm^2/g)	σ_I/ρ (cm^2/g)	σ_a/ρ (cm^2/g)	μ/ρ (cm^2/g)
0.5	7.15+3	5.44+0	1.96−3	2.66−6	7.15+3
0.6	4.78+3	5.41+0	2.75−3	4.46−6	4.79+3
0.7	3.41+3	5.37+0	3.63−3	6.83−6	3.42+3
0.8	2.56+3	5.33+0	4.58−3	9.82−6	2.57+3
0.9	1.92+3	5.29+0	5.58−3	1.34−5	1.92+3
0.96	1.66+3	5.26+0	6.19−3	1.58−5	1.67+3
1.0	1.53+3	5.24+0	6.61−3	1.75−5	1.54+3
1.0263 $L_{II,III}$	1.44+3	5.22+0	6.88−3	1.87−5	1.45+3
1.0277	4.42+3	5.22+0	6.89−3	1.88−5	4.42+3
1.1	8.95+3	5.19+0	7.65−3	2.22−5	8.96+3
1.1933 L_I	7.28+3	5.14+0	8.67−3	2.72−5	7.28+3
1.1947	8.48+3	5.14+0	8.69−3	2.72−5	8.49+3
1.2	8.32+3	5.14+0	8.75−3	2.75−5	8.33+3
1.3	6.81+3	5.08+0	9.77−3	3.32−5	6.81+3
1.5	4.82+3	4.97+0	1.19−2	4.63−5	4.83+3
2.0	2.35+3	4.67+0	1.70−2	8.60−5	2.36+3
2.5	1.32+3	4.37+0	2.18−2	1.36−4	1.32+3
3.0	8.19+2	4.08+0	2.65−2	1.95−4	8.23+2
3.5	5.48+2	3.80+0	3.10−2	2.64−4	5.52+2
4.0	3.83+2	3.54+0	3.54−2	3.42−4	3.87+2
5.0	2.11+2	3.05+0	4.37−2	5.23−4	2.14+2
6.0	1.29+2	2.64+0	5.15−2	7.30−4	1.32+2
7.0	8.56+1	2.28+0	5.86−2	9.60−4	8.79+1
8.0	5.99+1	1.99+0	6.51−2	1.21−3	6.19+1
9.0	4.37+1	1.74+0	7.12−2	1.47−3	4.55+1
9.659 $_K$	3.61+1	1.61+0	7.48−2	1.65−3	3.78+1
9.659	2.73+2	1.61+0	7.48−2	1.65−3	2.75+2
10.0	2.49+2	1.54+0	7.67−2	1.74−3	2.51+2
12.0	1.53+2	1.23+0	8.62−2	2.31−3	1.54+2
15.0	8.28+1	9.32−1	9.72−2	3.16−3	8.38+1
17.0	5.84+1	7.93−1	1.03−1	3.73−3	5.93+1
20.0	3.70+1	6.40−1	1.10−1	4.56−3	3.77+1
25.0	1.95+1	4.68−1	1.18−1	5.91−3	2.01+1
30.0	1.15+1	3.56−1	1.23−1	7.19−3	1.20+1
35.0	7.34+0	2.80−1	1.27−1	8.39−3	7.75+0
40.0	4.96+0	2.26−1	1.30−1	9.50−3	5.31+0
50.0	2.56+0	1.56−1	1.32−1	1.15−2	2.84+0
60.0	1.48+0	1.15−1	1.32−1	1.32−2	1.73+0
70.0	9.33−1	8.81−2	1.31−1	1.47−2	1.15+0
80.0	6.24−1	6.99−2	1.30−1	1.61−2	8.24−1
90.0	4.37−1	5.69−2	1.29−1	1.73−2	6.23−1
100.0	3.18−1	4.72−2	1.27−1	1.83−2	4.92−1
120.0	1.83−1	3.39−2	1.23−1	2.01−2	3.40−1
150.0	9.31−2	2.25−2	1.18−1	2.20−2	2.33−1
170.0	6.38−2	1.78−2	1.14−1	2.30−2	1.96−1
200.0	3.91−2	1.31−2	1.09−1	2.42−2	1.62−1
250.0	2.00−2	8.52−3	1.02−1	2.55−2	1.31−1
300.0	1.16−2	5.99−3	9.63−2	2.63−2	1.14−1
350.0	7.31−3	4.44−3	9.11−2	2.68−2	1.03−1
400.0	4.92−3	3.42−3	8.67−2	2.71−2	9.50−2
500.0	2.56−3	2.21−3	7.94−2	2.73−2	8.41−2

TABLE 3 (continued)

Energy (keV)	τ/ρ (cm²/g)	σ_c/ρ (cm²/g)	σ_I/ρ (cm²/g)	σ_a/ρ (cm²/g)	μ/ρ (cm²/g)
600.0	1.51–3	1.54–3	7.35–2	2.72–2	7.66–2
700.0	9.67–4	1.14–3	6.87–2	2.69–2	7.08–2
800.0	6.61–4	8.71–4	6.47–2	2.65–2	6.62–2
900.0	4.74–4	6.89–4	6.12–2	2.61–2	6.24–2
1,000.0	3.53–4	5.58–4	5.82–2	2.57–2	5.91–2

Gallium **Z = 31**

Energy (keV)	τ/ρ (cm²/g)	σ_c/ρ (cm²/g)	σ_I/ρ (cm²/g)	σ_a/ρ (cm²/g)	μ/ρ (cm²/g)
0.1	6.13+4	5.51+0	9.42–5	2.51–8	6.14+4
0.1035 $M_{II,III}$	6.03+4	5.51+0	1.00–4	2.75–8	6.03+4
0.1049	6.41+4	5.51+0	1.02–4	2.86–8	6.41+4
0.15	4.82+4	5.51+0	1.95–4	7.88–8	4.82+4
0.1574 M_I	4.61+4	5.51+0	2.14–4	9.09–8	4.61+4
0.1588	4.85+4	5.51+0	2.18–4	9.33–8	4.85+4
0.2	3.73+4	5.51+0	3.36–4	1.82–7	3.73+4
0.3	2.03+4	5.49+0	7.35–4	5.99–7	2.04+4
0.4	1.20+4	5.47+0	1.27–3	1.38–6	1.20+4
0.5	7.72+3	5.44+0	1.94–3	2.63–6	7.73+3
0.6	5.20+3	5.40+0	2.72–3	4.40–6	5.21+3
0.7	3.74+3	5.36+0	3.58–3	6.74–6	3.74+3
0.8	2.79+3	5.32+0	4.51–3	9.67–6	2.80+3
0.9	2.11+3	5.27+0	5.49–3	1.32–5	2.12+3
1.0	1.65+3	5.22+0	6.51–3	1.73–5	1.65+3
1.1	1.33+3	5.16+0	7.53–3	2.19–5	1.33+3
1.1233 $L_{II,III}$	1.26+3	5.15+0	7.78–3	2.30–5	1.26+3
1.1247	3.70+3	5.15+0	7.79–3	2.31–5	3.71+3
1.2	7.68+3	5.11+0	8.61–3	2.71–5	7.69+3
1.2973 L_I	6.28+3	5.04+0	9.61–3	3.25–5	6.29+3
1.2987	7.32+3	5.04+0	9.62–3	3.26–5	7.33+3
1.3	7.26+3	5.04+0	9.64–3	3.27–5	7.27+3
1.5	5.08+3	4.93+0	1.18–2	4.57–5	5.08+3
2.0	2.49+3	4.62+0	1.69–2	8.55–5	2.50+3
3.0	8.72+2	4.04+0	2.61–2	1.92–4	8.76+2
4.0	4.03+2	3.52+0	3.44–2	3.31–4	4.06+2
5.0	2.26+2	3.06+0	4.22–2	5.01–4	2.29+2
6.0	1.38+2	2.65+0	4.94–2	6.98–4	1.41+2
7.0	9.10+1	2.31+0	5.61–2	9.16–4	9.34+1
8.0	6.34+1	2.02+0	6.23–2	1.15–3	6.55+1
9.0	4.61+1	1.77+0	6.79–2	1.40–3	4.80+1
10.0	3.47+1	1.57+0	7.31–2	1.66–3	3.63+1
10.37 K	3.14+1	1.50+0	7.49–2	1.76–3	3.30+1
10.37	2.33+2	1.50+0	7.49–2	1.76–3	2.35+2
12.0	1.58+2	1.26+0	8.22–2	2.20–3	1.59+2
15.0	8.58+1	9.49–1	9.29–2	3.02–3	8.69+1
17.0	6.07+1	8.06–1	9.86–2	3.57–3	6.16+1
20.0	3.85+1	6.50–1	1.05–1	4.38–3	3.93+1
25.0	2.04+1	4.77–1	1.13–1	5.68–3	2.10+1
30.0	1.21+1	3.63–1	1.19–1	6.92–3	1.26+1
35.0	7.72+0	2.86–1	1.22–1	8.09–3	8.13+0
40.0	5.22+0	2.31–1	1.25–1	9.17–3	5.58+0
50.0	2.70+0	1.59–1	1.27–1	1.11–2	2.99+0
60.0	1.57+0	1.17–1	1.28–1	1.28–2	1.82+0
70.0	9.93–1	8.99–2	1.27–1	1.43–2	1.21+0

TABLE 3 (continued)

Energy (keV)	τ/ρ (cm²/g)	σ_c/ρ (cm²/g)	σ_I/ρ (cm²/g)	σ_a/ρ (cm²/g)	μ/ρ (cm²/g)
80.0	6.65–1	7.14–2	1.26–1	1.56–2	8.62–1
90.0	4.67–1	5.81–2	1.24–1	1.67–2	6.50–1
100.0	3.40–1	4.82–2	1.23–1	1.77–2	5.11–1
120.0	1.96–1	3.47–2	1.19–1	1.94–2	3.50–1
150.0	1.00–1	2.30–2	1.14–1	2.13–2	2.37–1
170.0	6.88–2	1.82–2	1.11–1	2.23–2	1.98–1
200.0	4.22–2	1.34–2	1.06–1	2.34–2	1.62–1
250.0	2.16–2	8.72–3	9.90–2	2.47–2	1.29–1
300.0	1.26–2	6.13–3	9.32–2	2.55–2	1.12–1
350.0	7.97–3	4.55–3	8.82–2	2.59–2	1.01–1
400.0	5.37–3	3.51–3	8.39–2	2.62–2	9.29–2
500.0	2.80–3	2.26–3	7.69–2	2.64–2	8.19–2
600.0	1.65–3	1.58–3	7.12–2	2.63–2	7.45–2
700.0	1.06–3	1.16–3	6.66–2	2.61–2	6.88–2
800.0	7.28–4	8.93–4	6.27–2	2.57–2	6.43–2
900.0	5.23–4	7.07–4	5.93–2	2.53–2	6.06–2
1,000.0	3.90–4	5.73–4	5.64–2	2.49–2	5.74–2

Germanium Z = 32

Energy (keV)	τ/ρ (cm²/g)	σ_c/ρ (cm²/g)	σ_I/ρ (cm²/g)	σ_a/ρ (cm²/g)	μ/ρ (cm²/g)
0.1	5.86+4	5.64+0	8.81–5	2.33–8	5.86+4
0.1225 $M_{II,III}$	5.44+4	5.64+0	1.25–4	4.05–8	5.44+4
0.1239	5.73+4	5.64+0	1.27–4	4.19–8	5.73+4
0.15	5.03+4	5.64+0	1.80–4	7.27–8	5.03+4
0.1793 M_I	4.27+4	5.64+0	2.54–4	1.23–7	4.27+4
0.1807	4.48+4	5.64+0	2.57–4	1.26–7	4.48+4
0.2	3.99+4	5.64+0	3.11–4	1.69–7	3.99+4
0.3	2.23+4	5.62+0	6.83–4	5.57–7	2.24+4
0.4	1.33+4	5.59+0	1.19–3	1.29–6	1.33+4
0.5	8.57+3	5.56+0	1.82–3	2.47–6	8.58+3
0.6	5.82+3	5.53+0	2.55–3	4.14–6	5.83+3
0.7	4.17+3	5.49+0	3.38–3	6.37–6	4.17+3
0.8	3.11+3	5.44+0	4.28–3	9.20–6	3.11+3
0.9	2.37+3	5.39+0	5.23–3	1.26–5	2.37+3
1.0	1.84+3	5.33+0	6.22–3	1.66–5	1.85+3
1.1	1.48+3	5.27+0	7.23–3	2.11–5	1.49+3
1.2	1.21+3	5.22+0	8.30–3	2.62–5	1.21+3
1.2263 $L_{II,III}$	1.15+3	5.20+0	8.56–3	2.76–5	1.15+3
1.2277	3.55+3	5.20+0	8.58–3	2.77–5	3.56+3
1.3	6.80+3	5.15+0	9.33–3	3.18–5	6.80+3
1.4133 L_I	5.50+3	5.08+0	1.05–2	3.88–5	5.50+3
1.4147	6.34+3	5.08+0	1.05–2	3.89–5	6.34+3
1.5	5.49+3	5.03+0	1.15–2	4.48–5	5.50+3
2.0	2.70+3	4.71+0	1.67–2	8.50–5	2.70+3
3.0	9.52+2	4.10+0	2.61–2	1.92–4	9.56+2
4.0	4.40+2	3.57+0	3.43–2	3.30–4	4.44+2
5.0	2.44+2	3.12+0	4.18–2	4.96–4	2.47+2
6.0	1.49+2	2.72+0	4.88–2	6.86–4	1.52+2
7.0	9.79+1	2.38+0	5.52–2	8.98–4	1.00+2
8.0	6.81+1	2.09+0	6.11–2	1.13–3	7.02+1
9.0	4.94+1	1.84+0	6.66–2	1.37–3	5.13+1
10.0	3.71+1	1.63+0	7.16–2	1.62–3	3.88+1
11.1 K	2.79+1	1.44+0	7.66–2	1.91–3	2.95+1

TABLE 3 (continued)

Energy (keV)	τ/ρ (cm²/g)	σ_c/ρ (cm²/g)	σ_I/ρ (cm²/g)	σ_a/ρ (cm²/g)	μ/ρ (cm²/g)
11.1	2.03+2	1.44+0	7.66–2	1.91–3	2.05+2
12.0	1.65+2	1.31+0	8.05–2	2.15–3	1.66+2
15.0	9.04+1	9.86–1	9.10–2	2.96–3	9.15+1
17.0	6.41+1	8.37–1	9.67–2	3.51–3	6.51+1
20.0	4.09+1	6.75–1	1.03–1	4.31–3	4.16+1
25.0	2.18+1	4.95–1	1.11–1	5.60–3	2.24+1
30.0	1.29+1	3.78–1	1.17–1	6.82–3	1.34+1
35.0	8.29+0	2.98–1	1.21–1	7.98–3	8.71+0
40.0	5.62+0	2.41–1	1.23–1	9.06–3	5.99+0
50.0	2.92+0	1.66–1	1.26–1	1.10–2	3.21+0
60.0	1.70+0	1.22–1	1.26–1	1.27–2	1.95+0
70.0	1.08+0	9.38–2	1.26–1	1.41–2	1.30+0
80.0	7.24–1	7.44–2	1.24–1	1.54–2	9.23–1
90.0	5.09–1	6.06–2	1.23–1	1.65–2	6.93–1
100.0	3.72–1	5.03–2	1.22–1	1.75–2	5.43–1
120.0	2.15–1	3.62–2	1.18–1	1.92–2	3.69–1
150.0	1.10–1	2.40–2	1.13–1	2.11–2	2.47–1
170.0	7.57–2	1.90–2	1.10–1	2.21–2	2.04–1
200.0	4.65–2	1.40–2	1.05–1	2.32–2	1.65–1
250.0	2.39–2	9.11–3	9.81–2	2.45–2	1.31–1
300.0	1.39–2	6.41–3	9.23–2	2.52–2	1.13–1
350.0	8.83–3	4.76–3	8.74–2	2.57–2	1.01–1
400.0	5.97–3	3.67–3	8.32–2	2.60–2	9.28–2
500.0	3.12–3	2.37–3	7.62–2	2.62–2	8.17–2
600.0	1.84–3	1.65–3	7.06–2	2.61–2	7.41–2
700.0	1.19–3	1.22–3	6.60–2	2.58–2	6.84–2
800.0	8.15–4	9.35–4	6.21–2	2.55–2	6.39–2
900.0	5.86–4	7.40–4	5.88–2	2.51–2	6.01–2
1,000.0	4.38–4	6.00–4	5.59–2	2.47–2	5.69–2

Arsenic **Z = 33**

Energy (keV)	τ/ρ (cm²/g)	σ_c/ρ (cm²/g)	σ_I/ρ (cm²/g)	σ_a/ρ (cm²/g)	μ/ρ (cm²/g)
0.1	5.21+4	5.82+0	7.97–5	2.12–8	5.21+4
0.1418 $M_{II,III}$	4.98+4	5.81+0	1.49–4	5.68–8	4.98+4
0.1432	5.24+4	5.81+0	1.52–4	5.85–8	5.24+4
0.15	5.15+4	5.81+0	1.65–4	6.69–8	5.15+4
0.2	4.04+4	5.81+0	2.87–4	1.55–7	4.04+4
0.2028 M_I	3.98+4	5.81+0	2.95–4	1.62–7	3.98+4
0.2042	4.16+4	5.81+0	2.99–4	1.65–7	4.16+4
0.3	2.45+4	5.79+0	6.30–4	5.15–7	2.45+4
0.4	1.48+4	5.77+0	1.10–3	1.20–6	1.48+4
0.5	9.54+3	5.74+0	1.69–3	2.29–6	9.55+3
0.6	6.52+3	5.70+0	2.37–3	3.85–6	6.53+3
0.7	4.66+3	5.66+0	3.15–3	5.95–6	4.67+3
0.8	3.47+3	5.61+0	4.00–3	8.62–6	3.48+3
0.9	2.66+3	5.56+0	4.90–3	1.18–5	2.66+3
1.0	2.07+3	5.50+0	5.85–3	1.56–5	2.08+3
1.3343 $L_{II,III}$	1.05+3	5.29+0	9.18–3	3.22–5	1.06+3
1.3357	3.48+3	5.29+0	9.20–3	3.23–5	3.48+3
1.4	6.12+3	5.25+0	9.86–3	3.62–5	6.12+3
1.5	5.19+3	5.19+0	1.09–2	4.28–5	5.19+3

TABLE 3 (continued)

Energy (keV)	τ/ρ (cm^2/g)	σ_c/ρ (cm^2/g)	σ_I/ρ (cm^2/g)	σ_a/ρ (cm^2/g)	μ/ρ (cm^2/g)
1.5253 L_I	4.96+3	5.17+0	1.12−2	4.45−5	4.96+3
1.5267	5.66+3	5.17+0	1.12−2	4.46−5	5.66+3
1.7	4.39+3	5.05+0	1.30−2	5.72−5	4.39+3
2.0	2.93+3	4.84+0	1.61−2	8.22−5	2.94+3
3.0	1.04+3	4.20+0	2.57−2	1.91−4	1.04+3
4.0	4.82+2	3.66+0	3.41−2	3.30−4	4.86+2
5.0	2.70+2	3.20+0	4.16−2	4.95−4	2.73+2
6.0	1.65+2	2.81+0	4.85−2	6.82−4	1.68+2
7.0	1.09+2	2.47+0	5.48−2	8.90−4	1.11+2
8.0	7.56+1	2.17+0	6.05−2	1.11−3	7.79+1
9.0	5.50+1	1.92+0	6.59−2	1.35−3	5.70+1
10.0	4.13+1	1.70+0	7.08−2	1.60−3	4.31+1
10.547	3.58+1	1.60+0	7.32−2	1.74−3	3.75+1
11.87 K	2.60+1	1.39+0	7.90−2	2.09−3	2.75+1
11.87	1.89+2	1.39+0	7.90−2	2.09−3	1.90+2
12.0	1.83+2	1.37+0	7.95−2	2.12−3	1.85+2
15.0	1.00+2	1.03+0	8.99−2	2.92−3	1.01+2
17.0	7.12+1	8.75−1	9.56−2	3.47−3	7.22+1
20.0	4.53+1	7.04−1	1.02−1	4.27−3	4.61+1
25.0	2.42+1	5.17−1	1.10−1	5.55−3	2.48+1
30.0	1.43+1	3.96−1	1.16−1	6.78−3	1.49+1
35.0	9.19+0	3.12−1	1.20−1	7.94−3	9.62+0
40.0	6.23+0	2.52−1	1.22−1	9.02−3	6.61+0
50.0	3.24+0	1.74−1	1.25−1	1.09−2	3.54+0
60.0	1.89+0	1.28−1	1.25−1	1.26−2	2.14+0
70.0	1.20+0	9.84−2	1.25−1	1.41−2	1.42+0
80.0	8.03−1	7.81−2	1.24−1	1.54−2	1.00+0
90.0	5.64−1	6.35−2	1.23−1	1.65−2	7.51−1
100.0	4.12−1	5.28−2	1.21−1	1.75−2	5.86−1
120.0	2.38−1	3.80−2	1.18−1	1.92−2	3.94−1
150.0	1.22−1	2.52−2	1.13−1	2.11−2	2.60−1
170.0	8.40−2	2.00−2	1.09−1	2.20−2	2.13−1
200.0	5.17−2	1.47−2	1.05−1	2.32−2	1.71−1
250.0	2.66−2	9.58−3	9.79−2	2.44−2	1.34−1
300.0	1.55−2	6.75−3	9.22−2	2.52−2	1.14−1
350.0	9.84−3	5.01−3	8.73−2	2.57−2	1.02−1
400.0	6.66−3	3.86−3	8.30−2	2.60−2	9.36−2
500.0	3.48−3	2.50−3	7.61−2	2.62−2	8.21−2
600.0	2.06−3	1.74−3	7.05−2	2.61−2	7.43−2
700.0	1.33−3	1.28−3	6.59−2	2.58−2	6.86−2
800.0	9.15−4	9.86−4	6.21−2	2.55−2	6.40−2
900.0	6.59−4	7.80−4	5.88−2	2.51−2	6.02−2
1,000.0	4.93−4	6.32−4	5.59−2	2.46−2	5.70−2

Selenium **Z = 34**

Energy (keV)	τ/ρ (cm^2/g)	σ_c/ρ (cm^2/g)	σ_I/ρ (cm^2/g)	σ_a/ρ (cm^2/g)	μ/ρ (cm^2/g)
0.1	4.05+4	5.86+0	7.35−5	1.94−8	4.05+4
0.15	4.77+4	5.86+0	1.50−4	6.05−8	4.77+4
0.1633 $M_{II,III}$	4.53+4	5.85+0	1.77−4	7.78−8	4.53+4
0.1647	4.79+4	5.85+0	1.80−4	7.99−8	4.79+4
0.2	4.22+4	5.85+0	2.59−4	1.40−7	4.22+4
0.2308 M_I	3.62+4	5.85+0	3.42−4	2.14−7	3.62+4
0.2322	3.78+4	5.84+0	3.46−4	2.18−7	3.78+4

TABLE 3 (continued)

Energy (keV)	τ/ρ (cm^2/g)	σ_c/ρ (cm^2/g)	σ_I/ρ (cm^2/g)	σ_a/ρ (cm^2/g)	μ/ρ (cm^2/g)
0.3	2.65+4	5.83+0	5.70−4	4.65−7	2.65+4
0.4	1.61+4	5.81+0	9.95−4	1.08−6	1.61+4
0.5	1.04+4	5.78+0	1.53−3	2.08−6	1.05+4
0.6	7.16+3	5.74+0	2.16−3	3.52−6	7.17+3
0.7	5.13+3	5.70+0	2.88−3	5.46−6	5.13+3
0.8	3.81+3	5.66+0	3.69−3	7.96−6	3.82+3
0.9	2.92+3	5.61+0	4.53−3	1.10−5	2.93+3
1.0	2.28+3	5.55+0	5.43−3	1.45−5	2.29+3
1.4483 $L_{II,III}$	9.43+2	5.27+0	9.82−3	3.74−5	9.49+2
1.4497	3.34+3	5.27+0	9.84−3	3.75−5	3.34+3
1.5	5.40+3	5.24+0	1.04−2	4.08−5	5.41+3
1.6533 L_I	4.32+3	5.13+0	1.19−2	5.14−5	4.33+3
1.6547	4.91+3	5.13+0	1.20−2	5.15−5	4.92+3
2.0	3.12+3	4.89+0	1.55−2	7.96−5	3.12+3
3.0	1.11+3	4.22+0	2.51−2	1.87−4	1.11+3
4.0	5.17+2	3.67+0	3.35−2	3.25−4	5.21+2
5.0	2.90+2	3.21+0	4.08−2	4.86−4	2.93+2
6.0	1.77+2	2.83+0	4.74−2	6.67−4	1.80+2
7.0	1.16+2	2.49+0	5.34−2	8.66−4	1.19+2
8.0	8.12+1	2.20+0	5.89−2	1.08−3	8.34+1
9.0	5.90+1	1.95+0	6.40−2	1.31−3	6.10+1
10.0	4.44+1	1.74+0	6.87−2	1.55−3	4.62+1
12.0	2.71+1	1.40+0	7.70−2	2.05−3	2.86+1
12.66 K	2.34+1	1.31+0	7.93−2	2.21−3	2.48+1
12.66	1.69+2	1.31+0	7.93−2	2.21−3	1.70+2
15.0	1.07+2	1.05+0	8.71−2	2.83−3	1.08+2
17.0	7.59+1	8.94−1	9.26−2	3.36−3	7.69+1
20.0	4.84+1	7.19−1	9.92−2	4.14−3	4.93+1
25.0	2.59+1	5.28−1	1.07−1	5.39−3	2.65+1
30.0	1.54+1	4.05−1	1.13−1	6.59−3	1.59+1
35.0	9.88+0	3.19−1	1.16−1	7.72−3	1.03+1
40.0	6.70+0	2.58−1	1.19−1	8.78−3	7.08+0
50.0	3.49+0	1.79−1	1.22−1	1.07−2	3.79+0
60.0	2.04+0	1.31−1	1.22−1	1.23−2	2.29+0
70.0	1.29+0	1.01−1	1.22−1	1.37−2	1.51+0
80.0	8.66−1	8.00−2	1.21−1	1.50−2	1.07+0
90.0	6.09−1	6.51−2	1.20−1	1.61−2	7.94−1
100.0	4.44−1	5.41−2	1.18−1	1.71−2	6.17−1
120.0	2.57−1	3.90−2	1.15−1	1.87−2	4.11−1
150.0	1.32−1	2.59−2	1.10−1	2.06−2	2.68−1
170.0	9.08−2	2.05−2	1.07−1	2.15−2	2.18−1
200.0	5.59−2	1.51−2	1.02−1	2.26−2	1.73−1
250.0	2.88−2	9.85−3	9.56−2	2.39−2	1.34−1
300.0	1.68−2	6.93−3	9.01−2	2.47−2	1.14−1
350.0	1.07−2	5.15−3	8.53−2	2.51−2	1.01−1
400.0	7.23−3	3.97−3	8.12−2	2.54−2	9.24−2
500.0	3.79−3	2.57−3	7.44−2	2.56−2	8.07−2
600.0	2.25−3	1.79−3	6.89−2	2.55−2	7.30−2
700.0	1.46−3	1.32−3	6.44−2	2.52−2	6.72−2
800.0	1.00−3	1.01−3	6.07−2	2.49−2	6.27−2
900.0	7.24−4	8.02−4	5.74−2	2.45−2	5.90−2
1,000.0	5.42−4	6.51−4	5.46−2	2.41−2	5.58−2

TABLE 3 (continued)

Energy (keV)	τ/ρ (cm^2/g)	σ_c/ρ (cm^2/g)	σ_I/ρ (cm^2/g)	σ_a/ρ (cm^2/g)	μ/ρ (cm^2/g)
Bromine	**Z = 35**				
0.1	2.70+4	6.14+0	6.73−5	1.79−8	2.70+4
0.15	4.53+4	6.13+0	1.40−4	5.66−8	4.53+4
0.1834 $M_{II,III}$	4.18+4	6.13+0	2.06−4	1.02−7	4.18+4
0.1848	4.46+4	6.13+0	2.09−4	1.05−7	4.46+4
0.2	4.35+4	6.13+0	2.43−4	1.32−7	4.36+4
0.2558 M_I	3.38+4	6.12+0	3.93−4	2.73−7	3.38+4
0.2572	3.52+4	6.12+0	3.97−4	2.78−7	3.52+4
0.3	2.87+4	6.11+0	5.36−4	4.38−7	2.87+4
0.4	1.78+4	6.09+0	9.39−4	1.02−6	1.78+4
0.5	1.16+4	6.06+0	1.45−3	1.97−6	1.16+4
0.6	8.00+3	6.02+0	2.05−3	3.34−6	8.00+3
0.7	5.75+3	5.98+0	2.74−3	5.20−6	5.76+3
0.8	4.28+3	5.93+0	3.52−3	7.60−6	4.29+3
1.0	2.58+3	5.83+0	5.22−3	1.40−5	2.58+3
1.4	1.16+3	5.56+0	9.07−3	3.36−5	1.17+3
1.5	9.80+2	5.50+0	1.01−2	4.00−5	9.85+2
1.5643 $L_{II,III}$	8.85+2	5.45+0	1.08−2	4.43−5	8.90+2
1.5657	3.32+3	5.45+0	1.08−2	4.44−5	3.33+3
1.7	4.45+3	5.36+0	1.22−2	5.42−5	4.45+3
1.7813 L_I	3.94+3	5.29+0	1.30−2	6.05−5	3.95+3
1.7827	4.46+3	5.29+0	1.31−2	6.06−5	4.47+3
2.0	3.43+3	5.14+0	1.53−2	7.93−5	3.43+3
3.0	1.23+3	4.43+0	2.52−2	1.89−4	1.23+3
4.0	5.73+2	3.83+0	3.40−2	3.32−4	5.77+2
5.0	3.21+2	3.35+0	4.16−2	4.96−4	3.24+2
6.0	1.96+2	2.95+0	4.83−2	6.80−4	1.99+2
7.0	1.29+2	2.61+0	5.43−2	8.80−4	1.31+2
8.0	8.96+1	2.32+0	5.98−2	1.10−3	9.19+1
9.0	6.51+1	2.06+0	6.48−2	1.32−3	6.72+1
10.0	4.89+1	1.84+0	6.95−2	1.56−3	5.08+1
12.0	2.98+1	1.48+0	7.78−2	2.06−3	3.14+1
12.02	2.97+1	1.48+0	7.79−2	2.07−3	3.12+1
13.47 K	2.18+1	1.28+0	8.28−2	2.44−3	2.32+1
13.47	1.55+2	1.28+0	8.28−2	2.44−3	1.57+2
15.0	1.16+2	1.12+0	8.79−2	2.85−3	1.17+2
17.0	8.28+1	9.48−1	9.34−2	3.38−3	8.38+1
20.0	5.29+1	7.62−1	1.00−1	4.17−3	5.38+1
25.0	2.84+1	5.60−1	1.08−1	5.45−3	2.90+1
30.0	1.69+1	4.30−1	1.14−1	6.67−3	1.75+1
35.0	1.09+1	3.40−1	1.18−1	7.82−3	1.13+1
40.0	7.39+0	2.75−1	1.20−1	8.89−3	7.79+0
50.0	3.85+0	1.90−1	1.23−1	1.08−2	4.17+0
60.0	2.25+0	1.40−1	1.24−1	1.25−2	2.52+0
70.0	1.43+0	1.07−1	1.24−1	1.40−2	1.66+0
80.0	9.62−1	8.52−2	1.23−1	1.52−2	1.17+0
90.0	6.77−1	6.93−2	1.21−1	1.64−2	8.68−1
100.0	4.95−1	5.76−2	1.20−1	1.74−2	6.72−1
120.0	2.87−1	4.15−2	1.17−1	1.90−2	4.45−1
150.0	1.48−1	2.76−2	1.12−1	2.09−2	2.87−1
170.0	1.02−1	2.19−2	1.08−1	2.19−2	2.32−1

TABLE 3 (continued)

Energy (keV)	τ/ρ (cm^2/g)	σ_c/ρ (cm^2/g)	σ_I/ρ (cm^2/g)	σ_a/ρ (cm^2/g)	μ/ρ (cm^2/g)
200.0	6.26–2	1.61–2	1.04–1	2.30–2	1.83–1
250.0	3.23–2	1.05–2	9.72–2	2.43–2	1.40–1
300.0	1.89–2	7.40–3	9.16–2	2.51–2	1.18–1
350.0	1.20–2	5.49–3	8.67–2	2.55–2	1.04–1
400.0	8.15–3	4.24–3	8.25–2	2.58–2	9.49–2
500.0	4.28–3	2.74–3	7.56–2	2.60–2	8.26–2
600.0	2.55–3	1.91–3	7.01–2	2.59–2	7.46–2
700.0	1.65–3	1.41–3	6.55–2	2.57–2	6.86–2
800.0	1.14–3	1.08–3	6.17–2	2.53–2	6.39–2
900.0	8.22–4	8.57–4	5.84–2	2.49–2	6.01–2
1,000.0	6.17–4	6.95–4	5.55–2	2.45–2	5.68–2
Krypton	**Z = 36**				
0.1	8.16+3	6.19+0	6.31–5	1.67–8	8.17+3
0.15	3.84+4	6.19+0	1.29–4	5.22–8	3.84+4
0.2	3.99+4	6.18+0	2.22–4	1.20–7	3.99+4
0.2161 $M_{II,III}$	3.74+4	6.18+0	2.58–4	1.51–7	3.74+4
0.2175	4.05+4	6.18+0	2.61–4	1.54–7	4.05+4
0.2883 M_I	3.11+4	6.17+0	4.52–4	3.54–7	3.11+4
0.2897	3.24+4	6.17+0	4.56–4	3.59–7	3.24+4
0.3	3.10+4	6.17+0	4.88–4	3.99–7	3.10+4
0.4	1.96+4	6.14+0	8.55–4	9.31–7	1.96+4
0.5	1.29+4	6.11+0	1.32–3	1.80–6	1.29+4
0.6	8.88+3	6.08+0	1.87–3	3.05–6	8.89+3
0.7	6.39+3	6.04+0	2.51–3	4.76–6	6.40+3
0.8	4.76+3	5.99+0	3.22–3	6.98–6	4.77+3
0.9	3.65+3	5.94+0	3.98–3	9.65–6	3.65+3
1.0	2.86+3	5.89+0	4.80–3	1.29–5	2.87+3
1.2	1.86+3	5.77+0	6.56–3	2.10–5	1.87+3
1.4	1.29+3	5.63+0	8.42–3	3.12–5	1.29+3
1.6	9.28+2	5.50+0	1.04–2	4.37–5	9.34+2
1.675 L_{III}	7.83+2	5.44+0	1.11–2	4.90–5	7.89+2
1.675	3.92+3	5.44+0	1.11–2	4.90–5	3.93+3
1.7	3.77+3	5.43+0	1.14–2	5.08–5	3.77+3
1.727 L_{II}	3.61+3	5.41+0	1.17–2	5.27–5	3.62+3
1.727	5.06+3	5.41+0	1.17–2	5.27–5	5.06+3
1.921 L_I	3.79+3	5.26+0	1.36–2	6.79–5	3.80+3
1.921	4.55+3	5.26+0	1.36–2	6.79–5	4.55+3
2.0	4.08+3	5.21+0	1.44–2	7.47–5	4.08+3
2.5	2.23+3	4.83+0	1.93–2	1.23–4	2.24+3
3.0	1.36+3	4.48+0	2.40–2	1.81–4	1.37+3
3.5	8.98+2	4.16+0	2.85–2	2.48–4	9.03+2
4.0	6.26+2	3.87+0	3.28–2	3.22–4	6.30+2
5.0	3.43+2	3.38+0	4.04–2	4.85–4	3.46+2
6.0	2.09+2	2.98+0	4.71–2	6.66–4	2.12+2
7.0	1.38+2	2.64+0	5.30–2	8.62–4	1.41+2
8.0	9.61+1	2.35+0	5.83–2	1.07–3	9.85+1
9.0	6.99+1	2.09+0	6.32–2	1.29–3	7.20+1
10.0	5.26+1	1.87+0	6.77–2	1.52–3	5.45+1
12.0	3.21+1	1.52+0	7.57–2	2.01–3	3.37+1
12.655	2.78+1	1.42+0	7.79–2	2.17–3	2.93+1
14.33 K	1.99+1	1.21+0	8.34–2	2.59–3	2.12+1
14.33	1.37+2	1.21+0	8.34–2	2.59–3	1.39+2

TABLE 3 (continued)

Energy (keV)	τ/ρ (cm^2/g)	σ_c/ρ (cm^2/g)	σ_I/ρ (cm^2/g)	σ_a/ρ (cm^2/g)	μ/ρ (cm^2/g)
15.0	1.22+2	1.14+0	8.55−2	2.77−3	1.23+2
17.0	8.69+1	9.69−1	9.08−2	3.29−3	8.79+1
20.0	5.57+1	7.78−1	9.74−2	4.06−3	5.66+1
25.0	3.00+1	5.72−1	1.05−1	5.31−3	3.07+1
30.0	1.79+1	4.39−1	1.11−1	6.50−3	1.85+1
35.0	1.15+1	3.48−1	1.15−1	7.63−3	1.20+1
40.0	7.86+0	2.82−1	1.17−1	8.69−3	8.26+0
50.0	4.11+0	1.95−1	1.20−1	1.06−2	4.43+0
60.0	2.41+0	1.44−1	1.21−1	1.22−2	2.67+0
70.0	1.53+0	1.10−1	1.21−1	1.37−2	1.76+0
80.0	1.03+0	8.73−2	1.20−1	1.49−2	1.24+0
90.0	7.27−1	7.11−2	1.19−1	1.60−2	9.17−1
100.0	5.32−1	5.90−2	1.17−1	1.70−2	7.08−1
120.0	3.09−1	4.26−2	1.14−1	1.87−2	4.66−1
150.0	1.59−1	2.83−2	1.09−1	2.05−2	2.97−1
170.0	1.10−1	2.24−2	1.06−1	2.15−2	2.38−1
200.0	6.76−2	1.65−2	1.02−1	2.26−2	1.86−1
250.0	3.49−2	1.08−2	9.53−2	2.38−2	1.41−1
300.0	2.04−2	7.60−3	8.98−2	2.46−2	1.18−1
350.0	1.30−2	5.65−3	8.50−2	2.51−2	1.04−1
400.0	8.84−3	4.36−3	8.09−2	2.53−2	9.41−2
500.0	4.65−3	2.82−3	7.42−2	2.55−2	8.16−2
600.0	2.77−3	1.97−3	6.87−2	2.54−2	7.34−2
700.0	1.80−3	1.45−3	6.43−2	2.52−2	6.75−2
800.0	1.24−3	1.11−3	6.05−2	2.48−2	6.29−2
900.0	8.98−4	8.82−4	5.73−2	2.44−2	5.91−2
1,000.0	6.74−4	7.15−4	5.45−2	2.40−2	5.58−2

Rubidium Z = 37

Energy (keV)	τ/ρ (cm^2/g)	σ_c/ρ (cm^2/g)	σ_I/ρ (cm^2/g)	σ_a/ρ (cm^2/g)	μ/ρ (cm^2/g)
0.1	3.30+3	6.41+0	1.38−4	3.65−8	3.31+3
0.1103 $M_{IV,V}$	3.11+3	6.40+0	1.63−4	4.77−8	3.12+3
0.1117	5.82+3	6.40+0	1.66−4	4.94−8	5.83+3
0.15	2.90+4	6.40+0	2.82−4	1.14−7	2.90+4
0.2	3.83+4	6.39+0	4.81−4	2.60−7	3.83+4
0.2408 $M_{II,III}$	3.43+4	6.38+0	6.82−4	4.44−7	3.43+4
0.2422	4.28+4	6.38+0	6.89−4	4.51−7	4.28+4
0.3	3.08+4	6.36+0	1.03−3	8.31−7	3.08+4
0.3214 M_I	2.80+4	6.36+0	1.16−3	1.01−6	2.80+4
0.3228	2.92+4	6.36+0	1.17−3	1.02−6	2.92+4
0.4	2.09+4	6.33+0	1.72−3	1.85−6	2.09+4
0.5	1.39+4	6.28+0	2.52−3	3.37−6	1.39+4
0.6	9.60+3	6.23+0	3.39−3	5.38−6	9.60+3
0.7	6.94+3	6.18+0	4.27−3	7.86−6	6.95+3
0.8	5.21+3	6.12+0	5.17−3	1.08−5	5.21+3
0.9	4.00+3	6.05+0	6.08−3	1.41−5	4.00+3
1.0	3.13+3	5.99+0	6.98−3	1.79−5	3.14+3
1.2	2.06+3	5.85+0	8.78−3	2.68−5	2.06+3
1.4	1.42+3	5.71+0	1.06−2	3.74−5	1.42+3
1.6	1.03+3	5.57+0	1.24−2	5.00−5	1.03+3
1.7	8.73+2	5.50+0	1.34−2	5.70−5	8.79+2
1.804 L_{III}	7.41+2	5.42+0	1.43−2	6.47−5	7.47+2
1.804	3.63+3	5.42+0	1.43−2	6.47−5	3.63+3

TABLE 3 (continued)

Energy (keV)	τ/ρ (cm²/g)	σ_c/ρ (cm²/g)	σ_I/ρ (cm²/g)	σ_a/ρ (cm²/g)	μ/ρ (cm²/g)
1.864 L_{II}	3.32+3	5.38+0	1.49−2	6.94−5	3.32+3
1.864	4.64+3	5.38+0	1.49−2	6.94−5	4.65+3
2.0	3.83+3	5.28+0	1.62−2	8.08−5	3.83+3
2.065 L_I	3.51+3	5.23+0	1.68−2	8.63−5	3.51+3
2.065	4.21+3	5.23+0	1.68−2	8.63−5	4.22+3
2.5	2.50+3	4.93+0	2.08−2	1.29−4	2.50+3
3.0	1.52+3	4.59+0	2.53−2	1.86−4	1.52+3
3.5	9.95+2	4.27+0	2.96−2	2.52−4	9.99+2
4.0	6.91+2	3.97+0	3.37−2	3.26−4	6.95+2
5.0	3.75+2	3.47+0	4.12−2	4.90−4	3.79+2
6.0	2.28+2	3.06+0	4.78−2	6.73−4	2.31+2
7.0	1.50+2	2.72+0	5.37−2	8.70−4	1.52+2
8.0	1.04+2	2.42+0	5.89−2	1.08−3	1.06+2
9.0	7.52+1	2.17+0	6.37−2	1.30−3	7.74+1
10.0	5.64+1	1.95+0	6.81−2	1.53−3	5.84+1
12.0	3.43+1	1.58+0	7.60−2	2.01−3	3.59+1
15.0	1.86+1	1.20+0	8.56−2	2.77−3	1.99+1
15.2 K	1.79+1	1.18+0	8.62−2	2.82−3	1.92+1
15.2	1.26+2	1.18+0	8.62−2	2.82−3	1.27+2
17.0	9.35+1	1.01+0	9.10−2	3.29−3	9.46+1
20.0	6.02+1	8.14−1	9.75−2	4.06−3	6.11+1
25.0	3.25+1	5.98−1	1.06−1	5.32−3	3.32+1
30.0	1.95+1	4.60−1	1.11−1	6.52−3	2.00+1
35.0	1.26+1	3.65−1	1.15−1	7.65−3	1.30+1
40.0	8.56+0	2.96−1	1.18−1	8.72−3	8.98+0
50.0	4.49+0	2.05−1	1.21−1	1.06−2	4.81+0
60.0	2.63+0	1.51−1	1.22−1	1.23−2	2.91+0
70.0	1.67+0	1.16−1	1.21−1	1.37−2	1.91+0
80.0	1.13+0	9.18−2	1.21−1	1.50−2	1.34+0
90.0	7.97−1	7.47−2	1.20−1	1.61−2	9.91−1
100.0	5.83−1	6.21−2	1.18−1	1.71−2	7.63−1
120.0	3.39−1	4.48−2	1.15−1	1.88−2	4.99−1
150.0	1.75−1	2.98−2	1.10−1	2.07−2	3.15−1
170.0	1.21−1	2.36−2	1.07−1	2.16−2	2.51−1
200.0	7.45−2	1.74−2	1.02−1	2.27−2	1.94−1
250.0	3.86−2	1.14−2	9.60−2	2.40−2	1.46−1
300.0	2.26−2	8.01−3	9.04−2	2.48−2	1.21−1
350.0	1.44−2	5.95−3	8.56−2	2.52−2	1.06−1
400.0	9.79−3	4.59−3	8.15−2	2.55−2	9.59−2
500.0	5.17−3	2.97−3	7.47−2	2.57−2	8.29−2
600.0	3.08−3	2.08−3	6.92−2	2.56−2	7.44−2
700.0	2.01−3	1.53−3	6.47−2	2.54−2	6.83−2
800.0	1.39−3	1.18−3	6.10−2	2.50−2	6.35−2
900.0	1.01−3	9.30−4	5.77−2	2.46−2	5.96−2
1,000.0	7.57−4	7.55−4	5.49−2	2.42−2	5.64−2

Strontium **Z = 38**

Energy (keV)	τ/ρ (cm²/g)	σ_c/ρ (cm²/g)	σ_I/ρ (cm²/g)	σ_a/ρ (cm²/g)	μ/ρ (cm²/g)
0.1	3.83+3	6.59+0	1.56−4	4.14−8	3.84+3
0.1332 $M_{IV,V}$	3.21+3	6.59+0	2.58−4	9.21−8	3.22+3
0.1346	5.72+3	6.59+0	2.63−4	9.49−8	5.73+3
0.15	1.45+4	6.58+0	3.21−4	1.30−7	1.45+4
0.2	3.52+4	6.57+0	5.51−4	2.98−7	3.53+4

TABLE 3 (continued)

Energy (keV)	τ/ρ (cm^2/g)	σ_c/ρ (cm^2/g)	σ_I/ρ (cm^2/g)	σ_a/ρ (cm^2/g)	μ/ρ (cm^2/g)
0.272 $M_{II,III}$	3.04+4	6.55+0	9.87−4	7.27−7	3.05+4
0.2734	3.51+4	6.55+0	9.96−4	7.38−7	3.51+4
0.3	3.17+4	6.54+0	1.19−3	9.64−7	3.17+4
0.3568 M_I	2.50+4	6.52+0	1.63−3	1.57−6	2.50+4
0.3582	2.64+4	6.52+0	1.64−3	1.59−6	2.64+4
0.4	2.21+4	6.50+0	2.01−3	2.17−6	2.21+4
0.5	1.49+4	6.45+0	2.98−3	4.00−6	1.49+4
0.6	1.04+4	6.40+0	4.03−3	6.44−6	1.04+4
0.7	7.54+3	6.33+0	5.13−3	9.47−6	7.55+3
0.8	5.67+3	6.26+0	6.23−3	1.30−5	5.67+3
0.9	4.37+3	6.19+0	7.33−3	1.71−5	4.37+3
1.0	3.43+3	6.11+0	8.40−3	2.16−5	3.44+3
1.2	2.26+3	5.95+0	1.05−2	3.18−5	2.26+3
1.4	1.56+3	5.79+0	1.24−2	4.33−5	1.57+3
1.6	1.13+3	5.64+0	1.43−2	5.65−5	1.14+3
1.7	9.77+2	5.57+0	1.52−2	6.37−5	9.83+2
1.94 L_{III}	6.85+2	5.38+0	1.74−2	8.26−5	6.91+2
1.94	3.23+3	5.38+0	1.74−2	8.26−5	3.24+3
2.0	2.97+3	5.34+0	1.79−2	8.77−5	2.98+3
2.007 L_{II}	2.94+3	5.34+0	1.80−2	8.83−5	2.95+3
2.007	4.12+3	5.34+0	1.80−2	8.83−5	4.13+3
2.216 L_I	3.14+3	5.18+0	1.99−2	1.07−4	3.15+3
2.216	3.77+3	5.18+0	1.99−2	1.07−4	3.78+3
2.5	2.71+3	4.99+0	2.24−2	1.36−4	2.72+3
3.0	1.65+3	4.65+0	2.66−2	1.92−4	1.65+3
3.5	1.08+3	4.34+0	3.07−2	2.58−4	1.09+3
4.0	7.51+2	4.05+0	3.47−2	3.30−4	7.55+2
5.0	4.08+2	3.55+0	4.19−2	4.94−4	4.11+2
6.0	2.48+2	3.13+0	4.84−2	6.76−4	2.51+2
7.0	1.62+2	2.78+0	5.42−2	8.73−4	1.65+2
8.0	1.13+2	2.48+0	5.94−2	1.08−3	1.15+2
9.0	8.17+1	2.23+0	6.40−2	1.30−3	8.40+1
10.0	6.12+1	2.00+0	6.83−2	1.53−3	6.33+1
12.0	3.72+1	1.64+0	7.60−2	2.00−3	3.89+1
15.0	2.02+1	1.24+0	8.54−2	2.75−3	2.15+1
16.1 K	1.66+1	1.13+0	8.83−2	3.03−3	1.79+1
16.1	1.16+2	1.13+0	8.83−2	3.03−3	1.17+2
17.0	1.00+2	1.05+0	9.07−2	3.27−3	1.02+2
20.0	6.47+1	8.45−1	9.71−2	4.04−3	6.56+1
25.0	3.50+1	6.21−1	1.05−1	5.29−3	3.57+1
30.0	2.10+1	4.78−1	1.11−1	6.49−3	2.16+1
35.0	1.36+1	3.79−1	1.15−1	7.63−3	1.41+1
40.0	9.27+0	3.08−1	1.17−1	8.70−3	9.69+0
50.0	4.87+0	2.14−1	1.20−1	1.06−2	5.20+0
60.0	2.86+0	1.57−1	1.22−1	1.23−2	3.14+0
70.0	1.82+0	1.21−1	1.21−1	1.37−2	2.06+0
80.0	1.23+0	9.57−2	1.21−1	1.50−2	1.44+0
90.0	8.67−1	7.79−2	1.19−1	1.61−2	1.06+0
100.0	6.35−1	6.47−2	1.18−1	1.71−2	8.18−1
120.0	3.70−1	4.67−2	1.15−1	1.88−2	5.32−1
150.0	1.91−1	3.11−2	1.10−1	2.07−2	3.32−1

TABLE 3 (continued)

Energy (keV)	τ/ρ (cm^2/g)	σ_c/ρ (cm^2/g)	σ_1/ρ (cm^2/g)	σ_a/ρ (cm^2/g)	μ/ρ (cm^2/g)
170.0	1.32–1	2.47–2	1.07–1	2.17–2	2.63–1
200.0	8.15–2	1.82–2	1.03–1	2.28–2	2.02–1
250.0	4.23–2	1.19–2	9.61–2	2.40–2	1.50–1
300.0	2.48–2	8.37–3	9.05–2	2.48–2	1.24–1
350.0	1.58–2	6.22–3	8.58–2	2.53–2	1.08–1
400.0	1.08–2	4.80–3	8.17–2	2.56–2	9.73–2
500.0	5.70–3	3.11–3	7.48–2	2.58–2	8.36–2
600.0	3.41–3	2.17–3	6.94–2	2.57–2	7.49–2
700.0	2.22–3	1.60–3	6.49–2	2.54–2	6.87–2
800.0	1.54–3	1.23–3	6.11–2	2.51–2	6.38–2
900.0	1.12–3	9.73–4	5.78–2	2.47–2	5.99–2
1,000.0	8.41–4	7.90–4	5.50–2	2.43–2	5.66–2

Yttrium Z = 39

Energy (keV)	τ/ρ (cm^2/g)	σ_c/ρ (cm^2/g)	σ_1/ρ (cm^2/g)	σ_a/ρ (cm^2/g)	μ/ρ (cm^2/g)
0.1	4.43+3	6.84+0	1.47–4	3.90–8	4.43+3
1.15	3.57+3	6.84+0	3.03–4	1.22–7	3.57+3
0.1576 $M_{IV,V}$	3.44+3	6.84+0	3.33–4	1.41–7	3.44+3
0.159	5.62+3	6.84+0	3.38–4	1.45–7	5.62+3
0.2	3.05+4	6.83+0	5.20–4	2.81–7	3.06+4
0.25	3.36+4	6.81+0	7.96–4	5.39–7	3.36+4
0.3	2.87+4	6.79+0	1.12–3	9.15–7	2.88+4
0.3036 $M_{II,III}$	2.83+4	6.79+0	1.15–3	9.46–7	2.83+4
0.305	3.24+4	6.79+0	1.16–3	9.59–7	3.24+4
0.3929 M_I	2.33+4	6.76+0	1.86–3	1.97–6	2.33+4
0.3943	2.47+4	6.76+0	1.87–3	1.99–6	2.47+4
0.4	2.40+4	6.76+0	1.92–3	2.07–6	2.40+4
0.5	1.63+4	6.71+0	2.86–3	3.85–6	1.63+4
0.6	1.14+4	6.65+0	3.91–3	6.26–6	1.14+4
0.7	8.33+3	6.58+0	5.01–3	9.29–6	8.34+3
0.8	6.26+3	6.51+0	6.14–3	1.29–5	6.27+3
0.9	4.84+3	6.43+0	7.28–3	1.71–5	4.84+3
1.0	3.81+3	6.36+0	8.40–3	2.17–5	3.82+3
1.2	2.50+3	6.19+0	1.06–2	3.24–5	2.51+3
1.5	1.47+3	5.94+0	1.36–2	5.11–5	1.48+3
2.0	7.26+2	5.54+0	1.83–2	8.98–5	7.32+2
2.08 L_{III}	6.53+2	5.47+0	1.90–2	9.69–5	6.58+2
2.08	2.93+3	5.47+0	1.90–2	9.69–5	2.93+3
2.156 L_{II}	2.65+3	5.41+0	1.97–2	1.04–4	2.66+3
2.156	3.71+3	5.41+0	1.97–2	1.04–4	3.72–3
2.373 L_I	2.86+3	5.25+0	2.17–2	1.25–4	2.86+3
2.373	3.43+3	5.25+0	2.17–2	1.25–4	3.43+3
2.5	2.97+3	5.16+0	2.28–2	1.38–4	2.98+3
3.0	1.80+3	4.81+0	2.71–2	1.96–4	1.81+3
3.5	1.18+3	4.49+0	3.12–2	2.61–4	1.19+3
4.0	8.22+2	4.19+0	3.51–2	3.34–4	8.26+2
5.0	4.46+2	3.66+0	4.24–2	4.99–4	4.50+2
6.0	2.71+2	3.23+0	4.90–2	6.84–4	2.74+2
7.0	1.78+2	2.87+0	5.48–2	8.83–4	1.81+2
8.0	1.23+2	2.57+0	6.01–2	1.09–3	1.26+2
9.0	8.94+1	2.31+0	6.47–2	1.31–3	9.18+1
10.0	6.70+1	2.09+0	6.90–2	1.54–3	6.92+1
12.0	4.07+1	1.71+0	7.66–2	2.02–3	4.25+1
15.0	2.21+1	1.30+0	8.60–2	2.77–3	2.35+1

TABLE 3 (continued)

Energy (keV)	τ/ρ (cm² /g)	σ_c/ρ (cm² /g)	σ_I/ρ (cm² /g)	σ_a/ρ (cm² /g)	μ/ρ (cm² /g)
17.0	1.57+1	1.10+0	9.12–2	3.28–3	1.69+1
17.04 K	1.56+1	1.10+0	9.12–2	3.29–3	1.68+1
17.04	1.08+2	1.10+0	9.12–2	3.29–3	1.09+2
20.0	7.01+1	8.87–1	9.77–2	4.06–3	7.11+1
25.0	3.80+1	6.51–1	1.06–1	5.32–3	3.88+1
30.0	2.29+1	5.01–1	1.11–1	6.53–3	2.35+1
35.0	1.48+1	3.98–1	1.15–1	7.69–3	1.53+1
40.0	1.01+1	3.24–1	1.18–1	8.77–3	1.05+1
50.0	5.31+0	2.25–1	1.21–1	1.07–2	5.66+0
60.0	3.13+0	1.66–1	1.22–1	1.24–2	3.42+0
70.0	1.99+0	1.27–1	1.22–1	1.39–2	2.24+0
80.0	1.35+0	1.01–1	1.22–1	1.52–2	1.57+0
90.0	9.51–1	8.20–2	1.21–1	1.63–2	1.15+0
100.0	6.97–1	6.81–2	1.19–1	1.73–2	8.84–1
120.0	4.06–1	4.92–2	1.16–1	1.90–2	5.72–1
150.0	2.10–1	3.28–2	1.11–1	2.09–2	3.54–1
170.0	1.45–1	2.60–2	1.08–1	2.19–2	2.79–1
200.0	8.98–2	1.91–2	1.04–1	2.30–2	2.13–1
250.0	4.67–2	1.25–2	9.71–2	2.43–2	1.56–1
300.0	2.74–2	8.83–3	9.15–2	2.51–2	1.28–1
350.0	1.75–2	6.57–3	8.67–2	2.56–2	1.11–1
400.0	1.19–2	5.07–3	8.25–2	2.58–2	9.95–2
500.0	6.32–3	3.28–3	7.57–2	2.60–2	8.53–2
600.0	3.79–3	2.29–3	7.01–2	2.60–2	7.62–2
700.0	2.47–3	1.69–3	6.56–2	2.57–2	6.98–2
800.0	1.71–3	1.30–3	6.18–2	2.54–2	6.48–2
900.0	1.25–3	1.03–3	5.85–2	2.50–2	6.07–2
1,000.0	9.40–4	8.35–4	5.56–2	2.45–2	5.74–2

Zirconium Z = 40

Energy (keV)	τ/ρ (cm² /g)	σ_c/ρ (cm² /g)	σ_I/ρ (cm² /g)	σ_a/ρ (cm² /g)	μ/ρ (cm² /g)
0.1	4.77+3	7.02+0	1.37–4	3.63–8	4.78+3
0.15	4.10+3	7.01+0	2.81–4	1.13–7	4.10+3
0.1803 $M_{IV,V}$	3.59+3	7.00+0	3.98–4	1.94–7	3.60+3
0.1817	5.44+3	7.00+0	4.04–4	1.98–7	5.45+3
0.2	1.65+4	7.00+0	4.83–4	2.61–7	1.65+4
0.25	3.21+4	6.99+0	7.39–4	5.01–7	3.22+4
0.3	2.93+4	6.97+0	1.05–3	8.50–7	2.93+4
0.3344 $M_{II,III}$	2.59+4	6.96+0	1.28–3	1.16–6	2.59+4
0.3358	2.95+4	6.96+0	1.29–3	1.18–6	2.95+4
0.4	2.40+4	6.93+0	1.79–3	1.94–6	2.40+4
0.4296 M_I	2.13+4	6.92+0	2.04–3	2.37–6	2.13+4
0.431	2.26+4	6.92+0	2.05–3	2.39–6	2.26+4
0.5	1.74+4	6.89+0	2.69–3	3.62–6	1.74+4
0.6	1.23+4	6.83+0	3.69–3	5.92–6	1.23+4
0.7	8.99+3	6.76+0	4.75–3	8.85–6	9.00+3
0.8	6.77+3	6.69+0	5.86–3	1.24–5	6.78+3
0.9	5.24+3	6.62+0	6.99–3	1.65–5	5.25+3
1.0	4.14+3	6.54+0	8.11–3	2.11–5	4.15+3
1.2	2.72+3	6.37+0	1.03–2	3.17–5	2.73+3
1.5	1.60+3	6.11+0	1.34–2	5.05–5	1.61+3
2.0	7.94+2	5.69+0	1.82–2	8.95–5	8.00+2
2.222 L_{III}	6.18+2	5.50+0	2.02–2	1.10–4	6.24+2
2.222	2.68+3	5.50+0	2.02–2	1.10–4	2.68+3

TABLE 3 (continued)

Energy (keV)	τ/ρ (cm^2/g)	σ_c/ρ (cm^2/g)	σ_I/ρ (cm^2/g)	σ_a/ρ (cm^2/g)	μ/ρ (cm^2/g)
$2.307_{L_{II}}$	2.41+3	5.44+0	2.09−2	1.18−4	2.42+3
2.307	3.38+3	5.44+0	2.09−2	1.18−4	3.38+3
2.5	2.71+3	5.30+0	2.27−2	1.38−4	2.71+3
2.532_{L_I}	2.62+3	5.27+0	2.30−2	1.41−4	2.62+3
2.532	3.14+3	5.27+0	2.30−2	1.41−4	3.14+3
3.0	1.97+3	4.93+0	2.70−2	1.95−4	1.97+3
3.5	1.29+3	4.60+0	3.11−2	2.60−4	1.29+3
4.0	8.92+2	4.29+0	3.50−2	3.32−4	8.97+2
5.0	4.83+2	3.75+0	4.22−2	4.96−4	4.87+2
6.0	2.93+2	3.31+0	4.87−2	6.80−4	2.96+2
7.0	1.91+2	2.94+0	5.46−2	8.80−4	1.94+2
8.0	1.33+2	2.63+0	5.99−2	1.09−3	1.35+2
9.0	9.59+1	2.37+0	6.46−2	1.31−3	9.83+1
10.0	7.18+1	2.14+0	6.88−2	1.54−3	7.40+1
12.0	4.35+1	1.76+0	7.63−2	2.01−3	4.53+1
15.0	2.35+1	1.35+0	8.55−2	2.75−3	2.50+1
17.0	1.67+1	1.14+0	9.07−2	3.26−3	1.79+1
18.0_K	1.43+1	1.06+0	9.29−2	3.51−3	1.54+1
18.0	9.51+1	1.06+0	9.29−2	3.51−3	9.63+1
20.0	7.23+1	9.18−1	9.71−2	4.03−3	7.33+1
25.0	3.99+1	6.73−1	1.05−1	5.29−3	4.07+1
30.0	2.43+1	5.18−1	1.11−1	6.50−3	2.49+1
35.0	1.58+1	4.12−1	1.15−1	7.65−3	1.63+1
40.0	1.09+1	3.36−1	1.18−1	8.73−3	1.13+1
50.0	5.76+0	2.34−1	1.21−1	1.07−2	6.11+0
60.0	3.40+0	1.72−1	1.22−1	1.24−2	3.70+0
70.0	2.17+0	1.32−1	1.22−1	1.38−2	2.42+0
80.0	1.47+0	1.05−1	1.21−1	1.51−2	1.69+0
90.0	1.04+0	8.52−2	1.20−1	1.63−2	1.24+0
100.0	7.61−1	7.08−2	1.19−1	1.73−2	9.50−1
120.0	4.43−1	5.12−2	1.16−1	1.90−2	6.10−1
150.0	2.29−1	3.41−2	1.11−1	2.09−2	3.74−1
170.0	1.58−1	2.71−2	1.08−1	2.19−2	2.93−1
200.0	9.76−2	1.99−2	1.04−1	2.30−2	2.21−1
250.0	5.06−2	1.30−2	9.70−2	2.43−2	1.61−1
300.0	2.97−2	9.20−3	9.14−2	2.51−2	1.30−1
350.0	1.90−2	6.84−3	8.66−2	2.56−2	1.12−1
400.0	1.29−2	5.28−3	8.25−2	2.58−2	1.01−1
500.0	6.85−3	3.42−3	7.56−2	2.60−2	8.59−2
600.0	4.12−3	2.39−3	7.01−2	2.59−2	7.67−2
700.0	2.70−3	1.76−3	6.56−2	2.57−2	7.00−2
800.0	1.88−3	1.35−3	6.17−2	2.53−2	6.50−2
900.0	1.37−3	1.07−3	5.84−2	2.49−2	6.09−2
1,000.0	1.04−3	8.71−4	5.56−2	2.45−2	5.75−2

Niobium **Z = 41**

Energy (keV)	τ/ρ (cm^2/g)	σ_c/ρ (cm^2/g)	σ_I/ρ (cm^2/g)	σ_a/ρ (cm^2/g)	μ/ρ (cm^2/g)
0.1	5.06+3	7.24+0	1.09−4	2.91−8	5.06+3
0.15	4.80+3	7.23+0	2.26−4	9.14−8	4.80+3
0.2	4.02+3	7.23+0	3.89−4	2.11−7	4.02+3
$0.205_{M_{IV,V}}$	3.93+3	7.23+0	4.08−4	2.27−7	3.94+3
0.2064	5.51+3	7.23+0	4.14−4	2.31−7	5.52+3

TABLE 3 (continued)

Energy (keV)	τ/ρ (cm^2/g)	σ_c/ρ (cm^2/g)	σ_I/ρ (cm^2/g)	σ_a/ρ (cm^2/g)	μ/ρ (cm^2/g)
0.25	2.83+4	7.21+0	5.97−4	4.05−7	2.83+4
0.3	3.06+4	7.20+0	8.46−4	6.88−7	3.06+4
0.3674 $M_{II,III}$	2.46+4	7.18+0	1.24−3	1.23−6	2.46+4
0.3688	2.83+4	7.18+0	1.25−3	1.25−6	2.83+4
0.4	2.61+4	7.16+0	1.45−3	1.57−6	2.61+4
0.4677 M_I	2.03+4	7.14+0	1.94−3	2.46−6	2.03+4
0.4691	2.15+4	7.14+0	1.95−3	2.48−6	2.15+4
0.5	1.92+4	7.12+0	2.19−3	2.96−6	1.92+4
0.6	1.36+4	7.07+0	3.02−3	4.87−6	1.36+4
0.7	9.95+3	7.01+0	3.93−3	7.34−6	9.96+3
0.8	7.51+3	6.95+0	4.88−3	1.04−5	7.52+3
0.9	5.80+3	6.88+0	5.86−3	1.39−5	5.81+3
1.0	4.59+3	6.80+0	6.85−3	1.80−5	4.59+3
1.2	3.02+3	6.64+0	8.85−3	2.75−5	3.02+3
1.5	1.78+3	6.39+0	1.18−2	4.51−5	1.78+3
2.0	8.78+2	5.96+0	1.65−2	8.27−5	8.84+2
2.371 L_{III}	5.70+2	5.64+0	1.99−2	1.17−4	5.76+2
2.371	2.45+3	5.64+0	1.99−2	1.17−4	2.45+3
2.465 L_{II}	2.20+3	5.57+0	2.08−2	1.26−4	2.21+3
2.465	3.08+3	5.57+0	2.08−2	1.26−4	3.09+3
2.5	2.96+3	5.55+0	2.11−2	1.30−4	2.97+3
2.698 L_I	2.40+3	5.38+0	2.28−2	1.51−4	2.41+3
2.698	2.88+3	5.38+0	2.28−2	1.51−4	2.89+3
3.0	2.15+3	5.15+0	2.55−2	1.86−4	2.16+3
3.5	1.41+3	4.79+0	2.96−2	2.51−4	1.41+3
4.0	9.76+2	4.45+0	3.36−2	3.23−4	9.81+2
5.0	5.28+2	3.88+0	4.11−2	4.88−4	5.32+2
6.0	3.20+2	3.42+0	4.79−2	6.74−4	3.23+2
7.0	2.09+2	3.04+0	5.40−2	8.76−4	2.12+2
8.0	1.45+2	2.72+0	5.94−2	1.09−3	1.48+2
9.0	1.05+2	2.45+0	6.43−2	1.31−3	1.07+2
10.0	7.85+1	2.22+0	6.86−2	1.54−3	8.08+1
12.0	4.75+1	1.83+0	7.62−2	2.01−3	4.94+1
15.0	2.57+1	1.40+0	8.55−2	2.75−3	2.72+1
17.0	1.82+1	1.19+0	9.07−2	3.27−3	1.95+1
18.99 K	1.34+1	1.03+0	9.50−2	3.77−3	1.46+1
18.99	8.74+1	1.03+0	9.50−2	3.77−3	8.85+1
20.0	7.64+1	9.57−1	9.71−2	4.04−3	7.75+1
25.0	4.25+1	7.02−1	1.05−1	5.29−3	4.33+1
30.0	2.60+1	5.40−1	1.11−1	6.51−3	2.67+1
35.0	1.71+1	4.30−1	1.15−1	7.66−3	1.76+1
40.0	1.18+1	3.50−1	1.18−1	8.75−3	1.23+1
50.0	6.29+0	2.44−1	1.21−1	1.07−2	6.66+0
60.0	3.74+0	1.80−1	1.22−1	1.24−2	4.04+0
70.0	2.40+0	1.38−1	1.23−1	1.39−2	2.66+0
80.0	1.63+0	1.09−1	1.22−1	1.52−2	1.86+0
90.0	1.15+0	8.91−2	1.21−1	1.64−2	1.36+0
100.0	8.47−1	7.40−2	1.19−1	1.74−2	1.04+0
120.0	4.95−1	5.35−2	1.16−1	1.91−2	6.65−1
150.0	2.57−1	3.57−2	1.12−1	2.10−2	4.04−1
170.0	1.77−1	2.83−2	1.08−1	2.20−2	3.14−1
200.0	1.10−1	2.09−2	1.04−1	2.31−2	2.35−1

TABLE 3 (continued)

Energy (keV)	τ/ρ (cm^2/g)	σ_c/ρ (cm^2/g)	σ_I/ρ (cm^2/g)	σ_a/ρ (cm^2/g)	μ/ρ (cm^2/g)
250.0	5.70–2	1.37–2	9.76–2	2.44–2	1.68–1
300.0	3.34–2	9.64–3	9.19–2	2.52–2	1.35–1
350.0	2.14–2	7.17–3	8.71–2	2.57–2	1.16–1
400.0	1.45–2	5.54–3	8.30–2	2.60–2	1.03–1
500.0	7.68–3	3.59–3	7.60–2	2.62–2	8.73–2
600.0	4.59–3	2.51–3	7.05–2	2.61–2	7.76–2
700.0	2.99–3	1.85–3	6.59–2	2.59–2	7.08–2
800.0	2.07–3	1.42–3	6.21–2	2.55–2	6.56–2
900.0	1.51–3	1.13–3	5.88–2	2.51–2	6.14–2
1,000.0	1.14–3	9.13–4	5.59–2	2.47–2	5.80–2

Molybdenum Z = 42

Energy (keV)	τ/ρ (cm^2/g)	σ_c/ρ (cm^2/g)	σ_I/ρ (cm^2/g)	σ_a/ρ (cm^2/g)	μ/ρ (cm^2/g)
0.1	5.00+3	7.36+0	1.01–4	2.68–8	5.01+3
0.15	5.10+3	7.35+0	2.09–4	8.44–8	5.11+3
0.2	4.42+3	7.34+0	3.58–4	1.94–7	4.43+3
0.2276 $M_{IV,V}$	3.97+3	7.34+0	4.59–4	2.83–7	3.98+3
0.229	5.31+3	7.34+0	4.65–4	2.88–7	5.32+3
0.25	1.38+4	7.33+0	5.50–4	3.73–7	1.38+4
0.3	2.94+4	7.32+0	7.79–4	6.35–7	2.95+4
0.3974 $M_{II,III}$	2.25+4	7.29+0	1.33–3	1.43–6	2.25+4
0.3988	2.57+4	7.29+0	1.33–3	1.44–6	2.57+4
0.4	2.58+4	7.29+0	1.34–3	1.45–6	2.58+4
0.5	1.88+4	7.24+0	2.03–3	2.74–6	1.88+4
0.5039 M_I	1.86+4	7.24+0	2.06–3	2.80–6	1.86+4
0.5053	1.96+4	7.24+0	2.07–3	2.82–6	1.97+4
0.6	1.43+4	7.19+0	2.81–3	4.53–6	1.43+4
0.7	1.05+4	7.14+0	3.66–3	6.85–6	1.05+4
0.8	7.96+3	7.07+0	4.56–3	9.71–6	7.97+3
0.9	6.16+3	7.01+0	5.50–3	1.31–5	6.17+3
1.0	4.88+3	6.94+0	6.45–3	1.69–5	4.89+3
1.2	3.22+3	6.78+0	8.37–3	2.61–5	3.23+3
1.5	1.90+3	6.53+0	1.12–2	4.31–5	1.91+3
2.0	9.42+2	6.10+0	1.59–2	7.97–5	9.49+2
2.5	5.61+2	5.67+0	2.03–2	1.26–4	5.66+2
2.52 L_{III}	5.50+2	5.65+0	2.05–2	1.28–4	5.55+2
2.52	2.22+3	5.65+0	2.05–2	1.28–4	2.23+3
2.625 L_{II}	1.98+3	5.56+0	2.14–2	1.39–4	1.99+3
2.625	2.78+3	5.56+0	2.14–2	1.39–4	2.78+3
2.866 L_I	2.18+3	5.36+0	2.35–2	1.65–4	2.19+3
2.866	2.62+3	5.36+0	2.35–2	1.65–4	2.62+3
3.0	2.31+3	5.27+0	2.46–2	1.81–4	2.31+3
3.5	1.51+3	4.89+0	2.87–2	2.44–4	1.51+3
4.0	1.04+3	4.55+0	3.26–2	3.14–4	1.05+3
5.0	5.62+2	3.96+0	4.00–2	4.75–4	5.66+2
6.0	3.40+2	3.48+0	4.67–2	6.59–4	3.43+2
7.0	2.22+2	3.09+0	5.28–2	8.60–4	2.25+2
8.0	1.53+2	2.76+0	5.83–2	1.07–3	1.56+2
9.0	1.11+2	2.49+0	6.32–2	1.29–3	1.13+2
10.0	8.28+1	2.26+0	6.75–2	1.52–3	8.51+1
12.0	5.00+1	1.87+0	7.51–2	1.99–3	5.20+1
15.0	2.70+1	1.44+0	8.43–2	2.72–3	2.85+1
17.0	1.91+1	1.22+0	8.94–2	3.22–3	2.04+1
20.0 K	1.22+1	9.82–1	9.58–2	3.98–3	1.33+1

TABLE 3 (continued)

Energy (keV)	τ/ρ (cm²/g)	σ_c/ρ (cm²/g)	σ_I/ρ (cm²/g)	σ_a/ρ (cm²/g)	μ/ρ (cm²/g)
20.0	8.19+1	9.82−1	9.58−2	3.98−3	8.30+1
25.0	4.54+1	7.20−1	1.04−1	5.22−3	4.62+1
30.0	2.77+1	5.54−1	1.09−1	6.43−3	2.84+1
35.0	1.82+1	4.41−1	1.14−1	7.57−3	1.87+1
40.0	1.25+1	3.60−1	1.16−1	8.65−3	1.30+1
50.0	6.68+0	2.51−1	1.20−1	1.06−2	7.05+0
60.0	3.97+0	1.85−1	1.21−1	1.23−2	4.28+0
70.0	2.55+0	1.42−1	1.21−1	1.38−2	2.81+0
80.0	1.73+0	1.13−1	1.21−1	1.51−2	1.96+0
90.0	1.23+0	9.16−2	1.20−1	1.62−2	1.44+0
100.0	9.03−1	7.62−2	1.18−1	1.72−2	1.10+0
120.0	5.29−1	5.51−2	1.15−1	1.89−2	6.99−1
150.0	2.75−1	3.67−2	1.11−1	2.08−2	4.22−1
170.0	1.90−1	2.92−2	1.07−1	2.18−2	3.27−1
200.0	1.18−1	2.15−2	1.03−1	2.29−2	2.43−1
250.0	6.14−2	1.41−2	9.67−2	2.42−2	1.72−1
300.0	3.61−2	9.94−3	9.11−2	2.50−2	1.37−1
350.0	2.31−2	7.39−3	8.64−2	2.55−2	1.17−1
400.0	1.57−2	5.71−3	8.22−2	2.58−2	1.04−1
500.0	8.32−3	3.70−3	7.54−2	2.60−2	8.74−2
600.0	4.98−3	2.59−3	6.99−2	2.59−2	7.75−2
700.0	3.25−3	1.91−3	6.54−2	2.56−2	7.06−2
800.0	2.25−3	1.47−3	6.16−2	2.53−2	6.53−2
900.0	1.64−3	1.16−3	5.83−2	2.49−2	6.11−2
1,000.0	1.23−3	9.42−4	5.55−2	2.45−2	5.76−2

Technetium Z = 43

Energy (keV)	τ/ρ (cm²/g)	σ_c/ρ (cm²/g)	σ_I/ρ (cm²/g)	σ_a/ρ (cm²/g)	μ/ρ (cm²/g)
0.1	5.35+3	7.48+0	1.09−4	2.89−8	5.36+3
0.15	5.48+3	7.47+0	2.24−4	9.07−8	5.49+3
0.2	4.73+3	7.46+0	3.86−4	2.09−7	4.74+3
0.2536 $M_{IV,V}$	3.86+3	7.45+0	6.09−4	4.19−7	3.87+3
0.255	5.05+3	7.45+0	6.15−4	4.26−7	5.05+3
0.27	1.01+4	7.44+0	6.86−4	5.03−7	1.01+4
0.3	2.70+4	7.43+0	8.40−4	6.84−7	2.70+4
0.4	2.26+4	7.40+0	1.45−3	1.57−6	2.26+4
0.4309 $M_{II,III}$	2.02+4	7.39+0	1.67−3	1.95−6	2.02+4
0.4323	2.27+4	7.39+0	1.68−3	1.96−6	2.27+4
0.5	1.93+4	7.35+0	2.19−3	2.96−6	1.93+4
0.5433 M_I	1.67+4	7.34+0	2.55−3	3.73−6	1.67+4
0.5447	1.78+4	7.33+0	2.56−3	3.76−6	1.78+4
0.6	1.48+4	7.30+0	3.04−3	4.90−6	1.48+4
0.7	1.10+4	7.24+0	3.96−3	7.42−6	1.10+4
0.8	8.35+3	7.17+0	4.94−3	1.05−5	8.35+3
0.9	6.49+3	7.11+0	5.95−3	1.41−5	6.50+3
1.0	5.15+3	7.03+0	6.97−3	1.83−5	5.16+3
1.5	2.03+3	6.61+0	1.20−2	4.57−5	2.03+3
2.0	1.01+3	6.16+0	1.66−2	8.26−5	1.01+3
2.5	6.10+2	5.73+0	2.09−2	1.28−4	6.16+2
2.677 L_{III}	5.14+2	5.58+0	2.24−2	1.46−4	5.19+2
2.677	1.97+3	5.58+0	2.24−2	1.46−4	1.97+3
2.793 L_{II}	1.75+3	5.48+0	2.33−2	1.59−4	1.76+3
2.793	2.45+3	5.48+0	2.33−2	1.59−4	2.46+3

TABLE 3 (continued)

Energy (keV)	τ/ρ (cm^2/g)	σ_c/ρ (cm^2/g)	σ_I/ρ (cm^2/g)	σ_a/ρ (cm^2/g)	μ/ρ (cm^2/g)
3.0	2.02+3	5.33+0	2.50–2	1.82–4	2.02+3
3.043 L_I	1.94+3	5.29+0	2.54–2	1.87–4	1.94+3
3.043	2.33+3	5.29+0	2.54–2	1.87–4	2.33+3
3.5	1.58+3	4.95+0	2.90–2	2.44–4	1.59+3
4.0	1.10+3	4.61+0	3.27–2	3.13–4	1.10+3
5.0	5.95+2	4.02+0	3.98–2	4.70–4	5.99+2
6.0	3.61+2	3.53+0	4.63–2	6.50–4	3.64+2
7.0	2.36+2	3.13+0	5.22–2	8.47–4	2.40+2
8.0	1.64+2	2.80+0	5.77–2	1.06–3	1.67+2
9.0	1.19+2	2.53+0	6.25–2	1.28–3	1.21+2
10.0	8.88+1	2.29+0	6.69–2	1.50–3	9.12+1
12.0	5.38+1	1.90+0	7.43–2	1.97–3	5.58+1
15.0	2.92+1	1.47+0	8.33–2	2.69–3	3.07+1
17.0	2.07+1	1.25+0	8.83–2	3.18–3	2.20+1
20.0	1.32+1	1.01+0	9.46–2	3.93–3	1.44+1
21.04 K	1.15+1	9.38–1	9.63–2	4.18–3	1.26+1
21.04	7.80+1	9.38–1	9.63–2	4.18–3	7.91+1
25.0	4.89+1	7.38–1	1.02–1	5.16–3	4.98+1
30.0	2.96+1	5.67–1	1.08–1	6.34–3	3.03+1
35.0	1.93+1	4.52–1	1.12–1	7.48–3	1.98+1
40.0	1.32+1	3.69–1	1.15–1	8.55–3	1.37+1
50.0	7.00+0	2.58–1	1.19–1	1.05–2	7.37+0
60.0	4.14+0	1.91–1	1.20–1	1.22–2	4.45+0
70.0	2.65+0	1.46–1	1.20–1	1.36–2	2.91+0
80.0	1.80+0	1.16–1	1.19–1	1.49–2	2.03+0
90.0	1.27+0	9.42–2	1.18–1	1.61–2	1.48+0
100.0	9.34–1	7.84–2	1.17–1	1.71–2	1.13+0
120.0	5.48–1	5.66–2	1.14–1	1.87–2	7.18–1
150.0	2.85–1	3.78–2	1.10–1	2.06–2	4.32–1
170.0	1.97–1	3.00–2	1.07–1	2.16–2	3.34–1
200.0	1.23–1	2.21–2	1.02–1	2.28–2	2.47–1
250.0	6.41–2	1.45–2	9.59–2	2.40–2	1.74–1
300.0	3.78–2	1.02–2	9.04–2	2.48–2	1.38–1
350.0	2.43–2	7.62–3	8.57–2	2.53–2	1.18–1
400.0	1.66–2	5.88–3	8.16–2	2.56–2	1.04–1
500.0	8.86–3	3.81–3	7.48–2	2.58–2	8.75–2
600.0	5.35–3	2.67–3	6.93–2	2.57–2	7.74–2
700.0	3.51–3	1.97–3	6.49–2	2.54–2	7.04–2
800.0	2.45–3	1.51–3	6.11–2	2.51–2	6.50–2
900.0	1.79–3	1.20–3	5.79–2	2.47–2	6.08–2
1,000.0	1.36–3	9.72–4	5.50–2	2.43–2	5.73–2

Ruthenium Z = 44

Energy (keV)	τ/ρ (cm^2/g)	σ_c/ρ (cm^2/g)	σ_I/ρ (cm^2/g)	σ_a/ρ (cm^2/g)	μ/ρ (cm^2/g)
0.1	5.05+3	7.67+0	8.78–5	2.33–8	5.06+3
0.15	5.74+3	7.66+0	1.81–4	7.29–8	5.75+3
0.2	5.36+3	7.65+0	3.10–4	1.68–7	5.36+3
0.2804 $M_{IV,V}$	4.12+3	7.64+0	5.94–4	4.52–7	4.12+3
0.2818	5.12+3	7.64+0	5.99–4	4.59–7	5.12+3
0.3	8.88+3	7.63+0	6.76–4	5.51–7	8.89+3
0.35	2.73+4	7.62+0	9.07–4	8.62–7	2.73+4
0.4	2.42+4	7.60+0	1.17–3	1.27–6	2.42+4
0.4673 $M_{II,III}$	1.92+4	7.57+0	1.57–3	1.99–6	1.92+4

TABLE 3 (continued)

Energy (keV)	τ/ρ (cm^2/g)	σ_c/ρ (cm^2/g)	σ_I/ρ (cm^2/g)	σ_a/ρ (cm^2/g)	μ/ρ (cm^2/g)
0.4687	2.17+4	7.57+0	1.58–3	2.00–6	2.17+4
0.5	2.10+4	7.56+0	1.78–3	2.40–6	2.10+4
0.5843 M_I	1.60+4	7.52+0	2.36–3	3.71–6	1.60+4
0.5857	1.69+4	7.52+0	2.37–3	3.74–6	1.70+4
0.6	1.61+4	7.51+0	2.47–3	3.99–6	1.61+4
0.7	1.20+4	7.46+0	3.24–3	6.08–6	1.20+4
0.8	9.13+3	7.40+0	4.07–3	8.69–6	9.14+3
0.9	7.11+3	7.34+0	4.93–3	1.18–5	7.12+3
1.0	5.65+3	7.26+0	5.82–3	1.54–5	5.65+3
1.5	2.22+3	6.87+0	1.04–2	4.03–5	2.23+3
2.0	1.10+3	6.43+0	1.50–2	7.59–5	1.11+3
2.5	6.31+2	5.99+0	1.94–2	1.21–4	6.37+2
2.838 L_{III}	4.86+2	5.69+0	2.23–2	1.56–4	4.92+2
2.838	1.80+3	5.69+0	2.23–2	1.56–4	1.81+3
2.967 L_{II}	1.59+3	5.59+0	2.34–2	1.71–4	1.60+3
2.967	2.23+3	5.59+0	2.34–2	1.71–4	2.24+3
3.0	2.17+3	5.57+0	2.37–2	1.75–4	2.17+3
3.224 L_I	1.78+3	5.38+0	2.55–2	2.01–4	1.78+3
3.224	2.13+3	5.38+0	2.55–2	2.01–4	2.14+3
3.5	1.70+3	5.17+0	2.77–2	2.37–4	1.71+3
4.0	1.18+3	4.80+0	3.15–2	3.05–4	1.19+3
5.0	6.40+2	4.17+0	3.87–2	4.62–4	6.44+2
6.0	3.88+2	3.65+0	4.54–2	6.41–4	3.92+2
7.0	2.54+2	3.23+0	5.14–2	8.40–4	2.57+2
8.0	1.76+2	2.89+0	5.70–2	1.05–3	1.79+2
9.0	1.28+2	2.60+0	6.19–2	1.27–3	1.30+2
10.0	9.55+1	2.36+0	6.63–2	1.50–3	9.80+1
12.0	5.79+1	1.96+0	7.39–2	1.96–3	5.99+1
15.0	3.14+1	1.52+0	8.30–2	2.68–3	3.30+1
17.0	2.23+1	1.30+0	8.80–2	3.18–3	2.37+1
20.0	1.43+1	1.05+0	9.43–2	3.92–3	1.54+1
22.12 K	1.08+1	9.08–1	9.78–2	4.43–3	1.18+1
22.12	7.26+1	9.08–1	9.78–2	4.43–3	7.37+1
25.0	5.21+1	7.66–1	1.02–1	5.15–3	5.30+1
30.0	3.16+1	5.88–1	1.08–1	6.33–3	3.23+1
35.0	2.06+1	4.68–1	1.12–1	7.47–3	2.12+1
40.0	1.41+1	3.82–1	1.15–1	8.53–3	1.46+1
50.0	7.50+0	2.68–1	1.18–1	1.05–2	7.88+0
60.0	4.44+0	1.98–1	1.20–1	1.22–2	4.76+0
70.0	2.84+0	1.52–1	1.20–1	1.37–2	3.11+0
80.0	1.93+0	1.20–1	1.19–1	1.49–2	2.17+0
90.0	1.37+0	9.80–2	1.18–1	1.61–2	1.58+0
100.0	1.01+0	8.14–2	1.17–1	1.71–2	1.20+0
120.0	5.90–1	5.89–2	1.14–1	1.88–2	7.63–1
150.0	3.07–1	3.93–2	1.10–1	2.07–2	4.56–1
170.0	2.13–1	3.12–2	1.07–1	2.17–2	3.51–1
200.0	1.32–1	2.30–2	1.02–1	2.28–2	2.58–1
250.0	6.93–2	1.51–2	9.60–2	2.41–2	1.80–1
300.0	4.10–2	1.06–2	9.05–2	2.49–2	1.42–1
350.0	2.63–2	7.93–3	8.58–2	2.54–2	1.20–1
400.0	1.80–2	6.13–3	8.18–2	2.56–2	1.06–1
500.0	9.64–3	3.97–3	7.50–2	2.58–2	8.85–2

TABLE 3 (continued)

Energy (keV)	τ/ρ (cm²/g)	σ_c/ρ (cm²/g)	σ_I/ρ (cm²/g)	σ_a/ρ (cm²/g)	μ/ρ (cm²/g)
600.0	5.82−3	2.78−3	6.95−2	2.57−2	7.81−2
700.0	3.83−3	2.05−3	6.50−2	2.55−2	7.09−2
800.0	2.67−3	1.58−3	6.13−2	2.52−2	6.55−2
900.0	1.96−3	1.25−3	5.80−2	2.48−2	6.12−2
1,000.0	1.48−3	1.01−3	5.51−2	2.44−2	5.76−2

Rhodium Z = 45

Energy (keV)	τ/ρ (cm²/g)	σ_c/ρ (cm²/g)	σ_I/ρ (cm²/g)	σ_a/ρ (cm²/g)	μ/ρ (cm²/g)
0.1	5.14+3	7.88+0	8.13−5	2.16−8	5.14+3
0.15	5.96+3	7.87+0	1.68−4	6.81−8	5.97+3
0.2	5.81+3	7.87+0	2.91−4	1.58−7	5.82+3
0.3	4.28+3	7.84+0	6.37−4	5.19−7	4.29+3
0.3082 $M_{IV,V}$	4.15+3	7.84+0	6.71−4	5.62−7	4.15+3
0.3096	5.02+3	7.84+0	6.77−4	5.69−7	5.03+3
0.35	2.23+4	7.83+0	8.55−4	8.13−7	2.23+4
0.4	2.52+4	7.81+0	1.10−3	1.20−6	2.52+4
0.5	1.83+4	7.77+0	1.68−3	2.27−6	1.83+4
0.5038 $M_{II,III}$	1.80+4	7.77+0	1.70−3	2.32−6	1.80+4
0.5052	2.02+4	7.77+0	1.71−3	2.34−6	2.02+4
0.6	1.62+4	7.73+0	2.34−3	3.79−6	1.63+4
0.6264 M_I	1.50+4	7.71+0	2.53−3	4.26−6	1.50+4
0.6278	1.59+4	7.71+0	2.54−3	4.29−6	1.59+4
0.7	1.29+4	7.67+0	3.07−3	5.78−6	1.29+4
0.8	9.83+3	7.61+0	3.87−3	8.28−6	9.83+3
0.9	7.67+3	7.55+0	4.70−3	1.12−5	7.68+3
1.0	6.10+3	7.48+0	5.56−3	1.47−5	6.10+3
1.5	2.40+3	7.09+0	1.01−2	3.90−5	2.41+3
2.0	1.20+3	6.65+0	1.46−2	7.40−5	1.20+3
2.5	6.86+2	6.20+0	1.90−2	1.19−4	6.93+2
3.0	4.62+2	5.77+0	2.32−2	1.72−4	4.68+2
3.004 L_{III}	4.61+2	5.76+0	2.32−2	1.72−4	4.66+2
3.004	1.63+3	5.76+0	2.32−2	1.72−4	1.63+3
3.146 L_{II}	1.44+3	5.64+0	2.44−2	1.89−4	1.44+3
3.146	2.01+3	5.64+0	2.44−2	1.89−4	2.02+3
3.412 L_I	1.61+3	5.42+0	2.65−2	2.22−4	1.62+3
3.412	1.93+3	5.42+0	2.65−2	2.22−4	1.94+3
3.5	1.80+3	5.36+0	2.72−2	2.33−4	1.81+3
4.0	1.25+3	4.97+0	3.10−2	3.01−4	1.26+3
5.0	6.81+2	4.31+0	3.82−2	4.56−4	6.85+2
6.0	4.14+2	3.77+0	4.48−2	6.34−4	4.18+2
7.0	2.72+2	3.33+0	5.09−2	8.33−4	2.75+2
8.0	1.89+2	2.98+0	5.65−2	1.05−3	1.92+2
9.0	1.37+2	2.68+0	6.15−2	1.27−3	1.40+2
10.0	1.03+2	2.43+0	6.60−2	1.50−3	1.05+2
12.0	6.23+1	2.03+0	7.37−2	1.96−3	6.44+1
15.0	3.39+1	1.58+0	8.29−2	2.68−3	3.56+1
17.0	2.41+1	1.35+0	8.80−2	3.18−3	2.55+1
20.0	1.55+1	1.09+0	9.42−2	3.92−3	1.66+1
23.22 K	1.03+1	8.81−1	9.94−2	4.70−3	1.13+1
23.22	6.63+1	8.81−1	9.94−2	4.70−3	6.72+1
25.0	5.44+1	7.95−1	1.02−1	5.15−3	5.53+1
30.0	3.33+1	6.10−1	1.08−1	6.33−3	3.40+1
35.0	2.18+1	4.86−1	1.12−1	7.47−3	2.24+1

TABLE 3 (continued)

Energy (keV)	τ/ρ (cm^2/g)	σ_c/ρ (cm^2/g)	σ_I/ρ (cm^2/g)	σ_a/ρ (cm^2/g)	μ/ρ (cm^2/g)
40.0	1.50+1	3.97−1	1.15−1	8.54−3	1.55+1
50.0	8.02+0	2.79−1	1.18−1	1.05−2	8.42+0
60.0	4.77+0	2.06−1	1.20−1	1.22−2	5.09+0
70.0	3.06+0	1.58−1	1.20−1	1.37−2	3.34+0
80.0	2.08+0	1.25−1	1.20−1	1.50−2	2.32+0
90.0	1.48+0	1.02−1	1.19−1	1.61−2	1.70+0
100.0	1.09+0	8.47−2	1.17−1	1.71−2	1.29+0
120.0	6.37−1	6.12−2	1.15−1	1.88−2	8.13−1
150.0	3.32−1	4.09−2	1.10−1	2.08−2	4.83−1
170.0	2.30−1	3.25−2	1.07−1	2.17−2	3.70−1
200.0	1.43−1	2.40−2	1.03−1	2.29−2	2.70−1
250.0	7.49−2	1.57−2	9.64−2	2.42−2	1.87−1
300.0	4.43−2	1.11−2	9.09−2	2.50−2	1.46−1
350.0	2.85−2	8.26−3	8.61−2	2.55−2	1.23−1
400.0	1.95−2	6.39−3	8.21−2	2.58−2	1.08−1
500.0	1.05−2	4.14−3	7.53−2	2.59−2	8.98−2
600.0	6.33−3	2.90−3	6.98−2	2.59−2	7.91−2
700.0	4.17−3	2.14−3	6.53−2	2.56−2	7.16−2
800.0	2.92−3	1.64−3	6.15−2	2.53−2	6.61−2
900.0	2.14−3	1.30−3	5.82−2	2.49−2	6.17−2
1,000.0	1.63−3	1.06−3	5.54−2	2.45−2	5.81−2

Palladium Z = 46

Energy (keV)	τ/ρ (cm^2/g)	σ_c/ρ (cm^2/g)	σ_I/ρ (cm^2/g)	σ_a/ρ (cm^2/g)	μ/ρ (cm^2/g)
0.1	5.98+3	7.96+0	5.53−5	1.47−8	5.98+3
0.15	5.78+3	7.96+0	1.14−4	4.60−8	5.78+3
0.2	6.23+3	7.95+0	1.97−4	1.07−7	6.24+3
0.3	4.91+3	7.94+0	4.35−4	3.55−7	4.92+3
0.3361 $M_{IV,V}$	4.29+3	7.93+0	5.42−4	4.97−7	4.30+3
0.3375	4.94+3	7.92+0	5.47−4	5.03−7	4.95+3
0.35	5.29+3	7.92+0	5.87−4	5.60−7	5.30+3
0.4	2.51+4	7.91+0	7.62−4	8.31−7	2.51+4
0.5	1.96+4	7.88+0	1.18−3	1.60−6	1.96+4
0.54 $M_{II,III}$	1.71+4	7.87+0	1.37−3	2.01−6	1.71+4
0.5414	1.96+4	7.86+0	1.37−3	2.02−6	1.96+4
0.6	1.73+4	7.84+0	1.67−3	2.73−6	1.74+4
0.6662 M_I	1.42+4	7.82+0	2.04−3	3.69−6	1.43+4
0.6676	1.49+4	7.82+0	2.05−3	3.71−6	1.49+4
0.7	1.37+4	7.80+0	2.24−3	4.26−6	1.38+4
0.8	1.05+4	7.75+0	2.89−3	6.25−6	1.05+4
0.9	8.22+3	7.69+0	3.57−3	8.67−6	8.23+3
1.0	6.55+3	7.63+0	4.31−3	1.16−5	6.55+3
1.5	2.58+3	7.27+0	8.51−3	3.37−5	2.59+3
2.0	1.29+3	6.84+0	1.30−2	6.76−5	1.29+3
2.5	7.36+2	6.39+0	1.75−2	1.11−4	7.43+2
3.0	4.81+2	5.94+0	2.16−2	1.63−4	4.87+2
3.173 L_{III}	4.17+2	5.78+0	2.30−2	1.82−4	4.23+2
3.173	1.53+3	5.78+0	2.30−2	1.82−4	1.54+3
3.33 L_{II}	1.34+3	5.65+0	2.42−2	2.00−4	1.35+3
3.33	1.88+3	5.65+0	2.42−2	2.00−4	1.88+3
3.5	1.64+3	5.51+0	2.56−2	2.21−4	1.64+3
3.604 L_I	1.51+3	5.42+0	2.63−2	2.34−4	1.51+3
3.604	1.81+3	5.42+0	2.63−2	2.34−4	1.82+3

TABLE 3 (continued)

Energy (keV)	τ/ρ (cm^2/g)	σ_c/ρ (cm^2/g)	σ_I/ρ (cm^2/g)	σ_a/ρ (cm^2/g)	μ/ρ (cm^2/g)
4.0	1.36+3	5.11+0	2.93−2	2.87−4	1.36+3
5.0	7.34+2	4.42+0	3.63−2	4.37−4	7.38+2
6.0	4.44+2	3.86+0	4.29−2	6.12−4	4.47+2
7.0	2.90+2	3.40+0	4.91−2	8.07−4	2.93+2
8.0	2.01+2	3.03+0	5.47−2	1.02−3	2.04+2
9.0	1.45+2	2.73+0	5.98−2	1.24−3	1.48+2
10.0	1.08+2	2.47+0	6.44−2	1.47−3	1.11+2
12.0	6.55+1	2.06+0	7.22−2	1.93−3	6.76+1
15.0	3.54+1	1.61+0	8.13−2	2.64−3	3.71+1
17.0	2.51+1	1.38+0	8.64−2	3.13−3	2.65+1
20.0	1.60+1	1.11+0	9.26−2	3.86−3	1.72+1
24.35$_K$	9.29+0	8.43−1	9.95−2	4.91−3	1.02+1
24.35	6.03+1	8.43−1	9.95−2	4.91−3	6.13+1
25.0	5.63+1	8.13−1	1.00−1	5.07−3	5.72+1
30.0	3.46+1	6.24−1	1.06−1	6.24−3	3.53+1
35.0	2.27+1	4.96−1	1.10−1	7.35−3	2.34+1
40.0	1.57+1	4.06−1	1.13−1	8.42−3	1.63+1
50.0	8.44+0	2.85−1	1.17−1	1.04−2	8.84+0
60.0	5.03+0	2.11−1	1.18−1	1.20−2	5.36+0
70.0	3.24+0	1.62−1	1.18−1	1.35−2	3.52+0
80.0	2.21+0	1.28−1	1.18−1	1.48−2	2.45+0
90.0	1.57+0	1.04−1	1.17−1	1.59−2	1.79+0
100.0	1.16+0	8.67−2	1.16−1	1.69−2	1.36+0
120.0	6.80−1	6.27−2	1.13−1	1.86−2	8.56−1
150.0	3.55−1	4.19−2	1.09−1	2.05−2	5.05−1
170.0	2.46−1	3.33−2	1.06−1	2.15−2	3.85−1
200.0	1.53−1	2.46−2	1.01−1	2.26−2	2.80−1
250.0	8.04−2	1.61−2	9.52−2	2.39−2	1.92−1
300.0	4.76−2	1.14−2	8.98−2	2.47−2	1.49−1
350.0	3.06−2	8.47−3	8.51−2	2.52−2	1.24−1
400.0	2.10−2	6.55−3	8.11−2	2.55−2	1.09−1
500.0	1.12−2	4.25−3	7.44−2	2.57−2	8.99−2
600.0	6.81−3	2.97−3	6.90−2	2.56−2	7.88−2
700.0	4.48−3	2.19−3	6.45−2	2.53−2	7.12−2
800.0	3.14−3	1.69−3	6.08−2	2.50−2	6.56−2
900.0	2.30−3	1.34−3	5.76−2	2.46−2	6.12−2
1,000.0	1.75−3	1.08−3	5.47−2	2.42−2	5.76−2
Silver	**Z = 47**				
0.1	5.67+3	8.20+0	7.20−5	1.91−8	5.68+3
0.15	6.05+3	8.19+0	1.49−4	6.03−8	6.06+3
0.2	6.48+3	8.18+0	2.58−4	1.40−7	6.49+3
0.3	5.17+3	8.16+0	5.64−4	4.60−7	5.17+3
0.35	4.38+3	8.15+0	7.57−4	7.20−7	4.39+3
0.3684$_{M_{IV,V}}$	4.12+3	8.15+0	8.35−4	8.36−7	4.13+3
0.3698	4.80+3	8.15+0	8.41−4	8.45−7	4.81+3
0.4	1.30+4	8.13+0	9.78−4	1.06−6	1.30+4
0.5	2.06+4	8.10+0	1.49−3	2.02−6	2.06+4
0.581$_{M_{II,III}}$	1.57+4	8.06+0	1.97−3	3.08−6	1.58+4
0.5824	1.75+4	8.06+0	1.97−3	3.11−6	1.75+4
0.6	1.80+4	8.06+0	2.08−3	3.38−6	1.80+4
0.7	1.37+4	8.01+0	2.75−3	5.17−6	1.37+4

TABLE 3 (continued)

Energy (keV)	τ/ρ (cm²/g)	σ_c/ρ (cm²/g)	σ_I/ρ (cm²/g)	σ_a/ρ (cm²/g)	μ/ρ (cm²/g)
0.7168 M_I	1.31+4	8.00+0	2.86−3	5.52−6	1.31+4
0.7182	1.38+4	8.00+0	2.87−3	5.55−6	1.39+4
0.8	1.12+4	7.95+0	3.47−3	7.43−6	1.12+4
0.9	8.75+3	7.89+0	4.22−3	1.01−5	8.76+3
1.0	7.00+3	7.82+0	5.01−3	1.33−5	7.00+3
1.5	2.78+3	7.44+0	9.20−3	3.58−5	2.78+3
2.0	1.39+3	7.01+0	1.35−2	6.88−5	1.40+3
2.5	7.96+2	6.55+0	1.77−2	1.11−4	8.02+2
3.0	5.21+2	6.11+0	2.18−2	1.62−4	5.27+2
3.351 L_{III}	3.94+2	5.80+0	2.45−2	2.03−4	4.00+2
3.351	1.40+3	5.80+0	2.45−2	2.03−4	1.41+3
3.5	1.24+3	5.68+0	2.57−2	2.21−4	1.25+3
3.524 L_{II}	1.22+3	5.66+0	2.59−2	2.24−4	1.23+3
3.524	1.71+3	5.66+0	2.59−2	2.24−4	1.71+3
3.806 L_I	1.38+3	5.42+0	2.80−2	2.60−4	1.39+3
3.806	1.66+3	5.42+0	2.80−2	2.60−4	1.66+3
4.0	1.45+3	5.28+0	2.94−2	2.86−4	1.45+3
5.0	7.83+2	4.57+0	3.64−2	4.36−4	7.88+2
6.0	4.75+2	3.99+0	4.29−2	6.10−4	4.79+2
7.0	3.11+2	3.52+0	4.89−2	8.03−4	3.14+2
8.0	2.15+2	3.13+0	5.45−2	1.01−3	2.18+2
9.0	1.56+2	2.81+0	5.97−2	1.24−3	1.59+2
10.0	1.17+2	2.55+0	6.43−2	1.46−3	1.19+2
12.0	7.06+1	2.13+0	7.22−2	1.93−3	7.29+1
15.0	3.83+1	1.66+0	8.15−2	2.65−3	4.00+1
17.0	2.71+1	1.43+0	8.66−2	3.14−3	2.86+1
20.0	1.74+1	1.15+0	9.28−2	3.87−3	1.86+1
25.0	9.40+0	8.45−1	1.01−1	5.08−3	1.03+1
25.51 K	8.89+0	8.20−1	1.01−1	5.20−3	9.81+0
25.51	5.58+1	8.20−1	1.01−1	5.20−3	5.68+1
30.0	3.64+1	6.48−1	1.06−1	6.26−3	3.72+1
35.0	2.41+1	5.16−1	1.11−1	7.39−3	2.47+1
40.0	1.68+1	4.22−1	1.14−1	8.45−3	1.73+1
50.0	9.04+0	2.97−1	1.17−1	1.04−2	9.45+0
60.0	5.41+0	2.20−1	1.19−1	1.21−2	5.75+0
70.0	3.49+0	1.69−1	1.19−1	1.36−2	3.78+0
80.0	2.38+0	1.34−1	1.19−1	1.49−2	2.64+0
90.0	1.70+0	1.09−1	1.18−1	1.60−2	1.93+0
100.0	1.25+0	9.03−2	1.17−1	1.70−2	1.46+0
120.0	7.39−1	6.53−2	1.14−1	1.87−2	9.18−1
150.0	3.86−1	4.37−2	1.09−1	2.07−2	5.39−1
170.0	2.68−1	3.47−2	1.06−1	2.16−2	4.09−1
200.0	1.67−1	2.56−2	1.02−1	2.28−2	2.95−1
250.0	8.75−2	1.68−2	9.59−2	2.41−2	2.00−1
300.0	5.18−2	1.19−2	9.04−2	2.49−2	1.54−1
350.0	3.33−2	8.84−3	8.58−2	2.54−2	1.28−1
400.0	2.28−2	6.84−3	8.17−2	2.56−2	1.11−1
500.0	1.22−2	4.44−3	7.49−2	2.58−2	9.16−2
600.0	7.40−3	3.11−3	6.95−2	2.58−2	8.00−2
700.0	4.87−3	2.29−3	6.50−2	2.55−2	7.22−2
800.0	3.41−3	1.76−3	6.12−2	2.52−2	6.64−2
900.0	2.50−3	1.40−3	5.80−2	2.48−2	6.19−2
1,000.0	1.90−3	1.13−3	5.52−2	2.44−2	5.82−2

TABLE 3 (continued)

Cadmium Z = 48

Energy (keV)	τ/ρ (cm²/g)	σ_c/ρ (cm²/g)	σ_I/ρ (cm²/g)	σ_a/ρ (cm²/g)	μ/ρ (cm²/g)
0.1	5.08+3	8.20+0	7.90–5	2.09–8	5.08+3
0.1069 N_I	4.22+3	8.20+0	8.85–5	2.51–8	4.22+3
0.1083	5.71+3	8.20+0	9.06–5	2.60–8	5.72+3
0.15	6.02+3	8.20+0	1.63–4	6.57–8	6.03+3
0.2	6.65+3	8.19+0	2.80–4	1.52–7	6.67+3
0.3	5.46+3	8.17+0	6.13–4	5.00–7	5.47+3
0.4	3.98+3	8.14+0	1.06–3	1.16–6	3.99+3
0.4057 $M_{IV,V}$	3.91+3	8.14+0	1.09–3	1.20–6	3.92+3
0.4071	4.56+3	8.14+0	1.10–3	1.22–6	4.57+3
0.5	2.17+4	8.10+0	1.62–3	2.20–6	2.17+4
0.6	1.55+4	8.06+0	2.26–3	3.67–6	1.55+4
0.6272 $M_{II,III}$	1.42+4	8.04+0	2.45–3	4.14–6	1.42+4
0.6286	1.56+4	8.04+0	2.46–3	4.17–6	1.56+4
0.7	1.42+4	8.00+0	2.98–3	5.61–6	1.42+4
0.7695 M_I	1.18+4	7.96+0	3.51–3	7.25–6	1.18+4
0.7709	1.26+4	7.96+0	3.53–3	7.28–6	1.26+4
0.8	1.16+4	7.95+0	3.76–3	8.04–6	1.16+4
0.9	9.15+3	7.88+0	4.56–3	1.09–5	9.15+3
1.0	7.32+3	7.81+0	5.40–3	1.43–5	7.33+3
2.0	1.46+3	6.98+0	1.39–2	7.01–5	1.47+3
2.5	8.40+2	6.53+0	1.79–2	1.11–4	8.47+2
3.0	5.29+2	6.09+0	2.17–2	1.60–4	5.35+2
3.5	3.89+2	5.67+0	2.54–2	2.17–4	3.94+2
3.538 L_{III}	3.78+2	5.64+0	2.57–2	2.22–4	3.84+2
3.538	1.27+3	5.64+0	2.57–2	2.22–4	1.28+3
3.727 L_{II}	1.10+3	5.49+0	2.71–2	2.45–4	1.11+3
3.727	1.54+3	5.49+0	2.71–2	2.45–4	1.55+3
4.0	1.27+3	5.28+0	2.90–2	2.81–4	1.27+3
4.018 L_I	1.25+3	5.27+0	2.91–2	2.83–4	1.26+3
4.018	1.50+3	5.27+0	2.91–2	2.83–4	1.51+3
5.0	8.22+2	4.59+0	3.57–2	4.26–4	8.27+2
6.0	4.97+2	4.01+0	4.19–2	5.93–4	5.01+2
7.0	3.25+2	3.53+0	4.77–2	7.80–4	3.28+2
8.0	2.25+2	3.14+0	5.31–2	9.84–4	2.28+2
9.0	1.62+2	2.82+0	5.80–2	1.20–3	1.65+2
10.0	1.21+2	2.55+0	6.26–2	1.42–3	1.24+2
12.0	7.34+1	2.13+0	7.04–2	1.89–3	7.55+1
15.0	3.96+1	1.67+0	7.95–2	2.59–3	4.14+1
17.0	2.81+1	1.44+0	8.45–2	3.07–3	2.96+1
20.0	1.79+1	1.16+0	9.06–2	3.78–3	1.92+1
25.0	9.68+0	8.53–1	9.83–2	4.96–3	1.06+1
26.71 K	8.06+0	7.75–1	1.00–1	5.35–3	8.94+0
26.71	5.17+1	7.75–1	1.00–1	5.35–3	5.26+1
30.0	3.80+1	6.54–1	1.04–1	6.11–3	3.88+1
35.0	2.51+1	5.20–1	1.08–1	7.21–3	2.57+1
40.0	1.74+1	4.26–1	1.11–1	8.25–3	1.80+1
50.0	9.39+0	3.00–1	1.15–1	1.02–2	9.81+0
60.0	5.62+0	2.22–1	1.16–1	1.18–2	5.96+0
70.0	3.63+0	1.71–1	1.16–1	1.33–2	3.91+0
80.0	2.47+0	1.35–1	1.16–1	1.46–2	2.72+0
90.0	1.76+0	1.10–1	1.15–1	1.57–2	1.99+0

Energy (keV)	τ/ρ (cm²/g)	σ_c/ρ (cm²/g)	σ_I/ρ (cm²/g)	σ_a/ρ (cm²/g)	μ/ρ (cm²/g)
100.0	1.30+0	9.15−2	1.14−1	1.67−2	1.50+0
120.0	7.65−1	6.62−2	1.11−1	1.83−2	9.42−1
150.0	3.99−1	4.42−2	1.07−1	2.02−2	5.51−1
170.0	2.78−1	3.51−2	1.04−1	2.12−2	4.17−1
200.0	1.73−1	2.59−2	1.00−1	2.23−2	2.99−1
250.0	9.08−2	1.70−2	9.39−2	2.36−2	2.02−1
300.0	5.38−2	1.20−2	8.86−2	2.44−2	1.54−1
350.0	3.47−2	8.97−3	8.40−2	2.49−2	1.28−1
400.0	2.38−2	6.94−3	8.00−2	2.51−2	1.11−1
500.0	1.28−2	4.51−3	7.34−2	2.53−2	9.07−2
600.0	7.76−3	3.15−3	6.81−2	2.52−2	7.90−2
700.0	5.13−3	2.33−3	6.37−2	2.50−2	7.12−2
800.0	3.60−3	1.79−3	6.00−2	2.47−2	6.54−2
900.0	2.65−3	1.42−3	5.68−2	2.43−2	6.09−2
1,000.0	2.03−3	1.15−3	5.41−2	2.39−2	5.72−2

Indium Z = 49

Energy (keV)	τ/ρ (cm²/g)	σ_c/ρ (cm²/g)	σ_I/ρ (cm²/g)	σ_a/ρ (cm²/g)	μ/ρ (cm²/g)
0.1	5.96+3	8.37+0	7.96−5	2.12−8	5.97+3
0.1212 N_I	3.99+3	8.37+0	1.12−4	3.63−8	4.00+3
0.1226	5.51+3	8.37+0	1.14−4	3.75−8	5.52+3
0.15	6.05+3	8.36+0	1.66−4	6.72−8	6.06+3
0.2	6.87+3	8.36+0	2.86−4	1.55−7	6.88+3
0.3	5.80+3	8.33+0	6.24−4	5.09−7	5.81+3
0.4	4.30+3	8.30+0	1.08−3	1.17−6	4.30+3
0.4455 $M_{IV,V}$	3.73+3	8.28+0	1.33−3	1.61−6	3.74+3
0.4469	4.27+3	8.28+0	1.34−3	1.62−6	4.28+3
0.5	2.42+4	8.26+0	1.65−3	2.23−6	2.42+4
0.6	1.64+4	8.20+0	2.30−3	3.72−6	1.64+4
0.6762 $M_{II,III}$	1.30+4	8.16+0	2.84−3	5.17−6	1.30+4
0.6776	1.44+4	8.16+0	2.85−3	5.20−6	1.44+4
0.7	1.48+4	8.15+0	3.02−3	5.69−6	1.48+4
0.8	1.16+4	8.08+0	3.81−3	8.16−6	1.16+4
0.8249 M_I	1.09+4	8.06+0	4.01−3	8.84−6	1.09+4
0.8263	1.16+4	8.06+0	4.02−3	8.88−6	1.16+4
0.9	9.67+3	8.01+0	4.63−3	1.11−5	9.68+3
1.0	7.76+3	7.94+0	5.48−3	1.45−5	7.77+3
2.0	1.57+3	7.06+0	1.42−2	7.19−5	1.57+3
2.5	9.01+2	6.61+0	1.83−2	1.14−4	9.08+2
3.0	5.68+2	6.17+0	2.21−2	1.63−4	5.74+2
3.5	4.17+2	5.76+0	2.58−2	2.19−4	4.23+2
3.73 L_{III}	3.56+2	5.57+0	2.74−2	2.47−4	3.61+2
3.73	1.16+3	5.57+0	2.74−2	2.47−4	1.17+3
3.938 L_{II}	9.99+2	5.41+0	2.88−2	2.74−4	1.00+3
3.938	1.40+3	5.41+0	2.88−2	2.74−4	1.40+3
4.0	1.34+3	5.37+0	2.93−2	2.82−4	1.35+3
4.238 L_I	1.14+3	5.19+0	3.08−2	3.14−4	1.15+3
4.238	1.37+3	5.19+0	3.08−2	3.14−4	1.38+3
5.0	8.71+2	4.68+0	3.58−2	4.26−4	8.76+2
6.0	5.28+2	4.09+0	4.19−2	5.91−4	5.32+2
7.0	3.46+2	3.61+0	4.75−2	7.75−4	3.49+2
8.0	2.40+2	3.21+0	5.28−2	9.76−4	2.43+2
9.0	1.73+2	2.88+0	5.77−2	1.19−3	1.76+2

TABLE 3 (continued)

Energy (keV)	τ/ρ (cm²/g)	σ_c/ρ (cm²/g)	σ_I/ρ (cm²/g)	σ_a/ρ (cm²/g)	μ/ρ (cm²/g)
10.0	1.30+2	2.61+0	6.22−2	1.41−3	1.32+2
12.0	7.87+1	2.18+0	7.00−2	1.87−3	8.09+1
15.0	4.26+1	1.71+0	7.91−2	2.58−3	4.44+1
17.0	3.02+1	1.47+0	8.41−2	3.05−3	3.18+1
20.0	1.93+1	1.19+0	9.02−2	3.77−3	2.06+1
25.0	1.05+1	8.78−1	9.78−2	4.94−3	1.15+1
27.94_K	7.72+0	7.46−1	1.01−1	5.61−3	8.57+0
27.94	5.12+1	7.46−1	1.01−1	5.61−3	5.20+1
30.0	4.21+1	6.73−1	1.03−1	6.08−3	4.29+1
35.0	2.75+1	5.35−1	1.07−1	7.18−3	2.81+1
40.0	1.89+1	4.38−1	1.10−1	8.22−3	1.95+1
50.0	1.01+1	3.09−1	1.14−1	1.01−2	1.05+1
60.0	5.99+0	2.29−1	1.16−1	1.18−2	6.34+0
70.0	3.85+0	1.76−1	1.16−1	1.33−2	4.14+0
80.0	2.62+0	1.40−1	1.16−1	1.45−2	2.87+0
90.0	1.86+0	1.14−1	1.15−1	1.57−2	2.09+0
100.0	1.37+0	9.43−2	1.14−1	1.67−2	1.58+0
120.0	8.10−1	6.82−2	1.11−1	1.83−2	9.90−1
150.0	4.24−1	4.56−2	1.07−1	2.02−2	5.77−1
170.0	2.95−1	3.63−2	1.04−1	2.12−2	4.36−1
200.0	1.85−1	2.68−2	9.99−2	2.23−2	3.12−1
250.0	9.74−2	1.76−2	9.38−2	2.36−2	2.09−1
300.0	5.79−2	1.24−2	8.85−2	2.44−2	1.59−1
350.0	3.75−2	9.26−3	8.39−2	2.48−2	1.31−1
400.0	2.58−2	7.16−3	7.99−2	2.51−2	1.13−1
500.0	1.39−2	4.65−3	7.33−2	2.53−2	9.18−2
600.0	8.43−3	3.25−3	6.80−2	2.52−2	7.97−2
700.0	5.57−3	2.40−3	6.37−2	2.50−2	7.16−2
800.0	3.91−3	1.85−3	6.00−2	2.47−2	6.57−2
900.0	2.87−3	1.46−3	5.68−2	2.43−2	6.12−2
1,000.0	2.19−3	1.19−3	5.40−2	2.39−2	5.74−2
Tin	**Z = 50**				
0.1	7.16+3	8.43+0	7.55−5	2.01−8	7.17+3
0.1358_{N_I}	4.28+3	8.42+0	1.30−4	4.74−8	4.29+3
0.1372	5.65+3	8.42+0	1.33−4	4.88−8	5.66+3
0.15	6.00+3	8.42+0	1.56−4	6.32−8	6.01+3
0.2	6.94+3	8.41+0	2.70−4	1.46−7	6.95+3
0.3	6.05+3	8.39+0	5.91−4	4.82−7	6.06+3
0.4	4.58+3	8.36+0	1.03−3	1.12−6	4.58+3
$0.4875_{M_{IV,V}}$	3.48+3	8.32+0	1.50−3	1.98−6	3.49+3
0.4889	3.91+3	8.32+0	1.50−3	1.99−6	3.91+3
0.5	6.39+3	8.31+0	1.57−3	2.13−6	6.40+3
0.6	1.73+4	8.26+0	2.19−3	3.56−6	1.73+4
0.7	1.27+4	8.20+0	2.90−3	5.46−6	1.27+4
$0.7277_{M_{II,III}}$	1.17+4	8.18+0	3.10−3	6.07−6	1.17+4
0.7291	1.33+4	8.18+0	3.11−3	6.11−6	1.33+4
0.8	1.21+4	8.13+0	3.66−3	7.86−6	1.21+4
0.8831_{M_I}	9.87+3	8.07+0	4.33−3	1.02−5	9.88+3
0.8845	1.05+4	8.07+0	4.34−3	1.02−5	1.05+4
0.9	1.01+4	8.06+0	4.46−3	1.07−5	1.01+4
1.0	8.13+3	7.98+0	5.30−3	1.41−5	8.14+3

TABLE 3 (continued)

Energy (keV)	τ/ρ (cm^2/g)	σ_c/ρ (cm^2/g)	σ_I/ρ (cm^2/g)	σ_a/ρ (cm^2/g)	μ/ρ (cm^2/g)
2.0	1.65+3	7.08+0	1.41−2	7.16−5	1.66+3
2.5	9.55+2	6.62+0	1.82−2	1.14−4	9.62+2
3.0	6.03+2	6.19+0	2.21−2	1.63−4	6.09+2
3.5	4.43+2	5.77+0	2.57−2	2.19−4	4.49+2
3.929 L_{III}	3.31+2	5.44+0	2.87−2	2.72−4	3.37+2
3.929	1.07+3	5.44+0	2.87−2	2.72−4	1.08+3
4.0	1.02+3	5.39+0	2.92−2	2.81−4	1.03+3
4.156 L_{II}	9.20+2	5.27+0	3.02−2	3.01−4	9.26+2
4.156	1.29+3	5.27+0	3.02−2	3.01−4	1.29+3
4.465 L_I	1.06+3	5.06+0	3.22−2	3.43−4	1.06+3
4.465	1.27+3	5.06+0	3.22−2	3.43−4	1.27+3
5.0	9.28+2	4.71+0	3.55−2	4.22−4	9.33+2
6.0	5.61+2	4.13+0	4.14−2	5.83−4	5.65+2
7.0	3.66+2	3.64+0	4.69−2	7.62−4	3.70+2
8.0	2.53+2	3.24+0	5.20−2	9.57−4	2.57+2
9.0	1.83+2	2.91+0	5.67−2	1.17−3	1.86+2
10.0	1.37+2	2.63+0	6.10−2	1.38−3	1.40+2
12.0	8.28+1	2.19+0	6.88−2	1.84−3	8.50+1
15.0	4.47+1	1.73+0	7.78−2	2.53−3	4.65+1
17.0	3.16+1	1.49+0	8.27−2	3.00−3	3.32+1
20.0	2.02+1	1.21+0	8.87−2	3.70−3	2.15+1
25.0	1.09+1	8.91−1	9.62−2	4.86−3	1.19+1
29.2 K	7.11+0	7.10−1	1.01−1	5.80−3	7.92+0
29.2	4.39+1	7.10−1	1.01−1	5.80−3	4.47+1
30.0	4.09+1	6.83−1	1.02−1	5.98−3	4.17+1
35.0	2.73+1	5.43−1	1.06−1	7.06−3	2.80+1
40.0	1.91+1	4.44−1	1.09−1	8.09−3	1.97+1
50.0	1.04+1	3.14−1	1.12−1	9.97−3	1.08+1
60.0	6.24+0	2.33−1	1.14−1	1.16−2	6.59+0
70.0	4.03+0	1.79−1	1.14−1	1.31−2	4.32+0
80.0	2.75+0	1.42−1	1.14−1	1.43−2	3.00+0
90.0	1.95+0	1.16−1	1.13−1	1.54−2	2.18+0
100.0	1.44+0	9.60−2	1.12−1	1.64−2	1.65+0
120.0	8.46−1	6.95−2	1.10−1	1.81−2	1.03+0
150.0	4.41−1	4.64−2	1.05−1	1.99−2	5.93−1
170.0	3.06−1	3.69−2	1.02−1	2.09−2	4.45−1
200.0	1.90−1	2.73−2	9.85−2	2.20−2	3.16−1
250.0	9.97−2	1.79−2	9.25−2	2.33−2	2.10−1
300.0	5.91−2	1.27−2	8.73−2	2.40−2	1.59−1
350.0	3.82−2	9.44−3	8.28−2	2.45−2	1.30−1
400.0	2.63−2	7.31−3	7.89−2	2.48−2	1.12−1
500.0	1.42−2	4.74−3	7.24−2	2.50−2	9.14−2
600.0	8.74−3	3.32−3	6.72−2	2.49−2	7.93−2
700.0	5.85−3	2.45−3	6.29−2	2.47−2	7.12−2
800.0	4.16−3	1.88−3	5.92−2	2.43−2	6.53−2
900.0	3.10−3	1.49−3	5.61−2	2.40−2	6.07−2
1,000.0	2.40−3	1.21−3	5.33−2	2.36−2	5.69−2

Antimony **Z = 51**

0.1	8.26+3	8.55+0	7.22−5	1.91−8	8.27+3
0.15	4.73+3	8.54+0	1.48−4	5.96−8	4.74+3

TABLE 3 (continued)

Energy (keV)	τ/ρ (cm^2/g)	σ_c/ρ (cm^2/g)	σ_I/ρ (cm^2/g)	σ_a/ρ (cm^2/g)	μ/ρ (cm^2/g)
0.1513 N_I	4.78+3	8.54+0	1.50–4	6.11–8	4.79+3
0.1527	6.02+3	8.54+0	1.53–4	6.28–8	6.03+3
0.2	7.07+3	8.54+0	2.54–4	1.38–7	7.08+3
0.3	6.32+3	8.51+0	5.56–4	4.54–7	6.33+3
0.4	4.82+3	8.47+0	9.68–4	1.05–6	4.83+3
0.5	3.60+3	8.43+0	1.48–3	2.01–6	3.60+3
0.5306 $M_{IV,V}$	3.30+3	8.41+0	1.65–3	2.38–6	3.31+3
0.5320	3.66+3	8.41+0	1.66–3	2.40–6	3.67+3
0.6	1.92+4	8.38+0	2.08–3	3.37–6	1.92+4
0.7	1.34+4	8.32+0	2.75–3	5.18–6	1.34+4
0.7803 $M_{II,III}$	1.07+4	8.27+0	3.33–3	6.98–6	1.07+4
0.7817	1.25+4	8.27+0	3.34–3	7.02–6	1.25+4
0.8	1.25+4	8.25+0	3.48–3	7.47–6	1.25+4
0.9	9.97+3	8.18+0	4.25–3	1.02–5	9.98+3
0.943 M_I	9.06+3	8.14+0	4.59–3	1.15–5	9.07+3
0.9444	9.56+3	8.14+0	4.60–3	1.16–5	9.57+3
1.0	8.53+3	8.10+0	5.06–3	1.34–5	8.54+3
2.0	1.76+3	7.16+0	1.37–2	6.99–5	1.77+3
2.5	1.01+3	6.69+0	1.79–2	1.12–4	1.02+3
3.0	6.42+2	6.24+0	2.19–2	1.62–4	6.48+2
3.5	4.63+2	5.83+0	2.56–2	2.19–4	4.69+2
4.0	3.30+2	5.45+0	2.91–2	2.81–4	3.35+2
4.132 L_{III}	3.04+2	5.35+0	2.99–2	2.98–4	3.09+2
4.132	9.44+2	5.35+0	2.99–2	2.98–4	9.49+2
4.38 L_{II}	8.06+2	5.17+0	3.15–2	3.32–4	8.11+2
4.38	1.13+3	5.17+0	3.15–2	3.32–4	1.13+3
4.698 L_I	9.33+2	4.96+0	3.36–2	3.76–4	9.38+2
4.698	1.12+3	4.96+0	3.36–2	3.76–4	1.12+3
5.0	9.46+2	4.77+0	3.54–2	4.21–4	9.51+2
6.0	5.77+2	4.19+0	4.12–2	5.80–4	5.81+2
7.0	3.80+2	3.70+0	4.65–2	7.56–4	3.83+2
8.0	2.64+2	3.29+0	5.15–2	9.48–4	2.68+2
9.0	1.92+2	2.95+0	5.61–2	1.15–3	1.95+2
10.0	1.44+2	2.67+0	6.04–2	1.37–3	1.47+2
12.0	8.80+1	2.23+0	6.80–2	1.82–3	9.03+1
15.0	4.81+1	1.75+0	7.70–2	2.51–3	4.99+1
17.0	3.42+1	1.52+0	8.19–2	2.97–3	3.58+1
20.0	2.20+1	1.24+0	8.79–2	3.67–3	2.34+1
25.0	1.20+1	9.10–1	9.53–2	4.82–3	1.30+1
30.0	7.34+0	6.98–1	1.01–1	5.93–3	8.13+0
30.49 K	7.02+0	6.81–1	1.01–1	6.03–3	7.80+0
30.49	4.37+1	6.81–1	1.01–1	6.03–3	4.45+1
35.0	3.00+1	5.55–1	1.05–1	7.00–3	3.07+1
40.0	2.08+1	4.54–1	1.08–1	8.02–3	2.13+1
50.0	1.11+1	3.21–1	1.11–1	9.88–3	1.16+1
60.0	6.64+0	2.38–1	1.13–1	1.15–2	6.99+0
70.0	4.28+0	1.83–1	1.13–1	1.30–2	4.58+0
80.0	2.92+0	1.46–1	1.13–1	1.42–2	3.18+0
90.0	2.08+0	1.18–1	1.12–1	1.53–2	2.31+0
100.0	1.53+0	9.84–2	1.11–1	1.63–2	1.74+0
120.0	9.04–1	7.12–2	1.09–1	1.79–2	1.08+0
150.0	4.73–1	4.76–2	1.05–1	1.98–2	6.26–1
170.0	3.30–1	3.79–2	1.02–1	2.08–2	4.69–1

TABLE 3 (continued)

Energy (keV)	τ/ρ (cm²/g)	σ_c/ρ (cm²/g)	σ_I/ρ (cm²/g)	σ_a/ρ (cm²/g)	μ/ρ (cm²/g)
200.0	2.06–1	2.80–2	9.79–2	2.19–2	3.32–1
250.0	1.09–1	1.84–2	9.19–2	2.31–2	2.19–1
300.0	6.47–2	1.30–2	8.68–2	2.39–2	1.64–1
350.0	4.18–2	9.70–3	8.23–2	2.44–2	1.34–1
400.0	2.88–2	7.51–3	7.84–2	2.46–2	1.15–1
500.0	1.56–2	4.88–3	7.20–2	2.48–2	9.24–2
600.0	9.50–3	3.42–3	6.68–2	2.48–2	7.97–2
700.0	6.30–3	2.53–3	6.25–2	2.45–2	7.13–2
800.0	4.45–3	1.94–3	5.89–2	2.42–2	6.52–2
900.0	3.28–3	1.54–3	5.57–2	2.38–2	6.05–2
1,000.0	2.51–3	1.25–3	5.30–2	2.34–2	5.67–2

Tellurium **Z = 52**

Energy (keV)	τ/ρ (cm²/g)	σ_c/ρ (cm²/g)	σ_I/ρ (cm²/g)	σ_a/ρ (cm²/g)	μ/ρ (cm²/g)
0.1	7.22+3	8.48+0	6.56–5	1.74–8	7.23+3
0.1095 $N_{II,III}$	4.00+3	8.48+0	7.67–5	2.24–8	4.01+3
0.1109	6.00+3	8.48+0	7.84–5	2.32–8	6.01+3
0.15	4.66+3	8.48+0	1.36–4	5.48–8	4.67+3
0.1676 N_I	5.18+3	8.47+0	1.68–4	7.61–8	5.19+3
0.169	6.30+3	8.47+0	1.71–4	7.80–8	6.31+3
0.2	7.03+3	8.47+0	2.34–4	1.27–7	7.04+3
0.3	6.43+3	8.44+0	5.13–4	4.18–7	6.44+3
0.4	4.97+3	8.41+0	8.94–4	9.72–7	4.98+3
0.5	3.75+3	8.37+0	1.37–3	1.86–6	3.76+3
0.5756 $M_{IV,V}$	3.06+3	8.33+0	1.79–3	2.79–6	3.07+3
0.577	3.37+3	8.33+0	1.79–3	2.81–6	3.38+3
0.6	2.96+4	8.32+0	1.93–3	3.14–6	2.96+4
0.7	1.38+4	8.25+0	2.56–3	4.85–6	1.38+4
0.8	1.05+4	8.18+0	3.26–3	7.03–6	1.05+4
0.835 $M_{II,III}$	9.56+3	8.16+0	3.51–3	7.89–6	9.57+3
0.8364	1.15+4	8.16+0	3.53–3	7.92–6	1.16+4
0.9	1.02+4	8.11+0	4.00–3	9.64–6	1.02+4
1.0	8.23+3	8.04+0	4.78–3	1.27–5	8.24+3
1.0053 M_I	8.14+3	8.03+0	4.82–3	1.29–5	8.15+3
1.0067	8.57+3	8.03+0	4.83–3	1.30–5	8.58+3
2.0	1.83+3	7.10+0	1.33–2	6.81–5	1.83+3
2.5	1.05+3	6.62+0	1.75–2	1.10–4	1.06+3
3.0	6.68+2	6.17+0	2.14–2	1.59–4	6.74+2
3.5	4.83+2	5.76+0	2.51–2	2.15–4	4.89+2
4.0	3.44+2	5.38+0	2.85–2	2.76–4	3.50+2
4.341 L_{III}	2.80+2	5.14+0	3.07–2	3.20–4	2.85+2
4.341	8.60+2	5.14+0	3.07–2	3.20+4	8.66+2
4.612 L_{II}	7.30+2	4.96+0	3.24–2	3.57–4	7.35+2
4.612	1.02+3	4.96+0	3.24–2	3.57–4	1.03+3
4.939 L_I	8.49+2	4.75+0	3.43–2	4.03–4	8.53+2
4.939	1.02+3	4.75+0	3.43–2	4.03–4	1.02+3
5.0	9.85+2	4.72+0	3.47–2	4.12–4	9.90+2
6.0	6.00+2	4.15+0	4.03–2	5.65–4	6.05+2
7.0	3.95+2	3.67+0	4.54–2	7.35–4	3.99+2
8.0	2.75+2	3.27+0	5.01–2	9.19–4	2.78+2
9.0	2.00+2	2.93+0	5.45–2	1.12–3	2.03+2
10.0	1.50+2	2.65+0	5.86–2	1.32–3	1.53+2
12.0	9.16+1	2.21+0	6.59–2	1.76–3	9.38+1
15.0	5.00+1	1.74+0	7.47–2	2.43–3	5.18+1

TABLE 3 (continued)

Energy (keV)	τ/ρ (cm^2/g)	σ_c/ρ (cm^2/g)	σ_I/ρ (cm^2/g)	σ_a/ρ (cm^2/g)	μ/ρ (cm^2/g)
17.0	3.56+1	1.51+0	7.94−2	2.88−3	3.72+1
20.0	2.29+1	1.23+0	8.52−2	3.56−3	2.42+1
25.0	1.25+1	9.09−1	9.25−2	4.67−3	1.35+1
30.0	7.62+0	6.98−1	9.77−2	5.75−3	8.41+0
31.81_K	6.49+0	6.40−1	9.92−2	6.12−3	7.24+0
31.81	3.99+1	6.40−1	9.92−2	6.12−3	4.06+1
35.0	3.08+1	5.55−1	1.02−1	6.79−3	3.15+1
40.0	2.14+1	4.54−1	1.04−1	7.77−3	2.20+1
50.0	1.16+1	3.21−1	1.08−1	9.59−3	1.20+1
60.0	6.92+0	2.39−1	1.10−1	1.12−2	7.27+0
70.0	4.46+0	1.84−1	1.10−1	1.26−2	4.76+0
80.0	3.04+0	1.46−1	1.10−1	1.38−2	3.30+0
90.0	2.17+0	1.19−1	1.09−1	1.49−2	2.40+0
100.0	1.60+0	9.86−2	1.08−1	1.59−2	1.81+0
120.0	9.43−1	7.14−2	1.06−1	1.74−2	1.12+0
150.0	4.93−1	4.77−2	1.02−1	1.93−2	6.43−1
170.0	3.43−1	3.80−2	9.90−2	2.02−2	4.80−1
200.0	2.14−1	2.81−2	9.52−2	2.13−2	3.38−1
250.0	1.13−1	1.84−2	8.93−2	2.25−2	2.21−1
300.0	6.70−2	1.30−2	8.44−2	2.32−2	1.64−1
350.0	4.34−2	9.73−3	8.00−2	2.37−2	1.33−1
400.0	2.99−2	7.53−3	7.63−2	2.40−2	1.14−1
500.0	1.61−2	4.89−3	7.00−2	2.42−2	9.10−2
600.0	9.87−3	3.43−3	6.49−2	2.41−2	7.83+2
700.0	6.57−3	2.53−3	6.08−2	2.39−2	6.99−2
800.0	4.64−3	1.95−3	5.73−2	2.35−2	6.39−2
900.0	3.44−3	1.54−3	5.42−2	2.32−2	5.92−2
1,000.0	2.64−3	1.25−3	5.15−2	2.28−2	5.54−2

Iodine **Z = 53**

Energy (keV)	τ/ρ (cm^2/g)	σ_c/ρ (cm^2/g)	σ_I/ρ (cm^2/g)	σ_a/ρ (cm^2/g)	μ/ρ (cm^2/g)
0.1	1.04+4	8.86+0	6.25−5	1.67−8	1.05+4
$0.122_{N_{II,III}}$	3.17+3	8.86+0	8.90−5	2.91−8	3.18+3
0.1234	5.20+3	8.86+0	9.09−5	3.01−8	5.21+3
0.15	4.86+3	8.86+0	1.31−4	5.31−8	4.87+3
0.17	5.40+3	8.85+0	1.67−4	7.69−8	5.41+3
0.1857_{N_I}	5.83+3	8.85+0	1.97−4	9.91−8	5.84+3
0.1871	6.89+3	8.85+0	2.00−4	1.01−7	6.90+3
0.2	7.26+3	8.85+0	2.26−4	1.23−7	7.27+3
0.3	6.89+3	8.82+0	4.97−4	4.06−7	6.90+3
0.4	5.40+3	8.78+0	8.68−4	9.46−7	5.41+3
0.5	4.11+3	8.74+0	1.34−3	1.82−6	4.12+3
0.6	3.16+3	8.69+0	1.89−3	3.07−6	3.16+3
$0.6235_{M_{IV,V}}$	2.97+3	8.68+0	2.02−3	3.42−6	2.98+3
0.6249	3.28+3	8.68+0	2.03−3	3.44−6	3.29+3
0.7	1.56+4	8.63+0	2.51−3	4.76−6	1.56+4
0.75	1.31+4	8.59+0	2.85−3	5.79−6	1.31+4
0.8	1.14+4	8.56+0	3.21−3	6.92−6	1.14+4
$0.8925_{M_{II,III}}$	9.03+3	8.49+0	3.88−3	9.31−6	9.04+3
0.8939	1.13+4	8.49+0	3.89−3	9.35−6	1.13+4
0.9	1.13+4	8.49+0	3.94−3	9.52−6	1.13+4
1.0	8.92+3	8.40+0	4.72−3	1.26−5	8.93+3
1.0713_{M_I}	7.72+3	8.33+0	5.29−3	1.51−5	7.73+3

TABLE 3 (continued)

Energy (keV)	τ/ρ (cm^2/g)	σ_c/ρ (cm^2/g)	σ_I/ρ (cm^2/g)	σ_a/ρ (cm^2/g)	μ/ρ (cm^2/g)
1.0727	8.12+3	8.33+0	5.30-3	1.52-5	8.12+3
2.0	1.99+3	7.42+0	1.35-2	6.93-5	2.00+3
3.0	7.30+2	6.44+0	2.19-2	1.64-4	7.37+2
3.5	5.26+2	6.00+0	2.58-2	2.22-4	5.32+2
4.0	3.75+2	5.60+0	2.94-2	2.86-4	3.80+2
4.557 L_{III}	2.69+2	5.21+0	3.30-2	3.61-4	2.74+2
4.557	8.21+2	5.21+0	3.30-2	3.61-4	8.26+2
4.852 L_{II}	6.92+2	5.01+0	3.48-2	4.03-4	6.97+2
4.852	9.69+2	5.01+0	3.48-2	4.03-4	9.74+2
5.0	8.93+2	4.92+0	3.58-2	4.25-4	8.97+2
5.188 L_I	8.07+2	4.80+0	3.69-2	4.54-4	8.12+2
5.188	9.69+2	4.80+0	3.69-2	4.54-4	9.73+2
6.0	6.52+2	4.34+0	4.14-2	5.82-4	6.56+2
7.0	4.28+2	3.84+0	4.66-2	7.54-4	4.32+2
8.0	2.98+2	3.42+0	5.13-2	9.41-4	3.01+2
9.0	2.16+2	3.07+0	5.58-2	1.14-3	2.19+2
10.0	1.62+2	2.77+0	5.99-2	1.35-3	1.65+2
12.0	9.86+1	2.31+0	6.73-2	1.79-3	1.01+2
15.0	5.37+1	1.82+0	7.63-2	2.48-3	5.56+1
17.0	3.82+1	1.58+0	8.12-2	2.95-3	3.98+1
20.0	2.45+1	1.29+0	8.71-2	3.64-3	2.59+1
25.0	1.33+1	9.56-1	9.44-2	4.77-3	1.44+1
30.0	8.12+0	7.34-1	9.98-2	5.88-3	8.96+0
33.17 K	6.18+0	6.32-1	1.02-1	6.54-3	6.91+0
33.17	3.84+1	6.32-1	1.02-1	6.54-3	3.91+1
35.0	3.31+1	5.83-1	1.04-1	6.93-3	3.38+1
40.0	2.29+1	4.77-1	1.07-1	7.94-3	2.35+1
50.0	1.22+1	3.38-1	1.10-1	9.80-3	1.27+1
60.0	7.31+0	2.52-1	1.12-1	1.14-2	7.67+0
70.0	4.71+0	1.94-1	1.13-1	1.29-2	5.02+0
80.0	3.22+0	1.54-1	1.12-1	1.41-2	3.48+0
90.0	2.29+0	1.25-1	1.12-1	1.53-2	2.53+0
100.0	1.69+0	1.04-1	1.11-1	1.62-2	1.91+0
120.0	1.00+0	7.54-2	1.08-1	1.79-2	1.19+0
150.0	5.28-1	5.04-2	1.04-1	1.97-2	6.82-1
170.0	3.68-1	4.01-2	1.01-1	2.07-2	5.10-1
200.0	2.31-1	2.97-2	9.74-2	2.18-2	3.58-1
250.0	1.22-1	1.95-2	9.15-2	2.30-2	2.33-1
300.0	7.32-2	1.38-2	8.64-2	2.38-2	1.73-1
350.0	4.76-2	1.03-2	8.20-2	2.43-2	1.40-1
400.0	3.28-2	7.97-3	7.81-2	2.46-2	1.19-1
500.0	1.78-2	5.17-3	7.17-2	2.48-2	9.47-2
600.0	1.09-2	3.62-3	6.65-2	2.47-2	8.11-2
700.0	7.24-3	2.68-3	6.23-2	2.44-2	7.22-2
800.0	5.11-3	2.06-3	5.87-2	2.41-2	6.58-2
900.0	3.78-3	1.63-3	5.55-2	2.38-2	6.09-2
1,000.0	2.89-3	1.32-3	5.28-2	2.34-2	5.70-2

Xenon **Z = 54**

Energy (keV)	τ/ρ (cm^2/g)	σ_c/ρ (cm^2/g)	σ_I/ρ (cm^2/g)	σ_a/ρ (cm^2/g)	μ/ρ (cm^2/g)
0.1	1.84+4	8.89+0	5.92-5	1.57-8	1.84+4
0.146 $N_{II,III}$	2.70+3	8.88+0	1.16-4	4.58-8	2.71+3
0.1474	5.00+3	8.88+0	1.19-4	4.71-8	5.00+3

TABLE 3 (continued)

Energy (keV)	τ/ρ (cm^2/g)	σ_c/ρ (cm^2/g)	σ_I/ρ (cm^2/g)	σ_a/ρ (cm^2/g)	μ/ρ (cm^2/g)
0.15	5.11+3	8.88+0	1.22−4	4.95−8	5.12+3
0.17	5.45+3	8.88+0	1.56−4	7.16−8	5.46+3
0.2	6.18+3	8.88+0	2.11−4	1.14−7	6.19+3
0.2073 N_I	6.32+3	8.88+0	2.26−4	1.27−7	6.33+3
0.2087	7.31+3	8.88+0	2.29−4	1.30−7	7.32+3
0.3	7.25+3	8.85+0	4.64−4	3.79−7	7.26+3
0.4	5.76+3	8.82+0	8.11−4	8.83−7	5.77+3
0.5	4.41+3	8.77+0	1.25−3	1.70−6	4.42+3
0.6	3.40+3	8.72+0	1.77−3	2.87−6	3.41+3
0.6767 $M_{IV,V}$	2.81+3	8.68+0	2.21−3	4.05−6	2.82+3
0.6781	3.17+3	8.68+0	2.22−3	4.07−6	3.17+3
0.7	2.35+4	8.66+0	2.36−3	4.46−6	2.35+4
0.75	1.43+4	8.63+0	2.68−3	5.44−6	1.43+4
0.8	1.21+4	8.60+0	3.01−3	6.51−6	1.21+4
0.9	9.42+3	8.52+0	3.71−3	8.97−6	9.43+3
0.957 $M_{II,III}$	8.22+3	8.48+0	4.13−3	1.06−5	8.23+3
0.9584	1.08+4	8.47+0	4.14−3	1.06−5	1.08+4
1.0	9.37+3	8.44+0	4.45−3	1.19−5	9.38+3
1.1443 M_I	7.06+3	8.31+0	5.57−3	1.70−5	7.07+3
1.1457	7.41+3	8.31+0	5.58−3	1.70−5	7.42+3
2.0	2.11+3	7.45+0	1.29−2	6.65−5	2.11+3
3.0	7.72+2	6.45+0	2.13−2	1.60−4	7.78+2
3.5	5.36+2	6.01+0	2.52−2	2.18−4	5.42+2
4.0	3.84+2	5.61+0	2.88−2	2.81−4	3.90+2
4.782 L_{III}	2.46+2	5.06+0	3.39−2	3.89−4	2.51+2
4.782	7.32+2	5.06+0	3.39−2	3.89−4	7.37+2
5.0	6.49+2	4.92+0	3.52−2	4.21−4	6.54+2
5.104 L_{II}	6.13+2	4.86+0	3.58−2	4.36−4	6.18+2
5.104	8.59+2	4.86+0	3.58−2	4.36−4	8.64+2
5.453 L_I	7.17+2	4.65+0	3.78−2	4.89−4	7.22+2
5.543	8.61+2	4.65+0	3.78−2	4.89−4	8.66+2
6.0	6.64+2	4.35+0	4.08−2	5.75−4	6.69+2
7.0	4.37+2	3.86+0	4.59−2	7.44−4	4.41+2
8.0	3.04+2	3.44+0	5.05−2	9.26−4	3.08+2
9.0	2.21+2	3.09+0	5.48−2	1.12−3	2.24+2
10.0	1.66+2	2.79+0	5.88−2	1.32−3	1.69+2
12.0	1.01+2	2.32+0	6.61−2	1.76−3	1.04+2
15.0	5.52+1	1.83+0	7.49−2	2.43−3	5.71+1
17.0	3.93+1	1.59+0	7.96−2	2.89−3	4.10+1
20.0	2.53+1	1.30+0	8.55−2	3.57−3	2.67+1
25.0	1.38+1	9.65−1	9.27−2	4.69−3	1.49+1
30.0	8.41+0	7.42−1	9.80−2	5.77−3	9.25+0
34.56 K	5.72+0	6.00−1	1.02−1	6.72−3	6.43+0
34.56	3.46+1	6.00−1	1.02−1	6.72−3	3.53+1
35.0	3.34+1	5.89−1	1.02−1	6.81−3	3.41+1
40.0	2.32+1	4.83−1	1.05−1	7.80−3	2.38+1
50.0	1.25+1	3.41−1	1.08−1	9.63−3	1.30+1
60.0	7.52+0	2.54−1	1.10−1	1.12−2	7.88+0
70.0	4.86+0	1.96−1	1.11−1	1.27−2	5.17+0
80.0	3.33+0	1.56−1	1.10−1	1.39−2	3.59+0
90.0	2.38+0	1.27−1	1.10−1	1.50−2	2.61+0
100.0	1.76+0	1.05−1	1.09−1	1.60−2	1.97+0

TABLE 3 (continued)

Energy (keV)	τ/ρ (cm^2/g)	σ_c/ρ (cm^2/g)	σ_I/ρ (cm^2/g)	σ_a/ρ (cm^2/g)	μ/ρ (cm^2/g)
120.0	1.04+0	7.63−2	1.06−1	1.76−2	1.23+0
150.0	5.50−1	5.10−2	1.02−1	1.94−2	7.03−1
170.0	3.84−1	4.06−2	9.97−2	2.03−2	5.24−1
200.0	2.41−1	3.00−2	9.58−2	2.14−2	3.67−1
250.0	1.28−1	1.98−2	9.01−2	2.27−2	2.38−1
300.0	7.65−2	1.40−2	8.50−2	2.34−2	1.75−1
350.0	4.97−2	1.04−2	8.07−2	2.39−2	1.41−1
400.0	3.43−2	8.09−3	7.69−2	2.42−2	1.19−1
500.0	1.87−2	5.27−3	7.06−2	2.44−2	9.45−2
600.0	1.14−2	3.69−3	6.55−2	2.43−2	8.06−2
700.0	7.62−3	2.73−3	6.13−2	2.41−2	7.16−2
800.0	5.39−3	2.10−3	5.77−2	2.38−2	6.52−2
900.0	3.99−3	1.67−3	5.47−2	2.34−2	6.03−2
1,000.0	3.06−3	1.35−3	5.20−2	2.30−2	5.64−2

Cesium **Z = 55**

Energy (keV)	τ/ρ (cm^2/g)	σ_c/ρ (cm^2/g)	σ_I/ρ (cm^2/g)	σ_a/ρ (cm^2/g)	μ/ρ (cm^2/g)
0.1	2.06+4	9.11+0	1.19−4	3.16−8	2.06+4
0.15	2.90+3	9.09+0	2.44−4	9.83−8	2.91+3
0.1645 $N_{II,III}$	3.06+3	9.09+0	2.90−4	1.29−7	3.06+3
0.1659	5.79+3	9.09+0	2.95−4	1.32−7	5.80+3
0.17	5.64+3	9.09+0	3.09−4	1.42−7	5.65+3
0.2	6.22+3	9.09+0	4.16−4	2.24−7	6.23+3
0.2301 N_I	6.67+3	9.07+0	5.40−4	3.36−7	6.68+3
0.2315	7.65+3	9.07+0	5.46−4	3.42−7	7.66+3
0.3	7.44+3	9.05+0	8.82−4	7.14−7	7.45+3
0.4	6.01+3	9.00+0	1.47−3	1.58−6	6.02+3
0.5	4.65+3	8.94+0	2.15−3	2.86−6	4.66+3
0.6	3.61+3	8.87+0	2.86−3	4.54−6	3.62+3
0.7	2.83+3	8.79+0	3.61−3	6.62−6	2.84+3
0.7304 $M_{IV,V}$	2.64+3	8.76+0	3.84−3	7.32−6	2.65+3
0.75	1.78+4	8.75+0	3.98−3	7.80−6	1.78+4
0.8	1.31+4	8.71+0	4.36−3	9.08−6	1.31+4
0.9	9.93+3	8.62+0	5.13−3	1.19−5	9.94+3
1.0	7.88+3	8.53+0	5.90−3	1.52−5	7.89+3
1.0193 $M_{II,III}$	7.56+3	8.51+0	6.05−3	1.58−5	7.57+3
1.0207	1.02+4	8.51+0	6.06−3	1.59−5	1.02+4
1.2163 M_I	6.52+3	8.33+0	7.59−3	2.35−5	6.53+3
1.2177	6.87+3	8.33+0	7.61−3	2.36−5	6.88+3
2.0	2.25+3	7.54+0	1.40−2	7.03−5	2.25+3
3.0	8.27+2	6.56+0	2.21−2	1.63−4	8.34+2
3.5	5.85+2	6.12+0	2.59−2	2.21−4	5.92+2
4.0	4.16+2	5.71+0	2.95−2	2.85−4	4.22+2
5.0	2.35+2	5.02+0	3.59−2	4.26−4	2.40+2
5.012 L_{III}	2.33+2	5.01+0	3.60−2	4.28−4	2.38+2
5.012	7.00+2	5.01+0	3.60−2	4.28−4	7.05+2
5.359 L_{II}	5.83+2	4.79+0	3.80−2	4.80−4	5.88+2
5.359	8.17+2	4.79+0	3.80−2	4.80−4	8.22+2
5.714 L_I	6.86+2	4.59+0	3.99−2	5.36−4	6.91+2
5.714	8.23+2	4.59+0	3.99−2	5.36−4	8.28+2
6.0	7.20+2	4.43+0	4.15−2	5.82−4	7.25+2
7.0	4.74+2	3.94+0	4.65−2	7.51−4	4.78+2
8.0	3.29+2	3.52+0	5.11−2	9.32−4	3.33+2

TABLE 3 (continued)

Energy (keV)	τ/ρ (cm²/g)	σ_c/ρ (cm²/g)	σ_I/ρ (cm²/g)	σ_a/ρ (cm²/g)	μ/ρ (cm²/g)
9.0	2.39+2	3.16+0	5.53−2	1.13−3	2.42+2
10.0	1.79+2	2.86+0	5.93−2	1.33−3	1.82+2
12.0	1.09+2	2.38+0	6.64−2	1.76−3	1.12+2
15.0	5.95+1	1.88+0	7.51−2	2.44−3	6.15+1
17.0	4.24+1	1.63+0	7.99−2	2.90−3	4.41+1
20.0	2.72+1	1.34+0	8.58−2	3.58−3	2.86+1
25.0	1.48+1	9.94−1	9.31−2	4.70−3	1.59+1
30.0	9.03+0	7.64−1	9.83−2	5.79−3	9.90+0
35.0	5.94+0	6.08−1	1.02−1	6.83−3	6.65+0
35.98_K	5.51+0	5.83−1	1.03−1	7.03−3	6.19+0
35.98	3.39+1	5.83−1	1.03−1	7.03−3	3.46+1
40.0	2.52+1	4.98−1	1.05−1	7.83−3	2.58+1
50.0	1.35+1	3.52−1	1.09−1	9.66−3	1.40+1
60.0	8.05+0	2.63−1	1.10−1	1.13−2	8.43+0
70.0	5.19+0	2.03−1	1.11−1	1.27−2	5.51+0
80.0	3.55+0	1.61−1	1.11−1	1.40−2	3.82+0
90.0	2.53+0	1.31−1	1.10−1	1.51−2	2.77+0
100.0	1.87+0	1.09−1	1.09−1	1.60−2	2.09+0
120.0	1.11+0	7.89−2	1.07−1	1.77−2	1.30+0
150.0	5.85−1	5.27−2	1.03−1	1.95−2	7.41−1
170.0	4.09−1	4.20−2	1.00−1	2.05−2	5.51−1
200.0	2.57−1	3.11−2	9.63−2	2.16−2	3.85−1
250.0	1.37−1	2.05−2	9.06−2	2.28−2	2.48−1
300.0	8.20−2	1.45−2	8.56−2	2.36−2	1.82−1
350.0	5.34−2	1.08−2	8.12−2	2.41−2	1.45−1
400.0	3.69−2	8.38−3	7.74−2	2.43−2	1.23−1
500.0	2.01−2	5.45−3	7.10−2	2.45−2	9.66−2
600.0	1.23−2	3.82−3	6.59−2	2.45−2	8.21−2
700.0	8.22−3	2.82−3	6.17−2	2.42−2	7.27−2
800.0	5.81−3	2.17−3	5.81−2	2.39−2	6.61−2
900.0	4.30−3	1.72−3	5.50−2	2.35−2	6.10−2
1,000.0	3.29−3	1.40−3	5.23−2	2.31−2	5.71−2
Barium	**Z = 56**				
0.1	1.55+4	9.13+0	1.35−4	3.58−8	1.55+4
0.15	3.14+3	9.13+0	2.78−4	1.12−7	3.15+3
0.17	3.31+3	9.12+0	3.52−4	1.62−7	3.32+3
$0.183_{N_{II,III}}$	3.61+3	9.12+0	4.03−4	1.99−7	3.61+3
0.1844	5.83+3	9.12+0	4.09−4	2.04−7	5.84+3
0.2	6.20+3	9.11+0	4.75−4	2.56−7	6.21+3
0.2523_{N_I}	6.76+3	9.09+0	7.35−4	5.02−7	6.77+3
0.2537	7.81+3	9.09+0	7.42−4	5.10−7	7.82+3
0.3	7.46+3	9.07+0	1.01−3	8.22−7	7.47+3
0.4	6.10+3	9.02+0	1.71−3	1.84−6	6.11+3
0.5	4.77+3	8.95+0	2.51−3	3.35−6	4.78+3
0.6	3.72+3	8.87+0	3.37−3	5.35−6	3.73+3
0.7	2.94+3	8.79+0	4.25−3	7.81−6	2.95+3
0.75	2.62+3	8.74+0	4.69−3	9.19−6	2.63+3
$0.7862_{M_{IV,V}}$	2.42+3	8.71+0	5.01−3	1.03−5	2.43+3
0.7876	3.86+3	8.70+0	5.02−3	1.03−5	3.87+3
0.8	1.28+4	8.70+0	5.13−3	1.07−5	1.28+4

TABLE 3 (continued)

Energy (keV)	τ/ρ (cm²/g)	σ_c/ρ (cm²/g)	σ_I/ρ (cm²/g)	σ_a/ρ (cm²/g)	μ/ρ (cm²/g)
0.9	1.02+4	8.60+0	6.01−3	1.40−5	1.03+4
1.0	8.16+3	8.50+0	6.86−3	1.76−5	8.17+3
1.0863 $M_{II,III}$	6.78+3	8.41+0	7.57−3	2.09−5	6.79+3
1.0877	8.31+3	8.41+0	7.59−3	2.10−5	8.31+3
1.2923 M_I	5.90+3	8.19+0	9.27−3	3.01−5	5.91+3
1.2937	6.28+3	8.19+0	9.28−3	3.02−5	6.29+3
2.0	2.34+3	7.48+0	1.49−2	7.34−5	2.34+3
3.0	8.64+2	6.53+0	2.26−2	1.64−4	8.70+2
3.5	6.11+2	6.10+0	2.62−2	2.21−4	6.17+2
4.0	4.35+2	5.70+0	2.96−2	2.84−4	4.41+2
5.0	2.46+2	5.00+0	3.59−2	4.23−4	2.51+2
5.247 L_{III}	2.18+2	4.85+0	3.73−2	4.60−4	2.22+2
5.247	6.43+2	4.85+0	3.73−2	4.60−4	6.48+2
5.624 L_{II}	5.32+2	4.63+0	3.94−2	5.18−4	5.37+2
5.624	7.45+2	4.63+0	3.94−2	5.18−4	7.50+2
5.989 L_I	6.28+2	4.43+0	4.13−2	5.75−4	6.33+2
5.989	7.54+2	4.43+0	4.13−2	5.75−4	7.59+2
6.0	7.50+2	4.43+0	4.13−2	5.77−4	7.55+2
7.0	4.93+2	3.94+0	4.62−2	7.43−4	4.97+2
8.0	3.43+2	3.53+0	5.06−2	9.20−4	3.46+2
9.0	2.49+2	3.17+0	5.47−2	1.11−3	2.52+2
10.0	1.87+2	2.87+0	5.85−2	1.31−3	1.90+2
12.0	1.14+2	2.39+0	6.54−2	1.73−3	1.16+2
15.0	6.20+1	1.88+0	7.39−2	2.39−3	6.39+1
17.0	4.41+1	1.63+0	7.86−2	2.85−3	4.58+1
20.0	2.83+1	1.34+0	8.44−2	3.52−3	2.98+1
25.0	1.54+1	1.00+0	9.15−2	4.62−3	1.65+1
30.0	9.40+0	7.71−1	9.66−2	5.69−3	1.03+1
35.0	6.18+0	6.13−1	1.00−1	6.71−3	6.89+0
37.44 K	5.14+0	5.54−1	1.02−1	7.19−3	5.80+0
37.44	3.12+1	5.54−1	1.02−1	7.19−3	3.19+1
40.0	2.60+1	5.02−1	1.03−1	7.69−3	2.66+1
50.0	1.39+1	3.55−1	1.07−1	9.50−3	1.44+1
60.0	8.32+0	2.65−1	1.09−1	1.11−2	8.70+0
70.0	5.37+0	2.05−1	1.09−1	1.25−2	5.69+0
80.0	3.67+0	1.63−1	1.09−1	1.37−2	3.94+0
90.0	2.62+0	1.33−1	1.08−1	1.48−2	2.86+0
100.0	1.94+0	1.10−1	1.08−1	1.58−2	2.16+0
120.0	1.15+0	7.99−2	1.05−1	1.74−2	1.34+0
150.0	6.09−1	5.34−2	1.01−1	1.92−2	7.63−1
170.0	4.26−1	4.25−2	9.86−2	2.01−2	5.67−1
200.0	2.68−1	3.15−2	9.48−2	2.12−2	3.95−1
250.0	1.43−1	2.07−2	8.92−2	2.25−2	2.53−1
300.0	8.58−2	1.47−2	8.42−2	2.32−2	1.85−1
350.0	5.59−2	1.10−2	7.99−2	2.37−2	1.47−1
400.0	3.87−2	8.49−3	7.62−2	2.40−2	1.23−1
500.0	2.11−2	5.52−3	6.99−2	2.42−2	9.66−2
600.0	1.30−2	3.87−3	6.49−2	2.41−2	8.17−2
700.0	8.64−3	2.86−3	6.07−2	2.39−2	7.22−2
800.0	6.11−3	2.20−3	5.72−2	2.36−2	6.56−2
900.0	4.53−3	1.74−3	5.42−2	2.32−2	6.05−2
1,000.0	3.47−3	1.42−3	5.16−2	2.28−2	5.64−2

TABLE 3 (continued)

Lanthanum **Z = 57**

Energy (keV)	τ/ρ (cm^2/g)	σ_c/ρ (cm^2/g)	σ_I/ρ (cm^2/g)	σ_a/ρ (cm^2/g)	μ/ρ (cm^2/g)
0.1	6.04+3	9.36+0	1.28–4	3.41–8	6.05+3
0.15	3.21+3	9.35+0	2.64–4	1.07–7	3.22+3
0.1955 $N_{II,III}$	3.95+3	9.33+0	4.33–4	2.29–7	3.96+3
0.1969	6.00+3	9.33+0	4.39–4	2.33–7	6.00+3
0.2	6.13+3	9.33+0	4.52–4	2.44–7	6.14+3
0.23	6.63+3	9.32+0	5.88–4	3.66–7	6.64+3
0.2697 N_I	6.77+3	9.31+0	7.94–4	5.80–7	6.78+3
0.2711	7.79+3	9.31+0	8.02–4	5.88–7	7.80+3
0.3	7.50+3	9.30+0	9.70–4	7.87–7	7.51+3
0.4	6.21+3	9.24+0	1.64–3	1.77–6	6.22+3
0.5	4.91+3	9.17+0	2.43–3	3.26–6	4.92+3
0.6	3.86+3	9.10+0	3.29–3	5.25–6	3.87+3
0.7	3.07+3	9.01+0	4.18–3	7.73–6	3.08+3
0.8	2.47+3	8.91+0	5.09–3	1.06–5	2.48+3
0.8377 $M_{IV,V}$	2.28+3	8.88+0	5.43–3	1.19–5	2.29+3
0.8391	3.01+3	8.87+0	5.45–3	1.19–5	3.02+3
0.9	1.07+4	8.82+0	6.00–3	1.40–5	1.07+4
0.95	9.49+3	8.77+0	6.45–3	1.58–5	9.50+3
1.0	8.50+3	8.71+0	6.89–3	1.77–5	8.51+3
1.1493 $M_{II,III}$	6.24+3	8.55+0	8.18–3	2.39–5	6.25+3
1.1507	7.56+3	8.55+0	8.19–3	2.40–5	7.57+3
1.3603 M_I	5.51+3	8.32+0	9.95–3	3.40–5	5.51+3
1.3617	5.88+3	8.32+0	9.96–3	3.41–5	5.89+3
2.0	2.46+3	7.64+0	1.52–2	7.46–5	2.47+3
3.0	9.17+2	6.66+0	2.28–2	1.66–4	9.23+2
4.0	4.41+2	5.81+0	2.99–2	2.86–4	4.47+2
5.0	2.62+2	5.10+0	3.62–2	4.27–4	2.67+2
5.483 L_{III}	2.07+2	4.81+0	3.90–2	5.01–4	2.12+2
5.483	6.12+2	4.81+0	3.90–2	5.01–4	6.17+2
5.891 L_{II}	5.03+2	4.58+0	4.12–2	5.65–4	5.07+2
5.891	7.04+2	4.58+0	4.12–2	5.65–4	7.08+2
6.0	6.69+2	4.52+0	4.18–2	5.83–4	6.74+2
6.266 L_I	5.94+2	4.38+0	4.31–2	6.26–4	5.99+2
6.266	7.13+2	4.38+0	4.31–2	6.26–4	7.18+2
7.0	5.27+2	4.03+0	4.67–2	7.50–4	5.31+2
8.0	3.65+2	3.61+0	5.10–2	9.28–4	3.69+2
9.0	2.64+2	3.25+0	5.51–2	1.12–3	2.68+2
10.0	1.98+2	2.94+0	5.89–2	1.31–3	2.01+2
12.0	1.20+2	2.45+0	6.57–2	1.74–3	1.23+2
15.0	6.52+1	1.93+0	7.42–2	2.40–3	6.72+1
17.0	4.63+1	1.67+0	7.89–2	2.85–3	4.80+1
20.0	2.97+1	1.38+0	8.47–2	3.53–3	3.11+1
25.0	1.61+1	1.03+0	9.19–2	4.64–3	1.72+1
30.0	9.76+0	7.95–1	9.70–2	5.71–3	1.07+1
35.0	6.40+0	6.32–1	1.01–1	6.74–3	7.13+0
38.92 K	4.78+0	5.39–1	1.03–1	7.51–3	5.42+0
38.92	2.91+1	5.39–1	1.03–1	7.51–3	2.98+1
40.0	2.70+1	5.18–1	1.04–1	7.72–3	2.77+1
50.0	1.46+1	3.66–1	1.07–1	9.53–3	1.51+1
60.0	8.81+0	2.74–1	1.09–1	1.11–2	9.19+0

TABLE 3 (continued)

Energy (keV)	τ/ρ (cm^2/g)	σ_c/ρ (cm^2/g)	σ_I/ρ (cm^2/g)	σ_a/ρ (cm^2/g)	μ/ρ (cm^2/g)
70.0	5.71+0	2.12−1	1.10−1	1.26−2	6.03+0
80.0	3.92+0	1.68−1	1.10−1	1.38−2	4.19+0
90.0	2.81+0	1.37−1	1.09−1	1.49−2	3.05+0
100.0	2.08+0	1.14−1	1.08−1	1.59−2	2.30+0
120.0	1.24+0	8.25−2	1.06−1	1.75−2	1.43+0
150.0	6.55−1	5.52−2	1.02−1	1.93−2	8.12−1
170.0	4.58−1	4.40−2	9.92−2	2.03−2	6.02−1
200.0	2.89−1	3.26−2	9.54−2	2.14−2	4.17−1
250.0	1.54−1	2.14−2	8.97−2	2.26−2	2.65−1
300.0	9.23−2	1.52−2	8.47−2	2.34−2	1.92−1
350.0	6.01−2	1.13−2	8.04−2	2.38−2	1.52−1
400.0	4.16−2	8.79−3	7.67−2	2.41−2	1.27−1
500.0	2.27−2	5.72−3	7.04−2	2.43−2	9.88−2
600.0	1.39−2	4.01−3	6.53−2	2.42−2	8.32−2
700.0	9.30−3	2.96−3	6.11−2	2.40−2	7.34−2
800.0	6.58−3	2.28−3	5.76−2	2.37−2	6.64−2
900.0	4.88−3	1.81−3	5.45−2	2.33−2	6.12−2
1,000.0	3.74−3	1.47−3	5.19−2	2.29−2	5.71−2

Cerium Z = 58

Energy (keV)	τ/ρ (cm^2/g)	σ_c/ρ (cm^2/g)	σ_I/ρ (cm^2/g)	σ_a/ρ (cm^2/g)	μ/ρ (cm^2/g)
0.1	8.76+3	9.60+0	1.24−4	3.29−8	8.76+3
0.1093 $N_{IV,V}$	8.08+3	9.60+0	1.44−4	4.20−8	8.09+3
0.1107	1.29+4	9.60+0	1.47−4	4.35−8	1.29+4
0.15	8.16+3	9.59+0	2.55−4	1.03−7	8.17+3
0.2	6.09+3	9.58+0	4.37−4	2.36−7	6.10+3
0.2119 $N_{II,III}$	6.08+3	9.58+0	4.88−4	2.80−7	6.09+3
0.2133	8.26+3	9.58+0	4.94−4	2.85−7	8.27+3
0.23	8.28+3	9.57+0	5.70−4	3.55−7	8.29+3
0.2889 N_I	7.89+3	9.55+0	8.76−4	6.85−7	7.90+3
0.2903	8.89+3	9.55+0	8.84−4	6.95−7	8.90+3
0.3	8.70+3	9.54+0	9.40−4	7.63−7	8.71+3
0.4	7.00+3	9.49+0	1.59−3	1.72−6	7.01+3
0.5	5.45+3	9.42+0	2.36−3	3.17−6	5.46+3
0.6	4.25+3	9.35+0	3.20−3	5.11−6	4.26+3
0.7	3.35+3	9.26+0	4.08−3	7.53−6	3.36+3
0.8	2.69+3	9.17+0	4.96−3	1.04−5	2.70+3
0.8898 $M_{IV,V}$	2.23+3	9.08+0	5.77−3	1.33−5	2.24+3
0.8912	3.10+3	9.08+0	5.78−3	1.34−5	3.11+3
0.9	9.29+3	9.07+0	5.86−3	1.37−5	9.30+3
0.95	1.07+4	9.02+0	6.30−3	1.55−5	1.07+4
1.0	9.45+3	8.97+0	6.74−3	1.74−5	9.46+3
1.2143 $M_{II,III}$	6.06+3	8.73+0	8.56−3	2.64−5	6.07+3
1.2157	7.48+3	8.73+0	8.57−3	2.65−5	7.49+3
1.4343 M_I	5.34+3	8.49+0	1.04−2	3.73−5	5.35+3
1.4357	5.69+3	8.49+0	1.04−2	3.74−5	5.70+3
2.0	2.67+3	7.89+0	1.49−2	7.35−5	2.67+3
3.0	9.90+2	6.89+0	2.26−2	1.64−4	9.97+2
4.0	4.75+2	6.01+0	2.96−2	2.84−4	4.81+2
5.0	2.79+2	5.29+0	3.60−2	4.25−4	2.84+2
5.723 L_{III}	1.97+2	4.84+0	4.01−2	5.37−4	2.02+2
5.723	5.76+2	4.84+0	4.01−2	5.37−4	5.81+2

TABLE 3 (continued)

Energy (keV)	τ/ρ (cm^2/g)	σ_c/ρ (cm^2/g)	σ_I/ρ (cm^2/g)	σ_a/ρ (cm^2/g)	μ/ρ (cm^2/g)
6.0	5.07+2	4.68+0	4.16−2	5.82−4	5.11+2
6.164 L_{II}	4.71+2	4.59+0	4.24−2	6.08−4	4.75+2
6.164	6.59+2	4.59+0	4.24−2	6.08−4	6.64+2
6.549 L_I	5.59+2	4.39+0	4.44−2	6.73−4	5.63+2
6.549	6.71+2	4.39+0	4.44−2	6.73−4	6.75+2
7.0	5.59+2	4.17+0	4.65−2	7.50−4	5.63+2
8.0	3.89+2	3.73+0	5.09−2	9.28−4	3.92+2
9.0	2.82+2	3.36+0	5.50−2	1.12−3	2.85+2
10.0	2.11+2	3.04+0	5.88−2	1.31−3	2.15+2
12.0	1.29+2	2.53+0	6.57−2	1.74−3	1.31+2
15.0	7.00+1	1.99+0	7.43−2	2.40−3	7.21+1
17.0	4.98+1	1.73+0	7.90−2	2.86−3	5.16+1
20.0	3.20+1	1.42+0	8.49−2	3.55−3	3.35+1
25.0	1.74+1	1.07+0	9.22−2	4.66−3	1.86+1
30.0	1.06+1	8.23−1	9.75−2	5.74−3	1.15+1
35.0	6.95+0	6.54−1	1.01−1	6.78−3	7.71+0
40.0	4.83+0	5.36−1	1.04−1	7.77−3	5.47+0
40.44 K	4.69+0	5.27−1	1.04−1	7.85−3	5.32+0
40.44	2.88+1	5.27−1	1.04−1	7.85−3	2.94+1
50.0	1.58+1	3.79−1	1.08−1	9.60−3	1.63+1
60.0	9.41+0	2.83−1	1.10−1	1.12−2	9.80+0
70.0	6.06+0	2.19−1	1.10−1	1.26−2	6.39+0
80.0	4.14+0	1.74−1	1.10−1	1.39−2	4.42+0
90.0	2.95+0	1.42−1	1.10−1	1.50−2	3.21+0
100.0	2.19+0	1.18−1	1.09−1	1.60−2	2.41+0
120.0	1.30+0	8.55−2	1.07−1	1.76−2	1.49+0
150.0	6.87−1	5.72−2	1.03−1	1.95−2	8.46−1
170.0	4.81−1	4.56−2	9.99−2	2.04−2	6.27−1
200.0	3.04−1	3.38−2	9.61−2	2.15−2	4.34−1
250.0	1.62−1	2.22−2	9.04−2	2.28−2	2.75−1
300.0	9.77−2	1.58−2	8.54−2	2.36−2	1.99−1
350.0	6.38−2	1.18−2	8.11−2	2.40−2	1.57−1
400.0	4.43−2	9.13−3	7.73−2	2.43−2	1.31−1
500.0	2.42−2	5.94−3	7.10−2	2.45−2	1.01−1
600.0	1.49−2	4.17−3	6.58−2	2.45−2	8.49−2
700.0	9.97−3	3.08−3	6.16−2	2.42−2	7.47−2
800.0	7.06−3	2.37−3	5.81−2	2.39−2	6.75−2
900.0	5.24−3	1.88−3	5.50−2	2.35−2	6.21−2
1,000.0	4.02−3	1.53−3	5.23−2	2.31−2	5.79−2

Praseodymium Z = 59

Energy (keV)	τ/ρ (cm^2/g)	σ_c/ρ (cm^2/g)	σ_I/ρ (cm^2/g)	σ_a/ρ (cm^2/g)	μ/ρ (cm^2/g)
0.1	1.22+4	9.88+0	1.23−4	3.27−8	1.22+4
0.1125 $N_{IV,V}$	1.11+4	9.88+0	1.51−4	4.52−8	1.11+4
0.1139	1.52+4	9.88+0	1.54−4	4.67−8	1.52+4
0.15	1.09+4	9.87+0	2.54−4	1.03−7	1.09+4
0.2	7.65+3	9.86+0	4.36−4	2.36−7	7.65+3
0.2231 $N_{II,III}$	7.32+3	9.85+0	5.36−4	3.23−7	7.33+3
0.2245	9.44+3	9.85+0	5.42−4	3.29−7	9.45+3
0.23	9.41+3	9.85+0	5.67−4	3.53−7	9.42+3
0.3	8.45+3	9.82+0	9.34−4	7.59−7	8.45+3
0.3038 N_I	8.38+3	9.82+0	9.56−4	7.86−7	8.39+3
0.3052	9.35+3	9.82+0	9.64−4	7.96−7	9.36+3

TABLE 3 (continued)

Energy (keV)	τ/ρ (cm²/g)	σ_c/ρ (cm²/g)	σ_I/ρ (cm²/g)	σ_a/ρ (cm²/g)	μ/ρ (cm²/g)
0.4	7.44+3	9.77+0	1.58−3	1.70−6	7.45+3
0.5	5.76+3	9.70+0	2.33−3	3.12−6	5.77+3
0.6	4.48+3	9.63+0	3.15−3	5.02−6	4.49+3
0.7	3.54+3	9.54+0	3.99−3	7.36−6	3.55+3
0.8	2.84+3	9.45+0	4.84−3	1.01−5	2.85+3
0.9	2.31+3	9.36+0	5.70−3	1.33−5	2.32+3
0.9383 $M_{IV,V}$	2.14+3	9.32+0	6.02−3	1.46−5	2.15+3
0.9397	2.85+3	9.32+0	6.04−3	1.46−5	2.86+3
0.95	8.97+3	9.31+0	6.12−3	1.50−5	8.98+3
1.0	1.01+4	9.26+0	6.54−3	1.68−5	1.01+4
1.2733 $M_{II,III}$	5.78+3	8.97+0	8.75−3	2.82−5	5.79+3
1.2747	7.15+3	8.97+0	8.77−3	2.82−5	7.16+3
1.5103 M_I	5.03+3	8.73+0	1.07−2	4.02−5	5.04+3
1.5117	5.38+3	8.73+0	1.07−2	4.03−5	5.39+3
2.0	2.83+3	8.22+0	1.45−2	7.16−5	2.84+3
3.0	1.06+3	7.21+0	2.21−2	1.61−4	1.06+3
4.0	5.07+2	6.31+0	2.91−2	2.79−4	5.14+2
5.0	2.94+2	5.55+0	3.54−2	4.19−4	3.00+2
5.964 L_{III}	1.87+2	4.93+0	4.08−2	5.68−4	1.92+2
5.964	5.46+2	4.93+0	4.08−2	5.68−4	5.51+2
6.0	5.37+2	4.91+0	4.09−2	5.74−4	5.42+2
6.44 L_{II}	4.43+2	4.65+0	4.32−2	6.46−4	4.48+2
6.44	6.20+2	4.65+0	4.32−2	6.46−4	6.25+2
6.835 L_I	5.27+2	4.45+0	4.51−2	7.13−4	5.32+2
6.835	6.33+2	4.45+0	4.51−2	7.13−4	6.37+2
7.0	5.93+2	4.37+0	4.59−2	7.42−4	5.98+2
8.0	4.12+2	3.91+0	5.04−2	9.20−4	4.16+2
9.0	2.99+2	3.51+0	5.45−2	1.11−3	3.02+2
10.0	2.24+2	3.17+0	5.84−2	1.31−3	2.27+2
12.0	1.36+2	2.63+0	6.54−2	1.73−3	1.39+2
15.0	7.42+1	2.07+0	7.41−2	2.41−3	7.63+1
17.0	5.27+1	1.79+0	7.90−2	2.87−3	5.46+1
20.0	3.39+1	1.48+0	8.51−2	3.57−3	3.54+1
25.0	1.84+1	1.11+0	9.27−2	4.70−3	1.96+1
30.0	1.12+1	8.55−1	9.81−2	5.79−3	1.22+1
35.0	7.36+0	6.80−1	1.02−1	6.84−3	8.14+0
40.0	5.12+0	5.57−1	1.05−1	7.84−3	5.78+0
41.99 K	4.48+0	5.17−1	1.06−1	8.21−3	5.10+0
41.99	2.74+1	5.17−1	1.06−1	8.21−3	2.81+1
50.0	1.68+1	3.94−1	1.09−1	9.69−3	1.73+1
60.0	9.98+0	2.94−1	1.11−1	1.13−2	1.04+1
70.0	6.43+0	2.28−1	1.11−1	1.28−2	6.77+0
80.0	4.39+0	1.81−1	1.11−1	1.41−2	4.69+0
90.0	3.14+0	1.48−1	1.11−1	1.52−2	3.40+0
100.0	2.32+0	1.23−1	1.10−1	1.62−2	2.56+0
120.0	1.38+0	8.90−2	1.08−1	1.78−2	1.58+0
150.0	7.32−1	5.95−2	1.04−1	1.97−2	8.95−1
170.0	5.13−1	4.74−2	1.01−1	2.06−2	6.61−1
200.0	3.42−1	3.51−2	9.72−2	2.18−2	4.56−1
250.0	1.73−1	2.31−2	9.14−2	2.31−2	2.88−1
300.0	1.04−1	1.64−2	8.63−2	2.38−2	2.07−1

TABLE 3 (continued)

Energy (keV)	τ/ρ (cm^2/g)	σ_c/ρ (cm^2/g)	σ_I/ρ (cm^2/g)	σ_a/ρ (cm^2/g)	μ/ρ (cm^2/g)
350.0	6.83−2	1.22−2	8.20−2	2.43−2	1.63−1
400.0	4.74−2	9.50−3	7.81−2	2.46−2	1.35−1
500.0	2.60−2	6.18−3	7.18−2	2.48−2	1.04−1
600.0	1.60−2	4.34−3	6.66−2	2.47−2	8.70−2
700.0	1.07−2	3.21−3	6.24−2	2.45−2	7.63−2
800.0	7.61−3	2.47−3	5.87−2	2.42−2	6.88−2
900.0	5.64−3	1.96−3	5.56−2	2.38−2	6.33−2
1,000.0	4.33−3	1.59−3	5.29−2	2.34−2	5.89−2

Neodymium Z = 60

Energy (keV)	τ/ρ (cm^2/g)	σ_c/ρ (cm^2/g)	σ_I/ρ (cm^2/g)	σ_a/ρ (cm^2/g)	μ/ρ (cm^2/g)
0.1	1.48+4	9.98+0	1.19−4	3.15−8	1.48+4
0.1168 $N_{IV,V}$	1.32+4	9.98+0	1.55−4	4.82−8	1.32+4
0.1182	1.68+4	9.98+0	1.58−4	4.99−8	1.68+4
0.15	1.33+4	9.97+0	2.44−4	9.85−8	1.34+4
0.2	9.03+3	9.96+0	4.18−4	2.26−7	9.04+3
0.23	8.29+3	9.95+0	5.44−4	3.39−7	8.30+3
0.2301 $N_{II,III}$	8.29+3	9.95+0	5.45−4	3.39−7	8.30+3
0.2315	1.03+4	9.95+0	5.51−4	3.45−7	1.03+4
0.3	8.99+3	9.92+0	8.97−4	7.28−7	8.99+3
0.3145 N_I	8.70+3	9.92+0	9.78−4	8.32−7	8.71+3
0.3159	9.61+3	9.92+0	9.86−4	8.42−7	9.62+3
0.4	7.74+3	9.87+0	1.52−3	1.63−6	7.75+3
0.5	5.96+3	9.81+0	2.24−3	3.00−6	5.97+3
0.6	4.63+3	9.74+0	3.03−3	4.84−6	4.64+3
0.7	3.66+3	9.66+0	3.85−3	7.10−6	3.67+3
0.8	2.93+3	9.57+0	4.68−3	9.77−6	2.94+3
0.9	2.39+3	9.47+0	5.51−3	1.29−5	2.40+3
0.95	2.16+3	9.42+0	5.92−3	1.45−5	2.17+3
0.9859 $M_{IV,V}$	2.02+3	9.39+0	6.20−3	1.58−5	2.03+3
0.9873	2.60+3	9.39+0	6.22−3	1.58−5	2.61+3
1.0	8.69+3	9.37+0	6.32−3	1.63−5	8.70+3
1.3323 $M_{II,III}$	5.40+3	9.03+0	8.94−3	3.00−5	5.41+3
1.3337	6.71+3	9.02+0	8.95−3	3.01−5	6.72+3
1.5743 M_I	4.75+3	8.78+0	1.08−2	4.25−5	4.76+3
1.5757	5.07+3	8.78+0	1.08−2	4.26−5	5.08+3
2.0	2.94+3	8.34+0	1.41−2	6.96−5	2.95+3
3.0	1.10+3	7.34+0	2.15−2	1.57−4	1.11+3
4.0	5.30+2	6.43+0	2.84−2	2.73−4	5.37+2
5.0	3.12+2	5.65+0	3.46−2	4.10−4	3.17+2
6.0	1.96+2	5.00+0	4.01−2	5.62−4	2.01+2
6.208 L_{III}	1.79+2	4.88+0	4.11−2	5.96−4	1.84+2
6.208	5.16+2	4.88+0	4.11−2	5.96−4	5.21+2
6.722 L_{II}	4.16+2	4.59+0	4.37−2	6.81−4	4.20+2
6.722	5.82+2	4.59+0	4.37−2	6.81−4	5.86+2
7.0	5.21+2	4.45+0	4.50−2	7.28−4	5.25+2
7.126 L_I	4.96+2	4.39+0	4.56−2	7.49−4	5.00+2
7.126	5.95+2	4.39+0	4.56−2	7.49−4	6.00+2
8.0	4.33+2	3.98+0	4.94−2	9.04−4	4.38+2
9.0	3.14+2	3.58+0	5.35−2	1.09−3	3.18+2
10.0	2.35+2	3.24+0	5.74−2	1.29−3	2.39+2
12.0	1.43+2	2.68+0	6.43−2	1.71−3	1.46+2
15.0	7.76+1	2.10+0	7.30−2	2.37−3	7.97+1

TABLE 3 (continued)

Energy (keV)	τ/ρ (cm^2/g)	σ_c/ρ (cm^2/g)	σ_I/ρ (cm^2/g)	σ_a/ρ (cm^2/g)	μ/ρ (cm^2/g)
17.0	5.51+1	1.82+0	7.79−2	2.83−3	5.70+1
20.0	3.53+1	1.50+0	8.40−2	3.52−3	3.69+1
25.0	1.92+1	1.13+0	9.16−2	4.65−3	2.04+1
30.0	1.16+1	8.71−1	9.70−2	5.74−3	1.26+1
35.0	7.63+0	6.94−1	1.01−1	6.78−3	8.42+0
40.0	5.29+0	5.67−1	1.04−1	7.77−3	5.96+0
43.57 K	4.19+0	4.97−1	1.06−1	8.44−3	4.79+0
43.57	2.55+1	4.97−1	1.06−1	8.44−3	2.61+1
50.0	1.73+1	4.01−1	1.08−1	9.60−3	1.78+1
60.0	1.03+1	3.00−1	1.10−1	1.12−2	1.08+1
70.0	6.68+0	2.32−1	1.10−1	1.27−2	7.03+0
80.0	4.57+0	1.85−1	1.10−1	1.39−2	4.87+0
90.0	3.27+0	1.51−1	1.10−1	1.51−2	3.53+0
100.0	2.42+0	1.25−1	1.09−1	1.60−2	2.66+0
120.0	1.44+0	9.08−2	1.07−1	1.77−2	1.64+0
150.0	7.66−1	6.07−2	1.03−1	1.96−2	9.29−1
170.0	5.37−1	4.84−2	1.00−1	2.05−2	6.86−1
200.0	3.40−1	3.58−2	9.65−2	2.16−2	4.72−1
250.0	1.82−1	2.36−2	9.07−2	2.29−2	2.96−1
300.0	1.10−1	1.67−2	8.58−2	2.37−2	2.12−1
350.0	7.19−2	1.25−2	8.14−2	2.42−2	1.66−1
400.0	4.99−2	9.70−3	7.76−2	2.44−2	1.37−1
500.0	2.74−2	6.31−3	7.12−2	2.46−2	1.05−1
600.0	1.69−2	4.43−3	6.61−2	2.46−2	8.75−2
700.0	1.13−2	3.27−3	6.19−2	2.43−2	7.65−2
800.0	8.03−3	2.52−3	5.83−2	2.40−2	6.89−2
900.0	5.96−3	2.00−3	5.53−2	2.37−2	6.33−2
1,000.0	4.58−3	1.62−3	5.26−2	2.33−2	5.88−2

Promethium **Z = 61**

Energy (keV)	τ/ρ (cm^2/g)	σ_c/ρ (cm^2/g)	σ_I/ρ (cm^2/g)	σ_a/ρ (cm^2/g)	μ/ρ (cm^2/g)
0.1	1.77+4	1.01+1	1.14−4	3.02−8	1.77+4
0.1197 $N_{IV,V}$	1.58+4	1.01+1	1.55−4	4.96−8	1.58+4
0.1211	1.89+4	1.01+1	1.59−4	5.13−8	1.90+4
0.14	1.85+4	1.01+1	2.07−4	7.78−8	1.85+4
0.15	1.60+4	1.01+1	2.35−4	9.48−8	1.61+4
0.2	1.08+4	1.01+1	4.03−4	2.18−7	1.08+4
0.2413 $N_{II,III}$	9.35+3	1.01+1	5.74−4	3.75−7	9.35+3
0.2427	1.13+4	1.01+1	5.81−4	3.81−7	1.13+4
0.3	9.78+3	1.01+1	8.64−4	7.02−7	9.79+3
0.3303 N_I	9.04+3	1.01+1	1.03−3	9.21−7	9.05+3
0.3317	9.91+3	1.01+1	1.04−3	9.32−7	9.91+3
0.4	8.20+3	1.00+1	1.46−3	1.58−6	8.21+3
0.5	6.26+3	9.96+0	2.17−3	2.90−6	6.27+3
0.6	4.85+3	9.89+0	2.93−3	4.68−6	4.85+3
0.7	3.82+3	9.80+0	3.73−3	6.88−6	3.83+3
0.8	3.06+3	9.72+0	4.53−3	9.48−6	3.07+3
0.9	2.49+3	9.62+0	5.34−3	1.25−5	2.50+3
1.0	2.05+3	9.53+0	6.14−3	1.58−5	2.06+3
1.0363 $M_{IV,V}$	1.92+3	9.49+0	6.42−3	1.71−5	1.93+3
1.0377	2.41+3	9.48+0	6.43−3	1.71−5	2.41+3
1.2	7.24+3	9.33+0	7.70−3	2.35−5	7.25+3
1.3	6.01+3	9.21+0	8.46−3	2.78−5	6.01+3

TABLE 3 (continued)

Energy (keV)	τ/ρ (cm^2/g)	σ_c/ρ (cm^2/g)	σ_I/ρ (cm^2/g)	σ_a/ρ (cm^2/g)	μ/ρ (cm^2/g)
1.3943 $M_{II,III}$	5.09+3	9.12+0	9.17−3	3.22−5	5.10+3
1.3957	6.35+3	9.12+0	9.19−3	3.23−5	6.35+3
1.4	6.39+3	9.11+0	9.22−3	3.25−5	6.40+3
1.6493 M_I	4.47+3	8.86+0	1.11−2	4.57−5	4.47+3
1.6507	4.77+3	8.86+0	1.11−2	4.58−5	4.78+3
2.0	3.07+3	8.50+0	1.38−2	6.80−5	3.08+3
3.0	1.16+3	7.50+0	2.11−2	1.54−4	1.16+3
4.0	5.57+2	6.58+0	2.78−2	2.67−4	5.64+2
5.0	3.27+2	5.79+0	3.39−2	4.02−4	3.33+2
6.0	2.05+2	5.13+0	3.94−2	5.53−4	2.10+2
6.459 L_{III}	1.70+2	4.85+0	4.17−2	6.27−4	1.75+2
6.459	4.84+2	4.85+0	4.17−2	6.27−4	4.89+2
7.0	3.89+2	4.56+0	4.42−2	7.17−4	3.93+2
7.013 L_{II}	3.87+2	4.55+0	4.43−2	7.19−4	3.91+2
7.013	5.41+2	4.55+0	4.43−2	7.19−4	5.46+2
7.428 L_I	4.63+2	4.34+0	4.62−2	7.90−4	4.67+2
7.428	5.55+2	4.34+0	4.62−2	7.90−4	5.60+2
8.0	4.54+2	4.08+0	4.87−2	8.91−4	4.58+2
9.0	3.29+2	3.67+0	5.28−2	1.08−3	3.32+2
10.0	2.47+2	3.31+0	5.65−2	1.27−3	2.50+2
12.0	1.50+2	2.74+0	6.34−2	1.68−3	1.53+2
15.0	8.15+1	2.15+0	7.21−2	2.35−3	8.37+1
17.0	5.79+1	1.86+0	7.70−2	2.80−3	5.99+1
20.0	3.72+1	1.54+0	8.32−2	3.49−3	3.88+1
25.0	2.02+1	1.15+0	9.08−2	4.62−3	2.14+1
30.0	1.23+1	8.91−1	9.63−2	5.70−3	1.33+1
35.0	8.06+0	7.10−1	1.00−1	6.74−3	8.87+0
40.0	5.60+0	5.81−1	1.03−1	7.73−3	6.28+0
45.18 K	4.02+0	4.81−1	1.06−1	8.70−3	4.60+0
45.18	2.42+1	4.81−1	1.06−1	8.70−3	2.48+1
50.0	1.82+1	4.10−1	1.07−1	9.55−3	1.87+1
60.0	1.09+1	3.07−1	1.09−1	1.12−2	1.13+1
70.0	7.01+0	2.38−1	1.10−1	1.26−2	7.36+0
80.0	4.79+0	1.89−1	1.10−1	1.39−2	5.09+0
90.0	3.43+0	1.54−1	1.09−1	1.50−2	3.69+0
100.0	2.54+0	1.28−1	1.09−1	1.60−2	2.78+0
120.0	1.51+0	9.30−2	1.06−1	1.76−2	1.71+0
150.0	8.03−1	6.22−2	1.02−1	1.95−2	9.67−1
170.0	5.63−1	4.95−2	9.99−2	2.04−2	7.13−1
200.0	3.57−1	3.67−2	9.62−2	2.16−2	4.90−1
250.0	1.91−1	2.42−2	9.05−2	2.28−2	3.06−1
300.0	1.15−1	1.72−2	8.55−2	2.36−2	2.18−1
350.0	7.56−2	1.28−2	8.12−2	2.41−2	1.70−1
400.0	5.26−2	9.94−3	7.74−2	2.44−2	1.40−1
500.0	2.89−2	6.47−3	7.10−2	2.46−2	1.06−1
600.0	1.79−2	4.54−3	6.60−2	2.45−2	8.84−2
700.0	1.20−2	3.35−3	6.17−2	2.43−2	7.71−2
800.0	8.51−3	2.58−3	5.82−2	2.40−2	6.93−2
900.0	6.32−3	2.05−3	5.51−2	2.36−2	6.35−2
1,000.0	4.86−3	1.66−3	5.24−2	2.32−2	5.90−2

TABLE 3 (continued)

Energy (keV)	τ/ρ (cm²/g)	σ_c/ρ (cm²/g)	σ_I/ρ (cm²/g)	σ_a/ρ (cm²/g)	μ/ρ (cm²/g)
Samarium Z = 62					
0.1	1.99+4	1.02+1	1.10–4	2.92–8	1.99+4
0.1283 $N_{IV,V}$	1.73+4	1.02+1	1.70–4	5.82–8	1.73+4
0.1297	2.02+4	1.02+1	1.73–4	6.01–8	2.02+4
0.14	2.14+4	1.02+1	1.99–4	7.48–8	2.14+4
0.15	1.94+4	1.02+1	2.26–4	9.12–8	1.94+4
0.2	1.25+4	1.02+1	3.87–4	2.09–7	1.25+4
0.2528 $N_{II,III}$	1.02+4	1.02+1	6.02–4	4.12–7	1.02+4
0.2542	1.20+4	1.02+1	6.09–4	4.19–7	1.20+4
0.3	1.06+4	1.02+1	8.31–4	6.75–7	1.06+4
0.345 N_I	9.36+3	1.02+1	1.08–3	1.00–6	9.37+3
0.3464	1.02+4	1.02+1	1.08–3	1.01–6	1.02+4
0.4	8.73+3	1.01+1	1.41–3	1.52–6	8.74+3
0.5	6.63+3	1.01+1	2.08–3	2.80–6	6.65+3
0.6	5.11+3	9.99+0	2.82–3	4.51–6	5.12+3
0.7	4.01+3	9.91+0	3.59–3	6.64–6	4.02+3
0.8	3.21+3	9.83+0	4.38–3	9.16–6	3.22+3
0.9	2.61+3	9.74+0	5.17–3	1.21–5	2.62+3
1.0	2.15+3	9.64+0	5.94–3	1.53–5	2.16+3
1.0903 $M_{IV,V}$	1.82+3	9.55+0	6.62–3	1.85–5	1.83+3
1.0917	2.23+3	9.55+0	6.63–3	1.85–5	2.24+3
1.2	7.63+3	9.45+0	7.46–3	2.28–5	7.64+3
1.3	6.32+3	9.33+0	8.20–3	2.70–5	6.33+3
1.4	5.31+3	9.23+0	8.94–3	3.15–5	5.32+3
1.4593 $M_{II,III}$	4.80+3	9.18+0	9.39–3	3.44–5	4.81+3
1.4607	6.00+3	9.18+0	9.40–3	3.45–5	6.01+3
1.7223 M_I	4.22+3	8.91+0	1.13–2	4.85–5	4.23+3
1.7237	4.51+3	8.91+0	1.13–2	4.86–5	4.52+3
2.0	3.21+3	8.63+0	1.34–2	6.61–5	3.22+3
3.0	1.21+3	7.63+0	2.05–2	1.50–4	1.22+3
4.0	5.84+2	6.70+0	2.71–2	2.61–4	5.91+2
5.0	3.43+2	5.90+0	3.31–2	3.93–4	3.49+2
6.0	2.15+2	5.23+0	3.85–2	5.41–4	2.21+2
6.716 L_{III}	1.61+2	4.81+0	4.20–2	6.55–4	1.66+2
6.716	4.56+2	4.81+0	4.20–2	6.55–4	4.61+2
7.0	4.08+2	4.65+0	4.33–2	7.03–4	4.12+2
7.312 L_{II}	3.62+2	4.49+0	4.47–2	7.55–4	3.66+2
7.312	5.07+2	4.49+0	4.47–2	7.55–4	5.11+2
7.737 L_I	4.34+2	4.28+0	4.66–2	8.28–4	4.38+2
7.737	5.21+2	4.28+0	4.66–2	8.28–4	5.25+2
8.0	4.75+2	4.16+0	4.77–2	8.74–4	4.79+2
9.0	3.45+2	3.74+0	5.17–2	1.06–3	3.48+2
10.0	2.58+2	3.38+0	5.55–2	1.25–3	2.62+2
12.0	1.57+2	2.80+0	6.22–2	1.66–3	1.60+2
15.0	8.53+1	2.19+0	7.09–2	2.31–3	8.76+1
17.0	6.06+1	1.90+0	7.58–2	2.76–3	6.26+1
20.0	3.89+1	1.56+0	8.20–2	3.45–3	4.05+1
25.0	2.11+1	1.17+0	8.96–2	4.57–3	2.24+1
30.0	1.28+1	9.08–1	9.52–2	5.65–3	1.38+1
35.0	8.42+0	7.23–1	9.93–2	6.68–3	9.25+0
40.0	5.85+0	5.92–1	1.02–1	7.66–3	6.54+0
46.83 K	3.80+0	4.63–1	1.05–1	8.92–3	4.37+0

TABLE 3 (continued)

Energy (keV)	τ/ρ (cm^2/g)	σ_c/ρ (cm^2/g)	σ_I/ρ (cm^2/g)	σ_a/ρ (cm^2/g)	μ/ρ (cm^2/g)
46.83	2.28+1	4.63−1	1.05−1	8.92−3	2.33+1
50.0	1.89+1	4.18−1	1.06−1	9.47−3	1.94+1
60.0	1.13+1	3.13−1	1.08−1	1.11−2	1.17+1
70.0	7.29+0	2.42−1	1.09−1	1.25−2	7.64+0
80.0	4.99+0	1.93−1	1.09−1	1.38−2	5.29+0
90.0	3.57+0	1.57−1	1.08−1	1.49−2	3.84+0
100.0	2.65+0	1.31−1	1.08−1	1.59−2	2.88+0
120.0	1.58+0	9.49−2	1.06−1	1.75−2	1.78+0
150.0	8.38−1	6.34−2	1.02−1	1.94−2	1.00+0
170.0	5.88−1	5.06−2	9.91−2	2.03−2	7.38−1
200.0	3.73−1	3.75−2	9.55−2	2.14−2	5.06−1
250.0	2.00−1	2.47−2	8.98−2	2.27−2	3.15−1
300.0	1.21−1	1.75−2	8.49−2	2.35−2	2.23−1
350.0	7.93−2	1.31−2	8.06−2	2.39−2	1.73−1
400.0	5.52−2	1.02−2	7.69−2	2.42−2	1.42−1
500.0	3.04−2	6.61−3	7.06−2	2.44−2	1.08−1
600.0	1.88−2	4.64−3	6.55−2	2.44−2	8.90−2
700.0	1.26−2	3.43−3	6.14−2	2.41−2	7.74−2
800.0	8.98−3	2.64−3	5.78−2	2.38−2	6.94−2
900.0	6.68−3	2.09−3	5.48−2	2.34−2	6.35−2
1,000.0	5.14−3	1.70−3	5.21−2	2.31−2	5.90−2

Europium Z = 63

Energy (keV)	τ/ρ (cm^2/g)	σ_c/ρ (cm^2/g)	σ_I/ρ (cm^2/g)	σ_a/ρ (cm^2/g)	μ/ρ (cm^2/g)
0.1	2.03+4	1.05+1	1.06−4	2.82−8	2.03+4
0.1325 $N_{IV,V}$	1.77+4	1.04+1	1.75−4	6.19−8	1.77+4
0.1339	2.05+4	1.04+1	1.78−4	6.38−8	2.05+4
0.14	2.13+4	1.04+1	1.93−4	7.26−8	2.13+4
0.15	2.05+4	1.04+1	2.19−4	8.85−8	2.06+4
0.2	1.34+4	1.04+1	3.76−4	2.03−7	1.34+4
0.265 $N_{II,III}$	1.05+4	1.04+1	6.40−4	4.59−7	1.05+4
0.2664	1.23+4	1.04+1	6.46−4	4.66−7	1.23+4
0.3	1.12+4	1.04+1	8.08−4	6.56−7	1.12+4
0.3595 N_I	9.49+3	1.04+1	1.13−3	1.10−6	9.50+3
0.3609	1.03+4	1.04+1	1.14−3	1.11−6	1.03+4
0.4	9.19+3	1.03+1	1.37−3	1.48−6	9.20+3
0.5	6.97+3	1.03+1	2.03−3	2.73−6	6.98+3
0.6	5.37+3	1.02+1	2.75−3	4.40−6	5.38+3
0.7	4.21+3	1.01+1	3.51−3	6.49−6	4.22+3
0.8	3.37+3	1.01+1	4.28−3	8.97−6	3.38+3
0.9	2.74+3	9.96+0	5.05−3	1.18−5	2.75+3
1.0	2.26+3	9.87+0	5.82−3	1.50−5	2.27+3
1.1423 $M_{IV,V}$	1.75+3	9.72+0	6.88−3	2.01−5	1.76+3
1.1437	2.11+3	9.72+0	6.89−3	2.01−5	2.12+3
1.2	8.05+3	9.67+0	7.32−3	2.24−5	8.05+3
1.3	6.68+3	9.56+0	8.04−3	2.65−5	6.69+3
1.4	5.60+3	9.46+0	8.77−3	3.10−5	5.60+3
1.5243 $M_{II,III}$	4.56+3	9.34+0	9.69−3	3.70−5	4.57+3
1.5257	5.73+3	9.34+0	9.70−3	3.71−5	5.74+3
1.7993 M_I	4.01+3	9.05+0	1.17−2	5.23−5	4.02+3
1.8007	4.29+3	9.05+0	1.17−2	5.24−5	4.30+3
2.0	3.37+3	8.85+0	1.31−2	6.51−5	3.38+3
3.0	1.28+3	7.85+0	2.02−2	1.48−4	1.28+3
4.0	6.17+2	6.91+0	2.68−2	2.58−4	6.24+2

TABLE 3 (continued)

Energy (keV)	τ/ρ (cm^2/g)	σ_c/ρ (cm^2/g)	σ_I/ρ (cm^2/g)	σ_a/ρ (cm^2/g)	μ/ρ (cm^2/g)
5.0	3.61+2	6.09+0	3.27−2	3.89−4	3.67+2
6.0	2.26+2	5.39+0	3.81−2	5.36−4	2.32+2
6.977$_{L_{III}}$	1.53+2	4.82+0	4.28−2	6.92−4	1.58+2
6.977	4.33+2	4.82+0	4.28−2	6.92−4	4.38+2
7.0	4.29+2	4.80+0	4.29−2	6.96−4	4.34+2
7.617$_{L_{II}}$	3.41+2	4.48+0	4.57−2	8.01−4	3.45+2
7.617	4.77+2	4.48+0	4.57−2	8.01−4	4.81+2
8.0	4.17+2	4.30+0	4.73−2	8.68−4	4.21+2
8.052$_{L_I}$	4.09+2	4.28+0	4.75−2	8.77−4	4.14+2
8.052	4.91+2	4.28+0	4.75−2	8.77−4	4.96+2
9.0	3.63+2	3.86+0	5.13−2	1.05−3	3.67+2
10.0	2.72+2	3.49+0	5.50−2	1.24−3	2.75+2
12.0	1.65+2	2.89+0	6.19−2	1.65−3	1.68+2
15.0	8.98+1	2.26+0	7.05−2	2.30−3	9.21+1
17.0	6.38+1	1.95+0	7.55−2	2.76−3	6.58+1
20.0	4.09+1	1.61+0	8.17−2	3.44−3	4.26+1
25.0	2.22+1	1.21+0	8.95−2	4.57−3	2.35+1
30.0	1.35+1	9.36−1	9.52−2	5.66−3	1.45+1
35.0	8.86+0	7.46−1	9.94−2	6.70−3	9.71+0
40.0	6.15+0	6.10−1	1.02−1	7.68−3	6.86+0
48.52$_K$	3.63+0	4.51−1	1.06−1	9.24−3	4.19+0
48.52	2.16+1	4.51−1	1.06−1	9.24−3	2.22+1
50.0	1.99+1	4.30−1	1.06−1	9.50−3	2.04+1
60.0	1.19+1	3.22−1	1.08−1	1.11−2	1.23+1
70.0	7.67+0	2.50−1	1.09−1	1.26−2	8.03+0
80.0	5.25+0	1.99−1	1.09−1	1.38−2	5.56+0
90.0	3.76+0	1.62−1	1.09−1	1.50−2	4.03+0
100.0	2.79+0	1.35−1	1.08−1	1.59−2	3.03+0
120.0	1.66+0	9.79−2	1.06−1	1.76−2	1.87+0
150.0	8.84−1	6.55−2	1.02−1	1.95−2	1.05+0
170.0	6.21−1	5.22−2	9.96−2	2.04−2	7.73−1
200.0	3.94−1	3.87−2	9.59−2	2.15−2	5.28−1
250.0	2.12−1	2.55−2	9.02−2	2.28−2	3.27−1
300.0	1.28−1	1.81−2	8.53−2	2.36−2	2.31−1
350.0	8.41−2	1.35−2	8.10−2	2.41−2	1.79−1
400.0	5.86−2	1.05−2	7.72−2	2.43−2	1.46−1
500.0	3.23−2	6.84−3	7.09−2	2.46−2	1.10−1
600.0	2.00−2	4.80−3	6.59−2	2.45−2	9.07−2
700.0	1.34−2	3.55−3	6.17−2	2.43−2	7.87−2
800.0	9.57−3	2.73−3	5.81−2	2.39−2	7.04−2
900.0	7.12−3	2.17−3	5.50−2	2.36−2	6.43−2
1,000.0	5.49−3	1.76−3	5.24−2	2.32−2	5.96−2

Gadolinium   Z = 64

0.1	1.80+4	1.04+1	9.88−5	2.63−8	1.80+4
0.1398$_{N_{IV,V}}$	1.61+4	1.04+1	1.79−4	6.73−8	1.61+4
0.1412	1.83+4	1.04+1	1.82−4	6.92−8	1.83+4
0.15	1.82+4	1.04+1	2.04−4	8.23−8	1.82+4
0.2	1.32+4	1.04+1	3.50−4	1.89−7	1.32+4
0.2761$_{N_{II,III}}$	1.01+4	1.04+1	6.45−4	4.82−7	1.01+4
0.2775	1.17+4	1.04+1	6.51−4	4.89−7	1.17+4
0.3	1.12+4	1.04+1	7.54−4	6.13−7	1.12+4
0.3751$_{N_I}$	9.08+3	1.03+1	1.14−3	1.16−6	9.09+3
0.3765	9.82+3	1.03+1	1.15−3	1.17−6	9.84+3

TABLE 3 (continued)

Energy (keV)	τ/ρ (cm^2/g)	σ_c/ρ (cm^2/g)	σ_I/ρ (cm^2/g)	σ_a/ρ (cm^2/g)	μ/ρ (cm^2/g)
0.4	9.16+3	1.03+1	1.28−3	1.39−6	9.17+3
0.5	6.98+3	1.03+1	1.92−3	2.57−6	6.99+3
0.6	5.40+3	1.02+1	2.61−3	4.19−6	5.41+3
0.7	4.25+3	1.01+1	3.35−3	6.21−6	4.26+3
0.8	3.41+3	1.00+1	4.11−3	8.64−6	3.42+3
0.9	2.78+3	9.94+0	4.87−3	1.15−5	2.79+3
1.0	2.30+3	9.85+0	5.63−3	1.46−5	2.31+3
1.1973 $M_{IV,V}$	1.63+3	9.65+0	7.11−3	2.18−5	1.64+3
1.1987	1.87+3	9.65+0	7.12−3	2.18−5	1.88+3
1.2	2.04+3	9.65+0	7.13−3	2.19−5	2.05+3
1.3	6.74+3	9.54+0	7.84−3	2.59−5	6.74+3
1.4	5.68+3	9.43+0	8.56−3	3.03−5	5.69+3
1.5913 $M_{II,III}$	4.18+3	9.24+0	9.94−3	3.96−5	4.19+3
1.5927	5.14+3	9.24+0	9.95−3	3.97−5	5.15+3
1.8803 M_I	3.67+3	8.94+0	1.20−2	5.59−5	3.68+3
1.8817	3.94+3	8.93+0	1.20−2	5.60−5	3.95+3
2.0	3.42+3	8.82+0	1.28−2	6.35−5	3.42+3
3.0	1.30+3	7.81+0	1.97−2	1.44−4	1.31+3
4.0	6.33+1	6.88+0	2.61−2	2.51−4	6.40+2
5.0	3.71+2	6.07+0	3.19−2	3.79−4	3.78+2
6.0	2.32+2	5.39+0	3.72−2	5.24−4	2.38+2
7.0	1.56+2	4.80+0	4.19−2	6.81−4	1.61+1
7.243 L_{III}	1.43+2	4.67+0	4.30−2	7.21−4	1.48+2
7.243	4.03+2	4.67+0	4.30−2	7.21−4	4.07+2
7.93 L_{II}	3.14+2	4.33+0	4.59−2	8.36−4	3.18+2
7.93	4.40+2	4.33+0	4.59−2	8.36−4	4.44+2
8.0	4.29+2	4.30+0	4.62−2	8.49−4	4.34+2
8.376 L_I	3.79+2	4.13+0	4.77−2	9.14−4	3.83+2
8.376	4.54+2	4.13+0	4.77−2	9.14−4	4.58+2
9.0	3.73+2	3.87+0	5.01−2	1.03−3	3.77+2
10.0	2.80+2	3.50+0	5.38−2	1.21−3	2.83+2
12.0	1.70+2	2.89+0	6.04−2	1.61−3	1.73+2
15.0	9.23+1	2.26+0	6.88−2	2.24−3	9.46+1
17.0	6.55+1	1.95+0	7.36−2	2.69−3	6.76+1
20.0	4.20+1	1.61+0	7.98−2	3.36−3	4.37+1
25.0	2.28+1	1.21+0	8.75−2	4.47−3	2.41+1
30.0	1.39+1	9.40−1	9.31−2	5.53−3	1.49+1
35.0	9.09+0	7.50−1	9.72−2	6.56−3	9.93+0
40.0	6.31+0	6.13−1	1.00−1	7.53−3	7.02+0
50.0	3.43+0	4.32−1	1.04−1	9.31−3	3.96+0
50.24 K	3.38+0	4.29−1	1.04−1	9.35−3	3.91+0
50.24	1.96+1	4.29−1	1.04−1	9.35−3	2.01+1
60.0	1.20+1	3.24−1	1.06−1	1.09−2	1.24+1
70.0	7.84+0	2.51−1	1.07−1	1.23−2	8.19+0
80.0	5.40+0	2.00−1	1.07−1	1.36−2	5.71+0
90.0	3.88+0	1.63−1	1.07−1	1.47−2	4.15+0
100.0	2.89+0	1.36−1	1.06−1	1.56−2	3.13+0
120.0	1.73+0	9.85−2	1.04−1	1.73−2	1.93+0
150.0	9.21−1	6.59−2	1.00−1	1.91−2	1.09+0
170.0	6.48−1	5.25−2	9.77−2	2.00−2	7.98−1
200.0	4.11−1	3.89−2	9.41−2	2.11−2	5.44−1
250.0	2.20−1	2.57−2	8.85−2	2.24−2	3.35−1
300.0	1.33−1	1.82−2	8.37−2	2.31−2	2.35−1
350.0	8.72−2	1.36−2	7.95−2	2.36−2	1.80−1

TABLE 3 (continued)

Energy (keV)	τ/ρ (cm^2/g)	σ_c/ρ (cm^2/g)	σ_I/ρ (cm^2/g)	σ_a/ρ (cm^2/g)	μ/ρ (cm^2/g)
400.0	6.07−2	1.06−2	7.58−2	2.39−2	1.47−1
500.0	3.35−2	6.89−3	6.96−2	2.41−2	1.10−1
600.0	2.07−2	4.84−3	6.46−2	2.40−2	9.02−2
700.0	1.39−2	3.58−3	6.06−2	2.38−2	7.81−2
800.0	9.95−3	2.75−3	5.70−2	2.35−2	6.97−2
900.0	7.42−3	2.18−3	5.40−2	2.31−2	6.37−2
1,000.0	5.74−3	1.78−3	5.14−2	2.28−2	5.89−2

Terbium **Z = 65**

Energy (keV)	τ/ρ (cm^2/g)	σ_c/ρ (cm^2/g)	σ_I/ρ (cm^2/g)	σ_a/ρ (cm^2/g)	μ/ρ (cm^2/g)
0.1	2.30+4	1.06+1	9.66−5	2.56−8	2.30+4
0.1463 $N_{IV,V}$	2.00+4	1.06+1	1.90−4	7.45−8	2.00+4
0.1477	2.24+4	1.06+1	1.93−4	7.66−8	2.24+4
0.15	2.25+4	1.06+1	1.98−4	8.01−8	2.25+4
0.2	1.68+4	1.06+1	3.40−4	1.84−7	1.68+4
0.2926 $N_{II,III}$	1.15+4	1.06+1	7.01−4	5.56−7	1.15+4
0.294	1.33+4	1.06+1	7.07−4	5.63−7	1.33+4
0.3	1.30+4	1.06+1	7.34−4	5.97−7	1.31+4
0.3972 N_I	9.75+3	1.05+1	1.24−3	1.33−6	9.77+3
0.3986	1.05+4	1.05+1	1.24−3	1.34−6	1.05+4
0.4	1.04+4	1.05+1	1.25−3	1.35−6	1.05+4
0.5	7.83+3	1.05+1	1.87−3	2.51−6	7.84+3
0.6	5.99+3	1.04+1	2.55−3	4.09−6	6.00+3
0.7	4.67+3	1.03+1	3.27−3	6.08−6	4.68+3
0.8	3.72+3	1.03+1	4.02−3	8.46−6	3.73+3
0.9	3.02+3	1.02+1	4.77−3	1.12−5	3.03+3
1.0	2.48+3	1.01+1	5.52−3	1.43−5	2.49+3
1.2	1.74+3	9.87+0	7.00−3	2.15−5	1.75+3
1.2543 $M_{IV,V}$	1.59+3	9.81+0	7.37−3	2.36−5	1.60+3
1.2557	1.86+3	9.80+0	7.39−3	2.37−5	1.87+3
1.3	7.27+3	9.76+0	7.70−3	2.55−5	7.28+3
1.4	6.18+3	9.66+0	8.41−3	2.98−5	6.19+3
1.6623 $M_{II,III}$	4.06+3	9.39+0	1.03−2	4.27−4	4.07+3
1.6637	5.15+3	9.39+0	1.03−2	4.28−5	5.16+3
1.9673 M_I	3.53+3	9.07+0	1.24−2	6.04−5	3.54+3
1.9687	3.79+3	9.07+0	1.24−2	6.05−5	3.80+3
2.0	3.65+3	9.04+0	1.26−2	6.25−5	3.66+3
3.0	1.39+3	8.02+0	1.94−2	1.42−4	1.40+3
4.0	6.74+2	7.08+0	2.57−2	2.48−4	6.81+2
5.0	3.92+2	6.26+0	3.16−2	3.76−4	3.98+2
6.0	2.45+2	5.56+0	3.68−2	5.20−4	2.51+2
7.0	1.65+2	4.96+0	4.16−2	6.77−4	1.70+2
7.514 L_{III}	1.38+2	4.68+0	4.39−2	7.62−4	1.42+2
7.514	3.84+2	4.68+0	4.39−2	7.62−4	3.89+2
8.0	3.24+2	4.44+0	4.59−2	8.44−4	3.28+2
8.252 L_{II}	2.97+2	4.32+0	4.69−2	8.88−4	3.02+2
8.252	4.16+2	4.32+0	4.69−2	8.88−4	4.20+2
8.708 L_I	3.59+2	4.12+0	4.87−2	9.69−4	3.63+2
8.708	4.31+2	4.12+0	4.87−2	9.69−4	4.35+2
9.0	3.94+2	3.99+0	4.98−2	1.02−3	3.98+2
10.0	2.95+2	3.61+0	5.35−2	1.21−3	2.99+2
12.0	1.79+2	2.99+0	6.01−2	1.60−3	1.82+2
15.0	9.74+1	2.33+0	6.86−2	2.24−3	9.97+1
17.0	6.91+1	2.01+0	7.34−2	2.68−3	7.12+1

TABLE 3 (continued)

Energy (keV)	τ/ρ (cm^2/g)	σ_c/ρ (cm^2/g)	σ_I/ρ (cm^2/g)	σ_a/ρ (cm^2/g)	μ/ρ (cm^2/g)
20.0	4.43+1	1.66+0	7.96−2	3.36−3	4.60+1
25.0	2.41+1	1.25+0	8.74−2	4.47−3	2.54+1
30.0	1.46+1	9.68−1	9.31−2	5.54−3	1.57+1
35.0	9.59+0	7.72−1	9.72−2	6.57−3	1.05+1
40.0	6.65+0	6.32−1	1.00−1	7.54−3	7.39+0
50.0	3.61+0	4.45−1	1.04−1	9.34−3	4.16+0
52.0 $_K$	3.25+0	4.19−1	1.05−1	9.67−3	3.77+0
52.0	1.93+1	4.19−1	1.05−1	9.67−3	1.98+1
60.0	1.28+1	3.33−1	1.06−1	1.09−2	1.33+1
70.0	8.28+0	2.59−1	1.07−1	1.24−2	8.65+0
80.0	5.67+0	2.07−1	1.07−1	1.36−2	5.98+0
90.0	4.05+0	1.68−1	1.07−1	1.47−2	4.33+0
100.0	3.01+0	1.40−1	1.06−1	1.57−2	3.25+0
120.0	1.79+0	1.02−1	1.04−1	1.73−2	2.00+0
150.0	9.56−1	6.79−2	1.01−1	1.92−2	1.12+0
170.0	6.73−1	5.42−2	9.80−2	2.01−2	8.25−1
200.0	4.27−1	4.02−2	9.44−2	2.12−2	5.62−1
250.0	2.30−1	2.65−2	8.89−2	2.25−2	3.46−1
300.0	1.40−1	1.88−2	8.41−2	2.32−2	2.43−1
350.0	9.20−2	1.41−2	7.98−2	2.37−2	1.86−1
400.0	6.42−2	1.09−2	7.61−2	2.40−2	1.51−1
500.0	3.55−2	7.11−3	7.00−2	2.42−2	1.13−1
600.0	2.21−2	4.99−3	6.50−2	2.41−2	9.20−2
700.0	1.48−2	3.69−3	6.08−2	2.39−2	7.94−2
800.0	1.06−2	2.84−3	5.73−2	2.36−2	7.07−2
900.0	7.88−3	2.25−3	5.43−2	2.33−2	6.44−2
1,000.0	6.07−3	1.83−3	5.17−2	2.29−2	5.96−2

Dysprosium Z = 66

Energy (keV)	τ/ρ (cm^2/g)	σ_c/ρ (cm^2/g)	σ_I/ρ (cm^2/g)	σ_a/ρ (cm^2/g)	μ/ρ (cm^2/g)
0.1	2.41+4	1.07+1	9.51−5	2.52−8	2.41+4
0.15	2.13+4	1.07+1	1.95−4	7.89−8	2.13+4
0.1535 $N_{IV,V}$	2.10+4	1.07+1	2.04−4	8.44−8	2.11+4
0.1549	2.33+4	1.07+1	2.08−4	8.67−8	2.33+4
0.2	1.86+4	1.07+1	3.35−4	1.81−7	1.86+4
0.3	1.23+4	1.07+1	7.20−4	5.85−7	1.23+4
0.3052 $N_{II,III}$	1.21+4	1.07+1	7.43−4	6.14−7	1.21+4
0.3066	1.38+4	1.07+1	7.49−4	6.22−7	1.38+4
0.4	1.03+4	1.06+1	1.22−3	1.32−6	1.04+4
0.4156 N_I	9.88+3	1.06+1	1.31−3	1.47−6	9.89+3
0.417	1.06+4	1.06+1	1.32−3	1.48−6	1.06+4
0.5	8.31+3	1.06+1	1.82−3	2.44−6	8.32+3
0.6	6.33+3	1.05+1	2.47−3	3.95−6	6.34+3
0.7	4.93+3	1.04+1	3.16−3	5.85−6	4.94+3
0.8	3.91+3	1.04+1	3.86−3	8.11−6	3.92+3
0.9	3.17+3	1.03+1	4.57−3	1.07−5	3.18+3
1.0	2.60+3	1.02+1	5.27−3	1.36−5	2.61+3
1.3093 $M_{IV,V}$	1.53+3	9.88+0	7.39−3	2.46−5	1.54+3
1.3107	1.76+3	9.87+0	7.40−3	2.46−5	1.77+3
1.4	6.44+3	9.79+0	8.01−3	2.83−5	6.45+3
1.6	4.65+3	9.60+0	9.36−3	3.75−5	4.66+3
1.7303 $M_{II,III}$	3.83+3	9.47+0	1.02−2	4.42−5	3.84+3
1.7317	4.89+3	9.47+0	1.02−2	4.43−5	4.90+3
1.8	4.48+3	9.40+0	1.07−2	4.80−5	4.49+3

TABLE 3 (continued)

Energy (keV)	τ/ρ (cm²/g)	σ_c/ρ (cm²/g)	σ_I/ρ (cm²/g)	σ_a/ρ (cm²/g)	μ/ρ (cm²/g)
2.0	3.53+3	9.20+0	1.21–2	5.99–5	3.54+3
2.0463 M_I	3.34+3	9.15+0	1.24–2	6.27–5	3.35+3
2.0477	3.58+3	9.15+0	1.24–2	6.29–5	3.59+3
3.0	1.44+3	8.21+0	1.87–2	1.37–4	1.45+3
4.0	7.01+2	7.27+0	2.49–2	2.40–4	7.08+2
5.0	4.08+2	6.43+0	3.06–2	3.65–4	4.15+2
6.0	2.55+2	5.71+0	3.58–2	5.05–4	2.61+2
7.0	1.71+2	5.09+0	4.04–2	6.59–4	1.76+2
7.79 L_{III}	1.30+2	4.66+0	4.38–2	7.88–4	1.35+2
7.79	3.61+2	4.66+0	4.38–2	7.88–4	3.66+2
8.0	3.36+2	4.56+0	4.47–2	8.24–4	3.40+2
8.581 L_{II}	2.77+2	4.28+0	4.70–2	9.24–4	2.81+2
8.581	3.88+2	4.28+0	4.70–2	9.24–4	3.92+2
9.0	3.40+2	4.10+0	4.86–2	9.98–4	3.45+2
9.046 L_I	3.36+2	4.08+0	4.88–2	1.01–3	3.40+2
9.046	4.03+2	4.08+0	4.88–2	1.01–3	4.07+2
10.0	3.06+2	3.70+0	5.23–2	1.18–3	3.10+2
12.0	1.86+2	3.06+0	5.88–2	1.57–3	1.89+2
15.0	1.01+2	2.38+0	6.72–2	2.20–3	1.04+2
17.0	7.18+1	2.06+0	7.21–2	2.64–3	7.39+1
20.0	4.60+1	1.69+0	7.83–2	3.31–3	4.78+1
25.0	2.50+1	1.27+0	8.62–2	4.41–3	2.64+1
30.0	1.52+1	9.87–1	9.19–2	5.48–3	1.63+1
35.0	9.97+0	7.88–1	9.61–2	6.50–3	1.09+1
40.0	6.92+0	6.45–1	9.92–2	7.47–3	7.66+0
50.0	3.76+0	4.54–1	1.03–1	9.25–3	4.31+0
53.79 K	3.08+0	4.04–1	1.04–1	9.87–3	3.59+0
53.79	1.81+1	4.04–1	1.04–1	9.87–3	1.86+1
60.0	1.33+1	3.40–1	1.05–1	1.08–2	1.37+1
70.0	8.58+0	2.64–1	1.06–1	1.22–2	8.95+0
80.0	5.87+0	2.11–1	1.06–1	1.35–2	6.19+0
90.0	4.21+0	1.72–1	1.06–1	1.46–2	4.48+0
100.0	3.12+0	1.43–1	1.05–1	1.56–2	3.37+0
120.0	1.86+0	1.04–1	1.03–1	1.72–2	2.07+0
150.0	9.94–1	6.93–2	9.97–2	1.90–2	1.16+0
170.0	7.00–1	5.52–2	9.73–2	2.00–2	8.52–1
200.0	4.45–1	4.10–2	9.37–2	2.11–2	5.80–1
250.0	2.40–1	2.70–2	8.82–2	2.23–2	3.55–1
300.0	1.46–1	1.92–2	8.34–2	2.31–2	2.48–1
350.0	9.61–2	1.44–2	7.92–2	2.36–2	1.90–1
400.0	6.71–2	1.11–2	7.56–2	2.38–2	1.54–1
500.0	3.72–2	7.26–3	6.95–2	2.40–2	1.14–1
600.0	2.31–2	5.09–3	6.45–2	2.40–2	9.27–2
700.0	1.56–2	3.77–3	6.04–2	2.38–2	7.97–2
800.0	1.11–2	2.90–3	5.69–2	2.34–2	7.09–2
900.0	8.28–3	2.30–3	5.39–2	2.31–2	6.45–2
1,000.0	6.39–3	1.87–3	5.13–2	2.27–2	5.96–2

Holmium **Z = 67**

Energy (keV)	τ/ρ (cm²/g)	σ_c/ρ (cm²/g)	σ_I/ρ (cm²/g)	σ_a/ρ (cm²/g)	μ/ρ (cm²/g)
0.1	2.41+4	1.09+1	9.11–5	2.42–8	2.41+4
0.15	2.21+4	1.09+1	1.89–4	7.62–8	2.21+4
0.1603 $N_{IV,V}$	2.14+4	1.09+1	2.14–4	9.27–8	2.14+4
0.1617	2.35+4	1.09+1	2.18–4	9.51–8	2.35+4

TABLE 3 (continued)

Energy (keV)		τ/ρ (cm^2/g)	σ_c/ρ (cm^2/g)	σ_I/ρ (cm^2/g)	σ_a/ρ (cm^2/g)	μ/ρ (cm^2/g)
0.2		2.00+4	1.09+1	3.24–4	1.75–7	2.00+4
0.3		1.31+4	1.08+1	6.98–4	5.67–7	1.31+4
0.3182	$N_{II,III}$	1.24+4	1.08+1	7.79–4	6.71–7	1.24+4
0.3196		1.40+4	1.08+1	7.85–4	6.79–7	1.40+4
0.4		1.10+4	1.08+1	1.19–3	1.28–6	1.10+4
0.435	N_I	9.91+3	1.08+1	1.38–3	1.62–6	9.92+3
0.4364		1.06+4	1.08+1	1.39–3	1.64–6	1.06+4
0.5		8.81+3	1.07+1	1.77–3	2.37–6	8.82+3
0.6		6.70+3	1.07+1	2.40–3	3.85–6	6.71+3
0.7		5.21+3	1.06+1	3.07–3	5.69–6	5.22+3
0.8		4.13+3	1.05+1	3.76–3	7.90–6	4.14+3
0.9		3.34+3	1.04+1	4.45–3	1.05–5	3.35+3
1.0		2.74+3	1.03+1	5.15–3	1.33–5	2.75+3
1.3663	$M_{IV,V}$	1.47+3	9.99+0	7.60–3	2.63–5	1.48+3
1.3677		1.68+3	9.99+0	7.61–3	2.63–5	1.69+3
1.4		6.30+3	9.96+0	7.82–3	2.77–5	6.31+3
1.6		4.89+3	9.78+0	9.15–3	3.67–5	4.90+3
1.8		3.65+3	9.57+0	1.05–2	4.70–5	3.66+3
1.8013	$M_{II,III}$	3.65+3	9.57+0	1.05–2	4.71–5	3.66+3
1.8027		4.68+3	9.57+0	1.05–2	4.72–5	4.69+3
2.0		3.68+3	9.38+0	1.18–2	5.86–5	3.69+3
2.1273	M_I	3.19+3	9.24+0	1.26–2	6.66–5	3.19+3
2.1287		3.42+3	9.24+0	1.26–2	6.67–5	3.43+3
3.0		1.51+3	8.39+0	1.83–2	1.35–4	1.52+3
4.0		7.35+2	7.44+0	2.45–2	2.36–4	7.42+2
5.0		4.27+2	6.59+0	3.01–2	3.59–4	4.34+3
6.0		2.67+2	5.86+0	3.52–2	4.98–4	2.73+2
7.0		1.79+2	5.23+0	3.99–2	6.51–4	1.84+2
8.0		1.27+2	4.68+0	4.41–2	8.14–4	1.32+2
8.071	L_{III}	1.24+2	4.64+0	4.44–2	8.26–4	1.29+2
8.071		3.41+2	4.64+0	4.44–2	8.26–4	3.45+2
8.918	L_{II}	2.59+2	4.25+0	4.77–2	9.72–4	2.64+2
8.918		3.63+2	4.25+0	4.77–2	9.72–4	3.67+2
9.0		3.54+2	4.21+0	4.80–2	9.87–4	3.59+2
9.394	L_I	3.15+2	4.04+0	4.95–2	1.06–3	3.19+2
9.394		3.78+2	4.04+0	4.95–2	1.06–3	3.82+2
10.0		3.19+2	3.80+0	5.16–2	1.17–3	3.23+2
12.0		1.94+2	3.14+0	5.82–2	1.56–3	1.97+2
15.0		1.06+2	2.44+0	6.66–2	2.18–3	1.08+2
17.0		7.50+1	2.11+0	7.14–2	2.62–3	7.72+1
20.0		4.82+1	1.73+0	7.77–2	3.29–3	5.00+1
25.0		2.62+1	1.30+0	8.56–2	4.39–3	2.76+1
30.0		1.60+1	1.01+0	9.14–2	5.46–3	1.71+1
35.0		1.05+1	8.08–1	9.57–2	6.49–3	1.14+1
40.0		7.28+0	6.61–1	9.88–2	7.45–3	8.04+0
50.0		3.96+0	4.65–1	1.03–1	9.23–3	4.53+0
55.62	K	2.96+0	3.93–1	1.04–1	1.01–2	3.46+0
55.62		1.72+1	3.93–1	1.04–1	1.01–2	1.76+1
60.0		1.38+1	3.48–1	1.05–1	1.08–2	1.43+1
70.0		8.95+0	2.70–1	1.06–1	1.22–2	9.33+0
80.0		6.14+0	2.16–1	1.06–1	1.35–2	6.46+0
90.0		4.40+0	1.76–1	1.06–1	1.46–2	4.68+0
100.0		3.26+0	1.47–1	1.05–1	1.56–2	3.52+0

TABLE 3 (continued)

Energy (keV)	τ/ρ (cm²/g)	σ_c/ρ (cm²/g)	σ_I/ρ (cm²/g)	σ_a/ρ (cm²/g)	μ/ρ (cm²/g)
120.0	1.95+0	1.06−1	1.03−1	1.72−2	2.16+0
150.0	1.04+0	7.11−2	9.97−2	1.90−2	1.21+0
170.0	7.34−1	5.66−2	9.72−2	1.99−2	8.88−1
200.0	4.67−1	4.20−2	9.36−2	2.11−2	6.03−1
250.0	2.52−1	2.77−2	8.82−2	2.23−2	3.68−1
300.0	1.53−1	1.97−2	8.34−2	2.31−2	2.56−1
350.0	1.01−1	1.47−2	7.92−2	2.36−2	1.95−1
400.0	7.05−2	1.14−2	7.56−2	2.38−2	1.58−1
500.0	3.91−2	7.45−3	6.94−2	2.40−2	1.16−1
600.0	2.44−2	5.23−3	6.45−2	2.40−2	9.41−2
700.0	1.64−2	3.87−3	6.04−2	2.38−2	8.07−2
800.0	1.17−2	2.98−3	5.69−2	2.35−2	7.16−2
900.0	8.75−3	2.36−3	5.39−2	2.31−2	6.50−2
1,000.0	6.76−3	1.92−3	5.13−2	2.27−2	6.00−2

Erbium Z = 68

Energy (keV)	τ/ρ (cm²/g)	σ_c/ρ (cm²/g)	σ_I/ρ (cm²/g)	σ_a/ρ (cm²/g)	μ/ρ (cm²/g)
0.1	2.48+4	1.11+1	8.88−5	2.36−8	2.48+4
0.15	2.33+4	1.11+1	1.83−4	7.39−8	2.33+4
0.1705 $N_{IV,V}$	2.19+4	1.11+1	2.34−4	1.08−7	2.19+4
0.1719	2.39+4	1.11+1	2.37−4	1.10−7	2.39+4
0.2	2.20+4	1.10+1	3.14−4	1.70−7	2.20+4
0.3	1.41+4	1.10+1	6.78−4	5.51−7	1.41+4
0.3347 $N_{II,III}$	1.26+4	1.10+1	8.31−4	7.53−7	1.26+4
0.3361	1.43+4	1.10+1	8.37−4	7.62−7	1.43+4
0.4	1.18+4	1.10+1	1.15−3	1.25−6	1.18+4
0.4484 N_I	1.02+4	1.09+1	1.42−3	1.72−6	1.02+4
0.4498	1.09+4	1.09+1	1.43−3	1.73−6	1.09+4
0.5	9.40+3	1.09+1	1.72−3	2.31−6	9.42+3
0.6	7.16+3	1.09+1	2.34−3	3.74−6	7.17+3
0.7	5.55+3	1.08+1	2.99−3	5.55−6	5.56+3
0.8	4.40+3	1.07+1	3.67−3	7.71−6	4.41+3
0.9	3.55+3	1.06+1	4.35−3	1.02−5	3.56+3
1.0	2.91+3	1.05+1	5.02−3	1.30−5	2.92+3
1.4	1.48+3	1.01+1	7.65−3	2.71−5	1.49+3
1.4263 $M_{IV,V}$	1.42+3	1.01+1	7.82−3	2.82−5	1.43+3
1.4277	1.61+3	1.01+1	7.83−3	2.83−5	1.62+3
1.6	5.17+3	9.96+0	8.95−3	3.60−5	5.18+3
1.8	3.85+3	9.76+0	1.03−2	4.61−5	3.86+3
1.8753 $M_{II,III}$	3.48+3	9.68+0	1.07−2	5.02−5	3.49+3
1.8767	4.50+3	9.68+0	1.08−2	5.03−5	4.51+3
2.0	3.85+3	9.56+0	1.16−2	5.75−5	3.86+3
2.2053 M_I	3.07+3	9.34+0	1.29−2	7.04−5	3.08+3
2.2067	3.29+3	9.34+0	1.29−2	7.05−5	3.30+3
3.0	1.58+3	8.57+0	1.80−2	1.32−4	1.59+3
4.0	7.71+2	7.62+0	2.41−2	2.33−4	7.78+2
5.0	4.46+2	6.76+0	2.96−2	3.54−4	4.53+2
6.0	2.78+2	6.01+0	3.47−2	4.91−4	2.84+2
7.0	1.86+2	5.37+0	3.94−2	6.43−4	1.92+2
8.0	1.32+2	4.81+0	4.36−2	8.05−4	1.37+2
8.358 L_{III}	1.17+2	4.63+0	4.50−2	8.65−4	1.22+2
8.358	3.22+2	4.63+0	4.50−2	8.65−4	3.27+2
9.0	2.64+2	4.33+0	4.75−2	9.77−4	2.68+2

TABLE 3 (continued)

Energy (keV)	τ/ρ (cm^2/g)	σ_c/ρ (cm^2/g)	σ_I/ρ (cm^2/g)	σ_a/ρ (cm^2/g)	μ/ρ (cm^2/g)
9.264 L_{II}	2.44+2	4.21+0	4.84−2	1.02−3	2.48+2
9.264	3.41+2	4.21+0	4.84−2	1.02−3	3.45+2
9.751 L_I	2.97+2	4.01+0	5.02−2	1.11−3	3.01+2
9.751	3.56+2	4.01+0	5.02−2	1.11−3	3.60+2
10.0	3.32+2	3.91+0	5.11−2	1.16−3	3.36+2
12.0	2.02+2	3.23+0	5.76−2	1.54−3	2.05+2
15.0	1.10+2	2.51+0	6.60−2	2.16−3	1.13+2
17.0	7.82+1	2.16+0	7.08−2	2.60−3	8.04+1
20.0	5.02+1	1.77+0	7.71−2	3.26−3	5.20+1
25.0	2.73+1	1.33+0	8.51−2	4.37−3	2.87+1
30.0	1.66+1	1.04+0	9.10−2	5.44−3	1.77+1
35.0	1.09+1	8.29−1	9.53−2	6.47−3	1.18+1
40.0	7.58+0	6.78−1	9.85−2	7.44−3	8.36+0
50.0	4.13+0	4.77−1	1.03−1	9.22−3	4.71+0
57.49 K	2.82+0	3.82−1	1.04−1	1.04−2	3.31+0
57.49	1.63+1	3.82−1	1.04−1	1.04−2	1.68+1
60.0	1.45+1	3.57−1	1.05−1	1.08−2	1.49+1
70.0	9.34+0	2.77−1	1.06−1	1.22−2	9.72+0
80.0	6.40+0	2.21−1	1.06−1	1.35−2	6.73+0
90.0	4.58+0	1.81−1	1.06−1	1.46−2	4.87+0
100.0	3.40+0	1.50−1	1.05−1	1.56−2	3.66+0
120.0	2.04+0	1.09−1	1.03−1	1.72−2	2.25+0
150.0	1.09+0	7.29−2	9.96−2	1.90−2	1.26+0
170.0	7.67−1	5.81−2	9.72−2	2.00−2	9.22−1
200.0	4.88−1	4.31−2	9.36−2	2.11−2	6.25−1
250.0	2.64−1	2.85−2	8.82−2	2.23−2	3.81−1
300.0	1.61−1	2.02−2	8.34−2	2.31−2	2.64−1
350.0	1.06−1	1.51−2	7.93−2	2.36−2	2.00−1
400.0	7.42−2	1.17−2	7.56−2	2.39−2	1.62−1
500.0	4.12−2	7.66−3	6.95−2	2.41−2	1.18−1
600.0	2.57−2	5.37−3	6.45−2	2.40−2	9.56−2
700.0	1.73−2	3.98−3	6.04−2	2.38−2	8.17−2
800.0	1.24−2	3.06−3	5.69−2	2.35−2	7.24−2
900.0	9.25−3	2.43−3	5.39−2	2.31−2	6.56−2
1,000.0	7.14−3	1.97−3	5.13−2	2.27−2	6.04−2

Thulium **Z = 69**

Energy (keV)	τ/ρ (cm^2/g)	σ_c/ρ (cm^2/g)	σ_I/ρ (cm^2/g)	σ_a/ρ (cm^2/g)	μ/ρ (cm^2/g)
0.1	2.50+4	1.13+1	8.74−5	2.32−8	2.51+4
0.15	2.42+4	1.13+1	1.79−4	7.23−8	2.42+4
0.1789 $N_{IV,V}$	2.24+4	1.13+1	2.50−4	1.21−7	2.24+4
0.1803	2.44+4	1.13+1	2.54−4	1.23−7	2.44+4
0.2	2.38+4	1.13+1	3.07−4	1.66−7	2.39+4
0.3	1.52+4	1.12+1	6.62−4	5.38−7	1.52+4
0.3523 $N_{II,III}$	1.28+4	1.12+1	8.92−4	8.50−7	1.29+4
0.3537	1.45+4	1.12+1	8.98−4	8.60−7	1.45+4
0.4	1.26+4	1.12+1	1.13−3	1.22−6	1.26+4
0.471 N_I	1.03+4	1.11+1	1.51−3	1.92−6	1.03+4
0.4724	1.09+4	1.11+1	1.52−3	1.93−6	1.09+4
0.5	1.01+4	1.11+1	1.68−3	2.25−6	1.01+4
0.6	7.68+3	1.11+1	2.29−3	3.66−6	7.69+3
0.7	5.95+3	1.10+1	2.93−3	5.43−6	5.96+3
0.8	4.71+3	1.09+1	3.59−3	7.55−6	4.72+3
0.9	3.79+3	1.08+1	4.26−3	1.00−5	3.80+3

TABLE 3 (continued)

Energy (keV)	τ/ρ (cm²/g)	σ_c/ρ (cm²/g)	σ_I/ρ (cm²/g)	σ_a/ρ (cm²/g)	μ/ρ (cm²/g)
1.0	3.10+3	1.07+1	4.92–3	1.28–5	3.11+3
1.4	1.57+3	1.04+1	7.51–3	2.66–5	1.58+3
1.4853 $M_{IV,V}$	1.39+3	1.03+1	8.07–3	3.02–5	1.40+3
1.4867	1.56+3	1.03+1	8.07–3	3.03–5	1.57+3
1.6	5.47+3	1.02+1	8.80–3	3.54–5	5.48+3
1.8	4.08+3	9.98+0	1.01–2	4.53–5	4.09+3
1.9523 $M_{II,III}$	3.33+3	9.83+0	1.11–2	5.38–5	3.34+3
1.9537	4.34+3	9.83+0	1.11–2	5.38–5	4.35+3
2.0	4.04+3	9.79+0	1.14–2	5.65–5	4.05+3
2.3063 M_I	2.90+3	9.47+0	1.33–2	7.61–5	2.91+3
2.3077	3.11+3	9.47+0	1.33–2	7.62–5	3.12+3
3.0	1.67+3	8.79+0	1.77–2	1.30–4	1.67+3
4.0	8.12+2	7.83+0	2.38–2	2.30–4	8.20+2
5.0	4.70+2	6.96+0	2.93–2	3.50–4	4.77+2
6.0	2.93+2	6.19+0	3.43–2	4.87–4	3.00+2
7.0	1.97+2	5.53+0	3.90–2	6.37–4	2.02+2
8.0	1.39+2	4.96+0	4.32–2	7.98–4	1.44+2
8.648 L_{III}	1.14+2	4.63+0	4.57–2	9.08–4	1.19+2
8.648	3.10+2	4.63+0	4.57–2	9.08–4	3.15+2
9.0	2.78+2	4.46+0	4.71–2	9.69–4	2.82+2
9.617 L_{II}	2.32+2	4.19+0	4.93–2	1.08–3	2.36+2
9.617	3.25+2	4.19+0	4.93–2	1.08–3	3.29+2
10.0	2.92+2	4.03+0	5.07–2	1.15–3	2.96+2
10.12 L_I	2.82+2	3.98+0	5.11–2	1.17–3	2.87+2
10.12	3.39+2	3.98+0	5.11–2	1.17–3	3.43+2
12.0	2.13+2	3.33+0	5.72–2	1.53–3	2.16+2
15.0	1.16+2	2.59+0	6.56–2	2.15–3	1.18+2
17.0	8.23+1	2.23+0	7.04–2	2.59–3	8.46+1
20.0	5.28+1	1.82+0	7.67–2	3.25–3	5.47+1
25.0	2.87+1	1.37+0	8.49–2	4.36–3	3.02+1
30.0	1.75+1	1.07+0	9.09–2	5.44–3	1.86+1
35.0	1.15+1	8.53–1	9.53–2	6.48–3	1.24+1
40.0	7.96+0	6.98–1	9.85–2	7.45–3	8.76+0
50.0	4.33+0	4.91–1	1.03–1	9.24–3	4.92+0
59.39 K	2.71+0	3.73–1	1.05–1	1.07–2	3.18+0
59.39	1.56+1	3.73–1	1.05–1	1.07–2	1.60+1
60.0	1.51+1	3.67–1	1.05–1	1.08–2	1.56+1
70.0	9.77+0	2.85–1	1.06–1	1.23–2	1.02+1
80.0	6.70+0	2.28–1	1.06–1	1.35–2	7.03+0
90.0	4.80+0	1.86–1	1.06–1	1.46–2	5.09+0
100.0	3.57+0	1.55–1	1.05–1	1.56–2	3.83+0
120.0	2.13+0	1.12–1	1.03–1	1.72–2	2.35+0
150.0	1.14+0	7.50–2	1.00–1	1.91–2	1.32+0
170.0	8.05–1	5.98–2	9.75–2	2.00–2	9.63–1
200.0	5.13–1	4.43–2	9.40–2	2.11–2	6.51–1
250.0	2.78–1	2.93–2	8.86–2	2.24–2	3.96–1
300.0	1.69–1	2.08–2	8.38–2	2.32–2	2.74–1
350.0	1.12–1	1.56–2	7.96–2	2.37–2	2.07–1
400.0	7.83–2	1.21–2	7.59–2	2.40–2	1.66–1
500.0	4.35–2	7.89–3	6.98–2	2.42–2	1.21–1
600.0	2.72–2	5.54–3	6.48–2	2.41–2	9.75–2
700.0	1.83–2	4.10–3	6.07–2	2.39–2	8.31–2
800.0	1.31–2	3.15–3	5.72–2	2.36–2	7.35–2

Energy (keV)	τ/ρ (cm^2/g)	σ_c/ρ (cm^2/g)	σ_I/ρ (cm^2/g)	σ_a/ρ (cm^2/g)	μ/ρ (cm^2/g)
900.0	9.81−3	2.50−3	5.42−2	2.32−2	6.65−2
1,000.0	7.58−3	2.04−3	5.15−2	2.28−2	6.12−2

Ytterbium Z = 70

Energy (keV)	τ/ρ (cm^2/g)	σ_c/ρ (cm^2/g)	σ_I/ρ (cm^2/g)	σ_a/ρ (cm^2/g)	μ/ρ (cm^2/g)
0.1	2.46+4	1.13+1	8.29−5	2.20−8	2.46+4
0.15	2.46+4	1.13+1	1.71−4	6.92−8	2.46+4
0.1895 $N_{IV,V}$	2.24+4	1.13+1	2.67−4	1.37−7	2.24+4
0.1909	2.43+4	1.13+1	2.70−4	1.40−7	2.43+4
0.2	2.44+4	1.13+1	2.95−4	1.59−7	2.44+4
0.3	1.60+4	1.13+1	6.36−4	5.18−7	1.60+4
0.3605 $N_{II,III}$	1.32+4	1.13+1	8.95−4	8.73−7	1.32+4
0.3619	1.48+4	1.13+1	9.01−4	8.83−7	1.48+4
0.4	1.32+4	1.12+1	1.08−3	1.17−6	1.32+4
0.4865 N_I	1.03+4	1.12+1	1.54−3	2.02−6	1.03+4
0.4879	1.09+4	1.12+1	1.55−3	2.03−6	1.09+4
0.5	1.05+4	1.12+1	1.62−3	2.17−6	1.06+4
0.6	8.05+3	1.11+1	2.20−3	3.53−6	8.06+3
0.7	6.24+3	1.11+1	2.83−3	5.24−6	6.25+3
0.8	4.93+3	1.10+1	3.47−3	7.29−6	4.94+3
0.9	3.96+3	1.09+1	4.12−3	9.68−6	3.97+3
1.0	3.24+3	1.08+1	4.76−3	1.23−5	3.25+3
1.5	1.41+3	1.04+1	7.91−3	2.99−5	1.42+3
1.5463 $M_{IV,V}$	1.32+3	1.03+1	8.20−3	3.19−5	1.33+3
1.5477	1.48+3	1.03+1	8.20−3	3.20−5	1.49+3
1.7	4.90+3	1.02+1	9.15−3	3.90−5	4.91+3
1.8	4.24+3	1.01+1	9.77−3	4.40−5	4.25+3
2.0233 $M_{II,III}$	3.15+3	9.84+0	1.12−2	5.62−5	3.16+3
2.0247	4.13+3	9.84+0	1.12−2	5.63−5	4.14+3
2.2	3.34+3	9.65+0	1.23−2	6.70−5	3.35+3
2.3973 M_I	2.73+3	9.47+0	1.35−2	8.01−5	2.74+3
2.3987	2.93+3	9.47+0	1.35−2	8.02−5	2.94+3
2.6	2.42+3	9.27+0	1.48−2	9.47−5	2.43+3
3.0	1.72+3	8.88+0	1.72−2	1.27−4	1.73+3
4.0	8.39+2	7.92+0	2.31−2	2.24−4	8.47+2
5.0	4.87+2	7.05+0	2.85−2	3.41−4	4.94+2
6.0	3.04+2	6.28+0	3.35−2	4.75−4	3.10+2
7.0	2.04+2	5.62+0	3.80−2	6.22−4	2.10+2
8.0	1.44+2	5.04+0	4.22−2	7.81−4	1.49+2
8.944 L_{III}	1.08+2	4.56+0	4.58−2	9.39−4	1.13+2
8.944	2.93+2	4.56+0	4.58−2	9.39−4	2.98+2
9.0	2.88+2	4.53+0	4.60−2	9.48−4	2.93+2
9.978 L_{II}	2.18+2	4.11+0	4.95−2	1.12−3	2.22+2
9.978	3.05+2	4.11+0	4.95−2	1.12−3	3.09+2
10.0	3.03+2	4.10+0	4.96−2	1.13−3	3.07+2
10.49 L_I	2.66+2	3.90+0	5.12−2	1.21−3	2.70+2
10.49	3.19+2	3.90+0	5.12−2	1.21−3	3.23+2
12.0	2.21+2	3.39+0	5.60−2	1.50−3	2.24+2
15.0	1.20+2	2.63+0	6.43−2	2.11−3	1.23+2
17.0	8.52+1	2.26+0	6.91−2	2.54−3	8.75+1
20.0	5.46+1	1.85+0	7.53−2	3.20−3	5.66+1
25.0	2.97+1	1.39+0	8.34−2	4.30−3	3.11+1
30.0	1.80+1	1.08+0	8.94−2	5.37−3	1.92+1

Energy (keV)	τ/ρ (cm²/g)	σ_c/ρ (cm²/g)	σ_I/ρ (cm²/g)	σ_a/ρ (cm²/g)	μ/ρ (cm²/g)
35.0	1.18+1	8.66−1	9.39−2	6.39−3	1.28+1
40.0	8.21+0	7.08−1	9.71−2	7.36−3	9.02+0
50.0	4.46+0	4.98−1	1.01−1	9.14−3	5.06+0
60.0	2.71+0	3.72−1	1.04−1	1.07−2	3.19+0
61.33 K	2.55+0	3.59−1	1.04−1	1.09−2	3.02+0
61.33	1.43+1	3.59−1	1.04−1	1.09−2	1.48+1
70.0	9.94+0	2.89−1	1.05−1	1.21−2	1.03+1
80.0	6.85+0	2.31−1	1.05−1	1.34−2	7.19+0
90.0	4.94+0	1.89−1	1.05−1	1.45−2	5.23+0
100.0	3.68+0	1.57−1	1.04−1	1.54−2	3.94+0
120.0	2.21+0	1.14−1	1.02−1	1.71−2	2.43+0
150.0	1.19+0	7.62−2	9.89−2	1.89−2	1.36+0
170.0	8.38−1	6.07−2	9.65−2	1.98−2	9.95−1
200.0	5.35−1	4.50−2	9.30−2	2.09−2	6.72−1
250.0	2.89−1	2.98−2	8.76−2	2.22−2	4.07−1
300.0	1.76−1	2.11−2	8.29−2	2.30−2	2.80−1
350.0	1.16−1	1.58−2	7.88−2	2.34−2	2.11−1
400.0	8.14−2	1.23−2	7.51−2	2.37−2	1.69−1
500.0	4.52−2	8.02−3	6.91−2	2.39−2	1.22−1
600.0	2.82−2	5.62−3	6.41−2	2.39−2	9.80−2
700.0	1.91−2	4.16−3	6.01−2	2.37−2	8.34−2
800.0	1.37−2	3.20−3	5.66−2	2.33−2	7.35−2
900.0	1.02−2	2.54−3	5.37−2	2.30−2	6.64−2
1,000.0	7.92−3	2.07−3	5.11−2	2.26−2	6.10−2

Lutetium Z = 71

Energy (keV)	τ/ρ (cm²/g)	σ_c/ρ (cm²/g)	σ_I/ρ (cm²/g)	σ_a/ρ (cm²/g)	μ/ρ (cm²/g)
0.1	2.13+4	1.15+1	8.05−5	2.13−8	2.13+4
0.15	2.28+4	1.15+1	1.65−4	6.64−8	2.28+4
0.1982 $N_{IV,V}$	2.10+4	1.15+1	2.78−4	1.49−7	2.10+4
0.1996	2.26+4	1.15+1	2.82−4	1.52−7	2.26+4
0.2	2.26+4	1.15+1	2.83−4	1.53−7	2.26+4
0.3	1.60+4	1.15+1	6.13−4	4.98−7	1.60+4
0.3755 $N_{II,III}$	1.28+4	1.15+1	9.32−4	9.48−7	1.28+4
0.3769	1.41+4	1.15+1	9.39−4	9.58−7	1.41+4
0.4	1.33+4	1.14+1	1.05−3	1.13−6	1.34+4
0.5	1.01+4	1.14+1	1.57−3	2.12−6	1.02+4
0.5055 N_I	9.99+3	1.14+1	1.60−3	2.18−6	1.00+4
0.5069	1.06+4	1.14+1	1.61−3	2.20−6	1.06+4
0.6	8.25+3	1.13+1	2.16−3	3.46−6	8.26+3
0.7	6.42+3	1.13+1	2.78−3	5.18−6	6.43+3
0.8	5.09+3	1.12+1	3.43−3	7.25−6	5.10+3
0.9	4.10+3	1.11+1	4.09−3	9.65−6	4.11+3
1.0	3.36+3	1.10+1	4.75−3	1.24−5	3.37+3
1.5	1.47+3	1.05+1	7.97−3	3.02−5	1.49+3
1.6083 $M_{IV,V}$	1.27+3	1.04+1	8.64−3	3.50−5	1.28+3
1.6097	1.39+3	1.04+1	8.65−3	3.50−5	1.40+3
1.7	5.00+3	1.03+1	9.21−3	3.93−5	5.02+3
1.8	4.39+3	1.02+1	9.83−3	4.43−5	4.40+3
2.1033 $M_{II,III}$	2.97+3	9.90+0	1.17−2	6.11−5	2.98+3
2.1047	3.74+3	9.90+0	1.17−2	6.12−5	3.75+3
2.2	3.45+3	9.80+0	1.23−2	6.71−5	3.46+3
2.4903 M_I	2.58+3	9.52+0	1.41−2	8.66−5	2.59+3
2.4917	2.78+3	9.52+0	1.41−2	8.67−5	2.79+3

TABLE 3 (continued)

Energy (keV)	τ/ρ (cm^2/g)	σ_c/ρ (cm^2/g)	σ_I/ρ (cm^2/g)	σ_a/ρ (cm^2/g)	μ/ρ (cm^2/g)
2.6	2.51+3	9.40+0	1.48−2	9.45−5	2.51+3
3.0	1.78+3	9.01+0	1.72−2	1.26−4	1.79+3
4.0	8.75+2	8.05+0	2.30−2	2.22−4	8.83+2
5.0	5.09+2	7.18+0	2.84−2	3.39−4	5.16+2
6.0	3.17+2	6.41+0	3.34−2	4.73−4	3.23+2
7.0	2.12+2	5.73+0	3.79−2	6.20−4	2.18+2
8.0	1.50+2	5.15+0	4.21−2	7.79−4	1.55+2
9.0	1.11+2	4.64+0	4.59−2	9.46−4	1.15+2
9.244$_{L_{III}}$	1.03+2	4.53+0	4.67−2	9.88−4	1.08+2
9.244	2.80+2	4.53+0	4.67−2	9.88−4	2.85+2
10.0	2.26+2	4.20+0	4.94−2	1.12−3	2.30+2
10.35$_{L_{II}}$	2.06+2	4.05+0	5.06−2	1.18−3	2.10+2
10.35	2.88+2	4.05+0	5.06−2	1.18−3	2.92+2
10.87$_{L_I}$	2.52+2	3.84+0	5.22−2	1.28−3	2.56+2
10.87	3.02+2	3.84+0	5.22−2	1.28−3	3.06+2
12.0	2.31+2	3.47+0	5.58−2	1.50−3	2.34+2
15.0	1.25+2	2.69+0	6.41−2	2.10−3	1.28+2
17.0	8.90+1	2.32+0	6.88−2	2.53−3	9.14+1
20.0	5.71+1	1.90+0	7.50−2	3.19−3	5.91+1
25.0	3.10+1	1.42+0	8.32−2	4.29−3	3.25+1
30.0	1.89+1	1.11+0	8.93−2	5.36−3	2.01+1
35.0	1.24+1	8.88−1	9.38−2	6.39−3	1.34+1
40.0	8.59+0	7.26−1	9.71−2	7.36−3	9.42+0
50.0	4.67+0	5.11−1	1.01−1	9.15−3	5.28+0
60.0	2.84+0	3.82−1	1.04−1	1.07−2	3.32+0
63.31$_K$	2.45+0	3.50−1	1.04−1	1.12−2	2.90+0
63.31	1.40+1	3.50−1	1.04−1	1.12−2	1.44+1
70.0	1.05+1	2.97−1	1.05−1	1.21−2	1.09+1
80.0	7.21+0	2.37−1	1.05−1	1.34−2	7.55+0
90.0	5.17+0	1.94−1	1.05−1	1.45−2	5.47+0
100.0	3.84+0	1.61−1	1.04−1	1.55−2	4.11+0
120.0	2.30+0	1.17−1	1.03−1	1.71−2	2.52+0
150.0	1.23+0	7.82−2	9.91−2	1.89−2	1.41+0
170.0	8.72−1	6.23−2	9.67−2	1.99−2	1.03+0
200.0	5.57−1	4.62−2	9.32−2	2.10−2	6.96−1
250.0	3.02−1	3.06−2	8.79−2	2.23−2	4.21−1
300.0	1.84−1	2.17−2	8.31−2	2.30−2	2.89−1
350.0	1.22−1	1.62−2	7.90−2	2.35−2	2.17−1
400.0	8.55−2	1.26−2	7.53−2	2.38−2	1.73−1
500.0	4.77−2	8.23−3	6.93−2	2.40−2	1.25−1
600.0	2.98−2	5.78−3	6.43−2	2.39−2	9.99−2
700.0	2.02−2	4.27−3	6.03−2	2.37−2	8.47−2
800.0	1.45−2	3.29−3	5.68−2	2.34−2	7.46−2
900.0	1.08−2	2.61−3	5.38−2	2.31−2	6.72−2
1,000.0	8.37−3	2.12−3	5.12−2	2.27−2	6.17−2

Hafnium $Z = 72$

0.1	1.85+4	1.16+1	7.60−5	2.02−8	1.85+4
0.15	2.18+4	1.16+1	1.56−4	6.29−8	2.18+4
0.2	2.10+4	1.16+1	2.68−4	1.45−7	2.10+4
0.217$_{N_{IV,V}}$	2.02+4	1.16+1	3.13−4	1.84−7	2.02+4
0.2184	2.17+4	1.16+1	3.17−4	1.87−7	2.17+4
0.3	1.65+4	1.16+1	5.80−4	4.72−7	1.65+4

TABLE 3 (continued)

Energy (keV)	τ/ρ (cm^2/g)	σ_c/ρ (cm^2/g)	σ_I/ρ (cm^2/g)	σ_a/ρ (cm^2/g)	μ/ρ (cm^2/g)
0.3986 $N_{II,III}$	1.25+4	1.15+1	9.89–4	1.07–6	1.25+4
0.4	1.37+4	1.15+1	9.96–4	1.08–6	1.37+4
0.5	1.06+4	1.15+1	1.50–3	2.02–6	1.07+4
0.5374 N_I	9.61+3	1.15+1	1.70–3	2.46–6	9.62+3
0.5388	1.02+4	1.15+1	1.71–3	2.48–6	1.02+4
0.6	8.63+3	1.14+1	2.06–3	3.32–6	8.64+3
0.7	6.75+3	1.14+1	2.67–3	4.99–6	6.76+3
0.8	5.34+3	1.13+1	3.31–3	7.02–6	5.35+3
0.9	4.33+3	1.12+1	3.97–3	9.40–6	4.34+3
1.0	3.53+3	1.11+1	4.63–3	1.21–5	3.54+3
1.5	1.56+3	1.06+1	7.85–3	2.99–5	1.57+3
1.6833 $M_{IV,V}$	1.20+3	1.04+1	8.99–3	3.81–5	1.22+3
1.6847	1.30+3	1.04+1	9.00–3	3.82–5	1.31+3
1.8	4.55+3	1.03+1	9.70–3	4.38–5	4.56+3
2.1933 $M_{II,III}$	2.79+3	9.88+0	1.21–2	6.59–5	2.80+3
2.1947	3.44+3	9.88+0	1.21–2	6.59–5	3.45+3
2.2	3.56+3	9.88+0	1.21–2	6.63–5	3.57+3
2.6	2.41+3	9.47+0	1.46–2	9.32–5	2.42+3
2.6003 M_I	2.41+3	9.47+0	1.46–2	9.33–5	2.42+3
2.6017	2.61+3	9.47+0	1.46–2	9.34–5	2.62+3
3.0	1.85+3	9.08+0	1.69–2	1.24–4	1.86+3
4.0	9.12+2	8.11+0	2.27–2	2.19–4	9.20+2
5.0	5.29+2	7.24+0	2.80–2	3.34–4	5.36+2
6.0	3.29+2	6.46+0	3.29–2	4.67–4	3.36+2
7.0	2.20+2	5.79+0	3.75–2	6.13–4	2.26+2
8.0	1.56+2	5.21+0	4.16–2	7.70–4	1.61+2
9.0	1.15+2	4.70+0	4.53–2	9.36–4	1.19+2
9.561 L_{III}	9.80+1	4.44+0	4.73–2	1.03–3	1.03+2
9.561	2.67+2	4.44+0	4.73–2	1.03–3	2.71+2
10.0	2.36+2	4.25+0	4.89–2	1.11–3	2.40+2
10.74 L_{II}	1.94+2	3.95+0	5.13–2	1.24–3	1.98+2
10.74	2.72+2	3.95+0	5.13–2	1.24–3	2.76+2
11.27 L_I	2.38+2	3.76+0	5.29–2	1.34–3	2.42+2
11.27	2.86+2	3.76+0	5.29–2	1.34–3	2.90+2
12.0	2.41+2	3.52+0	5.52–2	1.48–3	2.44+2
15.0	1.31+2	2.74+0	6.33–2	2.08–3	1.33+2
17.0	9.28+1	2.35+0	6.80–2	2.50–3	9.52+1
20.0	5.95+1	1.92+0	7.42–2	3.15–3	6.14+1
25.0	3.23+1	1.44+0	8.23–2	4.24–3	3.38+1
30.0	1.96+1	1.13+0	8.83–2	5.31–3	2.08+1
35.0	1.28+1	9.02–1	9.28–2	6.33–3	1.38+1
40.0	8.91+0	7.38–1	9.62–2	7.30–3	9.75+0
50.0	4.84+0	5.19–1	1.00–1	9.07–3	5.46+0
60.0	2.94+0	3.88–1	1.03–1	1.06–2	3.43+0
65.35 K	2.33+0	3.37–1	1.03–1	1.14–2	2.77+0
65.35	1.29+1	3.37–1	1.03–1	1.14–2	1.33+1
70.0	1.06+1	3.01–1	1.04–1	1.20–2	1.11+1
80.0	7.33+0	2.41–1	1.04–1	1.33–2	7.68+0
90.0	5.27+0	1.97–1	1.04–1	1.44–2	5.57+0
100.0	3.93+0	1.64–1	1.04–1	1.54–2	4.20+0
120.0	2.36+0	1.19–1	1.02–1	1.70–2	2.59+0
150.0	1.27+0	7.95–2	9.84–2	1.88–2	1.45+0

TABLE 3 (continued)

Energy (keV)	τ/ρ (cm²/g)	σ_c/ρ (cm²/g)	σ_I/ρ (cm²/g)	σ_a/ρ (cm²/g)	μ/ρ (cm²/g)
170.0	9.01–1	6.34–2	9.60–2	1.98–2	1.06+0
200.0	5.76–1	4.70–2	9.26–2	2.09–2	7.16–1
250.0	3.14–1	3.11–2	8.73–2	2.21–2	4.32–1
300.0	1.92–1	2.21–2	8.26–2	2.29–2	2.96–1
350.0	1.27–1	1.65–2	7.85–2	2.34–2	2.22–1
400.0	8.92–2	1.28–2	7.49–2	2.36–2	1.77–1
500.0	4.98–2	8.37–3	6.88–2	2.39–2	1.27–1
600.0	3.12–2	5.87–3	6.39–2	2.38–2	1.01–1
700.0	2.11–2	4.35–3	5.99–2	2.36–2	8.54–2
800.0	1.52–2	3.35–3	5.64–2	2.33–2	7.49–2
900.0	1.14–2	2.66–3	5.35–2	2.29–2	6.75–2
1,000.0	8.79–3	2.16–3	5.09–2	2.25–2	6.18–2

Tantalum Z = 73

Energy (keV)	τ/ρ (cm²/g)	σ_c/ρ (cm²/g)	σ_I/ρ (cm²/g)	σ_a/ρ (cm²/g)	μ/ρ (cm²/g)
0.1	1.53+4	1.18+1	7.22–5	1.92–8	1.53+4
0.15	2.02+4	1.18+1	1.48–4	5.99–8	2.02+4
0.2	2.05+4	1.18+1	2.55–4	1.38–7	2.05+4
0.2334 $N_{IV,V}$	1.93+4	1.18+1	3.42–4	2.16–7	1.93+4
0.2348	2.07+4	1.18+1	3.46–4	2.20–7	2.07+4
0.3	1.69+4	1.17+1	5.53–4	4.50–7	1.69+4
0.4	1.29+4	1.17+1	9.50–4	1.03–6	1.29+4
0.4239 $N_{II,III}$	1.21+4	1.17+1	1.06–3	1.22–6	1.21+4
0.4253	1.32+4	1.17+1	1.07–3	1.23–6	1.32+4
0.5	1.11+4	1.16+1	1.43–3	1.94–6	1.11+4
0.5648 N_I	9.35+3	1.16+1	1.78–3	2.71–6	9.36+3
0.5662	9.93+3	1.16+1	1.79–3	2.73–6	9.94+3
0.6	9.04+3	1.16+1	1.98–3	3.19–6	9.05+3
0.7	7.08+3	1.15+1	2.58–3	4.82–6	7.09+3
0.8	5.62+3	1.14+1	3.20–3	6.80–6	5.63+3
0.9	4.55+3	1.14+1	3.85–3	9.13–6	4.56+3
1.0	3.72+3	1.13+1	4.50–3	1.18–5	3.73+3
1.3	2.20+3	1.10+1	6.43–3	2.15–5	2.22+3
1.7	1.25+3	1.06+1	8.95–3	3.84–5	1.26+3
1.735 M_V	1.19+3	1.05+1	9.16–3	4.00–5	1.21+3
1.735	4.05+3	1.05+1	9.16–3	4.00–5	4.06+3
1.793 M_{IV}	3.71+3	1.05+1	9.51–3	4.29–5	3.72+3
1.793	5.57+3	1.05+1	9.51–3	4.29–5	5.58+3
2.0	4.18+3	1.02+1	1.08–2	5.38–5	4.19+3
2.194 M_{III}	3.28+3	1.00+1	1.19–2	6.50–5	3.29+3
2.194	3.94+3	1.00+1	1.19–2	6.50–5	3.95+3
2.469 M_{II}	2.89+3	9.75+0	1.36–2	8.28–5	2.90+3
2.469	3.18+3	9.75+0	1.36–2	8.28–5	3.19+3
2.5	3.08+3	9.72+0	1.38–2	8.50–5	3.09+3
2.708 M_I	2.49+3	9.49+0	1.50–2	9.98–5	2.50+3
2.708	2.74+3	9.49+0	1.50–2	9.98–5	2.75+3
3.0	2.10+3	9.20+0	1.67–2	1.23–4	2.11+3
3.5	1.40+3	8.70+0	1.96–2	1.67–4	1.41+3
4.0	9.87+2	8.22+0	2.24–2	2.16–4	9.95+2
5.0	5.50+2	7.34+0	2.77–2	3.31–4	5.57+3
6.0	3.41+2	6.56+0	3.26–2	4.63–4	3.47+2
7.0	2.27+2	5.89+0	3.71–2	6.09–4	2.33+2
8.0	1.60+2	5.30+0	4.13–2	7.67–4	1.66+2

TABLE 3 (continued)

Energy (keV)	τ/ρ (cm^2/g)	σ_c/ρ (cm^2/g)	σ_I/ρ (cm^2/g)	σ_a/ρ (cm^2/g)	μ/ρ (cm^2/g)
9.0	1.18+2	4.79+0	4.51−2	9.33−4	1.23+2
9.881 L_{III}	9.21+1	4.39+0	4.82−2	1.08−3	9.66+1
9.881	2.41+2	4.39+0	4.82−2	1.08−3	2.46+2
10.0	2.34+2	4.34+0	4.86−2	1.11−3	2.38+2
11.14 L_{II}	1.74+2	3.88+0	5.23−2	1.31−3	1.78+2
11.14	2.44+2	3.88+0	5.23−2	1.31−3	2.48+2
11.68 L_I	2.15+2	3.69+0	5.40−2	1.41−3	2.19+2
11.68	2.58+2	3.69+0	5.40−2	1.41−3	2.62+2
12.0	2.40+2	3.59+0	5.49−2	1.47−3	2.43+2
15.0	1.31+2	2.79+0	6.30−2	2.07−3	1.34+2
17.0	9.34+1	2.40+0	6.76−2	2.48−3	9.59+1
20.0	6.02+1	1.96+0	7.38−2	3.13−3	6.22+1
25.0	3.29+1	1.47+0	8.18−2	4.22−3	3.45+1
30.0	2.01+1	1.15+0	8.79−2	5.29−3	2.13+1
35.0	1.33+1	9.21−1	9.25−2	6.31−3	1.43+1
40.0	9.24+0	7.55−1	9.58−2	7.28−3	1.01+1
50.0	5.05+0	5.31−1	1.00−1	9.05−3	5.68+0
60.0	3.08+0	3.97−1	1.03−1	1.06−2	3.58+0
67.42 K	2.25+0	3.28−1	1.03−1	1.17−2	2.68+0
67.42	1.19+1	3.28−1	1.03−1	1.17−2	1.23+1
70.0	1.07+1	3.08−1	1.04−1	1.20−2	1.11+1
80.0	7.44+0	2.46−1	1.04−1	1.33−2	7.78+0
90.0	5.39+0	2.01−1	1.04−1	1.44−2	5.69+0
100.0	4.03+0	1.68−1	1.03−1	1.54−2	4.30+0
120.0	2.44+0	1.22−1	1.02−1	1.70−2	2.67+0
150.0	1.32+0	8.14−2	9.83−2	1.88−2	1.50+0
170.0	9.40−1	6.49−2	9.60−2	1.98−2	1.10+0
200.0	6.03−1	4.81−2	9.25−2	2.09−2	7.44−1
250.0	3.29−1	3.18−2	8.72−2	2.21−2	4.48−1
300.0	2.01−1	2.26−2	8.26−2	2.29−2	3.07−1
350.0	1.34−1	1.69−2	7.84−2	2.34−2	2.29−1
400.0	9.39−2	1.31−2	7.49−2	2.36−2	1.82−1
500.0	5.25−2	8.57−3	6.88−2	2.39−2	1.30−1
600.0	3.29−2	6.01−3	6.39−2	2.38−2	1.03−1
700.0	2.23−2	4.45−3	5.99−2	2.36−2	8.66−2
800.0	1.60−2	3.42−3	5.64−2	2.33−2	7.59−2
900.0	1.20−2	2.72−3	5.35−2	2.29−2	6.82−2
1,000.0	9.29−3	2.21−3	5.09−2	2.25−2	6.24−2

Tungsten Z = 74

Energy (keV)	τ/ρ (cm^2/g)	σ_c/ρ (cm^2/g)	σ_I/ρ (cm^2/g)	σ_a/ρ (cm^2/g)	μ/ρ (cm^2/g)
0.1	1.17+4	1.19+1	6.78−5	1.80−8	1.17+4
0.15	1.81+4	1.19+1	1.40−4	5.65−8	1.81+4
0.2	1.98+4	1.19+1	2.41−4	1.31−7	1.98+4
0.2501 $N_{IV,V}$	1.86+4	1.19+1	3.70−4	2.51−7	1.86+4
0.2515	1.99+4	1.19+1	3.74−4	2.56−7	1.99+4
0.3	1.72+4	1.19+1	5.25−4	4.28−7	1.73+4
0.4	1.34+4	1.18+1	9.05−4	9.82−7	1.34+4
0.4467 $N_{II,III}$	1.18+4	1.18+1	1.12−3	1.35−6	1.18+4
0.4481	1.29+4	1.18+1	1.12−3	1.36−6	1.29+4
0.5	1.15+4	1.18+1	1.37−3	1.85−6	1.15+4
0.5943 N_I	9.06+3	1.17+1	1.87−3	2.98−6	9.07+3
0.5957	9.62+3	1.17+1	1.87−3	3.00−6	9.63+3

TABLE 3 (continued)

Energy (keV)	τ/ρ (cm^2/g)	σ_c/ρ (cm^2/g)	σ_I/ρ (cm^2/g)	σ_a/ρ (cm^2/g)	μ/ρ (cm^2/g)
0.6	9.47+3	1.17+1	1.90−3	3.06−6	9.48+3
0.7	7.41+3	1.17+1	2.47−3	4.63−6	7.42+3
0.8	5.89+3	1.16+1	3.08−3	6.56−6	5.91+3
0.9	4.77+3	1.15+1	3.71−3	8.83−6	4.78+3
1.0	3.91+3	1.14+1	4.35−3	1.14−5	3.92+3
1.3	2.32+3	1.11+1	6.25−3	2.10−5	2.33+3
1.7	1.31+3	1.07+1	8.75−3	3.76−5	1.32+3
1.809_{M_V}	1.10+3	1.06+1	9.40−3	4.28−5	1.11+3
1.809	3.73+3	1.06+1	9.40−3	4.28−5	3.74+3
$1.872_{M_{IV}}$	3.41+3	1.05+1	9.78−3	4.60−5	3.42+3
1.872	5.11+3	1.05+1	9.78−3	4.60−5	5.12+3
2.0	4.30+3	1.04+1	1.06−2	5.28−5	4.31+3
$2.281_{M_{III}}$	3.05+3	1.01+1	1.22−2	6.91−5	3.07+3
2.281	3.67+3	1.01+1	1.22−2	6.91−5	3.68+3
2.5	2.89+3	9.84+0	1.35−2	8.33−5	2.90+3
$2.575_{M_{II}}$	2.67+3	9.75+0	1.39−2	8.84−5	2.68+3
2.575	2.94+3	9.75+0	1.39−2	8.84−5	2.95+3
2.82_{M_I}	2.32+3	9.49+0	1.53−2	1.06−4	2.33+3
2.82	2.55+3	9.49+0	1.53−2	1.06−4	2.56+3
3.0	2.17+3	9.31+0	1.64−2	1.20−4	2.18+3
3.5	1.45+3	8.80+0	1.92−2	1.64−4	1.46+3
4.0	1.03+3	8.31+0	2.20−2	2.13−4	1.03+3
5.0	5.73+2	7.43+0	2.72−2	3.26−4	5.80+2
6.0	3.56+2	6.64+0	3.22−2	4.58−4	3.63+2
7.0	2.38+2	5.97+0	3.67−2	6.04−4	2.44+2
8.0	1.68+2	5.38+0	4.09−2	7.61−4	1.74+2
9.0	1.24+2	4.86+0	4.47−2	9.26−4	1.29+2
10.0	9.40+1	4.41+0	4.82−2	1.10−3	9.85+1
$10.21_{L_{III}}$	8.90+1	4.31+0	4.89−2	1.14−3	9.34+1
10.21	2.42+2	4.31+0	4.89−2	1.14−3	2.47+2
$11.54_{L_{II}}$	1.73+2	3.81+0	5.31−2	1.38−3	1.77+2
11.54	2.42+2	3.81+0	5.31−2	1.38−3	2.46+2
12.0	2.18+2	3.66+0	5.45−2	1.46−3	2.22+2
12.1_{L_I}	2.13+2	3.63+0	5.48−2	1.48−3	2.17+2
12.1	2.56+2	3.63+0	5.48−2	1.48−3	2.59+2
15.0	1.42+2	2.85+0	6.25−2	2.05−3	1.45+2
17.0	1.01+2	2.45+0	6.71−2	2.47−3	1.03+2
20.0	6.45+1	2.00+0	7.32−2	3.11−3	6.66+1
25.0	3.50+1	1.50+0	8.12−2	4.19−3	3.66+1
30.0	2.12+1	1.17+0	8.73−2	5.25−3	2.25+1
35.0	1.39+1	9.39−1	9.19−2	6.27−3	1.50+1
40.0	9.66+0	7.69−1	9.53−2	7.24−3	1.05+1
50.0	5.24+0	5.41−1	9.96−2	9.01−3	5.88+0
60.0	3.18+0	4.05−1	1.02−1	1.06−2	3.69+0
69.53_K	2.12+0	3.17−1	1.03−1	1.19−2	2.54+0
69.53	1.13+1	3.17−1	1.03−1	1.19−2	1.17+1
70.0	1.10+1	3.14−1	1.03−1	1.20−2	1.15+1
80.0	7.70+0	2.51−1	1.04−1	1.32−2	8.06+0
90.0	5.60+0	2.05−1	1.03−1	1.43−2	5.90+0
100.0	4.20+0	1.71−1	1.03−1	1.53−2	4.47+0
120.0	2.55+0	1.24−1	1.01−1	1.69−2	2.77+0
150.0	1.38+0	8.30−2	9.79−2	1.88−2	1.56+0

TABLE 3 (continued)

Energy (keV)	τ/ρ (cm²/g)	σ_c/ρ (cm²/g)	σ_I/ρ (cm²/g)	σ_a/ρ (cm²/g)	μ/ρ (cm²/g)
170.0	9.81–1	6.62–2	9.56–2	1.97–2	1.14+0
200.0	6.29–1	4.91–2	9.22–2	2.08–2	7.70–1
250.0	3.43–1	3.24–2	8.70–2	2.20–2	4.62–1
300.0	2.09–1	2.31–2	8.23–2	2.28–2	3.15–1
350.0	1.39–1	1.73–2	7.83–2	2.33–2	2.34–1
400.0	9.75–2	1.34–2	7.47–2	2.36–2	1.86–1
500.0	5.44–2	8.74–3	6.86–2	2.38–2	1.32–1
600.0	3.42–2	6.14–3	6.38–2	2.37–2	1.04–1
700.0	2.32–2	4.54–3	5.98–2	2.35–2	8.75–2
800.0	1.67–2	3.50–3	5.63–2	2.32–2	7.65–2
900.0	1.26–2	2.78–3	5.34–2	2.29–2	6.87–2
1,000.0	9.80–3	2.26–3	5.08–2	2.25–2	6.28–2

Rhenium **Z = 75**

Energy (keV)	τ/ρ (cm²/g)	σ_c/ρ (cm²/g)	σ_I/ρ (cm²/g)	σ_a/ρ (cm²/g)	μ/ρ (cm²/g)
0.1	8.95+3	1.21+1	6.46–5	1.72–8	8.97+3
0.15	1.57+4	1.21+1	1.34–4	5.42–8	1.57+4
0.2	1.86+4	1.21+1	2.31–4	1.25–7	1.86+4
0.2649 $N_{IV,V}$	1.77+4	1.21+1	3.95–4	2.84–7	1.78+4
0.2663	1.89+4	1.21+1	3.99–4	2.89–7	1.89+4
0.3	1.72+4	1.20+1	5.02–4	4.09–7	1.73+4
0.4	1.36+4	1.20+1	8.67–4	9.40–7	1.36+4
0.4682 $N_{II,III}$	1.15+4	1.20+1	1.16–3	1.48–6	1.15+4
0.4696	1.24+4	1.20+1	1.17–3	1.49–6	1.24+4
0.5	1.18+4	1.20+1	1.31–3	1.78–6	1.18+4
0.6	9.23+3	1.19+1	1.82–3	2.94–6	9.24+3
0.6243 N_I	8.70+3	1.19+1	1.95–3	3.28–6	8.71+3
0.6257	9.24+3	1.19+1	1.96–3	3.30–6	9.25+3
0.7	7.68+3	1.18+1	2.38–3	4.46–6	7.69+3
0.8	6.12+3	1.18+1	2.98–3	6.34–6	6.14+3
0.9	4.96+3	1.17+1	3.59–3	8.56–6	4.97+3
1.0	4.08+3	1.16+1	4.22–3	1.11–5	4.09+3
1.3	2.42+3	1.13+1	6.10–3	2.05–5	2.44+3
1.7	1.38+3	1.09+1	8.57–3	3.69–5	1.39+3
1.883 M_V	1.08+3	1.07+1	9.65–3	4.58–5	1.09+3
1.883	3.49+3	1.07+1	9.65–3	4.58–5	3.50+3
1.949	3.19+3	1.06+1	1.00–2	4.92–5	3.20+3
1.949 M_{IV}	4.78+3	1.06+1	1.00–2	4.92–5	4.79+3
2.0	4.47+3	1.05+1	1.04–2	5.19–5	4.48+3
2.367 M_{III}	2.88+3	1.01+1	1.25–2	7.33–5	2.89+3
2.367	3.46+3	1.01+1	1.25–2	7.33–5	3.47+3
2.5	3.00+3	9.99+0	1.33–2	8.20–5	3.01+3
2.682 M_{II}	2.50+3	9.78+0	1.43–2	9.45–5	2.51+3
2.682	2.75+3	9.78+0	1.43–2	9.45–5	2.76+3
2.932 M_I	2.18+3	9.52+0	1.57–2	1.13–4	2.19+3
2.932	2.40+3	9.52+0	1.57–2	1.13–4	2.41+3
3.0	2.26+3	9.45+0	1.61–2	1.18–4	2.27+3
3.5	1.51+3	8.93+0	1.89–2	1.61–4	1.52+3
4.0	1.07+3	8.44+0	2.16–2	2.09–4	1.08+3
5.0	5.98+2	7.54+0	2.68–2	3.22–4	6.06+2
6.0	3.72+2	6.75+0	3.18–2	4.53–4	3.79+2
7.0	2.49+2	6.06+0	3.64–2	5.99–4	2.55+2
8.0	1.76+2	5.47+0	4.06–2	7.57–4	1.82+2

TABLE 3 (continued)

Energy (keV)	τ/ρ (cm²/g)	σ_c/ρ (cm²/g)	σ_I/ρ (cm²/g)	σ_a/ρ (cm²/g)	μ/ρ (cm²/g)
9.0	1.30+2	4.95+0	4.44–2	9.23–4	1.35+2
10.0	9.86+1	4.49+0	4.80–2	1.10–3	1.03+2
10.54 L_{III}	8.60+1	4.26+0	4.97–2	1.19–3	9.03+1
10.54	2.27+2	4.26+0	4.97–2	1.19–3	2.32+2
11.96 L_{II}	1.61+2	3.75+0	5.41–2	1.45–3	1.65+2
11.96	2.26+2	3.75+0	5.41–2	1.45–3	2.29+2
12.0	2.24+2	3.73+0	5.43–2	1.46–3	2.27+2
12.53 L_I	1.99+2	3.55+0	5.57–2	1.56–3	2.02+2
12.53	2.39+2	3.55+0	5.57–2	1.56–3	2.42+2
15.0	1.46+2	2.91+0	6.22–2	2.05–3	1.49+2
17.0	1.04+2	2.50+0	6.68–2	2.46–3	1.06+2
20.0	6.67+1	2.04+0	7.28–2	3.09–3	6.88+1
25.0	3.63+1	1.53+0	8.09–2	4.17–3	3.79+1
30.0	2.21+1	1.19+0	8.70–2	5.23–3	2.34+1
35.0	1.45+1	9.59–1	9.16–2	6.26–3	1.56+1
40.0	1.01+1	7.86–1	9.50–2	7.22–3	1.10+1
50.0	5.49+0	5.53–1	9.94–2	8.99–3	6.14+0
60.0	3.34+0	4.13–1	1.02–1	1.06–2	3.86+0
70.0	2.19+0	3.21–1	1.03–1	1.20–2	2.62+0
71.68 K	2.06+0	3.08–1	1.03–1	1.22–2	2.47+0
71.68	1.14+1	3.08–1	1.03–1	1.22–2	1.18+1
80.0	8.34+0	2.57–1	1.03–1	1.32–2	8.70+0
90.0	5.99+0	2.10–1	1.03–1	1.43–2	6.30+0
100.0	4.46+0	1.75–1	1.03–1	1.53–2	4.74+0
120.0	2.68+0	1.27–1	1.01–1	1.69–2	2.91+0
150.0	1.44+0	8.49–2	9.79–2	1.88–2	1.62+0
170.0	1.02+0	6.77–2	9.56–2	1.97–2	1.18+0
200.0	6.52–1	5.02–2	9.22–2	2.08–2	7.95–1
250.0	3.55–1	3.32–2	8.70–2	2.21–2	4.76–1
300.0	2.18–1	2.36–2	8.23–2	2.28–2	3.24–1
350.0	1.45–1	1.77–2	7.83–2	2.33–2	2.41–1
400.0	1.02–1	1.37–2	7.47–2	2.36–2	1.90–1
500.0	5.70–2	8.95–3	6.87–2	2.38–2	1.35–1
600.0	3.58–2	6.28–3	6.38–2	2.38–2	1.06–1
700.0	2.43–2	4.65–3	5.98–2	2.35–2	8.88–2
800.0	1.75–2	3.58–3	5.63–2	2.32–2	7.74–2
900.0	1.31–2	2.84–3	5.34–2	2.29–2	6.93–2
1,000.0	1.02–2	2.31–3	5.08–2	2.25–2	6.33–2

Osmium **Z = 76**

Energy (keV)	τ/ρ (cm²/g)	σ_c/ρ (cm²/g)	σ_I/ρ (cm²/g)	σ_a/ρ (cm²/g)	μ/ρ (cm²/g)
0.1	7.28+3	1.22+1	6.19–5	1.64–8	7.29+3
0.13	1.07+4	1.21+1	9.78–5	3.40–8	1.07+4
0.15	1.32+4	1.21+1	1.27–4	5.13–8	1.32+4
0.2	1.70+4	1.21+1	2.19–4	1.18–7	1.70+4
0.2787 $N_{IV,V}$	1.67+4	1.21+1	4.14–4	3.13–7	1.67+4
0.2801	1.78+4	1.21+1	4.18–4	3.18–7	1.78+4
0.3	1.69+4	1.21+1	4.77–4	3.88–7	1.69+4
0.4	1.36+4	1.21+1	8.23–4	8.94–7	1.37+4
0.4936 $N_{II,III}$	1.08+4	1.20+1	1.22–3	1.63–6	1.09+4
0.495	1.17+4	1.20+1	1.23–3	1.64–6	1.17+4
0.5	1.18+4	1.20+1	1.25–3	1.69–6	1.18+4

TABLE 3 (continued)

Energy (keV)	τ/ρ (cm^2/g)	σ_c/ρ (cm^2/g)	σ_I/ρ (cm^2/g)	σ_a/ρ (cm^2/g)	μ/ρ (cm^2/g)
0.6	9.40+3	1.20+1	1.74−3	2.81−6	9.41+3
0.6536 N_I	8.28+3	1.19+1	2.02−3	3.55−6	8.30+3
0.655	8.81+3	1.19+1	2.03−3	3.57−6	8.82+3
0.7	7.87+3	1.19+1	2.28−3	4.27−6	7.88+3
0.8	6.30+3	1.18+1	2.85−3	6.09−6	6.32+3
0.9	5.12+3	1.17+1	3.45−3	8.23−6	5.13+3
1.0	4.21+3	1.17+1	4.06−3	1.07−5	4.23+3
1.4	2.16+3	1.13+1	6.52−3	2.35−5	2.17+3
1.9	1.12+3	1.07+1	9.53−3	4.57−5	1.13+3
1.96 M_V	1.02+3	1.07+1	9.89−3	4.88−5	1.03+3
1.96	3.24+3	1.07+1	9.89−3	4.88−5	3.26+3
2.0	3.08+3	1.06+1	1.01−2	5.09−5	3.09+3
2.031 M_{IV}	2.96+3	1.06+1	1.03−2	5.25−5	2.97+3
2.031	4.44+3	1.06+1	1.03−2	5.25−5	4.45+3
2.457 M_{III}	2.70+3	1.01+1	1.28−2	7.78−5	2.71+3
2.457	3.24+3	1.01+1	1.28−2	7.78−5	3.26+3
2.5	3.10+3	1.01+1	1.30−2	8.06−5	3.11+3
2.792 M_{II}	2.33+3	9.73+0	1.46−2	1.01−4	2.34+3
2.792	2.56+3	9.73+0	1.46−2	1.01−4	2.57+3
3.0	2.12+3	9.52+0	1.58−2	1.16−4	2.13+3
3.049 M_I	2.04+3	9.46+0	1.61−2	1.20−4	2.04+3
3.049	2.24+3	9.46+0	1.61−2	1.20−4	2.25+3
3.5	1.56+3	8.99+0	1.86−2	1.58−4	1.57+3
4.0	1.11+3	8.50+0	2.12−2	2.06−4	1.11+3
5.0	6.18+2	7.58+0	2.64−2	3.17−4	6.26+2
6.0	3.85+2	6.79+0	3.13−2	4.46−4	3.92+2
7.0	2.58+2	6.10+0	3.58−2	5.91−4	2.64+2
8.0	1.82+2	5.51+0	4.01−2	7.47−4	1.88+2
9.0	1.34+2	4.99+0	4.39−2	9.12−4	1.39+2
10.0	1.02+2	4.53+0	4.74−2	1.08−3	1.07+2
10.87 L_{III}	8.21+1	4.17+0	5.02−2	1.24−3	8.63+1
10.87	2.15+2	4.17+0	5.02−2	1.24−3	2.19+2
12.0	1.64+2	3.77+0	5.36−2	1.44−3	1.68+2
12.39 L_{II}	1.51+2	3.64+0	5.47−2	1.52−3	1.54+2
12.39	2.11+2	3.64+0	5.47−2	1.52−3	2.14+2
12.97 L_I	1.86+2	3.46+0	5.63−2	1.62−3	1.90+2
12.97	2.23+2	3.46+0	5.63−2	1.62−3	2.27+2
15.0	1.50+2	2.94+0	6.15−2	2.02−3	1.53+2
17.0	1.07+2	2.53+0	6.60−2	2.43−3	1.10+2
20.0	6.87+1	2.06+0	7.19−2	3.05−3	7.09+1
25.0	3.75+1	1.55+0	7.99−2	4.12−3	3.91+1
30.0	2.28+1	1.21+0	8.59−2	5.17−3	2.41+1
35.0	1.50+1	9.71−1	9.05−2	6.18−3	1.61+1
40.0	1.04+1	7.95−1	9.39−2	7.14−3	1.13+1
50.0	5.69+0	5.60−1	9.83−2	8.90−3	6.35+0
60.0	3.46+0	4.19−1	1.01−1	1.05−2	3.98+0
70.0	2.28+0	3.25−1	1.02−1	1.18−2	2.70+0
73.87 K	1.97+0	2.97−1	1.02−1	1.23−2	2.37+0
73.87	1.07+1	2.97−1	1.02−1	1.23−2	1.11+1
80.0	8.59+0	2.60−1	1.02−1	1.31−2	8.95+0
90.0	6.17+0	2.13−1	1.02−1	1.42−2	6.48+0
100.0	4.59+0	1.77−1	1.02−1	1.52−2	4.87+0
120.0	2.76+0	1.29−1	1.00−1	1.68−2	2.99+0

Energy (keV)	τ/ρ (cm^2/g)	σ_c/ρ (cm^2/g)	σ_I/ρ (cm^2/g)	σ_a/ρ (cm^2/g)	μ/ρ (cm^2/g)
150.0	1.49+0	8.61−2	9.70−2	1.86−2	1.67+0
170.0	1.05+0	6.86−2	9.47−2	1.95−2	1.22+0
200.0	6.74−1	5.09−2	9.14−2	2.06−2	8.16−1
250.0	3.68−1	3.37−2	8.62−2	2.19−2	4.88−1
300.0	2.25−1	2.39−2	8.16−2	2.27−2	3.31−1
350.0	1.50−1	1.79−2	7.76−2	2.31−2	2.45−1
400.0	1.05−1	1.39−2	7.41−2	2.34−2	1.93−1
500.0	5.91−2	9.07−3	6.81−2	2.36−2	1.36−1
600.0	3.72−2	6.37−3	6.33−2	2.36−2	1.07−1
700.0	2.53−2	4.71−3	5.93−2	2.34−2	8.93−2
800.0	1.82−2	3.63−3	5.59−2	2.31−2	7.77−2
900.0	1.37−2	2.88−3	5.29−2	2.27−2	6.95−2
1,000.0	1.06−2	2.34−3	5.04−2	2.23−2	6.33−2

Iridium **Z = 77**

Energy (keV)	τ/ρ (cm^2/g)	σ_c/ρ (cm^2/g)	σ_I/ρ (cm^2/g)	σ_a/ρ (cm^2/g)	μ/ρ (cm^2/g)
0.1	6.66+3	1.23+1	5.91−5	1.57−8	6.67+3
0.13	7.84+3	1.23+1	9.38−5	3.27−8	7.86+3
0.15	1.04+4	1.23+1	1.22−4	4.93−8	1.04+4
0.2	1.55+4	1.23+1	2.10−4	1.14−7	1.56+4
0.3	1.63+4	1.23+1	4.58−4	3.73−7	1.63+4
0.3008 $N_{IV,V}$	1.62+4	1.23+1	4.60−4	3.76−7	1.62+4
0.3022	1.72+4	1.23+1	4.64−4	3.81−7	1.72+4
0.4	1.42+4	1.23+1	7.92−4	8.60−7	1.42+4
0.5	1.13+4	1.22+1	1.20−3	1.63−6	1.13+4
0.5212 $N_{II,III}$	1.07+4	1.22+1	1.30−3	1.83−6	1.07+4
0.5226	1.15+4	1.22+1	1.31−3	1.85−6	1.15+4
0.6	9.94+3	1.22+1	1.68−3	2.71−6	9.95+3
0.6894 N_I	8.08+3	1.21+1	2.14−3	3.96−6	8.09+3
0.6908	8.59+3	1.21+1	2.15−3	3.99−6	8.60+3
0.7	8.34+3	1.21+1	2.20−3	4.13−6	8.35+3
0.8	6.69+3	1.20+1	2.76−3	5.91−6	6.70+3
0.9	5.44+3	1.19+1	3.35−3	8.00−6	5.45+3
1.0	4.48+3	1.19+1	3.95−3	1.04−5	4.49+3
1.4	2.30+3	1.15+1	6.39−3	2.31−5	2.31+3
1.9	1.19+3	1.09+1	9.39−3	4.52−5	1.20+3
2.0	1.03+3	1.08+1	9.99−3	5.04−5	1.04+3
2.04 M_V	9.83+2	1.08+1	1.02−2	5.25−5	9.94+2
2.04	3.05+3	1.08+1	1.02−2	5.25−5	3.06+3
2.116 M_{IV}	2.77+3	1.07+1	1.07−2	5.66−5	2.78+3
2.116	4.15+3	1.07+1	1.07−2	5.66−5	4.16+3
2.5	2.69+3	1.02+1	1.29−2	8.00−5	2.70+3
2.551 M_{III}	2.56+3	1.02+1	1.32−2	8.33−5	2.57+3
2.551	3.07+3	1.02+1	1.32−2	8.33−5	3.08+3
2.909 M_{II}	2.18+3	9.78+0	1.52−2	1.09−4	2.19+3
2.909	2.40+3	9.78+0	1.52−2	1.09−4	2.41+3
3.0	2.21+3	9.69+0	1.57−2	1.16−4	2.22+3
3.174 M_I	1.91+3	9.49+0	1.66−2	1.30−4	1.92+3
3.174	2.10+3	9.49+0	1.66−2	1.30−4	2.11+3
3.5	1.63+3	9.15+0	1.84−2	1.58−4	1.64+3
4.0	1.15+3	8.64+0	2.11−2	2.05−4	1.16+3
5.0	6.45+2	7.71+0	2.63−2	3.15−4	6.53+2
6.0	4.02+2	6.91+0	3.11−2	4.44−4	4.09+2

TABLE 3 (continued)

Energy (keV)	τ/ρ (cm^2/g)	σ_c/ρ (cm^2/g)	σ_I/ρ (cm^2/g)	σ_a/ρ (cm^2/g)	μ/ρ (cm^2/g)
7.0	2.69+2	6.21+0	3.57−2	5.89−4	2.76+2
8.0	1.90+2	5.60+0	3.99−2	7.46−4	1.96+2
9.0	1.40+2	5.08+0	4.38−2	9.11−4	1.45+2
10.0	1.07+2	4.62+0	4.73−2	1.08−3	1.11+2
11.22 L_{III}	7.90+1	4.12+0	5.12−2	1.30−3	8.32+1
11.22	2.05+2	4.12+0	5.12−2	1.30−3	2.09+2
12.0	1.71+2	3.85+0	5.36−2	1.44−3	1.75+2
12.82 L_{II}	1.43+2	3.58+0	5.58−2	1.59−3	1.46+2
12.82	2.00+2	3.58+0	5.58−2	1.59−3	2.04+2
13.42 L_I	1.77+2	3.40+0	5.74−2	1.71−3	1.80+2
13.42	2.12+2	3.40+0	5.74−2	1.71−3	2.15+2
15.0	1.57+2	3.01+0	6.14−2	2.02−3	1.60+2
17.0	1.11+2	2.58+0	6.59−2	2.42−3	1.14+2
20.0	7.17+1	2.11+0	7.18−2	3.05−3	7.38+1
25.0	3.91+1	1.58+0	7.97−2	4.11−3	4.07+1
30.0	2.38+1	1.23+0	8.58−2	5.16−3	2.51+1
35.0	1.57+1	9.92−1	9.04−2	6.18−3	1.68+1
40.0	1.09+1	8.14−1	9.38−2	7.14−3	1.18+1
50.0	5.94+0	5.74−1	9.83−2	8.91−3	6.62+0
60.0	3.62+0	4.29−1	1.01−1	1.05−2	4.15+0
70.0	2.38+0	3.32−1	1.02−1	1.19−2	2.82+0
76.11 K	1.90+0	2.89−1	1.02−1	1.26−2	2.29+0
76.11	1.03+1	2.89−1	1.02−1	1.26−2	1.07+1
80.0	8.92+0	2.66−1	1.02−1	1.31−2	9.29+0
90.0	6.41+0	2.18−1	1.02−1	1.42−2	6.73+0
100.0	4.78+0	1.82−1	1.02−1	1.52−2	5.06+0
120.0	2.87+0	1.32−1	1.00−1	1.68−2	3.10+0
150.0	1.55+0	8.82−2	9.72−2	1.86−2	1.73+0
170.0	1.10+0	7.03−2	9.49−2	1.96−2	1.26+0
200.0	7.03−1	5.21−2	9.16−2	2.07−2	8.46−1
250.0	3.84−1	3.45−2	8.64−2	2.19−2	5.05−1
300.0	2.36−1	2.45−2	8.18−2	2.27−2	3.42−1
350.0	1.57−1	1.83−2	7.78−2	2.32−2	2.53−1
400.0	1.10−1	1.42−2	7.42−2	2.35−2	1.99−1
500.0	6.20−2	9.30−3	6.82−2	2.37−2	1.40−1
600.0	3.90−2	6.53−3	6.34−2	2.36−2	1.09−1
700.0	2.65−2	4.83−3	5.94−2	2.34−2	9.08−2
800.0	1.91−2	3.72−3	5.60−2	2.31−2	7.89−2
900.0	1.44−2	2.95−3	5.31−2	2.28−2	7.04−2
1,000.0	1.12−2	2.40−3	5.05−2	2.24−2	6.41−2

Platinum **Z = 78**

0.1	5.71+3	1.25+1	4.90−5	1.30−8	5.72+3
0.101 O_I	5.57+3	1.25+1	4.99−5	1.34−8	5.58+3
0.1024	6.09+3	1.25+1	5.11−5	1.39−8	6.11+3
0.13	5.54+3	1.25+1	7.78−5	2.71−8	5.56+3
0.15	7.27+3	1.25+1	1.01−4	4.09−8	7.29+3
0.2	1.33+4	1.25+1	1.74−4	9.41−8	1.33+4
0.3	1.64+4	1.24+1	3.80−4	3.10−7	1.64+4
0.3196 $N_{IV,V}$	1.60+4	1.24+1	4.29−4	3.72−7	1.60+4
0.321	1.69+4	1.24+1	4.32−4	3.77−7	1.69+4
0.4	1.47+4	1.24+1	6.59−4	7.16−7	1.47+4
0.5	1.18+4	1.24+1	1.01−3	1.36−6	1.18+4

TABLE 3 (continued)

Energy (keV)	τ/ρ (cm^2/g)	σ_c/ρ (cm^2/g)	σ_I/ρ (cm^2/g)	σ_a/ρ (cm^2/g)	μ/ρ (cm^2/g)
0.5484 $N_{II,III}$	1.05+4	1.23+1	1.19–3	1.77–6	1.05+4
0.5498	1.14+4	1.23+1	1.20–3	1.78–6	1.14+4
0.6	1.05+4	1.23+1	1.41–3	2.28–6	1.05+4
0.7	8.33+3	1.23+1	1.85–3	3.49–6	8.34+3
0.7213 N_I	7.94+3	1.22+1	1.95–3	3.79–6	7.95+3
0.7227	8.40+3	1.22+1	1.96–3	3.81–6	8.42+3
0.8	7.06+3	1.22+1	2.34–3	5.02–6	7.08+3
0.9	5.74+3	1.21+1	2.85–3	6.84–6	5.76+3
1.0	4.73+3	1.20+1	3.39–3	8.99–6	4.74+3
1.4	2.43+3	1.17+1	5.64–3	2.06–5	2.44+3
1.9	1.26+3	1.11+1	8.56–3	4.16–5	1.27+3
2.0	1.09+3	1.10+1	9.16–3	4.67–5	1.10+3
2.122 M_V	9.39+2	1.09+1	9.85–3	5.31–5	9.50+2
2.122	2.92+3	1.09+1	9.85–3	5.31–5	2.93+3
2.202 M_{IV}	2.65+3	1.08+1	1.03–2	5.76–5	2.66+3
2.202	3.98+3	1.08+1	1.03–2	5.76–5	3.99+3
2.5	2.85+3	1.05+1	1.20–2	7.58–5	2.86+3
2.645 M_{III}	2.46+3	1.03+1	1.29–2	8.53–5	2.47+3
2.645	2.95+3	1.03+1	1.29–2	8.53–5	2.96+3
3.0	2.12+3	9.88+0	1.49–2	1.11–4	2.13+3
3.027 M_{II}	2.07+3	9.85+0	1.50–2	1.13–4	2.08+3
3.027	2.28+3	9.85+0	1.50–2	1.13–4	2.29+3
3.296 M_I	1.82+3	9.54+0	1.65–2	1.34–4	1.83+3
3.296	2.00+3	9.54+0	1.65–2	1.34–4	2.01+3
3.5	1.71+3	9.33+0	1.76–2	1.52–4	1.72+3
4.0	1.21+3	8.79+0	2.03–2	1.98–4	1.21+3
5.0	6.71+2	7.83+0	2.54–2	3.07–4	6.79+2
6.0	4.16+2	7.00+0	3.03–2	4.36–4	4.23+2
7.0	2.78+2	6.29+0	3.50–2	5.81–4	2.84+2
8.0	1.96+2	5.68+0	3.93–2	7.38–4	2.01+2
9.0	1.44+2	5.16+0	4.32–2	9.04–4	1.49+2
10.0	1.09+2	4.69+0	4.68–2	1.08–3	1.14+2
11.56 L_{III}	7.45+1	4.07+0	5.17–2	1.35–3	7.86+1
11.56	1.96+2	4.07+0	5.17–2	1.35–3	2.00+2
12.0	1.77+2	3.92+0	5.31–2	1.44–3	1.81+2
13.27 L_{II}	1.35+2	3.51+0	5.65–2	1.67–3	1.38+2
13.27	1.89+2	3.51+0	5.65–2	1.67–3	1.92+2
13.88 L_I	1.67+2	3.34+0	5.81–2	1.79–3	1.70+2
13.88	2.00+2	3.34+0	5.81–2	1.79–3	2.04+2
15.0	1.62+2	3.06+0	6.09–2	2.01–3	1.65+2
17.0	1.15+2	2.63+0	6.54–2	2.41–3	1.18+2
20.0	7.42+1	2.15+0	7.13–2	3.03–3	7.64+1
25.0	4.05+1	1.61+0	7.92–2	4.08–3	4.22+1
30.0	2.47+1	1.26+0	8.53–2	5.13–3	2.60+1
35.0	1.62+1	1.01+0	8.99–2	6.15–3	1.73+1
40.0	1.13+1	8.29–1	9.33–2	7.11–3	1.22+1
50.0	6.15+0	5.85–1	9.79–2	8.87–3	6.83+0
60.0	3.75+0	4.37–1	1.00–1	1.04–2	4.28+0
70.0	2.46+0	3.39–1	1.02–1	1.18–2	2.91+0
78.39 K	1.81+0	2.81–1	1.02–1	1.29–2	2.19+0
78.39	9.68+0	2.81–1	1.02–1	1.29–2	1.01+1
80.0	9.13+0	2.71–1	1.02–1	1.31–2	9.50+0
90.0	6.51+0	2.22–1	1.02–1	1.42–2	6.83+0

TABLE 3 (continued)

Energy (keV)	τ/ρ (cm²/g)	σ_c/ρ (cm²/g)	σ_I/ρ (cm²/g)	σ_a/ρ (cm²/g)	μ/ρ (cm²/g)
100.0	4.82+0	1.85−1	1.02−1	1.51−2	5.11+0
120.0	2.89+0	1.34−1	1.00−1	1.68−2	3.12+0
150.0	1.56+0	8.99−2	9.69−2	1.86−2	1.75+0
170.0	1.11+0	7.17−2	9.46−2	1.95−2	1.27+0
200.0	7.16−1	5.32−2	9.13−2	2.06−2	8.60−1
250.0	3.96−1	3.51−2	8.62−2	2.19−2	5.17−1
300.0	2.45−1	2.50−2	8.16−2	2.27−2	3.52−1
350.0	1.65−1	1.87−2	7.76−2	2.31−2	2.61−1
400.0	1.17−1	1.45−2	7.40−2	2.34−2	2.05−1
500.0	6.62−2	9.48−3	6.81−2	2.36−2	1.44−1
600.0	4.18−2	6.66−3	6.33−2	2.36−2	1.12−1
700.0	2.84−2	4.93−3	5.93−2	2.34−2	9.26−2
800.0	2.04−2	3.79−3	5.59−2	2.31−2	8.00−2
900.0	1.52−2	3.01−3	5.30−2	2.27−2	7.12−2
1,000.0	1.17−2	2.45−3	5.04−2	2.23−2	6.45−2

Gold **Z = 79**

Energy (keV)	τ/ρ (cm²/g)	σ_c/ρ (cm²/g)	σ_I/ρ (cm²/g)	σ_a/ρ (cm²/g)	μ/ρ (cm²/g)
0.1	6.26+3	1.27+1	4.76−5	1.26−8	6.27+3
0.1071 O_{I}	5.19+3	1.27+1	5.35−5	1.52−8	5.20+3
0.1085	5.74+3	1.27+1	5.47−5	1.58−8	5.75+3
0.118	4.91+3	1.27+1	6.31−5	1.98−8	4.92+3
0.15	5.35+3	1.27+1	9.75−5	3.93−8	5.37+3
0.2	1.09+4	1.27+1	1.68−4	9.06−8	1.10+4
0.3	1.61+4	1.26+1	3.66−4	2.98−7	1.61+4
0.3404 $N_{IV,V}$	1.55+4	1.26+1	4.66−4	4.31−7	1.55+4
0.3418	1.63+4	1.26+1	4.70−4	4.36−7	1.63+4
0.4	1.50+4	1.26+1	6.35−4	6.90−7	1.50+4
0.5	1.22+4	1.26+1	9.70−4	1.31−6	1.23+4
0.5775 $N_{II,III}$	1.02+4	1.25+1	1.27−3	1.98−6	1.02+4
0.5789	1.10+4	1.25+1	1.27−3	1.99−6	1.10+4
0.6	1.09+4	1.25+1	1.36−3	2.20−6	1.09+4
0.7	8.71+3	1.25+1	1.79−3	3.38−6	8.72+3
0.7581 N_{I}	7.66+3	1.24+1	2.06−3	4.20−6	7.67+3
0.7595	8.11+3	1.24+1	2.07−3	4.23−6	8.12+3
0.8	7.39+3	1.24+1	2.27−3	4.86−6	7.40+3
0.9	6.03+3	1.23+1	2.76−3	6.64−6	6.04+3
1.0	4.97+3	1.22+1	3.29−3	8.73−6	4.98+3
1.2	3.50+3	1.21+1	4.38−3	1.38−5	3.51+3
1.5	2.22+3	1.18+1	6.09−3	2.38−5	2.23+3
2.0	1.19+3	1.12+1	8.99−3	4.59−5	1.21+3
2.206 M_{V}	9.05+2	1.10+1	1.01−2	5.69−5	9.16+2
2.206	2.60+3	1.10+1	1.01−2	5.69−5	2.61+3
2.291 M_{IV}	2.36+3	1.09+1	1.06−2	6.18−5	2.37+3
2.291	3.54+3	1.09+1	1.06−2	6.18−5	3.55+3
2.5	2.83+3	1.07+1	1.19−2	7.47−5	2.84+3
2.743 M_{III}	2.23+3	1.04+1	1.32−2	9.07−5	2.24+3
2.743	2.67+3	1.04+1	1.32−2	9.07−5	2.68+3
3.0	2.12+3	1.01+1	1.46−2	1.09−4	2.13+3
3.148 M_{II}	1.88+3	9.89+0	1.54−2	1.21−4	1.89+3
3.148	2.07+3	9.89+0	1.54−2	1.21−4	2.08+3
3.425 M_{I}	1.66+3	9.58+0	1.69−2	1.43−4	1.67+3
3.425	1.83+3	9.58+0	1.69−2	1.43−4	1.84+3

TABLE 3 (continued)

Energy (keV)	τ/ρ (cm²/g)	σ_c/ρ (cm²/g)	σ_I/ρ (cm²/g)	σ_a/ρ (cm²/g)	μ/ρ (cm²/g)
3.5	1.73+3	9.50+0	1.74−2	1.50−4	1.74+3
4.0	1.23+3	8.96+0	2.00−2	1.96−4	1.24+3
5.0	6.93+2	7.98+0	2.51−2	3.04−4	7.01+2
6.0	4.34+2	7.13+0	3.00−2	4.32−4	4.41+2
7.0	2.92+2	6.41+0	3.47−2	5.76−4	2.98+2
8.0	2.07+2	5.79+0	3.90−2	7.34−4	2.13+2
9.0	1.53+2	5.25+0	4.30−2	9.01−4	1.58+2
10.0	1.17+2	4.78+0	4.66−2	1.07−3	1.22+2
$11.92_{L_{III}}$	7.45+1	4.03+0	5.27−2	1.42−3	7.85+1
11.92	1.82+2	4.03+0	5.27−2	1.42−3	1.86+2
12.0	1.79+2	4.00+0	5.30−2	1.44−3	1.83+2
$13.73_{L_{II}}$	1.25+2	3.45+0	5.76−2	1.76−3	1.28+2
13.73	1.74+2	3.45+0	5.76−2	1.76−3	1.78+2
14.35_{L_I}	1.55+2	3.29+0	5.92−2	1.88−3	1.58+2
14.35	1.86+2	3.29+0	5.92−2	1.88−3	1.89+2
15.0	1.65+2	3.13+0	6.09−2	2.01−3	1.68+2
17.0	1.18+2	2.69+0	6.54−2	2.41−3	1.20+2
20.0	7.60+1	2.19+0	7.12−2	3.03−3	7.82+1
25.0	4.16+1	1.64+0	7.91−2	4.08−3	4.34+1
30.0	2.55+1	1.28+0	8.52−2	5.13−3	2.69+1
35.0	1.68+1	1.03+0	8.98−2	6.14−3	1.80+1
40.0	1.17+1	8.48−1	9.33−2	7.11−3	1.27+1
50.0	6.44+0	5.98−1	9.79−2	8.88−3	7.14+0
60.0	3.94+0	4.47−1	1.00−1	1.04−2	4.49+0
70.0	2.60+0	3.47−1	1.02−1	1.18−2	3.05+0
80.0	1.82+0	2.77−1	1.02−1	1.31−2	2.20+0
80.72_K	1.77+0	2.73−1	1.02−1	1.32−2	2.15+0
80.72	8.71+0	2.73−1	1.02−1	1.32−2	9.08+0
90.0	6.52+0	2.27−1	1.02−1	1.42−2	6.85+0
100.0	4.92+0	1.90−1	1.02−1	1.52−2	5.21+0
120.0	3.02+0	1.38−1	1.00−1	1.68−2	3.26+0
150.0	1.65+0	9.21−2	9.71−2	1.86−2	1.84+0
170.0	1.18+0	7.34−2	9.48−2	1.96−2	1.35+0
200.0	7.62−1	5.44−2	9.15−2	2.07−2	9.08−1
250.0	4.19−1	3.60−2	8.64−2	2.19−2	5.41−1
300.0	2.57−1	2.56−2	8.18−2	2.27−2	3.65−1
350.0	1.71−1	1.92−2	7.78−2	2.32−2	2.68−1
400.0	1.21−1	1.49−2	7.42−2	2.35−2	2.10−1
500.0	6.79−2	9.72−3	6.83−2	2.37−2	1.46−1
600.0	4.28−2	6.82−3	6.34−2	2.36−2	1.13−1
700.0	2.92−2	5.05−3	5.95−2	2.34−2	9.37−2
800.0	2.11−2	3.89−3	5.60−2	2.31−2	8.10−2
900.0	1.59−2	3.09−3	5.31−2	2.28−2	7.21−2
1,000.0	1.24−2	2.51−3	5.05−2	2.24−2	6.55−2

Mercury **Z = 80**

$0.1_{N_{VI,VII}}$	5.58+3	1.28+1	5.11−5	1.36−8	5.59+3
0.1108	6.00+3	1.28+1	6.06−5	1.78−8	6.01+3
0.1196_{O_I}	4.13+3	1.28+1	6.98−5	2.23−8	4.15+3
0.121	4.83+3	1.28+1	7.13−5	2.31−8	4.84+3
0.15	4.10+3	1.28+1	1.06−4	4.31−8	4.11+3
0.2	8.57+3	1.28+1	1.84−4	9.98−8	8.58+3

TABLE 3 (continued)

Energy (keV)	τ/ρ (cm^2/g)	σ_c/ρ (cm^2/g)	σ_I/ρ (cm^2/g)	σ_a/ρ (cm^2/g)	μ/ρ (cm^2/g)
0.23	1.18+4	1.28+1	2.41−4	1.51−7	1.18+4
0.3	1.53+4	1.27+1	4.04−4	3.29−7	1.53+4
0.3665 $N_{IV,V}$	1.46+4	1.27+1	5.92−4	5.90−7	1.47+4
0.3679	1.55+4	1.27+1	5.97−4	5.97−7	1.55+4
0.4	1.48+4	1.27+1	7.00−4	7.61−7	1.48+4
0.5	1.24+4	1.27+1	1.07−3	1.45−6	1.24+4
0.6	9.94+3	1.26+1	1.49−3	2.42−6	9.95+3
0.6056 $N_{II,III}$	9.81+3	1.26+1	1.52−3	2.48−6	9.83+3
0.607	1.05+4	1.26+1	1.53−3	2.50−6	1.05+4
0.7	8.95+3	1.25+1	1.97−3	3.71−6	8.96+3
0.7996 N_I	7.24+3	1.25+1	2.48−3	5.32−6	7.25+3
0.801	7.70+3	1.25+1	2.49−3	5.34−6	7.72+3
0.9	6.24+3	1.24+1	3.02−3	7.24−6	6.25+3
1.0	5.16+3	1.23+1	3.58−3	9.49−6	5.17+3
1.5	2.31+3	1.18+1	6.48−3	2.51−5	2.32+3
2.0	1.24+3	1.13+1	9.35−3	4.74−5	1.25+3
2.295 M_V	8.69+2	1.09+1	1.10−2	6.33−5	8.80+2
2.295	2.48+3	1.09+1	1.10−2	6.33−5	2.49+3
2.385 M_{IV}	2.25+3	1.08+1	1.15−2	6.86−5	2.26+3
2.385	3.37+3	1.08+1	1.15−2	6.86−5	3.38+3
2.5	2.99+3	1.07+1	1.21−2	7.58−5	3.00+3
2.847 M_{III}	2.13+3	1.03+1	1.40−2	9.89−5	2.14+3
2.847	2.56+3	1.03+1	1.40−2	9.89−5	2.57+3
3.0	2.23+3	1.01+1	1.48−2	1.10−4	2.24+3
3.279 M_{II}	1.78+3	9.78+0	1.63−2	1.32−4	1.79+3
3.279	1.95+3	9.78+0	1.63−2	1.32−4	1.96+3
3.5	1.65+3	9.55+0	1.75−2	1.50−4	1.66+3
3.562 M_I	1.58+3	9.48+0	1.78−2	1.55−4	1.59+3
3.562	1.73+3	9.48+0	1.78−2	1.55−4	1.74+3
4.0	1.28+3	9.01+0	2.01−2	1.96−4	1.29+3
5.0	7.21+2	8.03+0	2.51−2	3.02−4	7.29+2
6.0	4.49+2	7.18+0	2.99−2	4.28−4	4.57+2
7.0	3.02+2	6.45+0	3.44−2	5.70−4	3.08+2
8.0	2.14+2	5.83+0	3.87−2	7.26−4	2.19+2
9.0	1.57+2	5.29+0	4.26−2	8.92−4	1.63+2
10.0	1.20+2	4.82+0	4.62−2	1.06−3	1.25+2
12.0	7.47+1	4.04+0	5.26−2	1.42−3	7.88+1
12.28 L_{III}	7.04+1	3.94+0	5.33−2	1.47−3	7.44+1
12.28	1.77+2	3.94+0	5.33−2	1.47−3	1.81+2
14.21 L_{II}	1.19+2	3.36+0	5.84−2	1.84−3	1.23+2
14.21	1.67+2	3.36+0	5.84−2	1.84−3	1.71+2
14.84 L_I	1.49+2	3.20+0	6.00−2	1.96−3	1.52+2
14.84	1.78+2	3.20+0	6.00−2	1.96−3	1.82+2
15.0	1.73+2	3.17+0	6.04−2	1.99−3	1.77+2
17.0	1.24+2	2.72+0	6.48−2	2.39−3	1.26+2
20.0	7.97+1	2.22+0	7.06−2	3.00−3	8.20+1
25.0	4.36+1	1.66+0	7.84−2	4.04−3	4.54+1
30.0	2.67+1	1.30+0	8.44−2	5.08−3	2.80+1
35.0	1.76+1	1.05+0	8.90−2	6.09−3	1.87+1
40.0	1.23+1	8.59−1	9.25−2	7.05−3	1.32+1
50.0	6.70+0	6.07−1	9.71−2	8.81−3	7.41+0
60.0	4.10+0	4.53−1	9.96−2	1.04−2	4.65+0

TABLE 3 (continued)

Energy (keV)	τ/ρ (cm²/g)	σ_c/ρ (cm²/g)	σ_I/ρ (cm²/g)	σ_a/ρ (cm²/g)	μ/ρ (cm²/g)
70.0	2.70+0	3.51–1	1.01–1	1.17–2	3.15+0
80.0	1.88+0	2.81–1	1.01–1	1.30–2	2.27+0
83.1_K	1.70+0	2.64–1	1.01–1	1.33–2	2.06+0
83.1	8.83+0	2.64–1	1.01–1	1.33–2	9.20+0
90.0	7.04+0	2.30–1	1.01–1	1.41–2	7.37+0
100.0	5.22+0	1.92–1	1.01–1	1.51–2	5.51+0
120.0	3.12+0	1.40–1	9.95–2	1.67–2	3.36+0
150.0	1.68+0	9.34–2	9.64–2	1.85–2	1.87+0
170.0	1.19+0	7.45–2	9.42–2	1.95–2	1.36+0
200.0	7.61–1	5.52–2	9.09–2	2.06–2	9.07–1
250.0	4.17–1	3.65–2	8.58–2	2.18–2	5.39–1
300.0	2.57–1	2.60–2	8.13–2	2.26–2	3.64–1
350.0	1.71–1	1.95–2	7.73–2	2.31–2	2.68–1
400.0	1.21–1	1.51–2	7.38–2	2.33–2	2.10–1
500.0	6.87–2	9.87–3	6.79–2	2.36–2	1.46–1
600.0	4.35–2	6.93–3	6.31–2	2.35–2	1.13–1
700.0	2.97–2	5.13–3	5.91–2	2.33–2	9.40–2
800.0	2.15–2	3.95–3	5.57–2	2.30–2	8.12–2
900.0	1.62–2	3.13–3	5.28–2	2.27–2	7.22–2
1,000.0	1.26–2	2.55–3	5.03–2	2.23–2	6.55–2

Thallium Z = 81

Energy (keV)	τ/ρ (cm²/g)	σ_c/ρ (cm²/g)	σ_I/ρ (cm²/g)	σ_a/ρ (cm²/g)	μ/ρ (cm²/g)
0.1	7.59+3	1.29+1	5.30–5	1.41–8	7.60+3
$0.1196_{N_{VI,VII}}$	3.90+3	1.28+1	7.25–5	2.32–8	3.91+3
0.121	4.32+3	1.28+1	7.40–5	2.39–8	4.33+3
0.1356_{O_I}	3.57+3	1.28+1	9.14–5	3.32–8	3.58+3
0.137	4.28+3	1.28+1	9.31–5	3.42–8	4.29+3
0.15	3.70+3	1.28+1	1.10–4	4.45–8	3.71+3
0.2	6.27+3	1.28+1	1.89–4	1.02–7	6.28+3
0.23	9.60+3	1.28+1	2.48–4	1.54–7	9.61+3
0.3	1.44+4	1.28+1	4.13–4	3.37–7	1.45+4
$0.3937_{N_{IV,V}}$	1.40+4	1.28+1	6.95–4	7.42–7	1.40+4
0.3951	1.46+4	1.28+1	6.99–4	7.50–7	1.47+4
0.4	1.45+4	1.28+1	7.16–4	7.77–7	1.45+4
0.5	1.27+4	1.27+1	1.09–3	1.48–6	1.27+4
0.6	1.02+4	1.27+1	1.52–3	2.46–6	1.03+4
$0.6457_{N_{II,III}}$	9.24+3	1.26+1	1.74–3	3.02–6	9.25+3
0.6471	9.91+3	1.26+1	1.74–3	3.04–6	9.92+3
0.7	9.24+3	1.26+1	2.00–3	3.77–6	9.26+3
0.8	7.50+3	1.25+1	2.53–3	5.41–6	7.51+3
0.8448_{N_I}	6.85+3	1.25+1	2.77–3	6.24–6	6.86+3
0.8462	7.26+3	1.25+1	2.77–3	6.27–6	7.27+3
0.9	6.48+3	1.24+1	3.07–3	7.36–6	6.49+3
1.0	5.36+3	1.23+1	3.64–3	9.64–6	5.38+3
1.5	2.41+3	1.18+1	6.60–3	2.56–5	2.42+3
2.0	1.29+3	1.13+1	9.54–3	4.84–5	1.30+3
2.389_{M_V}	8.34+2	1.08+1	1.17–2	7.01–5	8.45+2
2.389	2.31+3	1.08+1	1.17–2	7.01–5	2.32+3
$2.485_{M_{IV}}$	2.08+3	1.07+1	1.23–2	7.61–5	2.09+3
2.485	3.12+3	1.07+1	1.23–2	7.61–5	3.14+3
2.5	3.08+3	1.07+1	1.24–2	7.71–5	3.09+3

TABLE 3 (continued)

Energy (keV)	τ/ρ (cm^2/g)	σ_c/ρ (cm^2/g)	σ_I/ρ (cm^2/g)	σ_a/ρ (cm^2/g)	μ/ρ (cm^2/g)
2.957 M_{III}	1.99+3	1.02+1	1.48–2	1.08–4	2.00+3
2.957	2.39+3	1.02+1	1.48–2	1.08–4	2.40+3
3.0	2.30+3	1.01+1	1.51–2	1.11–4	2.31+3
3.416 M_{II}	1.65+3	9.65+0	1.72–2	1.44–4	1.66+3
3.416	1.81+3	9.65+0	1.72–2	1.44–4	1.82+3
3.5	1.70+3	9.57+0	1.77–2	1.51–4	1.71+3
3.704 M_I	1.47+3	9.34+0	1.87–2	1.69–4	1.48+3
3.704	1.62+3	9.34+0	1.87–2	1.69–4	1.63+3
4.0	1.32+3	9.04+0	2.02–2	1.96–4	1.33+3
5.0	7.43+2	8.07+0	2.51–2	3.01–4	7.52+2
6.0	4.64+2	7.22+0	2.98–2	4.25–4	4.71+2
7.0	3.11+2	6.49+0	3.42–2	5.65–4	3.18+2
8.0	2.20+2	5.86+0	3.84–2	7.19–4	2.26+2
9.0	1.63+2	5.32+0	4.23–2	8.83–4	1.68+2
10.0	1.24+2	4.85+0	4.59–2	1.05–3	1.29+2
12.0	7.72+1	4.08+0	5.22–2	1.41–3	8.14+1
12.66 L_{III}	6.72+1	3.85+0	5.39–2	1.53–3	7.11+1
12.66	1.67+2	3.85+0	5.39–2	1.53–3	1.71+2
14.7 L_{II}	1.12+2	3.27+0	5.91–2	1.92–3	1.15+2
14.7	1.57+2	3.27+0	5.91–2	1.92–3	1.60+2
15.0	1.48+2	3.20+0	5.99–2	1.97–3	1.51+2
15.35 L_I	1.39+2	3.11+0	6.06–2	2.04–3	1.42+2
15.35	1.67+2	3.11+0	6.06–2	2.04–3	1.70+2
17.0	1.27+2	2.76+0	6.42–2	2.37–3	1.30+2
20.0	8.19+1	2.25+0	7.00–2	2.97–3	8.43+1
25.0	4.49+1	1.68+0	7.76–2	4.00–3	4.67+1
30.0	2.75+1	1.31+0	8.36–2	5.03–3	2.89+1
35.0	1.81+1	1.06+0	8.82–2	6.03–3	1.93+1
40.0	1.27+1	8.69–1	9.16–2	6.98–3	1.36+1
50.0	6.94+0	6.14–1	9.62–2	8.73–3	7.65+0
60.0	4.24+0	4.59–1	9.87–2	1.03–2	4.80+0
70.0	2.80+0	3.56–1	1.00–1	1.17–2	3.26+0
80.0	1.96+0	2.85–1	1.01–1	1.29–2	2.34+0
85.53 K	1.63+0	2.54–1	1.01–1	1.35–2	1.99+0
85.53	8.37+0	2.54–1	1.01–1	1.35–2	8.72+0
90.0	7.23+0	2.33–1	1.01–1	1.40–2	7.57+0
100.0	5.37+0	1.95–1	1.00–1	1.49–2	5.66+0
120.0	3.22+0	1.41–1	9.87–2	1.66–2	3.46+0
150.0	1.74+0	9.47–2	9.57–2	1.84–2	1.93+0
170.0	1.23+0	7.55–2	9.35–2	1.93–2	1.40+0
200.0	7.95–1	5.60–2	9.03–2	2.04–2	9.41–1
250.0	4.38–1	3.70–2	8.53–2	2.17–2	5.61–1
300.0	2.72–1	2.63–2	8.07–2	2.24–2	3.79–1
350.0	1.82–1	1.97–2	7.68–2	2.29–2	2.79–1
400.0	1.29–1	1.53–2	7.33–2	2.32–2	2.18–1
500.0	7.32–2	1.00–2	6.74–2	2.34–2	1.51–1
600.0	4.64–2	7.03–3	6.27–2	2.34–2	1.16–1
700.0	3.16–2	5.20–3	5.87–2	2.32–2	9.55–2
800.0	2.28–2	4.01–3	5.54–2	2.29–2	8.22–2
900.0	1.71–2	3.18–3	5.25–2	2.25–2	7.28–2
1,000.0	1.32–2	2.59–3	4.99–2	2.21–2	6.57–2

TABLE 3 (continued)

Energy (keV)	τ/ρ (cm²/g)	σ_c/ρ (cm²/g)	σ_I/ρ (cm²/g)	σ_a/ρ (cm²/g)	μ/ρ (cm²/g)
Lead	**Z = 82**				
0.1	8.49+3	1.30+1	5.19–5	1.38–8	8.51+3
0.1395 $N_{VI,VII}$	2.65+3	1.30+1	9.38–5	3.51–8	2.66+3
0.1409	3.20+3	1.30+1	9.56–5	3.62–8	3.21+3
0.1466 O_I	3.20+3	1.30+1	1.03–4	4.05–8	3.21+3
0.148	3.85+3	1.30+1	1.05–4	4.17–8	3.87+3
0.15	3.76+3	1.30+1	1.07–4	4.33–8	3.77+3
0.2	4.38+3	1.30+1	1.84–4	9.97–8	4.39+3
0.23	7.32+3	1.30+1	2.41–4	1.50–7	7.33+3
0.3	1.33+4	1.29+1	4.03–4	3.28–7	1.33+4
0.4	1.38+4	1.29+1	6.99–4	7.60–7	1.38+4
0.4211 $N_{IV,V}$	1.33+4	1.29+1	7.72–4	8.83–7	1.33+4
0.4225	1.39+4	1.29+1	7.77–4	8.92–7	1.39+4
0.5	1.29+4	1.29+1	1.07–3	1.45–6	1.29+4
0.6	1.05+4	1.28+1	1.49–3	2.42–6	1.05+4
0.6836 $N_{II,III}$	8.77+3	1.27+1	1.89–3	3.48–6	8.78+3
0.685	9.51+3	1.27+1	1.90–3	3.50–6	9.52+3
0.7	9.50+3	1.27+1	1.97–3	3.71–6	9.51+3
0.8	7.77+3	1.26+1	2.49–3	5.35–6	7.78+3
0.8929 N_I	6.46+3	1.26+1	3.00–3	7.14–6	6.47+3
0.8943	6.81+3	1.26+1	3.01–3	7.17–6	6.82+3
0.9	6.72+3	1.26+1	3.04–3	7.29–6	6.73+3
1.0	5.58+3	1.25+1	3.61–3	9.57–6	5.59+3
1.5	2.51+3	1.19+1	6.62–3	2.58–5	2.53+3
2.0	1.35+3	1.13+1	9.65–3	4.91–5	1.36+3
2.484 M_V	7.95+2	1.08+1	1.25–2	7.75–5	8.06+2
2.484	2.15+3	1.08+1	1.25–2	7.75–5	2.16+3
2.5	2.12+3	1.08+1	1.25–2	7.85–5	2.13+3
2.586 M_{IV}	1.94+3	1.07+1	1.30–2	8.40–5	1.95+3
2.586	2.91+3	1.07+1	1.30–2	8.40–5	2.92+3
3.0	1.99+3	1.02+1	1.53–2	1.13–4	2.00+3
3.066 M_{III}	1.88+3	1.01+1	1.56–2	1.18–4	1.89+3
3.066	2.25+3	1.01+1	1.56–2	1.18–4	2.26+3
3.5	1.60+3	9.63+0	1.79–2	1.53–4	1.61+3
3.554 M_{II}	1.54+3	9.57+0	1.82–2	1.58–4	1.55+3
3.554	1.69+3	9.57+0	1.82–2	1.58–4	1.70+3
3.851 M_I	1.38+3	9.25+0	1.97–2	1.84–4	1.39+3
3.851	1.51+3	9.25+0	1.97–2	1.84–4	1.52+3
4.0	1.37+3	9.11+0	2.05–2	1.98–4	1.38+3
5.0	7.72+2	8.14+0	2.53–2	3.02–4	7.80+2
6.0	4.83+2	7.29+0	2.99–2	4.24–4	4.90+2
7.0	3.24+2	6.56+0	3.42–2	5.63–4	3.31+2
8.0	2.30+2	5.93+0	3.83–2	7.16–4	2.36+2
9.0	1.70+2	5.38+0	4.22–2	8.79–4	1.75+2
10.0	1.29+2	4.91+0	4.58–2	1.05–3	1.34+2
12.0	8.07+1	4.13+0	5.20–2	1.41–3	8.49+1
13.04 L_{III}	6.52+1	3.78+0	5.47–2	1.59–3	6.90+1
13.04	1.67+2	3.78+0	5.47–2	1.59–3	1.71+2
15.0	1.14+2	3.25+0	5.97–2	1.97–3	1.17+2
15.2 L_{II}	1.10+2	3.20+0	6.01–2	2.01–3	1.13+2
15.2	1.54+2	3.20+0	6.01–2	2.01–3	1.57+2

TABLE 3 (continued)

Energy (keV)	τ/ρ (cm^2/g)	σ_c/ρ (cm^2/g)	σ_I/ρ (cm^2/g)	σ_a/ρ (cm^2/g)	μ/ρ (cm^2/g)
15.86_{L_I}	1.37+2	3.04+0	6.16–2	2.13–3	1.40+2
15.86	1.64+2	3.04+0	6.16–2	2.13–3	1.67+2
17.0	1.36+2	2.80+0	6.40–2	2.36–3	1.39+2
20.0	8.73+1	2.28+0	6.97–2	2.96–3	8.97+1
25.0	4.75+1	1.71+0	7.73–2	3.98–3	4.93+1
30.0	2.89+1	1.33+0	8.32–2	5.00–3	3.03+1
35.0	1.90+1	1.07+0	8.78–2	6.00–3	2.01+1
40.0	1.32+1	8.83–1	9.12–2	6.96–3	1.42+1
50.0	7.17+0	6.25–1	9.59–2	8.70–3	7.89+0
60.0	4.36+0	4.67–1	9.84–2	1.02–2	4.93+0
70.0	2.86+0	3.62–1	9.97–2	1.16–2	3.33+0
80.0	1.99+0	2.90–1	1.00–1	1.28–2	2.38+0
88.0_K	1.53+0	2.47–1	1.00–1	1.37–2	1.88+0
88.0	7.37+0	2.47–1	1.00–1	1.37–2	7.72+0
90.0	6.95+0	2.37–1	1.00–1	1.39–2	7.29+0
100.0	5.27+0	1.98–1	9.99–2	1.49–2	5.57+0
120.0	3.26+0	1.44–1	9.85–2	1.65–2	3.50+0
150.0	1.80+0	9.64–2	9.55–2	1.84–2	1.99+0
170.0	1.29+0	7.69–2	9.33–2	1.93–2	1.46+0
200.0	8.36–1	5.70–2	9.01–2	2.04–2	9.83–1
250.0	4.62–1	3.77–2	8.51–2	2.16–2	5.85–1
300.0	2.86–1	2.68–2	8.06–2	2.24–2	3.93–1
350.0	1.91–1	2.01–2	7.67–2	2.29–2	2.88–1
400.0	1.35–1	1.56–2	7.32–2	2.32–2	2.24–1
500.0	7.66–2	1.02–2	6.73–2	2.34–2	1.54–1
600.0	4.86–2	7.17–3	6.26–2	2.33–2	1.18–1
700.0	3.34–2	5.30–3	5.86–2	2.31–2	9.73–2
800.0	2.42–2	4.08–3	5.53–2	2.28–2	8.36–2
900.0	1.84–2	3.24–3	5.24–2	2.25–2	7.40–2
1,000.0	1.44–2	2.64–3	4.99–2	2.21–2	6.69–2

Bismuth **Z = 83**

Energy (keV)	τ/ρ (cm^2/g)	σ_c/ρ (cm^2/g)	σ_I/ρ (cm^2/g)	σ_a/ρ (cm^2/g)	μ/ρ (cm^2/g)
0.1	5.85+3	1.32+1	4.94–5	1.32–8	5.87+3
$0.1001_{O_{II,III}}$	5.82+3	1.32+1	4.95–5	1.32–8	5.84+3
0.1015	8.29+3	1.32+1	5.07–5	1.37–8	8.31+3
0.15	2.38+3	1.32+1	1.03–4	4.18–8	2.39+3
0.1586	2.11+3	1.32+1	1.15–4	4.92–8	2.12+3
0.16 $N_{VI,VII}O_I$	3.40+3	1.32+1	1.17–4	5.05–8	3.41+3
0.18	3.12+3	1.32+1	1.46–4	7.12–8	3.14+3
0.2	3.32+3	1.32+1	1.78–4	9.63–8	3.34+3
0.3	1.20+4	1.31+1	3.89–4	3.18–7	1.21+4
0.4	1.37+4	1.31+1	6.77–4	7.35–7	1.37+4
$0.4487_{N_{IV,V}}$	1.27+4	1.31+1	8.45–4	1.03–6	1.27+4
0.4501	1.32+4	1.31+1	8.50–4	1.04–6	1.32+4
0.5	1.31+4	1.31+1	1.03–3	1.40–6	1.31+4
0.6	1.08+4	1.30+1	1.45–3	2.35–6	1.08+4
0.7	8.74+3	1.29+1	1.92–3	3.61–6	8.75+3
$0.7203_{N_{II,III}}$	8.37+3	1.29+1	2.02–3	3.91–6	8.38+3
0.7217	9.20+3	1.29+1	2.02–3	3.93–6	9.21+3
0.8	8.03+3	1.28+1	2.43–3	5.21–6	8.04+3
0.9	6.61+3	1.27+1	2.96–3	7.11–6	6.62+3
0.9375_{N_I}	6.16+3	1.27+1	3.17–3	7.91–6	6.17+3
0.9389	6.46+3	1.27+1	3.17–3	7.94–6	6.48+3

TABLE 3 (continued)

Energy (keV)	τ/ρ (cm²/g)	σ_c/ρ (cm²/g)	σ_I/ρ (cm²/g)	σ_a/ρ (cm²/g)	μ/ρ (cm²/g)
1.0	5.80+3	1.26+1	3.52−3	9.35−6	5.81+3
1.5	2.63+3	1.21+1	6.51−3	2.54−5	2.64+3
2.0	1.42+3	1.15+1	9.58−3	4.89−5	1.43+3
2.5	8.59+2	1.09+1	1.26−2	7.90−5	8.69+2
2.58_{M_V}	7.76+2	1.08+1	1.30−2	8.43−5	7.86+2
2.58	2.03+3	1.08+1	1.30−2	8.43−5	2.04+3
$2.688_{M_{IV}}$	1.82+3	1.07+1	1.36−2	9.17−5	1.84+3
2.688	2.74+3	1.07+1	1.36−2	9.17−5	2.75+3
3.0	2.06+3	1.03+1	1.54−2	1.15−4	2.07+3
$3.177_{M_{III}}$	1.78+3	1.01+1	1.64−2	1.29−4	1.79+3
3.177	2.13+3	1.01+1	1.64−2	1.29−4	2.14+3
3.5	1.66+3	9.74+0	1.81−2	1.56−4	1.67+3
$3.696_{M_{II}}$	1.44+3	9.52+0	1.91−2	1.73−4	1.45+3
3.696	1.59+3	9.52+0	1.91−2	1.73−4	1.60+3
3.999_{M_I}	1.30+3	9.22+0	2.07−2	2.01−4	1.31+3
3.999	1.43+3	9.22+0	2.07−2	2.01−4	1.44+3
4.0	1.43+3	9.22+0	2.07−2	2.01−4	1.44+3
5.0	8.02+2	8.25+0	2.55−2	3.05−4	8.10+2
6.0	5.01+2	7.40+0	3.01−2	4.27−4	5.09+2
7.0	3.37+2	6.66+0	3.44−2	5.65−4	3.44+2
8.0	2.39+2	6.02+0	3.85−2	7.17−4	2.45+2
9.0	1.76+2	5.47+0	4.23−2	8.80−4	1.82+2
10.0	1.34+2	4.99+0	4.59−2	1.05−3	1.39+2
12.0	8.39+1	4.20+0	5.21−2	1.41−3	8.82+1
$13.42_{L_{III}}$	6.29+1	3.73+0	5.59−2	1.67−3	6.67+1
13.42	1.51+2	3.73+0	5.59−2	1.67−3	1.55+2
15.0	1.12+2	3.31+0	5.98−2	1.97−3	1.15+2
$15.71_{L_{II}}$	9.90+1	3.13+0	6.14−2	2.11−3	1.02+2
15.71	1.39+2	3.13+0	6.14−2	2.11−3	1.42+2
16.39_{L_I}	1.24+2	2.98+0	6.29−2	2.24−3	1.27+2
16.39	1.49+2	2.98+0	6.29−2	2.24−3	1.52+2
17.0	1.35+2	2.85+0	6.42−2	2.36−3	1.38+2
20.0	8.73+1	2.33+0	6.97−2	2.96−3	8.97+1
25.0	4.81+1	1.74+0	7.73−2	3.98−3	4.99+1
30.0	2.96+1	1.36+0	8.32−2	5.00−3	3.10+1
35.0	1.96+1	1.10+0	8.78−2	6.00−3	2.08+1
40.0	1.37+1	9.02−1	9.13−2	6.96−3	1.47+1
50.0	7.57+0	6.39−1	9.60−2	8.71−3	8.30+0
60.0	4.65+0	4.77−1	9.85−2	1.03−2	5.23+0
70.0	3.08+0	3.70−1	9.99−2	1.16−2	3.55+0
80.0	2.16+0	2.96−1	1.00−1	1.29−2	2.56+0
90.0	1.58+0	2.43−1	1.00−1	1.40−2	1.92+0
90.53_K	1.55+0	2.40−1	1.00−1	1.40−2	1.89+0
90.53	7.76+0	2.40−1	1.00−1	1.40−2	8.10+0
100.0	5.85+0	2.03−1	1.00−1	1.49−2	6.16+0
120.0	3.51+0	1.47−1	9.87−2	1.66−2	3.76+0
150.0	1.89+0	9.86−2	9.57−2	1.84−2	2.09+0
170.0	1.35+0	7.86−2	9.35−2	1.93−2	1.52+0
200.0	8.67−1	5.83−2	9.03−2	2.04−2	1.02+0
250.0	4.78−1	3.86−2	8.53−2	2.17−2	6.02−1
300.0	2.96−1	2.75−2	8.08−2	2.25−2	4.05−1
350.0	1.99−1	2.06−2	7.69−2	2.30−2	2.96−1

Energy (keV)	τ/ρ (cm²/g)	σ_c/ρ (cm²/g)	σ_I/ρ (cm²/g)	σ_a/ρ (cm²/g)	μ/ρ (cm²/g)
400.0	1.41–1	1.60–2	7.34–2	2.32–2	2.30–1
500.0	8.01–2	1.04–2	6.75–2	2.35–2	1.58–1
600.0	5.08–2	7.33–3	6.28–2	2.34–2	1.21–1
700.0	3.48–2	5.43–3	5.88–2	2.32–2	9.90–2
800.0	2.51–2	4.18–3	5.55–2	2.29–2	8.48–2
900.0	1.89–2	3.32–3	5.26–2	2.26–2	7.48–2
1,000.0	1.47–2	2.70–3	5.00–2	2.22–2	6.74–2

Polonium Z = 84

Energy (keV)	τ/ρ (cm²/g)	σ_c/ρ (cm²/g)	σ_I/ρ (cm²/g)	σ_a/ρ (cm²/g)	μ/ρ (cm²/g)
0.1	6.69+3	1.35+1	4.84–5	1.29–8	6.70+3
0.1123 $O_{II,III}$	4.16+3	1.35+1	5.91–5	1.77–8	4.17+3
0.1137	6.31+3	1.35+1	6.04–5	1.83–8	6.32+3
0.15	2.70+3	1.34+1	1.00–4	4.04–8	2.71+3
0.1763 O_I	1.97+3	1.34+1	1.36–4	6.50–8	1.98+3
0.1777	2.58+3	1.34+1	1.38–4	6.65–8	2.59+3
0.1833 $N_{VI,VII}$	2.53+3	1.34+1	1.46–4	7.27–8	2.54+3
0.1847	3.26+3	1.34+1	1.49–4	7.43–8	3.28+3
0.2	3.05+3	1.34+1	1.72–4	9.33–8	3.06+3
0.3	1.03+4	1.34+1	3.78–4	3.08–7	1.03+4
0.4	1.37+4	1.34+1	6.58–4	7.16–7	1.37+4
0.4834 $N_{IV,V}$	1.23+4	1.33+1	9.47–4	1.24–6	1.23+4
0.4848	1.27+4	1.33+1	9.52–4	1.25–6	1.27+4
0.5	1.40+4	1.33+1	1.01–3	1.37–6	1.40+4
0.6	1.13+4	1.32+1	1 42–3	2.30–6	1.13+4
0.7	9.18+3	1.32+1	1.88–3	3.55–6	9.20+3
0.753 $N_{II,III}$	8.22+3	1.31+1	2.15–3	4.36–6	8.23+3
0.7544	9.16+3	1.31+1	2.15–3	4.38–6	9.18+3
0.8	8.42+3	1.31+1	2.39–3	5.14–6	8.43+3
0.9	6.94+3	1.30+1	2.93–3	7.05–6	6.96+3
0.9946 N_I	5.83+3	1.29+1	3.46–3	9.18–6	5.84+3
0.996	6.11+3	1.29+1	3.47–3	9.21–6	6.13+3
1.0	6.08+3	1.29+1	3.49–3	9.31–6	6.09+3
1.5	2.78+3	1.23+1	6.55–3	2.56–5	2.79+3
2.0	1.50+3	1.17+1	9.71–3	4.97–5	1.51+3
2.5	9.08+2	1.11+1	1.28–2	8.07–5	9.19+2
2.683 M_V	7.73+2	1.08+1	1.39–2	9.33–5	7.83+2
2.683	1.91+3	1.08+1	1.39–2	9.33–5	1.92+3
2.798 M_{IV}	1.71+3	1.07+1	1.45–2	1.02–4	1.72+3
2.798	2.57+3	1.07+1	1.45–2	1.02–4	2.58+3
3.0	2.15+3	1.05+1	1.57–2	1.17–4	2.16+3
3.302 M_{III}	1.68+3	1.01+1	1.74–2	1.42–4	1.69+3
3.302	2.01+3	1.01+1	1.74–2	1.42–4	2.02+3
3.5	1.73+3	9.89+0	1.85–2	1.59–4	1.74+3
3.854 M_{II}	1.35+3	9.50+0	2.03–2	1.91–4	1.36+3
3.854	1.49+3	9.50+0	2.03–2	1.91–4	1.50+3
4.0	1.35+3	9.36+0	2.11–2	2.05–4	1.36+3
4.149 M_I	1.23+3	9.20+0	2.18–2	2.20–4	1.24+3
4.149	1.35+3	9.20+0	2.18–2	2.20–4	1.36+3
5.0	8.35+2	8.38+0	2.59–2	3.10–4	8.44+2
6.0	5.22+2	7.53+0	3.05–2	4.32–4	5.30+2
7.0	3.51+2	6.78+0	3.48–2	5.70–4	3.58+2

TABLE 3 (continued)

Energy (keV)	τ/ρ (cm²/g)	σ_c/ρ (cm²/g)	σ_I/ρ (cm²/g)	σ_a/ρ (cm²/g)	μ/ρ (cm²/g)
8.0	2.49+2	6.13+0	3.88−2	7.21−4	2.55+2
9.0	1.84+2	5.57+0	4.26−2	8.84−4	1.89+2
10.0	1.40+2	5.09+0	4.62−2	1.06−3	1.45+2
12.0	8.75+1	4.28+0	5.25−2	1.42−3	9.18+1
13.81 L_{III}	6.09+1	3.69+0	5.72−2	1.75−3	6.46+1
13.81	1.46+2	3.69+0	5.72−2	1.75−3	1.50+2
15.0	1.17+2	3.38+0	6.02−2	1.98−3	1.21+2
16.24 L_{II}	9.47+1	3.08+0	6.29−2	2.22−3	9.79+1
16.24	1.33+2	3.08+0	6.29−2	2.22−3	1.36+2
16.94 L_I	1.18+2	2.93+0	6.44−2	2.36−3	1.21+2
16.94	1.42+2	2.93+0	6.44−2	2.36−3	1.45+2
17.0	1.41+2	2.92+0	6.45−2	2.37−3	1.44+2
20.0	9.12+1	2.39+0	7.01−2	2.97−3	9.37+1
25.0	5.02+1	1.78+0	7.77−2	3.99−3	5.21+1
30.0	3.09+1	1.39+0	8.36−2	5.02−3	3.23+1
35.0	2.04+1	1.12+0	8.82−2	6.03−3	2.17+1
40.0	1.43+1	9.24−1	9.17−2	6.99−3	1.53+1
50.0	7.88+0	6.55−1	9.64−2	8.76−3	8.63+0
60.0	4.84+0	4.90−1	9.90−2	1.03−2	5.43+0
70.0	3.21+0	3.79−1	1.00−1	1.17−2	3.69+0
80.0	2.24+0	3.04−1	1.01−1	1.29−2	2.65+0
90.0	1.64+0	2.49−1	1.01−1	1.41−2	1.99+0
93.11 K	1.50+0	2.35−1	1.01−1	1.44−2	1.83+0
93.11	7.42+0	2.35−1	1.01−1	1.44−2	7.75+0
100.0	6.09+0	2.08−1	1.01−1	1.50−2	6.39+0
120.0	3.68+0	1.51−1	9.93−2	1.67−2	3.93+0
150.0	1.99+0	1.01−1	9.63−2	1.85−2	2.19+0
170.0	1.42+0	8.07−2	9.41−2	1.95−2	1.59+0
200.0	9.13−1	5.98−2	9.09−2	2.06−2	1.06+0
250.0	5.02−1	3.96−2	8.59−2	2.18−2	6.27−1
300.0	3.10−1	2.82−2	8.14−2	2.26−2	4.19−1
350.0	2.07−1	2.11−2	7.74−2	2.31−2	3.05−1
400.0	1.46−1	1.64−2	7.39−2	2.34−2	2.37−1
500.0	8.29−2	1.07−2	6.80−2	2.36−2	1.62−1
600.0	5.26−2	7.53−3	6.32−2	2.36−2	1.23−1
700.0	3.60−2	5.57−3	5.92−2	2.34−2	1.01−1
800.0	2.61−2	4.29−3	5.59−2	2.31−2	8.62−2
900.0	1.97−2	3.41−3	5.29−2	2.27−2	7.60−2
1,000.0	1.54−2	2.77−3	5.04−2	2.23−2	6.85−2

Astatine Z = 85

Energy (keV)	τ/ρ (cm²/g)	σ_c/ρ (cm²/g)	σ_I/ρ (cm²/g)	σ_a/ρ (cm²/g)	μ/ρ (cm²/g)
0.1	8.47+3	1.38+1	4.83−5	1.27−8	8.48+3
0.1253 $O_{II,III}$	3.32+3	1.38+1	7.07−5	2.35−8	3.34+3
0.1267	5.21+3	1.38+1	7.21−5	2.43−8	5.23+3
0.15	3.19+3	1.38+1	9.79−5	3.94−8	3.21+3
0.1943 O_I	1.96+3	1.38+1	1.59−4	8.36−8	1.98+3
0.1957	2.56+3	1.38+1	1.61−4	8.53−8	2.58+3
0.2	2.55+3	1.38+1	1.68−4	9.08−8	2.57+3
0.2093 $N_{VI,VII}$	2.51+3	1.38+1	1.84−4	1.04−7	2.52+3
0.2107	3.32+3	1.38+1	1.86−4	1.06−7	3.33+3
0.3	7.82+3	1.37+1	3.68−4	3.00−7	7.83+3
0.4	1.36+4	1.37+1	6.42−4	6.99−7	1.36+4

TABLE 3 (continued)

Energy (keV)	τ/ρ (cm²/g)	σ_c/ρ (cm²/g)	σ_I/ρ (cm²/g)	σ_a/ρ (cm²/g)	μ/ρ (cm²/g)
0.5	1.23+4	1.36+1	9.87–4	1.34–6	1.23+4
0.5168 $N_{IV,V}$	1.20+4	1.36+1	1.05–3	1.47–6	1.20+4
0.5182	1.23+4	1.36+1	1.06–3	1.48–6	1.23+4
0.6	1.18+4	1.36+1	1.39–3	2.26–6	1.18+4
0.7	9.69+3	1.35+1	1.85–3	3.50–6	9.70+3
0.788 $N_{II,III}$	8.10+3	1.34+1	2.29–3	4.87–6	8.11+3
0.7894	9.16+3	1.34+1	2.30–3	4.90–6	9.18+3
0.8	8.88+3	1.34+1	2.36–3	5.08–6	8.89+3
0.9	7.34+3	1.33+1	2.89–3	6.98–6	7.35+3
1.0	6.11+3	1.32+1	3.46–3	9.24–6	6.13+3
1.0413 N_I	5.68+3	1.32+1	3.70–3	1.03–5	5.69+3
1.0427	5.94+3	1.31+1	3.71–3	1.03–5	5.96+3
1.5	2.94+3	1.26+1	6.56–3	2.58–5	2.95+3
2.0	1.59+3	1.20+1	9.81–3	5.04–5	1.60+3
2.5	9.63+2	1.13+1	1.30–2	8.22–5	9.74+2
2.787 M_V	7.33+2	1.09+1	1.47–2	1.03–4	7.44+2
2.787	1.81+3	1.09+1	1.47–2	1.03–4	1.82+3
2.909 M_{IV}	1.62+3	1.08+1	1.55–2	1.13–4	1.63+3
2.909	2.43+3	1.08+1	1.55–2	1.13–4	2.45+3
3.0	2.25+3	1.07+1	1.60–2	1.20–4	2.26+3
3.426 M_{III}	1.60+3	1.02+1	1.85–2	1.56–4	1.61+3
3.426	1.92+3	1.02+1	1.85–2	1.56–4	1.93+3
3.5	1.81+3	1.01+1	1.89–2	1.63–4	1.82+3
4.0	1.29+3	9.55+0	2.16–2	2.10–4	1.30+3
4.008 M_{II}	1.28+3	9.54+0	2.16–2	2.11–4	1.29+3
4.008	1.41+3	9.54+0	2.16–2	2.11–4	1.42+3
4.317 M_I	1.16+3	9.21+0	2.32–2	2.42–4	1.17+3
4.317	1.28+3	9.21+0	2.32–2	2.42–4	1.29+3
5.0	8.76+2	8.56+0	2.65–2	3.17–4	8.84+2
6.0	5.47+2	7.69+0	3.10–2	4.39–4	5.55+2
7.0	3.68+2	6.94+0	3.53–2	5.77–4	3.75+2
8.0	2.61+2	6.28+0	3.93–2	7.30–4	2.67+2
9.0	1.93+2	5.71+0	4.32–2	8.94–4	1.98+2
10.0	1.47+2	5.21+0	4.67–2	1.07–3	1.52+2
12.0	9.18+1	4.39+0	5.31–2	1.43–3	9.62+1
14.21 L_{III}	5.94+1	3.68+0	5.88–2	1.85–3	6.31+1
14.21	1.42+2	3.68+0	5.88–2	1.85–3	1.45+2
15.0	1.23+2	3.47+0	6.08–2	2.00–3	1.26+2
16.78 L_{II}	9.09+1	3.05+0	6.47–2	2.35–3	9.40+1
16.78	1.27+2	3.05+0	6.47–2	2.35–3	1.30+2
17.0	1.23+2	3.00+0	6.52–2	2.40–3	1.26+2
17.49 L_I	1.14+2	2.90+0	6.61–2	2.49–3	1.17+2
17.49	1.37+2	2.90+0	6.61–2	2.49–3	1.40+2
20.0	9.56+1	2.45+0	7.08–2	3.00–3	9.81+1
25.0	5.27+1	1.84+0	7.84–2	4.03–3	5.46+1
30.0	3.24+1	1.43+0	8.43–2	5.06–3	3.39+1
35.0	2.14+1	1.15+0	8.90–2	6.08–3	2.27+1
40.0	1.50+1	9.50–1	9.25–2	7.05–3	1.61+1
50.0	8.27+0	6.75–1	9.73–2	8.84–3	9.05+0
60.0	5.08+0	5.04–1	1.00–1	1.04–2	5.69+0
70.0	3.37+0	3.91–1	1.01–1	1.18–2	3.86+0
80.0	2.36+0	3.13–1	1.02–1	1.31–2	2.77+0

TABLE 3 (continued)

Energy (keV)	τ/ρ (cm²/g)	σ_c/ρ (cm²/g)	σ_I/ρ (cm²/g)	σ_a/ρ (cm²/g)	μ/ρ (cm²/g)
90.0	1.72+0	2.56–1	1.02–1	1.42–2	2.08+0
95.73_K	1.46+0	2.31–1	1.02–1	1.48–2	1.79+0
95.73	7.18+0	2.31–1	1.02–1	1.48–2	7.51+0
100.0	6.36+0	2.14–1	1.02–1	1.52–2	6.68+0
120.0	3.85+0	1.56–1	1.00–1	1.69–2	4.10+0
150.0	2.09+0	1.04–1	9.74–2	1.87–2	2.29+0
170.0	1.48+0	8.31–2	9.52–2	1.97–2	1.66+0
200.0	9.57–1	6.16–2	9.19–2	2.08–2	1.11+0
250.0	5.27–1	4.08–2	8.68–2	2.21–2	6.54–1
300.0	3.25–1	2.91–2	8.23–2	2.29–2	4.36–1
350.0	2.17–1	2.18–2	7.83–2	2.34–2	3.17–1
400.0	1.54–1	1.69–2	7.47–2	2.37–2	2.46–1
500.0	8.73–2	1.10–2	6.88–2	2.39–2	1.67–1
600.0	5.54–2	7.76–3	6.40–2	2.38–2	1.27–1
700.0	3.80–2	5.74–3	5.99–2	2.36–2	1.04–1
800.0	2.75–2	4.43–3	5.65–2	2.33–2	8.84–2
900.0	2.08–2	3.51–3	5.35–2	2.30–2	7.78–2
1,000.0	1.62–2	2.86–3	5.10–2	2.26–2	7.01–2

Radon **Z = 86**

Energy (keV)	τ/ρ (cm²/g)	σ_c/ρ (cm²/g)	σ_I/ρ (cm²/g)	σ_a/ρ (cm²/g)	μ/ρ (cm²/g)
0.1	9.72+3	1.33+1	4.31–5	1.14–8	9.73+3
$0.1383_{O_{II,III}}$	2.56+3	1.33+1	7.67–5	2.85–8	2.57+3
0.1397	4.16+3	1.33+1	7.82–5	2.94–8	4.18+3
0.15	3.51+3	1.33+1	8.92–5	3.61–8	3.52+3
0.2	2.00+3	1.33+1	1.54–4	8.35–8	2.02+3
0.2133_{O_I}	1.89+3	1.33+1	1.75–4	1.01–7	1.90+3
0.2147	2.45+3	1.33+1	1.77–4	1.03–7	2.46+3
$0.2373_{N_{VI,VII}}$	2.39+3	1.33+1	2.15–4	1.38–7	2.40+3
0.2387	3.21+3	1.33+1	2.17–4	1.41–7	3.23+3
0.3	4.66+3	1.33+1	3.39–4	2.77–7	4.68+3
0.35	9.88+3	1.33+1	4.57–4	4.35–7	9.89+3
0.4	1.25+4	1.32+1	5.92–4	6.44–7	1.25+4
0.5	1.21+4	1.32+1	9.10–4	1.24–6	1.21+4
$0.5505_{N_{IV,V}}$	1.11+4	1.32+1	1.09–3	1.63–6	1.11+4
0.5519	1.14+4	1.32+1	1.10–3	1.64–6	1.14+4
0.6	1.18+4	1.31+1	1.28–3	2.09–6	1.18+4
0.7	9.67+3	1.31+1	1.71–3	3.24–6	9.68+3
0.8	7.92+3	1.30+1	2.18–3	4.71–6	7.93+3
$0.821_{N_{II,III}}$	7.59+3	1.30+1	2.29–3	5.06–6	7.61+3
0.8224	8.72+3	1.30+1	2.29–3	5.08–6	8.74+3
0.9	7.32+3	1.29+1	2.68–3	6.48–6	7.34+3
1.0	6.11+3	1.28+1	3.21–3	8.60–6	6.13+3
1.0963_{N_I}	5.17+3	1.27+1	3.74–3	1.09–5	5.18+3
1.0977	5.40+3	1.27+1	3.75–3	1.10–5	5.41+3
1.5	2.95+3	1.22+1	6.14–3	2.42–5	2.96+3
2.0	1.59+3	1.16+1	9.23–3	4.76–5	1.61+3
2.5	9.65+2	1.09+1	1.23–2	7.81–5	9.76+2
2.892_{M_V}	6.74+2	1.04+1	1.46–2	1.06–4	6.84+2
2.892	1.63+3	1.04+1	1.46–2	1.06–4	1.64+3
3.0	1.49+3	1.03+1	1.53–2	1.15–4	1.50+3
$3.022_{M_{IV}}$	1.46+3	1.03+1	1.54–2	1.16–4	1.47+3
3.022	2.19+3	1.03+1	1.54–2	1.16–4	2.20+3

TABLE 3 (continued)

Energy (keV)	τ/ρ (cm²/g)	σ_c/ρ (cm²/g)	σ_I/ρ (cm²/g)	σ_a/ρ (cm²/g)	μ/ρ (cm²/g)
3.5	1.50+3	9.75+0	1.81−2	1.57−4	1.51+3
3.538 M_{III}	1.46+3	9.70+0	1.83−2	1.60−4	1.47+3
3.538	1.75+3	9.70+0	1.83−2	1.60−4	1.76+3
4.0	1.27+3	9.22+0	2.07−2	2.03−4	1.28+3
4.159 M_{II}	1.15+3	9.05+0	2.15−2	2.18−4	1.16+3
4.159	1.27+3	9.05+0	2.15−2	2.18−4	1.28+3
4.482 M_I	1.05+3	8.74+0	2.31−2	2.50−4	1.05+3
4.482	1.15+3	8.74+0	2.31−2	2.50−4	1.16+3
5.0	8.68+2	8.27+0	2.55−2	3.05−4	8.76+2
6.0	5.43+2	7.44+0	2.98−2	4.23−4	5.50+2
7.0	3.65+2	6.71+0	3.39−2	5.54−4	3.72+2
8.0	2.59+2	6.08+0	3.77−2	6.99−4	2.65+2
9.0	1.91+2	5.53+0	4.13−2	8.55−4	1.97+2
10.0	1.46+2	5.05+0	4.47−2	1.02−3	1.51+2
12.0	9.10+1	4.26+0	5.08−2	1.37−3	9.53+1
14.62 L_{III}	5.47+1	3.46+0	5.73−2	1.84−3	5.83+1
14.62	1.30+2	3.46+0	5.73−2	1.84−3	1.34+2
15.0	1.22+2	3.37+0	5.82−2	1.91−3	1.25+2
17.0	8.70+1	2.92+0	6.23−2	2.29−3	9.00+1
17.34 L_{II}	8.25+1	2.85+0	6.30−2	2.35−3	8.54+1
17.34	1.16+2	2.85+0	6.30−2	2.35−3	1.18+2
18.05 L_I	1.04+2	2.71+0	6.43−2	2.49−3	1.07+2
18.05	1.25+2	2.71+0	6.43−2	2.49−3	1.27+2
20.0	9.47+1	2.39+0	6.77−2	2.86−3	9.72+1
25.0	5.22+1	1.78+0	7.49−2	3.85−3	5.41+1
30.0	3.21+1	1.39+0	8.05−2	4.83−3	3.36+1
35.0	2.13+1	1.12+0	8.49−2	5.80−3	2.25+1
40.0	1.49+1	9.25−1	8.84−2	6.73−3	1.59+1
50.0	8.21+0	6.57−1	9.29−2	8.45−3	8.96+0
60.0	5.05+0	4.91−1	9.55−2	9.96−3	5.63+0
70.0	3.34+0	3.80−1	9.68−2	1.13−2	3.82+0
80.0	2.34+0	3.05−1	9.74−2	1.25−2	2.74+0
90.0	1.71+0	2.50−1	9.75−2	1.36−2	2.06+0
98.4 K	1.35+0	2.14−1	9.73−2	1.44−2	1.66+0
98.4	6.58+0	2.14−1	9.73−2	1.44−2	6.89+0
100.0	6.29+0	2.09−1	9.72−2	1.45−2	6.59+0
120.0	3.81+0	1.52−1	9.59−2	1.61−2	4.05+0
150.0	2.07+0	1.02−1	9.31−2	1.79−2	2.26+0
170.0	1.47+0	8.10−2	9.10−2	1.88−2	1.64+0
200.0	9.48−1	6.01−2	8.79−2	1.99−2	1.10+0
250.0	5.22−1	3.98−2	8.31−2	2.11−2	6.45−1
300.0	3.23−1	2.83−2	7.87−2	2.19−2	4.30−1
350.0	2.16−1	2.12−2	7.49−2	2.24−2	3.12−1
400.0	1.53−1	1.65−2	7.15−2	2.27−2	2.41−1
500.0	8.69−2	1.08−2	6.58−2	2.29−2	1.63−1
600.0	5.52−2	7.57−3	6.12−2	2.28−2	1.24−1
700.0	3.78−2	5.60−3	5.73−2	2.26−2	1.01−1
800.0	2.74−2	4.32−3	5.41−2	2.23−2	8.58−2
900.0	2.08−2	3.43−3	5.12−2	2.20−2	7.54−2
1,000.0	1.62−2	2.79−3	4.88−2	2.16−2	6.78−2

TABLE 3 (continued)

Energy (keV)	τ/ρ (cm²/g)	σ_c/ρ (cm²/g)	σ_I/ρ (cm²/g)	σ_a/ρ (cm²/g)	μ/ρ (cm²/g)
Francium	**Z = 87**				
0.1	9.88+3	1.36+1	8.23–5	2.18–8	9.90+3
0.15	2.05+3	1.36+1	1.69–4	6.81–8	2.07+3
0.1533 $O_{II,III}$	1.91+3	1.36+1	1.76–4	7.25–8	1.93+3
0.1547	3.56+3	1.36+1	1.79–4	7.45–8	3.58+3
0.2	2.16+3	1.36+1	2.88–4	1.56–7	2.17+3
0.2333 O_I	1.89+3	1.35+1	3.84–4	2.42–7	1.90+3
0.2347	2.47+3	1.35+1	3.88–4	2.46–7	2.48+3
0.2673 $N_{VI,VII}$	2.33+3	1.35+1	4.94–4	3.57–7	2.34+3
0.2687	3.00+3	1.35+1	4.99–4	3.62–7	3.01+3
0.3	3.03+3	1.35+1	6.11–4	4.94–7	3.05+3
0.35	7.58+3	1.35+1	8.05–4	7.59–7	7.59+3
0.4	1.16+4	1.35+1	1.02–3	1.09–6	1.16+4
0.5	1.22+4	1.34+1	1.48–3	1.97–6	1.22+4
0.5868 $N_{IV,V}$	1.05+4	1.33+1	1.91–3	2.97–6	1.06+4
0.6	1.22+4	1.33+1	1.98–3	3.14–6	1.22+4
0.7	1.00+4	1.32+1	2.49–3	4.58–6	1.00+4
0.8	8.24+3	1.31+1	3.02–3	6.29–6	8.25+3
0.866 $N_{II,III}$	7.25+3	1.31+1	3.38–3	7.58–6	7.26+3
0.8674	8.31+3	1.31+1	3.38–3	7.60–6	8.33+3
0.9	7.62+3	1.30+1	3.56–3	8.28–6	7.63+3
1.0	6.37+3	1.29+1	4.11–3	1.06–5	6.38+3
1.1523 N_I	4.92+3	1.27+1	4.95–3	1.46–5	4.93+3
1.1537	5.16+3	1.27+1	4.96–3	1.46–5	5.17+3
1.5	3.09+3	1.23+1	6.97–3	2.65–5	3.10+3
2.0	1.68+3	1.17+1	9.96–3	5.01–5	1.69+3
2.5	1.02+3	1.11+1	1.29–2	8.06–5	1.03+3
3.0 M_V	6.65+2	1.05+1	1.59–2	1.17–4	6.76+2
3.0	1.53+3	1.05+1	1.59–2	1.17–4	1.54+3
3.136 M_{IV}	1.37+3	1.03+1	1.66–2	1.28–4	1.38+3
3.136	2.05+3	1.03+1	1.66–2	1.28–4	2.06+3
3.5	1.55+3	9.88+0	1.86–2	1.60–4	1.56+3
3.663 M_{III}	1.38+3	9.69+0	1.95–2	1.74–4	1.39+3
3.663	1.65+3	9.69+0	1.95–2	1.74–4	1.66+3
4.0	1.32+3	9.34+0	2.13–2	2.07–4	1.33+3
4.327 M_{II}	1.08+3	9.01+0	2.29–2	2.39–4	1.09+3
4.327	1.19+3	9.01+0	2.29–2	2.39–4	1.19+3
4.652 M_I	9.85+2	8.70+0	2.44–2	2.72–4	9.94+2
4.652	1.08+3	8.70+0	2.44–2	2.72–4	1.09+3
5.0	9.00+2	8.38+0	2.60–2	3.11–4	9.09+2
6.0	5.64+2	7.55+0	3.04–2	4.29–4	5.72+2
7.0	3.80+2	6.82+0	3.44–2	5.60–4	3.87+2
8.0	2.70+2	6.18+0	3.82–2	7.05–4	2.76+2
9.0	2.00+2	5.62+0	4.18–2	8.60–4	2.05+2
10.0	1.52+2	5.14+0	4.51–2	1.03–3	1.58+2
12.0	9.55+1	4.34+0	5.12–2	1.38–3	9.99+1
15.0	5.39+1	3.44+0	5.86–2	1.92–3	5.74+1
15.03 L_{III}	5.36+1	3.43+0	5.86–2	1.93–3	5.71+1
15.03	1.26+2	3.43+0	5.86–2	1.93–3	1.29+2
17.0	9.06+1	2.98+0	6.27–2	2.30–3	9.36+1
17.91 L_{II}	7.88+1	2.80+0	6.44–2	2.47–3	8.17+1
17.91	1.10+2	2.80+0	6.44–2	2.47–3	1.13+2

TABLE 3 (continued)

Energy (keV)	τ/ρ (cm^2/g)	σ_c/ρ (cm^2/g)	σ_I/ρ (cm^2/g)	σ_a/ρ (cm^2/g)	μ/ρ (cm^2/g)
18.64 L_I	9.92+1	2.66+0	6.57−2	2.61−3	1.02+2
18.64	1.19+2	2.66+0	6.57−2	2.61−3	1.22+2
20.0	9.87+1	2.44+0	6.81−2	2.88−3	1.01+2
25.0	5.44+1	1.83+0	7.52−2	3.86−3	5.63+1
30.0	3.35+1	1.42+0	8.09−2	4.85−3	3.50+1
35.0	2.22+1	1.15+0	8.53−2	5.83−3	2.34+1
40.0	1.55+1	9.46−1	8.88−2	6.76−3	1.66+1
50.0	8.57+0	6.73−1	9.34−2	8.49−3	9.33+0
60.0	5.27+0	5.03−1	9.60−2	1.00−2	5.87+0
70.0	3.49+0	3.90−1	9.74−2	1.14−2	3.98+0
80.0	2.45+0	3.12−1	9.80−2	1.26−2	2.85+0
90.0	1.79+0	2.56−1	9.81−2	1.37−2	2.14+0
100.0	1.35+0	2.14−1	9.78−2	1.46−2	1.66+0
101.1 K	1.31+0	2.10−1	9.77−2	1.47−2	1.62+0
101.1	6.25+0	2.10−1	9.77−2	1.47−2	6.56+0
120.0	3.92+0	1.55−1	9.65−2	1.62−2	4.17+0
150.0	2.14+0	1.04−1	9.36−2	1.80−2	2.34+0
170.0	1.53+0	8.31−2	9.16−2	1.90−2	1.70+0
200.0	9.88−1	6.16−2	8.85−2	2.00−2	1.14+0
250.0	5.46−1	4.08−2	8.36−2	2.13−2	6.70−1
300.0	3.38−1	2.90−2	7.92−2	2.21−2	4.46−1
350.0	2.26−1	2.17−2	7.54−2	2.25−2	3.23−1
400.0	1.60−1	1.69−2	7.20−2	2.28−2	2.49−1
500.0	9.10−2	1.10−2	6.62−2	2.30−2	1.68−1
600.0	5.78−2	7.76−3	6.16−2	2.30−2	1.27−1
700.0	3.97−2	5.74−3	5.77−2	2.28−2	1.03−1
800.0	2.88−2	4.43−3	5.44−2	2.25−2	8.77−2
900.0	2.18−2	3.51−3	5.16−2	2.22−2	7.69−2
1,000.0	1.71−2	2.86−3	4.91−2	2.18−2	6.90−2

Radium **Z = 88**

Energy (keV)	τ/ρ (cm^2/g)	σ_c/ρ (cm^2/g)	σ_I/ρ (cm^2/g)	σ_a/ρ (cm^2/g)	μ/ρ (cm^2/g)
0.1	9.52+3	1.37+1	9.51−5	2.53−8	9.53+3
0.15	2.16+3	1.37+1	1.96−4	7.92−8	2.18+3
0.168 $O_{II,III}$	1.57+3	1.37+1	2.43−4	1.10−7	1.59+3
0.1694	2.95+3	1.37+1	2.47−4	1.13−7	2.97+3
0.2	2.27+3	1.37+1	3.35−4	1.81−7	2.28+3
0.2537 O_I	1.89+3	1.37+1	5.24−4	3.60−7	1.90+3
0.2551	2.54+3	1.37+1	5.30−4	3.66−7	2.55+3
0.2982 $N_{VI,VII}$	2.27+3	1.36+1	7.08−4	5.70−7	2.29+3
0.2996	2.66+3	1.36+1	7.14−4	5.78−7	2.67+3
0.3	2.66+3	1.36+1	7.16−4	5.80−7	2.67+3
0.35	4.81+3	1.36+1	9.47−4	8.94−7	4.82+3
0.4	1.01+4	1.36+1	1.20−3	1.29−6	1.01+4
0.5	1.21+4	1.35+1	1.76−3	2.35−6	1.21+4
0.6	1.04+4	1.34+1	2.36−3	3.74−6	1.04+4
0.6153 $N_{IV,V}$	1.01+4	1.34+1	2.45−3	3.98−6	1.02+4
0.6167	1.07+4	1.34+1	2.46−3	4.01−6	1.08+4
0.7	1.02+4	1.33+1	2.97−3	5.45−6	1.02+4
0.8	8.45+3	1.32+1	3.58−3	7.44−6	8.47+3
0.9	6.98+3	1.31+1	4.19−3	9.73−6	6.99+3
0.9379 $N_{II,III}$	6.50+3	1.30+1	4.42−3	1.07−5	6.51+3
0.9393	7.26+3	1.30+1	4.43−3	1.07−5	7.27+3

TABLE 3 (continued)

Energy (keV)	τ/ρ (cm^2/g)	σ_c/ρ (cm^2/g)	σ_I/ρ (cm^2/g)	σ_a/ρ (cm^2/g)	μ/ρ (cm^2/g)
1.0	6.59+3	1.30+1	4.79–3	1.23–5	6.60+3
1.2073 N_I	4.67+3	1.27+1	6.02–3	1.84–5	4.68+3
1.2087	4.93+3	1.27+1	6.03–3	1.84–5	4.95+3
1.5	3.21+3	1.23+1	7.73–3	2.90–5	3.22–3
2.0	1.74+3	1.17+1	1.07–2	5.26–5	1.75+3
2.5	1.06+3	1.11+1	1.35–2	8.31–5	1.07+3
3.0	6.86+2	1.05+1	1.64–2	1.20–4	6.96+2
3.105 M_V	6.30+2	1.04+1	1.69–2	1.28–4	6.40+2
3.105	1.45+3	1.04+1	1.69–2	1.28–4	1.46+3
3.248 M_{IV}	1.29+3	1.02+1	1.77–2	1.40–4	1.30+3
3.248	1.93+3	1.02+1	1.77–2	1.40–4	1.94+3
3.5	1.60+3	9.92+0	1.91–2	1.62–4	1.61+3
3.792 M_{III}	1.30+3	9.59+0	2.06–2	1.89–4	1.31+3
3.792	1.56+3	9.59+0	2.06–2	1.89–4	1.57+3
4.0	1.36+3	9.38+0	2.17–2	2.09–4	1.37+3
4.49 M_{II}	1.01+3	8.89+0	2.41–2	2.58–4	1.02+3
4.49	1.11+3	8.89+0	2.41–2	2.58–4	1.12+3
4.822 M_I	9.27+2	8.58+0	2.56–2	2.93–4	9.36+2
4.822	1.02+3	8.58+0	2.56–2	2.93–4	1.03+3
5.0	9.30+2	8.42+0	2.64–2	3.13–4	9.38+2
6.0	5.83+2	7.59+0	3.07–2	4.31–3	5.90+2
7.0	3.92+2	6.86+0	3.46–2	5.62–4	3.99+2
8.0	2.79+2	6.23+0	3.83–2	7.05–4	2.85+2
9.0	2.06+2	5.67+0	4.18–2	8.59–4	2.12+2
10.0	1.57+2	5.18+0	4.51–2	1.02–3	1.63+2
12.0	9.87+1	4.38+0	5.11–2	1.37–3	1.03+2
15.0	5.57+1	3.48+0	5.85–2	1.92–3	5.92+1
15.44 L_{III}	5.17+1	3.36+0	5.94–2	2.00–3	5.51+1
15.44	1.21+2	3.36+0	5.94–2	2.00–3	1.24+2
17.0	9.36+1	3.02+0	6.26–2	2.29–3	9.67+1
18.48 L_{II}	7.49+1	2.72+0	6.53–2	2.57–3	7.77+1
18.48	1.05+2	2.72+0	6.53–2	2.57–3	1.08+2
19.24 L_I	9.42+1	2.59+0	6.66–2	2.72–3	9.68+1
19.24	1.13+2	2.59+0	6.66–2	2.72–3	1.16+2
20.0	1.02+2	2.47+0	6.79–2	2.87–3	1.04+2
25.0	5.62+1	1.85+0	7.50–2	3.84–3	5.81+1
30.0	3.46+1	1.44+0	8.05–2	4.83–3	3.61+1
35.0	2.29+1	1.16+0	8.49–2	5.80–3	2.42+1
40.0	1.60+1	9.59–1	8.84–2	6.73–3	1.71+1
50.0	8.85+0	6.83–1	9.30–2	8.45–3	9.63+0
60.0	5.44+0	5.10–1	9.56–2	9.97–3	6.05+0
70.0	3.61+0	3.95–1	9.70–2	1.13–2	4.10+0
80.0	2.53+0	3.17–1	9.76–2	1.25–2	2.94+0
90.0	1.85+0	2.60–1	9.77–2	1.36–2	2.20+0
100.0	1.39+0	2.17–1	9.74–2	1.46–2	1.71+0
103.9 K	1.26+0	2.03–1	9.71–2	1.49–2	1.56+0
103.9	5.98+0	2.03–1	9.71–2	1.49–2	6.28+0
120.0	4.04+0	1.58–1	9.61–2	1.62–2	4.30+0
150.0	2.21+0	1.06–1	9.34–2	1.80–2	2.41+0
170.0	1.58+0	8.44–2	9.13–2	1.89–2	1.75+0
200.0	1.02+0	6.26–2	8.82–2	2.00–2	1.17+0
250.0	5.63–1	4.14–2	8.34–2	2.12–2	6.88–1
300.0	3.49–1	2.95–2	7.90–2	2.20–2	4.57–1

TABLE 3 (continued)

Energy (keV)	τ/ρ (cm²/g)	σ_c/ρ (cm²/g)	σ_I/ρ (cm²/g)	σ_a/ρ (cm²/g)	μ/ρ (cm²/g)
350.0	2.34−1	2.21−2	7.52−2	2.25−2	3.31−1
400.0	1.66−1	1.72−2	7.18−2	2.28−2	2.55−1
500.0	9.43−2	1.12−2	6.61−2	2.30−2	1.72−1
600.0	6.00−2	7.88−3	6.14−2	2.29−2	1.29−1
700.0	4.12−2	5.83−3	5.76−2	2.27−2	1.05−1
800.0	2.99−2	4.49−3	5.43−2	2.24−2	8.87−2
900.0	2.27−2	3.57−3	5.15−2	2.21−2	7.77−2
1,000.0	1.77−2	2.90−3	4.90−2	2.17−2	6.96−2

Actinium Z = 89

Energy (keV)	τ/ρ (cm²/g)	σ_c/ρ (cm²/g)	σ_I/ρ (cm²/g)	σ_a/ρ (cm²/g)	μ/ρ (cm²/g)
0.1	1.16+4	1.40+1	9.21−5	2.45−8	1.17+4
0.15	2.67+3	1.40+1	1.90−4	7.67−8	2.68+3
0.1823 $O_{II,III}$	1.57+3	1.39+1	2.74−4	1.35−7	1.59+3
0.1837	2.84+3	1.39+1	2.78−4	1.38−7	2.86+3
0.2	2.51+3	1.39+1	3.25−4	1.76−7	2.53+3
0.2713 O_I	1.96+3	1.39+1	5.77−4	4.23−7	1.98+3
0.2727	2.61+3	1.39+1	5.82−4	4.30−7	2.62+3
0.3	2.42+3	1.39+1	6.96−4	5.65−7	2.43+3
0.3183 $N_{VI,VII}$	2.32+3	1.39+1	7.76−4	6.68−7	2.33+3
0.3197	2.63+3	1.39+1	7.82−4	6.76−7	2.64+3
0.4	8.74+3	1.38+1	1.18−3	1.27−6	8.75+3
0.5	1.19+4	1.37+1	1.74−3	2.32−6	1.19+4
0.6	1.04+4	1.37+1	2.34−3	3.74−6	1.04+4
0.6527 $N_{IV,V}$	9.41+3	1.36+1	2.67−3	4.62−6	9.43+3
0.6541	9.87+3	1.36+1	2.68−3	4.64−6	9.89+3
0.7	1.03+4	1.36+1	2.97−3	5.48−6	1.03+4
0.8	8.57+3	1.34+1	3.61−3	7.54−6	8.59+3
0.9	7.12+3	1.33+1	4.25−3	9.91−6	7.14+3
0.9526 $N_{II,III}$	6.47+3	1.33+1	4.58−3	1.13−5	6.48+3
0.954	7.13+3	1.33+1	4.59−3	1.13−5	7.15+3
1.0	6.69+3	1.32+1	4.88−3	1.25−5	6.71+3
1.2683 N_I	4.35+3	1.28+1	6.52−3	2.09−5	4.36+3
1.2697	4.61+3	1.28+1	6.53−3	2.10−5	4.63+3
1.5	3.31+3	1.26+1	7.93−3	2.98−5	3.32+3
2.0	1.81+3	1.19+1	1.09−2	5.39−5	1.82+3
3.0	7.24+2	1.06+1	1.67−2	1.22−4	7.35+2
3.219 M_V	5.99+2	1.04+1	1.79−2	1.40−4	6.09+2
3.219	1.37+3	1.04+1	1.79−2	1.40−4	1.38+3
3.37 M_{IV}	1.22+3	1.02+1	1.87−2	1.53−4	1.23+3
3.37	1.83+3	1.02+1	1.87−2	1.53−4	1.84+3
3.5	1.66+3	1.01+1	1.94−2	1.64−4	1.67+3
3.909 M_{III}	1.25+3	9.60+0	2.16−2	2.03−4	1.26+3
3.909	1.50+3	9.60+0	2.16−2	2.03−4	1.51+3
4.0	1.41+3	9.51+0	2.20−2	2.12−4	1.42+3
4.656 M_{II}	9.59+2	8.86+0	2.52−2	2.80−4	9.68+2
4.656	1.06+3	8.86+0	2.52−2	2.80−4	1.06+3
5.0	8.79+2	8.54+0	2.68−2	3.18−4	8.88+2
5.002 M_I	8.78+2	8.54+0	2.68−2	3.18−4	8.87+2
5.002	9.66+2	8.54+0	2.68−2	3.18−4	9.74+2
6.0	6.06+2	7.70+0	3.11−2	4.37−4	6.14+2
7.0	4.09+2	6.97+0	3.51−2	5.69−4	4.15+2
8.0	2.90+2	6.33+0	3.88−2	7.12−4	2.97+2

TABLE 3 (continued)

Energy (keV)	τ/ρ (cm^2/g)	σ_c/ρ (cm^2/g)	σ_I/ρ (cm^2/g)	σ_a/ρ (cm^2/g)	μ/ρ (cm^2/g)
9.0	2.15+2	5.77+0	4.23−2	8.66−4	2.20+2
10.0	1.64+2	5.27+0	4.56−2	1.03−3	1.69+2
12.0	1.03+2	4.46+0	5.15−2	1.38−3	1.07+2
15.0	5.80+1	3.55+0	5.89−2	1.93−3	6.17+1
15.87 L_{III}	5.02+1	3.33+0	6.07−2	2.09−3	5.36+1
15.87	1.17+2	3.33+0	6.07−2	2.09−3	1.21+2
17.0	9.76+1	3.08+0	6.30−2	2.31−3	1.01+2
19.08 L_{II}	7.17+1	2.67+0	6.68−2	2.70−3	7.44+1
19.08	1.00+2	2.67+0	6.68−2	2.70−3	1.03+2
19.84 L_I	9.04+1	2.55+0	6.81−2	2.85−3	9.31+1
19.84	1.09+2	2.55+0	6.81−2	2.85−3	1.11+2
20.0	1.06+2	2.53+0	6.83−2	2.88−3	1.09+2
25.0	5.86+1	1.89+0	7.54−2	3.86−3	6.05+1
30.0	3.60+1	1.47+0	8.09−2	4.85−3	3.76+1
35.0	2.39+1	1.19+0	8.53−2	5.82−3	2.52+1
40.0	1.67+1	9.80−1	8.88−2	6.76−3	1.78+1
50.0	9.22+0	6.99−1	9.35−2	8.49−3	1.00+1
60.0	5.67+0	5.23−1	9.61−2	1.00−2	6.29+0
70.0	3.76+0	4.05−1	9.75−2	1.14−2	4.26+0
80.0	2.63+0	3.24−1	9.81−2	1.26−2	3.05+0
90.0	1.92+0	2.66−1	9.82−2	1.37−2	2.29+0
100.0	1.45+0	2.22−1	9.80−2	1.47−2	1.77+0
106.8 K	1.22+0	1.98−1	9.75−2	1.52−2	1.51+0
106.8	5.75+0	1.98−1	9.75−2	1.52−2	6.04+0
120.0	4.19+0	1.62−1	9.67−2	1.63−2	4.45+0
150.0	2.30+0	1.08−1	9.39−2	1.81−2	2.50+0
170.0	1.64+0	8.65−2	9.18−2	1.90−2	1.82+0
200.0	1.06+0	8.41−2	8.88−2	2.01−2	1.21+0
250.0	5.88−1	4.24−2	8.39−2	2.14−2	7.14−1
300.0	3.64−1	3.02−2	7.95−2	2.22−2	4.74−1
350.0	2.44−1	2.26−2	7.57−2	2.26−2	3.43−1
400.0	1.73−1	1.76−2	7.23−2	2.29−2	2.63−1
500.0	9.86−2	1.15−2	6.65−2	2.31−2	1.77−1
600.0	6.28−2	8.07−3	6.19−2	2.31−2	1.33−1
700.0	4.31−2	5.97−3	5.80−2	2.29−2	1.07−1
800.0	3.14−2	4.60−3	5.47−2	2.26−2	9.07−2
900.0	2.38−2	3.65−3	5.18−2	2.23−2	7.93−2
1,000.0	1.86−2	2.97−3	4.93−2	2.19−2	7.09−2

Thorium Z = 90

Energy (keV)	τ/ρ (cm^2/g)	σ_c/ρ (cm^2/g)	σ_I/ρ (cm^2/g)	σ_a/ρ (cm^2/g)	μ/ρ (cm^2/g)
0.1	1.18+4	1.40+1	8.72−5	2.31−8	1.18+4
0.15	3.04+3	1.40+1	1.80−4	7.25−8	3.05+3
0.197 $O_{II,III}$	1.53+3	1.39+1	2.99−4	1.59−7	1.55+3
0.1984	2.71+3	1.39+1	3.03−4	1.63−7	2.72+3
0.2	2.68+3	1.39+1	3.08−4	1.66−7	2.69+3
0.2895 O_I	2.01+3	1.39+1	6.19−4	4.85−7	2.02+3
0.2909	2.64+3	1.39+1	6.25−4	4.92−7	2.65+3
0.3	2.52+3	1.39+1	6.62−4	5.38−7	2.54+3
0.3384 $N_{VI,VII}$	2.32+3	1.39+1	8.27−4	7.57−7	2.34+3
0.3398	2.57+3	1.39+1	8.33−4	7.66−7	2.59+3
0.4	6.99+3	1.38+1	1.12−3	1.21−6	7.00+3

TABLE 3 (continued)

Energy (keV)	τ/ρ (cm^2/g)	σ_c/ρ (cm^2/g)	σ_I/ρ (cm^2/g)	σ_a/ρ (cm^2/g)	μ/ρ (cm^2/g)
0.5	1.14+4	1.38+1	1.67−3	2.24−6	1.14+4
0.6	1.01+4	1.37+1	2.26−3	3.62−6	1.02+4
0.6908 $N_{IV,V}$	8.58+3	1.36+1	2.83−3	5.17−6	8.59+3
0.6922	8.97+3	1.36+1	2.84−3	5.20−6	8.98+3
0.7	9.87+3	1.36+1	2.89−3	5.35−6	9.88+3
0.8	8.52+3	1.35+1	3.53−3	7.40−6	8.53+3
0.9	7.12+3	1.33+1	4.17−3	9.78−6	7.13+3
1.0	5.97+3	1.32+1	4.81−3	1.24−5	5.98+3
1.0333 $N_{II,III}$	5.63+3	1.32+1	5.01−3	1.34−5	5.65+3
1.0347	6.26+3	1.32+1	5.02−3	1.34−5	6.27+3
1.3293 N_I	4.06+3	1.28+1	6.85−3	2.31−5	4.07+3
1.3307	4.32+3	1.28+1	6.85−3	2.31−5	4.33+3
1.5	3.39+3	1.26+1	7.90−3	2.98−5	3.41+3
2.0	1.86+3	1.19+1	1.09−2	5.39−5	1.87+3
3.0	7.50+2	1.06+1	1.66−2	1.21−4	7.60+2
3.332 M_V	5.70+2	1.02+1	1.84−2	1.49−4	5.80+2
3.332	1.28+3	1.02+1	1.84−2	1.49−4	1.29+3
3.491 M_{IV}	1.14+3	1.00+1	1.93−2	1.63−4	1.15+3
3.491	1.71+3	1.00+1	1.93−2	1.63−4	1.72+3
3.5	1.70+3	1.00+1	1.93−2	1.63−4	1.71+3
4.0	1.21+3	9.48+0	2.19−2	2.11−4	1.22+3
4.046 M_{III}	1.17+3	9.43+0	2.21−2	2.15−4	1.18+3
4.046	1.41+3	9.43+0	2.21−2	2.15−4	1.42+3
4.83 M_{II}	8.93+2	8.66+0	2.59−2	2.97−4	9.02+2
4.83	9.82+2	8.66+0	2.59−2	2.97−4	9.91+2
5.0	8.99+2	8.51+0	2.67−2	3.17−4	9.08+2
5.182 M_I	8.20+2	8.35+0	2.75−2	3.37−4	8.29+2
5.182	9.02+2	8.35+0	2.75−2	3.37−4	9.11+2
6.0	6.20+2	7.68+0	3.10−2	4.35−4	6.28+2
7.0	4.18+2	6.96+0	3.49−2	5.65−4	4.25+2
8.0	2.97+2	6.32+0	3.85−2	7.06−4	3.03+2
9.0	2.19+2	5.76+0	4.19−2	8.58−4	2.25+2
10.0	1.68+2	5.27+0	4.51−2	1.02−3	1.73+2
12.0	1.05+2	4.46+0	5.10−2	1.36−3	1.10+2
15.0	5.93+1	3.55+0	5.82−2	1.91−3	6.29+1
16.3 L_{III}	4.79+1	3.24+0	6.09−2	2.15−3	5.12+1
16.3	1.12+2	3.24+0	6.09−2	2.15−3	1.16+2
17.0	1.00+2	3.09+0	6.23−2	2.28−3	1.04+2
19.69 L_{II}	6.78+1	2.58+0	6.70−2	2.79−3	7.05+1
19.69	9.50+1	2.58+0	6.70−2	2.79−3	9.76+1
20.0	9.11+1	2.53+0	6.75−2	2.85−3	9.37+1
20.47 L_I	8.56+1	2.46+0	6.82−2	2.94−3	8.81+1
20.47	1.03+2	2.46+0	6.82−2	2.94−3	1.05+2
25.0	6.02+1	1.90+0	7.45−2	3.82−3	6.21+1
30.0	3.69+1	1.48+0	7.99−2	4.79−3	3.85+1
35.0	2.45+1	1.19+0	8.42−2	5.74−3	2.57+1
40.0	1.71+1	9.84−1	8.76−2	6.67−3	1.82+1
50.0	9.42+0	7.02−1	9.23−2	8.38−3	1.02+1
60.0	5.78+0	5.26−1	9.49−2	9.90−3	6.40+0
70.0	3.83+0	4.07−1	9.63−2	1.12−2	4.33+0
80.0	2.68+0	3.26−1	9.69−2	1.25−2	3.10+0

TABLE 3 (continued)

Energy (keV)	τ/ρ (cm²/g)	σ_c/ρ (cm²/g)	σ_I/ρ (cm²/g)	σ_a/ρ (cm²/g)	μ/ρ (cm²/g)
90.0	1.95+0	2.67–1	9.70–2	1.35–2	2.32+0
100.0	1.47+0	2.23–1	9.68–2	1.45–2	1.79+0
109.7_K	1.15+0	1.90–1	9.62–2	1.53–2	1.44+0
109.7	5.03+0	1.90–1	9.62–2	1.53–2	5.31+0
120.0	3.99+0	1.63–1	9.55–2	1.61–2	4.25+0
150.0	2.24+0	1.09–1	9.28–2	1.79–2	2.44+0
170.0	1.62+0	8.70–2	9.08–2	1.88–2	1.80+0
200.0	1.06+0	6.45–2	8.78–2	1.99–2	1.22+0
250.0	5.97–1	4.27–2	8.30–2	2.11–2	7.23–1
300.0	3.73–1	3.04–2	7.86–2	2.19–2	4.82–2
350.0	2.52–1	2.27–2	7.49–2	2.24–2	3.49–1
400.0	1.79–1	1.77–2	7.15–2	2.27–2	2.68–1
500.0	1.02–1	1.15–2	6.58–2	2.29–2	1.80–1
600.0	6.51–2	8.12–3	6.12–2	2.28–2	1.34–1
700.0	4.47–2	6.01–3	5.74–2	2.26–2	1.08–1
800.0	3.25–2	4.63–3	5.41–2	2.24–2	9.12–2
900.0	2.46–2	3.68–3	5.13–2	2.20–2	7.96–2
1,000.0	1.93–2	2.99–3	4.88–2	2.17–2	7.10–2

Protactinium Z = 91

Energy (keV)	τ/ρ (cm²/g)	σ_c/ρ (cm²/g)	σ_I/ρ (cm²/g)	σ_a/ρ (cm²/g)	μ/ρ (cm²/g)
0.1	1.56+4	1.43+1	8.72–5	2.31–8	1.56+4
0.15	3.86+3	1.43+1	1.79–4	7.23–8	3.87+3
0.2	1.56+3	1.43+1	3.07–4	1.66–7	1.57+3
$0.2222_{O_{II,III}}$	1.35+3	1.43+1	3.74–4	2.25–7	1.36+3
0.2236	2.68+3	1.43+1	3.79–4	2.29–7	2.69+3
0.3	2.23+3	1.43+1	6.58–4	5.34–7	2.24+3
0.3089_{O_I}	2.20+3	1.43+1	6.95–4	5.81–7	2.21+3
0.3103	2.84+3	1.43+1	7.01–4	5.88–7	2.85+3
$0.3638_{N_{VI,VII}}$	2.51+3	1.42+1	9.38–4	9.22–7	2.53+3
0.3652	2.78+3	1.42+1	9.45–4	9.32–7	2.79+3
0.4	3.60+3	1.42+1	1.11–3	1.20–6	3.62+3
0.5	1.15+4	1.41+1	1.65–3	2.21–6	1.15+4
0.6	1.08+4	1.40+1	2.23–3	3.57–6	1.08+4
0.7	9.03+3	1.39+1	2.84–3	5.26–6	9.04+3
$0.7216_{N_{IV,V}}$	8.65+3	1.39+1	2.98–3	5.66–6	8.66+3
0.723	9.02+3	1.39+1	2.99–3	5.69–6	9.04+3
0.8	9.05+3	1.38+1	3.46–3	7.26–6	9.07+3
0.9	7.58+3	1.37+1	4.09–3	9.57–6	7.60+3
1.0	6.36+3	1.36+1	4.71–3	1.21–5	6.38+3
$1.0783_{N_{II,III}}$	5.57+3	1.35+1	5.18–3	1.43–5	5.58+3
1.0797	6.21+3	1.35+1	5.19–3	1.44–5	6.23+3
1.3863_{N_I}	3.99+3	1.31+1	7.04–3	2.46–5	4.00+3
1.3877	4.24+3	1.31+1	7.05–3	2.47–5	4.25+3
1.5	3.62+3	1.29+1	7.73–3	2.91–5	3.63+3
2.0	1.98+3	1.23+1	1.07–2	5.31–5	2.00+3
3.0	7.98+2	1.10+1	1.65–2	1.21–4	8.09+2
3.442_{M_V}	5.67+2	1.04+1	1.89–2	1.58–4	5.77+2
3.442	1.24+3	1.04+1	1.89–2	1.58–4	1.25+3
3.5	1.19+3	1.04+1	1.92–2	1.63–4	1.20+3
$3.611_{M_{IV}}$	1.10+3	1.02+1	1.98–2	1.73–4	1.11+3
3.611	1.65+3	1.02+1	1.98–2	1.73–4	1.66+3

TABLE 3 (continued)

Energy (keV)	τ/ρ (cm^2/g)	σ_c/ρ (cm^2/g)	σ_I/ρ (cm^2/g)	σ_a/ρ (cm^2/g)	μ/ρ (cm^2/g)
4.0	1.27+3	9.81+0	2.19−2	2.10−4	1.28+3
$4.174_{M_{III}}$	1.14+3	9.61+0	2.27−2	2.28−4	1.15+3
4.174	1.36+3	9.61+0	2.27−2	2.28−4	1.37+3
5.0	8.59+2	8.80+0	2.67−2	3.17−4	8.68+2
$5.001_{M_{II}}$	8.58+2	8.80+0	2.67−2	3.17−4	8.67+2
5.001	9.44+2	8.80+0	2.67−2	3.17−4	9.53+2
5.367_{M_I}	7.88+2	8.46+0	2.83−2	3.59−4	7.96+2
5.367	8.67+2	8.46+0	2.83−2	3.59−4	8.75+2
6.0	6.51+2	7.93+0	3.10−2	4.36−4	6.59+2
7.0	4.39+2	7.17+0	3.50−2	5.68−4	4.46+2
8.0	3.11+2	6.51+0	3.87−2	7.10−4	3.18+2
9.0	2.30+2	5.93+0	4.21−2	8.64−4	2.36+2
10.0	1.76+2	5.43+0	4.54−2	1.03−3	1.81+2
12.0	1.10+2	4.59+0	5.14−2	1.38−3	1.15+2
15.0	6.21+1	3.66+0	5.88−2	1.93−3	6.58+1
$16.73_{L_{III}}$	4.70+1	3.24+0	6.25−2	2.26−3	5.03+1
16.73	1.10+2	3.24+0	6.25−2	2.26−3	1.14+2
17.0	1.06+2	3.18+0	6.30−2	2.31−3	1.09+2
20.0	6.85+1	2.62+0	6.83−2	2.89−3	7.12+1
$20.31_{L_{II}}$	6.58+1	2.57+0	6.88−2	2.95−3	6.84+1
20.31	9.21+1	2.57+0	6.88−2	2.95−3	9.47+1
21.1_{L_I}	8.31+1	2.44+0	6.99−2	3.10−3	8.57+1
21.1	9.98+1	2.44+0	6.99−2	3.10−3	1.02+2
25.0	6.34+1	1.96+0	7.54−2	3.86−3	6.54+1
30.0	3.89+1	1.53+0	8.09−2	4.85−3	4.05+1
35.0	2.58+1	1.23+0	8.53−2	5.82−3	2.71+1
40.0	1.80+1	1.02+0	8.87−2	6.76−3	1.91+1
50.0	9.93+0	7.26−1	9.35−2	8.50−3	1.07+1
60.0	6.10+0	5.43−1	9.62−2	1.00−2	6.74+0
70.0	4.04+0	4.21−1	9.76−2	1.14−2	4.56+0
80.0	2.83+0	3.37−1	9.83−2	1.26−2	3.26+0
90.0	2.06+0	2.76−1	9.84−2	1.37−2	2.44+0
100.0	1.56+0	2.31−1	9.81−2	1.47−2	1.88+0
112.6_K	1.13+0	1.88−1	9.73−2	1.57−2	1.42+0
112.6	5.34+0	1.88−1	9.73−2	1.57−2	5.63+0
120.0	4.49+0	1.68−1	9.69−2	1.63−2	4.76+0
150.0	2.46+0	1.13−1	9.42−2	1.82−2	2.67+0
170.0	1.76+0	8.99−2	9.21−2	1.91−2	1.94+0
200.0	1.14+0	6.67−2	8.91−2	2.02−2	1.30+0
250.0	6.32−1	4.41−2	8.42−2	2.15−2	7.60−1
300.0	3.92−1	3.14−2	7.99−2	2.22−2	5.03−1
350.0	2.63−1	2.35−2	7.60−2	2.27−2	3.63−1
400.0	1.87−1	1.83−2	7.26−2	2.30−2	2.78−1
500.0	1.07−1	1.19−2	6.68−2	2.32−2	1.85−1
600.0	6.80−2	8.38−3	6.21−2	2.32−2	1.39−1
700.0	4.69−2	6.21−3	5.82−2	2.30−2	1.11−1
800.0	3.41−2	4.78−3	5.49−2	2.27−2	9.38−2
900.0	2.59−2	3.80−3	5.21−2	2.24−2	8.17−2
1,000.0	2.03−2	3.09−3	4.96−2	2.20−2	7.29−2

Uranium **Z = 92**

0.1	1.30+4	1.42+1	8.28−5	2.20−8	1.30+4

TABLE 3 (continued)

Energy (keV)	τ/ρ (cm^2/g)	σ_c/ρ (cm^2/g)	σ_I/ρ (cm^2/g)	σ_a/ρ (cm^2/g)	μ/ρ (cm^2/g)
0.15	4.45+3	1.42+1	1.71–4	6.90–8	4.46+3
0.2	1.61+3	1.42+1	2.92–4	1.58–7	1.62+3
0.2158 $O_{II,III}$	1.41+3	1.42+1	3.38–4	1.97–7	1.42+3
0.2172	2.58+3	1.42+1	3.42–4	2.01–7	2.60+3
0.3	2.18+3	1.42+1	6.28–4	5.10–7	2.19+3
0.323 O_I	2.12+3	1.41+1	7.20–4	6.29–7	2.14+3
0.3244	2.74+3	1.41+1	7.26–4	6.37–7	2.76+3
0.3847 $N_{VI,VII}$	2.44+3	1.41+1	9.92–4	1.03–6	2.46–3
0.3861	2.68+3	1.41+1	9.98–4	1.04–6	2.69+3
0.4	2.69+3	1.41+1	1.06–3	1.15–6	2.70+3
0.5	1.05+4	1.40+1	1.58–3	2.12–6	1.06+4
0.55	1.12+4	1.40+1	1.85–3	2.72–6	1.12+4
0.6	1.06+4	1.39+1	2.14–3	3.42–6	1.07+4
0.7	9.00+3	1.38+1	2.73–3	5.04–6	9.01+3
0.7541 $N_{IV,V}$	8.11+3	1.38+1	3.05–3	6.05–6	8.12+3
0.7555	8.44+3	1.38+1	3.06–3	6.07–6	8.45+3
0.8	9.05+3	1.37+1	3.33–3	6.97–6	9.06+3
0.9	7.61+3	1.36+1	3.93–3	9.20–6	7.63+3
1.0	6.41+3	1.35+1	4.53–3	1.17–5	6.42+3
1.1203 $N_{II,III}$	5.25+3	1.34+1	5.24–3	1.50–5	5.27+3
1.1217	5.87+3	1.33+1	5.24–3	1.51–5	5.88+3
1.2	5.30+3	1.33+1	5.72–3	1.75–5	5.31+3
1.4403 N_I	3.75+3	1.29+1	7.11–3	2.58–5	3.76+3
1.4417	3.98+3	1.29+1	7.12–3	2.59–5	4.00+3
1.5	3.67+3	1.29+1	7.47–3	2.82–5	3.68+3
2.0	2.02+3	1.22+1	1.04–2	5.15–5	2.03+3
2.5	1.23+3	1.16+1	1.32–2	8.14–5	1.25+3
3.0	8.48+2	1.09+1	1.60–2	1.17–4	8.59+2
3.5	5.73+2	1.03+1	1.87–2	1.58–4	5.84+2
3.552 M_V	5.52+2	1.03+1	1.89–2	1.63–4	5.62+2
3.552	1.14+3	1.03+1	1.89–2	1.63–4	1.15+3
3.728 M_{IV}	1.01+3	1.00+1	1.98–2	1.79–4	1.02+3
3.728	1.51+3	1.00+1	1.98–2	1.79–4	1.52+3
4.0	1.26+3	9.75+0	2.12–2	2.05–4	1.27+3
4.303 M_{III}	1.05+3	9.42+0	2.27–2	2.34–4	1.06+3
4.303	1.26+3	9.42+0	2.27–2	2.34–4	1.27+3
5.0	8.56+2	8.74+0	2.59–2	3.08–4	8.65+2
5.182 M_{II}	7.82+2	8.57+0	2.67–2	3.28–4	7.90+2
5.182	8.60+2	8.57+0	2.67–2	3.28–4	8.69+2
5.548 M_I	7.22+2	8.25+0	2.83–2	3.71–4	7.31+2
5.548	7.95+2	8.25+0	2.83–2	3.71–4	8.03+2
6.0	6.51+2	7.87+0	3.02–2	4.25–4	6.59+2
7.0	4.39+2	7.12+0	3.41–2	5.54–4	4.46+2
8.0	3.12+2	6.47+0	3.77–2	6.93–4	3.19+2
9.0	2.31+2	5.89+0	4.11–2	8.44–4	2.37+2
10.0	1.77+2	5.39+0	4.43–2	1.00–3	1.82+2
12.0	1.11+2	4.56+0	5.01–2	1.34–3	1.16+2
15.0	6.27+1	3.64+0	5.75–2	1.89–3	6.64+1
17.0	4.56+1	3.17+0	6.16–2	2.26–3	4.88+1
17.17 L_{III}	4.45+1	3.13+0	6.19–2	2.29–3	4.76+1
17.17	1.03+2	3.13+0	6.19–2	2.29–3	1.06+2
20.0	6.86+1	2.61+0	6.69–2	2.83–3	7.13+1

Energy (keV)	τ/ρ (cm²/g)	σ_c/ρ (cm²/g)	σ_I/ρ (cm²/g)	σ_a/ρ (cm²/g)	μ/ρ (cm²/g)
$20.95_{L_{II}}$	6.07+1	2.45+0	6.83−2	3.01−3	6.32+1
20.95	8.49+1	2.45+0	6.83−2	3.01−3	8.75+1
21.76_{L_I}	7.68+1	2.34+0	6.94−2	3.16−3	7.92+1
21.76	9.21+1	2.34+0	6.94−2	3.16−3	9.45+1
25.0	6.37+1	1.95+0	7.38−2	3.79−3	6.57+1
30.0	3.92+1	1.52+0	7.92−2	4.74−3	4.08+1
35.0	2.60+1	1.23+0	8.35−2	5.69−3	2.73+1
40.0	1.82+1	1.01+0	8.69−2	6.61−3	1.93+1
50.0	1.01+1	7.24−1	9.15−2	8.32−3	1.09+1
60.0	6.19+0	5.42−1	9.41−2	9.83−3	6.82+0
70.0	4.11+0	4.20−1	9.56−2	1.12−2	4.62+0
80.0	2.88+0	3.36−1	9.62−2	1.24−2	3.31+0
90.0	2.10+0	2.76−1	9.64−2	1.34−2	2.47+0
100.0	1.59+0	2.30−1	9.61−2	1.44−2	1.91+0
115.6_K	1.08+0	1.79−1	9.52−2	1.57−2	1.35+0
115.6	4.67+0	1.79−1	9.52−2	1.57−2	4.95+0
120.0	4.24+0	1.68−1	9.50−2	1.60−2	4.50+0
150.0	2.36+0	1.13−1	9.23−2	1.78−2	2.57+0
170.0	1.71+0	8.98−2	9.03−2	1.87−2	1.89+0
200.0	1.12+0	6.66−2	8.73−2	1.98−2	1.28+0
250.0	6.32−1	4.40−2	8.26−2	2.11−2	7.59−1
300.0	3.97−1	3.13−2	7.83−2	2.18−2	5.07−1
350.0	2.69−1	2.35−2	7.45−2	2.23−2	3.67−1
400.0	1.93−1	1.82−2	7.12−2	2.26−2	2.82−1
500.0	1.11−1	1.19−2	6.55−2	2.28−2	1.88−1
600.0	7.09−2	8.37−3	6.10−2	2.28−2	1.40−1
700.0	4.88−2	6.20−3	5.71−2	2.26−2	1.12−1
800.0	3.55−2	4.77−3	5.39−2	2.23−2	9.41−2
900.0	2.68−2	3.79−3	5.11−2	2.19−2	8.17−2
1,000.0	2.10−2	3.08−3	4.86−2	2.16−2	7.27−2

Neptunium Z = 93

Energy (keV)	τ/ρ (cm²/g)	σ_c/ρ (cm²/g)	σ_I/ρ (cm²/g)	σ_a/ρ (cm²/g)	μ/ρ (cm²/g)
0.1	1.39+4	1.46+1	8.25−5	2.19−8	1.39+4
$0.1038_{O_{IV,V}}$	1.23+4	1.46+1	8.79−5	2.42−8	1.23+4
0.1052	1.51+4	1.46+1	9.00−5	2.51−8	1.51+4
0.15	5.31+3	1.46+1	1.69−4	6.83−8	5.32+3
0.2	1.71+3	1.46+1	2.90−4	1.57−7	1.73+3
$0.2312_{O_{II,III}}$	1.36+3	1.46+1	3.81−4	2.39−7	1.37+3
0.2326	2.55+3	1.46+1	3.86−4	2.43−7	2.56+3
0.3	2.31+3	1.45+1	6.23−4	5.06−7	2.33+3
0.3373_{O_I}	2.25+3	1.45+1	7.74−4	7.06−7	2.26+3
0.3387	2.86+3	1.45+1	7.79−4	7.14−7	2.88+3
0.4	2.56+3	1.45+1	1.06−3	1.14−6	2.58+3
$0.4082_{N_{VI,VII}}$	2.53+3	1.45+1	1.10−3	1.21−6	2.54+3
0.4096	2.75+3	1.45+1	1.10−3	1.22−6	2.77+3
0.5	9.21+3	1.44+1	1.57−3	2.10−6	9.22+3
0.6	1.09+4	1.43+1	2.13−3	3.40−6	1.10+4
0.7	9.36+3	1.42+1	2.72−3	5.03−6	9.37+3
$0.7878_{N_{IV,V}}$	7.94+3	1.41+1	3.24−3	6.71−6	7.96+3
0.7892	8.25+3	1.41+1	3.25−3	6.73−6	8.27+3
0.8	9.15+3	1.41+1	3.32−3	6.96−6	9.16+3
0.9	7.96+3	1.40+1	3.92−3	9.20−6	7.97+3

TABLE 3 (continued)

Energy (keV)	τ/ρ (cm²/g)	σ_c/ρ (cm²/g)	σ_I/ρ (cm²/g)	σ_a/ρ (cm²/g)	μ/ρ (cm²/g)
1.0	6.72+3	1.39+1	4.53−3	1.17−5	6.74+3
1.1663 $N_{II,III}$	5.13+3	1.37+1	5.51−3	1.65−5	5.14+3
1.1677	5.74+3	1.37+1	5.52−3	1.65−5	5.75+3
1.5	3.64+3	1.32+1	7.49−3	2.83−5	3.66+3
1.5003 N_I	3.64+3	1.32+1	7.49−3	2.83−5	3.65+3
1.5017	3.88+3	1.32+1	7.50−3	2.84−5	3.89+3
2.0	2.13+3	1.26+1	1.04−2	5.17−5	2.14+3
3.0	8.59+2	1.12+1	1.61−2	1.18−4	8.70+2
3.5	6.45+2	1.06+1	1.88−2	1.59−4	6.56+2
3.666 M_V	5.76+2	1.04+1	1.96−2	1.74−4	5.86+2
3.666	1.13+3	1.04+1	1.96−2	1.74−4	1.14+3
3.85 M_{IV}	9.96+2	1.02+1	2.06−2	1.91−4	1.01+3
3.85	1.49+3	1.02+1	2.06−2	1.91−4	1.50+3
4.0	1.35+3	1.00+1	2.13−2	2.06−4	1.36+3
4.435 M_{III}	1.04+3	9.57+0	2.34−2	2.49−4	1.05+3
4.435	1.25+3	9.57+0	2.34−2	2.49−4	1.26+3
5.0	9.15+2	9.00+0	2.61−2	3.10−4	9.24+2
5.366 M_{II}	7.63+2	8.65+0	2.77−2	3.52−4	7.72+2
5.366	8.39+2	8.65+0	2.77−2	3.52−4	8.48+2
5.723 M_I	7.11+2	8.33+0	2.92−2	3.94−4	7.20+2
5.723	7.82+2	8.33+0	2.92−2	3.94−4	7.91+2
6.0	6.93+2	8.10+0	3.04−2	4.28−4	7.01+2
7.0	4.66+2	7.32+0	3.44−2	5.59−4	4.73+2
8.0	3.30+2	6.65+0	3.80−2	7.00−4	3.37+2
9.0	2.44+2	6.06+0	4.14−2	8.52−4	2.50+2
10.0	1.86+2	5.54+0	4.47−2	1.01−3	1.92+2
12.0	1.16+2	4.69+0	5.06−2	1.36−3	1.21+2
15.0	6.56+1	3.75+0	5.81−2	1.91−3	6.94+1
17.0	4.75+1	3.26+0	6.24−2	2.29−3	5.08+1
17.61 L_{III}	4.34+1	3.13+0	6.35−2	2.40−3	4.66+1
17.61	1.03+2	3.13+0	6.35−2	2.40−3	1.06+2
20.0	7.33+1	2.69+0	6.77−2	2.87−3	7.60+1
21.6 L_{II}	5.96+1	2.43+0	7.00−2	3.17−3	6.21+1
21.6	8.35+1	2.43+0	7.00−2	3.17−3	8.60+1
22.43 L_I	7.54+1	2.32+0	7.12−2	3.33−3	7.78+1
22.43	9.05+1	2.32+0	7.12−2	3.33−3	9.29+1
25.0	6.77+1	2.01+0	7.47−2	3.83−3	6.98+1
30.0	4.15+1	1.57+0	8.02−2	4.81−3	4.32+1
35.0	2.75+1	1.26+0	8.45−2	5.77−3	2.88+1
40.0	1.92+1	1.04+0	8.79−2	6.70−3	2.04+1
50.0	1.06+1	7.47−1	9.27−2	8.43−3	1.14+1
60.0	6.49+0	5.59−1	9.54−2	9.96−3	7.14+0
70.0	4.29+0	4.33−1	9.69−2	1.13−2	4.82+0
80.0	3.00+0	3.47−1	9.76−2	1.25−2	3.45+0
90.0	2.19+0	2.84−1	9.77−2	1.36−2	2.57+0
100.0	1.65+0	2.38−1	9.75−2	1.46−2	1.99+0
118.7 K	1.04+0	1.76−1	9.64−2	1.61−2	1.32+0
118.7	4.89+0	1.76−1	9.64−2	1.61−2	5.17+0
120.0	4.75+0	1.73−1	9.63−2	1.62−2	5.02+0
150.0	2.61+0	1.16−1	9.36−2	1.81−2	2.82+0
170.0	1.87+0	9.28−2	9.16−2	1.90−2	2.05+0
200.0	1.21+0	6.88−2	8.86−2	2.01−2	1.37+0

TABLE 3 (continued)

Energy (keV)	τ/ρ (cm^2/g)	σ_c/ρ (cm^2/g)	σ_I/ρ (cm^2/g)	σ_a/ρ (cm^2/g)	μ/ρ (cm^2/g)
250.0	6.72−1	4.55−2	8.38−2	2.14−2	8.01−1
300.0	4.18−1	3.24−2	7.95−2	2.21−2	5.30−1
350.0	2.81−1	2.43−2	7.56−2	2.26−2	3.81−1
400.0	2.00−1	1.89−2	7.22−2	2.29−2	2.91−1
500.0	1.14−1	1.23−2	6.65−2	2.31−2	1.93−1
600.0	7.30−2	8.66−3	6.19−2	2.31−2	1.43−1
700.0	5.03−2	6.41−3	5.80−2	2.29−2	1.15−1
800.0	3.67−2	4.94−3	5.47−2	2.26−2	9.63−2
900.0	2.79−2	3.92−3	5.18−2	2.23−2	8.36−2
1,000.0	2.19−2	3.19−3	4.93−2	2.19−2	7.44−2

Plutonium Z = 94

Energy (keV)	τ/ρ (cm^2/g)	σ_c/ρ (cm^2/g)	σ_I/ρ (cm^2/g)	σ_a/ρ (cm^2/g)	μ/ρ (cm^2/g)
0.1	2.04+4	1.46+1	8.11−5	2.15−8	2.04+4
0.1089 $O_{IV,V}$	1.55+4	1.46+1	9.39−5	2.72−8	1.56+4
0.1103	1.84+4	1.46+1	9.60−5	2.82−8	1.84+4
0.15	7.35+3	1.46+1	1.67−4	6.75−8	7.36+3
0.2	1.89+3	1.46+1	2.87−4	1.55−7	1.91+3
0.2283 $O_{II,III}$	1.38+3	1.46+1	3.68−4	2.27−7	1.40+3
0.2297	2.54+3	1.46+1	3.73−4	2.31−7	2.55+3
0.3	2.30+3	1.45+1	6.15−4	5.00−7	2.31+3
0.3512 O_I	2.27+3	1.45+1	8.22−4	7.80−7	2.28+3
0.3526	2.86+3	1.45+1	8.28−4	7.89−7	2.88+3
0.4	2.68+3	1.45+1	1.04−3	1.12−6	2.69+3
0.4374 $N_{VI,VII}$	2.53+3	1.45+1	1.22−3	1.44−6	2.55+3
0.4388	2.77+3	1.45+1	1.23−3	1.45−6	2.79+3
0.5	5.08+3	1.44+1	1.54−3	2.06−6	5.09+3
0.6	1.11+4	1.43+1	2.08−3	3.32−6	1.11+4
0.7	9.84+3	1.42+1	2.65−3	4.90−6	9.85+3
0.8	8.19+3	1.41+1	3.23−3	6.76−6	8.20+3
0.8197 $N_{IV,V}$	7.88+3	1.41+1	3.34−3	7.16−6	7.90+3
0.8211	8.17+3	1.41+1	3.35−3	7.19−6	8.19+3
0.9	8.33+3	1.40+1	3.81−3	8.91−6	8.35+3
1.0	7.05+3	1.39+1	4.39−3	1.13−5	7.06+3
1.2003 $N_{II,III}$	5.09+3	1.37+1	5.54−3	1.70−5	5.11+3
1.2017	5.72+3	1.37+1	5.55−3	1.70−5	5.74+3
1.5	3.79+3	1.33+1	7.25−3	2.74−5	3.81+3
1.5583 N_I	3.51+3	1.32+1	7.59−3	2.97−5	3.52+3
1.5597	3.73+3	1.32+1	7.59−3	2.98−5	3.74+3
2.0	2.21+3	1.27+1	1.01−2	5.03−5	2.23+3
3.0	8.88+2	1.14+1	1.56−2	1.14−4	9.00+2
3.8553 $M_{IV,V}$	4.91+2	1.03+1	2.00−2	1.86−4	5.01+2
3.8567	5.71+2	1.03+1	2.00−2	1.86−4	5.81+2
4.0	1.42+3	1.01+1	2.07−2	1.99−4	1.43+3
4.5	1.04+3	9.58+0	2.30−2	2.48−4	1.05+3
4.8834 $M_{II,III}$	8.36+2	9.18+0	2.48−2	2.88−4	8.46+2
4.8857	1.10+3	9.18+0	2.48−2	2.88−4	1.11+3
5.0	1.07+3	9.07+0	2.53−2	3.01−4	1.08+3
5.9323 M_I	6.96+2	8.21+0	2.93−2	4.08−4	7.04+2
5.9337	7.70+2	8.21+0	2.93−2	4.08−4	7.79+2
7.0	5.02+2	7.36+0	3.34−2	5.44−4	5.10+2
8.0	3.53+2	6.68+0	3.70−2	6.83−4	3.60+2
9.0	2.49+2	6.08+0	4.04−2	8.33−4	2.55+2
10.0	1.90+2	5.56+0	4.37−2	9.92−4	1.95+2

TABLE 3 (continued)

Energy (keV)	τ/ρ (cm² /g)	σ_c/ρ (cm² /g)	σ_I/ρ (cm² /g)	σ_a/ρ (cm² /g)	μ/ρ (cm² /g)
12.0	1.19+2	4.71+0	4.96−2	1.33−3	1.23+2
15.0	6.67+1	3.77+0	5.71−2	1.88−3	7.05+1
17.0	4.83+1	3.28+0	6.13−2	2.26−3	5.16+1
18.06 L_{III}	4.13+1	3.05+0	6.33−2	2.46−3	4.44+1
18.06	9.82+1	3.05+0	6.33−2	2.46−3	1.01+2
20.0	7.47+1	2.70+0	6.67−2	2.83−3	7.74+1
22.27 L_{II}	5.60+1	2.35+0	7.00−2	3.26−3	5.84+1
22.27	7.84+1	2.35+0	7.00−2	3.26−3	8.08+1
23.1 L_I	7.11+1	2.24+0	7.11−2	3.41−3	7.34+1
23.1	8.53+1	2.24+0	7.11−2	3.41−3	8.76+1
25.0	6.90+1	2.03+0	7.37−2	3.79−3	7.11+1
30.0	4.24+1	1.58+0	7.91−2	4.75−3	4.40+1
35.0	2.80+1	1.27+0	8.34−2	5.69−3	2.94+1
40.0	1.96+1	1.05+0	8.68−2	6.61−3	2.07+1
50.0	1.08+1	7.51−1	9.15−2	8.32−3	1.16+1
60.0	6.62+0	5.63−1	9.42−2	9.84−3	7.27+0
70.0	4.38+0	4.36−1	9.57−2	1.12−2	4.91+0
80.0	3.06+0	3.49−1	9.64−2	1.24−2	3.51+0
90.0	2.23+0	2.86−1	9.66−2	1.35−2	2.62+0
100.0	1.68+0	2.39−1	9.63−2	1.44−2	2.02+0
120.0	1.03+0	1.74−1	9.52−2	1.60−2	1.30+0
121.8 K	9.93−1	1.70−1	9.50−2	1.62−2	1.26+0
121.8	4.22+0	1.70−1	9.50−2	1.62−2	4.48+0
150.0	2.50+0	1.17−1	9.26−2	1.79−2	2.71+0
170.0	1.82+0	9.34−2	9.06−2	1.88−2	2.00+0
200.0	1.20+0	6.93−2	8.76−2	1.99−2	1.36+0
250.0	6.83−1	4.58−2	8.29−2	2.11−2	8.12−1
300.0	4.30−1	3.26−2	7.86−2	2.19−2	5.41−1
350.0	2.91−1	2.44−2	7.48−2	2.24−2	3.90−1
400.0	2.08−1	1.90−2	7.15−2	2.27−2	2.99−1
500.0	1.19−1	1.24−2	6.58−2	2.29−2	1.98−1
600.0	7.63−2	8.73−3	6.12−2	2.29−2	1.46−1
700.0	5.25−2	6.46−3	5.74−2	2.27−2	1.16−1
800.0	3.82−2	4.98−3	5.41−2	2.24−2	9.73−2
900.0	2.89−2	3.95−3	5.13−2	2.21−2	8.42−2
1,000.0	2.26−2	3.22−3	4.89−2	2.17−2	7.47−2

IV. ATTENUATION CROSS SECTIONS IN cm^2/g AT SELECTED WAVELENGTHS FOR 94 ELEMENTS

William J. Veigele, Kaman Sciences Corporation

Total mass attenuation cross sections (μ/ρ) in cm^2/g from the preceding tables were interpolated to provide values at 280 selected emission wavelengths of primary interest in spectroscopy. They are given in Table 4. Entries such as 3.06 + 3 are read 3.06×10^3 cm^2/g. Wavelengths, in Å, are for

46 $K\alpha_1\alpha_2$	lines for emitters from B through Sn
31 $K\beta_1$	lines for emitters from Ne through Zr
73 $L\alpha_1$	lines for emitters from Ca through U
72 $L\beta_1$	lines for emitters from Ca through U
29 $M\alpha$	lines for emitters from La through U
29 $M\beta$	lines for emitters from La through U.

Wavelengths were taken from Bearden, J. A., *Rev. Mod. Phys.*, 39, 78, 1967, and the cross sections were taken from Bracewell, B. and Veigele, W. J., *Advances in X-ray Analysis,* Vol. 15, Heinrich, K. F. J., Barrett, C. S., Newkirk, J. B., and Rudd, C. O., Eds., Plenum Press, New York, 1972.

TABLE 4

Attenuation Cross Sections in cm^2/g at Selected Wavelengths for 94 Elements

Mass Attenuation Coefficients for $L\alpha$ Lines

Emitter	Ca	Sc	Ti	V	Cr	Mn	Fe	Co	Ni	Cu	Zn	Ga	Ge	As
Wavelength	3.63+1	3.14+1	2.74+1	2.42+1	2.16+1	1.95+1	1.76+1	1.60+1	1.46+1	1.33+1	1.23+1	1.13+1	1.04+1	9.67+0
Energy (keV)	3.41-1	3.95-1	4.52-1	5.11-1	5.73-1	6.37-1	7.05-1	7.76-1	8.52-1	9.30-1	1.01+0	1.10+0	1.19+0	1.28+0
Absorber														
1 H	2.42+2	1.46+2	9.52+1	6.37+1	4.35+1	3.15+1	2.28+1	1.62+1	1.21+1	9.16+0	6.73+0	5.53+0	4.28+0	3.57+0
2 He	2.05+3	1.20+3	8.39+2	5.42+2	3.87+2	2.72+2	1.91+2	1.42+2	1.05+2	7.81+1	5.97+1	4.82+1	3.62+1	2.98+1
3 Li	5.78+3	3.55+3	2.53+3	1.69+3	1.25+3	9.07+2	6.57+2	5.01+2	3.80+2	2.89+2	2.23+2	1.82+2	1.38+2	1.14+2
4 Be	1.28+4	8.14+3	5.89+3	4.01+3	2.99+3	2.21+3	1.63+3	1.25+3	9.49+2	7.33+2	5.79+2	4.78+2	3.72+2	3.09+2
5 B	2.28+4	1.49+4	1.10+4	7.64+3	5.75+3	4.29+3	3.19+3	2.48+3	1.92+3	1.49+3	1.17+3	9.71+2	7.65+2	6.39+2
6 C	3.41+4	2.38+4	1.80+4	1.29+4	9.80+3	7.40+3	5.56+3	4.35+3	3.39+3	2.66+3	2.11+3	1.75+3	1.37+3	1.15+3
7 N	2.71+3	1.78+3	2.43+4	1.82+4	1.41+4	1.08+4	8.19+3	6.47+3	5.09+3	4.01+3	3.20+3	2.69+3	2.15+3	1.81+3
8 O	3.97+3	2.60+3	1.94+3	1.36+3	1.72+4	1.41+4	1.08+4	8.65+3	6.88+3	5.48+3	4.41+3	3.72+3	3.00+3	2.54+3
9 F	5.57+3	3.62+3	2.68+3	1.89+3	1.43+3	1.08+3	1.24+4	1.04+4	8.46+3	6.77+3	5.51+3	4.70+3	3.85+3	3.27+3
10 Ne	8.54+3	5.54+3	4.09+3	2.86+3	2.17+3	1.64+3	1.23+3	9.65+2	7.47+2	9.03+3	7.50+3	6.33+3	5.11+3	4.34+3
11 Na	1.07+4	7.06+3	5.25+3	3.71+3	2.84+3	2.15+3	1.61+3	1.28+3	1.00+3	7.89+2	6.29+2	7.80+3	6.33+3	5.39+3
12 Mg	1.46+4	9.74+3	7.26+3	5.15+3	3.95+3	3.00+3	2.26+3	1.80+3	1.41+3	1.11+3	8.86+2	7.40+2	5.88+2	4.73+2
13 Al	1.78+4	1.20+4	9.00+3	6.43+3	4.94+3	3.77+3	2.86+3	2.26+3	1.79+3	1.42+3	1.13+3	9.44+2	7.48+2	6.32+2
14 Si	2.27+4	1.54+4	1.16+4	8.36+3	6.44+3	4.92+3	3.75+3	2.97+3	2.35+3	1.86+3	1.49+3	1.25+3	1.01+3	8.52+2
15 P	2.76+4	1.88+4	1.42+4	1.03+4	7.91+3	6.05+3	4.61+3	3.66+3	2.89+3	2.29+3	1.84+3	1.54+3	1.23+3	1.04+3
16 S	3.36+4	2.32+4	1.76+4	1.28+4	9.89+3	7.59+3	5.81+3	4.62+3	3.66+3	2.91+3	2.33+3	1.96+3	1.57+3	1.33+3
17 Cl	3.69+4	2.61+4	2.00+4	1.46+4	1.13+4	8.72+3	6.69+3	5.33+3	4.23+3	3.37+3	2.71+3	2.28+3	1.83+3	1.55+3
18 Ar	3.96+4	2.95+4	2.27+4	1.67+4	1.30+4	9.98+3	7.66+3	6.10+3	4.84+3	3.86+3	3.10+3	2.61+3	2.09+3	1.77+3
19 K	4.12+4	3.47+4	2.74+4	2.04+4	1.59+4	1.24+4	9.55+3	7.63+3	6.07+3	4.85+3	3.92+3	3.30+3	2.65+3	2.25+3
20 Ca	4.67+3	3.45+4	3.00+4	2.32+4	1.83+4	1.43+4	1.12+4	8.94+3	7.13+3	5.72+3	4.64+3	3.88+3	3.09+3	2.63+3
21 Sc	5.33+3	3.89+3	2.78+4	2.46+4	1.92+4	1.54+4	1.20+4	9.66+3	7.73+3	6.20+3	5.01+3	4.20+3	3.36+3	2.86+3
22 Ti	5.81+3	4.27+3	3.26+3	2.32+4	2.08+4	1.67+4	1.31+4	1.06+4	8.53+3	6.87+3	5.57+3	4.68+3	3.74+3	3.19+3
23 V	6.36+3	4.68+3	3.58+3	2.80+3	1.96+4	1.79+4	1.42+4	1.15+4	9.33+3	7.55+3	6.14+3	5.16+3	4.14+3	3.54+3
24 Cr	7.54+3	5.49+3	4.33+3	3.29+3	2.58+3	1.86+4	1.64+4	1.32+4	1.08+4	8.76+3	7.14+3	6.00+3	4.81+3	4.11+3
25 Mn	8.20+3	6.01+3	4.75+3	3.63+3	2.88+3	2.28+3	1.53+4	1.42+4	1.15+4	9.39+3	7.68+3	6.48+3	5.23+3	4.47+3
26 Fe	9.52+3	6.95+3	5.49+3	4.19+3	3.33+3	2.64+3	2.11+3	1.45+4	1.30+4	1.06+4	8.68+3	7.33+3	5.93+3	5.08+3
27 Co	1.05+4	7.69+3	6.06+3	4.62+3	3.69+3	2.93+3	2.33+3	1.89+3	1.21+4	1.14+4	9.33+3	7.89+3	6.40+3	5.49+3
28 Ni	1.24+4	9.01+3	7.14+3	5.49+3	4.40+3	3.47+3	2.71+3	2.25+3	1.78+3	1.14+4	1.08+4	9.09+3	7.34+3	6.29+3
29 Cu	1.34+4	9.76+3	7.89+3	6.23+3	4.91+3	3.78+3	2.84+3	2.51+3	1.99+3	1.56+3	1.02+4	9.20+3	7.81+3	6.73+3
30 Zn	1.56+4	1.14+4	9.03+3	6.89+3	5.43+3	4.27+3	3.37+3	2.77+3	2.24+3	1.80+3	1.50+3	8.83+3	7.38+3	7.08+3
31 Ga	1.69+4	1.24+4	9.78+3	7.44+3	5.89+3	4.66+3	3.70+3	3.02+3	2.45+3	1.98+3	1.61+3	1.34+3	7.05+3	6.51+3
32 Ge	1.86+4	1.37+4	1.08+4	8.27+3	6.58+3	5.21+3	4.12+3	3.36+3	2.73+3	2.22+3	1.81+3	1.49+3	1.25+3	6.00+3
33 As	2.05+4	1.52+4	1.20+4	9.21+3	7.35+3	5.83+3	4.61+3	3.76+3	3.06+3	2.49+3	2.04+3	1.78+3	1.50+3	1.22+3
34 Se	2.22+4	1.66+4	1.32+4	1.01+4	8.06+3	6.41+3	5.07+3	4.13+3	3.36+3	2.74+3	2.25+3	2.00+3	1.73+3	1.45+3
35 Br	2.42+4	1.83+4	1.46+4	1.12+4	8.99+3	7.16+3	5.68+3	4.64+3	3.85+3	3.18+3	2.54+3	2.24+3	1.92+3	1.58+3
36 Kr	2.60+4	2.01+4	1.61+4	1.24+4	9.97+3	7.96+3	6.32+3	5.15+3	4.19+3	3.42+3	2.81+3	2.38+3	1.93+3	1.63+3
37 Rb	2.72+4	2.14+4	1.72+4	1.34+4	1.08+4	8.61+3	6.86+3	5.63+3	4.59+3	3.75+3	3.08+3	2.61+3	2.13+3	1.80+3

TABLE 4 (continued)

Mass Attenuation Coefficients for $L\alpha$ Lines

Emitter		Ca	Sc	Ti	V	Cr	Mn	Fe	Co	Ni	Cu	Zn	Ga	Ge	As
Wavelength		3.63+1	3.14+1	2.74+1	2.42+1	2.16+1	1.95+1	1.76+1	1.60+1	1.46+1	1.33+1	1.23+1	1.13+1	1.04+1	9.67+0
Energy (keV)		3.41-1	3.95-1	4.52-1	5.11-1	5.73-1	6.37-1	7.05-1	7.76-1	8.52-1	9.30-1	1.01+0	1.10+0	1.19+0	1.28+0
Absorber															
38	Sr	2.69+4	2.26+4	1.83+4	1.44+4	1.16+4	9.32+3	7.45+3	6.12+3	5.00+3	4.09+3	3.37+3	2.86+3	2.33+3	1.98+3
39	Y	2.86+4	2.46+4	2.00+4	1.58+4	1.28+4	1.03+4	8.24+3	6.76+3	5.54+3	4.54+3	3.74+3	3.18+3	2.59+3	2.23+3
40	Zr	2.90+4	2.44+4	2.10+4	1.68+4	1.37+4	1.11+4	8.89+3	7.31+3	5.99+3	4.92+3	4.06+3	3.45+3	2.82+3	2.42+3
41	Nb	2.69+4	2.65+4	2.16+4	1.85+4	1.51+4	1.22+4	9.84+3	8.10+3	6.64+3	5.45+3	4.50+3	3.82+3	3.12+3	2.68+3
42	Mo	2.65+4	2.27+4	2.22+4	1.93+4	1.58+4	1.29+4	1.04+4	8.57+3	7.04+3	5.79+3	4.79+3	4.07+3	3.33+3	2.87+3
43	Tc	2.52+4	2.28+4	2.17+4	1.87+4	1.63+4	1.34+4	1.08+4	8.98+3	7.40+3	6.10+3	5.08+3	4.55+3	3.98+3	3.39+3
44	Ru	2.41+4	2.45+4	2.04+4	2.04+4	1.67+4	1.46+4	1.19+4	9.82+3	8.10+3	6.69+3	5.57+3	4.98+3	4.37+3	3.72+3
45	Rh	1.86+4	2.50+4	2.16+4	2.00+4	1.74+4	1.55+4	1.27+4	1.06+4	8.72+3	7.21+3	6.02+3	5.38+3	4.72+3	4.02+3
46	Pd	5.05+3	2.33+4	2.22+4	1.89+4	1.84+4	1.56+4	1.36+4	1.13+4	9.35+3	7.73+3	6.46+3	5.78+3	5.06+3	4.32+3
47	Ag	4.53+3	1.18+4	1.70+4	1.99+4	1.62+4	1.64+4	1.35+4	1.20+4	9.94+3	8.24+3	6.90+3	6.18+3	5.42+3	4.62+3
48	Cd	4.86+3	4.06+3	1.29+4	2.10+4	1.72+4	1.54+4	1.41+4	1.24+4	1.03+4	8.61+3	7.26+3	6.76+3	6.23+3	5.68+3
49	In	5.19+3	4.37+3	6.27+3	2.33+4	1.85+4	1.47+4	1.47+4	1.23+4	1.09+4	9.11+3	7.70+3	7.16+3	6.60+3	6.02+3
50	Sn	5.45+3	4.65+3	3.93+3	7.63+3	1.44+4	1.56+4	1.25+4	1.25+4	1.07+4	9.51+3	8.07+3	7.51+3	6.93+3	6.32+3
51	Sb	5.71+3	4.90+3	4.19+3	3.50+3	1.30+4	1.70+4	1.32+4	1.08+4	1.12+4	9.35+3	8.46+3	7.88+3	7.27+3	6.63+3
52	Te	5.84+3	5.05+3	4.34+3	3.66+3	3.09+3	2.37+4	1.37+4	1.13+4	1.12+4	9.63+3	8.55+3	7.96+3	7.35+3	6.71+3
53	I	6.28+3	5.47+3	4.73+3	4.01+3	3.42+3	5.34+3	1.54+4	1.22+4	1.01+4	1.06+4	8.73+3	7.96+3	7.36+3	6.74+3
54	Xe	6.64+3	5.84+3	5.07+3	4.31+3	3.68+3	3.12+3	2.26+4	1.32+4	1.07+4	8.80+3	9.19+3	7.81+3	7.16+3	6.57+3
55	Cs	6.86+3	6.08+3	5.31+3	4.54+3	3.90+3	3.33+3	2.81+3	1.53+4	1.15+4	9.33+3	7.70+3	8.73+3	7.06+3	6.50+3
56	Ba	6.91+3	6.17+3	5.41+3	4.66+3	4.02+3	3.44+3	2.92+3	2.49+3	1.15+4	9.63+3	7.98+3	8.19+3	7.13+3	6.03+3
57	La	6.98+3	6.28+3	5.54+3	4.80+3	4.16+3	3.57+3	3.05+3	2.62+3	4.58+3	9.99+3	8.33+3	7.02+3	7.20+3	6.28+3
58	Ce	8.01+3	7.09+3	6.20+3	5.33+3	4.59+3	3.92+3	3.33+3	2.85+3	2.43+3	1.01+4	9.27+3	7.91+3	6.49+3	6.84+3
59	Pr	8.63+3	7.54+3	6.57+3	5.63+3	4.84+3	4.14+3	3.51+3	3.01+3	2.57+3	2.19+3	9.96+3	8.58+3	7.15+3	7.10+3
60	Nd	9.05+3	7.85+3	6.82+3	5.82+3	5.00+3	4.28+3	3.63+3	3.11+3	2.66+3	2.27+3	8.59+3	7.73+3	6.84+3	5.91+3
61	Pm	9.68+3	8.33+3	7.20+3	6.11+3	5.24+3	4.47+3	3.79+3	3.25+3	2.78+3	2.37+3	2.02+3	4.21+3	6.89+3	6.24+3
62	Sm	9.48+3	8.87+3	7.65+3	6.47+3	5.53+3	4.70+3	3.98+3	3.41+3	2.91+3	2.48+3	2.12+3	2.55+3	7.04+3	6.57+3
63	Eu	1.00+4	9.33+3	8.04+3	6.80+3	5.81+3	4.95+3	4.18+3	3.58+3	3.06+3	2.61+3	2.23+3	1.92+3	6.79+3	6.94+3
64	Gd	1.00+4	9.30+3	8.04+3	6.81+3	5.84+3	4.98+3	4.22+3	3.62+3	3.10+3	2.65+3	2.27+3	1.98+3	1.67+3	5.90+3
65	Tb	1.17+4	9.83+3	9.09+3	7.64+3	6.50+3	5.51+3	4.64+3	3.96+3	3.37+3	2.87+3	2.45+3	2.13+3	1.80+3	5.08+3
66	Dy	1.25+4	1.05+4	9.63+3	8.10+3	6.88+3	5.82+3	4.89+3	4.17+3	3.54+3	3.01+3	2.57+3	2.27+3	1.96+3	1.63+3
67	Ho	1.32+4	1.12+4	1.02+4	8.58+3	7.28+3	6.15+3	5.16+3	4.40+3	3.73+3	3.17+3	2.71+3	2.41+3	2.10+3	1.77+3
68	Er	1.41+4	1.20+4	1.08+4	9.16+3	7.78+3	6.57+3	5.51+3	4.69+3	3.97+3	3.37+3	2.83+3	2.57+3	2.25+3	1.91+3
69	Tm	1.33+4	1.28+4	1.09+4	9.81+3	8.34+3	7.04+3	5.90+3	5.01+3	4.24+3	3.60+3	3.07+3	2.74+3	2.39+3	2.03+3
70	Yb	1.41+4	1.34+4	1.15+4	1.03+4	8.74+3	7.38+3	6.18+3	5.25+3	4.44+3	3.76+3	3.21+3	2.89+3	2.56+3	2.22+3
71	Lu	1.42+4	1.35+4	1.17+4	1.05+4	8.94+3	7.58+3	6.37+3	5.42+3	4.59+3	3.89+3	3.33+3	3.00+3	2.66+3	2.31+3
72	Hf	1.48+4	1.26+4	1.21+4	1.03+4	9.34+3	7.94+3	6.69+3	5.68+3	4.83+3	4.10+3	3.50+3	3.16+3	2.80+3	2.43+3
73	Ta	1.52+4	1.31+4	1.25+4	1.08+4	9.77+3	8.32+3	7.02+3	5.98+3	5.08+3	4.31+3	3.68+3	3.24+3	2.78+3	2.31+3
74	W	1.57+4	1.36+4	1.28+4	1.12+4	9.64+3	8.71+3	7.34+3	6.27+3	5.33+3	4.52+3	3.86+3	3.40+3	2.92+3	2.42+3

TABLE 4 (continued)

Mass Attenuation Coefficients for $L\ \alpha$ Lines

Emitter	Ca	Sc	Ti	V	Cr	Mn	Fe	Co	Ni	Cu	Zn	Ga	Ge	As
Wavelength	3.63+1	3.14+1	2.74+1	2.42+1	2.16+1	1.95+1	1.76+1	1.60+1	1.46+1	1.33+1	1.23+1	1.13+1	1.04+1	9.67+0
Energy (keV)	3.41-1	3.95-1	4.52-1	5.11-1	5.73-1	6.37-1	7.05-1	7.76-1	8.52-1	9.30-1	1.01+0	1.10+0	1.19+0	1.28+0
Absorber														
75 Re	1.58+4	1.38+4	1.20+4	1.15+4	9.95+3	9.01+3	7.61+3	6.51+3	5.54+3	4.71+3	4.03+3	3.55+3	3.05+3	2.53+3
76 Os	1.55+4	1.38+4	1.21+4	1.15+4	1.01+4	8.63+3	7.80+3	6.69+3	5.71+3	4.86+3	4.17+3	3.72+3	3.26+3	2.78+3
77 Ir	1.60+4	1.43+4	1.27+4	1.10+4	1.05+4	9.17+3	8.27+3	7.10+3	6.06+3	5.17+3	4.43+3	3.96+3	3.46+3	2.95+3
78 Pt	1.63+4	1.49+4	1.32+4	1.15+4	1.10+4	9.67+3	8.25+3	7.49+3	6.40+3	5.46+3	4.67+3	4.18+3	3.66+3	3.12+3
79 Au	1.60+4	1.51+4	1.36+4	1.20+4	1.04+4	1.01+4	8.63+3	7.81+3	6.70+3	5.73+3	4.90+3	4.26+3	3.60+3	3.16+3
80 Hg	1.51+4	1.49+4	1.35+4	1.21+4	1.05+4	9.95+3	8.86+3	7.60+3	6.91+3	5.90+3	5.05+3	4.30+3	3.68+3	3.16+3
81 Tl	1.42+4	1.46+4	1.35+4	1.24+4	1.09+4	9.44+3	9.17+3	7.93+3	7.19+3	6.16+3	5.31+3	4.80+3	4.26+3	3.71+3
82 Pb	1.35+4	1.38+4	1.35+4	1.26+4	1.12+4	9.75+3	9.43+3	8.19+3	7.05+3	6.39+3	5.52+3	4.99+3	4.44+3	3.86+3
83 Bi	1.27+4	1.36+4	1.32+4	1.29+4	1.14+4	1.00+4	8.66+3	8.40+3	7.31+3	6.26+3	5.73+3	5.19+3	4.62+3	4.02+3
84 Po	1.17+4	1.35+4	1.28+4	1.37+4	1.20+4	1.05+4	9.11+3	8.82+3	7.67+3	6.61+3	6.02+3	5.45+3	4.85+3	4.23+3
85 At	1.02+4	1.33+4	1.29+4	1.21+4	1.20+4	1.10+4	9.61+3	8.32+3	8.10+3	6.99+3	6.00+3	5.59+3	5.00+3	4.39+3
86 Rn	8.99+3	1.22+4	1.23+4	1.18+4	1.16+4	1.10+4	9.59+3	8.35+3	8.21+3	6.98+3	6.01+3	5.41+3	4.86+3	4.29+3
87 Fr	6.80+3	1.12+4	1.19+4	1.20+4	1.08+4	1.14+4	9.94+3	8.68+3	7.48+3	7.26+3	6.27+3	5.45+3	4.96+3	4.40+3
88 Ra	4.45+3	9.62+3	1.12+4	1.19+4	1.09+4	1.06+4	1.02+4	8.89+3	7.71+3	6.62+3	6.49+3	5.69+3	4.86+3	4.51+3
89 Ac	4.28+3	8.40+3	1.04+4	1.17+4	1.08+4	9.71+3	1.02+4	9.00+3	7.84+3	6.77+3	6.60+3	5.85+3	5.06+3	4.56+3
90 Th	2.70+3	6.66+3	9.32+3	1.13+4	1.05+4	9.51+3	9.81+3	8.85+3	7.81+3	6.79+3	5.86+3	5.80+3	5.13+3	4.42+3
91 Pa	2.66+3	3.51+3	7.72+3	1.14+4	1.10+4	1.02+4	8.95+3	9.06+3	8.31+3	7.23+3	6.26+3	6.09+3	5.44+3	4.76+3
92 U	2.67+3	2.70+3	6.80+3	1.07+4	1.09+4	1.00+4	8.93+3	8.74+3	8.32+3	7.27+3	6.31+3	5.48+3	5.40+3	4.78+3
93 Np	2.87+3	2.60+3	5.81+3	9.42+3	1.05+4	1.04+4	9.29+3	8.15+3	8.55+3	7.61+3	6.62+3	5.80+3	5.62+3	5.03+3
94 Pu	2.29+3	2.71+3	3.29+3	5.77+3	9.46+3	1.06+4	9.77+3	8.59+3	8.25+3	7.97+3	6.95+3	6.11+3	5.23+3	5.22+3

TABLE 4 (continued)

Mass Attenuation Coefficients for $L\ \alpha$ Lines

Emitter	Se	Br	Kr	Rb	Sr	Y	Zr	Nb	Mo	Tc	Ru	Rh	Pd	Ag
Wavelength	8.99+0	8.37+0	7.82+0	7.32+0	6.86+0	6.45+0	6.07+0	5.72+0	5.41+0	5.11+0	4.85+0	4.60+0	4.37+0	4.15+0
Energy (keV)	1.38+0	1.48+0	1.59+0	1.69+0	1.81+0	1.92+0	2.04+0	2.17+0	2.29+0	2.42+0	2.56+0	2.70+0	2.84+0	2.98+0
Absorber														
1 H	2.94+0	2.27+0	1.89+0	1.56+0	1.37+0	1.18+0	1.03+0	9.41-1	8.51-1	7.59-1	6.89-1	6.49-1	6.07-1	5.65-1
2 He	2.40+1	1.80+1	1.45+1	1.15+1	9.69+0	7.93+0	6.47+0	5.64+0	4.79+0	3.91+0	3.23+0	2.85+0	2.45+0	2.04+0
3 Li	9.22+1	6.96+1	5.60+1	4.44+1	3.75+1	3.07+1	2.50+1	2.17+1	1.84+1	1.49+1	1.22+1	1.07+1	9.06+0	7.42+0
4 Be	2.52+2	1.92+2	1.56+2	1.25+2	1.06+2	8.70+1	7.13+1	6.21+1	5.26+1	4.29+1	3.53+1	3.08+1	2.63+1	2.16+1
5 B	5.23+2	4.01+2	3.27+2	2.62+2	2.23+2	1.84+2	1.51+2	1.32+2	1.12+2	9.17+1	7.53+1	6.63+1	5.66+1	4.66+1
6 C	9.48+2	7.35+2	6.02+2	4.87+2	4.15+2	3.45+2	2.85+2	2.49+2	2.12+2	1.75+2	1.45+2	1.27+2	1.09+2	9.01+1
7 N	1.49+3	1.16+3	9.58+2	7.78+2	6.65+2	5.54+2	4.59+2	4.03+2	3.44+2	2.84+2	2.37+2	2.08+2	1.78+2	1.48+2
8 O	2.11+3	1.66+3	1.37+3	1.12+3	9.63+2	8.05+2	6.72+2	5.90+2	5.06+2	4.19+2	3.51+2	3.09+2	2.66+2	2.22+2
9 F	2.72+3	2.15+3	1.78+3	1.46+3	1.25+3	1.05+3	8.78+2	7.72+2	6.63+2	5.51+2	4.62+2	4.08+2	3.51+2	2.94+2
10 Ne	3.63+3	2.88+3	2.40+3	1.98+3	1.71+3	1.44+3	1.21+3	1.06+3	9.15+2	7.63+2	6.44+2	5.69+2	4.92+2	4.13+2
11 Na	4.50+3	3.58+3	2.99+3	2.46+3	2.13+3	1.79+3	1.51+3	1.33+3	1.14+3	9.57+2	8.08+2	7.14+2	6.18+2	5.19+2
12 Mg	5.41+3	4.45+3	3.75+3	3.11+3	2.69+3	2.28+3	1.92+3	1.70+3	1.47+3	1.23+3	1.04+3	9.24+2	8.02+2	6.76+2
13 Al	5.25+2	4.14+2	4.32+3	3.64+3	3.16+3	2.69+3	2.28+3	2.02+3	1.75+3	1.48+3	1.26+3	1.12+3	9.72+2	8.23+2
14 Si	7.10+2	5.61+2	4.67+2	3.85+2	3.25+2	3.36+3	2.89+3	2.56+3	2.21+3	1.86+3	1.58+3	1.41+3	1.22+3	1.03+3
15 P	8.69+2	6.89+2	5.75+2	4.75+2	4.11+2	3.47+2	2.89+2	2.79+3	2.45+3	2.11+3	1.82+3	1.61+3	1.41+3	1.19+3
16 S	1.11+3	8.78+2	7.32+2	6.04+2	5.23+2	4.42+2	3.73+2	3.29+2	2.84+2	2.38+2	2.19+3	1.95+3	1.70+3	1.44+3
17 Cl	1.30+3	1.03+3	8.61+2	7.11+2	6.16+2	5.21+2	4.40+2	3.90+2	3.38+2	2.85+2	2.41+2	2.12+2	1.83+3	1.60+3
18 Ar	1.48+3	1.17+3	9.74+2	8.03+2	6.94+2	5.86+2	4.94+2	4.37+2	3.79+2	3.18+2	2.71+2	2.40+2	2.09+2	1.78+2
19 K	1.88+3	1.49+3	1.25+3	1.03+3	8.91+2	7.53+2	6.36+2	5.63+2	4.88+2	4.11+2	3.50+2	3.11+2	2.71+2	2.30+2
20 Ca	2.21+3	1.77+3	1.53+3	1.33+3	1.13+3	9.25+2	7.57+2	6.71+2	5.83+2	4.93+2	4.20+2	3.74+2	3.26+2	2.77+2
21 Sc	2.40+3	1.92+3	1.67+3	1.45+3	1.24+3	1.01+3	8.26+2	7.33+2	6.37+2	5.38+2	4.59+2	4.08+2	3.56+2	3.02+2
22 Ti	2.69+3	2.16+3	1.87+3	1.63+3	1.39+3	1.14+3	9.32+2	8.28+2	7.22+2	6.12+2	5.23+2	4.65+2	4.05+2	3.43+2
23 V	2.98+3	2.40+3	2.08+3	1.82+3	1.55+3	1.27+3	1.04+3	9.24+2	8.02+2	6.77+2	5.77+2	5.12+2	4.46+2	3.78+2
24 Cr	3.46+3	2.79+3	2.41+3	2.11+3	1.80+3	1.48+3	1.21+3	1.08+3	9.35+2	7.90+2	6.74+2	5.99+2	5.21+2	4.42+2
25 Mn	3.77+3	3.05+3	2.64+3	2.32+3	1.98+3	1.62+3	1.34+3	1.19+3	1.04+3	8.81+2	7.54+2	6.69+2	5.83+2	4.93+2
26 Fe	4.29+3	3.47+3	3.01+3	2.64+3	2.26+3	1.86+3	1.53+3	1.37+3	1.19+3	1.02+3	8.73+2	7.74+2	6.74+2	5.70+2
27 Co	4.64+3	3.76+3	3.27+3	2.87+3	2.45+3	2.02+3	1.68+3	1.49+3	1.31+3	1.12+3	9.58+2	8.51+2	7.40+2	6.27+2
28 Ni	5.33+3	4.32+3	3.76+3	3.30+3	2.82+3	2.33+3	1.93+3	1.72+3	1.51+3	1.29+3	1.11+3	9.83+2	8.55+2	7.23+2
29 Cu	5.69+3	4.59+3	3.99+3	3.51+3	3.01+3	2.49+3	2.06+3	1.83+3	1.60+3	1.35+3	1.15+3	1.02+3	8.89+2	7.52+2
30 Zn	6.03+3	5.02+3	4.40+3	3.87+3	3.31+3	2.74+3	2.27+3	2.02+3	1.75+3	1.48+3	1.27+3	1.13+3	9.85+2	8.38+2
31 Ga	6.41+3	5.30+3	4.64+3	4.08+3	3.50+3	2.90+3	2.43+3	2.23+3	2.02+3	1.81+3	1.59+3	1.37+3	1.14+3	9.01+2
32 Ge	5.90+3	5.69+3	5.02+3	4.41+3	3.78+3	3.14+3	2.63+3	2.41+3	2.19+3	1.96+3	1.73+3	1.49+3	1.24+3	9.83+2
33 As	5.26+3	5.37+3	5.23+3	4.44+3	3.88+3	3.31+3	2.86+3	2.62+3	2.38+3	2.13+3	1.88+3	1.62+3	1.35+3	1.07+3
34 Se	1.16+3	4.60+3	4.80+3	4.71+3	4.13+3	3.52+3	3.04+3	2.79+3	2.53+3	2.27+3	2.00+3	1.72+3	1.44+3	1.15+3
35 Br	1.24+3	1.02+3	3.50+3	4.40+3	4.35+3	3.80+3	3.34+3	3.07+3	2.79+3	2.50+3	2.20+3	1.90+3	1.59+3	1.26+3
36 Kr	1.35+3	1.15+3	9.59+2	3.81+3	4.54+3	4.55+3	3.93+3	3.47+3	3.00+3	2.52+3	2.13+3	1.89+3	1.65+3	1.39+3
37 Rb	1.49+3	1.27+3	1.06+3	8.88+2	3.62+3	4.30+3	3.62+3	3.82+3	3.32+3	2.80+3	2.39+3	2.12+3	1.84+3	1.55+3

TABLE 4 (continued)

Mass Attenuation Coefficients for $L\ \alpha$ Lines

Emitter		Se	Br	Kr	Rb	Sr	Y	Zr	Nb	Mo	Tc	Ru	Rh	Pd	Ag
Wavelength		8.99+0	8.37+0	7.82+0	7.32+0	6.86+0	6.45+0	6.07+0	5.72+0	5.41+0	5.11+0	4.85+0	4.60+0	4.37+0	4.15+0
Energy (keV)		1.38+0	1.48+0	1.59+0	1.69+0	1.81+0	1.92+0	2.04+0	2.17+0	2.29+0	2.42+0	2.56+0	2.70+0	2.84+0	2.98+0
Absorber															
38	Sr	1.64+3	1.39+3	1.17+3	9.92+2	8.53+2	7.12+2	3.96+3	3.38+3	3.49+3	3.00+3	2.59+3	2.30+3	2.00+3	1.69+3
39	Y	1.89+3	1.54+3	1.35+3	1.19+3	1.02+3	8.47+2	6.93+2	3.68+3	3.18+3	3.25+3	2.84+3	2.52+3	2.19+3	1.85+3
40	Zr	2.06+3	1.68+3	1.47+3	1.30+3	1.11+3	9.26+2	7.66+2	6.68+2	2.46+3	2.98+3	3.08+3	2.73+3	2.38+3	2.01+3
41	Nb	2.28+3	1.86+3	1.63+3	1.43+3	1.23+3	1.02+3	8.48+2	7.46+2	6.40+2	2.31+3	2.83+3	2.41+3	2.55+3	2.20+3
42	Mo	2.44+3	1.99+3	1.74+3	1.54+3	1.32+3	1.10+3	9.16+2	8.22+2	7.24+2	6.24+2	2.14+3	2.61+3	2.25+3	2.35+3
43	Tc	2.79+3	2.15+3	1.86+3	1.64+3	1.41+3	1.17+3	9.79+2	8.81+2	7.80+2	6.76+2	5.84+2	1.94+3	2.36+3	2.05+3
44	Ru	3.06+3	2.36+3	2.03+3	1.79+3	1.54+3	1.28+3	1.07+3	9.52+2	8.32+2	7.09+2	6.12+2	5.53+2	1.81+3	2.20+3
45	Rh	3.30+3	2.56+3	2.20+3	1.94+3	1.67+3	1.39+3	1.16+3	1.03+3	9.04+2	7.71+2	6.67+2	6.04+2	5.41+2	4.75+2
46	Pd	3.55+3	2.74+3	2.36+3	2.08+3	1.79+3	1.49+3	1.25+3	1.11+3	9.70+2	8.26+2	7.13+2	6.42+2	5.69+2	4.95+2
47	Ag	3.80+3	2.95+3	2.55+3	2.25+3	1.93+3	1.61+3	1.34+3	1.20+3	1.05+3	8.92+2	7.70+2	6.94+2	6.16+2	5.36+2
48	Cd	5.11+3	4.51+3	3.90+3	3.26+3	2.60+3	1.92+3	1.42+3	1.26+3	1.10+3	9.41+2	8.10+2	7.24+2	6.36+2	5.45+2
49	In	5.42+3	4.79+3	4.14+3	3.47+3	2.77+3	2.05+3	1.52+3	1.35+3	1.18+3	1.01+3	8.69+2	7.76+2	6.82+2	5.84+2
50	Sn	5.69+3	5.03+3	4.35+3	3.64+3	2.92+3	2.16+3	1.60+3	1.43+3	1.25+3	1.07+3	9.21+2	8.23+2	7.23+2	6.20+2
51	Sb	5.97+3	5.29+3	4.57+3	3.84+3	3.08+3	2.29+3	1.70+3	1.52+3	1.33+3	1.13+3	9.78+2	8.75+2	7.69+2	6.60+2
52	Te	6.05+3	5.36+3	4.65+3	3.91+3	3.15+3	2.36+3	1.77+3	1.58+3	1.38+3	1.18+3	1.02+3	9.09+2	7.99+2	6.86+2
53	I	6.10+3	5.43+3	4.74+3	4.02+3	3.28+3	2.51+3	1.95+3	1.79+3	1.63+3	1.47+3	1.30+3	1.12+3	9.41+2	7.57+2
54	Xe	5.97+3	5.34+3	4.69+3	4.01+3	3.32+3	2.59+3	2.06+3	1.89+3	1.72+3	1.55+3	1.37+3	1.18+3	9.93+2	7.99+2
55	Cs	5.93+3	5.33+3	4.70+3	4.06+3	3.40+3	2.71+3	2.19+3	2.02+3	1.84+3	1.65+3	1.46+3	1.26+3	1.06+3	8.57+2
56	Ba	5.82+3	5.25+3	4.66+3	4.05+3	3.43+3	2.78+3	2.28+3	2.10+3	1.91+3	1.72+3	1.52+3	1.32+3	1.11+3	8.94+2
57	La	5.79+3	5.25+3	4.69+3	4.11+3	3.50+3	2.88+3	2.40+3	2.21+3	2.01+3	1.81+3	1.61+3	1.39+3	1.17+3	9.48+2
58	Ce	5.89+3	5.46+3	4.90+3	4.32+3	3.71+3	3.09+3	2.60+3	2.40+3	2.18+3	1.96+3	1.74+3	1.51+3	1.27+3	1.02+3
59	Pr	6.22+3	5.31+3	5.00+3	4.44+3	3.85+3	3.25+3	2.77+3	2.55+3	2.32+3	2.09+3	1.85+3	1.60+3	1.35+3	1.09+3
60	Nd	6.35+3	5.52+3	5.03+3	4.49+3	3.92+3	3.34+3	2.87+3	2.64+3	2.41+3	2.17+3	1.92+3	1.67+3	1.41+3	1.14+3
61	Pm	5.24+3	5.78+3	4.96+3	4.57+3	4.02+3	3.46+3	3.00+3	2.76+3	2.52+3	2.27+3	2.01+3	1.75+3	1.47+3	1.19+3
62	Sm	5.53+3	5.88+3	5.16+3	4.42+3	4.13+3	3.58+3	3.13+3	2.89+3	2.63+3	2.37+3	2.10+3	1.82+3	1.54+3	1.25+3
63	Eu	5.83+3	4.93+3	5.36+3	4.68+3	4.27+3	3.74+3	3.29+3	3.03+3	2.76+3	2.49+3	2.21+3	1.92+3	1.62+3	1.32+3
64	Gd	5.91+3	5.06+3	4.23+3	4.63+3	4.06+3	3.77+3	3.34+3	3.07+3	2.81+3	2.53+3	2.24+3	1.95+3	1.65+3	1.34+3
65	Tb	6.42+3	5.54+3	4.68+3	5.00+3	4.40+3	3.78+3	3.56+3	3.28+3	3.00+3	2.70+3	2.40+3	2.08+3	1.76+3	1.43+3
66	Dy	5.36+3	5.73+3	4.79+3	4.07+3	4.46+3	3.91+3	3.37+3	3.33+3	3.04+3	2.75+3	2.44+3	2.13+3	1.81+3	1.49+3
67	Ho	3.32+3	5.75+3	5.00+3	4.32+3	4.67+3	4.08+3	3.53+3	3.34+3	3.07+3	2.78+3	2.48+3	2.18+3	1.87+3	1.55+3
68	Er	1.56+3	2.71+3	4.89+3	4.56+3	3.83+3	4.27+3	3.70+3	3.23+3	3.11+3	2.83+3	2.54+3	2.24+3	1.94+3	1.63+3
69	Tm	1.66+3	1.41+3	5.00+3	4.83+3	4.06+3	3.48+3	3.89+3	3.43+3	2.96+3	2.88+3	2.60+3	2.31+3	2.01+3	1.71+3
70	Yb	1.87+3	1.50+3	2.35+3	4.78+3	4.22+3	3.65+3	4.06+3	3.50+3	3.06+3	2.88+3	2.54+3	2.26+3	2.01+3	1.76+3
71	Lu	1.94+3	1.56+3	1.32+3	4.78+3	4.37+3	3.83+3	3.26+3	3.56+3	3.18+3	2.78+3	2.62+3	2.34+3	2.08+3	1.82+3
72	Hf	2.05+3	1.65+3	1.40+3	1.58+3	4.53+3	4.01+3	3.47+3	2.92+3	3.30+3	2.93+3	2.54+3	2.44+3	2.17+3	1.89+3
73	Ta	2.03+3	1.78+3	1.53+3	1.27+3	5.49+3	4.71+3	4.00+3	3.42+3	3.57+3	3.07+3	2.92+3	2.54+3	2.46+3	2.14+3
74	W	2.13+3	1.87+3	1.61+3	1.34+3	1.11+3	4.80+3	4.13+3	3.58+3	3.63+3	3.17+3	2.73+3	2.64+3	2.52+3	2.21+3

TABLE 4 (continued)

Mass Attenuation Coefficients for $L\ \alpha$ Lines

Emitter		Se	Br	Kr	Rb	Sr	Y	Zr	Nb	Mo	Tc	Ru	Rh	Pd	Ag
Wavelength		8.99+0	8.37+0	7.82+0	7.32+0	6.86+0	6.45+0	6.07+0	5.72+0	5.41+0	5.11+0	4.85+0	4.60+0	4.37+0	4.15+0
Energy (keV)		1.38+0	1.48+0	1.59+0	1.69+0	1.81+0	1.92+0	2.04+0	2.17+0	2.29+0	2.42+0	2.56+0	2.70+0	2.84+0	2.98+0
Absorber															
75	Re	2.23+3	1.96+3	1.69+3	1.40+3	1.21+3	3.32+3	4.30+3	3.76+3	3.21+3	3.27+3	2.85+3	2.73+3	2.40+3	2.30+3
76	Os	2.28+3	2.00+3	1.79+3	1.56+3	1.33+3	1.09+3	4.40+3	3.90+3	3.38+3	2.85+3	2.96+3	2.59+3	2.47+3	2.17+3
77	Ir	2.42+3	2.13+3	1.90+3	1.66+3	1.41+3	1.17+3	3.05+3	3.97+3	3.49+3	2.99+3	3.06+3	2.72+3	2.36+3	2.25+3
78	Pt	2.56+3	2.25+3	2.00+3	1.75+3	1.49+3	1.23+3	1.05+3	2.78+3	3.64+3	3.15+3	2.70+3	2.84+3	2.51+3	2.17+3
79	Au	2.75+3	2.32+3	2.06+3	1.83+3	1.60+3	1.36+3	1.15+3	9.72+2	3.54+3	3.10+3	2.69+3	2.35+3	2.48+3	2.17+3
80	Hg	2.74+3	2.38+3	2.06+3	1.78+3	1.55+3	1.36+3	1.20+3	1.04+3	8.82+2	3.25+3	2.85+3	2.51+3	2.16+3	2.28+3
81	Tl	3.13+3	2.53+3	2.23+3	1.99+3	1.74+3	1.48+3	1.25+3	1.11+3	9.58+2	2.24+3	2.95+3	2.62+3	2.28+3	2.35+3
82	Pb	3.27+3	2.65+3	2.33+3	2.07+3	1.81+3	1.54+3	1.32+3	1.17+3	1.03+3	8.75+2	2.01+3	2.68+3	2.36+3	2.03+3
83	Bi	3.41+3	2.76+3	2.43+3	2.17+3	1.90+3	1.62+3	1.38+3	1.24+3	1.10+3	9.55+2	8.03+2	2.73+3	2.42+3	2.11+3
84	Po	3.59+3	2.92+3	2.57+3	2.30+3	2.01+3	1.71+3	1.46+3	1.32+3	1.17+3	1.01+3	8.76+2	1.90+3	2.49+3	2.19+3
85	At	3.75+3	3.08+3	2.72+3	2.43+3	2.13+3	1.81+3	1.55+3	1.39+3	1.23+3	1.07+3	9.27+2	8.16+2	1.74+3	2.29+3
86	Rn	3.70+3	3.08+3	2.73+3	2.44+3	2.13+3	1.82+3	1.55+3	1.40+3	1.24+3	1.07+3	9.33+2	8.30+2	7.24+2	1.52+3
87	Fr	3.82+3	3.22+3	2.86+3	2.55+3	2.24+3	1.91+3	1.63+3	1.47+3	1.30+3	1.13+3	9.86+2	8.89+2	7.89+2	6.87+2
88	Ra	3.94+3	3.34+3	2.97+3	2.65+3	2.32+3	1.98+3	1.70+3	1.53+3	1.35+3	1.17+3	1.02+3	9.22+2	8.16+2	7.08+2
89	Ac	4.01+3	3.43+3	3.06+3	2.74+3	2.40+3	2.05+3	1.77+3	1.64+3	1.50+3	1.36+3	1.21+3	1.06+3	9.09+2	7.52+2
90	Th	4.07+3	3.51+3	3.14+3	2.81+3	2.47+3	2.11+3	1.83+3	1.69+3	1.55+3	1.40+3	1.25+3	1.10+3	9.40+2	7.78+2
91	Pa	4.06+3	3.74+3	3.35+3	3.00+3	2.63+3	2.25+3	1.95+3	1.80+3	1.65+3	1.49+3	1.33+3	1.17+3	1.00+3	8.28+2
92	U	4.15+3	3.79+3	3.40+3	3.04+3	2.67+3	2.29+3	1.96+3	1.77+3	1.57+3	1.36+3	1.20+3	1.09+3	9.84+2	8.71+2
93	Np	4.42+3	3.78+3	3.59+3	3.21+3	2.82+3	2.41+3	2.09+3	1.93+3	1.77+3	1.60+3	1.43+3	1.26+3	1.08+3	8.90+2
94	Pu	4.59+3	3.93+3	3.65+3	3.28+3	2.89+3	2.49+3	2.17+3	2.01+3	1.84+3	1.66+3	1.49+3	1.30+3	1.11+3	9.21+2

TABLE 4 (continued)

Mass Attenuation Coefficients for $L\ \alpha$ Lines

Emitter	Cd	In	Sn	Sb	Te	I	Xe	Cs	Ba	La	Ce	Pr	Nd	Pm
Wavelength	3.96+0	3.77+0	3.60+0	3.44+0	3.29+0	3.15+0	3.02+0	2.89+0	2.78+0	2.67+0	2.56+0	2.46+0	2.37+0	2.28+0
Energy (keV)	3.13+0	3.29+0	3.44+0	3.60+0	3.77+0	3.94+0	4.11+0	4.29+0	4.47+0	4.65+0	4.84+0	5.03+0	5.23+0	5.43+0
Absorber														
1 H	5.42-1	5.21-1	4.99-1	4.84-1	4.71-1	4.59-1	4.50-1	4.44-1	4.38-1	4.31-1	4.25-1	4.18-1	4.16-1	4.12-1
2 He	1.81+0	1.60+0	1.39+0	1.23+0	1.11+0	9.84-1	8.99-1	8.35-1	7.71-1	7.04-1	6.36-1	5.74-1	5.43-1	5.12-1
3 Li	6.50+0	5.66+0	4.80+0	4.17+0	3.68+0	3.18+0	2.83+0	2.58+0	2.32+0	2.06+0	1.79+0	1.54+0	1.42+0	1.30+0
4 Be	1.89+1	1.64+1	1.39+1	1.21+1	1.06+1	9.14+0	8.12+0	7.37+0	6.60+0	5.81+0	5.00+0	4.26+0	3.90+0	3.54+0
5 B	4.09+1	3.56+1	3.02+1	2.63+1	2.31+1	1.99+1	1.77+1	1.60+1	1.44+1	1.26+1	1.09+1	9.26+0	8.47+0	7.66+0
6 C	7.93+1	6.92+1	5.89+1	5.13+1	4.53+1	3.90+1	3.47+1	3.15+1	2.83+1	2.49+1	2.15+1	1.83+1	1.67+1	1.51+1
7 N	1.30+2	1.14+2	9.73+1	8.50+1	7.50+1	6.49+1	5.78+1	5.25+1	4.71+1	4.16+1	3.59+1	3.07+1	2.80+1	2.54+1
8 O	1.96+2	1.72+2	1.47+2	1.29+2	1.14+2	9.86+1	8.80+1	8.00+1	7.19+1	6.35+1	5.50+1	4.71+1	4.31+1	3.91+1
9 F	2.60+2	2.28+2	1.95+2	1.71+2	1.52+2	1.32+2	1.18+2	1.07+2	9.63+1	8.53+1	7.39+1	6.34+1	5.81+1	5.27+1
10 Ne	3.66+2	3.21+2	2.76+2	2.43+2	2.15+2	1.87+2	1.68+2	1.53+2	1.38+2	1.22+2	1.06+2	9.12+1	8.37+1	7.59+1
11 Na	4.60+2	4.05+2	3.49+2	3.07+2	2.72+2	2.37+2	2.13+2	1.94+2	1.75+2	1.55+2	1.35+2	1.16+2	1.07+2	9.68+1
12 Mg	6.01+2	5.30+2	4.57+2	4.03+2	3.58+2	3.13+2	2.80+2	2.56+2	2.31+2	2.05+2	1.79+2	1.54+2	1.42+2	1.29+2
13 Al	7.33+2	6.48+2	5.61+2	4.95+2	4.41+2	3.86+2	3.47+2	3.17+2	2.86+2	2.55+2	2.22+2	1.93+2	1.77+2	1.61+2
14 Si	9.19+2	8.12+2	7.02+2	6.20+2	5.52+2	4.83+2	4.34+2	3.96+2	3.58+2	3.18+2	2.78+2	2.40+2	2.21+2	2.01+2
15 P	1.06+3	9.41+2	8.16+2	7.21+2	6.43+2	5.64+2	5.07+2	4.64+2	4.19+2	3.74+2	3.27+2	2.83+2	2.61+2	2.37+2
16 S	1.29+3	1.14+3	9.91+2	8.77+2	7.83+2	6.87+2	6.19+2	5.66+2	5.12+2	4.57+2	4.00+2	3.47+2	3.20+2	2.91+2
17 Cl	1.44+3	1.27+3	1.11+3	9.82+2	8.78+2	7.71+2	6.95+2	6.36+2	5.76+2	5.14+2	4.51+2	3.92+2	3.61+2	3.29+2
18 Ar	1.56+2	1.40+3	1.23+3	1.10+3	9.81+2	8.62+2	7.77+2	7.11+2	6.44+2	5.75+2	5.04+2	4.39+2	4.04+2	3.68+2
19 K	2.06+2	1.83+2	1.59+2	1.39+2	1.16+3	1.03+3	9.33+2	8.55+2	7.75+2	6.93+2	6.09+2	5.31+2	4.90+2	4.47+2
20 Ca	2.47+2	2.19+2	1.91+2	1.69+2	1.52+2	1.34+2	1.07+3	9.86+2	8.96+2	8.03+2	7.08+2	6.20+2	5.72+2	5.23+2
21 Sc	2.70+2	2.39+2	2.08+2	1.85+2	1.65+2	1.46+2	1.30+2	1.17+2	1.04+2	8.13+2	7.32+2	6.55+2	6.05+2	5.53+2
22 Ti	3.06+2	2.71+2	2.36+2	2.09+2	1.87+2	1.64+2	1.48+2	1.36+2	1.23+2	1.10+2	9.67+1	7.08+2	6.55+2	6.00+2
23 V	3.37+2	2.98+2	2.59+2	2.29+2	2.05+2	1.80+2	1.63+2	1.49+2	1.35+2	1.21+2	1.07+2	9.29+1	8.45+1	7.58+1
24 Cr	3.94+2	3.49+2	3.03+2	2.69+2	2.41+2	2.12+2	1.91+2	1.75+2	1.59+2	1.43+2	1.25+2	1.10+2	1.01+2	9.27+1
25 Mn	4.40+2	3.90+2	3.38+2	3.00+2	2.68+2	2.36+2	2.13+2	1.95+2	1.77+2	1.58+2	1.39+2	1.22+2	1.12+2	1.03+2
26 Fe	5.08+2	4.50+2	3.91+2	3.46+2	3.09+2	2.72+2	2.45+2	2.25+2	2.04+2	1.82+2	1.60+2	1.40+2	1.29+2	1.18+2
27 Co	5.59+2	4.95+2	4.30+2	3.81+2	3.40+2	2.99+2	2.70+2	2.47+2	2.24+2	2.01+2	1.77+2	1.54+2	1.42+2	1.30+2
28 Ni	6.45+2	5.71+2	4.95+2	4.38+2	3.92+2	3.44+2	3.10+2	2.84+2	2.58+2	2.31+2	2.03+2	1.77+2	1.63+2	1.49+2
29 Cu	6.74+2	6.02+2	5.28+2	4.70+2	4.20+2	3.69+2	3.33+2	3.05+2	2.77+2	2.48+2	2.18+2	1.90+2	1.76+2	1.61+2
30 Zn	7.50+2	6.67+2	5.82+2	5.17+2	4.63+2	4.07+2	3.68+2	3.37+2	3.06+2	2.74+2	2.41+2	2.11+2	1.95+2	1.78+2
31 Ga	8.13+2	7.41+2	6.67+2	5.92+2	5.15+2	4.36+2	3.87+2	3.56+2	3.24+2	2.91+2	2.57+2	2.26+2	2.09+2	1.91+2
32 Ge	8.87+2	8.09+2	7.28+2	6.46+2	5.62+2	4.76+2	4.22+2	3.87+2	3.52+2	3.16+2	2.79+2	2.44+2	2.25+2	2.06+2
33 As	9.68+2	8.83+2	7.96+2	7.06+2	6.15+2	5.21+2	4.63+2	4.25+2	3.87+2	3.48+2	3.07+2	2.70+2	2.49+2	2.28+2
34 Se	1.03+3	9.44+2	8.51+2	7.56+2	6.58+2	5.58+2	4.96+2	4.56+2	4.15+2	3.72+2	3.23+2	2.89+2	2.67+2	2.44+2
35 Br	1.14+3	1.04+3	9.40+2	8.35+2	7.28+2	6.18+2	5.49+2	5.04+2	4.59+2	4.12+2	3.65+2	3.20+2	2.95+2	2.70+2
36 Kr	1.24+3	1.10+3	9.55+2	8.46+2	7.56+2	6.64+2	5.99+2	5.49+2	4.98+2	4.45+2	3.91+2	3.41+2	3.15+2	2.88+2
37 Rb	1.38+3	1.22+3	1.06+3	9.35+2	8.35+2	7.33+2	6.60+2	6.04+2	5.47+2	4.89+2	4.29+2	3.74+2	3.45+2	3.15+2

TABLE 4 (continued)

Mass Attenuation Coefficients for $L\alpha$ Lines

Emitter	Cd	In	Sn	Sb	Te	I	Xe	Cs	Ba	La	Ce	Pr	Nd	Pm
Wavelength	3.96+0	3.77+0	3.60+0	3.44+0	3.29+0	3.15+0	3.02+0	2.89+0	2.78+0	2.67+0	2.56+0	2.46+0	2.37+0	2.28+0
Energy (keV)	3.13+0	3.29+0	3.44+0	3.60+0	3.77+0	3.94+0	4.11+0	4.29+0	4.47+0	4.65+0	4.84+0	5.03+0	5.23+0	5.43+0
Absorber														
38 Sr	1.50+3	1.33+3	1.15+3	1.02+3	9.07+2	7.96+2	7.17+2	6.56+2	5.95+2	5.31+2	4.66+2	4.06+2	3.74+2	3.42+2
39 Y	1.64+3	1.45+3	1.26+3	1.11+3	9.93+2	8.71+2	7.84+2	7.18+2	6.51+2	5.81+2	5.10+2	4.44+2	4.09+2	3.74+2
40 Zr	1.79+3	1.58+3	1.37+3	1.21+3	1.08+3	9.46+2	8.52+2	7.79+2	7.06+2	6.30+2	5.52+2	4.80+2	4.43+2	4.04+2
41 Nb	1.96+3	1.73+3	1.50+3	1.32+3	1.18+3	1.03+3	9.31+2	8.52+2	7.72+2	6.89+2	6.04+2	5.25+2	4.84+2	4.42+2
42 Mo	2.10+3	1.85+3	1.60+3	1.41+3	1.26+3	1.10+3	9.93+2	9.08+2	8.22+2	7.33+2	6.43+2	5.59+2	5.15+2	4.70+2
43 Tc	2.18+3	1.94+3	1.68+3	1.49+3	1.33+3	1.16+3	1.05+3	9.59+2	8.68+2	7.75+2	6.80+2	5.91+2	5.45+2	4.98+2
44 Ru	1.94+3	2.04+3	1.80+3	1.60+3	1.43+3	1.25+3	1.13+3	1.03+3	9.33+2	8.33+2	7.31+2	6.36+2	5.86+2	5.35+2
45 Rh	1.46+3	1.80+3	1.89+3	1.69+3	1.51+3	1.33+3	1.19+3	1.09+3	9.91+2	8.85+2	7.77+2	6.76+2	6.24+2	5.70+2
46 Pd	4.37+2	1.40+3	1.72+3	1.81+3	1.63+3	1.43+3	1.29+3	1.18+3	1.07+3	9.56+2	8.38+2	7.28+2	6.71+2	6.12+2
47 Ag	4.79+2	4.23+2	1.31+3	1.62+3	1.43+3	1.52+3	1.38+3	1.26+3	1.14+3	1.02+3	8.94+2	7.78+2	7.17+2	6.54+2
48 Cd	4.97+2	4.54+2	4.10+2	1.22+3	1.51+3	1.34+3	1.45+3	1.32+3	1.20+3	1.07+3	9.38+2	8.16+2	7.52+2	6.86+2
49 In	5.33+2	4.87+2	4.40+2	3.95+2	1.14+3	1.01+3	1.25+3	1.35+3	1.23+3	1.11+3	9.81+2	8.64+2	7.97+2	7.27+2
50 Sn	5.66+2	5.17+2	4.67+2	4.21+2	3.78+2	1.07+3	9.56+2	1.20+3	1.27+3	1.15+3	1.03+3	9.20+2	8.48+2	7.74+2
51 Sb	6.00+2	5.45+2	4.89+2	4.41+2	3.97+2	3.52+2	3.14+2	8.63+2	1.08+3	9.67+2	1.04+3	9.38+2	8.66+2	7.91+2
52 Te	6.25+2	5.68+2	5.10+2	4.60+2	4.14+2	3.67+2	3.29+2	2.95+2	8.05+2	1.01+3	9.06+2	9.77+2	9.01+2	8.23+2
53 I	6.82+2	6.19+2	5.55+2	5.00+2	4.50+2	3.99+2	3.59+2	3.26+2	2.91+2	7.85+2	7.02+2	8.82+2	9.57+2	8.78+2
54 Xe	7.15+2	6.43+2	5.69+2	5.10+2	4.60+2	4.09+2	3.71+2	3.39+2	3.07+2	2.75+2	7.15+2	6.42+2	8.13+2	7.31+2
55 Cs	7.69+2	6.95+2	6.19+2	5.56+2	5.00+2	4.43+2	4.02+2	3.70+2	3.37+2	3.03+2	2.69+2	6.98+2	6.32+2	7.94+2
56 Ba	8.03+2	7.25+2	6.46+2	5.80+2	5.22+2	4.63+2	4.20+2	3.86+2	3.52+2	3.17+2	2.81+2	2.47+2	2.24+2	5.94+2
57 La	8.60+2	7.87+2	7.12+2	6.35+2	5.57+2	4.76+2	4.27+2	3.95+2	3.63+2	3.30+2	2.96+2	2.63+2	2.41+2	2.17+2
58 Ce	9.28+2	8.49+2	7.68+2	6.85+2	6.00+2	5.13+2	4.59+2	4.24+2	3.89+2	3.53+2	3.15+2	2.80+2	2.58+2	2.35+2
59 Pr	9.90+2	9.05+2	8.19+2	7.31+2	6.40+2	5.48+2	4.90+2	4.52+2	4.14+2	3.75+2	3.34+2	2.96+2	2.74+2	2.51+2
60 Nd	1.03+3	9.44+2	8.55+2	7.63+2	6.68+2	5.72+2	5.12+2	4.74+2	4.34+2	3.94+2	3.52+2	3.14+2	2.91+2	2.67+2
61 Pm	1.08+3	9.91+2	8.97+2	8.01+2	7.02+2	6.01+2	5.38+2	4.98+2	4.56+2	4.13+2	3.70+2	3.29+2	3.05+2	2.80+2
62 Sm	1.13+3	1.04+3	9.39+2	8.38+2	7.35+2	6.30+2	5.64+2	5.22+2	4.78+2	4.34+2	3.88+2	3.45+2	3.20+2	2.94+2
63 Eu	1.20+3	1.09+3	9.91+2	8.85+2	7.76+2	6.65+2	5.96+2	5.50+2	5.04+2	4.57+2	4.08+2	3.63+2	3.36+2	3.09+2
64 Gd	1.22+3	1.12+3	1.01+3	9.06+2	7.95+2	6.82+2	6.11+2	5.65+2	5.18+2	4.69+2	4.20+2	3.73+2	3.45+2	3.17+2
65 Tb	1.30+3	1.19+3	1.08+3	9.65+2	8.47+2	7.26+2	6.50+2	6.00+2	5.49+2	4.97+2	4.43+2	3.93+2	3.64+2	3.35+2
66 Dy	1.35+3	1.24+3	1.12+3	1.00+3	8.80+2	7.55+2	6.76+2	6.24+2	5.71+2	5.17+2	4.62+2	4.10+2	3.79+2	3.48+2
67 Ho	1.41+3	1.30+3	1.17+3	1.05+3	9.21+2	7.90+2	7.08+2	6.54+2	5.98+2	5.41+2	4.83+2	4.28+2	3.97+2	3.64+2
68 Er	1.48+3	1.36+3	1.23+3	1.10+3	9.66+2	8.29+2	7.42+2	6.85+2	6.27+2	5.66+2	5.05+2	4.47+2	4.14+2	3.80+2
69 Tm	1.56+3	1.43+3	1.30+3	1.16+3	1.02+3	8.74+2	7.83+2	7.22+2	6.60+2	5.97+2	5.32+2	4.71+2	4.36+2	4.00+2
70 Yb	1.61+3	1.48+3	1.34+3	1.20+3	1.05+3	9.02+2	8.09+2	7.46+2	6.83+2	6.17+2	5.50+2	4.88+2	4.52+2	4.14+2
71 Lu	1.67+3	1.53+3	1.39+3	1.24+3	1.09+3	9.39+2	8.42+2	7.78+2	7.12+2	6.44+2	5.75+2	5.09+2	4.72+2	4.33+2
72 Hf	1.74+3	1.59+3	1.44+3	1.29+3	1.14+3	9.79+2	8.78+2	8.10+2	7.41+2	6.70+2	5.97+2	5.29+2	4.90+2	4.49+2
73 Ta	1.92+3	1.71+3	1.49+3	1.32+3	1.19+3	1.05+3	9.47+2	8.69+2	7.91+2	7.10+2	6.27+2	5.50+2	5.09+2	4.66+2
74 W	1.99+3	1.77+3	1.54+3	1.37+3	1.23+3	1.09+3	9.84+2	9.04+2	8.22+2	7.39+2	6.53+2	5.73+2	5.30+2	4.86+2

TABLE 4 (continued)

Mass Attenuation Coefficients for $L\alpha$ Lines

Emitter	Cd	In	Sn	Sb	Te	I	Xe	Cs	Ba	La	Ce	Pr	Nd	Pm
Wavelength	3.96+0	3.77+0	3.60+0	3.44+0	3.29+0	3.15+0	3.02+0	2.89+0	2.78+0	2.67+0	2.56+0	2.46+0	2.37+0	2.28+0
Energy (keV)	3.13+0	3.29+0	3.44+0	3.60+0	3.77+0	3.94+0	4.11+0	4.29+0	4.47+0	4.65+0	4.84+0	5.03+0	5.23+0	5.43+0
Absorber														
75 Re	2.07+3	1.84+3	1.61+3	1.43+3	1.28+3	1.13+3	1.03+3	9.43+2	8.58+2	7.71+2	6.81+2	5.98+2	5.54+2	5.08+2
76 Os	2.12+3	1.89+3	1.66+3	1.48+3	1.33+3	1.17+3	1.06+3	9.74+2	8.86+2	7.96+2	7.04+2	6.18+2	5.72+2	5.25+2
77 Ir	1.99+3	1.95+3	1.72+3	1.54+3	1.38+3	1.22+3	1.11+3	1.02+3	9.25+2	8.31+2	7.35+2	6.45+2	5.97+2	5.48+2
78 Pt	2.11+3	1.85+3	1.80+3	1.62+3	1.45+3	1.28+3	1.16+3	1.06+3	9.65+2	8.66+2	7.65+2	6.71+2	6.20+2	5.69+2
79 Au	1.91+3	1.87+3	1.81+3	1.63+3	1.47+3	1.30+3	1.18+3	1.08+3	9.87+2	8.88+2	7.87+2	6.92+2	6.41+2	5.88+2
80 Hg	2.02+3	1.95+3	1.74+3	1.70+3	1.53+3	1.36+3	1.23+3	1.13+3	1.03+3	9.26+2	8.19+2	7.20+2	6.66+2	6.11+2
81 Tl	2.10+3	1.86+3	1.78+3	1.59+3	1.56+3	1.39+3	1.27+3	1.17+3	1.06+3	9.55+2	8.45+2	7.42+2	6.87+2	6.30+2
82 Pb	2.16+3	1.93+3	1.70+3	1.65+3	1.47+3	1.44+3	1.32+3	1.21+3	1.10+3	9.90+2	8.77+2	7.71+2	7.13+2	6.55+2
83 Bi	1.86+3	1.98+3	1.75+3	1.56+3	1.53+3	1.37+3	1.37+3	1.26+3	1.14+3	1.03+3	9.10+2	8.00+2	7.41+2	6.80+2
84 Po	1.95+3	1.71+3	1.82+3	1.63+3	1.45+3	1.42+3	1.27+3	1.28+3	1.17+3	1.06+3	9.41+2	8.33+2	7.71+2	7.08+2
85 At	2.05+3	1.82+3	1.90+3	1.71+3	1.54+3	1.36+3	1.34+3	1.20+3	1.20+3	1.09+3	9.79+2	8.73+2	8.08+2	7.42+2
86 Rn	2.04+3	1.81+3	1.59+3	1.69+3	1.52+3	1.35+3	1.20+3	1.19+3	1.07+3	1.07+3	9.63+2	8.65+2	8.01+2	7.35+2
87 Fr	1.38+3	1.85+3	1.63+3	1.45+3	1.56+3	1.39+3	1.25+3	1.12+3	1.11+3	9.94+2	9.93+2	8.98+2	8.31+2	7.63+2
88 Ra	1.43+3	1.89+3	1.68+3	1.50+3	1.33+3	1.43+3	1.29+3	1.17+3	1.04+3	1.03+3	1.02+3	9.26+2	8.58+2	7.87+2
89 Ac	6.58+2	1.31+3	1.74+3	1.57+3	1.40+3	1.48+3	1.35+3	1.23+3	1.10+3	9.72+2	9.70+2	9.63+2	8.92+2	8.19+2
90 Th	6.88+2	6.05+2	1.19+3	1.60+3	1.44+3	1.28+3	1.37+3	1.26+3	1.14+3	1.02+3	9.86+2	8.93+2	8.94+2	8.24+2
91 Pa	7.39+2	6.59+2	1.25+3	1.11+3	1.50+3	1.34+3	1.20+3	1.31+3	1.19+3	1.08+3	9.66+2	9.39+2	8.55+2	8.53+2
92 U	7.85+2	7.01+2	6.15+2	1.11+3	1.48+3	1.33+3	1.19+3	1.07+3	1.17+3	1.07+3	9.57+2	8.51+2	8.50+2	7.74+2
93 Np	8.13+2	7.47+2	6.80+2	6.12+2	1.07+3	1.42+3	1.28+3	1.16+3	1.24+3	1.13+3	1.02+3	9.10+2	8.28+2	8.24+2
94 Pu	8.37+2	7.66+2	6.93+2	6.18+2	5.41+2	1.06+3	1.34+3	1.21+3	1.07+3	9.68+2	8.69+2	1.06+3	9.86+2	9.04+2

TABLE 4 (continued)

Mass Attenuation Coefficients for $L\ \alpha$ Lines

Emitter	Sm	Eu	Gd	Ib	Dy	Ho	Er	Tm	Yb	Lu	Hf	Ta	W	Re
Wavelength	2.20+0	2.12+0	2.05+0	1.98+0	1.91+0	1.84+0	1.78+0	1.73+0	1.67+0	1.62+0	1.57+0	1.52+0	1.48+0	1.43+0
Energy (keV)	5.64+0	5.85+0	6.06+0	6.27+0	6.50+0	6.72+0	6.95+0	7.18+0	7.42+0	7.66+0	7.90+0	8.15+0	8.40+0	8.65+0
Absorber														
1 H	4.09-1	4.06-1	4.04-1	4.02-1	4.00-1	3.98-1	3.96-1	3.95-1	3.94-1	3.93-1	3.92-1	3.91-1	3.90-1	3.89-1
2 He	4.80-1	4.47-1	4.19-1	4.02-1	3.84-1	3.66-1	3.48-1	3.36-1	3.25-1	3.14-1	3.03-1	2.94-1	2.87-1	2.80-1
3 Li	1.18+0	1.05+0	9.40-1	8.76-1	8.10-1	7.43-1	6.75-1	6.31-1	5.92-1	5.53-1	5.13-1	4.82-1	4.58-1	4.33-1
4 Be	3.17+0	2.78+0	2.45+0	2.26+0	2.06+0	1.86+0	1.65+0	1.52+0	1.40+0	1.29+0	1.17+0	1.08+0	1.00+0	9.29-1
5 B	6.84+0	6.00+0	5.27+0	4.84+0	4.39+0	3.94+0	3.49+0	3.19+0	2.93+0	2.67+0	2.40+0	2.20+0	2.03+0	1.87+0
6 C	1.35+1	1.19+1	1.04+1	9.56+0	8.67+0	7.78+0	6.87+0	6.27+0	5.75+0	5.22+0	4.68+0	4.27+0	3.94+0	3.61+0
7 N	2.27+1	1.99+1	1.75+1	1.61+1	1.46+1	1.31+1	1.15+1	1.05+1	9.65+0	8.76+0	7.85+0	7.15+0	6.59+0	6.02+0
8 O	3.49+1	3.07+1	2.70+1	2.48+1	2.25+1	2.02+1	1.79+1	1.63+1	1.50+1	1.36+1	1.22+1	1.11+1	1.02+1	9.34+0
9 F	4.72+1	4.15+1	3.66+1	3.36+1	3.05+1	2.74+1	2.43+1	2.22+1	2.03+1	1.85+1	1.66+1	1.51+1	1.39+1	1.27+1
10 Ne	6.81+1	6.00+1	5.30+1	4.87+1	4.43+1	3.98+1	3.53+1	3.23+1	2.96+1	2.69+1	2.42+1	2.21+1	2.03+1	1.86+1
11 Na	8.69+1	7.67+1	6.77+1	6.23+1	5.67+1	5.10+1	4.53+1	4.14+1	3.80+1	3.46+1	3.11+1	2.84+1	2.62+1	2.40+1
12 Mg	1.16+2	1.02+2	9.04+1	8.32+1	7.58+1	6.82+1	6.06+1	5.54+1	5.09+1	4.64+1	4.17+1	3.81+1	3.51+1	3.22+1
13 Al	1.45+2	1.28+2	1.14+2	1.05+2	9.54+1	8.60+1	7.65+1	7.00+1	6.44+1	5.87+1	5.28+1	4.83+1	4.46+1	4.08+1
14 Si	1.81+2	1.60+2	1.42+2	1.31+2	1.19+2	1.07+2	9.55+1	8.75+1	8.04+1	7.33+1	6.60+1	6.03+1	5.57+1	5.10+1
15 P	2.14+2	1.90+2	1.68+2	1.55+2	1.42+2	1.28+2	1.14+2	1.04+2	9.61+1	8.76+1	7.90+1	7.23+1	6.68+1	6.12+1
16 S	2.63+2	2.33+2	2.07+2	1.91+2	1.74+2	1.57+2	1.40+2	1.29+2	1.19+2	1.08+2	9.76+1	8.93+1	8.26+1	7.58+1
17 Cl	2.97+2	2.64+2	2.35+2	2.17+2	1.98+2	1.79+2	1.60+2	1.47+2	1.35+2	1.23+2	1.11+2	1.02+2	9.43+1	8.66+1
18 Ar	3.32+2	2.95+2	2.63+2	2.42+2	2.21+2	2.00+2	1.79+2	1.64+2	1.51+2	1.38+2	1.25+2	1.14+2	1.06+2	9.69+1
19 K	4.04+2	3.59+2	3.20+2	2.96+2	2.70+2	2.45+2	2.19+2	2.01+2	1.85+2	1.69+2	1.53+2	1.40+2	1.30+2	1.20+2
20 Ca	4.73+2	4.21+2	3.76+2	3.47+2	3.18+2	2.88+2	2.58+2	2.37+2	2.19+2	2.00+2	1.81+2	1.66+2	1.54+2	1.42+2
21 Sc	5.00+2	4.47+2	3.99+2	3.69+2	3.38+2	3.07+2	2.75+2	2.53+2	2.33+2	2.14+2	1.94+2	1.78+2	1.65+2	1.52+2
22 Ti	5.45+2	4.88+2	4.38+2	4.05+2	3.72+2	3.38+2	3.04+2	2.80+2	2.59+2	2.37+2	2.16+2	1.98+2	1.84+2	1.69+2
23 V	5.87+2	5.33+2	4.84+2	4.48+2	4.11+2	3.73+2	3.35+2	3.09+2	2.85+2	2.62+2	2.37+2	2.18+2	2.03+2	1.87+2
24 Cr	8.40+1	7.50+1	5.59+2	5.17+2	4.75+2	4.32+2	3.88+2	3.57+2	3.31+2	3.03+2	2.75+2	2.53+2	2.35+2	2.16+2
25 Mn	9.32+1	8.33+1	7.43+1	6.81+1	6.17+1	4.57+2	4.16+2	3.85+2	3.56+2	3.27+2	2.97+2	2.73+2	2.54+2	2.34+2
26 Fe	1.07+2	9.56+1	8.55+1	7.92+1	7.27+1	6.61+1	5.94+1	4.28+2	3.97+2	3.65+2	3.33+2	3.07+2	2.86+2	2.63+2
27 Co	1.18+2	1.05+2	9.43+1	8.74+1	8.02+1	7.29+1	6.56+1	6.02+1	5.55+1	5.06+1	3.70+2	3.43+2	3.19+2	2.94+2
28 Ni	1.35+2	1.21+2	1.08+2	1.00+2	9.18+1	8.34+1	7.50+1	6.91+1	6.40+1	5.88+1	5.35+1	4.89+1	3.37+2	3.13+2
29 Cu	1.46+2	1.30+2	1.16+2	1.08+2	9.87+1	8.98+1	8.06+1	7.44+1	6.89+1	6.32+1	5.75+1	5.30+1	4.93+1	4.55+1
30 Zn	1.62+2	1.45+2	1.29+2	1.20+2	1.10+2	1.00+2	9.02+1	8.32+1	7.71+1	7.09+1	6.45+1	5.95+1	5.54+1	5.12+1
31 Ga	1.73+2	1.54+2	1.38+2	1.28+2	1.17+2	1.07+2	9.58+1	8.84+1	8.18+1	7.51+1	6.83+1	6.29+1	5.85+1	5.41+1
32 Ge	1.86+2	1.66+2	1.49+2	1.38+2	1.26+2	1.15+2	1.03+2	9.49+1	8.78+1	8.06+1	7.33+1	6.75+1	6.27+1	5.79+1
33 As	2.06+2	1.84+2	1.64+2	1.52+2	1.40+2	1.27+2	1.14+2	1.05+2	9.73+1	8.93+1	8.12+1	7.48+1	6.96+1	6.42+1
34 Se	2.21+2	1.97+2	1.76+2	1.63+2	1.50+2	1.36+2	1.22+2	1.13+2	1.04+2	9.57+1	8.70+1	8.02+1	7.45+1	6.88+1
35 Br	2.44+2	2.18+2	1.95+2	1.80+2	1.65+2	1.50+2	1.35+2	1.24+2	1.15+2	1.06+2	9.59+1	8.83+1	8.21+1	7.58+1
36 Kr	2.61+2	2.33+2	2.08+2	1.93+2	1.77+2	1.61+2	1.44+2	1.33+2	1.23+2	1.13+2	1.03+2	9.47+1	8.80+1	8.12+1
37 Rb	2.85+2	2.54+2	2.27+2	2.10+2	1.92+2	1.74+2	1.56+2	1.44+2	1.33+2	1.22+2	1.11+2	1.02+2	9.48+1	8.75+1

TABLE 4 (continued)

Mass Attenuation Coefficients for $L\ \alpha$ Lines

Emitter	Sm	Eu	Gd	Tb	Dy	Ho	Er	Tm	Yb	Lu	Hf	Ta	W	Re
Wavelength	2.20+0	2.12+0	2.05+0	1.98+0	1.91+0	1.84+0	1.78+0	1.73+0	1.67+0	1.62+0	1.57+0	1.52+0	1.48+0	1.43+0
Energy (keV)	5.64+0	5.85+0	6.06+0	6.27+0	6.50+0	6.72+0	6.95+0	7.18+0	7.42+0	7.66+0	7.90+0	8.15+0	8.40+0	8.65+0
Absorber														
38 Sr	3.09+2	2.75+2	2.46+2	2.27+2	2.08+2	1.89+2	1.70+2	1.56+2	1.44+2	1.32+2	1.20+2	1.11+2	1.03+2	9.49+1
39 Y	3.38+2	3.01+2	2.69+2	2.49+2	2.28+2	2.07+2	1.85+2	1.71+2	1.58+2	1.45+2	1.32+2	1.21+2	1.12+2	1.04+2
40 Zr	3.65+2	3.25+2	2.90+2	2.68+2	2.46+2	2.23+2	2.00+2	1.84+2	1.70+2	1.56+2	1.41+2	1.30+2	1.21+2	1.11+2
41 Nb	3.99+2	3.56+2	3.17+2	2.93+2	2.68+2	2.44+2	2.18+2	2.01+2	1.86+2	1.70+2	1.54+2	1.42+2	1.32+2	1.21+2
42 Mo	4.24+2	3.78+2	3.36+2	3.11+2	2.85+2	2.58+2	2.31+2	2.13+2	1.96+2	1.80+2	1.63+2	1.50+2	1.39+2	1.28+2
43 Tc	4.50+2	4.01+2	3.57+2	3.30+2	3.03+2	2.75+2	2.46+2	2.26+2	2.09+2	1.92+2	1.74+2	1.60+2	1.49+2	1.37+2
44 Ru	4.84+2	4.31+2	3.84+2	3.55+2	3.25+2	2.95+2	2.64+2	2.43+2	2.25+2	2.06+2	1.87+2	1.72+2	1.60+2	1.47+2
45 Rh	5.15+2	4.59+2	4.09+2	3.79+2	3.47+2	3.15+2	2.82+2	2.60+2	2.40+2	2.20+2	2.00+2	1.84+2	1.71+2	1.58+2
46 Pd	5.53+2	4.92+2	4.39+2	4.05+2	3.71+2	3.37+2	3.01+2	2.77+2	2.56+2	2.35+2	2.13+2	1.95+2	1.81+2	1.67+2
47 Ag	5.91+2	5.27+2	4.69+2	4.34+2	3.97+2	3.60+2	3.23+2	2.97+2	2.74+2	2.51+2	2.28+2	2.10+2	1.95+2	1.79+2
48 Cd	6.20+2	5.51+2	4.91+2	4.54+2	4.16+2	3.77+2	3.37+2	3.10+2	2.87+2	2.63+2	2.38+2	2.19+2	2.03+2	1.87+2
49 In	6.57+2	5.85+2	5.22+2	4.82+2	4.42+2	4.01+2	3.59+2	3.30+2	3.05+2	2.80+2	2.54+2	2.33+2	2.16+2	1.99+2
50 Sn	6.99+2	6.22+2	5.54+2	5.12+2	4.69+2	4.25+2	3.80+2	3.50+2	3.23+2	2.96+2	2.68+2	2.46+2	2.29+2	2.11+2
51 Sb	7.16+2	6.38+2	5.70+2	5.27+2	4.83+2	4.39+2	3.94+2	3.63+2	3.35+2	3.08+2	2.79+2	2.57+2	2.39+2	2.20+2
52 Te	7.45+2	6.64+2	5.93+2	5.49+2	5.03+2	4.57+2	4.10+2	3.77+2	3.49+2	3.20+2	2.91+2	2.67+2	2.48+2	2.29+2
53 I	7.98+2	7.17+2	6.44+2	5.95+2	5.45+2	4.95+2	4.44+2	4.09+2	3.78+2	3.46+2	3.14+2	2.89+2	2.68+2	2.48+2
54 Xe	8.00+2	7.24+2	6.56+2	6.07+2	5.56+2	5.05+2	4.53+2	4.17+2	3.86+2	3.54+2	3.21+2	2.95+2	2.74+2	2.53+2
55 Cs	7.19+2	7.81+2	7.11+2	6.58+2	6.03+2	5.47+2	4.90+2	4.52+2	4.17+2	3.83+2	3.48+2	3.20+2	2.97+2	2.74+2
56 Ba	7.46+2	6.79+2	7.40+2	6.84+2	6.27+2	5.69+2	5.10+2	4.70+2	4.35+2	3.98+2	3.62+2	3.33+2	3.09+2	2.85+2
57 La	5.76+2	5.19+2	6.58+2	7.16+2	6.59+2	6.02+2	5.44+2	5.02+2	4.63+2	4.25+2	3.85+2	3.54+2	3.29+2	3.03+2
58 Ce	2.12+2	5.50+2	4.99+2	6.35+2	5.77+2	6.33+2	5.76+2	5.33+2	4.92+2	4.51+2	4.10+2	3.77+2	3.50+2	3.22+2
59 Pr	2.29+2	2.05+2	5.30+2	4.84+2	6.12+2	5.59+2	6.10+2	5.65+2	5.22+2	4.78+2	4.34+2	3.99+2	3.71+2	3.42+2
60 Nd	2.43+2	2.19+2	1.96+2	5.09+2	4.65+2	4.20+2	5.37+2	5.90+2	5.46+2	5.01+2	4.56+2	4.20+2	3.90+2	3.59+2
61 Pm	2.55+2	2.29+2	2.06+2	1.89+2	4.82+2	4.43+2	4.02+2	5.14+2	4.69+2	5.19+2	4.76+2	4.39+2	4.08+2	3.76+2
62 Sm	2.67+2	2.40+2	2.16+2	2.00+2	1.83+2	4.61+2	4.21+2	3.86+2	4.93+2	4.52+2	4.97+2	4.60+2	4.27+2	3.94+2
63 Eu	2.81+2	2.52+2	2.27+2	2.11+2	1.94+2	1.78+2	1.60+2	4.08+2	3.74+2	4.75+2	4.37+2	4.83+2	4.49+2	4.14+2
64 Gd	2.89+2	2.59+2	2.33+2	2.17+2	2.00+2	1.83+2	1.65+2	1.51+2	3.85+2	3.54+2	3.22+2	4.14+2	4.56+2	4.22+2
65 Tb	3.05+2	2.74+2	2.46+2	2.29+2	2.11+2	1.93+2	1.74+2	1.60+2	1.48+2	3.71+2	3.41+2	3.13+2	4.02+2	3.70+2
66 Dy	3.17+2	2.84+2	2.56+2	2.38+2	2.19+2	2.00+2	1.81+2	1.67+2	1.54+2	1.42+2	3.52+2	3.25+2	3.00+2	3.84+2
67 Ho	3.31+2	2.97+2	2.68+2	2.49+2	2.29+2	2.09+2	1.89+2	1.75+2	1.63+2	1.50+2	1.37+2	3.38+2	3.14+2	2.89+2
68 Er	3.45+2	3.10+2	2.79+2	2.59+2	2.38+2	2.17+2	1.96+2	1.82+2	1.69+2	1.55+2	1.42+2	1.31+2	3.24+2	3.00+2
69 Tm	3.64+2	3.27+2	2.94+2	2.73+2	2.51+2	2.30+2	2.07+2	1.92+2	1.78+2	1.64+2	1.50+2	1.39+2	1.29+2	3.14+2
70 Yb	3.77+2	3.38+2	3.04+2	2.83+2	2.60+2	2.38+2	2.15+2	1.99+2	1.85+2	1.70+2	1.56+2	1.44+2	1.34+2	1.24+2
71 Lu	3.94+2	3.53+2	3.17+2	2.95+2	2.71+2	2.48+2	2.24+2	2.07+2	1.92+2	1.77+2	1.62+2	1.50+2	1.39+2	1.29+2
72 Hf	4.09+2	3.67+2	3.29+2	3.06+2	2.81+2	2.57+2	2.32+2	2.15+2	1.99+2	1.84+2	1.68+2	1.55+2	1.45+2	1.34+2
73 Ta	4.24+2	3.80+2	3.41+2	3.16+2	2.91+2	2.65+2	2.39+2	2.21+2	2.05+2	1.89+2	1.72+2	1.59+2	1.48+2	1.37+2
74 W	4.42+2	3.97+2	3.56+2	3.31+2	3.04+2	2.78+2	2.50+2	2.32+2	2.15+2	1.98+2	1.81+2	1.67+2	1.56+2	1.44+2

TABLE 4 (continued)

Mass Attenuation Coefficients for $L\ \alpha$ Lines

Emitter	Sm	Eu	Gd	Ib	Dy	Ho	Er	Tm	Yb	Lu	Hf	Ta	W	Re
Wavelength	2.20+0	2.12+0	2.05+0	1.98+0	1.91+0	1.84+0	1.78+0	1.73+0	1.67+0	1.62+0	1.57+0	1.52+0	1.48+0	1.43+0
Energy (keV)	5.64+0	5.85+0	6.06+0	6.27+0	6.50+0	6.72+0	6.95+0	7.18+0	7.42+0	7.66+0	7.90+0	8.15+0	8.40+0	8.65+0
Absorber														
75 Re	4.62+2	4.14+2	3.72+2	3.45+2	3.18+2	2.90+2	2.62+2	2.42+2	2.25+2	2.07+2	1.89+2	1.75+2	1.63+2	1.51+2
76 Os	4.77+2	4.28+2	3.84+2	3.57+2	3.28+2	3.00+2	2.71+2	2.50+2	2.32+2	2.14+2	1.95+2	1.81+2	1.68+2	1.56+2
77 Ir	4.98+2	4.47+2	4.01+2	3.73+2	3.43+2	3.13+2	2.82+2	2.61+2	2.42+2	2.23+2	2.04+2	1.89+2	1.76+2	1.63+2
78 Pt	5.16+2	4.63+2	4.15+2	3.85+2	3.54+2	3.23+2	2.91+2	2.69+2	2.50+2	2.30+2	2.10+2	1.94+2	1.81+2	1.67+2
79 Au	5.35+2	4.81+2	4.33+2	4.02+2	3.70+2	3.38+2	3.06+2	2.83+2	2.63+2	2.42+2	2.22+2	2.05+2	1.91+2	1.77+2
80 Hg	5.56+2	4.99+2	4.48+2	4.16+2	3.83+2	3.50+2	3.16+2	2.92+2	2.71+2	2.50+2	2.28+2	2.11+2	1.97+2	1.82+2
81 Tl	5.73+2	5.14+2	4.62+2	4.29+2	3.95+2	3.61+2	3.26+2	3.01+2	2.80+2	2.58+2	2.36+2	2.18+2	2.03+2	1.88+2
82 Pb	5.96+2	5.35+2	4.81+2	4.46+2	4.11+2	3.75+2	3.39+2	3.14+2	2.91+2	2.68+2	2.45+2	2.27+2	2.12+2	1.96+2
83 Bi	6.18+2	5.55+2	4.99+2	4.64+2	4.27+2	3.90+2	3.52+2	3.26+2	3.03+2	2.79+2	2.55+2	2.36+2	2.20+2	2.04+2
84 Po	6.44+2	5.78+2	5.20+2	4.83+2	4.44+2	4.06+2	3.66+2	3.39+2	3.15+2	2.90+2	2.65+2	2.45+2	2.29+2	2.12+2
85 At	6.75+2	6.06+2	5.45+2	5.06+2	4.66+2	4.25+2	3.84+2	3.55+2	3.30+2	3.04+2	2.78+2	2.57+2	2.40+2	2.22+2
86 Rn	6.69+2	6.00+2	5.40+2	5.01+2	4.62+2	4.22+2	3.81+2	3.52+2	3.27+2	3.02+2	2.76+2	2.55+2	2.38+2	2.20+2
87 Fr	6.95+2	6.24+2	5.61+2	5.22+2	4.80+2	4.39+2	3.96+2	3.67+2	3.41+2	3.14+2	2.87+2	2.66+2	2.48+2	2.30+2
88 Ra	7.17+2	6.44+2	5.79+2	5.38+2	4.96+2	4.53+2	4.09+2	3.79+2	3.52+2	3.24+2	2.97+2	2.74+2	2.56+2	2.37+2
89 Ac	7.45+2	6.70+2	6.03+2	5.60+2	5.16+2	4.71+2	4.26+2	3.94+2	3.66+2	3.38+2	3.09+2	2.85+2	2.66+2	2.47+2
90 Th	7.54+2	6.81+2	6.16+2	5.72+2	5.27+2	4.81+2	4.35+2	4.03+2	3.74+2	3.45+2	3.15+2	2.92+2	2.72+2	2.52+2
91 Pa	7.83+2	7.12+2	6.47+2	6.01+2	5.53+2	5.05+2	4.57+2	4.23+2	3.92+2	3.62+2	3.31+2	3.06+2	2.85+2	2.65+2
92 U	7.75+2	7.08+2	6.46+2	6.01+2	5.53+2	5.06+2	4.57+2	4.23+2	3.93+2	3.63+2	3.32+2	3.07+2	2.86+2	2.65+2
93 Np	7.51+2	7.51+2	6.88+2	6.39+2	5.88+2	5.37+2	4.85+2	4.49+2	4.17+2	3.84+2	3.51+2	3.24+2	3.03+2	2.80+2
94 Pu	8.23+2	7.39+2	7.48+2	6.93+2	6.37+2	5.80+2	5.23+2	4.83+2	4.47+2	4.11+2	3.75+2	3.44+2	3.18+2	2.91+2

TABLE 4 (continued)

Mass Attenuation Coefficients for $L\ \alpha$ Lines

Emitter	Os	Ir	Pt	Au	Hg	Tl	Pb	Bi	Po	At	Rn	Fr	Ra	Ag
Wavelength	1.39+0	1.35+0	1.31+0	1.28+0	1.24+0	1.21+0	1.17+0	1.14+0	1.11+0	1.08+0	1.06+0	1.03+0	1.00+0	9.80-1
Energy (keV)	8.91+0	9.18+0	9.44+0	9.71+0	9.99+0	1.03+1	1.06+1	1.08+1	1.11+1	1.14+1	1.17+1	1.20+1	1.23+1	1.27+1
Absorber														
1 H	3.88-1	3.87-1	3.87-1	3.86-1	3.85-1	3.85-1	3.84-1	3.83-1	3.83-1	3.82-1	3.82-1	3.81-1	3.81-1	3.80-1
2 He	2.73-1	2.67-1	2.62-1	2.57-1	2.52-1	2.49-1	2.45-1	2.42-1	2.39-1	2.35-1	2.32-1	2.29-1	2.27-1	2.25-1
3 Li	4.08-1	3.88-1	3.72-1	3.55-1	3.38-1	3.28-1	3.18-1	3.08-1	2.97-1	2.87-1	2.76-1	2.66-1	2.61-1	2.56-1
4 Be	8.54-1	7.96-1	7.47-1	6.98-1	6.48-1	6.19-1	5.90-1	5.61-1	5.31-1	5.01-1	4.71-1	4.42-1	4.28-1	4.14-1
5 B	1.70+0	1.57+0	1.46+0	1.35+0	1.24+0	1.17+0	1.11+0	1.04+0	9.75-1	9.08-1	8.40-1	7.75-1	7.44-1	7.13-1
6 C	3.27+0	3.01+0	2.78+0	2.56+0	2.33+0	2.20+0	2.07+0	1.94+0	1.80+0	1.67+0	1.53+0	1.40+0	1.33+0	1.27+0
7 N	5.45+0	5.00+0	4.63+0	4.25+0	3.86+0	3.63+0	3.41+0	3.18+0	2.95+0	2.72+0	2.48+0	2.26+0	2.15+0	2.04+0
8 O	8.44+0	7.75+0	7.16+0	6.57+0	5.96+0	5.60+0	5.25+0	4.90+0	4.54+0	4.17+0	3.80+0	3.45+0	3.28+0	3.11+0
9 F	1.15+1	1.06+1	9.78+0	8.97+0	8.14+0	7.65+0	7.18+0	6.69+0	6.19+0	5.69+0	5.19+0	4.70+0	4.47+0	4.23+0
10 Ne	1.68+1	1.55+1	1.43+1	1.31+1	1.19+1	1.12+1	1.05+1	9.79+0	9.06+0	8.33+0	7.58+0	6.87+0	6.53+0	6.19+0
11 Na	2.17+1	1.99+1	1.84+1	1.69+1	1.54+1	1.45+1	1.36+1	1.26+1	1.17+1	1.08+1	9.80+0	8.88+0	8.44+0	7.99+0
12 Mg	2.91+1	2.68+1	2.48+1	2.27+1	2.07+1	1.94+1	1.82+1	1.70+1	1.57+1	1.45+1	1.32+1	1.19+1	1.13+1	1.07+1
13 Al	3.70+1	3.40+1	3.15+1	2.89+1	2.63+1	2.47+1	2.32+1	2.16+1	2.00+1	1.84+1	1.63+1	1.52+1	1.45+1	1.37+1
14 Si	4.63+1	4.26+1	3.94+1	3.62+1	3.29+1	3.10+1	2.90+1	2.71+1	2.51+1	2.31+1	2.10+1	1.91+1	1.81+1	1.72+1
15 P	5.56+1	5.12+1	4.74+1	4.36+1	3.97+1	3.73+1	3.50+1	3.27+1	3.03+1	2.79+1	2.54+1	2.31+1	2.20+1	2.08+1
16 S	6.88+1	6.34+1	5.88+1	5.40+1	4.92+1	4.63+1	4.35+1	4.06+1	3.76+1	3.46+1	3.16+1	2.87+1	2.73+1	2.59+1
17 Cl	7.87+1	7.25+1	6.72+1	6.19+1	5.64+1	5.31+1	4.98+1	4.65+1	4.32+1	3.98+1	3.63+1	3.30+1	3.14+1	2.97+1
18 Ar	8.81+1	8.12+1	7.53+1	6.93+1	6.32+1	5.95+1	5.58+1	5.21+1	4.84+1	4.46+1	4.07+1	3.70+1	3.52+1	3.33+1
19 K	1.09+2	1.00+2	9.31+1	8.58+1	7.83+1	7.37+1	6.92+1	6.47+1	6.01+1	5.54+1	5.06+1	4.61+1	4.38+1	4.15+1
20 Ca	1.29+2	1.19+2	1.10+2	1.02+2	9.30+1	8.76+1	8.23+1	7.69+1	7.14+1	6.59+1	6.03+1	5.49+1	5.22+1	4.95+1
21 Sc	1.38+2	1.28+2	1.19+2	1.09+2	9.99+1	9.41+1	8.84+1	8.27+1	7.68+1	7.09+1	6.49+1	5.91+1	5.63+1	5.33+1
22 Ti	1.55+2	1.43+2	1.33+2	1.23+2	1.12+2	1.06+2	9.97+1	9.33+1	8.67+1	8.01+1	7.34+1	6.70+1	6.38+1	6.05+1
23 V	1.70+2	1.58+2	1.46+2	1.35+2	1.24+2	1.17+2	1.10+2	1.03+2	9.54+1	8.81+1	8.08+1	7.37+1	7.01+1	6.65+1
24 Cr	1.98+2	1.83+2	1.70+2	1.57+2	1.44+2	1.36+2	1.27+2	1.19+2	1.11+2	1.03+2	9.40+1	8.58+1	8.16+1	7.74+1
25 Mn	2.14+2	1.98+2	1.84+2	1.70+2	1.55+2	1.47+2	1.38+2	1.29+2	1.20+2	1.11+2	1.02+2	9.30+1	8.86+1	8.40+1
26 Fe	2.41+2	2.23+2	2.08+2	1.92+2	1.76+2	1.66+2	1.57+2	1.47+2	1.37+2	1.26+2	1.16+2	1.06+2	1.01+2	9.59+1
27 Co	2.68+2	2.48+2	2.31+2	2.14+2	1.96+2	1.85+2	1.74+2	1.63+2	1.51+2	1.40+2	1.28+2	1.17+2	1.12+2	1.06+2
28 Ni	2.89+2	2.69+2	2.50+2	2.32+2	2.13+2	2.02+2	1.90+2	1.78+2	1.66+2	1.54+2	1.42+2	1.30+2	1.24+2	1.18+2
29 Cu	4.17+1	2.83+2	2.64+2	2.45+2	2.25+2	2.12+2	2.00+2	1.88+2	1.75+2	1.62+2	1.50+2	1.37+2	1.31+2	1.24+2
30 Zn	4.69+1	4.34+1	4.03+1	2.71+2	2.52+2	2.38+2	2.24+2	2.10+2	1.96+2	1.82+2	1.67+2	1.53+2	1.46+2	1.39+2
31 Ga	4.95+1	4.59+1	4.28+1	3.97+1	3.65+1	3.39+1	2.26+2	2.13+2	1.99+2	1.86+2	1.72+2	1.58+2	1.51+2	1.43+2
32 Ge	5.30+1	4.91+1	4.58+1	4.24+1	3.90+1	3.65+1	3.41+1	3.17+1	2.03+2	1.91+2	1.78+2	1.66+2	1.58+2	1.50+2
33 As	5.88+1	5.45+1	5.08+1	4.71+1	4.33+1	4.03+1	3.74+1	3.53+1	3.30+1	3.08+1	2.85+1	1.84+2	1.75+2	1.67+2
34 Se	6.30+1	5.84+1	5.45+1	5.04+1	4.63+1	4.38+1	4.13+1	3.88+1	3.62+1	3.36+1	3.10+1	2.84+1	2.66+1	2.49+1
35 Br	6.94+1	6.43+1	6.00+1	5.55+1	5.10+1	4.82+1	4.54+1	4.27+1	3.98+1	3.69+1	3.40+1	3.12+1	2.95+1	2.77+1
36 Kr	7.44+1	6.89+1	6.43+1	5.95+1	5.47+1	5.17+1	4.88+1	4.58+1	4.27+1	3.97+1	3.65+1	3.35+1	3.14+1	2.93+1
37 Rb	8.00+1	7.41+1	6.90+1	6.39+1	5.86+1	5.54+1	5.22+1	4.90+1	4.57+1	4.24+1	3.90+1	3.57+1	3.41+1	3.24+1

TABLE 4 (continued)

Mass Attenuation Coefficients for $L\alpha$ Lines

Emitter	Os	Ir	Pt	Au	Hg	Tl	Pb	Bi	Po	At	Rn	Fr	Ra	Ac
Wavelength	1.39+0	1.35+0	1.31+0	1.28+0	1.24+0	1.21+0	1.17+0	1.14+0	1.11+0	1.08+0	1.06+0	1.03+0	1.00+0	9.80-1
Energy (keV)	8.91+0	9.18+0	9.44+0	9.71+0	9.99+0	1.03+1	1.06+1	1.08+1	1.11+1	1.14+1	1.17+1	1.20+1	1.23+1	1.27+1
Absorber														
38 Sr	8.68+1	8.04+1	7.48+1	6.92+1	6.35+1	6.00+1	5.66+1	5.31+1	4.95+1	4.59+1	4.22+1	3.87+1	3.69+1	3.51+1
39 Y	9.48+1	8.78+1	8.18+1	7.57+1	6.94+1	6.56+1	6.18+1	5.80+1	5.41+1	5.01+1	4.61+1	4.23+1	4.03+1	3.83+1
40 Zr	1.02+2	9.41+1	8.76+1	8.10+1	7.43+1	7.02+1	6.61+1	6.20+1	5.78+1	5.35+1	4.92+1	4.51+1	4.30+1	4.09+1
41 Nb	1.11+2	1.03+2	9.56+1	8.84+1	8.11+1	7.66+1	7.21+1	6.76+1	6.31+1	5.84+1	5.37+1	4.92+1	4.69+1	4.46+1
42 Mo	1.17+2	1.08+2	1.01+2	9.32+1	8.54+1	8.07+1	7.60+1	7.12+1	6.64+1	6.15+1	5.65+1	5.17+1	4.93+1	4.69+1
43 Tc	1.25+2	1.16+2	1.08+2	9.98+1	9.15+1	8.64+1	8.14+1	7.64+1	7.12+1	6.60+1	6.06+1	5.56+1	5.30+1	5.04+1
44 Ru	1.35+2	1.25+2	1.16+2	1.07+2	9.83+1	9.29+1	8.75+1	8.20+1	7.65+1	7.08+1	6.51+1	5.97+1	5.69+1	5.41+1
45 Rh	1.44+2	1.33+2	1.24+2	1.15+2	1.05+2	9.96+1	9.39+1	8.80+1	8.21+1	7.61+1	7.00+1	6.41+1	6.12+1	5.82+1
46 Pd	1.53+2	1.41+2	1.31+2	1.21+2	1.11+2	1.05+2	9.90+1	9.27+1	8.64+1	8.00+1	7.35+1	6.73+1	6.42+1	6.10+1
47 Ag	1.64+2	1.52+2	1.41+2	1.31+2	1.20+2	1.13+2	1.06+2	9.98+1	9.30+1	8.61+1	7.92+1	7.25+1	6.91+1	6.57+1
48 Cd	1.71+2	1.58+2	1.47+2	1.36+2	1.24+2	1.17+2	1.11+2	1.04+2	9.66+1	8.94+1	8.22+1	7.52+1	7.17+1	6.81+1
49 In	1.82+2	1.69+2	1.57+2	1.45+2	1.33+2	1.26+2	1.18+2	1.11+2	1.03+2	9.57+1	8.80+1	8.06+1	7.68+1	7.30+1
50 Sn	1.92+2	1.78+2	1.66+2	1.53+2	1.40+2	1.32+2	1.25+2	1.17+2	1.09+2	1.01+2	9.25+1	8.46+1	8.07+1	7.67+1
51 Sb	2.02+2	1.87+2	1.74+2	1.61+2	1.48+2	1.39+2	1.31+2	1.23+2	1.15+2	1.07+2	9.81+1	8.99+1	8.57+1	8.15+1
52 Te	2.09+2	1.94+2	1.81+2	1.67+2	1.53+2	1.45+2	1.37+2	1.28+2	1.19+2	1.11+2	1.02+2	9.34+1	8.91+1	8.47+1
53 I	2.26+2	2.10+2	1.95+2	1.80+2	1.65+2	1.56+2	1.47+2	1.38+2	1.29+2	1.19+2	1.10+2	1.01+2	9.58+1	9.11+1
54 Xe	2.31+2	2.14+2	2.00+2	1.85+2	1.69+2	1.60+2	1.51+2	1.41+2	1.32+2	1.22+2	1.12+2	1.03+2	9.83+1	9.35+1
55 Cs	2.50+2	2.32+2	2.16+2	2.00+2	1.83+2	1.73+2	1.63+2	1.53+2	1.42+2	1.32+2	1.21+2	1.11+2	1.06+2	1.01+2
56 Ba	2.60+2	2.41+2	2.25+2	2.08+2	1.90+2	1.80+2	1.69+2	1.59+2	1.48+2	1.37+2	1.26+2	1.16+2	1.10+2	1.05+2
57 La	2.77+2	2.56+2	2.38+2	2.20+2	2.02+2	1.91+2	1.80+2	1.68+2	1.57+2	1.45+2	1.33+2	1.22+2	1.16+2	1.11+2
58 Ce	2.95+2	2.73+2	2.54+2	2.35+2	2.15+2	2.03+2	1.92+2	1.80+2	1.67+2	1.55+2	1.43+2	1.31+2	1.25+2	1.18+2
59 Pr	3.12+2	2.89+2	2.69+2	2.49+2	2.28+2	2.16+2	2.03+2	1.90+2	1.77+2	1.64+2	1.51+2	1.38+2	1.32+2	1.25+2
60 Nd	3.28+2	3.04+2	2.83+2	2.61+2	2.40+2	2.26+2	2.13+2	2.00+2	1.86+2	1.72+2	1.58+2	1.45+2	1.38+2	1.31+2
61 Pm	3.43+2	3.18+2	2.96+2	2.74+2	2.51+2	2.37+2	2.23+2	2.09+2	1.95+2	1.81+2	1.66+2	1.52+2	1.45+2	1.38+2
62 Sm	3.60+2	3.33+2	3.10+2	2.87+2	2.63+2	2.48+2	2.34+2	2.19+2	2.04+2	1.89+2	1.74+2	1.59+2	1.52+2	1.44+2
63 Eu	3.79+2	3.51+2	3.26+2	3.02+2	2.76+2	2.61+2	2.46+2	2.30+2	2.15+2	1.99+2	1.83+2	1.67+2	1.60+2	1.52+2
64 Gd	3.89+2	3.61+2	3.36+2	3.10+2	2.84+2	2.69+2	2.53+2	2.37+2	2.21+2	2.05+2	1.88+2	1.72+2	1.64+2	1.56+2
65 Tb	4.09+2	3.81+2	3.54+2	3.27+2	3.00+2	2.83+2	2.67+2	2.50+2	2.33+2	2.16+2	1.98+2	1.81+2	1.73+2	1.64+2
66 Dy	3.55+2	3.94+2	3.67+2	3.39+2	3.11+2	2.94+2	2.77+2	2.59+2	2.42+2	2.24+2	2.06+2	1.88+2	1.79+2	1.71+2
67 Ho	2.64+2	3.41+2	3.78+2	3.51+2	3.24+2	3.06+2	2.88+2	2.70+2	2.52+2	2.33+2	2.14+2	1.96+2	1.87+2	1.78+2
68 Er	2.76+2	2.55+2	3.29+2	3.04+2	3.37+2	3.19+2	3.00+2	2.81+2	2.62+2	2.43+2	2.23+2	2.04+2	1.95+2	1.85+2
69 Tm	2.91+2	2.69+2	2.49+2	3.21+2	2.97+2	3.33+2	3.14+2	2.95+2	2.75+2	2.55+2	2.35+2	2.15+2	2.05+2	1.95+2
70 Yb	1.14+2	2.80+2	2.61+2	2.41+2	3.08+2	2.86+2	3.19+2	3.00+2	2.81+2	2.62+2	2.42+2	2.23+2	2.13+2	2.02+2
71 Lu	1.19+2	1.10+2	2.70+2	2.51+2	2.31+2	2.15+2	2.78+2	2.58+2	2.90+2	2.71+2	2.52+2	2.33+2	2.22+2	2.11+2
72 Hf	1.23+2	1.14+2	1.06+2	2.61+2	2.41+2	2.25+2	2.09+2	2.69+2	2.51+2	2.80+2	2.61+2	2.43+2	2.32+2	2.20+2
73 Ta	1.26+2	1.17+2	1.09+2	1.01+2	2.39+2	2.24+2	2.09+2	1.94+2	1.79+2	2.32+2	2.59+2	2.42+2	2.31+2	2.20+2
74 W	1.33+2	1.23+2	1.15+2	1.07+2	9.88+1	2.44+2	2.29+2	2.14+2	1.98+2	1.83+2	2.36+2	2.20+2	2.50+2	2.37+2

TABLE 4 (continued)

Mass Attenuation Coefficients for $L\ \alpha$ Lines

Emitter		Os	Ir	Pt	Au	Hg	Tl	Pb	Bi	Po	At	Rn	Fr	Ra	Ac
Wavelength		1.39+0	1.35+0	1.31+0	1.28+0	1.24+0	1.21+0	1.17+0	1.14+0	1.11+0	1.08+0	1.06+0	1.03+0	1.00+0	9.80-1
Energy (keV)		8.91+0	9.18+0	9.44+0	9.71+0	9.99+0	1.03+1	1.06+1	1.08+1	1.11+1	1.14+1	1.17+1	1.20+1	1.23+1	1.27+1
Absorber															
75	Re	1.39+2	1.29+2	1.21+2	1.12+2	1.03+2	9.68+1	2.31+2	2.18+2	2.04+2	1.90+2	1.76+2	2.26+2	2.11+2	2.38+2
76	Os	1.43+2	1.33+2	1.25+2	1.16+2	1.07+2	1.00+2	9.37+1	8.70+1	2.07+2	1.94+2	1.80+2	1.67+2	1.56+2	2.03+2
77	Ir	1.50+2	1.39+2	1.30+2	1.21+2	1.12+2	1.05+2	9.86+1	9.20+1	8.52+1	2.00+2	1.87+2	1.74+2	1.63+2	1.52+2
78	Pt	1.53+2	1.43+2	1.33+2	1.24+2	1.14+2	1.08+2	1.01+2	9.48+1	8.83+1	8.16+1	1.93+2	1.80+2	1.70+2	1.59+2
79	Au	1.63+2	1.52+2	1.42+2	1.32+2	1.22+2	1.16+2	1.09+2	1.03+2	9.63+1	8.96+1	8.29+1	1.82+2	1.72+2	1.62+2
80	Hg	1.68+2	1.56+2	1.46+2	1.36+2	1.25+2	1.19+2	1.12+2	1.05+2	9.88+1	9.20+1	8.51+1	7.83+1	1.79+2	1.70+2
81	Tl	1.73+2	1.61+2	1.51+2	1.40+2	1.29+2	1.22+2	1.16+2	1.09+2	1.02+2	9.49+1	8.78+1	8.09+1	7.61+1	7.13+1
82	Pb	1.80+2	1.68+2	1.57+2	1.46+2	1.35+2	1.28+2	1.21+2	1.14+2	1.06+2	9.91+1	9.17+1	8.45+1	7.97+1	7.49+1
83	Bi	1.87+2	1.74+2	1.63+2	1.51+2	1.40+2	1.32+2	1.25+2	1.18+2	1.10+2	1.03+2	9.52+1	8.77+1	8.30+1	7.83+1
84	Po	1.95+2	1.81+2	1.70+2	1.58+2	1.46+2	1.38+2	1.30+2	1.23+2	1.15+2	1.07+2	9.91+1	9.13+1	8.67+1	8.20+1
85	At	2.04+2	1.90+2	1.78+2	1.65+2	1.53+2	1.45+2	1.37+2	1.29+2	1.20+2	1.12+2	1.04+2	9.57+1	9.11+1	8.65+1
86	Rn	2.03+2	1.89+2	1.76+2	1.64+2	1.51+2	1.43+2	1.35+2	1.27+2	1.19+2	1.11+2	1.03+2	9.49+1	9.05+1	8.61+1
87	Fr	2.12+2	1.97+2	1.84+2	1.71+2	1.58+2	1.50+2	1.42+2	1.33+2	1.25+2	1.16+2	1.08+2	9.94+1	9.51+1	9.06+1
88	Ra	2.18+2	2.03+2	1.90+2	1.77+2	1.63+2	1.55+2	1.46+2	1.38+2	1.29+2	1.20+2	1.11+2	1.03+2	9.81+1	9.35+1
89	Ac	2.27+2	2.12+2	1.98+2	1.84+2	1.70+2	1.61+2	1.52+2	1.43+2	1.34+2	1.25+2	1.16+2	1.07+2	1.02+2	9.74+1
90	Th	2.32+2	2.16+2	2.02+2	1.88+2	1.73+2	1.64+2	1.55+2	1.46+2	1.37+2	1.28+2	1.18+2	1.09+2	1.04+2	9.94+1
91	Pa	2.43+2	2.27+2	2.12+2	1.97+2	1.82+2	1.72+2	1.63+2	1.53+2	1.44+2	1.34+2	1.24+2	1.14+2	1.09+2	1.04+2
92	U	2.44+2	2.27+2	2.13+2	1.98+2	1.83+2	1.73+2	1.64+2	1.54+2	1.44+2	1.35+2	1.25+2	1.15+2	1.10+2	1.05+2
93	Np	2.58+2	2.40+2	2.24+2	2.08+2	1.92+2	1.82+2	1.72+2	1.62+2	1.52+2	1.41+2	1.31+2	1.21+2	1.15+2	1.10+2
94	Pu	2.64+2	2.45+2	2.29+2	2.13+2	1.96+2	1.86+2	1.76+2	1.65+2	1.55+2	1.44+2	1.33+2	1.23+2	1.17+2	1.12+2

TABLE 4 (continued)

Mass Attenuation Coefficients for $L\ \alpha$ Lines

Emitter		Th	Pa	U
Wavelength		9.56-1	9.33-1	9.11-1
Energy (keV)		1.30+1	1.33+1	1.36+1
Absorber				
1	H	3.80-1	3.79-1	3.79-1
2	He	2.23-1	2.21-1	2.19-1
3	Li	2.51-1	2.46-1	2.41-1
4	Be	4.00-1	3.85-1	3.71-1
5	B	6.81-1	6.49-1	6.17-1
6	C	1.21+0	1.14+0	1.08+0
7	N	1.93+0	1.82+0	1.71+0
8	O	2.94+0	2.76+0	2.59+0
9	F	4.00+0	3.76+0	3.51+0
10	Ne	5.84+0	5.48+0	5.13+0
11	Na	7.54+0	7.08+0	6.62+0
12	Mg	1.01+1	9.52+0	8.89+0
13	Al	1.29+1	1.21+1	1.13+1
14	Si	1.62+1	1.52+1	1.42+1
15	P	1.96+1	1.84+1	1.72+1
16	S	2.44+1	2.29+1	2.14+1
17	Cl	2.81+1	2.64+1	2.47+1
18	Ar	3.15+1	2.95+1	2.76+1
19	K	3.92+1	3.69+1	3.45+1
20	Ca	4.67+1	4.39+1	4.11+1
21	Sc	5.04+1	4.74+1	4.44+1
22	Ti	5.72+1	5.38+1	5.04+1
23	V	6.29+1	5.92+1	5.54+1
24	Cr	7.32+1	6.89+1	6.45+1
25	Mn	7.94+1	7.48+1	7.01+1
26	Fe	9.07+1	8.54+1	8.01+1
27	Co	1.00+2	9.43+1	8.84+1
28	Ni	1.11+2	1.05+2	9.86+1
29	Cu	1.17+2	1.11+2	1.04+2
30	Zn	1.31+2	1.24+2	1.16+2
31	Ga	1.36+2	1.28+2	1.20+2
32	Ge	1.42+2	1.34+2	1.26+2
33	As	1.58+2	1.49+2	1.40+2
34	Se	1.62+2	1.53+2	1.45+2
35	Br	2.59+1	2.42+1	1.53+2
36	Kr	2.78+1	2.62+1	2.46+1
37	Rb	3.07+1	2.90+1	2.73+1
38	Sr	3.33+1	3.14+1	2.96+1
39	Y	3.63+1	3.43+1	3.23+1
40	Zr	3.87+1	3.66+1	3.44+1
41	Nb	4.23+1	3.99+1	3.75+1
42	Mo	4.44+1	4.19+1	3.94+1
43	Tc	4.77+1	4.50+1	4.23+1
44	Ru	5.12+1	4.84+1	4.54+1
45	Rh	5.51+1	5.20+1	4.89+1
46	Pd	5.78+1	5.45+1	5.12+1
47	Ag	6.23+1	5.87+1	5.52+1
48	Cd	6.45+1	6.08+1	5.72+1
49	In	6.91+1	6.52+1	6.13+1
50	Sn	7.26+1	6.85+1	6.43+1
51	Sb	7.73+1	7.29+1	6.86+1
52	Te	8.03+1	7.57+1	7.12+1
53	I	8.63+1	8.14+1	7.65+1
54	Xe	8.86+1	8.36+1	7.86+1
55	Cs	9.55+1	9.01+1	8.47+1
56	Ba	9.93+1	9.37+1	8.81+1
57	La	1.05+2	9.89+1	9.29+1
58	Ce	1.12+2	1.06+2	9.94+1
59	Pr	1.19+2	1.12+2	1.05+2
60	Nd	1.24+2	1.17+2	1.10+2
61	Pm	1.30+2	1.23+2	1.16+2
62	Sm	1.36+2	1.29+2	1.21+2
63	Eu	1.44+2	1.35+2	1.27+2
64	Gd	1.48+2	1.39+2	1.31+2
65	Tb	1.56+2	1.47+2	1.38+2
66	Dy	1.62+2	1.52+2	1.43+2
67	Ho	1.68+2	1.59+2	1.49+2
68	Er	1.75+2	1.65+2	1.55+2
69	Tm	1.85+2	1.74+2	1.64+2
70	Yb	1.91+2	1.80+2	1.69+2
71	Lu	2.00+2	1.89+2	1.77+2
72	Hf	2.08+2	1.97+2	1.85+2
73	Ta	2.08+2	1.96+2	1.84+2
74	W	2.25+2	2.12+2	1.99+2
75	Re	2.26+2	2.13+2	2.01+2
76	Os	1.90+2	2.15+2	2.04+2
77	Ir	1.98+2	1.85+2	2.08+2
78	Pt	1.48+2	1.91+2	1.80+2
79	Au	1.52+2	1.42+2	1.32+2
80	Hg	1.60+2	1.51+2	1.41+2
81	Tl	1.63+2	1.54+2	1.45+2
82	Pb	7.01+1	1.64+2	1.55+2
83	Bi	7.35+1	6.86+1	1.50+2
84	Po	7.73+1	7.24+1	6.76+1
85	At	8.17+1	7.69+1	7.20+1
86	Rn	8.16+1	7.71+1	7.25+1
87	Fr	8.62+1	8.16+1	7.70+1
88	Ra	8.89+1	8.42+1	7.95+1
89	Ac	9.26+1	8.77+1	8.27+1
90	Th	9.45+1	8.95+1	8.44+1
91	Pa	9.89+1	9.37+1	8.84+1
92	U	9.97+1	9.44+1	8.91+1
93	Np	1.04+2	9.89+1	9.33+1
94	Pu	1.06+2	1.01+2	9.49+1

TABLE 4 (continued)

Mass Attenuation Coefficients for $L\ \beta_1$ Lines

Emitter	Ca	Sc	Ti	V	Cr	Mn	Fe	Co	Ni	Cu	Zn	Ga	Ge	As
Wavelength	3.59+1	3.10+1	2.70+1	2.39+1	2.13+1	1.91+1	1.73+1	1.57+1	1.43+1	1.31+1	1.20+1	1.10+1	1.02+1	9.41+0
Energy (keV)	3.45-1	4.00-1	4.58-1	5.19-1	5.83-1	6.49-1	7.18-1	7.91-1	8.69-1	9.50-1	1.03+0	1.12+0	1.22+0	1.32+0
Absorber														
1 H	2.32+2	1.40+2	9.17+1	6.07+1	4.12+1	2.98+1	2.14+1	1.51+1	1.15+1	8.42+0	6.41+0	5.16+0	3.99+0	3.34+0
2 He	1.99+3	1.14+3	8.04+2	5.22+2	3.62+2	2.58+2	1.82+2	1.32+2	9.78+1	7.33+1	5.67+1	4.47+1	3.36+1	2.77+1
3 Li	5.63+3	3.37+3	2.43+3	1.64+3	1.18+3	8.64+2	6.28+2	4.68+2	3.57+2	2.72+2	2.12+2	1.69+2	1.28+2	1.06+2
4 Be	1.25+4	7.78+3	5.67+3	3.88+3	2.82+3	2.11+3	1.56+3	1.16+3	8.93+2	6.93+2	5.52+2	4.46+2	3.47+2	2.89+2
5 B	2.22+4	1.43+4	1.06+4	7.39+3	5.44+3	4.10+3	3.05+3	2.32+3	1.81+3	1.40+3	1.12+3	9.10+2	7.15+2	5.97+2
6 C	3.34+4	2.30+4	1.74+4	1.25+4	9.30+3	7.08+3	5.33+3	4.09+3	3.21+3	2.51+3	2.01+3	1.64+3	1.29+3	1.08+3
7 N	2.65+3	1.71+3	2.36+4	1.77+4	1.34+4	1.03+4	7.87+3	6.11+3	4.82+3	3.80+3	3.06+3	2.52+3	2.02+3	1.70+3
8 O	3.87+3	2.50+3	1.87+3	1.31+3	1.68+4	1.35+4	1.04+4	8.20+3	6.53+3	5.20+3	4.22+3	3.51+3	2.82+3	2.39+3
9 F	5.44+3	3.47+3	2.59+3	1.83+3	1.36+3	1.03+3	1.20+4	9.98+3	8.03+3	6.44+3	5.29+3	4.45+3	3.64+3	3.08+3
10 Ne	8.34+3	5.30+3	3.94+3	2.77+3	2.06+3	1.57+3	1.18+3	9.09+2	9.18+3	8.64+3	7.19+3	5.97+3	4.81+3	4.09+3
11 Na	1.04+4	6.78+3	5.07+3	3.60+3	2.70+3	2.05+3	1.55+3	1.21+3	9.48+2	7.47+2	6.00+2	7.36+3	5.96+3	5.07+3
12 Mg	1.43+4	9.36+3	7.02+3	5.00+3	3.76+3	2.87+3	2.17+3	1.70+3	1.33+3	1.05+3	8.47+2	6.95+2	5.46+2	5.99+3
13 Al	1.74+4	1.15+4	8.70+3	6.24+3	4.70+3	3.61+3	2.74+3	2.14+3	1.69+3	1.34+3	1.08+3	8.85+2	7.02+2	5.94+2
14 Si	2.22+4	1.48+4	1.12+4	8.11+3	6.12+3	4.72+3	3.60+3	2.80+3	2.22+3	1.77+3	1.43+3	1.18+3	9.45+2	8.01+2
15 P	2.70+4	1.81+4	1.38+4	9.95+3	7.52+3	5.80+3	4.43+3	3.45+3	2.74+3	2.17+3	1.76+3	1.45+3	1.15+3	9.80+2
16 S	3.29+4	2.24+4	1.71+4	1.24+4	9.41+3	7.28+3	5.58+3	4.36+3	3.47+3	2.76+3	2.23+3	1.84+3	1.47+3	1.25+3
17 Cl	3.62+4	2.53+4	1.94+4	1.42+4	1.08+4	8.37+3	6.44+3	5.04+3	4.02+3	3.20+3	2.60+3	2.15+3	1.72+3	1.46+3
18 Ar	3.90+4	2.87+4	2.20+4	1.62+4	1.23+4	9.58+3	7.36+3	5.77+3	4.60+3	3.66+3	2.97+3	2.45+3	1.96+3	1.66+3
19 K	4.02+4	3.42+4	2.66+4	1.98+4	1.52+4	1.19+4	9.19+3	7.22+3	5.77+3	4.61+3	3.75+3	3.11+3	2.50+3	2.12+3
20 Ca	4.57+3	3.38+4	2.93+4	2.26+4	1.75+4	1.38+4	1.07+4	8.47+3	6.77+3	5.44+3	4.44+3	3.65+3	2.91+3	2.48+3
21 Sc	5.24+3	3.78+3	2.71+4	2.39+4	1.85+4	1.48+4	1.16+4	9.15+3	7.34+3	5.89+3	4.80+3	3.95+3	3.16+3	2.69+3
22 Ti	5.71+3	4.15+3	2.01+4	2.25+4	2.00+4	1.61+4	1.26+4	1.01+4	8.11+3	6.53+3	5.33+3	4.40+3	3.52+3	3.01+3
23 V	6.24+3	4.55+3	3.49+3	1.60+4	1.89+4	1.73+4	1.37+4	1.10+4	8.89+3	7.18+3	5.88+3	4.86+3	3.90+3	3.33+3
24 Cr	7.40+3	5.33+3	4.21+3	3.20+3	1.89+4	1.77+4	1.58+4	1.27+4	1.03+4	8.34+3	6.83+3	5.65+3	4.53+3	3.87+3
25 Mn	8.05+3	5.84+3	4.62+3	3.53+3	2.76+3	1.14+4	1.47+4	1.35+4	1.10+4	8.94+3	7.36+3	6.10+3	4.93+3	4.22+3
26 Fe	9.35+3	6.76+3	5.34+3	4.08+3	3.18+3	2.54+3	9.71+3	1.33+4	1.24+4	1.01+4	8.32+3	6.91+3	5.59+3	4.79+3
27 Co	1.03+4	7.47+3	5.90+3	4.50+3	3.54+3	2.83+3	2.25+3	1.13+4	1.16+4	1.09+4	8.94+3	7.45+3	6.04+3	5.18+3
28 Ni	1.21+4	8.75+3	6.95+3	5.35+3	4.22+3	3.34+3	2.62+3	2.16+3	7.44+3	1.09+4	1.03+4	8.57+3	6.93+3	5.95+3
29 Cu	1.32+4	9.47+3	7.71+3	6.06+3	4.70+3	3.61+3	2.78+3	2.44+3	1.86+3	9.08+3	9.62+3	8.79+3	7.42+3	6.36+3
30 Zn	1.53+4	1.11+4	8.79+3	6.70+3	5.19+3	4.12+3	3.26+3	2.64+3	2.12+3	1.71+3	4.86+3	8.51+3	8.05+3	6.64+3
31 Ga	1.66+4	1.20+4	9.51+3	7.24+3	5.64+3	4.49+3	3.57+3	2.88+3	2.33+3	1.88+3	1.54+3	3.71+3	7.42+3	7.08+3
32 Ge	1.83+4	1.33+4	1.05+4	8.05+3	6.30+3	5.02+3	3.98+3	3.20+3	2.60+3	2.11+3	1.72+3	1.42+3	1.17+3	6.61+3
33 As	2.02+4	1.48+4	1.17+4	8.97+3	7.05+3	5.62+3	4.45+3	3.58+3	2.92+3	2.37+3	1.97+3	1.70+3	1.41+3	1.11+3
34 Se	2.19+4	1.62+4	1.28+4	9.83+3	7.74+3	6.18+3	4.89+3	3.93+3	3.20+3	2.61+3	2.19+3	1.92+3	1.64+3	1.34+3
35 Br	2.38+4	1.78+4	1.42+4	1.09+4	8.63+3	6.91+3	5.49+3	4.41+3	3.70+3	3.01+3	2.46+3	2.14+3	1.81+3	1.46+3
36 Kr	2.56+4	1.97+4	1.57+4	1.21+4	9.58+3	7.67+3	6.10+3	4.91+3	4.00+3	3.26+3	2.70+3	2.25+3	1.82+3	1.53+3
37 Rb	2.68+4	2.09+4	1.68+4	1.31+4	1.03+4	8.31+3	6.63+3	5.36+3	4.38+3	3.57+3	2.95+3	2.47+3	2.01+3	1.69+3

TABLE 4 (continued)

Mass Attenuation Coefficients for $L\ \beta_1$ Lines

Emitter	Ca	Sc	Ti	V	Cr	Mn	Fe	Co	Ni	Cu	Zn	Ga	Ge	As
Wavelength	3.59+1	3.10+1	2.70+1	2.39+1	2.13+1	1.91+1	1.73+1	1.57+1	1.43+1	1.31+1	1.20+1	1.10+1	1.02+1	9.41+0
Energy (keV)	3.45-1	4.00-1	4.58-1	5.19-1	5.83-1	6.49-1	7.18-1	7.91-1	8.69-1	9.50-1	1.03+0	1.12+0	1.22+0	1.32+0
Absorber														
38 Sr	2.64+4	2.22+4	1.79+4	1.40+4	1.12+4	9.00+3	7.20+3	5.83+3	4.78+3	3.91+3	3.23+3	2.70+3	2.20+3	1.86+3
39 Y	2.83+4	2.41+4	1.95+4	1.54+4	1.23+4	9.93+3	7.96+3	6.45+3	5.29+3	4.33+3	3.59+3	3.00+3	2.44+3	2.11+3
40 Zr	2.87+4	2.40+4	2.06+4	1.64+4	1.32+4	1.07+4	8.59+3	6.97+3	5.72+3	4.70+3	3.90+3	3.26+3	2.66+3	2.29+3
41 Nb	2.66+4	2.62+4	2.11+4	1.81+4	1.46+4	1.18+4	9.51+3	7.73+3	6.34+3	5.20+3	4.32+3	3.61+3	2.95+3	2.54+3
42 Mo	2.63+4	2.58+4	2.17+4	1.89+4	1.53+4	1.24+4	1.00+4	8.19+3	6.73+3	5.53+3	4.60+3	3.85+3	3.15+3	2.71+3
43 Tc	2.50+4	2.26+4	2.14+4	1.82+4	1.57+4	1.29+4	1.05+4	8.58+3	7.08+3	5.83+3	4.94+3	4.38+3	3.79+3	3.18+3
44 Ru	2.54+4	2.43+4	1.99+4	1.99+4	1.61+4	1.41+4	1.15+4	9.39+3	7.75+3	6.39+3	5.42+3	4.80+3	4.16+3	3.48+3
45 Rh	2.01+4	2.52+4	2.12+4	1.96+4	1.70+4	1.50+4	1.23+4	1.01+4	8.35+3	6.89+3	5.85+3	5.18+3	4.49+3	3.76+3
46 Pd	5.15+3	2.50+4	2.19+4	1.84+4	1.80+4	1.51+4	1.32+4	1.08+4	8.95+3	7.40+3	6.28+3	5.56+3	4.82+3	4.04+3
47 Ag	4.47+3	1.29+4	1.74+4	1.94+4	1.75+4	1.59+4	1.38+4	1.15+4	9.52+3	7.88+3	6.71+3	5.95+3	5.16+3	4.33+3
48 Cd	4.81+3	4.00+3	1.40+4	2.05+4	1.65+4	1.52+4	1.36+4	1.19+4	9.92+3	8.24+3	7.13+3	6.60+3	6.05+3	5.47+3
49 In	5.14+3	4.31+3	8.59+3	2.27+4	1.77+4	1.42+4	1.42+4	1.18+4	1.05+4	8.73+3	7.55+3	7.00+3	6.41+3	5.80+3
50 Sn	5.40+3	4.59+3	3.85+3	8.50+3	1.54+4	1.51+4	1.20+4	1.22+4	1.03+4	9.12+3	7.92+3	7.33+3	6.73+3	6.09+3
51 Sb	5.65+3	4.84+3	4.11+3	3.42+3	1.53+4	1.64+4	1.28+4	1.25+4	1.08+4	9.47+3	8.31+3	7.70+3	7.06+3	6.39+3
52 Te	5.79+3	4.99+3	4.27+3	3.58+3	1.00+4	2.19+4	1.32+4	1.08+4	1.09+4	9.24+3	8.39+3	7.78+3	7.14+3	6.47+3
53 I	6.23+3	5.41+3	4.65+3	3.94+3	3.33+3	7.21+3	1.47+4	1.17+4	9.65+3	1.01+4	8.34+3	7.78+3	7.16+3	6.51+3
54 Xe	6.59+3	5.78+3	4.98+3	4.23+3	3.58+3	3.03+3	2.01+4	1.25+4	1.03+4	8.38+3	8.82+3	7.38+3	6.97+3	6.36+3
55 Cs	6.81+3	6.02+3	5.23+3	4.46+3	3.80+3	3.24+3	2.72+3	1.39+4	1.09+4	8.92+3	9.91+3	8.23+3	6.88+3	6.30+3
56 Ba	6.86+3	6.11+3	5.33+3	4.58+3	3.91+3	3.35+3	2.83+3	6.62+3	1.11+4	9.22+3	7.61+3	7.88+3	6.78+3	6.16+3
57 La	6.93+3	6.23+3	5.46+3	4.72+3	4.05+3	3.48+3	2.97+3	2.53+3	6.76+3	9.50+3	7.98+3	6.62+3	6.91+3	5.94+3
58 Ce	7.95+3	7.02+3	6.11+3	5.23+3	4.47+3	3.82+3	3.24+3	2.75+3	2.35+3	1.07+4	8.91+3	7.49+3	7.46+3	6.50+3
59 Pr	8.56+3	7.46+3	6.47+3	5.52+3	4.71+3	4.03+3	3.42+3	2.91+3	2.48+3	8.86+3	9.59+3	8.16+3	6.66+3	6.78+3
60 Nd	8.97+3	7.76+3	6.71+3	5.72+3	4.87+3	4.17+3	3.53+3	3.00+3	2.57+3	2.18+3	8.36+3	7.46+3	6.54+3	5.56+3
61 Pm	9.59+3	8.22+3	7.08+3	6.00+3	5.10+3	4.35+3	3.69+3	3.13+3	2.68+3	2.28+3	1.94+3	5.01+3	7.02+3	5.85+3
62 Sm	9.38+3	8.76+3	7.52+3	6.35+3	5.38+3	4.58+3	3.87+3	3.29+3	2.81+3	2.39+3	2.03+3	3.89+3	7.40+3	6.16+3
63 Eu	9.93+3	9.21+3	7.91+3	6.68+3	5.65+3	4.82+3	4.07+3	3.45+3	2.95+3	2.51+3	2.15+3	1.82+3	7.80+3	6.51+3
64 Gd	9.93+3	9.18+3	7.90+3	6.69+3	5.68+3	4.85+3	4.11+3	3.49+3	2.99+3	2.55+3	2.19+3	1.89+3	2.92+3	6.56+3
65 Tb	1.15+4	1.05+4	8.93+3	7.49+3	6.32+3	5.36+3	4.51+3	3.81+3	3.25+3	2.76+3	2.36+3	2.03+3	1.70+3	7.10+3
66 Dy	1.24+4	1.04+4	9.46+3	7.94+3	6.69+3	5.66+3	4.75+3	4.01+3	3.41+3	2.90+3	2.49+3	2.18+3	1.85+3	2.10+3
67 Ho	1.31+4	1.10+4	9.99+3	8.41+3	7.07+3	5.98+3	5.02+3	4.23+3	3.60+3	3.05+3	2.63+3	2.32+3	1.99+3	1.65+3
68 Er	1.39+4	1.18+4	1.06+4	8.98+3	7.56+3	6.39+3	5.35+3	4.51+3	3.82+3	3.24+3	2.80+3	2.47+3	2.14+3	1.79+3
69 Tm	1.32+4	1.26+4	1.07+4	9.62+3	8.10+3	6.84+3	5.73+3	4.82+3	4.09+3	3.46+3	2.98+3	2.64+3	2.28+3	1.90+3
70 Yb	1.39+4	1.32+4	1.13+4	1.01+4	8.49+3	7.17+3	6.01+3	5.05+3	4.28+3	3.61+3	3.12+3	2.80+3	2.45+3	2.09+3
71 Lu	1.41+4	1.34+4	1.15+4	1.03+4	8.69+3	7.37+3	6.19+3	5.22+3	4.42+3	3.74+3	3.24+3	2.90+3	2.55+3	2.18+3
72 Hf	1.47+4	1.33+4	1.19+4	1.01+4	9.08+3	7.72+3	6.50+3	5.47+3	4.65+3	3.94+3	3.41+3	3.05+3	2.68+3	2.29+3
73 Ta	1.51+4	1.29+4	1.23+4	1.06+4	9.50+3	8.09+3	6.82+3	5.75+3	4.89+3	4.15+3	3.56+3	3.10+3	2.63+3	2.17+3
74 W	1.55+4	1.34+4	1.26+4	1.10+4	9.37+3	8.48+3	7.14+3	6.04+3	5.13+3	4.35+3	3.74+3	3.26+3	2.76+3	2.29+3

TABLE 4 (continued)

Mass Attenuation Coefficients for $L\ \beta_1$ Lines

Emitter		Ca	Sc	Ti	V	Cr	Mn	Fe	Co	Ni	Cu	Zn	Ga	Ge	As
Wavelength		3.59+1	3.10+1	2.70+1	2.39+1	2.13+1	1.91+1	1.73+1	1.57+1	1.43+1	1.31+1	1.20+1	1.10+1	1.02+1	9.41+0
Energy (keV)		3.45-1	4.00-1	4.58-1	5.19-1	5.83-1	6.49-1	7.18-1	7.91-1	8.69-1	9.50-1	1.03+0	1.12+0	1.22+0	1.32+0
Absorber															
75	Re	1.56+4	1.37+4	1.18+4	1.13+4	9.69+3	8.77+3	7.40+3	6.27+3	5.34+3	4.53+3	3.90+3	3.40+3	2.89+3	2.39+3
76	Os	1.54+4	1.37+4	1.19+4	1.14+4	9.83+3	8.40+3	7.59+3	6.45+3	5.50+3	4.68+3	4.05+3	3.59+3	3.10+3	2.60+3
77	Ir	1.59+4	1.42+4	1.25+4	1.08+4	1.03+4	8.94+3	8.05+3	6.84+3	5.84+3	4.97+3	4.30+3	3.81+3	3.30+3	2.76+3
78	Pt	1.62+4	1.48+4	1.30+4	1.13+4	1.08+4	9.43+3	8.00+3	7.22+3	6.17+3	5.25+3	4.54+3	4.02+3	3.48+3	2.92+3
79	Au	1.62+4	1.50+4	1.34+4	1.18+4	1.10+4	9.83+3	8.39+3	7.55+3	6.46+3	5.51+3	4.73+3	4.07+3	3.43+3	3.01+3
80	Hg	1.50+4	1.48+4	1.33+4	1.19+4	1.03+4	9.75+3	8.60+3	7.37+3	6.66+3	5.67+3	4.83+3	4.10+3	3.50+3	3.00+3
81	Tl	1.42+4	1.45+4	1.34+4	1.22+4	1.07+4	9.90+3	8.93+3	7.66+3	6.94+3	5.94+3	5.17+3	4.64+3	4.08+3	3.50+3
82	Pb	1.35+4	1.38+4	1.34+4	1.25+4	1.09+4	9.51+3	9.19+3	7.93+3	6.81+3	6.16+3	5.38+3	4.82+3	4.25+3	3.65+3
83	Bi	1.28+4	1.37+4	1.32+4	1.27+4	1.12+4	9.80+3	8.41+3	8.17+3	7.06+3	6.36+3	5.59+3	5.02+3	4.42+3	3.80+3
84	Po	1.18+4	1.37+4	1.27+4	1.35+4	1.17+4	1.03+4	8.86+3	8.57+3	7.42+3	6.37+3	5.87+3	5.27+3	4.65+3	4.00+3
85	At	1.04+4	1.36+4	1.29+4	1.23+4	1.19+4	1.08+4	9.37+3	9.12+3	7.83+3	6.74+3	5.76+3	5.42+3	4.80+3	4.16+3
86	Rn	9.36+3	1.24+4	1.22+4	1.17+4	1.16+4	1.08+4	9.36+3	8.08+3	7.90+3	6.73+3	5.78+3	5.25+3	4.68+3	4.08+3
87	Fr	7.13+3	1.16+4	1.19+4	1.18+4	1.06+4	1.12+4	9.70+3	8.41+3	8.30+3	7.01+3	6.05+3	5.19+3	4.78+3	4.19+3
88	Ra	4.60+3	1.01+4	1.13+4	1.18+4	1.07+4	1.06+4	9.91+3	8.62+3	7.45+3	7.16+3	6.28+3	5.44+3	4.89+3	4.31+3
89	Ac	4.56+3	8.72+3	1.06+4	1.16+4	1.07+4	9.50+3	1.00+4	8.74+3	7.59+3	6.52+3	6.40+3	5.62+3	4.80+3	4.36+3
90	Th	2.96+3	6.97+3	9.60+3	1.12+4	1.04+4	9.32+3	9.63+3	8.65+3	7.57+3	6.56+3	6.27+3	5.60+3	4.90+3	4.16+3
91	Pa	2.64+3	3.61+3	8.21+3	1.14+4	1.09+4	9.95+3	8.72+3	9.06+3	8.06+3	6.99+3	6.02+3	5.90+3	5.22+3	4.51+3
92	U	2.65+3	2.70+3	7.29+3	1.08+4	1.08+4	9.85+3	8.71+3	8.95+3	8.07+3	7.03+3	6.09+3	5.86+3	5.19+3	4.55+3
93	Np	2.85+3	2.58+3	6.25+3	9.55+3	1.07+4	1.02+4	9.08+3	8.45+3	8.35+3	7.36+3	6.40+3	5.54+3	5.43+3	4.81+3
94	Pu	2.29+3	2.69+3	3.53+3	6.25+3	1.01+4	1.05+4	9.55+3	8.34+3	8.28+3	7.71+3	6.72+3	5.84+3	5.63+3	4.99+3

TABLE 4 (continued)

Mass Attenuation Coefficients for $L\,\beta_1$ Lines

Emitter	Se	Br	Kr	Rb	Sr	Y	Zr	Nb	Mo	Tc	Ru	Rh	Rd	Ag
Wavelength	8.74+0	8.13+0	7.58+0	7.08+0	6.62+0	6.21+0	5.84+0	5.49+0	5.18+0	4.89+0	4.62+0	4.37+0	4.15+0	3.93+0
Energy (keV)	1.42+0	1.53+0	1.64+0	1.75+0	1.87+0	2.00+0	2.12+0	2.26+0	2.39+0	2.54+0	2.68+0	2.83+0	2.99+0	3.15+0
Absorber														
1 H	2.67+0	2.07+0	1.73+0	1.46+0	1.27+0	1.06+0	9.70-1	8.76-1	7.80-1	6.95-1	6.52-1	6.09-1	5.63-1	5.40-1
2 He	2.17+1	1.62+1	1.31+1	1.05+1	8.70+0	6.82+0	5.92+0	5.03+0	4.11+0	3.30+0	2.88+0	2.46+0	2.02+0	1.79+0
3 Li	8.33+1	6.25+1	5.06+1	4.07+1	3.37+1	2.64+1	2.28+1	1.93+1	1.57+1	1.24+1	1.08+1	9.10+0	7.35+0	6.41+0
4 Be	2.28+2	1.73+2	1.41+2	1.15+2	9.52+1	7.51+1	6.52+1	5.53+1	4.50+1	3.60+1	3.13+1	2.64+1	2.14+1	1.86+1
5 B	4.75+2	3.63+2	2.97+2	2.41+2	2.01+2	1.59+2	1.39+2	1.18+2	9.63+1	7.73+1	6.73+1	5.69+1	4.62+1	4.03+1
6 C	8.63+2	6.66+2	5.48+2	4.49+2	3.76+2	3.00+2	2.61+2	2.23+2	1.83+2	1.48+2	1.29+2	1.09+2	8.94+1	7.82+1
7 N	1.36+3	1.06+3	8.73+2	7.18+2	6.03+2	4.83+2	4.22+2	3.60+2	2.97+2	2.41+2	2.11+2	1.79+2	1.47+2	1.29+2
8 O	1.93+3	1.51+3	1.25+3	1.04+3	8.74+2	7.05+2	6.17+2	5.29+2	4.39+2	3.58+2	3.13+2	2.67+2	2.20+2	1.93+2
9 F	2.49+3	1.96+3	1.63+3	1.35+3	1.14+3	9.22+2	8.08+2	6.94+2	5.76+2	4.71+2	4.13+2	3.53+2	2.91+2	2.56+2
10 Ne	3.33+3	2.64+3	2.20+3	1.83+3	1.55+3	1.26+3	1.11+3	9.56+2	7.97+2	6.55+2	5.76+2	4.94+2	4.09+2	3.61+2
11 Na	4.14+3	3.28+3	2.74+3	2.28+3	1.94+3	1.58+3	1.39+3	1.20+3	9.99+2	8.22+2	7.23+2	6.21+2	5.15+2	4.54+2
12 Mg	5.03+3	4.11+3	3.45+3	2.89+3	2.46+3	2.01+3	1.77+3	1.53+3	1.28+3	1.06+3	9.36+2	8.05+2	6.71+2	5.93+2
13 Al	4.81+2	3.75+2	4.00+3	3.39+3	2.90+3	2.39+3	2.11+3	1.83+3	1.54+3	1.28+3	1.13+3	9.76+2	8.17+2	7.23+2
14 Si	6.51+2	5.13+2	4.29+2	3.53+2	3.59+3	3.02+3	2.67+3	2.31+3	1.94+3	1.61+3	1.42+3	1.23+3	1.03+3	9.07+2
15 P	7.98+2	6.31+2	5.28+2	4.41+2	3.75+2	3.07+2	2.60+2	2.55+3	2.18+3	1.85+3	1.63+3	1.41+3	1.18+3	1.05+3
16 S	1.02+3	8.03+2	6.73+2	5.61+2	4.77+2	3.91+2	3.44+2	2.97+2	2.48+2	2.23+3	1.97+3	1.71+3	1.43+3	1.27+3
17 Cl	1.19+3	9.44+2	7.91+2	6.61+2	5.63+2	4.61+2	4.07+2	3.53+2	2.97+2	2.46+2	2.15+2	1.84+3	1.59+3	1.42+3
18 Ar	1.35+3	1.07+3	8.94+2	7.45+2	6.33+2	5.18+2	4.56+2	3.95+2	3.32+2	2.75+2	2.43+2	2.10+2	1.76+2	1.54+2
19 K	1.73+3	1.37+3	1.14+3	9.55+2	8.13+2	6.66+2	5.88+2	5.09+2	4.28+2	3.56+2	3.15+2	2.72+2	2.29+2	2.03+2
20 Ca	2.03+3	1.64+3	1.44+3	1.23+3	1.02+3	7.93+2	7.00+2	6.08+2	5.13+2	4.28+2	3.78+2	3.27+2	2.75+2	2.44+2
21 Sc	2.21+3	1.78+3	1.57+3	1.34+3	1.11+3	8.66+2	7.64+2	6.64+2	5.60+2	4.67+2	4.13+2	3.57+2	3.00+2	2.66+2
22 Ti	2.48+3	2.00+3	1.76+3	1.51+3	1.25+3	9.77+2	8.63+2	7.52+2	6.36+2	5.32+2	4.70+2	4.06+2	3.40+2	3.02+2
23 V	2.75+3	2.22+3	1.96+3	1.68+3	1.39+3	1.09+3	9.63+2	8.36+2	7.05+2	5.87+2	5.19+2	4.48+2	3.75+2	3.32+2
24 Cr	3.19+3	2.58+3	2.27+3	1.95+3	1.62+3	1.27+3	1.12+3	9.75+2	8.22+2	6.86+2	6.06+2	5.24+2	4.39+2	3.89+2
25 Mn	3.48+3	2.83+3	2.49+3	2.14+3	1.78+3	1.40+3	1.24+3	1.08+3	9.16+2	7.67+2	6.78+2	5.85+2	4.90+2	4.34+2
26 Fe	3.96+3	3.22+3	2.84+3	2.44+3	2.03+3	1.60+3	1.42+3	1.24+3	1.06+3	8.88+2	7.84+2	6.77+2	5.66+2	5.02+2
27 Co	4.29+3	3.50+3	3.08+3	2.66+3	2.21+3	1.75+3	1.55+3	1.36+3	1.16+3	9.75+2	8.61+2	7.43+2	6.22+2	5.52+2
28 Ni	4.93+3	4.01+3	3.54+3	3.05+3	2.55+3	2.02+3	1.79+3	1.57+3	1.34+3	1.13+3	9.95+2	8.59+2	7.18+2	6.36+2
29 Cu	5.25+3	4.26+3	3.77+3	3.25+3	2.72+3	2.16+3	1.91+3	1.66+3	1.41+3	1.17+3	1.04+3	8.93+2	7.47+2	6.66+2
30 Zn	5.63+3	4.70+3	4.15+3	3.58+3	2.99+3	2.38+3	2.10+3	1.83+3	1.54+3	1.29+3	1.14+3	9.89+2	8.33+2	7.41+2
32 Ga	5.97+3	4.95+3	4.38+3	3.78+3	3.16+3	2.52+3	2.30+3	2.08+3	1.86+3	1.63+3	1.39+3	1.14+3	8.92+2	8.05+2
32 Ge	6.30+3	5.35+3	4.73+3	4.09+3	3.42+3	2.73+3	2.49+3	2.25+3	2.01+3	1.77+3	1.51+3	1.25+3	9.73+2	8.78+2
33 As	5.94+3	5.26+3	4.86+3	4.14+3	3.56+3	2.96+3	2.70+3	2.45+3	2.19+3	1.92+3	1.64+3	1.36+3	1.06+3	9.59+2
34 Se	1.04+3	5.23+3	4.45+3	4.41+3	3.79+3	3.14+3	2.87+3	2.61+3	2.33+3	2.04+3	1.75+3	1.45+3	1.13+3	1.02+3
35 Br	1.13+3	9.47+2	3.92+3	4.13+3	4.04+3	3.45+3	3.16+3	2.86+3	2.56+3	2.25+3	1.93+3	1.59+3	1.25+3	1.13+3
36 Kr	1.26+3	1.07+3	8.63+2	4.90+3	4.12+3	4.11+3	3.63+3	3.13+3	2.63+3	2.17+3	1.92+3	1.66+3	1.38+3	1.23+3
37 Rb	1.39+3	1.18+3	9.76+2	8.13+2	4.60+3	3.86+3	3.98+3	3.46+3	2.92+3	2.43+3	2.14+3	1.85+3	1.54+3	1.36+3

TABLE 4 (continued)

Mass Attenuation Coefficients for $L\beta_1$ Lines

Emitter		Se	Br	Kr	Rb	Sr	Y	Zr	Nb	Mo	Tc	Ru	Rh	Pd	As
Wavelength		8.74+0	8.13+0	7.58+0	7.08+0	6.62+0	6.21+0	5.84+0	5.49+0	5.18+0	4.89+0	4.62+0	4.37+0	4.15+0	3.93+0
Energy (keV)		1.42+0	1.53+0	1.64+0	1.75+0	1.87+0	2.00+0	2.12+0	2.26+0	2.39+0	2.54+0	2.68+0	2.83+0	2.99+0	3.15+0
Absorber															
38	Sr	1.53+3	1.30+3	1.08+3	9.19+2	7.74+2	3.00+3	3.58+3	3.62+3	3.11+3	2.64+3	2.33+3	2.01+3	1.67+3	1.48+3
39	Y	1.75+3	1.44+3	1.27+3	1.10+3	9.23+2	7.38+2	2.77+3	3.32+3	3.35+3	2.89+3	2.55+3	2.20+3	1.83+3	1.62+3
40	Zr	1.91+3	1.57+3	1.39+3	1.20+3	1.01+3	8.07+2	7.01+2	2.57+3	3.08+3	3.13+3	2.77+3	2.39+3	2.00+3	1.77+3
41	Nb	2.12+3	1.74+3	1.54+3	1.33+3	1.11+3	8.91+2	7.80+2	6.70+2	2.39+3	2.86+3	2.45+3	2.56+3	2.18+3	1.93+3
42	Mo	2.26+3	1.86+3	1.65+3	1.42+3	1.19+3	9.56+2	8.53+2	7.52+2	6.47+2	2.19+3	2.64+3	2.26+3	2.33+3	2.07+3
43	Tc	2.54+3	1.98+3	1.75+3	1.52+3	1.27+3	1.02+3	9.14+2	8.08+2	6.99+2	5.96+2	1.96+3	2.37+3	2.04+3	2.16+3
44	Ru	2.78+3	2.17+3	1.92+3	1.66+3	1.40+3	1.12+3	9.91+2	8.66+2	7.36+2	6.21+2	5.58+2	4.93+2	2.19+3	1.91+3
45	Rh	3.01+3	2.35+3	2.08+3	1.80+3	1.51+3	1.21+3	1.08+3	9.41+2	8.00+2	6.76+2	6.10+2	5.42+2	4.72+2	2.01+3
46	Pd	3.23+3	2.52+3	2.23+3	1.93+3	1.62+3	1.30+3	1.16+3	1.01+3	8.58+2	7.24+2	6.49+2	5.71+2	4.92+2	4.31+2
47	Ag	3.47+3	2.71+3	2.41+3	2.08+3	1.75+3	1.41+3	1.25+3	1.09+3	9.27+2	7.82+2	7.02+2	6.19+2	5.33+2	4.73+2
48	Cd	4.87+3	4.25+3	3.60+3	2.92+3	2.22+3	1.49+3	1.32+3	1.15+3	9.78+2	8.24+2	7.32+2	6.38+2	5.41+2	4.93+2
49	In	5.17+3	4.51+3	3.82+3	3.11+3	2.37+3	1.60+3	1.41+3	1.23+3	1.05+3	8.83+2	7.85+2	6.84+2	5.80+2	5.28+2
50	Sn	5.43+3	4.73+3	4.02+3	3.27+3	2.49+3	1.69+3	1.49+3	1.30+3	1.11+3	9.36+2	8.33+2	7.26+2	6.16+2	5.61+2
51	Sb	5.70+3	4.98+3	4.23+3	3.45+3	2.64+3	1.79+3	1.58+3	1.38+3	1.18+3	9.94+2	8.85+2	7.72+2	6.55+2	5.94+2
52	Te	5.78+3	5.05+3	4.30+3	3.52+3	2.70+3	1.86+3	1.64+3	1.44+3	1.22+3	1.03+3	9.19+2	8.02+2	6.82+2	6.18+2
53	I	5.84+3	5.13+3	4.40+3	3.64+3	2.85+3	2.03+3	1.84+3	1.68+3	1.50+3	1.32+3	1.14+3	9.46+2	7.49+2	6.75+2
54	Xe	5.72+3	5.06+3	4.37+3	3.65+3	2.91+3	2.14+3	1.95+3	1.77+3	1.59+3	1.40+3	1.20+3	9.99+2	7.91+2	7.07+2
55	Cs	5.69+3	5.06+3	4.40+3	3.72+3	3.01+3	2.28+3	2.08+3	1.89+3	1.69+3	1.49+3	1.28+3	1.07+3	8.48+2	7.61+2
56	Ba	5.59+3	4.99+3	4.38+3	3.73+3	3.06+3	2.37+3	2.16+3	1.96+3	1.76+3	1.55+3	1.34+3	1.11+3	8.85+2	7.94+2
57	La	5.58+3	5.01+3	4.41+3	3.80+3	3.15+3	2.49+3	2.28+3	2.07+3	1.86+3	1.64+3	1.41+3	1.18+3	9.39+2	8.51+2
58	Ce	5.49+3	5.22+3	4.63+3	4.00+3	3.36+3	2.70+3	2.47+3	2.24+3	2.01+3	1.77+3	1.53+3	1.27+3	1.01+3	9.19+2
59	Pr	5.86+3	5.32+3	4.74+3	4.14+3	3.51+3	2.86+3	2.62+3	2.38+3	2.14+3	1.89+3	1.63+3	1.36+3	1.08+3	9.80+2
60	Nd	6.02+3	5.15+3	4.78+3	4.19+3	3.59+3	2.97+3	2.72+3	2.48+3	2.22+3	1.96+3	1.69+3	1.41+3	1.13+3	1.02+3
61	Pm	6.25+3	5.42+3	4.57+3	4.29+3	3.71+3	3.10+3	2.84+3	2.59+3	2.32+3	2.05+3	1.77+3	1.48+3	1.18+3	1.07+3
62	Sm	5.15+3	5.57+3	4.81+3	4.38+3	3.82+3	3.24+3	2.97+3	2.70+3	2.43+3	2.14+3	1.85+3	1.55+3	1.24+3	1.12+3
63	Eu	5.44+3	5.74+3	5.04+3	4.32+3	3.97+3	3.40+3	3.12+3	2.84+3	2.55+3	2.25+3	1.95+3	1.63+3	1.30+3	1.18+3
64	Gd	5.54+3	4.70+3	4.93+3	4.34+3	3.72+3	3.44+3	3.16+3	2.88+3	2.59+3	2.29+3	1.98+3	1.66+3	1.33+3	1.21+3
65	Tb	6.03+3	5.17+3	4.27+3	4.69+3	4.05+3	3.68+3	3.38+3	3.08+3	2.77+3	2.45+3	2.11+3	1.77+3	1.42+3	1.29+3
66	Dy	6.28+3	5.33+3	4.43+3	4.78+3	4.15+3	3.56+3	3.42+3	3.12+3	2.81+3	2.49+3	2.16+3	1.82+3	1.47+3	1.34+3
67	Ho	6.18+3	5.42+3	4.67+3	3.96+3	4.34+3	3.71+3	3.21+3	3.14+3	2.84+3	2.53+3	2.21+3	1.88+3	1.54+3	1.40+3
68	Er	1.45+3	3.65+3	4.94+3	4.18+3	3.51+3	3.89+3	3.39+3	3.19+3	2.89+3	2.59+3	2.27+3	1.95+3	1.61+3	1.47+3
69	Tm	1.54+3	2.93+3	5.23+3	4.42+3	3.73+3	4.07+3	3.58+3	3.09+3	2.94+3	2.64+3	2.34+3	2.02+3	1.70+3	1.55+3
70	Yb	1.72+3	1.37+3	3.49+3	4.57+3	3.90+3	3.29+3	3.69+3	3.17+3	2.74+3	2.59+3	2.28+3	2.02+3	1.74+3	1.59+3
71	Lu	1.79+3	1.44+3	2.47+3	4.69+3	4.06+3	3.48+3	3.69+3	3.28+3	2.87+3	2.67+3	2.36+3	2.09+3	1.81+3	1.65+3
72	Hf	1.89+3	1.52+3	1.30+3	3.21+3	4.24+3	3.68+3	3.11+3	3.40+3	3.01+3	2.60+3	2.47+3	2.18+3	1.88+3	1.72+3
73	Ta	1.93+3	1.67+3	1.41+3	3.96+3	5.05+3	4.22+3	3.62+3	3.71+3	3.18+3	2.98+3	2.57+3	2.47+3	2.13+3	1.90+3
74	W	2.03+3	1.76+3	1.48+3	1.22+3	3.42+3	4.34+3	3.76+3	3.17+3	3.27+3	2.79+3	2.68+3	2.53+3	2.20+3	1.96+3

TABLE 4 (continued)

Mass Attenuation Coefficients for $L\ \beta_1$ Lines

Emitter		Se	Br	Kr	Rb	Sr	Y	Zr	Nb	Mo	Tc	Ru	Rh	Rd	Ag
Wavelength		8.74+0	8.13+0	7.58+0	7.08+0	6.62+0	6.21+0	5.84+0	5.49+0	5.18+0	4.89+0	4.62+0	4.37+0	4.15+0	3.93+0
Energy (keV)		1.42+0	1.53+0	1.64+0	1.75+0	1.87+0	2.00+0	2.12+0	2.26+0	2.39+0	2.54+0	2.68+0	2.83+0	2.99+0	3.15+0
Absorber															
75	Re	2.12+3	1.84+3	1.55+3	1.30+3	1.11+3	4.51+3	3.94+3	3.37+3	3.37+3	2.91+3	2.76+3	2.41+3	2.29+3	2.04+3
76	Os	2.13+3	1.91+3	1.68+3	1.44+3	1.19+3	3.11+3	4.07+3	3.52+3	2.97+3	3.01+3	2.62+3	2.48+3	2.15+3	2.10+3
77	Ir	2.27+3	2.03+3	1.78+3	1.53+3	1.27+3	1.05+3	4.13+3	3.63+3	3.10+3	2.60+3	2.75+3	2.37+3	2.24+3	1.96+3
78	Pt	2.39+3	2.14+3	1.89+3	1.62+3	1.34+3	1.11+3	2.92+3	3.78+3	3.26+3	2.76+3	2.87+3	2.52+3	2.15+3	2.08+3
79	Au	2.58+3	2.18+3	1.95+3	1.71+3	1.47+3	1.21+3	1.03+3	2.46+3	3.20+3	2.75+3	2.39+3	2.49+3	2.16+3	2.07+3
80	Hg	2.59+3	2.23+3	1.92+3	1.66+3	1.44+3	1.26+3	1.10+3	9.28+2	3.35+3	2.91+3	2.55+3	2.17+3	2.27+3	2.00+3
81	Tl	2.90+3	2.36+3	2.11+3	1.86+3	1.59+3	1.31+3	1.16+3	1.00+3	2.30+3	3.00+3	2.65+3	2.29+3	2.33+3	2.08+3
82	Pb	3.02+3	2.47+3	2.21+3	1.94+3	1.66+3	1.37+3	1.22+3	1.07+3	9.09+2	2.05+3	2.71+3	2.37+3	2.02+3	2.14+3
83	Bi	3.15+3	2.58+3	2.31+3	2.03+3	1.74+3	1.44+3	1.29+3	1.14+3	9.87+2	8.31+2	1.84+3	2.43+3	2.09+3	1.83+3
84	Po	3.33+3	2.73+3	2.44+3	2.15+3	1.84+3	1.52+3	1.37+3	1.21+3	1.04+3	8.92+2	1.92+3	2.50+3	2.18+3	1.92+3
85	At	3.48+3	2.88+3	2.58+3	2.27+3	1.95+3	1.61+3	1.45+3	1.28+3	1.11+3	9.45+2	8.27+2	1.75+3	2.28+3	2.03+3
86	Rn	3.45+3	2.89+3	2.59+3	2.28+3	1.95+3	1.62+3	1.45+3	1.28+3	1.11+3	9.49+2	8.40+2	7.27+2	1.51+3	2.01+3
87	Fr	3.58+3	3.03+3	2.72+3	2.39+3	2.05+3	1.70+3	1.52+3	1.35+3	1.17+3	1.00+3	8.98+2	7.92+2	6.83+2	2.04+3
88	Ra	3.70+3	3.15+3	2.82+3	2.48+3	2.13+3	1.77+3	1.58+3	1.40+3	1.21+3	1.04+3	9.32+2	8.19+2	7.03+2	1.41+3
89	Ac	3.78+3	3.24+3	2.91+3	2.56+3	2.20+3	1.83+3	1.68+3	1.54+3	1.39+3	1.24+3	1.08+3	9.14+2	7.45+2	6.48+2
90	Th	3.85+3	3.33+3	2.99+3	2.63+3	2.27+3	1.89+3	1.74+3	1.59+3	1.43+3	1.28+3	1.11+3	9.45+2	7.71+2	6.78+2
91	Pa	4.08+3	3.55+3	3.19+3	2.81+3	2.42+3	2.01+3	1.85+3	1.69+3	1.53+3	1.36+3	1.19+3	1.01+3	8.21+2	7.30+2
92	U	3.90+3	3.60+3	3.23+3	2.85+3	2.46+3	2.04+3	1.84+3	1.63+3	1.41+3	1.22+3	1.10+3	9.87+2	8.66+2	7.76+2
93	Np	4.17+3	3.80+3	3.42+3	3.01+3	2.59+3	2.16+3	1.99+3	1.82+3	1.64+3	1.46+3	1.27+3	1.08+3	8.83+2	8.06+2
94	Pu	4.33+3	3.68+3	3.48+3	3.08+3	2.67+3	2.24+3	2.06+3	1.88+3	1.70+3	1.51+3	1.32+3	1.12+3	9.13+2	8.29+2

TABLE 4 (continued)

Mass Attenuation Coefficients for $L\ \beta_1$ Lines

Emitter	Cd	In	Sn	Sb	Te	I	Cs	Ba	La	Ce	Pr	Nd	Pm	Sm
Wavelength	3.74+0	3.56+0	3.38+0	3.23+0	3.08+0	2.94+0	2.68+0	2.57+0	2.46+0	2.36+0	2.26+0	2.17+0	2.08+0	2.00+0
Energy (keV)	3.32+0	3.49+0	3.66+0	3.84+0	4.03+0	4.22+0	4.62+0	4.83+0	5.04+0	5.26+0	5.49+0	5.72+0	5.96+0	6.21+0
Absorber														
1 H	5.17-1	4.93-1	4.79-1	4.66-1	4.53-1	4.47-1	4.32-1	4.25-1	4.18-1	4.15-1	4.12-1	4.08-1	4.05-1	4.02-1
2 He	1.56+0	1.33+0	1.19+0	1.05+0	9.27-1	8.59-1	7.16-1	6.41-1	5.73-1	5.38-1	5.03-1	4.67-1	4.29-1	4.07-1
3 Li	5.50+0	4.56+0	4.00+0	3.46+0	2.95+0	2.67+0	2.10+0	1.81+0	1.54+0	1.40+0	1.27+0	1.13+0	9.81-1	8.96-1
4 Be	1.60+1	1.32+1	1.16+1	9.97+0	8.46+0	7.65+0	5.94+0	5.06+0	4.25+0	3.85+0	3.43+0	3.01+0	2.57+0	2.32+0
5 B	3.46+1	2.87+1	2.52+1	2.17+1	1.84+1	1.67+1	1.29+1	1.10+1	9.23+0	8.34+0	7.43+0	6.50+0	5.54+0	4.97+0
6 C	6.73+1	5.60+1	4.92+1	4.25+1	3.62+1	3.27+1	2.55+1	2.17+1	1.82+1	1.65+1	1.47+1	1.28+1	1.09+1	9.82+0
7 N	1.11+2	9.27+1	8.15+1	7.05+1	6.02+1	5.45+1	4.25+1	3.63+1	3.05+1	2.76+1	2.46+1	2.16+1	1.84+1	1.65+1
8 O	1.67+2	1.40+2	1.23+2	1.07+2	9.16+1	8.30+1	6.50+1	5.56+1	4.69+1	4.25+1	3.79+1	3.32+1	2.84+1	2.55+1
9 F	2.22+2	1.86+2	1.64+2	1.43+2	1.23+2	1.11+2	8.71+1	7.47+1	6.32+1	5.73+1	5.11+1	4.49+1	3.84+1	3.45+1
10 Ne	3.13+2	2.64+2	2.33+2	2.03+2	1.75+2	1.58+2	1.25+2	1.07+2	9.09+1	8.24+1	7.37+1	6.48+1	5.56+1	5.01+1
11 Na	3.95+2	3.33+2	2.95+2	2.57+2	2.21+2	2.01+2	1.58+2	1.36+2	1.16+2	1.05+2	9.40+1	8.27+1	7.11+1	6.40+1
12 Mg	5.16+2	4.37+2	3.87+2	3.38+2	2.92+2	2.65+2	2.09+2	1.80+2	1.54+2	1.40+2	1.25+2	1.10+2	9.48+1	8.54+1
13 Al	6.31+2	5.37+2	4.76+2	4.17+2	3.61+2	3.28+2	2.60+2	2.25+2	1.92+2	1.74+2	1.57+2	1.38+2	1.19+2	1.07+2
14 Si	7.91+2	6.72+2	5.96+2	5.22+2	4.51+2	4.10+2	3.25+2	2.81+2	2.40+2	2.18+2	1.95+2	1.72+2	1.49+2	1.34+2
15 P	9.17+2	7.81+2	6.94+2	6.08+2	5.27+2	4.80+2	3.81+2	3.30+2	2.83+2	2.57+2	2.31+2	2.04+2	1.76+2	1.59+2
16 S	1.11+3	9.49+2	8.44+2	7.41+2	6.43+2	5.85+2	4.66+2	4.04+2	3.46+2	3.15+2	2.83+2	2.50+2	2.17+2	1.96+2
17 Cl	1.24+3	1.06+3	9.46+2	8.31+2	7.22+2	6.58+2	5.25+2	4.55+2	3.91+2	3.56+2	3.20+2	2.84+2	2.46+2	2.22+2
18 Ar	1.36+3	1.19+3	1.06+3	9.29+2	8.07+2	7.36+2	5.87+2	5.09+2	4.37+2	3.98+2	3.58+2	3.17+2	2.75+2	2.49+2
19 K	1.78+2	1.53+2	1.25+3	1.11+3	9.69+2	8.84+2	7.07+2	6.15+2	5.29+2	4.83+2	4.35+2	3.86+2	3.35+2	3.03+2
20 Ca	2.14+2	1.83+2	1.63+2	1.44+2	1.24+2	1.02+3	8.19+2	7.15+2	6.18+2	5.64+2	5.09+2	4.52+2	3.93+2	3.56+2
21 Sc	2.33+2	1.99+2	1.78+2	1.57+2	1.36+2	1.22+2	8.26+2	7.37+2	6.53+2	5.96+2	5.38+2	4.79+2	4.17+2	3.79+2
22 Ti	2.64+2	2.26+2	2.01+2	1.77+2	1.54+2	1.40+2	1.12+2	9.76+1	7.06+2	6.46+2	5.85+2	5.22+2	4.57+2	4.15+2
23 V	2.91+2	2.48+2	2.21+2	1.94+2	1.69+2	1.54+2	1.23+2	1.08+2	9.25+1	8.31+1	6.25+2	5.65+2	5.03+2	4.59+2
24 Cr	3.41+2	2.91+2	2.59+2	2.28+2	1.98+2	1.81+2	1.45+2	1.27+2	1.09+2	9.99+1	9.03+1	8.03+1	7.01+1	5.30+2
25 Mn	3.80+2	3.24+2	2.89+2	2.54+2	2.21+2	2.02+2	1.62+2	1.41+2	1.21+2	1.11+2	1.00+2	8.92+1	7.78+1	7.01+1
26 Fe	4.39+2	3.74+2	3.33+2	2.93+2	2.54+2	2.32+2	1.86+2	1.62+2	1.40+2	1.27+2	1.15+2	1.02+2	8.93+1	8.12+1
27 Co	4.83+2	4.12+2	3.66+2	3.22+2	2.80+2	2.56+2	2.05+2	1.78+2	1.54+2	1.41+2	1.27+2	1.13+2	9.85+1	8.96+1
28 Ni	5.56+2	4.74+2	4.22+2	3.71+2	3.22+2	2.94+2	2.35+2	2.05+2	1.76+2	1.61+2	1.46+2	1.29+2	1.13+2	1.03+2
29 Cu	5.88+2	5.08+2	4.53+2	3.98+2	3.46+2	3.16+2	2.53+2	2.20+2	1.90+2	1.73+2	1.56+2	1.39+2	1.21+2	1.10+2
30 Zn	6.51+2	5.59+2	4.98+2	4.38+2	3.82+2	3.49+2	2.80+2	2.44+2	2.10+2	1.92+2	1.74+2	1.55+2	1.35+2	1.23+2
31 Ga	7.27+2	6.47+2	5.65+2	4.80+2	4.01+2	3.67+2	2.96+2	2.60+2	2.25+2	2.06+2	1.86+2	1.65+2	1.44+2	1.31+2
32 Ge	7.94+2	7.06+2	6.16+2	5.24+2	4.38+2	4.00+2	3.22+2	2.81+2	2.43+2	2.22+2	2.01+2	1.78+2	1.55+2	1.41+2
33 As	8.66+2	7.71+2	6.74+2	5.73+2	4.80+2	4.39+2	3.54+2	3.10+2	2.69+2	2.46+2	2.22+2	1.97+2	1.72+2	1.56+2
34 Se	9.26+2	8.25+2	7.21+2	6.14+2	5.14+2	4.71+2	3.80+2	3.32+2	2.88+2	2.63+2	2.38+2	2.11+2	1.84+2	1.67+2
35 Br	1.02+3	9.12+2	7.97+2	6.79+2	5.69+2	5.21+2	4.20+2	3.68+2	3.19+2	2.91+2	2.63+2	2.34+2	2.03+2	1.85+2
36 Kr	1.07+3	9.15+2	8.14+2	7.15+2	6.22+2	5.67+2	4.54+2	3.95+2	3.40+2	3.11+2	2.81+2	2.49+2	2.17+2	1.98+2
37 Rb	1.19+3	1.01+3	9.00+2	7.90+2	6.85+2	6.25+2	4.99+2	4.33+2	3.73+2	3.40+2	3.07+2	2.72+2	2.37+2	2.15+2

TABLE 4 (continued)

Mass Attenuation Coefficients for $L\ \beta_1$ Lines

Emitter		Cd	In	Sn	Sb	Te	I	Cs	Ba	La	Ce	Pr	Nd	Pm	Sm
Wavelength		3.74+0	3.56+0	3.38+0	3.23+0	3.08+0	2.94+0	2.68+0	2.57+0	2.46+0	2.36+0	2.26+0	2.17+0	2.08+0	2.00+0
Energy (keV)		3.32+0	3.49+0	3.66+0	3.84+0	4.03+0	4.22+0	4.62+0	4.83+0	5.04+0	5.26+0	5.49+0	5.72+0	5.96+0	6.21+0
Absorber															
38	Sr	1.29+3	1.10+3	9.78+2	8.58+2	7.45+2	6.79+2	5.42+2	4.70+2	4.04+2	3.69+2	3.33+2	2.95+2	2.57+2	2.33+2
39	Y	1.42+3	1.20+3	1.07+3	9.39+2	8.15+2	7.43+2	5.93+2	5.15+2	4.43+2	4.04+2	3.64+2	3.23+2	2.81+2	2.55+2
40	Zr	1.54+3	1.31+3	1.16+3	1.02+3	8.84+2	8.06+2	6.43+2	5.57+2	4.79+2	4.37+2	3.93+2	3.49+2	3.03+2	2.75+2
41	Nb	1.69+3	1.43+3	1.27+3	1.12+3	9.68+2	8.82+2	7.03+2	6.10+2	5.23+2	4.78+2	4.30+2	3.82+2	3.32+2	3.01+2
42	Mo	1.80+3	1.53+3	1.36+3	1.19+3	1.03+3	9.40+2	7.48+2	6.49+2	5.57+2	5.08+2	4.57+2	4.05+2	3.52+2	3.19+2
43	Tc	1.89+3	1.61+3	1.43+3	1.26+3	1.09+3	9.92+2	7.91+2	6.86+2	5.89+2	5.38+2	4.84+2	4.30+2	3.74+2	3.39+2
44	Ru	1.99+3	1.73+3	1.54+3	1.35+3	1.17+3	1.07+3	8.50+2	7.37+2	6.34+2	5.78+2	5.21+2	4.62+2	4.02+2	3.64+2
45	Rh	1.76+3	1.83+3	1.63+3	1.43+3	1.24+3	1.13+3	9.03+2	7.84+2	6.74+2	6.15+2	5.54+2	4.92+2	4.28+2	3.88+2
46	Pd	1.36+3	1.66+3	1.75+3	1.54+3	1.34+3	1.23+3	9.76+2	8.46+2	7.26+2	6.62+2	5.96+2	5.28+2	4.59+2	4.16+2
47	Ag	4.13+2	1.26+3	1.55+3	1.62+3	1.43+3	1.31+3	1.04+3	9.03+2	7.75+2	7.07+2	6.37+2	5.65+2	4.91+2	4.45+2
48	Cd	4.46+2	3.98+2	1.16+3	1.43+3	1.50+3	1.37+3	1.09+3	9.47+2	8.13+2	7.41+2	6.68+2	5.92+2	5.14+2	4.66+2
49	In	4.78+2	4.27+2	3.79+2	1.08+3	1.32+3	1.16+3	1.13+3	9.89+2	8.61+2	7.86+2	7.08+2	6.28+2	5.46+2	4.95+2
50	Sn	5.07+2	4.53+2	4.06+2	3.59+2	1.01+3	1.24+3	1.17+3	1.04+3	9.17+2	8.36+2	7.53+2	6.68+2	5.80+2	5.25+2
51	Sb	5.35+2	4.73+2	4.25+2	3.77+2	3.29+2	9.00+2	9.86+2	1.05+3	9.35+2	8.54+2	7.70+2	6.84+2	5.96+2	5.41+2
52	Te	5.57+2	4.94+2	4.44+2	3.94+2	3.44+2	3.08+2	1.02+3	9.13+2	9.74+2	8.89+2	8.01+2	7.12+2	6.20+2	5.62+2
53	I	6.07+2	5.37+2	4.83+2	4.28+2	3.75+2	3.38+2	7.99+2	7.08+2	8.78+2	9.44+2	8.56+2	7.65+2	6.72+2	6.10+2
54	Xe	6.29+2	5.48+2	4.93+2	4.38+2	3.85+2	3.51+2	2.80+2	7.20+2	6.39+2	8.00+2	8.53+2	7.69+2	6.83+2	6.22+2
55	Cs	6.81+2	5.98+2	5.36+2	4.75+2	4.16+2	3.82+2	3.09+2	2.71+2	6.95+2	6.21+2	7.74+2	8.25+2	7.39+2	6.74+2
56	Ba	7.10+2	6.24+2	5.60+2	4.96+2	4.35+2	3.99+2	3.23+2	2.84+2	2.46+2	6.44+2	5.77+2	7.19+2	6.42+2	7.02+2
57	La	7.72+2	6.91+2	6.07+2	5.21+2	4.41+2	4.07+2	3.35+2	2.98+2	2.62+2	2.37+2	6.15+2	5.53+2	6.86+2	6.16+2
58	Ce	8.34+2	7.45+2	6.55+2	5.61+2	4.75+2	4.37+2	3.59+2	3.18+2	2.79+2	2.54+2	2.29+2	2.02+2	5.21+2	6.53+2
59	Pr	8.89+2	7.95+2	6.99+2	6.00+2	5.07+2	4.67+2	3.81+2	3.37+2	2.95+2	2.70+2	2.45+2	2.19+2	1.92+2	4.98+2
60	Nd	9.27+2	8.30+2	7.29+2	6.26+2	5.30+2	4.88+2	4.01+2	3.55+2	3.13+2	2.87+2	2.60+2	2.33+2	2.05+2	1.84+2
61	Pm	9.73+2	8.71+2	7.66+2	6.58+2	5.57+2	5.13+2	4.21+2	3.73+2	3.28+2	3.01+2	2.73+2	2.44+2	2.15+2	1.94+2
62	Sm	1.02+3	9.12+2	8.02+2	6.89+2	5.84+2	5.38+2	4.41+2	3.91+2	3.44+2	3.15+2	2.86+2	2.56+2	2.26+2	2.05+2
63	Eu	1.07+3	9.62+2	8.46+2	7.27+2	6.16+2	5.67+2	4.65+2	4.12+2	3.62+2	3.32+2	3.01+2	2.69+2	2.37+2	2.16+2
64	Gd	1.10+3	9.84+2	8.67+2	7.45+2	6.33+2	5.82+2	4.78+2	4.23+2	3.72+2	3.41+2	3.09+2	2.77+2	2.43+2	2.22+2
65	Tb	1.17+3	1.05+3	9.23+2	7.93+2	6.73+2	6.19+2	5.06+2	4.47+2	3.92+2	3.60+2	3.26+2	2.92+2	2.57+2	2.34+2
66	Dy	1.22+3	1.09+3	9.59+2	8.25+2	7.00+2	6.43+2	5.26+2	4.65+2	4.08+2	3.74+2	3.39+2	3.04+2	2.67+2	2.43+2
67	Ho	1.27+3	1.14+3	1.00+3	8.63+2	7.33+2	6.74+2	5.51+2	4.87+2	4.27+2	3.92+2	3.55+2	3.17+2	2.79+2	2.55+2
68	Er	1.33+3	1.20+3	1.05+3	9.05+2	7.68+2	7.06+2	5.77+2	5.09+2	4.46+2	4.09+2	3.70+2	3.31+2	2.91+2	2.65+2
69	Tm	1.40+3	1.26+3	1.11+3	9.54+2	8.10+2	7.45+2	6.08+2	5.36+2	4.70+2	4.30+2	3.90+2	3.49+2	3.07+2	2.80+2
70	Yb	1.45+3	1.30+3	1.14+3	9.85+2	8.37+2	7.69+2	6.28+2	5.55+2	4.86+2	4.46+2	4.04+2	3.61+2	3.17+2	2.89+2
71	Lu	1.50+3	1.35+3	1.19+3	1.02+3	8.72+2	8.02+2	6.55+2	5.79+2	5.08+2	4.65+2	4.22+2	3.77+2	3.31+2	3.02+2
72	Hf	1.56+3	1.40+3	1.24+3	1.07+3	9.08+2	8.35+2	6.82+2	6.02+2	5.28+2	4.84+2	4.38+2	3.91+2	3.43+2	3.13+2
73	Ta	1.67+3	1.43+3	1.27+3	1.12+3	9.82+2	8.98+2	7.23+2	6.32+2	5.48+2	5.02+2	4.54+2	4.06+2	3.56+2	3.24+2
74	W	1.73+3	1.48+3	1.32+3	1.17+3	1.02+3	9.34+2	7.53+2	6.59+2	5.71+2	5.23+2	4.74+2	4.24+2	3.71+2	3.39+2

TABLE 4 (continued)

Mass Attenuation Coefficients for $L\ \beta_1$ Lines

Emitter		Cd	In	Sn	Sb	Te	I	Cs	Ba	La	Ce	Pr	Nd	Pm	Sm
Wavelength		3.74+0	3.56+0	3.38+0	3.23+0	3.08+0	2.94+0	2.68+0	2.57+0	2.46+0	2.36+0	2.26+0	2.17+0	2.08+0	2.00+0
Energy (keV)		3.32+0	3.49+0	3.66+0	3.84+0	4.03+0	4.22+0	4.62+0	4.83+0	5.04+0	5.26+0	5.49+0	5.72+0	5.96+0	6.21+0
Absorber															
75	Re	1.80+3	1.54+3	1.38+3	1.22+3	1.06+3	9.74+2	7.85+2	6.87+2	5.97+2	5.47+2	4.95+2	4.42+2	3.88+2	3.54+2
76	Os	1.85+3	1.59+3	1.42+3	1.26+3	1.10+3	1.01+3	8.11+2	7.10+2	6.16+2	5.65+2	5.11+2	4.57+2	4.01+2	3.65+2
77	Ir	1.91+3	1.66+3	1.48+3	1.31+3	1.15+3	1.05+3	8.47+2	7.41+2	6.43+2	5.89+2	5.34+2	4.77+2	4.18+2	3.82+2
78	Pt	1.98+3	1.74+3	1.56+3	1.37+3	1.20+3	1.10+3	8.83+2	7.72+2	6.69+2	6.12+2	5.54+2	4.95+2	4.33+2	3.95+2
79	Au	1.83+3	1.76+3	1.58+3	1.39+3	1.22+3	1.12+3	9.05+2	7.93+2	6.90+2	6.33+2	5.74+2	5.13+2	4.51+2	4.12+2
80	Hg	1.91+3	1.68+3	1.64+3	1.45+3	1.28+3	1.17+3	9.43+2	8.26+2	7.17+2	6.57+2	5.96+2	5.32+2	4.67+2	4.26+2
81	Tl	1.81+3	1.73+3	1.53+3	1.49+3	1.32+3	1.21+3	9.73+2	8.52+2	7.40+2	6.78+2	6.15+2	5.49+2	4.82+2	4.40+2
82	Pb	1.89+3	1.63+3	1.59+3	1.39+3	1.36+3	1.25+3	1.01+3	8.84+2	7.68+2	7.04+2	6.38+2	5.71+2	5.01+2	4.57+2
83	Bi	1.94+3	1.69+3	1.49+3	1.46+3	1.42+3	1.30+3	1.05+3	9.18+2	7.98+2	7.31+2	6.63+2	5.93+2	5.20+2	4.75+2
84	Po	2.00+3	1.76+3	1.57+3	1.37+3	1.33+3	1.32+3	1.07+3	9.48+2	8.31+2	7.61+2	6.90+2	6.17+2	5.42+2	4.94+2
85	At	1.77+3	1.84+3	1.65+3	1.46+3	1.40+3	1.25+3	1.11+3	9.86+2	8.70+2	7.98+2	7.23+2	6.47+2	5.68+2	5.18+2
86	Rn	1.77+3	1.53+3	1.63+3	1.44+3	1.26+3	1.23+3	1.08+3	9.70+2	8.63+2	7.91+2	7.17+2	6.41+2	5.63+2	5.14+2
87	Fr	1.81+3	1.57+3	1.39+3	1.48+3	1.31+3	1.17+3	1.01+3	1.00+3	8.95+2	8.21+2	7.44+2	6.66+2	5.85+2	5.34+2
88	Ra	1.85+3	1.62+3	1.44+3	1.52+3	1.35+3	1.21+3	1.05+3	1.03+3	9.23+2	8.47+2	7.68+2	6.87+2	6.04+2	5.51+2
89	Ac	1.28+3	1.69+3	1.51+3	1.33+3	1.40+3	1.27+3	9.93+2	9.76+2	9.60+2	8.80+2	7.99+2	7.15+2	6.28+2	5.73+2
90	Th	5.88+2	1.15+3	1.55+3	1.37+3	1.19+3	1.30+3	1.04+3	9.03+2	8.89+2	8.83+2	8.05+2	7.24+2	6.41+2	5.86+2
91	Pa	6.43+2	1.21+3	1.61+3	1.43+3	1.26+3	1.35+3	1.10+3	9.73+2	9.35+2	8.41+2	8.33+2	7.54+2	6.72+2	6.15+2
92	U	6.85+2	5.91+2	1.07+3	1.41+3	1.25+3	1.11+3	1.08+3	9.64+2	8.48+2	8.38+2	7.53+2	7.48+2	6.71+2	6.15+2
93	Np	7.35+2	6.62+2	5.88+2	1.01+3	1.34+3	1.20+3	1.15+3	1.03+3	9.07+2	8.15+2	8.04+2	7.20+2	7.14+2	6.54+2
94	Pu	7.52+2	6.73+2	5.91+2	5.06+2	1.40+3	1.26+3	9.84+2	8.75+2	1.06+3	9.73+2	8.82+2	7.88+2	7.72+2	7.10+2

TABLE 4 (continued)

Mass Attenuation Coefficients for $L\ \beta_1$ Lines

Emitter	Eu	Gd	Tb	Dy	Ho	Er	Tm	Yb	Lu	Hf	Ta	W	Re	Os
Wavelength	1.92+0	1.85+0	1.78+0	1.71+0	1.65+0	1.59+0	1.53+0	1.48+0	1.42+0	1.37+0	1.33+0	1.28+0	1.24+0	1.20+0
Energy (keV)	6.46+0	6.71+0	6.98+0	7.25+0	7.53+0	7.81+0	8.10+0	8.40+0	8.71+0	9.02+0	9.34+0	9.67+0	1.00+1	1.04+1
Absorber														
1 H	4.00-1	3.98-1	3.96-1	3.95-1	3.93-1	3.92-1	3.91-1	3.90-1	3.89-1	3.88-1	3.87-1	3.86-1	3.85-1	3.84-1
2 He	3.87-1	3.67-1	3.46-1	3.33-1	3.20-1	3.07-1	2.96-1	2.87-1	2.78-1	2.70-1	2.64-1	2.58-1	2.51-1	2.48-1
3 Li	8.22-1	7.45-1	6.67-1	6.20-1	5.74-1	5.27-1	4.87-1	4.57-1	4.27-1	3.98-1	3.78-1	3.57-1	3.37-1	3.25-1
4 Be	2.09+0	1.86+0	1.63+0	1.49+0	1.35+0	1.21+0	1.09+0	1.00+0	9.12-1	8.24-1	7.66-1	7.06-1	6.45-1	6.10-1
5 B	4.47+0	3.96+0	3.43+0	3.11+0	2.81+0	2.50+0	2.22+0	2.03+0	1.83+0	1.63+0	1.50+0	1.37+0	1.23+0	1.15+0
6 C	8.83+0	7.80+0	6.75+0	6.12+0	5.51+0	4.88+0	4.33+0	3.93+0	3.53+0	3.13+0	2.87+0	2.59+0	2.32+0	2.16+0
7 N	1.48+1	1.31+1	1.13+1	1.03+1	9.24+0	8.18+0	7.25+0	6.58+0	5.90+0	5.22+0	4.77+0	4.30+0	3.84+0	3.56+0
8 O	2.29+1	2.03+1	1.76+1	1.59+1	1.43+1	1.27+1	1.12+1	1.02+1	9.14+0	8.08+0	7.38+0	6.66+0	5.92+0	5.50+0
9 F	3.11+1	2.75+1	2.39+1	2.17+1	1.95+1	1.73+1	1.53+1	1.39+1	1.25+1	1.10+1	1.01+1	9.09+0	8.09+0	7.51+0
10 Ne	4.51+1	4.00+1	3.47+1	3.15+1	2.84+1	2.52+1	2.24+1	2.03+1	1.82+1	1.61+1	1.47+1	1.33+1	1.18+1	1.10+1
11 Na	5.77+1	5.12+1	4.45+1	4.04+1	3.65+1	3.24+1	2.88+1	2.61+1	2.35+1	2.08+1	1.90+1	1.72+1	1.53+1	1.42+1
12 Mg	7.70+1	6.85+1	5.96+1	5.42+1	4.88+1	4.34+1	3.86+1	3.51+1	3.15+1	2.79+1	2.55+1	2.31+1	2.05+1	1.91+1
13 Al	9.70+1	8.63+1	7.53+1	6.84+1	6.18+1	5.49+1	4.89+1	4.45+1	4.00+1	3.55+1	3.24+1	2.93+1	2.61+1	2.42+1
14 Si	1.21+2	1.08+2	9.40+1	8.54+1	7.72+1	6.86+1	6.11+1	5.56+1	5.00+1	4.44+1	4.06+1	3.67+1	3.27+1	3.04+1
15 P	1.44+2	1.28+2	1.12+2	1.02+2	9.22+1	8.21+1	7.32+1	6.67+1	6.00+1	5.33+1	4.88+1	4.42+1	3.94+1	3.66+1
16 S	1.77+2	1.58+2	1.38+2	1.26+2	1.14+2	1.01+2	9.06+1	8.25+1	7.43+1	6.61+1	6.05+1	5.47+1	4.89+1	4.54+1
17 Cl	2.01+2	1.80+2	1.57+2	1.43+2	1.30+2	1.16+2	1.03+2	9.42+1	8.49+1	7.56+1	6.92+1	6.27+1	5.61+1	5.21+1
18 Ar	2.25+2	2.01+2	1.76+2	1.60+2	1.45+2	1.29+2	1.16+2	1.05+2	9.50+1	8.46+1	7.75+1	7.02+1	6.28+1	5.84+1
19 K	2.75+2	2.46+2	2.16+2	1.97+2	1.78+2	1.59+2	1.42+2	1.30+2	1.17+2	1.05+2	9.58+1	8.69+1	7.78+1	7.23+1
20 Ca	3.23+2	2.89+2	2.54+2	2.32+2	2.10+2	1.88+2	1.68+2	1.54+2	1.39+2	1.24+2	1.14+2	1.03+2	9.24+1	8.59+1
21 Sc	3.43+2	3.08+2	2.71+2	2.47+2	2.24+2	2.01+2	1.80+2	1.65+2	1.49+2	1.33+2	1.22+2	1.11+2	9.93+1	9.24+1
22 Ti	3.78+2	3.39+2	2.99+2	2.74+2	2.49+2	2.24+2	2.01+2	1.84+2	1.66+2	1.49+2	1.37+2	1.24+2	1.12+2	1.04+2
23 V	4.17+2	3.74+2	3.30+2	3.02+2	2.75+2	2.46+2	2.21+2	2.02+2	1.83+2	1.64+2	1.51+2	1.37+2	1.23+2	1.14+2
24 Cr	4.82+2	4.33+2	3.82+2	3.50+2	3.18+2	2.85+2	2.56+2	2.35+2	2.12+2	1.90+2	1.75+2	1.59+2	1.43+2	1.33+2
25 Mn	6.29+1	4.58+2	4.11+2	3.77+2	3.43+2	3.08+2	2.77+2	2.53+2	2.29+2	2.06+2	1.89+2	1.72+2	1.55+2	1.44+2
26 Fe	7.38+1	6.63+1	5.85+1	4.19+2	3.82+2	3.45+2	3.11+2	2.85+2	2.59+2	2.32+2	2.14+2	1.95+2	1.75+2	1.63+2
27 Co	8.15+1	7.32+1	6.46+1	5.89+1	5.32+1	3.82+2	3.48+2	3.18+2	2.88+2	2.58+2	2.38+2	2.16+2	1.94+2	1.81+2
28 Ni	9.32+1	8.37+1	7.39+1	6.76+1	6.16+1	5.54+1	4.97+1	3.36+2	3.08+2	2.79+2	2.57+2	2.35+2	2.12+2	1.98+2
29 Cu	1.00+2	9.00+1	7.95+1	7.28+1	6.63+1	5.96+1	5.37+1	4.92+1	4.47+1	2.94+2	2.71+2	2.47+2	2.24+2	2.09+2
30 Zn	1.12+2	1.01+2	8.89+1	8.15+1	7.43+1	6.68+1	6.02+1	5.53+1	5.03+1	4.52+1	4.15+1	2.74+2	2.50+2	2.34+2
31 Ga	1.19+2	1.07+2	9.44+1	8.65+1	7.87+1	7.08+1	6.37+1	5.84+1	5.31+1	4.77+1	4.40+1	4.01+1	3.62+1	3.32+1
32 Ge	1.28+2	1.15+2	1.01+2	9.29+1	8.45+1	7.59+1	6.83+1	6.26+1	5.68+1	5.10+1	4.70+1	4.29+1	3.87+1	3.58+1
33 As	1.42+2	1.27+2	1.12+2	1.03+2	9.36+1	8.42+1	7.58+1	6.95+1	6.31+1	5.67+1	5.22+1	4.77+1	4.30+1	3.94+1
34 Se	1.52+2	1.36+2	1.20+2	1.10+2	1.00+2	9.02+1	8.12+1	7.44+1	6.75+1	6.07+1	5.59+1	5.10+1	4.61+1	4.30+1
35 Br	1.68+2	1.51+2	1.33+2	1.22+2	1.11+2	9.94+1	8.94+1	8.20+1	7.44+1	6.68+1	6.16+1	5.62+1	5.07+1	4.74+1
36 Kr	1.80+2	1.61+2	1.42+2	1.30+2	1.18+2	1.06+2	9.59+1	8.79+1	7.97+1	7.16+1	6.60+1	6.02+1	5.44+1	5.08+1
37 Rb	1.95+2	1.75+2	1.54+2	1.41+2	1.28+2	1.15+2	1.03+2	9.47+1	8.58+1	7.70+1	7.09+1	6.46+1	5.83+1	5.44+1

TABLE 4 (continued)

Mass Attenuation Coefficients for $L\ \beta_1$ Lines

Emitter	Eu	Gd	Tb	Dy	Ho	Er	Tm	Yb	Lu	Hf	Ta	W	Re	Os
Wavelength	1.92+0	1.85+0	1.78+0	1.71+0	1.65+0	1.59+0	1.53+0	1.48+0	1.42+0	1.37+0	1.33+0	1.28+0	1.24+0	1.20+0
Energy (keV)	6.46+0	6.71+0	6.98+0	7.25+0	7.53+0	7.81+0	8.10+0	8.40+0	8.71+0	9.02+0	9.34+0	9.67+0	1.00+1	1.04+1
Absorber														
38 Sr	2.12+2	1.90+2	1.67+2	1.53+2	1.39+2	1.25+2	1.12+2	1.03+2	9.31+1	8.35+1	7.69+1	7.01+1	6.32+1	5.90+1
39 Y	2.32+2	2.08+2	1.83+2	1.67+2	1.52+2	1.36+2	1.23+2	1.12+2	1.02+2	9.13+1	8.40+1	7.66+1	6.90+1	6.44+1
40 Zr	2.50+2	2.24+2	1.97+2	1.80+2	1.63+2	1.46+2	1.32+2	1.20+2	1.09+2	9.78+1	9.00+1	8.20+1	7.39+1	6.89+1
41 Nb	2.73+2	2.44+2	2.15+2	1.96+2	1.79+2	1.60+2	1.44+2	1.32+2	1.19+2	1.07+2	9.83+1	8.95+1	8.06+1	7.52+1
42 Mo	2.89+2	2.59+2	2.28+2	2.08+2	1.89+2	1.69+2	1.52+2	1.39+2	1.26+2	1.13+2	1.04+2	9.44+1	8.50+1	7.92+1
43 Tc	3.07+2	2.75+2	2.42+2	2.22+2	2.01+2	1.80+2	1.62+2	1.48+2	1.34+2	1.20+2	1.11+2	1.01+2	9.10+1	8.49+1
44 Ru	3.30+2	2.96+2	2.60+2	2.38+2	2.16+2	1.94+2	1.74+2	1.59+2	1.44+2	1.29+2	1.19+2	1.09+2	9.78+1	9.12+1
45 Rh	3.53+2	3.16+2	2.78+2	2.54+2	2.31+2	2.07+2	1.86+2	1.71+2	1.55+2	1.39+2	1.28+2	1.16+2	1.05+2	9.78+1
46 Pd	3.77+2	3.38+2	2.97+2	2.71+2	2.46+2	2.21+2	1.98+2	1.81+2	1.64+2	1.47+2	1.35+2	1.23+2	1.11+2	1.03+2
47 Ag	4.04+2	3.61+2	3.18+2	2.91+2	2.64+2	2.37+2	2.12+2	1.94+2	1.76+2	1.58+2	1.45+2	1.32+2	1.19+2	1.11+2
48 Cd	4.22+2	3.78+2	3.32+2	3.03+2	2.76+2	2.47+2	2.22+2	2.03+2	1.83+2	1.64+2	1.51+2	1.37+2	1.24+2	1.15+2
49 In	4.49+2	4.02+2	3.54+2	3.23+2	2.93+2	2.63+2	2.36+2	2.16+2	1.96+2	1.75+2	1.61+2	1.47+2	1.32+2	1.23+2
50 Sn	4.76+2	4.26+2	3.74+2	3.42+2	3.11+2	2.78+2	2.50+2	2.28+2	2.07+2	1.85+2	1.70+2	1.55+2	1.39+2	1.30+2
51 Sb	4.91+2	4.40+2	3.88+2	3.55+2	3.23+2	2.90+2	2.60+2	2.39+2	2.16+2	1.94+2	1.79+2	1.63+2	1.47+2	1.37+2
52 Te	5.11+2	4.58+2	4.03+2	3.69+2	3.36+2	3.01+2	2.71+2	2.48+2	2.25+2	2.02+2	1.86+2	1.69+2	1.53+2	1.42+2
53 I	5.54+2	4.96+2	4.37+2	4.00+2	3.63+2	3.26+2	2.93+2	2.68+2	2.43+2	2.18+2	2.00+2	1.83+2	1.65+2	1.54+2
54 Xe	5.65+2	5.06+2	4.46+2	4.08+2	3.71+2	3.33+2	2.99+2	2.74+2	2.48+2	2.23+2	2.05+2	1.87+2	1.69+2	1.57+2
55 Cs	6.12+2	5.49+2	4.83+2	4.42+2	4.02+2	3.60+2	3.24+2	2.97+2	2.69+2	2.41+2	2.22+2	2.02+2	1.82+2	1.70+2
56 Ba	6.37+2	5.71+2	5.03+2	4.60+2	4.18+2	3.75+2	3.37+2	3.09+2	2.80+2	2.51+2	2.31+2	2.10+2	1.89+2	1.77+2
57 La	6.69+2	6.04+2	5.36+2	4.91+2	4.46+2	3.99+2	3.59+2	3.28+2	2.97+2	2.66+2	2.45+2	2.23+2	2.01+2	1.87+2
58 Ce	5.87+2	6.34+2	5.69+2	5.21+2	4.74+2	4.25+2	3.81+2	3.49+2	3.16+2	2.84+2	2.61+2	2.38+2	2.14+2	2.00+2
59 Pr	6.21+2	5.60+2	6.03+2	5.53+2	5.02+2	4.50+2	4.04+2	3.70+2	3.35+2	3.01+2	2.77+2	2.52+2	2.27+2	2.12+2
60 Nd	4.72+2	4.22+2	5.30+2	5.77+2	5.26+2	4.73+2	4.25+2	3.89+2	3.53+2	3.16+2	2.91+2	2.65+2	2.38+2	2.22+2
61 Pm	1.75+2	4.44+2	3.97+2	5.01+2	5.42+2	4.91+2	4.45+2	4.07+2	3.69+2	3.31+2	3.04+2	2.77+2	2.49+2	2.33+2
62 Sm	1.86+2	1.66+2	4.16+2	3.76+2	4.75+2	5.12+2	4.66+2	4.27+2	3.87+2	3.46+2	3.19+2	2.90+2	2.61+2	2.44+2
63 Eu	1.97+2	1.78+2	4.37+2	3.98+2	3.58+2	4.51+2	4.89+2	4.48+2	4.06+2	3.64+2	3.35+2	3.05+2	2.75+2	2.56+2
64 Gd	2.03+2	1.83+2	1.63+2	4.07+2	3.71+2	3.34+2	4.20+2	4.55+2	4.15+2	3.75+2	3.45+2	3.14+2	2.83+2	2.64+2
65 Tb	2.14+2	1.93+2	1.72+2	1.57+2	3.87+2	3.52+2	3.17+2	4.02+2	4.35+2	3.96+2	3.64+2	3.31+2	2.98+2	2.78+2
66 Dy	2.22+2	2.01+2	1.78+2	1.63+2	1.49+2	3.63+2	3.30+2	3.00+2	3.78+2	3.42+2	3.77+2	3.43+2	3.09+2	2.89+2
67 Ho	2.32+2	2.10+2	1.86+2	1.71+2	1.57+2	1.42+2	3.42+2	3.13+2	2.84+2	3.56+2	3.24+2	3.55+2	3.22+2	3.00+2
68 Er	2.42+2	2.18+2	1.94+2	1.78+2	1.63+2	1.47+2	1.32+2	3.23+2	2.95+2	2.66+2	3.38+2	3.08+2	3.36+2	3.13+2
69 Tm	2.55+2	2.30+2	2.05+2	1.88+2	1.72+2	1.55+2	1.40+2	1.28+2	3.09+2	2.81+2	2.57+2	3.24+2	2.95+2	3.27+2
70 Yb	2.64+2	2.38+2	2.12+2	1.95+2	1.78+2	1.61+2	1.46+2	1.34+2	1.22+2	2.91+2	2.68+2	2.44+2	3.06+2	2.80+2
71 Lu	2.75+2	2.48+2	2.21+2	2.03+2	1.85+2	1.67+2	1.51+2	1.39+2	1.27+2	1.15+2	2.78+2	2.54+2	2.30+2	2.92+2
72 Hf	2.86+2	2.58+2	2.29+2	2.10+2	1.92+2	1.73+2	1.57+2	1.44+2	1.32+2	1.19+2	1.09+2	2.63+2	2.40+2	2.20+2
73 Ta	2.95+2	2.66+2	2.36+2	2.17+2	1.98+2	1.78+2	1.61+2	1.48+2	1.35+2	1.22+2	1.12+2	1.03+2	2.37+2	2.19+2
74 W	3.09+2	2.78+2	2.47+2	2.27+2	2.07+2	1.87+2	1.69+2	1.56+2	1.42+2	1.28+2	1.18+2	1.08+2	9.82+1	2.39+2

TABLE 4 (continued)

Mass Attenuation Coefficients for $L\,\beta_1$ Lines

Emitter		Eu	Gd	Tb	Dy	Ho	Er	Tm	Yb	Lu	Hf	Ta	W	Re	Os
Wavelength		1.92+0	1.85+0	1.78+0	1.71+0	1.65+0	1.59+0	1.53+0	1.48+0	1.42+0	1.37+0	1.33+0	1.28+0	1.24+0	1.20+0
Energy (keV)		6.46+0	6.71+0	6.98+0	7.25+0	7.53+0	7.81+0	8.10+0	8.40+0	8.71+0	9.02+0	9.34+0	9.67+0	1.00+1	1.04+1
Absorber															
75	Re	3.23+2	2.91+2	2.58+2	2.37+2	2.17+2	1.96+2	1.77+2	1.63+2	1.48+2	1.34+2	1.24+2	1.13+2	1.03+2	9.47+1
76	Os	3.33+2	3.01+2	2.67+2	2.45+2	2.24+2	2.02+2	1.83+2	1.68+2	1.53+2	1.38+2	1.28+2	1.17+2	1.06+2	9.83+1
77	Ir	3.48+2	3.14+2	2.78+2	2.56+2	2.34+2	2.11+2	1.91+2	1.76+2	1.60+2	1.44+2	1.34+2	1.22+2	1.11+2	1.03+2
78	Pt	3.60+2	3.24+2	2.87+2	2.64+2	2.41+2	2.17+2	1.96+2	1.80+2	1.64+2	1.48+2	1.37+2	1.25+2	1.13+2	1.06+2
79	Au	3.76+2	3.39+2	3.02+2	2.77+2	2.54+2	2.29+2	2.08+2	1.91+2	1.74+2	1.58+2	1.46+2	1.34+2	1.21+2	1.14+2
80	Hg	3.89+2	3.51+2	3.11+2	2.86+2	2.61+2	2.36+2	2.14+2	1.97+2	1.79+2	1.62+2	1.50+2	1.37+2	1.24+2	1.17+2
81	Tl	4.01+2	3.62+2	3.21+2	2.95+2	2.70+2	2.44+2	2.20+2	2.03+2	1.85+2	1.67+2	1.54+2	1.42+2	1.28+2	1.20+2
82	Pb	4.17+2	3.76+2	3.34+2	3.07+2	2.81+2	2.54+2	2.30+2	2.11+2	1.93+2	1.74+2	1.61+2	1.48+2	1.34+2	1.25+2
83	Bi	4.33+2	3.91+2	3.47+2	3.19+2	2.92+2	2.64+2	2.38+2	2.19+2	2.00+2	1.81+2	1.67+2	1.53+2	1.39+2	1.30+2
84	Po	4.51+2	4.07+2	3.61+2	3.32+2	3.04+2	2.74+2	2.48+2	2.29+2	2.08+2	1.88+2	1.74+2	1.60+2	1.45+2	1.36+2
85	At	4.73+2	4.27+2	3.79+2	3.48+2	3.18+2	2.88+2	2.60+2	2.40+2	2.18+2	1.97+2	1.82+2	1.67+2	1.52+2	1.42+2
86	Rn	4.69+2	4.23+2	3.76+2	3.45+2	3.16+2	2.85+2	2.58+2	2.37+2	2.16+2	1.96+2	1.81+2	1.66+2	1.51+2	1.41+2
87	Fr	4.88+2	4.40+2	3.91+2	3.60+2	3.29+2	2.97+2	2.69+2	2.48+2	2.26+2	2.04+2	1.89+2	1.73+2	1.57+2	1.47+2
88	Ra	5.03+2	4.54+2	4.04+2	3.71+2	3.39+2	3.07+2	2.78+2	2.56+2	2.33+2	2.11+2	1.95+2	1.79+2	1.62+2	1.52+2
89	Ac	5.23+2	4.72+2	4.20+2	3.86+2	3.53+2	3.19+2	2.89+2	2.66+2	2.43+2	2.19+2	2.03+2	1.86+2	1.69+2	1.58+2
90	Th	5.35+2	4.83+2	4.29+2	3.95+2	3.61+2	3.26+2	2.95+2	2.72+2	2.48+2	2.24+2	2.07+2	1.90+2	1.73+2	1.62+2
91	Pa	5.62+2	5.07+2	4.50+2	4.14+2	3.78+2	3.42+2	3.10+2	2.85+2	2.60+2	2.35+2	2.17+2	1.99+2	1.81+2	1.69+2
92	U	5.62+2	5.07+2	4.51+2	4.15+2	3.79+2	3.43+2	3.11+2	2.86+2	2.61+2	2.36+2	2.18+2	2.00+2	1.82+2	1.70+2
93	Np	5.97+2	5.39+2	4.78+2	4.40+2	4.02+2	3.63+2	3.28+2	3.02+2	2.76+2	2.49+2	2.30+2	2.11+2	1.91+2	1.79+2
94	Pu	6.47+2	5.82+2	5.15+2	4.73+2	4.31+2	3.88+2	3.49+2	3.18+2	2.86+2	2.54+2	2.35+2	2.15+2	1.95+2	1.83+2

TABLE 4 (continued)

Mass Attenuation Coefficients for $L\,\beta_1$ Lines

Emitter	Ir	Pt	Au	Hg	Tl	Pb	Bi	Po	At	Rn	Fr	Ra	Ac	Th
Wavelength	1.16+0	1.12+0	1.08+0	1.05+0	1.02+0	9.83-1	9.52-1	9.22-1	8.93-1	8.66-1	8.39-1	8.14-1	7.89-1	7.65-1
Energy (keV)	1.07+1	1.11+1	1.14+1	1.18+1	1.22+1	1.26+1	1.30+1	1.34+1	1.39+1	1.43+1	1.48+1	1.52+1	1.57+1	1.62+1
Absorber														
1 H	3.84-1	3.83-1	3.82-1	3.81-1	3.81-1	3.80-1	3.80-1	3.79-1	3.78-1	3.77-1	3.77-1	3.76-1	3.75-1	3.75-1
2 He	2.44-1	2.39-1	2.35-1	2.31-1	2.28-1	2.25-1	2.23-1	2.20-1	2.18-1	2.15-1	2.13-1	2.11-1	2.09-1	2.07-1
3 Li	3.12-1	2.99-1	2.86-1	2.73-1	2.63-1	2.57-1	2.50-1	2.43-1	2.36-1	2.29-1	2.22-1	2.16-1	2.12-1	2.08-1
4 Be	5.74-1	5.37-1	5.00-1	4.61-1	4.33-1	4.15-1	3.97-1	3.78-1	3.59-1	3.39-1	3.19-1	3.03-1	2.93-1	2.82-1
5 B	1.07+0	9.89-1	9.04-1	8.18-1	7.56-1	7.17-1	6.76-1	6.34-1	5.91-1	5.48-1	5.02-1	4.68-1	4.45-1	4.22-1
6 C	2.00+0	1.83+0	1.66+0	1.48+0	1.36+0	1.28+0	1.20+0	1.11+0	1.03+0	9.37-1	8.45-1	7.76-1	7.30-1	6.82-1
7 N	3.29+0	3.00+0	2.71+0	2.41+0	2.19+0	2.06+0	1.92+0	1.77+0	1.62+0	1.47+0	1.31+0	1.19+0	1.11+0	1.03+0
8 O	5.06+0	4.61+0	4.15+0	3.68+0	3.35+0	3.13+0	2.91+0	2.68+0	2.45+0	2.21+0	1.96+0	1.77+0	1.65+0	1.52+0
9 F	6.91+0	6.30+0	5.67+0	5.02+0	4.56+0	4.26+0	3.96+0	3.64+0	3.32+0	2.99+0	2.65+0	2.39+0	2.21+0	2.04+0
10 Ne	1.01+1	9.21+0	8.29+0	7.35+0	6.67+0	6.23+0	5.78+0	5.31+0	4.84+0	4.35+0	3.85+0	3.47+0	3.21+0	2.95+0
11 Na	1.30+1	1.19+1	1.07+1	9.49+0	8.62+0	8.05+0	7.46+0	6.86+0	6.24+0	5.61+0	4.97+0	4.47+0	4.14+0	3.79+0
12 Mg	1.76+1	1.60+1	1.44+1	1.28+1	1.16+1	1.08+1	1.00+1	9.21+0	8.39+0	7.54+0	6.66+0	6.00+0	5.54+0	5.08+0
13 Al	2.23+1	2.04+1	1.83+1	1.63+1	1.48+1	1.38+1	1.28+1	1.17+1	1.07+1	9.60+0	8.48+0	7.63+0	7.05+0	6.45+0
14 Si	2.80+1	2.55+1	2.30+1	2.04+1	1.85+1	1.73+1	1.60+1	1.47+1	1.34+1	1.20+1	1.06+1	9.57+0	8.85+0	8.10+0
15 P	3.38+1	3.08+1	2.78+1	2.47+1	2.24+1	2.09+1	1.94+1	1.78+1	1.63+1	1.46+1	1.29+1	1.16+1	1.08+1	9.86+0
16 S	4.19+1	3.82+1	3.45+1	3.07+1	2.79+1	2.60+1	2.42+1	2.22+1	2.02+1	1.82+1	1.61+1	1.45+1	1.34+1	1.23+1
17 Cl	4.80+1	4.39+1	3.96+1	3.52+1	3.21+1	2.99+1	2.78+1	2.55+1	2.33+1	2.10+1	1.86+1	1.67+1	1.55+1	1.42+1
18 Ar	5.38+1	4.91+1	4.44+1	3.95+1	3.59+1	3.36+1	3.11+1	2.86+1	2.61+1	2.35+1	2.08+1	1.87+1	1.73+1	1.59+1
19 K	6.68+1	6.10+1	5.51+1	4.91+1	4.48+1	4.18+1	3.88+1	3.57+1	3.26+1	2.94+1	2.60+1	2.35+1	2.17+1	1.99+1
20 Ca	7.93+1	7.25+1	6.56+1	5.85+1	5.33+1	4.98+1	4.63+1	4.26+1	3.88+1	3.50+1	3.11+1	2.80+1	2.59+1	2.38+1
21 Sc	8.53+1	7.80+1	7.06+1	6.30+1	5.74+1	5.37+1	4.99+1	4.59+1	4.19+1	3.78+1	3.36+1	3.03+1	2.81+1	2.57+1
22 Ti	9.62+1	8.81+1	7.98+1	7.13+1	6.51+1	6.09+1	5.66+1	5.21+1	4.76+1	4.30+1	3.82+1	3.46+1	3.20+1	2.94+1
23 V	1.06+2	9.69+1	8.78+1	7.84+1	7.16+1	6.70+1	6.22+1	5.74+1	5.24+1	4.73+1	4.21+1	3.80+1	3.52+1	3.23+1
24 Cr	1.23+2	1.13+2	1.02+2	9.12+1	8.33+1	7.80+1	7.25+1	6.68+1	6.10+1	5.51+1	4.90+1	4.43+1	4.11+1	3.77+1
25 Mn	1.33+2	1.22+2	1.11+2	9.89+1	9.04+1	8.46+1	7.87+1	7.25+1	6.63+1	5.99+1	5.33+1	4.83+1	4.47+1	4.10+1
26 Fe	1.51+2	1.39+2	1.26+2	1.13+2	1.03+2	9.65+1	8.98+1	8.29+1	7.58+1	6.86+1	6.11+1	5.54+1	5.13+1	4.72+1
27 Co	1.68+2	1.54+2	1.39+2	1.25+2	1.14+2	1.07+2	9.92+1	9.14+1	8.36+1	7.56+1	6.73+1	6.09+1	5.64+1	5.18+1
28 Ni	1.84+2	1.69+2	1.53+2	1.38+2	1.26+2	1.18+2	1.10+2	1.02+2	9.34+1	8.47+1	7.57+1	6.87+1	6.37+1	5.86+1
29 Cu	1.93+2	1.78+2	1.62+2	1.45+2	1.33+2	1.25+2	1.16+2	1.08+2	9.86+1	8.94+1	7.99+1	7.25+1	6.73+1	6.19+1
30 Zn	2.17+2	1.99+2	1.81+2	1.63+2	1.49+2	1.40+2	1.30+2	1.20+2	1.10+2	9.98+1	8.92+1	8.09+1	7.51+1	6.91+1
31 Ga	2.19+2	2.02+2	1.85+2	1.67+2	1.54+2	1.44+2	1.34+2	1.24+2	1.14+2	1.03+2	9.24+1	8.39+1	7.79+1	7.17+1
32 Ge	3.28+1	2.97+1	1.90+2	1.74+2	1.61+2	1.51+2	1.41+2	1.30+2	1.20+2	1.09+2	9.73+1	8.84+1	8.21+1	7.56+1
33 As	3.62+1	3.35+1	3.07+1	2.78+1	1.79+2	1.68+2	1.56+2	1.45+2	1.33+2	1.20+2	1.08+2	9.80+1	9.10+1	8.38+1
34 Se	3.99+1	3.67+1	3.35+1	3.01+1	2.74+1	2.51+1	1.60+2	1.49+2	1.38+2	1.26+2	1.14+2	1.04+2	9.69+1	8.93+1
35 Br	4.39+1	4.04+1	3.68+1	3.31+1	3.02+1	2.79+1	2.56+1	2.33+1	1.46+2	1.35+2	1.23+2	1.14+2	1.05+2	9.72+1
36 Kr	4.71+1	4.34+1	3.95+1	3.55+1	3.23+1	2.96+1	2.75+1	2.55+1	2.34+1	2.12+1	1.28+2	1.19+2	1.10+2	1.02+2
37 Rb	5.04+1	4.64+1	4.22+1	3.79+1	3.48+1	3.26+1	3.04+1	2.82+1	2.59+1	2.35+1	2.11+1	1.27+2	1.18+2	1.09+2

TABLE 4 (continued)

Mass Attenuation Coefficients for $L\ \beta_1$ Lines

Emitter	Ir	Pt	Au	Hg	Tl	Pb	Bi	Po	At	Rn	Fr	Ra	Ac	Th
Wavelength	1.16+0	1.12+0	1.08+0	1.05+0	1.02+0	9.83-1	9.52-1	9.22-1	8.93-1	8.66-1	8.39-1	8.14-1	7.89-1	7.65-1
Energy (keV)	1.07+1	1.11+1	1.14+1	1.18+1	1.22+1	1.26+1	1.30+1	1.34+1	1.39+1	1.43+1	1.48+1	1.52+1	1.57+1	1.62+1
Absorber														
38 Sr	5.47+1	5.02+1	4.57+1	4.11+1	3.77+1	3.54+1	3.30+1	3.05+1	2.80+1	2.55+1	2.29+1	2.07+1	1.92+1	1.16+2
39 Y	5.97+1	5.49+1	4.99+1	4.48+1	4.11+1	3.86+1	3.60+1	3.33+1	3.06+1	2.78+1	2.49+1	2.27+1	2.11+1	1.95+1
40 Zr	6.38+1	5.86+1	5.33+1	4.79+1	4.39+1	4.11+1	3.84+1	3.55+1	3.26+1	2.96+1	2.65+1	2.41+1	2.24+1	2.07+1
41 Nb	6.97+1	6.40+1	5.82+1	5.22+1	4.79+1	4.49+1	4.19+1	3.87+1	3.55+1	3.23+1	2.89+1	2.63+1	2.45+1	2.26+1
42 Mo	7.34+1	6.74+1	6.12+1	5.49+1	5.03+1	4.72+1	4.40+1	4.07+1	3.73+1	3.39+1	3.03+1	2.76+1	2.56+1	2.37+1
43 Tc	7.87+1	7.23+1	6.57+1	5.90+1	5.40+1	5.07+1	4.73+1	4.37+1	4.01+1	3.65+1	3.27+1	2.97+1	2.76+1	2.55+1
44 Ru	8.45+1	7.76+1	7.05+1	6.33+1	5.80+1	5.44+1	5.08+1	4.69+1	4.31+1	3.91+1	3.51+1	3.19+1	2.97+1	2.74+1
45 Rh	9.07+1	8.33+1	7.58+1	6.80+1	6.24+1	5.85+1	5.46+1	5.05+1	4.64+1	4.21+1	3.78+1	3.44+1	3.20+1	2.95+1
46 Pd	9.56+1	8.77+1	7.97+1	7.15+1	6.55+1	6.14+1	5.72+1	5.29+1	4.85+1	4.40+1	3.94+1	3.58+1	3.33+1	3.07+1
47 Ag	1.03+2	9.44+1	8.58+1	7.70+1	7.05+1	6.61+1	6.17+1	5.70+1	5.23+1	4.75+1	4.25+1	3.87+1	3.60+1	3.32+1
48 Cd	1.07+2	9.81+1	8.91+1	7.98+1	7.31+1	6.86+1	6.39+1	5.91+1	5.42+1	4.92+1	4.40+1	4.00+1	3.72+1	3.43+1
49 In	1.14+2	1.05+2	9.53+1	8.55+1	7.83+1	7.35+1	6.85+1	6.33+1	5.81+1	5.27+1	4.72+1	4.29+1	3.99+1	3.68+1
50 Sn	1.20+2	1.10+2	1.00+2	8.99+1	8.23+1	7.72+1	7.19+1	6.65+1	6.09+1	5.53+1	4.95+1	4.49+1	4.18+1	3.85+1
51 Sb	1.27+2	1.17+2	1.06+2	9.54+1	8.75+1	8.21+1	7.65+1	7.08+1	6.51+1	5.91+1	5.30+1	4.83+1	4.49+1	4.14+1
52 Te	1.32+2	1.21+2	1.10+2	9.91+1	9.08+1	8.52+1	7.95+1	7.35+1	6.75+1	6.14+1	5.50+1	5.01+1	4.66+1	4.30+1
53 I	1.42+2	1.31+2	1.19+2	1.07+2	9.78+1	9.17+1	8.55+1	7.91+1	7.26+1	6.59+1	5.91+1	5.37+1	5.00+1	4.61+1
54 Xe	1.46+2	1.34+2	1.22+2	1.09+2	1.00+2	9.41+1	8.77+1	8.12+1	7.45+1	6.77+1	6.07+1	5.52+1	5.14+1	4.74+1
55 Cs	1.57+2	1.45+2	1.31+2	1.18+2	1.08+2	1.01+2	9.46+1	8.75+1	8.03+1	7.29+1	6.53+1	5.94+1	5.53+1	5.10+1
56 Ba	1.64+2	1.50+2	1.37+2	1.23+2	1.12+2	1.06+2	9.84+1	9.10+1	8.35+1	7.59+1	6.79+1	6.18+1	5.75+1	5.30+1
57 La	1.73+2	1.59+2	1.45+2	1.30+2	1.19+2	1.11+2	1.04+2	9.60+1	8.80+1	7.99+1	7.15+1	6.50+1	6.04+1	5.57+1
58 Ce	1.85+2	1.70+2	1.54+2	1.39+2	1.27+2	1.19+2	1.11+2	1.03+2	9.43+1	8.56+1	7.66+1	6.97+1	6.48+1	5.98+1
59 Pr	1.96+2	1.80+2	1.64+2	1.47+2	1.35+2	1.26+2	1.18+2	1.09+2	9.98+1	9.06+1	8.11+1	7.38+1	6.86+1	6.33+1
60 Nd	2.06+2	1.89+2	1.72+2	1.54+2	1.41+2	1.32+2	1.23+2	1.14+2	1.04+2	9.48+1	8.48+1	7.71+1	7.16+1	6.60+1
61 Pm	2.15+2	1.98+2	1.80+2	1.61+2	1.48+2	1.39+2	1.29+2	1.19+2	1.10+2	9.94+1	8.90+1	8.09+1	7.52+1	6.94+1
62 Sm	2.26+2	2.07+2	1.88+2	1.69+2	1.55+2	1.45+2	1.35+2	1.25+2	1.15+2	1.04+2	9.31+1	8.46+1	7.87+1	7.25+1
63 Eu	2.37+2	2.18+2	1.98+2	1.78+2	1.63+2	1.53+2	1.42+2	1.31+2	1.21+2	1.09+2	9.79+1	8.90+1	8.27+1	7.63+1
64 Gd	2.44+2	2.24+2	2.04+2	1.83+2	1.67+2	1.57+2	1.46+2	1.35+2	1.24+2	1.12+2	1.01+2	9.14+1	8.50+1	7.84+1
65 Tb	2.58+2	2.36+2	2.15+2	1.93+2	1.76+2	1.65+2	1.54+2	1.42+2	1.31+2	1.19+2	1.06+2	9.64+1	8.96+1	8.26+1
66 Dy	2.67+2	2.45+2	2.23+2	2.00+2	1.83+2	1.72+2	1.60+2	1.48+2	1.36+2	1.23+2	1.10+2	1.00+2	9.30+1	8.57+1
67 Ho	2.78+2	2.56+2	2.32+2	2.08+2	1.91+2	1.79+2	1.67+2	1.54+2	1.41+2	1.28+2	1.15+2	1.04+2	9.71+1	8.95+1
68 Er	2.90+2	2.66+2	2.42+2	2.17+2	1.99+2	1.86+2	1.74+2	1.61+2	1.47+2	1.34+2	1.20+2	1.09+2	1.01+2	9.32+1
69 Tm	3.03+2	2.79+2	2.54+2	2.28+2	2.09+2	1.96+2	1.83+2	1.69+2	1.55+2	1.41+2	1.26+2	1.14+2	1.06+2	9.81+1
70 Yb	3.08+2	2.85+2	2.61+2	2.36+2	2.17+2	2.03+2	1.90+2	1.75+2	1.61+2	1.46+2	1.30+2	1.18+2	1.10+2	1.02+2
71 Lu	2.67+2	2.93+2	2.70+2	2.45+2	2.27+2	2.12+2	1.98+2	1.83+2	1.68+2	1.52+2	1.36+2	1.24+2	1.15+2	1.06+2
72 Hf	2.00+2	2.55+2	2.79+2	2.55+2	2.36+2	2.22+2	2.06+2	1.91+2	1.75+2	1.59+2	1.42+2	1.29+2	1.20+2	1.10+2
73 Ta	2.01+2	1.82+2	2.32+2	2.53+2	2.36+2	2.21+2	2.06+2	1.91+2	1.75+2	1.59+2	1.42+2	1.29+2	1.20+2	1.11+2
74 W	2.21+2	2.02+2	1.82+2	2.31+2	2.55+2	2.39+2	2.23+2	2.06+2	1.89+2	1.72+2	1.54+2	1.40+2	1.30+2	1.20+2

TABLE 4 (continued)

Mass Attenuation Coefficients for $L\ \beta_1$ Lines

Emitter		Ir	Pt	Au	Hg	Tl	Pb	Bi	Po	At	Rn	Fr	Ra	Ac	Th
Wavelength		1.16+0	1.12+0	1.08+0	1.05+0	1.02+0	9.83-1	9.52-1	9.22-1	8.93-1	8.66-1	8.39-1	8.14-1	7.89-1	7.65-1
Energy (keV)		1.07+1	1.11+1	1.14+1	1.18+1	1.22+1	1.26+1	1.30+1	1.34+1	1.39+1	1.43+1	1.48+1	1.52+1	1.57+1	1.62+1
Absorber															
75	Re	2.24+2	2.07+2	1.89+2	1.71+2	2.17+2	2.39+2	2.24+2	2.08+2	1.91+2	1.75+2	1.58+2	1.44+2	1.34+2	1.23+2
76	Os	9.01+1	2.10+2	1.93+2	1.76+2	1.61+2	2.05+2	2.25+2	2.10+2	1.94+2	1.78+2	1.62+2	1.48+2	1.38+2	1.27+2
77	Ir	9.50+1	8.66+1	1.99+2	1.83+2	1.67+2	1.54+2	1.96+2	2.14+2	1.99+2	1.84+2	1.68+2	1.54+2	1.43+2	1.32+2
78	Pt	9.78+1	8.96+1	8.12+1	1.89+2	1.74+2	1.60+2	1.47+2	1.86+2	1.70+2	1.89+2	1.73+2	1.60+2	1.49+2	1.37+2
79	Au	1.06+2	9.76+1	8.93+1	8.07+1	1.76+2	1.63+2	1.50+2	1.37+2	1.73+2	1.59+2	1.75+2	1.62+2	1.51+2	1.39+2
80	Hg	1.08+2	1.00+2	9.16+1	8.29+1	7.55+1	1.71+2	1.59+2	1.46+2	1.33+2	1.68+2	1.54+2	1.71+2	1.59+2	1.46+2
81	Tl	1.12+2	1.03+2	9.46+1	8.56+1	7.81+1	7.19+1	1.61+2	1.50+2	1.38+2	1.26+2	1.58+2	1.45+2	1.61+2	1.49+2
82	Pb	1.17+2	1.08+2	9.87+1	8.93+1	8.17+1	7.55+1	6.93+1	1.60+2	1.48+2	1.36+2	1.24+2	1.56+2	1.44+2	1.59+2
83	Bi	1.21+2	1.12+2	1.02+2	9.27+1	8.50+1	7.89+1	7.27+1	1.54+2	1.43+2	1.32+2	1.21+2	1.11+2	1.42+2	1.31+2
84	Po	1.26+2	1.17+2	1.07+2	9.65+1	8.86+1	8.26+1	7.64+1	7.01+1	1.48+2	1.37+2	1.26+2	1.16+2	1.07+2	9.85+1
85	At	1.32+2	1.22+2	1.12+2	1.01+2	9.30+1	8.70+1	8.09+1	7.45+1	6.81+1	1.43+2	1.32+2	1.22+2	1.13+2	1.04+2
86	Rn	1.31+2	1.21+2	1.11+2	1.00+2	9.23+1	8.66+1	8.09+1	7.49+1	6.88+1	6.26+1	1.30+2	1.21+2	1.12+2	1.04+2
87	Fr	1.37+2	1.27+2	1.16+2	1.05+2	9.69+1	9.12+1	8.54+1	7.94+1	7.33+1	6.71+1	6.06+1	1.26+2	1.17+2	1.08+2
88	Ra	1.42+2	1.31+2	1.20+2	1.08+2	1.00+2	9.41+1	8.81+1	8.19+1	7.57+1	6.92+1	6.26+1	5.70+1	1.20+2	1.11+2
89	Ac	1.47+2	1.36+2	1.25+2	1.13+2	1.04+2	9.80+1	9.17+1	8.53+1	7.88+1	7.21+1	6.52+1	5.95+1	5.51+1	1.15+2
90	Th	1.50+2	1.39+2	1.27+2	1.15+2	1.06+2	1.00+2	9.36+1	8.70+1	8.04+1	7.35+1	6.65+1	6.08+1	5.65+1	5.21+1
91	Pa	1.58+2	1.46+2	1.33+2	1.21+2	1.11+2	1.05+2	9.80+1	9.11+1	8.41+1	7.70+1	6.96+1	6.37+1	5.94+1	5.50+1
92	U	1.59+2	1.46+2	1.34+2	1.21+2	1.12+2	1.05+2	9.88+1	9.19+1	8.48+1	7.76+1	7.02+1	6.44+1	6.02+1	5.59+1
93	Np	1.67+2	1.54+2	1.41+2	1.27+2	1.18+2	1.11+2	1.04+2	9.62+1	8.88+1	8.12+1	7.33+1	6.72+1	6.28+1	5.82+1
94	Pu	1.70+2	1.57+2	1.43+2	1.30+2	1.20+2	1.13+2	1.05+2	9.79+1	9.03+1	8.26+1	7.46+1	6.83+1	6.38+1	5.92+1

TABLE 4 (continued)

Mass Attenuation Coefficients for $L\ \beta_1$ Lines

Emitter	Pa	U	Emitter	Pa	U
Wavelength	7.42-1	7.20-1	Wavelength	7.42-1	7.20-1
Energy (keV)	1.67+1	1.72+1	Energy (keV)	1.67+1	1.72+1
Absorber			Absorber		
1 H	3.74-1	3.73-1	48 Cd	3.13+1	2.88+1
2 He	2.06-1	2.04-1	49 In	3.37+1	3.10+1
3 Li	2.04-1	2.01-1	50 Sn	3.52+1	3.24+1
4 Be	2.71-1	2.62-1	51 Sb	3.79+1	3.49+1
5 B	3.97-1	3.77-1	52 Te	3.93+1	3.62+1
6 C	6.34-1	5.93-1	53 I	4.22+1	3.88+1
7 N	9.49-1	8.79-1	54 Xe	4.34+1	3.99+1
8 O	1.39+0	1.28+0	55 Cs	4.67+1	4.29+1
9 F	1.85+0	1.70+0	56 Ba	4.85+1	4.46+1
10 Ne	2.68+0	2.45+0	57 La	5.09+1	4.68+1
11 Na	3.44+0	3.14+0	58 Ce	5.46+1	5.02+1
12 Mg	4.60+0	4.20+0	59 Pr	5.79+1	5.32+1
13 Al	5.84+0	5.33+0	60 Nd	6.03+1	5.55+1
14 Si	7.34+0	6.69+0	61 Pm	6.34+1	5.83+1
15 P	8.93+0	8.15+0	62 Sm	6.63+1	6.09+1
16 S	1.11+1	1.02+1	63 Eu	6.97+1	6.41+1
17 Cl	1.28+1	1.17+1	64 Gd	7.16+1	6.58+1
18 Ar	1.44+1	1.31+1	65 Tb	7.55+1	6.94+1
19 K	1.81+1	1.65+1	66 Dy	7.83+1	7.20+1
20 Ca	2.16+1	1.97+1	67 Ho	8.18+1	7.52+1
21 Sc	2.34+1	2.13+1	68 Er	8.52+1	7.83+1
22 Ti	2.67+1	2.44+1	69 Tm	8.96+1	8.24+1
23 V	2.94+1	2.69+1	70 Yb	9.27+1	8.52+1
24 Cr	3.42+1	3.13+1	71 Lu	9.69+1	8.90+1
25 Mn	3.73+1	3.41+1	72 Hf	1.01+2	9.27+1
26 Fe	4.29+1	3.93+1	73 Ta	1.02+2	9.35+1
27 Co	4.71+1	4.31+1	74 W	1.09+2	1.01+2
28 Ni	5.34+1	4.90+1	75 Re	1.13+2	1.04+2
29 Cu	5.64+1	5.18+1	76 Os	1.16+2	1.07+2
30 Zn	6.30+1	5.77+1	77 Ir	1.21+2	1.11+2
31 Ga	6.54+1	6.00+1	78 Pt	1.25+2	1.15+2
32 Ge	6.90+1	6.34+1	79 Au	1.28+2	1.17+2
33 As	7.65+1	7.02+1	80 Hg	1.34+2	1.23+2
34 Se	8.15+1	7.49+1	81 Tl	1.37+2	1.26+2
35 Br	8.88+1	8.16+1	82 Pb	1.46+2	1.35+2
36 Kr	9.31+1	8.56+1	83 Bi	1.44+2	1.34+2
37 Rb	1.00+2	9.22+1	84 Po	1.26+2	1.40+2
38 Sr	1.07+2	9.89+1	85 At	9.54+1	1.22+2
39 Y	1.79+1	1.07+2	86 Rn	9.52+1	8.70+1
40 Zr	1.90+1	1.74+1	87 Fr	9.90+1	9.07+1
41 Nb	2.07+1	1.90+1	88 Ra	1.02+2	9.38+1
42 Mo	2.16+1	1.98+1	89 Ac	1.06+2	9.79+1
43 Tc	2.33+1	2.15+1	90 Th	1.09+2	1.01+2
44 Ru	2.50+1	2.31+1	91 Pa	5.05+1	1.06+2
45 Rh	2.70+1	2.49+1	92 U	5.15+1	1.06+2
46 Pd	2.81+1	2.58+1	93 Np	5.36+1	4.93+1
47 Ag	3.03+1	2.79+1	94 Pu	5.45+1	5.01+1

TABLE 4 (continued)

Mass Attenuation Coefficients for $M\alpha$ Lines

Emitter		La	Ce	Pr	Nd	Sm	Eu	Gd	Tb	Dy	Ho	Er	Tm	Yb	Lu
Wavelength		1.49+1	1.40+1	1.33+1	1.27+1	1.15+1	1.10+1	1.05+1	1.00+1	9.59+0	9.20+0	8.82+0	8.48+0	8.15+0	7.84+0
Energy (keV)		8.33-1	8.83-1	9.29-1	9.78-1	1.08+0	1.13+0	1.19+0	1.24+0	1.29+0	1.35+0	1.41+0	1.46+0	1.52+0	1.58+0
Absorber															
1	H	1.30+1	1.09+1	9.18+0	7.56+0	5.77+0	5.07+0	4.32+0	3.85+0	3.50+0	3.14+0	2.76+0	2.40+0	2.08+0	1.90+0
2	He	1.12+2	9.21+1	7.82+1	6.65+1	5.05+1	4.38+1	3.66+1	3.23+1	2.91+1	2.59+1	2.25+1	1.91+1	1.63+1	1.46+1
3	Li	4.05+2	3.38+2	2.90+2	2.48+2	1.90+2	1.66+2	1.40+2	1.23+2	1.11+2	9.92+1	8.62+1	7.37+1	6.29+1	5.65+1
4	Be	1.01+3	8.47+2	7.34+2	6.36+2	4.97+2	4.39+2	3.75+2	3.34+2	3.03+2	2.70+2	2.36+2	2.03+2	1.75+2	1.57+2
5	B	2.03+3	1.72+3	1.49+3	1.29+3	1.01+3	8.95+2	7.72+2	6.90+2	6.26+2	5.60+2	4.91+2	4.23+2	3.65+2	3.30+2
6	C	3.59+3	3.06+3	2.66+3	2.31+3	1.82+3	1.61+3	1.39+3	1.24+3	1.13+3	1.01+3	8.91+2	7.73+2	6.71+2	6.07+2
7	N	5.38+3	4.60+3	4.02+3	3.50+3	2.79+3	2.49+3	2.17+3	1.95+3	1.77+3	1.60+3	1.41+3	1.22+3	1.07+3	9.65+2
8	O	7.26+3	6.24+3	5.48+3	4.80+3	3.85+3	3.46+3	3.03+3	2.73+3	2.49+3	2.25+3	1.99+3	1.74+3	1.52+3	1.38+3
9	F	8.92+3	7.68+3	6.78+3	5.98+3	4.86+3	4.39+3	3.88+3	3.51+3	3.21+3	2.90+3	2.57+3	2.25+3	1.97+3	1.79+3
10	Ne	7.94+2	9.66+3	9.04+3	8.09+3	6.56+3	5.88+3	5.15+3	4.65+3	4.26+3	3.86+3	3.43+3	3.02+3	2.66+3	2.42+3
11	Na	1.06+3	9.03+2	7.90+2	6.89+2	8.07+3	7.26+3	6.38+3	5.77+3	5.29+3	4.79+3	4.26+3	3.75+3	3.30+3	3.01+3
12	Mg	1.49+3	1.27+3	1.11+3	9.70+2	7.69+2	6.84+2	5.93+2	5.21+2	4.60+2	5.70+3	5.15+3	4.62+3	4.14+3	3.78+3
13	Al	1.89+3	1.62+3	1.42+3	1.24+3	9.81+2	8.72+2	7.55+2	6.78+2	6.20+2	5.60+2	4.96+2	4.34+2	3.78+2	4.34+3
14	Si	2.48+3	2.12+3	1.86+3	1.63+3	1.30+3	1.16+3	1.01+3	9.13+2	8.36+2	7.55+2	6.70+2	5.88+2	5.16+2	4.71+2
15	P	3.05+3	2.62+3	2.30+3	2.01+3	1.60+3	1.43+3	1.24+3	1.12+3	1.02+3	9.25+2	8.22+2	7.22+2	6.35+2	5.79+2
16	S	3.86+3	3.31+3	2.91+3	2.55+3	2.03+3	1.81+3	1.58+3	1.42+3	1.30+3	1.18+3	1.05+3	9.20+2	8.09+2	7.38+2
17	Cl	4.46+3	3.84+3	3.38+3	2.96+3	2.37+3	2.12+3	1.85+3	1.66+3	1.53+3	1.38+3	1.23+3	1.08+3	9.50+2	8.67+2
18	Ar	5.11+3	4.39+3	3.86+3	3.39+3	2.70+3	2.42+3	2.10+3	1.90+3	1.74+3	1.57+3	1.39+3	1.22+3	1.08+3	9.81+2
19	K	6.40+3	5.51+3	4.86+3	4.27+3	3.42+3	3.06+3	2.67+3	2.41+3	2.21+3	2.00+3	1.78+3	1.56+3	1.38+3	1.26+3
20	Ca	7.52+3	6.48+3	5.72+3	5.04+3	4.03+3	3.59+3	3.12+3	2.81+3	2.58+3	2.34+3	2.09+3	1.85+3	1.64+3	1.54+3
21	Sc	8.14+3	7.03+3	6.21+3	5.46+3	4.36+3	3.89+3	3.39+3	3.06+3	2.81+3	2.55+3	2.28+3	2.01+3	1.79+3	1.67+3
22	Ti	8.97+3	7.77+3	6.88+3	6.06+3	4.85+3	4.33+3	3.77+3	3.41+3	3.13+3	2.85+3	2.55+3	2.25+3	2.01+3	1.88+3
23	V	9.80+3	8.52+3	7.56+3	6.67+3	5.36+3	4.79+3	4.18+3	3.78+3	3.47+3	3.16+3	2.82+3	2.50+3	2.23+3	2.09+3
24	Cr	1.14+4	9.88+3	8.77+3	7.75+3	6.22+3	5.56+3	4.85+3	4.39+3	4.03+3	3.67+3	3.28+3	2.91+3	2.60+3	2.43+3
25	Mn	1.21+4	1.06+4	9.40+3	8.32+3	6.71+3	6.02+3	5.27+3	4.77+3	4.39+3	4.00+3	3.58+3	3.18+3	2.84+3	2.66+3
26	Fe	1.18+4	1.19+4	1.06+4	9.39+3	7.60+3	6.82+3	5.98+3	5.42+3	4.99+3	4.54+3	4.07+3	3.62+3	3.24+3	3.03+3
27	Co	1.26+4	1.11+4	1.14+4	1.01+4	8.18+3	7.34+3	6.45+3	5.85+3	5.39+3	4.91+3	4.41+3	3.92+3	3.51+3	3.29+3
28	Ni	1.90+3	9.62+3	1.14+4	1.01+4	9.42+3	8.45+3	7.40+3	6.71+3	6.18+3	5.64+3	5.06+3	4.50+3	4.03+3	3.78+3
29	Cu	2.14+3	1.74+3	1.57+3	1.09+4	8.46+3	8.69+3	7.85+3	7.19+3	6.62+3	6.02+3	5.39+3	4.79+3	4.28+3	4.01+3
30	Zn	2.36+3	2.03+3	1.80+3	1.61+3	7.77+3	8.40+3	7.43+3	7.72+3	6.92+3	6.34+3	5.76+3	5.20+3	4.72+3	4.43+3
31	Ga	2.57+3	2.23+3	1.98+3	1.75+3	1.39+3	4.04+3	6.90+3	7.11+3	6.35+3	6.75+3	6.11+3	5.50+3	4.97+3	4.66+3
32	Ge	2.87+3	2.50+3	2.22+3	1.96+3	1.55+3	1.40+3	1.26+3	4.11+3	6.49+3	6.25+3	5.59+3	5.87+3	5.38+3	5.04+3
33	As	3.21+3	2.80+3	2.49+3	2.21+3	1.83+3	1.68+3	1.51+3	1.34+3	1.18+3	3.99+3	6.07+3	5.55+3	5.00+3	5.26+3
34	Se	3.52+3	3.08+3	2.74+3	2.43+3	2.05+3	1.90+3	1.74+3	1.57+3	1.41+3	1.25+3	1.08+3	3.85+3	5.26+3	4.84+3
35	Br	4.01+3	3.58+3	3.19+3	2.77+3	2.30+3	2.12+3	1.93+3	1.73+3	1.55+3	1.35+3	1.16+3	1.05+3	9.53+2	3.46+3
36	Kr	4.40+3	3.84+3	3.43+3	3.04+3	2.46+3	2.22+3	1.95+3	1.76+3	1.60+3	1.44+3	1.28+3	1.18+3	1.07+3	9.67+2
37	Rb	4.82+3	4.21+3	3.75+3	3.33+3	2.70+3	2.44+3	2.15+3	1.94+3	1.77+3	1.59+3	1.41+3	1.30+3	1.19+3	1.07+3

TABLE 4 (continued)

Mass Attenuation Coefficients for $M\alpha$ Lines

Emitter	La	Ce	Pr	Nd	Sm	Eu	Gd	Tb	Dy	Ho	Er	Tm	Yb	Lu
Wavelength	1.49+1	1.40+1	1.33+1	1.27+1	1.15+1	1.10+1	1.05+1	1.00+1	9.59+0	9.20+0	8.82+0	8.48+0	8.15+0	7.84+0
Energy (keV)	8.33−1	8.83−1	9.29−1	9.78−1	1.08+0	1.13+0	1.19+0	1.24+0	1.29+0	1.35+0	1.41+0	1.46+0	1.52+0	1.58+0
Absorber														
38 Sr	5.24+3	4.59+3	4.10+3	3.64+3	2.96+3	2.67+3	2.35+3	2.12+3	1.94+3	1.75+3	1.56+3	1.43+3	1.31+3	1.18+3
39 Y	5.80+3	5.09+3	4.54+3	4.04+3	3.29+3	2.96+3	2.61+3	2.37+3	2.19+3	2.00+3	1.80+3	1.61+3	1.44+3	1.36+3
40 Zr	6.27+3	5.51+3	4.92+3	4.39+3	3.57+3	3.22+3	2.84+3	2.58+3	2.38+3	2.18+3	1.96+3	1.75+3	1.58+3	1.48+3
41 Nb	6.96+3	6.10+3	5.45+3	4.86+3	3.96+3	3.56+3	3.14+3	2.86+3	2.64+3	2.41+3	2.17+3	1.94+3	1.74+3	1.64+3
42 Mo	7.37+3	6.48+3	5.80+3	5.17+3	4.22+3	3.80+3	3.35+3	3.05+3	2.82+3	2.58+3	2.32+3	2.08+3	1.87+3	1.75+3
43 Tc	7.74+3	6.81+3	6.11+3	5.45+3	4.65+3	4.34+3	4.00+3	3.66+3	3.33+3	2.98+3	2.62+3	2.27+3	1.99+3	1.87+3
44 Ru	8.47+3	7.46+3	6.69+3	5.98+3	5.10+3	4.76+3	4.39+3	4.01+3	3.65+3	3.27+3	2.87+3	2.49+3	2.18+3	2.05+3
45 Rh	9.12+3	8.04+3	7.22+3	6.45+3	5.51+3	5.14+3	4.74+3	4.33+3	3.94+3	3.53+3	3.11+3	2.69+3	2.36+3	2.22+3
46 Pd	9.78+3	8.62+3	7.74+3	6.92+3	5.91+3	5.51+3	5.09+3	4.65+3	4.23+3	3.79+3	3.33+3	2.89+3	2.53+3	2.38+3
47 Ag	1.04+4	9.17+3	8.25+3	7.39+3	6.32+3	5.90+3	5.44+3	4.98+3	4.53+3	4.07+3	3.58+3	3.11+3	2.73+3	2.56+3
48 Cd	1.08+4	9.57+3	8.62+3	7.73+3	6.86+3	6.56+3	6.25+3	5.92+3	5.61+3	5.29+3	4.95+3	4.62+3	4.27+3	3.92+3
49 In	1.14+4	1.01+4	9.12+3	8.19+3	7.27+3	6.96+3	6.62+3	6.28+3	5.95+3	5.61+3	5.25+3	4.91+3	4.54+3	4.17+3
50 Sn	1.12+4	9.89+3	9.52+3	8.57+3	7.62+3	7.29+3	6.94+3	6.59+3	6.24+3	5.89+3	5.51+3	5.15+3	4.76+3	4.38+3
51 Sb	1.17+4	1.04+4	9.36+3	8.95+3	7.99+3	7.66+3	7.29+3	6.92+3	6.56+3	6.18+3	5.79+3	5.41+3	5.01+3	4.60+3
52 Te	9.62+3	1.06+4	9.64+3	8.68+3	8.08+3	7.74+3	7.37+3	7.00+3	6.64+3	6.26+3	5.87+3	5.49+3	5.08+3	4.68+3
53 I	1.06+4	9.28+3	1.06+4	9.45+3	8.07+3	7.74+3	7.38+3	7.02+3	6.67+3	6.31+3	5.92+3	5.55+3	5.16+3	4.77+3
54 Xe	1.12+4	9.89+3	8.81+3	1.01+4	8.08+3	7.29+3	7.18+3	6.84+3	6.51+3	6.16+3	5.80+3	5.46+3	5.09+3	4.71+3
55 Cs	1.20+4	1.05+4	9.34+3	8.34+3	9.05+3	8.12+3	7.11+3	6.75+3	6.44+3	6.11+3	5.77+3	5.44+3	5.09+3	4.73+3
56 Ba	1.20+4	1.07+4	9.64+3	8.63+3	6.87+3	7.80+3	7.17+3	6.52+3	6.10+3	5.99+3	5.66+3	5.35+3	5.02+3	4.68+3
57 La	2.32+3	8.55+3	1.00+4	8.94+3	7.28+3	6.52+3	7.23+3	6.69+3	6.17+3	5.64+3	5.65+3	5.35+3	5.03+3	4.71+3
58 Ce	2.53+3	2.27+3	1.01+4	1.00+4	8.18+3	7.39+3	6.53+3	7.25+3	6.73+3	6.19+3	5.62+3	5.56+3	5.24+3	4.92+3
59 Pr	2.67+3	2.41+3	2.19+3	9.63+3	8.85+3	8.06+3	7.20+3	6.32+3	7.00+3	6.50+3	5.98+3	5.48+3	5.34+3	5.03+3
60 Nd	2.76+3	2.49+3	2.27+3	2.06+3	7.90+3	7.40+3	6.87+3	6.32+3	5.80+3	6.60+3	6.13+3	5.67+3	5.19+3	5.05+3
61 Pm	2.88+3	2.60+3	2.37+3	2.16+3	3.70+3	5.19+3	6.80+3	6.75+3	6.10+3	5.55+3	6.35+3	5.92+3	5.46+3	5.00+3
62 Sm	3.02+3	2.72+3	2.49+3	2.26+3	1.87+3	4.20+3	6.89+3	7.12+3	6.42+3	5.84+3	5.26+3	6.00+3	5.60+3	5.19+3
63 Eu	3.17+3	2.86+3	2.61+3	2.38+3	1.98+3	1.80+3	6.47+3	7.51+3	6.79+3	6.17+3	5.55+3	5.09+3	4.59+3	5.39+3
64 Gd	3.21+3	2.90+3	2.65+3	2.41+3	2.03+3	1.86+3	1.68+3	3.93+3	6.42+3	6.24+3	5.64+3	5.20+3	4.73+3	4.26+3
65 Tb	3.50+3	3.15+3	2.87+3	2.61+3	2.19+3	2.01+3	1.81+3	1.64+3	6.43+3	6.76+3	6.14+3	5.69+3	5.21+3	4.72+3
66 Dy	3.68+3	3.30+3	3.01+3	2.74+3	2.33+3	2.16+3	1.97+3	1.78+3	1.60+3	3.73+3	6.40+3	5.90+3	5.37+3	4.83+3
67 Ho	3.88+3	3.48+3	3.17+3	2.88+3	2.47+3	2.30+3	2.11+3	1.92+3	1.73+3	1.54+3	6.27+3	5.88+3	5.46+3	5.03+3
68 Er	4.13+3	3.70+3	3.37+3	3.06+3	2.63+3	2.45+3	2.26+3	2.06+3	1.87+3	1.68+3	1.48+3	2.33+3	3.56+3	4.80+3
69 Tm	4.41+3	3.96+3	3.60+3	3.27+3	2.80+3	2.61+3	2.41+3	2.20+3	1.99+3	1.78+3	1.57+3	1.45+3	2.77+3	4.84+3
70 Yb	4.62+3	4.14+3	3.76+3	3.41+3	2.96+3	2.77+3	2.58+3	2.37+3	2.18+3	1.98+3	1.77+3	1.56+3	1.38+3	2.24+3
71 Lu	4.78+3	4.28+3	3.90+3	3.54+3	3.07+3	2.88+3	2.67+3	2.47+3	2.27+3	2.06+3	1.84+3	1.63+3	1.44+3	1.33+3
72 Hf	5.02+3	4.51+3	4.11+3	3.72+3	3.22+3	3.03+3	2.81+3	2.59+3	2.39+3	2.17+3	1.94+3	1.72+3	1.53+3	1.41+3
73 Ta	5.28+3	4.74+3	4.32+3	3.92+3	3.32+3	3.07+3	2.80+3	2.52+3	2.25+3	2.10+3	1.96+3	1.83+3	1.69+3	1.54+3
74 W	5.53+3	4.97+3	4.53+3	4.11+3	3.49+3	3.23+3	2.94+3	2.65+3	2.36+3	2.21+3	2.06+3	1.92+3	1.77+3	1.62+3

TABLE 4 (continued)

Mass Attenuation Coefficients for $M\alpha$ Lines

Emitter	La	Ce	Pr	Nd	Sm	Eu	Gd	Tb	Dy	Ho	Er	Tm	Yb	Lu
Wavelength	1.49+1	1.40+1	1.33+1	1.27+1	1.15+1	1.10+1	1.05+1	1.00+1	9.59+0	9.20+0	8.82+0	8.48+0	8.15+0	7.84+0
Energy (keV)	8.33-1	8.83-1	9.29-1	9.78-1	1.08+0	1.13+0	1.19+0	1.24+0	1.29+0	1.35+0	1.41+0	1.46+0	1.52+0	1.58+0
Absorber														
75 Re	5.75+3	5.17+3	4.72+3	4.29+3	3.64+3	3.37+3	3.07+3	2.77+3	2.47+3	2.31+3	2.16+3	2.01+3	1.86+3	1.70+3
76 Os	5.93+3	5.33+3	4.87+3	4.43+3	3.81+3	3.55+3	3.28+3	2.99+3	2.72+3	2.44+3	2.16+3	2.04+3	1.92+3	1.80+3
77 Ir	6.29+3	5.66+3	5.17+3	4.70+3	4.05+3	3.78+3	3.48+3	3.18+3	2.89+3	2.59+3	2.29+3	2.17+3	2.04+3	1.91+3
78 Pt	6.64+3	5.98+3	5.46+3	4.97+3	4.28+3	3.99+3	3.68+3	3.36+3	3.05+3	2.74+3	2.42+3	2.29+3	2.15+3	2.01+3
79 Au	6.95+3	6.27+3	5.73+3	5.22+3	4.39+3	4.02+3	3.62+3	3.34+3	3.12+3	2.88+3	2.63+3	2.39+3	2.19+3	2.07+3
80 Hg	7.19+3	6.47+3	5.90+3	5.38+3	4.43+3	4.05+3	3.70+3	3.38+3	3.11+3	2.86+3	2.63+3	2.44+3	2.25+3	2.07+3
81 Tl	7.03+3	6.74+3	6.17+3	5.62+3	4.90+3	4.60+3	4.28+3	3.96+3	3.64+3	3.32+3	2.97+3	2.64+3	2.37+3	2.24+3
82 Pb	7.32+3	6.61+3	6.40+3	5.84+3	5.09+3	4.79+3	4.46+3	4.12+3	3.79+3	3.46+3	3.10+3	2.76+3	2.48+3	2.34+3
83 Bi	7.57+3	6.86+3	6.27+3	6.05+3	5.29+3	4.98+3	4.64+3	4.29+3	3.95+3	3.60+3	3.24+3	2.88+3	2.59+3	2.44+3
84 Po	7.95+3	7.21+3	6.61+3	6.04+3	5.56+3	5.23+3	4.87+3	4.51+3	4.16+3	3.80+3	3.41+3	3.04+3	2.74+3	2.58+3
85 At	8.39+3	7.61+3	6.99+3	6.40+3	5.71+3	5.38+3	5.02+3	4.66+3	4.31+3	3.95+3	3.57+3	3.20+3	2.90+3	2.73+3
86 Rn	8.55+3	7.64+3	6.98+3	6.39+3	5.33+3	5.21+3	4.88+3	4.55+3	4.22+3	3.89+3	3.54+3	3.19+3	2.90+3	2.74+3
87 Fr	7.76+3	7.99+3	7.27+3	6.66+3	5.61+3	5.13+3	4.98+3	4.65+3	4.34+3	4.01+3	3.66+3	3.33+3	3.04+3	2.87+3
88 Ra	7.98+3	7.24+3	6.62+3	6.84+3	5.85+3	5.39+3	4.89+3	4.76+3	4.45+3	4.12+3	3.78+3	3.45+3	3.16+3	2.98+3
89 Ac	8.11+3	7.38+3	6.77+3	6.92+3	6.00+3	5.56+3	5.09+3	4.61+3	4.49+3	4.18+3	3.85+3	3.54+3	3.26+3	3.08+3
90 Th	8.07+3	7.37+3	6.80+3	6.24+3	5.92+3	5.55+3	5.15+3	4.74+3	4.34+3	4.24+3	3.92+3	3.61+3	3.34+3	3.16+3
91 Pa	8.58+3	7.85+3	7.24+3	6.65+3	6.22+3	5.85+3	5.46+3	5.06+3	4.68+3	4.28+3	4.15+3	3.84+3	3.56+3	3.37+3
92 U	8.59+3	7.87+3	7.27+3	6.69+3	5.64+3	5.81+3	5.42+3	5.05+3	4.71+3	4.35+3	3.98+3	3.89+3	3.61+3	3.42+3
93 Np	8.77+3	8.18+3	7.61+3	7.01+3	5.96+3	5.48+3	5.64+3	5.29+3	4.96+3	4.61+3	4.25+3	3.90+3	3.82+3	3.61+3
94 Pu	8.21+3	8.31+3	7.97+3	7.34+3	6.27+3	5.78+3	5.26+3	5.49+3	5.15+3	4.79+3	4.41+3	4.05+3	3.70+3	3.67+3

TABLE 4 (continued)

Mass Attenuation Coefficients for $M\alpha$ Lines

Emitter	Hf	Ta	W	Re	Os	Ir	Pt	Au	Hg	Tl	Pb	Bi	Th	Pa
Wavelength	7.54+0	7.25+0	6.99+0	6.73+0	6.49+0	6.27+0	6.05+0	5.85+0	5.65+0	5.47+0	5.29+0	5.12+0	4.14+0	4.03+0
Energy (keV)	1.64+0	1.71+0	1.77+0	1.84+0	1.91+0	1.98+0	2.05+0	2.12+0	2.20+0	2.27+0	2.34+0	2.42+0	2.99+0	3.08+0
Absorber														
1 H	1.71+0	1.53+0	1.42+0	1.31+0	1.20+0	1.09+0	1.02+0	9.72-1	9.20-1	8.69-1	8.16-1	7.62-1	5.63-1	5.50-1
2 He	1.28+1	1.12+1	1.02+1	9.14+0	8.12+0	7.09+0	6.43+0	5.94+0	5.44+0	4.95+0	4.45+0	3.93+0	2.02+0	1.89+0
3 Li	4.98+1	4.33+1	3.94+1	3.54+1	3.14+1	2.74+1	2.48+1	2.29+1	2.09+1	1.90+1	1.70+1	1.50+1	7.33+0	6.81+0
4 Be	1.39+2	1.22+2	1.11+2	1.00+2	8.90+1	7.80+1	7.08+1	6.54+1	5.99+1	5.44+1	4.89+1	4.31+1	2.13+1	1.98+1
5 B	2.92+2	2.56+2	2.34+2	2.11+2	1.88+2	1.65+2	1.50+2	1.39+2	1.27+2	1.16+2	1.04+2	9.23+1	4.61+1	4.28+1
6 C	5.40+2	4.75+2	4.35+2	3.94+2	3.52+2	3.11+2	2.83+2	2.62+2	2.41+2	2.20+2	1.98+2	1.76+2	8.91+1	8.30+1
7 N	8.60+2	7.59+2	6.96+2	6.31+2	5.65+2	5.00+2	4.56+2	4.23+2	3.89+2	3.55+2	3.21+2	2.86+2	1.46+2	1.36+2
8 O	1.24+3	1.09+3	1.01+3	9.14+2	8.22+2	7.30+2	6.67+2	6.20+2	5.71+2	5.22+2	4.73+2	4.22+2	2.20+2	2.05+2
9 F	1.61+3	1.42+3	1.31+3	1.19+3	1.07+3	9.53+2	8.72+2	8.11+2	7.47+2	6.84+2	6.20+2	5.54+2	2.91+2	2.71+2
10 Ne	2.17+3	1.93+3	1.78+3	1.62+3	1.46+3	1.31+3	1.20+3	1.11+3	1.03+3	9.43+2	8.57+2	7.68+2	4.08+2	3.82+2
11 Na	2.70+3	2.41+3	2.22+3	2.02+3	1.83+3	1.63+3	1.50+3	1.39+3	1.29+3	1.18+3	1.07+3	9.62+2	5.14+2	4.80+2
12 Mg	3.41+3	3.04+3	2.81+3	2.56+3	2.32+3	2.08+3	1.91+3	1.78+3	1.65+3	1.51+3	1.38+3	1.24+3	6.69+2	6.26+2
13 Al	3.95+3	3.56+3	3.30+3	3.02+3	2.74+3	2.46+3	2.27+3	2.12+3	1.96+3	1.81+3	1.65+3	1.49+3	8.15+2	7.64+2
14 Si	4.23+2	3.75+2	3.42+2	3.72+3	3.41+3	3.10+3	2.87+3	2.68+3	2.48+3	2.28+3	2.08+3	1.87+3	1.02+3	9.58+2
15 P	5.21+2	4.64+2	4.28+2	3.91+2	3.54+2	3.17+2	2.87+2	2.61+2	2.71+3	2.52+3	2.32+3	2.12+3	1.18+3	1.11+3
16 S	6.63+2	5.91+2	5.45+2	4.98+2	4.50+2	4.03+2	3.70+2	3.45+2	3.19+2	2.93+2	2.66+2	2.39+2	1.43+3	1.34+3
17 Cl	7.80+2	6.95+2	6.42+2	5.87+2	5.31+2	4.76+2	4.38+2	4.08+2	3.78+2	3.48+2	3.18+2	2.86+2	1.59+3	1.50+3
18 Ar	8.81+2	7.85+2	7.24+2	6.61+2	5.98+2	5.34+2	4.91+2	4.58+2	4.24+2	3.90+2	3.56+2	3.20+2	1.76+2	1.64+2
19 K	1.13+3	1.01+3	9.29+2	8.48+2	7.68+2	6.87+2	6.32+2	5.90+2	5.46+2	5.03+2	4.59+2	4.13+2	2.28+2	2.14+2
20 Ca	1.42+3	1.31+3	1.19+3	1.07+3	9.47+2	8.25+2	7.52+2	7.02+2	6.51+2	6.00+2	5.49+2	4.95+2	2.74+2	2.57+2
21 Sc	1.55+3	1.42+3	1.30+3	1.17+3	1.03+3	9.01+2	8.21+2	7.67+2	7.11+2	6.56+2	5.99+2	5.41+2	2.99+2	2.81+2
22 Ti	1.74+3	1.60+3	1.46+3	1.31+3	1.16+3	1.02+3	9.26+2	8.66+2	8.04+2	7.42+2	6.80+2	6.15+2	3.40+2	3.19+2
23 V	1.94+3	1.78+3	1.62+3	1.46+3	1.30+3	1.13+3	1.04+3	9.67+2	8.96+2	8.26+2	7.55+2	6.81+2	3.74+2	3.51+2
24 Cr	2.25+3	2.07+3	1.89+3	1.70+3	1.51+3	1.32+3	1.21+3	1.13+3	1.04+3	9.63+2	8.80+2	7.94+2	4.38+2	4.10+2
25 Mn	2.47+3	2.27+3	2.07+3	1.87+3	1.66+3	1.46+3	1.33+3	1.24+3	1.15+3	1.07+3	9.78+2	8.85+2	4.89+2	4.58+2
26 Fe	2.81+3	2.59+3	2.37+3	2.13+3	1.90+3	1.67+3	1.52+3	1.43+3	1.33+3	1.23+3	1.13+3	1.02+3	5.65+2	5.30+2
27 Co	3.05+3	2.81+3	2.57+3	2.32+3	2.07+3	1.82+3	1.67+3	1.56+3	1.45+3	1.34+3	1.23+3	1.12+3	6.21+2	5.82+2
28 Ni	3.51+3	3.23+3	2.96+3	2.67+3	2.38+3	2.10+3	1.92+3	1.80+3	1.67+3	1.55+3	1.42+3	1.29+3	7.16+2	6.72+2
29 Cu	3.73+3	3.44+3	3.15+3	2.85+3	2.55+3	2.24+3	2.05+3	1.92+3	1.78+3	1.64+3	1.50+3	1.36+3	7.45+2	7.01+2
30 Zn	4.11+3	3.79+3	3.47+3	3.14+3	2.80+3	2.47+3	2.26+3	2.11+3	1.96+3	1.80+3	1.65+3	1.49+3	8.31+2	7.80+2
31 Ga	4.34+3	4.00+3	3.67+3	3.31+3	2.96+3	2.61+3	2.42+3	2.30+3	2.18+3	2.06+3	1.94+3	1.82+3	8.89+2	8.39+2
32 Ge	4.69+3	4.33+3	3.96+3	3.58+3	3.21+3	2.83+3	2.62+3	2.49+3	2.36+3	2.23+3	2.10+3	1.97+3	9.70+2	9.16+2
33 As	4.80+3	4.35+3	4.03+3	3.70+3	3.37+3	3.04+3	2.84+3	2.71+3	2.57+3	2.43+3	2.29+3	2.14+3	1.06+3	9.99+2
34 Se	4.39+3	4.63+3	4.29+3	3.94+3	3.59+3	3.24+3	3.02+3	2.88+3	2.73+3	2.58+3	2.43+3	2.28+3	1.13+3	1.07+3
35 Br	3.99+3	4.39+3	3.99+3	4.18+3	3.86+3	3.54+3	3.32+3	3.17+3	3.00+3	2.84+3	2.68+3	2.51+3	1.25+3	1.18+3
36 Kr	8.48+2	3.72+3	4.75+3	4.31+3	3.87+3	4.22+3	3.90+3	3.64+3	3.36+3	3.09+3	2.82+3	2.53+3	1.38+3	1.30+3
37 Rb	9.63+2	8.67+2	7.84+2	3.43+3	4.37+3	3.96+3	3.59+3	3.99+3	3.70+3	3.41+3	3.12+3	2.82+3	1.54+3	1.44+3

TABLE 4 (continued)

Mass Attenuation Coefficients for $M\alpha$ Lines

Emitter	Hf	Ta	W	Rf	Os	Ir	Pt	Au	Hg	Tl	Pb	Bi	Th	Pa
Wavelength	7.54+0	7.25+0	6.99+0	6.73+0	6.49+0	6.27+0	6.05+0	5.85+0	5.65+0	5.47+0	5.29+0	5.12+0	4.14+0	4.03+0
Energy (keV)	1.64+0	1.71+0	1.77+0	1.84+0	1.91+0	1.98+0	2.05+0	2.12+0	2.20+0	2.27+0	2.34+0	2.42+0	2.99+0	3.08+0
Absorber														
38 Sr	1.07+3	9.71+2	8.92+2	8.09+2	7.27+2	3.07+3	3.93+3	3.59+3	3.25+3	3.58+3	3.30+3	3.02+3	1.67+3	1.56+3
39 Y	1.26+3	1.16+3	1.07+3	9.66+2	8.65+2	7.64+2	6.87+2	2.78+3	3.56+3	3.27+3	2.98+3	3.26+3	1.83+3	1.71+3
40 Zr	1.38+3	1.27+3	1.17+3	1.06+3	9.46+2	8.36+2	7.61+2	7.04+2	6.45+2	2.54+3	3.26+3	2.99+3	1.99+3	1.87+3
41 Nb	1.52+3	1.41+3	1.29+3	1.17+3	1.04+3	9.23+2	8.43+2	7.83+2	7.22+2	6.61+2	5.99+2	2.32+3	2.18+3	2.04+3
42 Mo	1.63+3	1.51+3	1.38+3	1.25+3	1.12+3	9.91+2	9.11+2	8.56+2	7.99+2	7.43+2	6.86+2	6.27+2	2.33+3	2.19+3
43 Tc	1.74+3	1.60+3	1.47+3	1.33+3	1.20+3	1.06+3	9.73+2	9.16+2	8.57+2	7.99+2	7.40+2	6.79+2	2.04+3	2.27+3
44 Ru	1.90+3	1.76+3	1.61+3	1.46+3	1.31+3	1.16+3	1.06+3	9.94+2	9.24+2	8.55+2	7.85+2	7.12+2	2.19+3	2.04+3
45 Rh	2.06+3	1.91+3	1.75+3	1.58+3	1.42+3	1.26+3	1.15+3	1.08+3	1.00+3	9.29+2	8.53+2	7.74+2	4.72+2	1.53+3
46 Pd	2.21+3	2.04+3	1.88+3	1.70+3	1.53+3	1.35+3	1.24+3	1.16+3	1.08+3	9.98+2	9.16+2	8.31+2	4.91+2	4.58+2
47 Ag	2.38+3	2.20+3	2.02+3	1.83+3	1.64+3	1.46+3	1.34+3	1.25+3	1.16+3	1.08+3	9.88+2	8.97+2	5.32+2	4.99+2
48 Cd	3.55+3	3.17+3	2.79+3	2.39+3	2.00+3	1.60+3	1.41+3	1.32+3	1.23+3	1.14+3	1.04+3	9.46+2	5.40+2	5.13+2
49 In	3.78+3	3.37+3	2.97+3	2.55+3	2.13+3	1.71+3	1.51+3	1.41+3	1.31+3	1.22+3	1.12+3	1.01+3	5.79+2	5.50+2
50 Sn	3.97+3	3.54+3	3.12+3	2.68+3	2.24+3	1.80+3	1.59+3	1.49+3	1.39+3	1.29+3	1.18+3	1.07+3	6.15+2	5.84+2
51 Sb	4.17+3	3.73+3	3.29+3	2.83+3	2.37+3	1.91+3	1.69+3	1.59+3	1.48+3	1.37+3	1.26+3	1.14+3	6.54+2	6.20+2
52 Te	4.25+3	3.81+3	3.37+3	2.90+3	2.44+3	1.98+3	1.76+3	1.65+3	1.53+3	1.42+3	1.30+3	1.18+3	6.80+2	6.45+2
53 I	4.35+3	3.92+3	3.49+3	3.04+3	2.59+3	2.15+3	1.94+3	1.85+3	1.75+3	1.66+3	1.57+3	1.47+3	7.47+2	7.05+2
54 Xe	4.32+3	3.92+3	3.51+3	3.09+3	2.67+3	2.25+3	2.05+3	1.95+3	1.85+3	1.75+3	1.66+3	1.55+3	7.89+2	7.41+2
55 Cs	4.36+3	3.97+3	3.59+3	3.19+3	2.79+3	2.38+3	2.18+3	2.08+3	1.98+3	1.87+3	1.77+3	1.66+3	8.46+2	7.96+2
56 Ba	4.33+3	3.97+3	3.61+3	3.22+3	2.85+3	2.47+3	2.27+3	2.17+3	2.06+3	1.95+3	1.84+3	1.72+3	8.82+2	8.31+2
57 La	4.37+3	4.02+3	3.68+3	3.31+3	2.95+3	2.58+3	2.39+3	2.28+3	2.17+3	2.05+3	1.94+3	1.82+3	9.36+2	8.86+2
58 Ce	4.58+3	4.23+3	3.89+3	3.52+3	3.16+3	2.79+3	2.59+3	2.47+3	2.35+3	2.22+3	2.10+3	1.97+3	1.01+3	9.57+2
59 Pr	4.70+3	4.36+3	4.02+3	3.66+3	3.31+3	2.96+3	2.76+3	2.63+3	2.50+3	2.36+3	2.23+3	2.09+3	1.08+3	1.02+3
60 Nd	4.74+3	4.41+3	4.08+3	3.74+3	3.40+3	3.06+3	2.86+3	2.73+3	2.59+3	2.45+3	2.32+3	2.18+3	1.12+3	1.06+3
61 Pm	4.51+3	4.49+3	4.18+3	3.85+3	3.52+3	3.19+3	2.99+3	2.85+3	2.71+3	2.57+3	2.42+3	2.28+3	1.18+3	1.12+3
62 Sm	4.76+3	4.32+3	4.28+3	3.96+3	3.64+3	3.32+3	3.12+3	2.98+3	2.83+3	2.68+3	2.53+3	2.38+3	1.23+3	1.17+3
63 Eu	4.99+3	4.58+3	4.18+3	4.10+3	3.79+3	3.48+3	3.28+3	3.13+3	2.97+3	2.82+3	2.66+3	2.50+3	1.30+3	1.23+3
64 Gd	4.89+3	4.55+3	4.22+3	3.87+3	3.82+3	3.52+3	3.32+3	3.17+3	3.01+3	2.86+3	2.70+3	2.54+3	1.33+3	1.26+3
65 Tb	4.21+3	4.92+3	4.57+3	4.21+3	3.85+3	3.76+3	3.55+3	3.39+3	3.22+3	3.05+3	2.88+3	2.71+3	1.42+3	1.34+3
66 Dy	4.38+3	3.97+3	4.65+3	4.29+3	3.97+3	3.64+3	3.59+3	3.43+3	3.26+3	3.10+3	2.93+3	2.75+3	1.47+3	1.39+3
67 Ho	4.62+3	4.22+3	3.82+3	4.49+3	4.15+3	3.80+3	3.50+3	3.22+3	3.28+3	3.12+3	2.96+3	2.79+3	1.54+3	1.46+3
68 Er	4.89+3	4.46+3	4.03+3	3.65+3	4.33+3	3.98+3	3.68+3	3.40+3	3.12+3	3.16+3	3.00+3	2.84+3	1.61+3	1.53+3
69 Tm	5.17+3	4.72+3	4.27+3	3.88+3	3.55+3	4.19+3	3.86+3	3.60+3	3.32+3	3.05+3	3.05+3	2.89+3	1.69+3	1.61+3
70 Yb	3.67+3	4.85+3	4.42+3	4.04+3	3.71+3	3.38+3	4.03+3	3.71+3	3.37+3	3.14+3	2.91+3	2.89+3	1.74+3	1.66+3
71 Lu	2.79+3	4.96+3	4.56+3	4.20+3	3.88+3	3.57+3	3.23+3	3.70+3	3.47+3	3.25+3	3.03+3	2.80+3	1.81+3	1.72+3
72 Hf	1.29+3	2.01+3	3.84+3	4.37+3	4.07+3	3.76+3	3.44+3	3.12+3	3.46+3	3.37+3	3.16+3	2.94+3	1.88+3	1.79+3
73 Ta	1.39+3	1.24+3	3.83+3	5.25+3	4.80+3	4.34+3	3.97+3	3.63+3	3.94+3	3.66+3	3.38+3	3.09+3	2.12+3	2.00+3
74 W	1.46+3	1.30+3	1.18+3	3.57+3	4.88+3	4.45+3	4.10+3	3.78+3	3.45+3	3.12+3	3.45+3	3.18+3	2.20+3	2.07+3

TABLE 4 (continued)

Mass Attenuation Coefficients for $M\alpha$ Lines

Emitter		Hf	Ta	W	Rf	Os	Ir	Pt	Au	Hg	Tl	Pb	Bi	Th	Pa
Wavelength		7.54+0	7.25+0	6.99+0	6.73+0	6.49+0	6.27+0	6.05+0	5.85+0	5.65+0	5.47+0	5.29+0	5.12+0	4.14+0	4.03+0
Energy (keV)		1.64+0	1.71+0	1.77+0	1.84+0	1.91+0	1.98+0	2.05+0	2.12+0	2.20+0	2.27+0	2.34+0	2.42+0	2.99+0	3.08+0
Absorber															
75	Re	1.53+3	1.37+3	1.27+3	1.16+3	3.37+3	4.61+3	4.27+3	3.96+3	3.64+3	3.32+3	3.00+3	3.29+3	2.29+3	2.15+3
76	Os	1.66+3	1.53+3	1.39+3	1.25+3	1.12+3	3.18+3	4.37+3	4.08+3	3.78+3	3.48+3	3.18+3	2.86+3	2.15+3	2.20+3
77	Ir	1.77+3	1.62+3	1.48+3	1.33+3	1.19+3	1.08+3	3.02+3	4.15+3	3.86+3	3.58+3	3.30+3	3.01+3	2.24+3	2.09+3
78	Pt	1.87+3	1.71+3	1.56+3	1.40+3	1.25+3	1.14+3	1.04+3	9.51+2	2.68+3	3.74+3	3.45+3	3.16+3	2.15+3	2.20+3
79	Au	1.94+3	1.80+3	1.67+3	1.53+3	1.39+3	1.25+3	1.14+3	1.04+3	9.31+2	2.43+3	3.37+3	3.11+3	2.15+3	2.00+3
80	Hg	1.90+3	1.75+3	1.62+3	1.49+3	1.28+3	1.38+3	1.19+3	1.10+3	1.01+3	9.14+2	2.37+3	3.27+3	2.26+3	2.12+3
81	Tl	2.10+3	1.95+3	1.81+3	1.66+3	1.50+3	1.35+3	1.25+3	1.16+3	1.07+3	9.87+2	8.99+2	2.24+3	2.33+3	2.19+3
82	Pb	2.19+3	2.04+3	1.89+3	1.73+3	1.57+3	1.42+3	1.31+3	1.23+3	1.14+3	1.05+3	9.69+2	8.80+2	2.01+3	2.24+3
83	Bi	2.29+3	2.13+3	1.98+3	1.81+3	1.65+3	1.48+3	1.38+3	1.29+3	1.21+3	1.13+3	1.05+3	9.59+2	2.09+3	1.95+3
84	Po	2.42+3	2.26+3	2.09+3	1.92+3	1.74+3	1.57+3	1.46+3	1.37+3	1.28+3	1.19+3	1.11+3	1.01+3	2.17+3	2.04+3
85	At	2.56+3	2.39+3	2.21+3	2.03+3	1.85+3	1.66+3	1.54+3	1.45+3	1.36+3	1.27+3	1.17+3	1.07+3	2.28+3	2.14+3
86	Rn	2.57+3	2.39+3	2.22+3	2.03+3	1.85+3	1.67+3	1.54+3	1.45+3	1.36+3	1.27+3	1.17+3	1.08+3	1.51+3	2.12+3
87	Fr	2.69+3	2.51+3	2.33+3	2.13+3	1.94+3	1.75+3	1.62+3	1.53+3	1.43+3	1.33+3	1.23+3	1.13+3	6.82+2	1.45+3
88	Ra	2.80+3	2.61+3	2.42+3	2.22+3	2.02+3	1.82+3	1.69+3	1.59+3	1.49+3	1.39+3	1.28+3	1.18+3	7.02+2	6.54+2
89	Ac	2.89+3	2.69+3	2.50+3	2.29+3	2.09+3	1.88+3	1.76+3	1.69+3	1.61+3	1.53+3	1.45+3	1.36+3	7.43+2	6.90+2
90	Th	2.96+3	2.76+3	2.57+3	2.36+3	2.15+3	1.94+3	1.82+3	1.74+3	1.66+3	1.57+3	1.49+3	1.41+3	7.69+2	7.18+2
91	Pa	3.16+3	2.95+3	2.74+3	2.51+3	2.29+3	2.07+3	1.94+3	1.85+3	1.77+3	1.68+3	1.59+3	1.50+3	8.19+2	7.68+2
92	U	3.21+3	2.99+3	2.78+3	2.55+3	2.33+3	2.10+3	1.95+3	1.84+3	1.72+3	1.61+3	1.49+3	1.37+3	8.65+2	8.16+2
93	Np	3.39+3	3.16+3	2.93+3	2.70+3	2.46+3	2.22+3	2.08+3	1.99+3	1.90+3	1.80+3	1.71+3	1.61+3	8.81+2	8.37+2
94	Pu	3.45+3	3.23+3	3.00+3	2.77+3	2.54+3	2.30+3	2.16+3	2.07+3	1.97+3	1.87+3	1.77+3	1.67+3	9.10+2	8.63+2

TABLE 4 (continued)

Mass Attenuation Coefficients for $M\alpha$ Lines

Emitter	U	Emitter	U
Wavelength	3.92+0	Wavelength	3.92+0
Energy (keV)	3.17+0	Energy (keV)	3.17+0
Absorber		Absorber	
1 H	5.38-1	48 Cd	4.88+2
2 He	1.77+0	49 In	5.24+2
3 Li	6.33+0	50 Sn	5.56+2
4 Be	1.84+1	51 Sb	5.88+2
5 B	3.98+1	52 Te	6.13+2
6 C	7.72+1	53 I	6.69+2
7 N	1.27+2	54 Xe	7.00+2
8 O	1.91+2	55 Cs	7.54+2
9 F	2.53+2	56 Ba	7.86+2
10 Ne	3.56+2	57 La	8.44+2
11 Na	4.49+2	58 Ce	9.11+2
12 Mg	5.86+2	59 Pr	9.72+2
13 Al	7.15+2	60 Nd	1.01+3
14 Si	8.97+2	61 Pm	1.06+3
15 P	1.04+3	62 Sm	1.11+3
16 S	1.26+3	63 Eu	1.17+3
17 Cl	1.40+3	64 Gd	1.20+3
18 Ar	1.52+2	65 Tb	1.28+3
19 K	2.01+2	66 Dy	1.33+3
20 Ca	2.41+2	67 Ho	1.39+3
21 Sc	2.63+2	68 Er	1.46+3
22 Ti	2.99+2	69 Tm	1.53+3
23 V	3.29+2	70 Yb	1.58+3
24 Cr	3.85+2	71 Lu	1.64+3
25 Mn	4.29+2	72 Hf	1.71+3
26 Fe	4.96+2	73 Ta	1.88+3
27 Co	5.45+2	74 W	1.94+3
28 Ni	6.29+2	75 Re	2.02+3
29 Cu	6.59+2	76 Os	2.07+3
30 Zn	7.33+2	77 Ir	1.93+3
31 Ga	7.98+2	78 Pt	2.05+3
32 Ge	8.71+2	79 Au	2.05+3
33 As	9.50+2	80 Hg	1.97+3
34 Se	1.02+3	81 Tl	2.05+3
35 Br	1.12+3	82 Pb	2.11+3
36 Kr	1.21+3	83 Bi	1.81+3
37 Rb	1.35+3	84 Po	1.90+3
38 Sr	1.46+3	85 At	2.01+3
39 Y	1.60+3	86 Rn	1.99+3
40 Zr	1.75+3	87 Fr	2.02+3
41 Nb	1.91+3	88 Ra	1.39+3
42 Mo	2.05+3	89 Ac	6.40+2
43 Tc	2.13+3	90 Th	6.70+2
44 Ru	1.88+3	91 Pa	7.22+2
45 Rm	1.99+3	92 U	7.67+2
46 Pd	4.25+2	93 Np	7.99+2
47 Ag	4.67+2	94 Pu	8.22+2

TABLE 4 (continued)

Mass Attenuation Coefficients for $M\beta$ Lines

Emitter	La	Ce	Pr	Nd	Sm	Eu	Gd	Tb	Dy	Ho	Er	Tm	Yb	Lu
Wavelength	1.45+1	1.37+1	1.31+1	1.24+1	1.13+1	1.08+1	1.03+1	9.79+0	9.36+0	8.96+0	8.59+0	8.25+0	7.91+0	7.60+0
Energy (keV)	8.54−1	9.02−1	9.50−1	9.97−1	1.10+0	1.15+0	1.21+0	1.27+0	1.33+0	1.38+0	1.44+0	1.50+0	1.57+0	1.63+0
Absorber														
1 H	1.20+1	1.02+1	8.41+0	6.99+0	5.50+0	4.76+0	4.05+0	3.68+0	3.29+0	2.91+0	2.52+0	2.14+0	1.94+0	1.75+0
2 He	1.04+2	8.47+1	7.32+1	6.20+1	4.80+1	4.09+1	3.41+1	3.07+1	2.72+1	2.38+1	2.03+1	1.68+1	1.50+1	1.32+1
3 Li	3.77+2	3.13+2	2.72+2	2.31+2	1.81+2	1.55+2	1.30+2	1.18+2	1.04+2	9.14+1	7.80+1	6.49+1	5.80+1	5.12+1
4 Be	9.41+2	7.88+2	6.92+2	5.99+2	4.75+2	4.12+2	3.52+2	3.19+2	2.84+2	2.50+2	2.14+2	1.80+2	1.61+2	1.43+2
5 B	1.90+3	1.60+3	1.40+3	1.21+3	9.67+2	8.44+2	7.27+2	6.58+2	5.88+2	5.18+2	4.46+2	3.76+2	3.38+2	3.00+2
6 C	3.37+3	2.86+3	2.51+3	2.18+3	1.74+3	1.52+3	1.31+3	1.19+3	1.06+3	9.40+2	8.13+2	6.90+2	6.22+2	5.54+2
7 N	5.05+3	4.31+3	3.80+3	3.30+3	2.67+3	2.35+3	2.05+3	1.86+3	1.67+3	1.48+3	1.29+3	1.10+3	9.88+2	8.82+2
8 O	6.83+3	5.86+3	5.19+3	4.54+3	3.70+3	3.28+3	2.87+3	2.61+3	2.35+3	2.09+3	1.83+3	1.56+3	1.42+3	1.27+3
9 F	8.40+3	7.23+3	6.44+3	5.67+3	4.68+3	4.18+3	3.69+3	3.36+3	3.03+3	2.70+3	2.36+3	2.03+3	1.83+3	1.65+3
10 Ne	7.40+2	9.58+3	8.64+3	7.72+3	6.31+3	5.58+3	4.88+3	4.46+3	4.03+3	3.60+3	3.16+3	2.73+3	2.47+3	2.22+3
11 Na	9.95+2	8.46+2	7.47+2	6.50+2	7.76+3	6.89+3	6.05+3	5.53+3	5.00+3	4.47+3	3.92+3	3.39+3	3.08+3	2.77+3
12 Mg	1.40+3	1.19+3	1.05+3	9.15+2	7.37+2	6.47+2	5.57+2	4.91+2	5.92+3	5.37+3	4.83+3	4.25+3	3.86+3	3.49+3
13 Al	1.77+3	1.52+3	1.34+3	1.17+3	9.40+2	8.24+2	7.12+2	6.49+2	5.85+2	5.21+2	4.55+2	3.91+2	4.43+3	4.03+3
14 Si	2.33+3	1.99+3	1.76+3	1.54+3	1.25+3	1.10+3	9.58+2	8.75+2	7.89+2	7.04+2	6.16+2	5.30+2	4.81+2	4.33+2
15 P	2.87+3	2.46+3	2.17+3	1.90+3	1.53+3	1.35+3	1.17+3	1.07+3	9.65+2	8.62+2	7.56+2	6.52+2	5.92+2	5.33+2
16 S	3.63+3	3.11+3	2.76+3	2.41+3	1.95+3	1.72+3	1.49+3	1.36+3	1.23+3	1.10+3	9.63+2	8.31+2	7.54+2	6.79+2
17 Cl	4.20+3	3.61+3	3.20+3	2.80+3	2.27+3	2.00+3	1.75+3	1.60+3	1.44+3	1.29+3	1.13+3	9.76+2	8.86+2	7.98+2
18 Ar	4.81+3	4.13+3	3.66+3	3.20+3	2.59+3	2.29+3	1.99+3	1.82+3	1.64+3	1.46+3	1.28+3	1.10+3	1.00+3	9.02+2
19 K	6.03+3	5.19+3	4.61+3	4.04+3	3.28+3	2.90+3	2.53+3	2.31+3	2.09+3	1.87+3	1.64+3	1.41+3	1.28+3	1.16+3
20 Ca	7.08+3	6.10+3	5.43+3	4.78+3	3.86+3	3.40+3	2.95+3	2.70+3	2.44+3	2.19+3	1.93+3	1.68+3	1.56+3	1.45+3
21 Sc	7.67+3	6.62+3	5.89+3	5.17+3	4.19+3	3.68+3	3.20+3	2.93+3	2.66+3	2.38+3	2.10+3	1.83+3	1.70+3	1.58+3
22 Ti	8.47+3	7.33+3	6.53+3	5.74+3	4.66+3	4.10+3	3.57+3	3.27+3	2.97+3	2.67+3	2.35+3	2.05+3	1.91+3	1.77+3
23 V	9.27+3	8.05+3	7.18+3	6.33+3	5.14+3	4.54+3	3.95+3	3.63+3	3.29+3	2.96+3	2.61+3	2.28+3	2.12+3	1.97+3
24 Cr	1.07+4	9.34+3	8.34+3	7.35+3	5.98+3	5.27+3	4.59+3	4.21+3	3.82+3	3.43+3	3.03+3	2.65+3	2.47+3	2.29+3
25 Mn	1.14+4	1.00+4	8.94+3	7.91+3	6.45+3	5.71+3	4.99+3	4.58+3	4.16+3	3.74+3	3.31+3	2.90+3	2.70+3	2.51+3
26 Fe	1.29+4	1.12+4	1.01+4	8.93+3	7.30+3	6.47+3	5.67+3	5.21+3	4.73+3	4.26+3	3.77+3	3.30+3	3.08+3	2.86+3
27 Co	1.21+4	1.05+4	1.09+4	9.60+3	7.86+3	6.97+3	6.12+3	5.62+3	5.11+3	4.61+3	4.09+3	3.58+3	3.34+3	3.10+3
28 Ni	1.77+3	1.22+4	1.09+4	9.57+3	9.05+3	8.02+3	7.02+3	6.45+3	5.87+3	5.29+3	4.69+3	4.11+3	3.84+3	3.57+3
29 Cu	1.97+3	1.61+3	9.12+3	1.05+4	9.18+3	8.35+3	7.52+3	6.91+3	6.27+3	5.64+3	4.99+3	4.36+3	4.08+3	3.79+3
30 Zn	2.22+3	1.91+3	1.71+3	1.55+3	8.95+3	8.00+3	8.19+3	7.32+3	6.56+3	5.99+3	5.39+3	4.81+3	4.49+3	4.18+3
31 Ga	2.43+3	2.11+3	1.88+3	1.66+3	1.33+3	5.22+3	7.56+3	6.74+3	7.00+3	6.36+3	5.71+3	5.07+3	4.74+3	4.41+3
32 Ge	2.71+3	2.36+3	2.11+3	1.87+3	1.49+3	1.34+3	1.19+3	5.28+3	6.52+3	5.85+3	6.06+3	5.48+3	5.12+3	4.76+3
33 As	3.04+3	2.65+3	2.37+3	2.10+3	1.77+3	1.61+3	1.44+3	1.26+3	1.08+3	5.42+3	5.72+3	5.17+3	5.36+3	4.90+3
34 Se	3.34+3	2.91+3	2.61+3	2.31+3	1.99+3	1.83+3	1.66+3	1.49+3	1.32+3	1.14+3	9.65+2	5.39+3	4.93+3	4.48+3
35 Br	3.83+3	3.42+3	3.01+3	2.61+3	2.23+3	2.04+3	1.84+3	1.64+3	1.43+3	1.23+3	1.09+3	9.81+2	3.34+3	3.88+3
36 Kr	4.17+3	3.64+3	3.26+3	2.89+3	2.37+3	2.10+3	1.84+3	1.68+3	1.51+3	1.34+3	1.22+3	1.11+3	9.92+2	8.73+2
37 Rb	4.56+3	3.99+3	3.57+3	3.16+3	2.60+3	2.32+3	2.04+3	1.85+3	1.66+3	1.48+3	1.34+3	1.22+3	1.10+3	9.84+2

TABLE 4 (continued)

Mass Attenuation Coefficients for $M\beta$ Lines

Emitter		La	Ce	Pr	Nd	Sm	Eu	Gd	Tb	Dy	Ho	Fr	Tm	Yb	Lu
Wavelength		1.45+1	1.37+1	1.31+1	1.24+1	1.13+1	1.08+1	1.03+1	9.79+0	9.36+0	8.96+0	8.59+0	8.25+0	7.91+0	7.60+0
Energy (keV)		8.54-1	9.02-1	9.50-1	9.97-1	1.10+0	1.15+0	1.21+0	1.27+0	1.33+0	1.38+0	1.44+0	1.50+0	1.57+0	1.63+0
Absorber															
38	Sr	4.97+3	4.35+3	3.91+3	3.47+3	2.85+3	2.54+3	2.23+3	2.03+3	1.83+3	1.63+3	1.48+3	1.35+3	1.21+3	1.09+3
39	Y	5.50+3	4.82+3	4.33+3	3.85+3	3.16+3	2.81+3	2.48+3	2.28+3	2.08+3	1.88+3	1.67+3	1.47+3	1.38+3	1.28+3
40	Zr	5.95+3	5.22+3	4.70+3	4.18+3	3.44+3	3.06+3	2.70+3	2.48+3	2.26+3	2.05+3	1.82+3	1.61+3	1.50+3	1.40+3
41	Nb	6.60+3	5.79+3	5.20+3	4.63+3	3.81+3	3.39+3	2.98+3	2.75+3	2.51+3	2.27+3	2.02+3	1.78+3	1.66+3	1.55+3
42	Mo	7.00+3	6.14+3	5.53+3	4.93+3	4.06+3	3.62+3	3.19+3	2.94+3	2.68+3	2.42+3	2.16+3	1.90+3	1.78+3	1.66+3
43	Tc	7.35+3	6.47+3	5.83+3	5.20+3	4.53+3	4.20+3	3.85+3	3.49+3	3.13+3	2.76+3	2.39+3	2.03+3	1.89+3	1.76+3
44	Ru	8.05+3	7.09+3	6.39+3	5.70+3	4.97+3	4.60+3	4.22+3	3.83+3	3.43+3	3.03+3	2.62+3	2.22+3	2.08+3	1.93+3
45	Rh	8.67+3	7.65+3	6.89+3	6.15+3	5.37+3	4.97+3	4.56+3	4.14+3	3.70+3	3.28+3	2.83+3	2.40+3	2.25+3	2.09+3
46	Pd	9.29+3	8.20+3	7.39+3	6.60+3	5.76+3	5.34+3	4.89+3	4.44+3	3.97+3	3.51+3	3.04+3	2.58+3	2.41+3	2.25+3
47	Ag	9.87+3	8.72+3	7.88+3	7.05+3	6.16+3	5.71+3	5.24+3	4.76+3	4.26+3	3.77+3	3.27+3	2.78+3	2.60+3	2.42+3
48	Cd	1.03+4	9.12+3	8.24+3	7.38+3	6.75+3	6.43+3	6.10+3	5.77+3	5.43+3	5.09+3	4.73+3	4.38+3	4.00+3	3.63+3
49	In	1.09+4	9.64+3	8.73+3	7.83+3	7.15+3	6.82+3	6.47+3	6.12+3	5.76+3	5.40+3	5.02+3	4.65+3	4.25+3	3.86+3
50	Sn	1.07+4	1.01+4	9.12+3	8.20+3	7.50+3	7.15+3	6.79+3	6.42+3	6.04+3	5.66+3	5.27+3	4.88+3	4.47+3	4.05+3
51	Sb	1.11+4	9.94+3	9.46+3	8.60+3	7.87+3	7.50+3	7.13+3	6.74+3	6.34+3	5.95+3	5.54+3	5.13+3	4.70+3	4.27+3
52	Te	1.12+4	1.02+4	9.23+3	8.30+3	7.95+3	7.58+3	7.21+3	6.82+3	6.42+3	6.02+3	5.62+3	5.21+3	4.77+3	4.34+3
53	I	1.00+4	1.12+4	1.01+4	9.00+3	7.95+3	7.59+3	7.22+3	6.85+3	6.46+3	6.08+3	5.68+3	5.28+3	4.86+3	4.44+3
54	Xe	1.07+4	9.38+3	8.38+3	9.48+3	7.78+3	7.37+3	7.03+3	6.67+3	6.31+3	5.95+3	5.57+3	5.20+3	4.80+3	4.40+3
55	Cs	1.14+4	9.90+3	8.92+3	7.96+3	8.70+3	7.70+3	6.66+3	6.60+3	6.25+3	5.91+3	5.55+3	5.19+3	4.81+3	4.44+3
56	Ba	1.14+4	1.02+4	9.21+3	8.23+3	8.17+3	7.54+3	6.89+3	6.22+3	6.12+3	5.79+3	5.46+3	5.12+3	4.76+3	4.41+3
57	La	4.90+3	1.07+4	9.50+3	8.57+3	7.00+3	7.54+3	7.00+3	6.44+3	5.86+3	5.77+3	5.45+3	5.13+3	4.78+3	4.44+3
58	Ce	2.42+3	9.35+3	1.07+4	9.53+3	7.88+3	7.03+3	6.15+3	7.00+3	6.42+3	5.85+3	5.66+3	5.34+3	5.00+3	4.65+3
59	Pr	2.56+3	2.31+3	8.98+3	1.01+4	8.55+3	7.70+3	6.81+3	5.90+3	6.71+3	6.19+3	5.65+3	5.11+3	5.10+3	4.77+3
60	Nd	2.65+3	2.39+3	2.17+3	7.26+3	7.71+3	7.18+3	6.63+3	6.06+3	5.48+3	6.32+3	5.83+3	5.34+3	4.82+3	4.80+3
61	Pm	2.76+3	2.49+3	2.28+3	2.08+3	4.26+3	5.86+3	7.14+3	6.43+3	5.77+3	5.21+3	6.06+3	5.60+3	5.10+3	4.61+3
62	Sm	2.90+3	2.61+3	2.39+3	2.17+3	2.65+3	5.31+3	7.52+3	6.78+3	6.08+3	5.49+3	4.95+3	5.72+3	5.28+3	4.85+3
63	Eu	3.04+3	2.74+3	2.51+3	2.28+3	1.91+3	3.13+3	7.93+3	7.15+3	6.42+3	5.79+3	5.25+3	4.75+3	5.48+3	5.08+3
64	Gd	3.08+3	2.78+3	2.55+3	2.32+3	1.97+3	1.79+3	2.48+3	5.15+3	6.48+3	5.87+3	5.35+3	4.88+3	4.37+3	4.95+3
65	Tb	3.35+3	3.02+3	2.76+3	2.51+3	2.12+3	1.92+3	1.73+3	3.14+3	7.01+3	6.37+3	5.84+3	5.36+3	4.83+3	4.32+3
66	Dy	3.52+3	3.17+3	2.89+3	2.63+3	2.27+3	2.08+3	1.89+3	1.69+3	2.52+3	5.56+3	6.07+3	5.53+3	4.95+3	4.47+3
67	Ho	3.71+3	3.34+3	3.05+3	2.77+3	2.40+3	2.22+3	2.03+3	1.83+3	1.62+3	3.88+3	6.01+3	5.59+3	5.13+3	4.71+3
68	Er	3.95+3	3.55+3	3.24+3	2.94+3	2.56+3	2.37+3	2.17+3	1.97+3	1.76+3	1.55+3	1.94+3	3.18+3	4.51+3	4.98+3
69	Tm	4.22+3	3.79+3	3.46+3	3.14+3	2.73+3	2.53+3	2.31+3	2.10+3	1.87+3	1.65+3	1.49+3	2.13+3	4.36+3	5.27+3
70	Yb	4.42+3	3.96+3	3.61+3	3.27+3	2.89+3	2.69+3	2.49+3	2.28+3	2.06+3	1.85+3	1.63+3	1.42+3	1.93+3	3.36+3
71	Lu	4.57+3	4.10+3	3.74+3	3.40+3	3.00+3	2.79+3	2.58+3	2.37+3	2.15+3	1.93+3	1.70+3	1.48+3	1.36+3	2.26+3
72	Hf	4.80+3	4.32+3	3.94+3	3.57+3	3.15+3	2.94+3	2.72+3	2.49+3	2.26+3	2.03+3	1.79+3	1.56+3	1.44+3	1.32+3
73	Ta	5.05+3	4.54+3	4.15+3	3.76+3	3.23+3	2.96+3	2.68+3	2.39+3	2.16+3	2.02+3	1.87+3	1.73+3	1.57+3	1.42+3
74	W	5.30+3	4.76+3	4.35+3	3.95+3	3.39+3	3.11+3	2.81+3	2.51+3	2.26+3	2.12+3	1.97+3	1.82+3	1.66+3	1.50+3

TABLE 4 (continued)

Mass Attenuation Coefficients for $M\ \beta$ Lines

Emitter		La	Ce	Pr	Nd	Sm	Eu	Gd	Tb	Dy	Ho	Er	Tm	Yb	Lu
Wavelength		1.45+1	1.37+1	1.31+1	1.24+1	1.13+1	1.08+1	1.03+1	9.79+0	9.36+0	8.96+0	8.59+0	8.25+0	7.91+0	7.60+0
Energy (keV)		8.54−1	9.02−1	9.50−1	9.97−1	1.10+0	1.15+0	1.21+0	1.27+0	1.33+0	1.38+0	1.44+0	1.50+0	1.57+0	1.63+0
Absorber															
75	Re	5.51+3	4.96+3	4.53+3	4.12+3	3.54+3	3.25+3	2.94+3	2.62+3	2.37+3	2.22+3	2.06+3	1.90+3	1.73+3	1.57+3
76	Os	5.68+3	5.11+3	4.68+3	4.25+3	3.71+3	3.44+3	3.15+3	2.86+3	2.56+3	2.26+3	2.08+3	1.96+3	1.82+3	1.69+3
77	Ir	6.03+3	5.43+3	4.97+3	4.52+3	3.95+3	3.65+3	3.35+3	3.04+3	2.72+3	2.40+3	2.21+3	2.08+3	1.94+3	1.80+3
78	Pt	6.36+3	5.74+3	5.25+3	4.77+3	4.17+3	3.86+3	3.54+3	3.21+3	2.87+3	2.54+3	2.34+3	2.20+3	2.05+3	1.90+3
79	Au	6.67+3	6.02+3	5.51+3	5.02+3	4.25+3	3.86+3	3.47+3	3.23+3	2.98+3	2.73+3	2.48+3	2.23+3	2.09+3	1.96+3
80	Hg	6.87+3	6.23+3	5.67+3	5.20+3	4.28+3	3.90+3	3.55+3	3.24+3	2.96+3	2.72+3	2.50+3	2.31+3	2.11+3	1.94+3
81	Tl	7.16+3	6.47+3	5.93+3	5.41+3	4.78+3	4.47+3	4.14+3	3.80+3	3.45+3	3.11+3	2.75+3	2.41+3	2.27+3	2.13+3
82	Pb	7.02+3	6.71+3	6.16+3	5.62+3	4.98+3	4.65+3	4.31+3	3.96+3	3.60+3	3.24+3	2.87+3	2.52+3	2.37+3	2.22+3
83	Bi	7.27+3	6.60+3	6.35+3	5.84+3	5.17+3	4.84+3	4.48+3	4.12+3	3.75+3	3.38+3	3.00+3	2.63+3	2.48+3	2.32+3
84	Po	7.64+3	6.93+3	6.37+3	6.12+3	5.44+3	5.08+3	4.71+3	4.34+3	3.95+3	3.56+3	3.17+3	2.78+3	2.62+3	2.46+3
85	At	8.06+3	7.33+3	6.74+3	6.16+3	5.58+3	5.23+3	4.86+3	4.49+3	4.10+3	3.72+3	3.33+3	2.95+3	2.77+3	2.60+3
86	Rn	8.17+3	7.31+3	6.73+3	6.16+3	5.40+3	5.08+3	4.74+3	4.39+3	4.03+3	3.68+3	3.31+3	2.95+3	2.78+3	2.61+3
87	Fr	7.44+3	7.61+3	7.01+3	6.42+3	5.43+3	5.10+3	4.84+3	4.50+3	4.15+3	3.80+3	3.44+3	3.09+3	2.91+3	2.73+3
88	Ra	7.67+3	6.97+3	7.15+3	6.63+3	5.67+3	5.18+3	4.95+3	4.61+3	4.26+3	3.91+3	3.56+3	3.21+3	3.02+3	2.84+3
89	Ac	7.80+3	7.11+3	6.52+3	6.74+3	5.83+3	5.37+3	4.88+3	4.38+3	4.31+3	3.98+3	3.64+3	3.31+3	3.12+3	2.93+3
90	Th	7.77+3	7.11+3	6.56+3	6.02+3	5.78+3	5.38+3	4.97+3	4.54+3	4.10+3	4.04+3	3.72+3	3.40+3	3.20+3	3.01+3
91	Pa	8.27+3	7.57+3	6.99+3	6.41+3	6.08+3	5.69+3	5.29+3	4.88+3	4.45+3	4.03+3	3.95+3	3.62+3	3.41+3	3.20+3
92	U	8.29+3	7.60+3	7.02+3	6.46+3	5.46+3	5.65+3	5.25+3	4.88+3	4.50+3	4.13+3	3.99+3	3.67+3	3.46+3	3.25+3
93	Np	8.52+3	7.95+3	7.36+3	6.77+3	5.78+3	5.27+3	5.49+3	5.13+3	4.76+3	4.39+3	4.02+3	3.88+3	3.66+3	3.43+3
94	Pu	8.25+3	8.32+3	7.70+3	7.10+3	6.09+3	5.57+3	5.69+3	5.32+3	4.94+3	4.56+3	4.17+3	3.79+3	3.72+3	3.50+3

TABLE 4 (continued)

Mass Attenuation Coefficients for $M\beta$ Lines

Emitter	Hf	Ta	W	Re	Os	Ir	Pt	Au	Hg	Tl	Pb	Bi	Th	Pa
Wavelength	7.30+0	7.02+0	6.76+0	6.50+0	6.27+0	6.04+0	5.83+0	5.62+0	5.43+0	5.25+0	5.08+0	4.91+0	3.94+0	3.83+0
Energy (keV)	1.70+0	1.77+0	1.83+0	1.91+0	1.98+0	2.05+0	2.13+0	2.20+0	2.28+0	2.36+0	2.44+0	2.53+0	3.15+0	3.24+0
Absorber														
1 H	1.55+0	1.44+0	1.32+0	1.21+0	1.09+0	1.02+0	9.68-1	9.14-1	8.59-1	8.03-1	7.46-1	6.98-1	5.40-1	5.27-1
2 He	1.14+1	1.03+1	9.26+0	8.18+0	7.08+0	6.40+0	5.90+0	5.38+0	4.86+0	4.32+0	3.78+0	3.33+0	1.80+0	1.67+0
3 Li	4.41+1	4.00+1	3.59+1	3.17+1	2.74+1	2.47+1	2.28+1	2.07+1	1.86+1	1.65+1	1.44+1	1.26+1	6.44+0	5.92+0
4 Be	1.24+2	1.12+2	1.01+2	8.97+1	7.80+1	7.05+1	6.50+1	5.92+1	5.34+1	4.75+1	4.15+1	3.64+1	1.87+1	1.72+1
5 B	2.60+2	2.37+2	2.14+2	1.90+2	1.65+2	1.50+2	1.38+2	1.26+2	1.14+2	1.01+2	8.88+1	7.81+1	4.05+1	3.73+1
6 C	4.83+2	4.41+2	3.98+2	3.55+2	3.11+2	2.82+2	2.60+2	2.38+2	2.16+2	1.93+2	1.69+2	1.49+2	7.85+1	7.23+1
7 N	7.72+2	7.05+2	6.38+2	5.69+2	5.00+2	4.54+2	4.20+2	3.85+2	3.49+2	3.12+2	2.75+2	2.43+2	1.29+2	1.19+2
8 O	1.11+3	1.02+3	9.24+2	8.27+2	7.29+2	6.64+2	6.16+2	5.64+2	5.13+2	4.60+2	4.07+2	3.61+2	1.94+2	1.79+2
9 F	1.45+3	1.33+3	1.20+3	1.08+3	9.52+2	8.68+2	8.05+2	7.39+2	6.72+2	6.04+2	5.35+2	4.76+2	2.57+2	2.38+2
10 Ne	1.96+3	1.80+3	1.64+3	1.47+3	1.31+3	1.19+3	1.11+3	1.02+3	9.27+2	8.35+2	7.42+2	6.61+2	3.62+2	3.35+2
11 Na	2.45+3	2.25+3	2.04+3	1.84+3	1.63+3	1.49+3	1.38+3	1.27+3	1.16+3	1.05+3	9.30+2	8.30+2	4.56+2	4.22+2
12 Mg	3.09+3	2.84+3	2.59+3	2.34+3	2.08+3	1.90+3	1.77+3	1.63+3	1.49+3	1.34+3	1.20+3	1.07+3	5.95+2	5.51+2
13 Al	3.62+3	3.33+3	3.05+3	2.76+3	2.46+3	2.26+3	2.10+3	1.94+3	1.78+3	1.61+3	1.44+3	1.29+3	7.26+2	6.74+2
14 Si	3.82+2	3.46+2	3.10+2	3.43+3	3.10+3	2.86+3	2.66+3	2.45+3	2.24+3	2.03+3	1.81+3	1.63+3	9.11+2	8.45+2
15 P	4.71+2	4.33+2	3.95+2	3.56+2	3.16+2	2.85+2	2.59+2	2.69+3	2.48+3	2.27+3	2.06+3	1.87+3	1.05+3	9.79+2
16 S	6.00+2	5.52+2	5.03+2	4.53+2	4.03+2	3.69+2	3.43+2	3.15+2	2.88+2	2.60+2	2.31+2	2.25+3	1.28+3	1.19+3
17 Cl	7.07+2	6.50+2	5.93+2	5.35+2	4.75+2	4.36+2	4.06+2	3.74+2	3.43+2	3.10+2	2.77+2	2.48+2	1.42+3	1.33+3
18 Ar	7.97+2	7.33+2	6.68+2	6.01+2	5.34+2	4.89+2	4.55+2	4.19+2	3.84+2	3.47+2	3.10+2	2.78+2	1.54+2	1.45+3
19 K	1.02+3	9.39+2	8.57+2	7.72+2	6.87+2	6.29+2	5.86+2	5.40+2	4.94+2	4.47+2	4.00+2	3.59+2	2.04+2	1.90+2
20 Ca	1.33+3	1.21+3	1.08+3	9.54+2	8.25+2	7.49+2	6.98+2	6.44+2	5.90+2	5.35+2	4.80+2	4.31+2	2.45+2	2.28+2
21 Sc	1.45+3	1.32+3	1.18+3	1.04+3	9.00+2	8.18+2	7.62+2	7.04+2	6.45+2	5.85+2	5.24+2	4.72+2	2.67+2	2.49+2
22 Ti	1.63+3	1.48+3	1.33+3	1.17+3	1.01+3	9.23+2	8.61+2	7.96+2	7.31+2	6.64+2	5.96+2	5.37+2	3.03+2	2.82+2
23 V	1.81+3	1.65+3	1.48+3	1.31+3	1.13+3	1.03+3	9.61+2	8.87+2	8.12+2	7.36+2	6.59+2	5.93+2	3.34+2	3.10+2
24 Cr	2.10+3	1.91+3	1.72+3	1.52+3	1.32+3	1.20+3	1.12+3	1.03+3	9.47+2	8.59+2	7.69+2	6.92+2	3.91+2	3.63+2
25 Mn	2.31+3	2.10+3	1.89+3	1.67+3	1.45+3	1.32+3	1.24+3	1.14+3	1.05+3	9.55+2	8.58+2	7.74+2	4.36+2	4.05+2
26 Fe	2.63+3	2.40+3	2.16+3	1.91+3	1.67+3	1.52+3	1.42+3	1.31+3	1.21+3	1.10+3	9.92+2	8.96+2	5.04+2	4.68+2
27 Co	2.86+3	2.61+3	2.35+3	2.09+3	1.82+3	1.66+3	1.55+3	1.44+3	1.32+3	1.21+3	1.09+3	9.84+2	5.54+2	5.15+2
28 Ni	3.29+3	3.00+3	2.70+3	2.40+3	2.09+3	1.91+3	1.79+3	1.66+3	1.53+3	1.39+3	1.26+3	1.14+3	6.39+2	5.94+2
29 Cu	3.50+3	3.19+3	2.88+3	2.56+3	2.24+3	2.04+3	1.91+3	1.76+3	1.62+3	1.47+3	1.32+3	1.18+3	6.69+2	6.24+2
30 Zn	3.85+3	3.52+3	3.17+3	2.82+3	2.47+3	2.25+3	2.10+3	1.94+3	1.77+3	1.61+3	1.44+3	1.30+3	7.44+2	6.93+2
31 Ga	4.06+3	3.71+3	3.35+3	2.98+3	2.61+3	2.41+3	2.29+3	2.17+3	2.04+3	1.91+3	1.78+3	1.65+3	8.07+2	7.63+2
32 Ge	4.39+3	4.01+3	3.63+3	3.23+3	2.83+3	2.61+3	2.48+3	2.35+3	2.21+3	2.07+3	1.93+3	1.79+3	8.81+2	8.33+2
33 As	4.41+3	4.07+3	3.74+3	3.39+3	3.04+3	2.84+3	2.70+3	2.55+3	2.40+3	2.25+3	2.10+3	1.94+3	9.61+2	9.09+2
34 Se	4.69+3	4.34+3	3.98+3	3.61+3	3.23+3	3.01+3	2.87+3	2.71+3	2.55+3	2.39+3	2.23+3	2.07+3	1.03+3	9.72+2
35 Br	4.43+3	4.05+3	4.22+3	3.88+3	3.53+3	3.31+3	3.15+3	2.98+3	2.81+3	2.63+3	2.46+3	2.27+3	1.13+3	1.07+3
36 Kr	3.79+3	4.81+3	4.36+3	3.89+3	4.21+3	3.89+3	3.61+3	3.33+3	3.04+3	2.75+3	2.45+3	2.19+3	1.23+3	1.14+3
37 Rb	8.82+2	7.96+2	3.47+3	4.40+3	3.96+3	3.57+3	3.97+3	3.67+3	3.36+3	3.04+3	2.73+3	2.45+3	1.37+3	1.27+3

TABLE 4 (continued)

Mass Attenuation Coefficients for $M\beta$ Lines

Emitter	Hf	Ta	W	Re	Os	Ir	Pt	Au	Hg	Tl	Pb	Bi	Th	Pa
Wavelength	7.30+0	7.02+0	6.76+0	6.50+0	6.27+0	6.84+0	5.83+0	5.62+0	5.43+0	5.25+0	5.08+0	4.91+0	3.94+0	3.83+0
Energy (keV)	1.70+0	1.77+0	1.83+0	1.91+0	1.98+0	2.05+0	2.13+0	2.20+0	2.28+0	2.36+0	2.44+0	2.53+0	3.15+0	3.24+0
Absorber														
38 Sr	9.87+2	9.03+2	8.19+2	7.32+2	3.07+3	3.91+3	3.56+3	3.20+3	3.53+3	3.23+3	2.93+3	2.66+3	1.49+3	1.38+3
39 Y	1.18+3	1.08+3	9.77+2	8.71+2	7.64+2	6.83+2	2.76+3	3.53+3	3.22+3	2.90+3	3.18+3	2.92+3	1.63+3	1.51+3
40 Zr	1.29+3	1.18+3	1.07+3	9.52+2	8.35+2	7.58+2	6.99+2	6.37+2	2.49+3	3.19+3	2.91+3	2.64+3	1.77+3	1.65+3
41 Nb	1.43+3	1.30+3	1.18+3	1.05+3	9.23+2	8.39+2	7.78+2	7.14+2	6.49+2	5.83+2	2.26+3	2.90+3	1.94+3	1.80+3
42 Mo	1.53+3	1.40+3	1.27+3	1.13+3	9.90+2	9.08+2	8.51+2	7.92+2	7.33+2	6.72+2	6.10+2	2.21+3	2.08+3	1.93+3
43 Tc	1.63+3	1.49+3	1.35+3	1.20+3	1.06+3	9.70+2	9.11+2	8.50+2	7.88+2	7.25+2	6.61+2	6.02+2	2.16+3	2.01+3
44 Ru	1.79+3	1.63+3	1.48+3	1.32+3	1.16+3	1.06+3	9.88+2	9.15+2	8.42+2	7.67+2	6.91+2	6.26+2	1.92+3	2.11+3
45 Rh	1.93+3	1.77+3	1.60+3	1.43+3	1.26+3	1.15+3	1.07+3	9.95+2	9.15+2	8.34+2	7.51+2	6.81+2	1.44+3	1.88+3
46 Pd	2.07+3	1.90+3	1.72+3	1.54+3	1.35+3	1.23+3	1.15+3	1.07+3	9.82+2	8.95+2	8.06+2	7.30+2	4.33+2	1.46+3
47 Ag	2.24+3	2.05+3	1.85+3	1.66+3	1.46+3	1.33+3	1.24+3	1.15+3	1.06+3	9.66+2	8.70+2	7.88+2	4.75+2	4.40+2
48 Cd	3.24+3	2.84+3	2.44+3	2.02+3	1.60+3	1.40+3	1.31+3	1.22+3	1.12+3	1.02+3	9.18+2	8.31+2	4.94+2	4.68+2
49 In	3.45+3	3.03+3	2.60+3	2.16+3	1.71+3	1.50+3	1.40+3	1.30+3	1.20+3	1.09+3	9.84+2	8.91+2	5.30+2	5.02+2
50 Sn	3.62+3	3.18+3	2.73+3	2.27+3	1.80+3	1.59+3	1.48+3	1.38+3	1.27+3	1.15+3	1.04+3	9.44+2	5.62+2	5.32+2
51 Sb	3.82+3	3.36+3	2.88+3	2.40+3	1.91+3	1.69+3	1.58+3	1.46+3	1.35+3	1.23+3	1.11+3	1.00+3	5.96+2	5.62+2
52 Te	3.89+3	3.43+3	2.96+3	2.47+3	1.98+3	1.75+3	1.64+3	1.52+3	1.40+3	1.27+3	1.15+3	1.04+3	6.20+2	5.86+2
53 I	4.00+3	3.55+3	3.09+3	2.62+3	2.15+3	1.93+3	1.84+3	1.74+3	1.64+3	1.54+3	1.44+3	1.34+3	6.77+2	6.39+2
54 Xe	3.99+3	3.57+3	3.14+3	2.70+3	2.25+3	2.04+3	1.94+3	1.84+3	1.74+3	1.63+3	1.52+3	1.41+3	7.09+2	6.65+2
55 Cs	4.04+3	3.64+3	3.23+3	2.81+3	2.38+3	2.18+3	2.07+3	1.96+3	1.85+3	1.74+3	1.63+3	1.51+3	7.64+2	7.18+2
56 Ba	4.03+3	3.66+3	3.27+3	2.87+3	2.47+3	2.27+3	2.16+3	2.04+3	1.93+3	1.81+3	1.69+3	1.57+3	7.97+2	7.49+2
57 La	4.09+3	3.72+3	3.35+3	2.97+3	2.58+3	2.38+3	2.27+3	2.15+3	2.03+3	1.91+3	1.78+3	1.66+3	8.54+2	8.09+2
58 Ce	4.30+3	3.93+3	3.56+3	3.18+3	2.79+3	2.58+3	2.46+3	2.33+3	2.20+3	2.07+3	1.93+3	1.79+3	9.22+2	8.73+2
59 Pr	4.42+3	4.07+3	3.70+3	3.33+3	2.96+3	2.75+3	2.62+3	2.48+3	2.34+3	2.20+3	2.05+3	1.91+3	9.83+2	9.31+2
60 Nd	4.47+3	4.13+3	3.78+3	3.42+3	3.06+3	2.85+3	2.71+3	2.57+3	2.43+3	2.28+3	2.13+3	1.98+3	1.03+3	9.71+2
61 Pm	4.55+3	4.22+3	3.89+3	3.54+3	3.19+3	2.98+3	2.84+3	2.69+3	2.54+3	2.39+3	2.23+3	2.07+3	1.08+3	1.02+3
62 Sm	4.40+3	4.32+3	3.99+3	3.66+3	3.32+3	3.11+3	2.96+3	2.81+3	2.65+3	2.49+3	2.33+3	2.17+3	1.13+3	1.07+3
63 Eu	4.66+3	4.23+3	4.14+3	3.81+3	3.48+3	3.27+3	3.11+3	2.95+3	2.79+3	2.62+3	2.45+3	2.28+3	1.19+3	1.13+3
64 Gd	4.61+3	4.27+3	3.91+3	3.84+3	3.52+3	3.31+3	3.16+3	2.99+3	2.83+3	2.66+3	2.49+3	2.31+3	1.21+3	1.15+3
65 Tb	4.98+3	4.62+3	4.25+3	3.87+3	3.75+3	3.54+3	3.37+3	3.20+3	3.02+3	2.84+3	2.66+3	2.47+3	1.29+3	1.23+3
66 Dy	4.05+3	4.70+3	4.33+3	3.99+3	3.64+3	3.58+3	3.41+3	3.24+3	3.06+3	2.89+3	2.70+3	2.52+3	1.34+3	1.27+3
67 Ho	4.30+3	3.88+3	4.53+3	4.17+3	3.80+3	3.48+3	3.19+3	3.26+3	3.09+3	2.91+3	2.74+3	2.56+3	1.41+3	1.33+3
68 Er	4.54+3	4.09+3	3.69+3	4.35+3	3.98+3	3.66+3	3.38+3	3.08+3	3.13+3	2.96+3	2.79+3	2.61+3	1.47+3	1.40+3
69 Tm	4.80+3	4.33+3	3.92+3	3.57+3	4.19+3	3.85+3	3.57+3	3.29+3	3.00+3	3.01+3	2.84+3	2.67+3	1.55+3	1.47+3
70 Yb	4.86+3	4.48+3	4.08+3	3.73+3	3.38+3	4.01+3	3.68+3	3.34+3	3.09+3	2.85+3	2.83+3	2.62+3	1.60+3	1.52+3
71 Lu	4.92+3	4.61+3	4.24+3	3.90+3	3.56+3	3.21+3	3.68+3	3.44+3	3.21+3	2.97+3	2.73+3	2.70+3	1.66+3	1.57+3
72 Hf	1.67+3	3.59+3	4.40+3	4.08+3	3.76+3	3.42+3	3.09+3	3.55+3	3.33+3	3.10+3	2.87+3	2.64+3	1.72+3	1.64+3
73 Ta	1.26+3	3.88+3	5.30+3	4.82+3	4.34+3	3.95+3	3.60+3	3.91+3	3.61+3	3.31+3	3.00+3	3.01+3	1.90+3	1.77+3
74 W	1.33+3	1.19+3	3.61+3	4.91+3	4.45+3	4.08+3	3.75+3	3.40+3	3.67+3	3.39+3	3.10+3	2.82+3	1.97+3	1.84+3

TABLE 4 (continued)

Mass Attenuation Coefficients for $M\beta$ Lines

Emitter		Hf	Ta	W	Re	Os	Ir	Pt	Au	Hg	Tl	Pb	Bi	Th	Pa
Wavelength		7.30+0	7.02+0	6.76+0	6.50+0	6.27+0	6.84+0	5.83+0	5.62+0	5.43+0	5.25+0	5.08+0	4.91+0	3.94+0	3.83+0
Energy (keV)		1.70+0	1.77+0	1.83+0	1.91+0	1.98+0	2.05+0	2.13+0	2.20+0	2.28+0	2.36+0	2.44+0	2.53+0	3.15+0	3.24+0
Absorber															
75	Re	1.39+3	1.28+3	1.17+3	3.39+3	4.61+3	4.25+3	3.93+3	3.60+3	3.26+3	2.91+3	3.21+3	2.94+3	2.05+3	1.91+3
76	Os	1.55+3	1.41+3	1.27+3	1.12+3	3.18+3	4.35+3	4.05+3	3.74+3	3.42+3	3.10+3	2.77+3	3.04+3	2.10+3	1.96+3
77	Ir	1.65+3	1.50+3	1.35+3	1.19+3	1.08+3	3.01+3	4.12+3	3.83+3	3.53+3	3.23+3	2.92+3	2.63+3	1.97+3	2.02+3
78	Pt	1.74+3	1.58+3	1.42+3	1.26+3	1.14+3	1.04+3	2.91+3	3.98+3	3.68+3	3.38+3	3.08+3	2.79+3	2.09+3	1.93+3
79	Au	1.83+3	1.69+3	1.54+3	1.40+3	1.25+3	1.13+3	1.03+3	9.18+2	2.39+3	3.31+3	3.03+3	2.78+3	1.89+3	1.94+3
80	Hg	1.78+3	1.63+3	1.50+3	1.39+3	1.28+3	1.19+3	1.09+3	9.95+2	8.96+2	2.32+3	3.19+3	2.93+3	2.00+3	1.85+3
81	Tl	1.98+3	1.83+3	1.67+3	1.51+3	1.35+3	1.24+3	1.15+3	1.06+3	9.71+2	8.77+2	2.19+3	3.03+3	2.08+3	1.93+3
82	Pb	2.07+3	1.91+3	1.75+3	1.58+3	1.42+3	1.30+3	1.22+3	1.13+3	1.04+3	9.47+2	8.54+2	2.08+3	2.14+3	2.00+3
83	Bi	2.16+3	2.00+3	1.83+3	1.66+3	1.48+3	1.37+3	1.29+3	1.20+3	1.11+3	1.02+3	9.34+2	8.43+2	1.84+3	2.05+3
84	Po	2.29+3	2.11+3	1.94+3	1.75+3	1.57+3	1.45+3	1.36+3	1.27+3	1.18+3	1.08+3	9.87+2	9.00+2	1.93+3	1.78+3
85	At	2.42+3	2.24+3	2.05+3	1.86+3	1.66+3	1.54+3	1.44+3	1.35+3	1.25+3	1.15+3	1.05+3	9.54+2	2.04+3	1.89+3
86	Rn	2.43+3	2.24+3	2.05+3	1.86+3	1.66+3	1.54+3	1.45+3	1.35+3	1.25+3	1.15+3	1.05+3	9.57+2	2.02+3	1.88+3
87	Fr	2.54+3	2.35+3	2.16+3	1.95+3	1.75+3	1.62+3	1.52+3	1.42+3	1.31+3	1.21+3	1.10+3	1.01+3	2.05+3	1.92+3
88	Ra	2.64+3	2.44+3	2.24+3	2.03+3	1.82+3	1.68+3	1.58+3	1.47+3	1.37+3	1.26+3	1.15+3	1.05+3	1.41+3	1.31+3
89	Ac	2.73+3	2.52+3	2.31+3	2.10+3	1.88+3	1.76+3	1.68+3	1.60+3	1.51+3	1.43+3	1.34+3	1.25+3	6.51+2	1.36+3
90	Th	2.80+3	2.59+3	2.38+3	2.16+3	1.94+3	1.81+3	1.73+3	1.65+3	1.56+3	1.47+3	1.38+3	1.29+3	6.81+2	6.30+2
91	Pa	2.99+3	2.76+3	2.54+3	2.30+3	2.07+3	1.93+3	1.85+3	1.75+3	1.66+3	1.57+3	1.47+3	1.37+3	7.33+2	6.83+2
92	U	3.03+3	2.81+3	2.58+3	2.34+3	2.10+3	1.95+3	1.83+3	1.71+3	1.59+3	1.46+3	1.34+3	1.23+3	7.79+2	7.27+2
93	Np	3.20+3	2.96+3	2.72+3	2.47+3	2.22+3	2.08+3	1.98+3	1.88+3	1.78+3	1.68+3	1.58+3	1.47+3	8.08+2	7.68+2
94	Pu	3.27+3	3.03+3	2.79+3	2.55+3	2.30+3	2.15+3	2.06+3	1.95+3	1.85+3	1.75+3	1.64+3	1.53+3	8.32+2	7.88+2

TABLE 4 (continued)

Mass Attenuation Coefficients for $M\beta$ Lines

Emitter		U	Emitter		U
Wavelength		3.72+0	Wavelength		3.72+0
Energy (keV)		3.34+0	Energy (keV)		3.34+0
Absorber			Absorber		
1	H	5.14-1	48	Cd	4.40+2
2	He	1.53+0	49	In	4.72+2
3	Li	5.39+0	50	Sn	5.01+2
4	Be	1.56+1	51	Sb	5.27+2
5	B	3.39+1	52	Te	5.50+2
6	C	6.59+1	53	I	5.99+2
7	N	1.09+2	54	Xe	6.19+2
8	O	1.64+2	55	Cs	6.71+2
9	F	2.18+2	56	Ba	7.00+2
10	Ne	3.07+2	57	La	7.63+2
11	Na	3.87+2	58	Ce	8.23+2
12	Mg	5.07+2	59	Pr	8.78+2
13	Al	6.20+2	60	Nd	9.16+2
14	Si	7.77+2	61	Pm	9.61+2
15	P	9.01+2	62	Sm	1.01+3
16	S	1.09+3	63	Eu	1.06+3
17	Cl	1.22+3	64	Gd	1.09+3
18	Ar	1.34+3	65	Tb	1.16+3
19	K	1.75+2	66	Dy	1.20+3
20	Ca	2.10+2	67	Ho	1.26+3
21	Sc	2.29+2	68	Er	1.32+3
22	Ti	2.60+2	69	Tm	1.39+3
23	V	2.86+2	70	Yb	1.43+3
24	Cr	3.35+2	71	Lu	1.49+3
25	Mn	3.74+2	72	Hf	1.54+3
26	Fe	4.31+2	73	Ta	1.64+3
27	Co	4.74+2	74	W	1.70+3
28	Ni	5.47+2	75	Re	1.77+3
29	Cu	5.79+2	76	Os	1.82+3
30	Zn	6.40+2	77	Ir	1.88+3
31	Ga	7.18+2	78	Pt	1.96+3
32	Ge	7.83+2	79	Au	1.80+3
33	As	8.55+2	80	Hg	1.88+3
34	Se	9.15+2	81	Tl	1.78+3
35	Br	1.01+3	82	Pb	1.86+3
36	Kr	1.05+3	83	Bi	1.91+3
37	Rb	1.17+3	84	Po	1.97+3
38	Sr	1.27+3	85	At	1.74+3
39	Y	1.39+3	86	Rn	1.74+3
40	Zr	1.52+3	87	Fr	1.78+3
41	Nb	1.66+3	88	Ra	1.82+3
42	Mo	1.77+3	89	Ac	1.26+3
43	Tc	1.85+3	90	Th	1.29+3
44	Ru	1.96+3	91	Pa	6.32+2
45	Rh	1.73+3	92	U	6.74+2
46	Pd	1.87+3	93	Np	7.26+2
47	Ag	4.05+2	94	Pu	7.43+2

TABLE 4 (continued)

Mass Attenuation Coefficients for $K\alpha$ Lines

Emitter	B	C	N	O	F	Ne	Na	Mg	Al	Si	P	S	Cl	Ar
Wavelength	6.76+1	4.48+1	3.16+1	2.36+1	1.83+1	1.46+1	1.19+1	9.89+0	8.34+0	7.13+0	6.16+0	5.37+0	4.73+0	4.19+0
Energy (keV)	1.83-1	2.77-1	3.92-1	5.25-1	6.77-1	8.49-1	1.04+0	1.25+0	1.49+0	1.74+0	2.01+0	2.31+0	2.62+0	2.96+0
Absorber														
1 H	1.81+3	4.89+2	1.51+2	5.85+1	2.62+1	1.22+1	6.32+0	3.76+0	2.23+0	1.48+0	1.05+0	8.41-1	6.70-1	5.73-1
2 He	1.20+4	4.06+3	1.25+3	5.07+2	2.23+2	1.06+2	5.58+1	3.15+1	1.77+1	1.07+1	6.67+0	4.69+0	3.06+0	2.12+0
3 Li	2.98+4	1.08+4	3.67+3	1.60+3	7.57+2	3.84+2	2.09+2	1.20+2	6.82+1	4.15+1	2.58+1	1.80+1	1.15+1	7.73+0
4 Be	5.82+4	2.29+4	8.40+3	3.78+3	1.86+3	9.59+2	5.44+2	3.26+2	1.89+2	1.17+2	7.34+1	5.15+1	3.33+1	2.24+1
5 B	3.93+3	3.75+4	1.53+4	7.22+3	3.63+3	1.93+3	1.10+3	6.73+2	3.94+2	2.46+2	1.56+2	1.10+2	7.15+1	4.85+1
6 C	7.32+3	2.75+3	2.44+4	1.22+4	6.29+3	3.43+3	1.98+3	1.21+3	7.22+2	4.56+2	2.93+2	2.08+2	1.37+2	9.37+1
7 N	1.19+4	4.71+3	1.83+3	1.73+4	9.23+3	5.14+3	3.02+3	1.90+3	1.14+3	7.30+2	4.73+2	3.37+2	2.23+2	1.54+2
8 O	1.74+4	6.90+3	2.68+3	1.27+3	1.21+4	6.94+3	4.17+3	2.67+3	1.63+3	1.05+3	6.91+2	4.96+2	3.32+2	2.30+2
9 F	2.45+4	9.73+3	3.73+3	1.79+3	9.12+2	8.54+3	5.23+3	3.44+3	2.11+3	1.37+3	9.03+2	6.51+2	4.37+2	3.05+2
10 Ne	3.72+4	1.36+4	5.70+3	2.71+3	1.39+3	7.54+2	7.11+3	4.55+3	2.84+3	1.86+3	1.24+3	8.98+2	6.09+2	4.27+2
11 Na	4.25+4	1.80+4	7.26+3	3.52+3	1.83+3	1.01+3	5.93+2	5.65+3	3.53+3	2.32+3	1.55+3	1.12+3	7.65+2	5.38+2
12 Mg	5.62+4	2.44+4	1.00+4	4.89+3	2.55+3	1.42+3	8.37+2	5.06+2	4.39+3	2.93+3	1.98+3	1.44+3	9.89+2	7.00+2
13 Al	6.44+4	2.92+4	1.23+4	6.10+3	3.22+3	1.80+3	1.07+3	6.63+2	4.07+2	3.44+3	2.34+3	1.72+3	1.19+3	8.51+2
14 Si	7.48+4	3.47+4	1.58+4	7.93+3	4.22+3	2.37+3	1.41+3	8.93+2	5.52+2	3.60+2	2.97+3	2.18+3	1.50+3	1.07+3
15 P	7.49+4	4.19+4	1.93+4	9.74+3	5.19+3	2.92+3	1.74+3	1.09+3	6.78+2	4.47+2	3.00+2	2.41+3	1.72+3	1.23+3
16 S	8.18+4	4.95+4	2.38+4	1.21+4	6.52+3	3.69+3	2.21+3	1.39+3	8.64+2	5.70+2	3.83+2	2.79+2	2.08+3	1.49+3
17 Cl	7.44+3	5.17+4	2.67+4	1.39+4	7.50+3	4.27+3	2.57+3	1.63+3	1.01+3	6.71+2	4.52+2	3.32+2	2.28+2	1.65+3
18 Ar	9.51+3	5.24+4	3.00+4	1.59+4	8.59+3	4.89+3	2.93+3	1.85+3	1.15+3	7.56+2	5.08+2	3.72+2	2.57+2	1.84+2
19 K	1.14+4	5.92+3	3.51+4	1.94+4	1.07+4	6.13+3	3.71+3	2.36+3	1.47+3	9.70+2	6.53+2	4.80+2	3.32+2	2.38+2
20 Ca	1.31+4	7.15+3	3.49+4	2.21+4	1.24+4	7.19+3	4.38+3	2.75+3	1.74+3	1.25+3	7.77+2	5.73+2	3.99+2	2.86+2
21 Sc	1.43+4	7.80+3	3.97+3	2.34+4	1.34+4	7.79+3	4.74+3	2.99+3	1.90+3	1.37+3	8.48+2	6.26+2	4.36+2	3.12+2
22 Ti	1.54+4	8.45+3	4.35+3	2.20+4	1.45+4	8.59+3	5.27+3	3.34+3	2.13+3	1.53+3	9.56+2	7.10+2	4.96+2	3.55+2
23 V	1.68+4	9.22+3	4.77+3	1.66+4	1.57+4	9.40+3	5.81+3	3.70+3	2.36+3	1.71+3	1.07+3	7.89+2	5.47+2	3.90+2
24 Cr	2.09+4	1.11+4	5.61+3	3.13+3	1.58+4	1.09+4	6.75+3	4.30+3	2.74+3	1.99+3	1.25+3	9.19+2	6.39+2	4.57+2
25 Mn	2.23+4	1.20+4	6.13+3	3.46+3	1.68+4	1.16+4	7.27+3	4.67+3	3.00+3	2.18+3	1.37+3	1.02+3	7.15+2	5.10+2
26 Fe	2.61+4	1.40+4	7.10+3	4.00+3	2.31+3	1.31+4	8.22+3	5.31+3	3.42+3	2.49+3	1.57+3	1.17+3	8.28+2	5.90+2
27 Co	2.86+4	1.54+4	7.85+3	4.41+3	2.58+3	1.22+4	8.84+3	5.73+3	3.71+3	2.70+3	1.72+3	1.29+3	9.09+2	6.48+2
28 Ni	3.34+4	1.81+4	9.19+3	5.25+3	3.01+3	1.80+3	1.02+4	6.58+3	4.26+3	3.11+3	1.98+3	1.48+3	1.05+3	7.48+2
29 Cu	3.65+4	1.96+4	9.96+3	5.94+3	3.20+3	2.01+3	9.47+3	7.04+3	4.52+3	3.31+3	2.12+3	1.57+3	1.09+3	7.78+2
30 Zn	4.03+4	2.26+4	1.17+4	6.56+3	3.73+3	2.25+3	5.26+3	7.51+3	4.96+3	3.64+3	2.33+3	1.72+3	1.20+3	8.66+2
31 Ga	4.18+4	2.42+4	1.26+4	7.10+3	4.08+3	2.47+3	1.52+3	6.92+3	5.23+3	3.84+3	2.48+3	2.00+3	1.49+3	9.46+2
32 Ge	4.41+4	2.64+4	1.40+4	7.89+3	4.56+3	2.75+3	1.70+3	4.72+3	5.63+3	4.16+3	2.68+3	2.17+3	1.62+3	1.03+3
33 As	4.41+4	2.86+4	1.55+4	8.80+3	5.10+3	3.08+3	1.95+3	1.30+3	5.32+3	4.20+3	2.91+3	2.35+3	1.76+3	1.12+3
34 Se	4.49+4	3.03+4	1.69+4	9.64+3	5.61+3	3.38+3	2.17+3	1.53+3	4.86+3	4.47+3	3.09+3	2.50+3	1.87+3	1.20+3
35 Br	4.19+4	3.22+4	1.86+4	1.07+4	6.28+3	3.87+3	2.44+3	1.68+3	1.01+3	4.20+3	3.40+3	2.75+3	2.06+3	1.32+3
36 Kr	3.94+4	3.28+4	2.05+4	1.19+4	6.98+3	4.23+3	2.66+3	1.72+3	1.14+3	4.98+3	4.04+3	2.95+3	2.02+3	1.44+3
37 Rb	3.52+4	3.56+4	2.17+4	1.28+4	7.57+3	4.63+3	2.92+3	1.89+3	1.25+3	8.28+2	3.77+3	3.26+3	2.26+3	1.61+3

TABLE 4 (continued)

Mass Attenuation Coefficients for $K\alpha$ Lines

Emitter	B	C	N	O	F	Ne	Na	Mg	Al	Si	P	S	Cl	Ar
Wavelength	6.76+1	4.48+1	3.16+1	2.36+1	1.83+1	1.46+1	1.19+1	9.89+0	8.34+0	7.13+0	6.16+0	5.37+0	4.73+0	4.19+0
Energy (keV)	1.83-1	2.77-1	3.92-1	5.25-1	6.77-1	8.49-1	1.04+0	1.25+0	1.49+0	1.74+0	2.01+0	2.31+0	2.62+0	2.96+0
Absorber														
38 Sr	2.83+4	3.47+4	2.29+4	1.37+4	8.21+3	5.04+3	3.20+3	2.08+3	1.38+3	9.34+2	4.10+3	3.44+3	2.46+3	1.74+3
39 Y	2.04+4	3.10+4	2.34+4	1.51+4	9.06+3	5.58+3	3.55+3	2.32+3	1.52+3	1.12+3	7.19+2	3.12+3	2.69+3	1.91+3
40 Zr	6.41+3	3.06+4	2.46+4	1.61+4	9.77+3	6.03+3	3.86+3	2.53+3	1.66+3	1.22+3	7.90+2	3.38+3	2.92+3	2.08+3
41 Nb	4.28+3	2.96+4	2.67+4	1.78+4	1.08+4	6.69+3	4.27+3	2.80+3	1.84+3	1.35+3	8.72+2	6.29+2	2.62+3	2.26+3
42 Mo	4.66+3	2.23+4	2.29+4	1.85+4	1.14+4	7.09+3	4.55+3	2.99+3	1.97+3	1.45+3	9.38+2	7.14+2	2.00+3	2.41+3
43 Tc	4.99+3	1.41+4	2.29+4	1.78+4	1.19+4	7.45+3	4.90+3	3.57+3	2.12+3	1.54+3	1.00+3	7.68+2	5.49+2	2.11+3
44 Ru	5.49+3	4.18+3	2.47+4	1.95+4	1.30+4	8.16+3	5.37+3	3.92+3	2.32+3	1.69+3	1.10+3	8.19+2	5.85+2	1.62+3
45 Rh	5.87+3	4.64+3	2.48+4	1.94+4	1.38+4	8.79+3	5.80+3	4.23+3	2.51+3	1.83+3	1.19+3	8.90+2	6.38+2	4.87+2
46 Pd	6.09+3	5.22+3	2.21+4	1.80+4	1.46+4	9.42+3	6.23+3	4.54+3	2.69+3	1.97+3	1.28+3	9.55+2	6.80+2	5.09+2
47 Ag	6.34+3	5.48+3	1.10+4	1.91+4	1.47+4	1.00+4	6.66+3	4.86+3	2.90+3	2.12+3	1.38+3	1.03+3	7.35+2	5.51+2
48 Cd	6.45+3	5.75+3	4.10+3	2.01+4	1.47+4	1.04+4	7.09+3	5.84+3	4.48+3	2.99+3	1.45+3	1.09+3	7.71+2	5.62+2
49 In	6.61+3	6.06+3	4.42+3	2.23+4	1.36+4	1.10+4	7.51+3	6.20+3	4.75+3	3.19+3	1.56+3	1.16+3	8.26+2	6.03+2
50 Sn	6.64+3	6.27+3	4.70+3	9.12+3	1.38+4	1.08+4	7.88+3	6.50+3	4.99+3	3.35+3	1.64+3	1.23+3	8.76+2	6.39+2
51 Sb	6.71+3	6.50+3	4.94+3	3.36+3	1.48+4	1.13+4	8.26+3	6.82+3	5.25+3	3.53+3	1.75+3	1.31+3	9.30+2	6.80+2
52 Te	6.65+3	6.58+3	5.09+3	3.53+3	1.75+4	1.13+4	8.35+3	6.90+3	5.32+3	3.60+3	1.81+3	1.36+3	9.67+2	7.07+2
53 I	5.77+3	6.99+3	5.52+3	3.88+3	1.18+4	1.02+4	8.24+3	6.93+3	5.39+3	3.72+3	1.98+3	1.61+3	1.22+3	7.91+2
54 Xe	5.79+3	7.27+3	5.88+3	4.17+3	2.84+3	1.08+4	8.72+3	6.75+3	5.30+3	3.73+3	2.10+3	1.70+3	1.28+3	8.35+2
55 Cs	5.91+3	7.52+3	6.13+3	4.40+3	3.02+3	1.15+4	9.79+3	6.67+3	5.29+3	3.79+3	2.23+3	1.82+3	1.37+3	8.95+2
56 Ba	4.09+3	7.64+3	6.21+3	4.52+3	3.13+3	1.16+4	7.51+3	6.36+3	5.21+3	3.80+3	2.32+3	1.89+3	1.43+3	9.34+2
57 La	3.76+3	7.74+3	6.32+3	4.66+3	3.26+3	4.21+3	7.89+3	6.56+3	5.22+3	3.86+3	2.45+3	1.99+3	1.51+3	9.90+2
58 Ce	6.79+3	7.98+3	7.14+3	5.16+3	3.57+3	2.45+3	8.81+3	7.12+3	5.43+3	4.07+3	2.65+3	2.16+3	1.63+3	1.07+3
59 Pr	8.74+3	8.77+3	7.60+3	5.45+3	3.77+3	2.59+3	9.49+3	6.10+3	5.26+3	4.20+3	2.82+3	2.30+3	1.74+3	1.14+3
60 Nd	1.05+4	9.43+3	7.92+3	5.64+3	3.89+3	2.68+3	8.29+3	6.19+3	5.47+3	4.26+3	2.92+3	2.38+3	1.80+3	1.19+3
61 Pm	1.26+4	1.04+4	8.40+3	5.92+3	4.07+3	2.79+3	2.51+3	6.59+3	5.73+3	4.35+3	3.06+3	2.49+3	1.89+3	1.25+3
62 Sm	1.48+4	1.13+4	8.95+3	6.26+3	4.27+3	2.93+3	2.01+3	6.94+3	5.84+3	4.44+3	3.19+3	2.60+3	1.97+3	1.30+3
63 Eu	1.58+4	1.20+4	9.42+3	6.58+3	4.49+3	3.08+3	2.12+3	7.32+3	4.88+3	4.39+3	3.35+3	2.73+3	2.08+3	1.37+3
64 Gd	1.49+4	1.12+4	9.39+3	6.60+3	4.53+3	3.12+3	2.17+3	4.57+3	5.01+3	4.40+3	3.40+3	2.78+3	2.11+3	1.40+3
65 Tb	1.87+4	1.24+4	9.93+3	7.38+3	4.99+3	3.39+3	2.34+3	1.61+3	5.49+3	4.76+3	3.63+3	2.96+3	2.25+3	1.50+3
66 Dy	2.04+4	1.37+4	1.06+4	7.83+3	5.26+3	3.56+3	2.47+3	1.73+3	5.68+3	4.85+3	3.48+3	3.01+3	2.30+3	1.55+3
67 Ho	2.16+4	1.47+4	1.13+4	8.29+3	5.56+3	3.76+3	2.61+3	1.87+3	5.70+3	4.04+3	3.64+3	3.03+3	2.35+3	1.61+3
68 Er	2.32+4	1.60+4	1.21+4	8.86+3	5.94+3	4.00+3	2.77+3	2.01+3	2.84+3	4.26+3	3.81+3	3.08+3	2.40+3	1.68+3
69 Tm	2.43+4	1.72+4	1.29+4	9.49+3	6.36+3	4.27+3	2.96+3	2.14+3	1.56+3	4.51+3	4.00+3	3.08+3	2.47+3	1.76+3
70 Yb	2.28+4	1.79+4	1.35+4	9.94+3	6.67+3	4.47+3	3.10+3	2.32+3	1.47+3	4.65+3	3.21+3	3.02+3	2.39+3	1.80+3
71 Lu	2.15+4	1.75+4	1.36+4	1.01+4	6.86+3	4.62+3	3.22+3	2.42+3	1.54+3	4.77+3	3.40+3	3.13+3	2.48+3	1.87+3
72 Hf	2.13+4	1.80+4	1.27+4	9.96+3	7.20+3	4.86+3	3.38+3	2.54+3	1.62+3	2.86+3	3.60+3	3.26+3	2.58+3	1.94+3
73 Ta	2.04+4	1.82+4	1.32+4	1.04+4	7.54+3	5.11+3	3.53+3	2.45+3	1.77+3	4.03+3	4.13+3	3.52+3	2.75+3	2.20+3
74 W	1.93+4	1.85+4	1.37+4	1.09+4	7.90+3	5.36+3	3.70+3	2.57+3	1.86+3	1.24+3	4.25+3	3.58+3	2.83+3	2.27+3

TABLE 4 (continued)

Mass Attenuation Coefficients for $K\alpha$ Lines

Emitter	B	C	N	O	F	Ne	Na	Mg	Al	Si	P	S	Cl	Ar
Wavelength	6.76+1	4.48+1	3.16+1	2.36+1	1.83+1	1.46+1	1.19+1	9.89+0	8.34+0	7.13+0	6.16+0	5.37+0	4.73+0	4.19+0
Energy (keV)	1.83-1	2.77-1	3.92-1	5.25-1	6.77-1	8.49-1	1.04+0	1.25+0	1.49+0	1.74+0	2.01+0	2.31+0	2.62+0	2.96+0
Absorber														
75 Re	1.76+4	1.84+4	1.39+4	1.12+4	8.18+3	5.57+3	3.87+3	2.69+3	1.95+3	1.32+3	4.42+3	3.15+3	2.68+3	2.36+3
76 Os	1.58+4	1.67+4	1.39+4	1.12+4	8.36+3	5.74+3	4.02+3	2.92+3	1.99+3	1.47+3	3.04+3	3.32+3	2.79+3	2.22+3
77 Ir	1.38+4	1.61+4	1.44+4	1.15+4	8.36+3	6.09+3	4.27+3	3.11+3	2.12+3	1.56+3	1.03+3	3.44+3	2.90+3	2.31+3
78 Pt	1.13+4	1.57+4	1.50+4	1.12+4	8.83+3	6.43+3	4.51+3	3.28+3	2.24+3	1.64+3	1.08+3	3.59+3	2.53+3	2.23+3
79 Au	9.09+3	1.49+4	1.51+4	1.16+4	9.23+3	6.74+3	4.68+3	3.28+3	2.29+3	1.74+3	1.19+3	3.49+3	2.54+3	2.23+3
80 Hg	6.62+3	1.47+4	1.50+4	1.17+4	9.30+3	6.95+3	4.77+3	3.31+3	2.36+3	1.69+3	1.24+3	2.46+3	2.70+3	2.34+3
81 Tl	5.42+3	1.29+4	1.40+4	1.21+4	9.55+3	7.24+3	5.13+3	3.88+3	2.50+3	1.88+3	1.29+3	9.41+2	2.80+3	2.00+3
82 Pb	4.19+3	1.14+4	1.38+4	1.23+4	8.93+3	7.10+3	5.34+3	4.04+3	2.61+3	1.97+3	1.35+3	1.01+3	2.84+3	2.09+3
83 Bi	3.17+3	1.01+4	1.35+4	1.26+4	9.23+3	7.35+3	5.55+3	4.20+3	2.72+3	2.06+3	1.42+3	1.09+3	1.96+3	2.17+3
84 Po	2.54+3	8.62+3	1.34+4	1.33+4	9.68+3	7.72+3	5.82+3	4.42+3	2.88+3	2.18+3	1.50+3	1.15+3	8.29+2	2.25+3
85 At	2.28+3	6.67+3	1.31+4	1.23+4	1.02+4	8.14+3	5.70+3	4.57+3	3.04+3	2.31+3	1.59+3	1.22+3	8.76+2	2.35+3
86 Rn	2.52+3	4.13+3	1.21+4	1.16+4	1.02+4	8.26+3	5.72+3	4.46+3	3.04+3	2.31+3	1.59+3	1.22+3	8.85+2	1.55+3
87 Fr	2.69+3	3.02+3	1.10+4	1.17+4	1.05+4	7.52+3	5.99+3	4.57+3	3.18+3	2.42+3	1.67+3	1.28+3	9.41+2	7.06+2
88 Ra	2.66+3	2.42+3	9.31+3	1.17+4	1.04+4	7.75+3	6.22+3	4.68+3	3.30+3	2.52+3	1.74+3	1.33+3	9.78+2	7.28+2
89 Ac	2.49+3	2.59+3	8.17+3	1.15+4	1.01+4	7.88+3	6.35+3	4.49+3	3.40+3	2.60+3	1.80+3	1.48+3	1.14+3	7.81+2
90 Th	1.99+3	2.12+3	6.44+3	1.11+4	8.83+3	7.85+3	6.22+3	4.64+3	3.48+3	2.67+3	1.86+3	1.53+3	1.18+3	8.08+2
91 Pa	2.34+3	2.38+3	3.44+3	1.13+4	9.45+3	8.35+3	5.96+3	4.97+3	3.71+3	2.85+3	1.98+3	1.63+3	1.26+3	8.60+2
92 U	2.57+3	2.30+3	2.70+3	1.09+4	9.39+3	8.36+3	6.03+3	4.96+3	3.76+3	2.89+3	2.01+3	1.55+3	1.15+3	8.92+2
93 Np	2.93+3	2.41+3	2.62+3	9.65+3	9.74+3	8.59+3	6.34+3	5.21+3	3.74+3	3.05+3	2.13+3	1.75+3	1.35+3	9.25+2
94 Pu	3.73+3	2.39+3	2.72+3	6.59+3	1.01+4	8.24+3	6.66+3	5.40+3	3.89+3	3.12+3	2.21+3	1.82+3	1.40+3	9.57+2

TABLE 4 (continued)

Mass Attenuation Coefficients for $K\alpha$ Lines

Emitter	K	Ca	Sc	Ti	V	Cr	Mn	Fe	Co	Ni	Cu	Zn	Ga	Ge
Wavelength	3.74+0	3.36+0	3.03+0	2.75+0	2.50+0	2.29+0	2.10+0	1.94+0	1.79+0	1.66+0	1.54+0	1.44+0	1.34+0	1.26+0
Energy (keV)	3.31+0	3.69+0	4.09+0	4.51+0	4.95+0	5.41+0	5.90+0	6.40+0	6.93+0	7.47+0	8.04+0	8.63+0	9.24+0	9.88+0
Absorber														
1 H	5.17-1	4.77-1	4.51-1	4.36-1	4.21-1	4.13-1	4.06-1	4.01-1	3.97-1	3.94-1	3.91-1	3.89-1	3.87-1	3.86-1
2 He	1.57+0	1.17+0	9.06-1	7.55-1	5.97-1	5.15-1	4.40-1	3.92-1	3.50-1	3.22-1	2.97-1	2.81-1	2.66-1	2.54-1
3 Li	5.52+0	3.92+0	2.86+0	2.26+0	1.63+0	1.31+0	1.02+0	8.39-1	6.82-1	5.83-1	4.93-1	4.35-1	3.84-1	3.45-1
4 Be	1.60+1	1.13+1	8.21+0	6.42+0	4.54+0	3.57+0	2.69+0	2.15+0	1.67+0	1.38+0	1.11+0	9.35-1	7.84-1	6.69-1
5 B	3.47+1	2.46+1	1.79+1	1.40+1	9.87+0	7.74+0	5.80+0	4.58+0	3.53+0	2.87+0	2.26+0	1.88+0	1.54+0	1.28+0
6 C	6.75+1	4.82+1	3.51+1	2.75+1	1.95+1	1.53+1	1.15+1	9.05+0	6.96+0	5.62+0	4.41+0	3.63+0	2.95+0	2.43+0
7 N	1.11+2	7.98+1	5.84+1	4.58+1	3.26+1	2.57+1	1.93+1	1.52+1	1.17+1	9.44+0	7.39+0	6.07+0	4.91+0	4.02+0
8 O	1.68+2	1.21+2	8.89+1	7.00+1	5.00+1	3.95+1	2.97+1	2.35+1	1.81+1	1.46+1	1.15+1	9.41+0	7.60+0	6.21+0
9 F	2.23+2	1.61+2	1.19+2	9.38+1	6.73+1	5.32+1	4.02+1	3.19+1	2.46+1	1.99+1	1.56+1	1.28+1	1.04+1	8.48+0
10 Ne	3.14+2	2.29+2	1.70+2	1.34+2	9.68+1	7.67+1	5.82+1	4.62+1	3.58+1	2.90+1	2.28+1	1.88+1	1.52+1	1.24+1
11 Na	3.96+2	2.89+2	2.15+2	1.70+2	1.23+2	9.78+1	7.43+1	5.91+1	4.59+1	3.72+1	2.93+1	2.41+1	1.96+1	1.60+1
12 Mg	5.18+2	3.79+2	2.83+2	2.25+2	1.63+2	1.30+2	9.90+1	7.89+1	6.14+1	4.99+1	3.93+1	3.24+1	2.63+1	2.15+1
13 Al	6.33+2	4.67+2	3.50+2	2.79+2	2.04+2	1.63+2	1.24+2	9.94+1	7.75+1	6.30+1	4.98+1	4.11+1	3.34+1	2.74+1
14 Si	7.94+2	5.84+2	4.38+2	3.49+2	2.55+2	2.03+2	1.55+2	1.24+2	9.67+1	7.87+1	6.22+1	5.14+1	4.18+1	3.43+1
15 P	9.20+2	6.81+2	5.12+2	4.09+2	3.00+2	2.40+2	1.84+2	1.47+2	1.15+2	9.41+1	7.45+1	6.17+1	5.02+1	4.13+1
16 S	1.12+3	8.28+2	6.25+2	4.99+2	3.67+2	2.94+2	2.26+2	1.81+2	1.42+2	1.16+2	9.22+1	7.64+1	6.22+1	5.12+1
17 Cl	1.25+3	9.28+2	7.02+2	5.62+2	4.14+2	3.33+2	2.56+2	2.06+2	1.62+2	1.32+2	1.05+2	8.72+1	7.12+1	5.86+1
18 Ar	1.37+3	1.04+3	7.85+2	6.28+2	4.63+2	3.72+2	2.87+2	2.30+2	1.81+2	1.48+2	1.18+2	9.77+1	7.97+1	6.57+1
19 K	1.79+2	1.23+3	9.43+2	7.56+2	5.61+2	4.51+2	3.49+2	2.81+2	2.22+2	1.82+2	1.45+2	1.20+2	9.85+1	8.13+1
20 Ca	2.14+2	1.60+2	1.08+3	8.74+2	6.54+2	5.28+2	4.09+2	3.31+2	2.61+2	2.14+2	1.71+2	1.43+2	1.17+2	9.66+1
21 Sc	2.34+2	1.75+2	1.32+2	8.74+2	6.85+2	5.58+2	4.34+2	3.51+2	2.78+2	2.29+2	1.83+2	1.53+2	1.25+2	1.04+2
22 Ti	2.65+2	1.97+2	1.50+2	1.20+2	8.90+1	6.06+2	4.75+2	3.86+2	3.07+2	2.54+2	2.04+2	1.71+2	1.41+2	1.17+2
23 V	2.92+2	2.17+2	1.64+2	1.32+2	9.82+1	7.67+1	5.20+2	4.27+2	3.39+2	2.80+2	2.25+2	1.88+2	1.55+2	1.28+2
24 Cr	3.42+2	2.54+2	1.93+2	1.55+2	1.16+2	9.36+1	7.29+1	4.93+2	3.92+2	3.24+2	2.61+2	2.18+2	1.80+2	1.49+2
25 Mn	3.81+2	2.83+2	2.15+2	1.73+2	1.28+2	1.04+2	8.09+1	6.45+1	4.21+2	3.49+2	2.81+2	2.35+2	1.94+2	1.61+2
26 Fe	4.40+2	3.27+2	2.48+2	1.99+2	1.48+2	1.19+2	9.29+1	7.55+1	6.01+1	3.89+2	3.16+2	2.65+2	2.19+2	1.83+2
27 Co	4.84+2	3.60+2	2.73+2	2.19+2	1.63+2	1.32+2	1.03+2	8.33+1	6.63+1	5.43+1	3.53+2	2.96+2	2.44+2	2.03+2
28 Ni	5.58+2	4.14+2	3.14+2	2.52+2	1.87+2	1.51+2	1.17+2	9.53+1	7.58+1	6.28+1	5.06+1	3.15+2	2.64+2	2.21+2
29 Cu	5.90+2	4.44+2	3.36+2	2.70+2	2.01+2	1.62+2	1.26+2	1.03+2	8.16+1	6.75+1	5.46+1	4.58+1	2.78+2	2.33+2
30 Zn	6.53+2	4.89+2	3.71+2	2.99+2	2.23+2	1.80+2	1.41+2	1.14+2	9.12+1	7.56+1	6.12+1	5.15+1	4.27+1	2.60+2
31 Ga	7.29+2	5.52+2	3.91+2	3.16+2	2.38+2	1.93+2	1.50+2	1.22+2	9.69+1	8.02+1	6.48+1	5.44+1	4.51+1	3.78+1
32 Ge	7.96+2	6.02+2	4.26+2	3.44+2	2.57+2	2.08+2	1.62+2	1.31+2	1.04+2	8.61+1	6.94+1	5.83+1	4.83+1	4.04+1
33 As	8.68+2	6.58+2	4.67+2	3.78+2	2.84+2	2.30+2	1.79+2	1.45+2	1.15+2	9.54+1	7.70+1	6.47+1	5.36+1	4.48+1
34 Se	9.29+2	7.05+2	5.01+2	4.05+2	3.04+2	2.46+2	1.92+2	1.55+2	1.24+2	1.02+2	8.25+1	6.93+1	5.74+1	4.80+1
35 Br	1.03+3	7.79+2	5.54+2	4.48+2	3.37+2	2.73+2	2.12+2	1.72+2	1.36+2	1.13+2	9.09+1	7.63+1	6.32+1	5.28+1
36 Kr	1.08+3	7.99+2	6.05+2	4.85+2	3.60+2	2.91+2	2.26+2	1.84+2	1.46+2	1.21+2	9.74+1	8.18+1	6.78+1	5.67+1
37 Rb	1.19+3	8.83+2	6.66+2	5.34+2	3.95+2	3.18+2	2.47+2	2.00+2	1.58+2	1.31+2	1.05+2	8.81+1	7.28+1	6.08+1

TABLE 4 (continued)

Mass Attenuation Coefficients for $K\ \alpha$ Lines

Emitter	K	Ca	Sc	Ti	V	Cr	Mn	Fe	Co	Ni	Cu	Zn	Ga	Ge
Wavelength	3.74+0	3.36+0	3.03+0	2.75+0	2.50+0	2.29+0	2.10+0	1.94+0	1.79+0	1.66+0	1.54+0	1.44+0	1.34+0	1.26+0
Energy (keV)	3.31+0	3.69+0	4.09+0	4.51+0	4.95+0	5.41+0	5.90+0	6.40+0	6.93+0	7.47+0	8.04+0	8.63+0	9.24+0	9.88+0
Absorber														
38 Sr	1.30+3	9.59+2	7.24+2	5.80+2	4.28+2	3.45+2	2.68+2	2.17+2	1.72+2	1.42+2	1.14+2	9.55+1	7.90+1	6.59+1
39 Y	1.42+3	1.05+3	7.92+2	6.35+2	4.69+2	3.78+2	2.93+2	2.37+2	1.88+2	1.55+2	1.25+2	1.04+2	8.63+1	7.20+1
40 Zr	1.55+3	1.14+3	8.60+2	6.88+2	5.07+2	4.08+2	3.16+2	2.55+2	2.02+2	1.66+2	1.34+2	1.12+2	9.24+1	7.70+1
41 Nb	1.69+3	1.25+3	9.41+2	7.53+2	5.55+2	4.46+2	3.45+2	2.79+2	2.21+2	1.82+2	1.46+2	1.22+2	1.01+2	8.41+1
42 Mo	1.81+3	1.33+3	1.00+3	8.02+2	5.90+2	4.74+2	3.67+2	2.96+2	2.34+2	1.92+2	1.54+2	1.29+2	1.06+2	8.86+1
43 Tc	1.89+3	1.40+3	1.06+3	8.47+2	6.25+2	5.03+2	3.89+2	3.15+2	2.49+2	2.05+2	1.65+2	1.38+2	1.14+2	9.49+1
44 Ru	2.00+3	1.51+3	1.14+3	9.10+2	6.71+2	5.40+2	4.18+2	3.38+2	2.67+2	2.20+2	1.77+2	1.48+2	1.22+2	1.02+2
45 Rh	1.77+3	1.60+3	1.21+3	9.66+2	7.14+2	5.75+2	4.46+2	3.61+2	2.86+2	2.36+2	1.90+2	1.59+2	1.31+2	1.09+2
46 Pd	1.37+3	1.72+3	1.31+3	1.05+3	7.70+2	6.18+2	4.78+2	3.86+2	3.05+2	2.51+2	2.01+2	1.68+2	1.39+2	1.15+2
47 Ag	4.14+2	1.52+3	1.39+3	1.11+3	8.22+2	6.61+2	5.11+2	4.13+2	3.27+2	2.69+2	2.16+2	1.81+2	1.49+2	1.24+2
48 Cd	4.47+2	1.14+3	1.46+3	1.17+3	8.62+2	6.93+2	5.35+2	4.32+2	3.41+2	2.81+2	2.25+2	1.88+2	1.55+2	1.29+2
49 In	4.79+2	3.72+2	1.27+3	1.20+3	9.09+2	7.35+2	5.68+2	4.59+2	3.63+2	2.99+2	2.40+2	2.01+2	1.66+2	1.38+2
50 Sn	5.09+2	3.99+2	9.69+2	1.25+3	9.65+2	7.81+2	6.04+2	4.87+2	3.85+2	3.17+2	2.54+2	2.12+2	1.75+2	1.45+2
51 Sb	5.36+2	4.18+2	3.18+2	1.05+3	9.80+2	7.99+2	6.20+2	5.02+2	3.98+2	3.29+2	2.65+2	2.22+2	1.83+2	1.53+2
52 Te	5.59+2	4.36+2	3.33+2	7.85+2	1.02+3	8.31+2	6.45+2	5.22+2	4.14+2	3.42+2	2.75+2	2.31+2	1.91+2	1.59+2
53 I	6.09+2	4.74+2	3.63+2	2.83+2	9.23+2	8.86+2	6.97+2	5.67+2	4.49+2	3.70+2	2.98+2	2.49+2	2.06+2	1.72+2
54 Xe	6.30+2	4.84+2	3.74+2	3.00+2	6.73+2	7.39+2	7.07+2	5.78+2	4.58+2	3.78+2	3.04+2	2.55+2	2.11+2	1.76+2
55 Cs	6.83+2	5.27+2	4.05+2	3.29+2	2.49+2	8.02+2	7.63+2	6.26+2	4.96+2	4.09+2	3.29+2	2.76+2	2.28+2	1.90+2
56 Ba	7.12+2	5.50+2	4.24+2	3.44+2	2.61+2	6.00+2	6.63+2	6.52+2	5.16+2	4.26+2	3.43+2	2.87+2	2.37+2	1.97+2
57 La	7.74+2	5.94+2	4.31+2	3.55+2	2.76+2	2.20+2	7.07+2	6.84+2	5.50+2	4.54+2	3.65+2	3.05+2	2.52+2	2.09+2
58 Ce	8.36+2	6.40+2	4.63+2	3.81+2	2.94+2	2.37+2	5.38+2	6.02+2	5.82+2	4.83+2	3.88+2	3.25+2	2.68+2	2.23+2
59 Pr	8.91+2	6.84+2	4.95+2	4.05+2	3.11+2	2.54+2	2.00+2	4.57+2	6.16+2	5.12+2	4.11+2	3.44+2	2.84+2	2.37+2
60 Nd	9.30+2	7.14+2	5.17+2	4.25+2	3.29+2	2.69+2	2.13+2	4.84+2	5.42+2	5.35+2	4.33+2	3.62+2	2.98+2	2.48+2
61 Pm	9.76+2	7.49+2	5.43+2	4.46+2	3.45+2	2.82+2	2.23+2	1.79+2	4.06+2	5.52+2	4.52+2	3.79+2	3.12+2	2.60+2
62 Sm	1.02+3	7.85+2	5.69+2	4.68+2	3.61+2	2.96+2	2.34+2	1.90+2	4.25+2	4.84+2	4.74+2	3.97+2	3.27+2	2.73+2
63 Eu	1.08+3	8.28+2	6.01+2	4.93+2	3.80+2	3.11+2	2.46+2	2.02+2	1.62+2	3.66+2	4.15+2	4.17+2	3.44+2	2.87+2
64 Gd	1.10+3	8.48+2	6.17+2	5.07+2	3.91+2	3.20+2	2.53+2	2.07+2	1.67+2	3.78+2	4.28+2	4.25+2	3.54+2	2.95+2
65 Tb	1.17+3	9.03+2	6.56+2	5.37+2	4.13+2	3.38+2	2.66+2	2.19+2	1.76+2	1.45+2	3.24+2	3.73+2	3.74+2	3.11+2
66 Dy	1.22+3	9.39+2	6.82+2	5.59+2	4.29+2	3.51+2	2.77+2	2.27+2	1.83+2	1.51+2	3.36+2	3.86+2	3.87+2	3.23+2
67 Ho	1.28+3	9.82+2	7.15+2	5.85+2	4.49+2	3.67+2	2.90+2	2.37+2	1.91+2	1.60+2	1.30+2	2.91+2	3.34+2	3.35+2
68 Er	1.34+3	1.03+3	7.49+2	6.13+2	4.69+2	3.83+2	3.02+2	2.47+2	1.99+2	1.66+2	1.35+2	3.02+2	2.49+2	3.48+2
69 Tm	1.41+3	1.08+3	7.90+2	6.46+2	4.94+2	4.04+2	3.18+2	2.61+2	2.10+2	1.75+2	1.43+2	1.19+2	2.64+2	3.07+2
70 Yb	1.45+3	1.12+3	8.16+2	6.68+2	5.12+2	4.18+2	3.29+2	2.70+2	2.17+2	1.81+2	1.48+2	1.25+2	2.75+2	2.29+2
71 Lu	1.51+3	1.16+3	8.50+2	6.96+2	5.34+2	4.37+2	3.44+2	2.81+2	2.26+2	1.89+2	1.54+2	1.30+2	1.08+2	2.39+2
72 Hf	1.57+3	1.21+3	8.86+2	7.25+2	5.55+2	4.54+2	3.57+2	2.92+2	2.34+2	1.95+2	1.59+2	1.35+2	1.12+2	2.49+2
73 Ta	1.67+3	1.25+3	9.56+2	7.72+2	5.79+2	4.71+2	3.69+2	3.02+2	2.42+2	2.01+2	1.64+2	1.38+2	1.15+2	9.67+1
74 W	1.73+3	1.30+3	9.93+2	8.03+2	6.03+2	4.91+2	3.86+2	3.16+2	2.53+2	2.11+2	1.72+2	1.45+2	1.21+2	1.02+2

TABLE 4 (continued)

Mass Attenuation Coefficients for $K\ \alpha$ Lines

Emitter		K	Ca	Sc	Ti	V	Cr	Mn	Fe	Co	Ni	Cu	Zn	Ga	Ge
Wavelength		3.74+0	3.36+0	3.03+0	2.75+0	2.50+0	2.29+0	2.10+0	1.94+0	1.79+0	1.66+0	1.54+0	1.44+0	1.34+0	1.26+0
Energy (keV)		3.31+0	3.69+0	4.09+0	4.51+0	4.95+0	5.41+0	5.90+0	6.40+0	6.93+0	7.47+0	8.04+0	8.63+0	9.24+0	9.88+0
Absorber															
75	Re	1.80+3	1.35+3	1.04+3	8.38+2	6.30+2	5.13+2	4.03+2	3.30+2	2.65+2	2.21+2	1.80+2	1.52+2	1.27+2	1.07+2
76	Os	1.85+3	1.40+3	1.07+3	8.66+2	6.51+2	5.30+2	4.16+2	3.41+2	2.74+2	2.28+2	1.86+2	1.57+2	1.31+2	1.11+2
77	Ir	1.91+3	1.46+3	1.12+3	9.03+2	6.79+2	5.53+2	4.35+2	3.56+2	2.85+2	2.38+2	1.94+2	1.64+2	1.37+2	1.15+2
78	Pt	1.99+3	1.53+3	1.17+3	9.42+2	7.06+2	5.74+2	4.50+2	3.68+2	2.94+2	2.45+2	1.99+2	1.68+2	1.40+2	1.18+2
79	Au	1.84+3	1.55+3	1.19+3	9.64+2	7.28+2	5.94+2	4.68+2	3.84+2	3.09+2	2.58+2	2.11+2	1.79+2	1.50+2	1.26+2
80	Hg	1.92+3	1.61+3	1.24+3	1.01+3	7.57+2	6.17+2	4.85+2	3.97+2	3.19+2	2.66+2	2.17+2	1.84+2	1.53+2	1.29+2
81	Tl	1.82+3	1.49+3	1.28+3	1.04+3	7.81+2	6.36+2	5.01+2	4.10+2	3.29+2	2.75+2	2.24+2	1.89+2	1.58+2	1.34+2
82	Pb	1.89+3	1.56+3	1.33+3	1.08+3	8.11+2	6.61+2	5.20+2	4.26+2	3.43+2	2.86+2	2.33+2	1.97+2	1.65+2	1.39+2
83	Bi	1.95+3	1.46+3	1.38+3	1.12+3	8.42+2	6.86+2	5.40+2	4.43+2	3.56+2	2.97+2	2.42+2	2.05+2	1.71+2	1.45+2
84	Po	2.01+3	1.54+3	1.29+3	1.14+3	8.74+2	7.14+2	5.63+2	4.61+2	3.70+2	3.09+2	2.52+2	2.13+2	1.79+2	1.51+2
85	At	1.78+3	1.62+3	1.35+3	1.17+3	9.14+2	7.49+2	5.90+2	4.83+2	3.88+2	3.24+2	2.64+2	2.24+2	1.87+2	1.58+2
86	Rn	1.78+3	1.60+3	1.22+3	1.14+3	9.04+2	7.42+2	5.84+2	4.79+2	3.85+2	3.21+2	2.62+2	2.22+2	1.85+2	1.56+2
87	Fr	1.82+3	1.63+3	1.26+3	1.08+3	9.36+2	7.70+2	6.07+2	4.98+2	4.01+2	3.35+2	2.73+2	2.31+2	1.94+2	1.63+2
88	Ra	1.86+3	1.41+3	1.31+3	1.11+3	9.63+2	7.95+2	6.27+2	5.14+2	4.14+2	3.45+2	2.82+2	2.39+2	2.00+2	1.69+2
89	Ac	1.29+3	1.48+3	1.36+3	1.07+3	9.13+2	8.26+2	6.52+2	5.35+2	4.30+2	3.59+2	2.93+2	2.49+2	2.08+2	1.76+2
90	Th	5.90+2	1.52+3	1.39+3	1.11+3	9.32+2	8.31+2	6.64+2	5.47+2	4.40+2	3.67+2	3.00+2	2.54+2	2.12+2	1.79+2
91	Pa	6.45+2	1.58+3	1.21+3	1.17+3	8.98+2	8.60+2	6.95+2	5.74+2	4.62+2	3.85+2	3.14+2	2.66+2	2.23+2	1.88+2
92	U	6.87+2	1.04+3	1.21+3	1.15+3	8.94+2	7.82+2	6.92+2	5.74+2	4.62+2	3.86+2	3.15+2	2.67+2	2.24+2	1.89+2
93	Np	7.36+2	1.12+3	1.30+3	1.21+3	9.54+2	8.32+2	7.35+2	6.10+2	4.90+2	4.09+2	3.34+2	2.82+2	2.36+2	1.99+2
94	Pu	7.54+2	5.78+2	1.36+3	1.04+3	1.09+3	9.13+2	7.19+2	6.61+2	5.29+2	4.39+2	3.55+2	2.94+2	2.41+2	2.03+2

TABLE 4 (continued)

Mass Attenuation Coefficients for $K\alpha$ Lines

Emitter	As	Se	Br	Kr	Rb	Sr	Y	Zr	Nb	Mo	Tc	Ru	Rh	Pd
Wavelength	1.18+0	1.11+0	1.04+0	9.81-1	9.27-1	8.77-1	8.30-1	7.87-1	7.48-1	7.11-1	6.76-1	6.45-1	6.15-1	5.87-1
Energy (keV)	1.05+1	1.12+1	1.19+1	1.26+1	1.34+1	1.41+1	1.49+1	1.57+1	1.66+1	1.74+1	1.83+1	1.92+1	2.02+1	2.11+1
Absorber														
1 H	3.84-1	3.83-1	3.81-1	3.80-1	3.79-1	3.78-1	3.76-1	3.75-1	3.74-1	3.73-1	3.72-1	3.70-1	3.69-1	3.68-1
2 He	2.46-1	2.38-1	2.30-1	2.25-1	2.21-1	2.16-1	2.12-1	2.09-1	2.06-1	2.04-1	2.02-1	1.99-1	1.97-1	1.96-1
3 Li	3.18-1	2.95-1	2.70-1	2.57-1	2.45-1	2.32-1	2.19-1	2.12-1	2.05-1	1.99-1	1.95-1	1.90-1	1.86-1	1.83-1
4 Be	5.92-1	5.23-1	4.52-1	4.15-1	3.81-1	3.47-1	3.12-1	2.92-1	2.74-1	2.59-1	2.48-1	2.36-1	2.26-1	2.20-1
5 B	1.11+0	9.57-1	7.98-1	7.15-1	6.41-1	5.65-1	4.86-1	4.44-1	4.03-1	3.71-1	3.47-1	3.22-1	2.99-1	2.87-1
6 C	2.08+0	1.77+0	1.44+0	1.28+0	1.13+0	9.72-1	8.13-1	7.27-1	6.45-1	5.80-1	5.32-1	4.83-1	4.37-1	4.12-1
7 N	3.42+0	2.89+0	2.34+0	2.05+0	1.79+0	1.53+0	1.26+0	1.11+0	9.69-1	8.58-1	7.75-1	6.90-1	6.12-1	5.71-1
8 O	5.28+0	4.44+0	3.58+0	3.12+0	2.72+0	2.30+0	1.87+0	1.64+0	1.42+0	1.24+0	1.11+0	9.80-1	8.56-1	7.91-1
9 F	7.21+0	6.06+0	4.88+0	4.25+0	3.69+0	3.12+0	2.53+0	2.20+0	1.90+0	1.65+0	1.47+0	1.29+0	1.12+0	1.02+0
10 Ne	1.05+1	8.87+0	7.13+0	6.21+0	5.39+0	4.54+0	3.67+0	3.19+0	2.74+0	2.38+0	2.11+0	1.84+0	1.58+0	1.45+0
11 Na	1.36+1	1.15+1	9.22+0	8.02+0	6.96+0	5.86+0	4.73+0	4.11+0	3.52+0	3.05+0	2.70+0	2.35+0	2.01+0	1.84+0
12 Mg	1.83+1	1.54+1	1.24+1	1.08+1	9.35+0	7.87+0	6.35+0	5.51+0	4.71+0	4.08+0	3.61+0	3.12+0	2.67+0	2.43+0
13 Al	2.33+1	1.96+1	1.58+1	1.37+1	1.19+1	1.00+1	8.08+0	7.01+0	5.99+0	5.17+0	4.57+0	3.94+0	3.37+0	3.06+0
14 Si	2.92+1	2.46+1	1.98+1	1.72+1	1.49+1	1.26+1	1.01+1	8.79+0	7.52+0	6.50+0	5.73+0	4.95+0	4.22+0	3.84+0
15 P	3.52+1	2.97+1	2.40+1	2.09+1	1.81+1	1.53+1	1.23+1	1.07+1	9.15+0	7.91+0	6.98+0	6.03+0	5.14+0	4.67+0
16 S	4.37+1	3.68+1	2.98+1	2.60+1	2.25+1	1.90+1	1.54+1	1.33+1	1.14+1	9.87+0	8.71+0	7.52+0	6.41+0	5.82+0
17 Cl	5.01+1	4.23+1	3.42+1	2.98+1	2.59+1	2.19+1	1.77+1	1.54+1	1.32+1	1.14+1	1.00+1	8.67+0	7.40+0	6.71+0
18 Ar	5.61+1	4.74+1	3.84+1	3.34+1	2.90+1	2.45+1	1.98+1	1.72+1	1.47+1	1.27+1	1.12+1	9.71+0	8.28+0	7.51+0
19 K	6.95+1	5.88+1	4.78+1	4.17+1	3.63+1	3.06+1	2.49+1	2.16+1	1.85+1	1.60+1	1.42+1	1.22+1	1.04+1	9.48+0
20 Ca	8.26+1	7.00+1	5.69+1	4.97+1	4.32+1	3.65+1	2.97+1	2.58+1	2.21+1	1.91+1	1.69+1	1.46+1	1.25+1	1.13+1
21 Sc	8.88+1	7.53+1	6.13+1	5.35+1	4.66+1	3.94+1	3.21+1	2.79+1	2.39+1	2.07+1	1.83+1	1.58+1	1.35+1	1.23+1
22 Ti	1.00+2	8.50+1	6.94+1	6.07+1	5.29+1	4.48+1	3.65+1	3.18+1	2.73+1	2.37+1	2.09+1	1.81+1	1.55+1	1.40+1
23 V	1.10+2	9.35+1	7.63+1	6.68+1	5.82+1	4.93+1	4.02+1	3.50+1	3.01+1	2.61+1	2.31+1	1.99+1	1.71+1	1.55+1
24 Cr	1.28+2	1.09+2	8.88+1	7.77+1	6.77+1	5.75+1	4.69+1	4.08+1	3.51+1	3.04+1	2.69+1	2.33+1	1.99+1	1.81+1
25 Mn	1.39+2	1.18+2	9.63+1	8.43+1	7.36+1	6.24+1	5.10+1	4.44+1	3.82+1	3.32+1	2.93+1	2.54+1	2.17+1	1.98+1
26 Fe	1.57+2	1.34+2	1.10+2	9.62+1	8.40+1	7.14+1	5.85+1	5.10+1	4.39+1	3.82+1	3.38+1	2.93+1	2.51+1	2.28+1
27 Co	1.74+2	1.48+2	1.21+2	1.06+2	9.27+1	7.88+1	6.43+1	5.61+1	4.82+1	4.19+1	3.71+1	3.21+1	2.75+1	2.50+1
28 Ni	1.91+2	1.63+2	1.34+2	1.18+2	1.03+2	8.81+1	7.24+1	6.34+1	5.47+1	4.76+1	4.22+1	3.67+1	3.15+1	2.86+1
29 Cu	2.01+2	1.72+2	1.42+2	1.25+2	1.09+2	9.30+1	7.65+1	6.69+1	5.77+1	5.03+1	4.46+1	3.88+1	3.33+1	3.03+1
30 Zn	2.25+2	1.92+2	1.58+2	1.39+2	1.22+2	1.04+2	8.54+1	7.47+1	6.44+1	5.61+1	4.98+1	4.32+1	3.71+1	3.38+1
31 Ga	2.27+2	1.96+2	1.63+2	1.44+2	1.26+2	1.08+2	8.85+1	7.74+1	6.69+1	5.83+1	5.17+1	4.49+1	3.86+1	3.51+1
32 Ge	3.43+1	2.00+2	1.70+2	1.51+2	1.32+2	1.13+2	9.32+1	8.16+1	7.06+1	6.16+1	5.47+1	4.76+1	4.10+1	3.73+1
33 As	3.76+1	3.25+1	1.89+2	1.67+2	1.47+2	1.25+2	1.03+2	9.05+1	7.82+1	6.83+1	6.06+1	5.28+1	4.54+1	4.13+1
34 Se	4.15+1	3.55+1	2.94+1	2.50+1	1.51+2	1.31+2	1.10+2	9.64+1	8.34+1	7.28+1	6.47+1	5.63+1	4.85+1	4.41+1
35 Br	4.56+1	3.91+1	3.23+1	2.78+1	2.37+1	1.39+2	1.19+2	1.05+2	9.08+1	7.94+1	7.05+1	6.14+1	5.30+1	4.82+1
36 Kr	4.90+1	4.19+1	3.46+1	2.95+1	2.58+1	2.21+1	1.25+2	1.10+2	9.52+1	8.33+1	7.40+1	6.46+1	5.57+1	5.08+1
37 Rb	5.24+1	4.48+1	3.69+1	3.25+1	2.86+1	2.45+1	2.02+1	1.17+2	1.02+2	8.97+1	7.98+1	6.96+1	6.01+1	5.48+1

TABLE 4 (continued)

Mass Attenuation Coefficients for $K\alpha$ Lines

Emitter	As	Se	Br	Kr	Rb	Sr	Y	Zr	Nb	Mo	Tc	Ru	Rh	Pd
Wavelength	1.18+0	1.11+0	1.04+0	9.81−1	9.27−1	8.77−1	8.30−1	7.87−1	7.48−1	7.11−1	6.76−1	6.45−1	6.15−1	5.87−1
Energy (keV)	1.05+1	1.12+1	1.19+1	1.26+1	1.34+1	1.41+1	1.49+1	1.57+1	1.66+1	1.74+1	1.83+1	1.92+1	2.02+1	2.11+1
Absorber														
38 Sr	5.68+1	4.86+1	4.00+1	3.52+1	3.09+1	2.65+1	2.19+1	1.90+1	1.09+2	9.62+1	8.56+1	7.48+1	6.46+1	5.89+1
39 Y	6.21+1	5.30+1	4.37+1	3.85+1	3.38+1	2.89+1	2.39+1	2.10+1	1.83+1	1.04+2	9.26+1	8.09+1	7.00+1	6.38+1
40 Zr	6.64+1	5.67+1	4.66+1	4.10+1	3.60+1	3.08+1	2.54+1	2.23+1	1.94+1	1.68+1	9.25+1	8.21+1	7.22+1	6.59+1
41 Nb	7.24+1	6.18+1	5.09+1	4.48+1	3.93+1	3.36+1	2.77+1	2.43+1	2.11+1	1.84+1	1.62+1	8.58+1	7.63+1	6.98+1
42 Mo	7.63+1	6.51+1	5.35+1	4.70+1	4.12+1	3.52+1	2.90+1	2.55+1	2.21+1	1.91+1	1.70+1	1.50+1	8.17+1	7.47+1
43 Tc	8.18+1	6.98+1	5.74+1	5.05+1	4.43+1	3.79+1	3.13+1	2.75+1	2.38+1	2.09+1	1.86+1	1.63+1	1.41+1	7.85+1
44 Ru	8.79+1	7.50+1	6.17+1	5.43+1	4.76+1	4.07+1	3.36+1	2.95+1	2.56+1	2.24+1	2.00+1	1.75+1	1.51+1	1.35+1
45 Rh	9.43+1	8.05+1	6.63+1	5.84+1	5.12+1	4.38+1	3.62+1	3.18+1	2.76+1	2.42+1	2.16+1	1.89+1	1.63+1	1.47+1
46 Pd	9.94+1	8.47+1	6.96+1	6.12+1	5.36+1	4.58+1	3.78+1	3.31+1	2.87+1	2.51+1	2.24+1	1.96+1	1.69+1	1.49+1
47 Ag	1.07+2	9.12+1	7.50+1	6.59+1	5.78+1	4.94+1	4.07+1	3.58+1	3.10+1	2.71+1	2.42+1	2.12+1	1.83+1	1.67+1
48 Cd	1.11+2	9.47+1	7.78+1	6.84+1	5.99+1	5.11+1	4.21+1	3.70+1	3.20+1	2.80+1	2.50+1	2.18+1	1.89+1	1.72+1
49 In	1.19+2	1.01+2	8.33+1	7.32+1	6.42+1	5.49+1	4.52+1	3.97+1	3.44+1	3.01+1	2.68+1	2.35+1	2.03+1	1.86+1
50 Sn	1.25+2	1.07+2	8.75+1	7.69+1	6.74+1	5.75+1	4.74+1	4.15+1	3.60+1	3.15+1	2.80+1	2.45+1	2.12+1	1.93+1
51 Sb	1.32+2	1.13+2	9.29+1	8.18+1	7.18+1	6.15+1	5.08+1	4.47+1	3.88+1	3.40+1	3.03+1	2.65+1	2.30+1	2.10+1
52 Te	1.37+2	1.17+2	9.65+1	8.50+1	7.45+1	6.38+1	5.27+1	4.63+1	4.02+1	3.52+1	3.14+1	2.75+1	2.38+1	2.18+1
53 I	1.48+2	1.26+2	1.04+2	9.14+1	8.02+1	6.86+1	5.66+1	4.97+1	4.31+1	3.78+1	3.37+1	2.94+1	2.55+1	2.33+1
54 Xe	1.51+2	1.29+2	1.07+2	9.38+1	8.23+1	7.04+1	5.81+1	5.11+1	4.43+1	3.89+1	3.46+1	3.03+1	2.63+1	2.40+1
55 Cs	1.64+2	1.40+2	1.15+2	1.01+2	8.87+1	7.59+1	6.26+1	5.50+1	4.77+1	4.18+1	3.72+1	3.26+1	2.82+1	2.58+1
56 Ba	1.70+2	1.45+2	1.20+2	1.05+2	9.22+1	7.89+1	6.51+1	5.72+1	4.96+1	4.34+1	3.87+1	3.38+1	2.93+1	2.68+1
57 La	1.80+2	1.54+2	1.26+2	1.11+2	9.73+1	8.31+1	6.85+1	6.01+1	5.20+1	4.55+1	4.05+1	3.54+1	3.06+1	2.80+1
58 Ce	1.92+2	1.64+2	1.35+2	1.19+2	1.04+2	8.90+1	7.34+1	6.44+1	5.58+1	4.89+1	4.36+1	3.81+1	3.30+1	3.01+1
59 Pr	2.04+2	1.74+2	1.43+2	1.26+2	1.10+2	9.43+1	7.77+1	6.82+1	5.91+1	5.18+1	4.61+1	4.03+1	3.49+1	3.19+1
60 Nd	2.14+2	1.82+2	1.50+2	1.32+2	1.15+2	9.86+1	8.12+1	7.12+1	6.17+1	5.40+1	4.81+1	4.20+1	3.63+1	3.32+1
61 Pm	2.24+2	1.91+2	1.57+2	1.38+2	1.21+2	1.03+2	8.52+1	7.48+1	6.48+1	5.67+1	5.05+1	4.41+1	3.82+1	3.49+1
62 Sm	2.35+2	2.00+2	1.64+2	1.45+2	1.27+2	1.08+2	8.92+1	7.82+1	6.78+1	5.93+1	5.28+1	4.61+1	3.99+1	3.64+1
63 Eu	2.47+2	2.11+2	1.73+2	1.52+2	1.33+2	1.14+2	9.38+1	8.23+1	7.13+1	6.24+1	5.55+1	4.85+1	4.20+1	3.83+1
64 Gd	2.54+2	2.17+2	1.78+2	1.56+2	1.37+2	1.17+2	9.64+1	8.45+1	7.32+1	6.40+1	5.70+1	4.98+1	4.30+1	3.93+1
65 Tb	2.68+2	2.28+2	1.88+2	1.65+2	1.44+2	1.23+2	1.02+2	8.91+1	7.71+1	6.75+1	6.01+1	5.24+1	4.53+1	4.14+1
66 Dy	2.78+2	2.37+2	1.95+2	1.71+2	1.50+2	1.28+2	1.05+2	9.25+1	8.01+1	7.00+1	6.23+1	5.45+1	4.71+1	4.30+1
67 Ho	2.89+2	2.47+2	2.03+2	1.78+2	1.56+2	1.34+2	1.10+2	9.66+1	8.37+1	7.32+1	6.52+1	5.69+1	4.92+1	4.50+1
68 Er	3.01+2	2.57+2	2.11+2	1.86+2	1.63+2	1.39+2	1.15+2	1.01+2	8.71+1	7.62+1	6.78+1	5.93+1	5.12+1	4.68+1
69 Tm	3.15+2	2.70+2	2.22+2	1.96+2	1.71+2	1.46+2	1.21+2	1.06+2	9.16+1	8.01+1	7.13+1	6.23+1	5.39+1	4.92+1
70 Yb	3.20+2	2.76+2	2.30+2	2.03+2	1.78+2	1.52+2	1.25+2	1.09+2	9.48+1	8.29+1	7.38+1	6.44+1	5.57+1	5.08+1
71 Lu	2.79+2	2.85+2	2.40+2	2.12+2	1.86+2	1.58+2	1.30+2	1.14+2	9.91+1	8.66+1	7.71+1	6.73+1	5.82+1	5.31+1
72 Hf	2.10+2	2.46+2	2.50+2	2.21+2	1.93+2	1.65+2	1.36+2	1.19+2	1.03+2	9.02+1	8.02+1	7.00+1	6.05+1	5.52+1
73 Ta	2.10+2	2.44+2	2.49+2	2.20+2	1.93+2	1.65+2	1.36+2	1.20+2	1.04+2	9.09+1	8.10+1	7.08+1	6.13+1	5.60+1
74 W	2.30+2	1.94+2	2.26+2	2.38+2	2.09+2	1.79+2	1.47+2	1.29+2	1.12+2	9.78+1	8.70+1	7.59+1	6.56+1	5.98+1

TABLE 4 (continued)

Mass Attenuation Coefficients for $K\alpha$ Lines

Emitter		As	Se	Br	Kr	Rb	Sr	Y	Zr	Nb	Mo	Tc	Ru	Rh	Pd
Wavelength		1.18+0	1.11+0	1.04+0	9.81-1	9.27-1	8.77-1	8.30-1	7.87-1	7.48-1	7.11-1	6.76-1	6.45-1	6.15-1	5.87-1
Energy (keV)		1.05+1	1.12+1	1.19+1	1.26+1	1.34+1	1.41+1	1.49+1	1.57+1	1.66+1	1.74+1	1.83+1	1.92+1	2.02+1	2.11+1
Absorber															
75	Re	9.05+1	2.00+2	1.67+2	2.38+2	2.10+2	1.81+2	1.52+2	1.33+2	1.15+2	1.01+2	8.98+1	7.84+1	6.78+1	6.18+1
76	Os	9.42+1	2.04+2	1.72+2	2.04+2	2.12+2	1.84+2	1.56+2	1.37+2	1.19+2	1.04+2	9.24+1	8.07+1	6.98+1	6.37+1
77	Ir	9.90+1	8.35+1	1.79+2	1.53+2	1.82+2	1.90+2	1.62+2	1.43+2	1.24+2	1.08+2	9.63+1	8.41+1	7.27+1	6.64+1
78	Pt	1.02+2	8.65+1	1.85+2	1.60+2	1.88+2	1.95+2	1.68+2	1.48+2	1.28+2	1.12+2	9.97+1	8.71+1	7.53+1	6.87+1
79	Au	1.10+2	9.45+1	7.88+1	1.63+2	1.39+2	1.65+2	1.70+2	1.50+2	1.30+2	1.14+2	1.02+2	8.90+1	7.70+1	7.04+1
80	Hg	1.12+2	9.70+1	8.09+1	1.71+2	1.48+2	1.25+2	1.79+2	1.58+2	1.37+2	1.20+2	1.07+2	9.33+1	8.08+1	7.38+1
81	Tl	1.16+2	1.00+2	8.35+1	7.16+1	1.51+2	1.30+2	1.53+2	1.61+2	1.40+2	1.23+2	1.10+2	9.58+1	8.30+1	7.58+1
82	Pb	1.21+2	1.04+2	8.72+1	7.53+1	1.62+2	1.41+2	1.19+2	1.43+2	1.49+2	1.32+2	1.17+2	1.02+2	8.83+1	8.06+1
83	Bi	1.26+2	1.08+2	9.05+1	7.86+1	6.74+1	1.37+2	1.17+2	1.41+2	1.47+2	1.31+2	1.16+2	1.02+2	8.84+1	8.08+1
84	Po	1.31+2	1.13+2	9.42+1	8.23+1	7.12+1	1.42+2	1.22+2	1.07+2	1.29+2	1.36+2	1.22+2	1.06+2	9.23+1	8.43+1
85	At	1.37+2	1.18+2	9.88+1	8.68+1	7.56+1	6.41+1	1.28+2	1.13+2	9.76+1	1.18+2	1.26+2	1.11+2	9.66+1	8.83+1
86	Rn	1.36+2	1.17+2	9.79+1	8.64+1	7.59+1	6.50+1	1.26+2	1.12+2	9.73+1	1.17+2	1.23+2	1.09+2	9.57+1	8.75+1
87	Fr	1.42+2	1.23+2	1.03+2	9.09+1	8.04+1	6.95+1	5.83+1	1.16+2	1.01+2	8.78+1	1.07+2	1.13+2	9.97+1	9.11+1
88	Ra	1.47+2	1.27+2	1.06+2	9.38+1	8.30+1	7.18+1	6.02+1	1.19+2	1.04+2	9.10+1	7.96+1	9.69+1	1.03+2	9.40+1
89	Ac	1.53+2	1.32+2	1.10+2	9.77+1	8.64+1	7.47+1	6.27+1	5.48+1	1.08+2	9.51+1	8.39+1	1.01+2	1.07+2	9.80+1
90	Th	1.56+2	1.35+2	1.12+2	9.97+1	8.82+1	7.62+1	6.40+1	5.62+1	1.11+2	9.82+1	8.73+1	7.61+1	9.17+1	9.90+1
91	Pa	1.63+2	1.41+2	1.18+2	1.04+2	9.23+1	7.98+1	6.69+1	5.91+1	5.16+1	1.03+2	9.23+1	8.09+1	6.97+1	1.02+2
92	U	1.64+2	1.42+2	1.19+2	1.05+2	9.30+1	8.05+1	6.75+1	5.99+1	5.25+1	1.03+2	9.19+1	8.07+1	6.99+1	8.57+1
93	Np	1.73+2	1.49+2	1.24+2	1.10+2	9.74+1	8.42+1	7.05+1	6.25+1	5.47+1	4.78+1	9.71+1	8.57+1	7.46+1	6.63+1
94	Pu	1.76+2	1.52+2	1.27+2	1.12+2	9.91+1	8.56+1	7.17+1	6.35+1	5.56+1	4.86+1	9.80+1	8.68+1	7.60+1	6.80+1

TABLE 4 (continued)

Mass Attenuation Coefficients for $K\alpha$ Lines

Emitter	Ag	Cd	In	Sn
Wavelength	5.61-1	5.36-1	5.14-1	4.92-1
Energy (keV)	2.21+1	2.31+1	2.41+1	2.52+1
Absorber				
1 H	3.67-1	3.65-1	3.64-1	3.63-1
2 He	1.94-1	1.93-1	1.91-1	1.90-1
3 Li	1.81-1	1.78-1	1.75-1	1.73-1
4 Be	2.14-1	2.07-1	2.01-1	1.95-1
5 B	2.74-1	2.61-1	2.48-1	2.36-1
6 C	3.88-1	3.62-1	3.36-1	3.12-1
7 N	5.29-1	4.85-1	4.41-1	4.00-1
8 O	7.25-1	6.57-1	5.87-1	5.23-1
9 F	9.32-1	8.37-1	7.40-1	6.51-1
10 Ne	1.31+0	1.17+0	1.02+0	8.91-1
11 Na	1.66+0	1.47+0	1.28+0	1.11+0
12 Mg	2.19+0	1.94+0	1.68+0	1.45+0
13 Al	2.75+0	2.43+0	2.10+0	1.80+0
14 Si	3.44+0	3.04+0	2.62+0	2.24+0
15 P	4.19+0	3.69+0	3.19+0	2.72+0
16 S	5.22+0	4.60+0	3.96+0	3.38+0
17 Cl	6.02+0	5.30+0	4.57+0	3.89+0
18 Ar	6.73+0	5.93+0	5.10+0	4.34+0
19 K	8.49+0	7.48+0	6.45+0	5.49+0
20 Ca	1.01+1	8.93+0	7.69+0	6.55+0
21 Sc	1.10+1	9.68+0	8.34+0	7.10+0
22 Ti	1.26+1	1.11+1	9.55+0	8.13+0
23 V	1.39+1	1.22+1	1.05+1	8.99+0
24 Cr	1.62+1	1.43+1	1.23+1	1.05+1
25 Mn	1.77+1	1.56+1	1.35+1	1.15+1
26 Fe	2.05+1	1.80+1	1.56+1	1.33+1
27 Co	2.24+1	1.97+1	1.70+1	1.45+1
28 Ni	2.57+1	2.27+1	1.96+1	1.68+1
29 Cu	2.72+1	2.40+1	2.08+1	1.78+1
30 Zn	3.03+1	2.68+1	2.31+1	1.98+1
31 Ga	3.16+1	2.79+1	2.41+1	2.07+1
32 Ge	3.35+1	2.97+1	2.57+1	2.20+1
33 As	3.71+1	3.28+1	2.85+1	2.44+1
34 Se	3.97+1	3.51+1	3.04+1	2.61+1
35 Br	4.34+1	3.84+1	3.33+1	2.86+1
36 Kr	4.57+1	4.05+1	3.51+1	3.02+1
37 Rb	4.93+1	4.37+1	3.80+1	3.27+1
38 Sr	5.30+1	4.70+1	4.09+1	3.52+1
39 Y	5.75+1	5.10+1	4.43+1	3.82+1
40 Zr	5.95+1	5.30+1	4.63+1	4.00+1
41 Nb	6.31+1	5.62+1	4.92+1	4.27+1
42 Mo	6.75+1	6.01+1	5.25+1	4.55+1
43 Tc	7.12+1	6.38+1	5.61+1	4.90+1
44 Ru	1.18+1	6.65+1	5.92+1	5.22+1
45 Rh	1.31+1	1.14+1	6.11+1	5.45+1
46 Pd	1.35+1	1.20+1	1.05+1	5.63+1
47 Ag	1.51+1	1.35+1	1.18+1	1.01+1
48 Cd	1.56+1	1.39+1	1.21+1	1.04+1
49 In	1.68+1	1.49+1	1.30+1	1.13+1
50 Sn	1.75+1	1.55+1	1.35+1	1.17+1
51 Sb	1.90+1	1.69+1	1.48+1	1.28+1
52 Te	1.97+1	1.75+1	1.53+1	1.33+1
53 I	2.11+1	1.87+1	1.64+1	1.42+1
54 Xe	2.17+1	1.93+1	1.69+1	1.46+1
55 Cs	2.33+1	2.07+1	1.81+1	1.57+1
56 Ba	2.42+1	2.15+1	1.88+1	1.63+1
57 La	2.53+1	2.25+1	1.96+1	1.70+1
58 Ce	2.72+1	2.42+1	2.11+1	1.83+1
59 Pr	2.88+1	2.56+1	2.23+1	1.93+1
60 Nd	2.99+1	2.66+1	2.32+1	2.01+1
61 Pm	3.15+1	2.80+1	2.44+1	2.11+1
62 Sm	3.29+1	2.92+1	2.55+1	2.21+1
63 Eu	3.46+1	3.07+1	2.68+1	2.32+1
64 Gd	3.55+1	3.15+1	2.75+1	2.38+1
65 Tb	3.74+1	3.32+1	2.89+1	2.50+1
66 Dy	3.88+1	3.45+1	3.01+1	2.60+1
67 Ho	4.06+1	3.61+1	3.15+1	2.72+1
68 Er	4.22+1	3.75+1	3.27+1	2.83+1
69 Tm	4.44+1	3.94+1	3.44+1	2.97+1
70 Yb	4.59+1	4.08+1	3.55+1	3.07+1
71 Lu	4.79+1	4.26+1	3.71+1	3.21+1
72 Hf	4.98+1	4.43+1	3.86+1	3.33+1
73 Ta	5.06+1	4.50+1	3.93+1	3.40+1
74 W	5.39+1	4.79+1	4.17+1	3.60+1
75 Re	5.58+1	4.96+1	4.32+1	3.73+1
76 Os	5.75+1	5.11+1	4.46+1	3.85+1
77 Ir	5.99+1	5.32+1	4.64+1	4.01+1
78 Pt	6.20+1	5.51+1	4.81+1	4.15+1
79 Au	6.35+1	5.65+1	4.93+1	4.27+1
80 Hg	6.66+1	5.92+1	5.17+1	4.47+1
81 Tl	6.84+1	6.09+1	5.31+1	4.60+1
82 Pb	7.27+1	6.46+1	5.62+1	4.86+1
83 Bi	7.30+1	6.50+1	5.68+1	4.92+1
84 Po	7.62+1	6.78+1	5.93+1	5.13+1
85 At	7.98+1	7.10+1	6.21+1	5.38+1
86 Rn	7.90+1	7.04+1	6.15+1	5.33+1
87 Fr	8.23+1	7.33+1	6.40+1	5.55+1
88 Ra	8.50+1	7.56+1	6.61+1	5.73+1
89 Ac	8.85+1	7.88+1	6.88+1	5.96+1
90 Th	8.97+1	8.01+1	7.03+1	6.12+1
91 Pa	9.28+1	8.33+1	7.36+1	6.45+1
92 U	9.15+1	8.25+1	7.33+1	6.47+1
93 Np	8.10+1	8.68+1	7.75+1	6.88+1
94 Pu	5.98+1	8.75+1	7.86+1	7.01+1

TABLE 4 (continued)

Mass Attenuation Coefficients for $K\,\beta_1$ Lines

Emitter		Ne	Na	Mg	Al	Si	P	S	Cl	Ar	K	Ca	Sc	Ti	V
Wavelength		1.45+1	1.16+1	9.52+0	7.96+0	6.75+0	5.80+0	5.03+0	4.40+0	3.89+0	3.45+0	3.09+0	2.78+0	2.51+0	2.28+0
Energy (keV)		8.58-1	1.07+0	1.30+0	1.56+0	1.84+0	2.14+0	2.46+0	2.82+0	3.19+0	3.59+0	4.01+0	4.46+0	4.93+0	5.43+0
Absorber															
1	H	1.19+1	5.90+0	3.44+0	1.97+0	1.32+0	9.60-1	7.31-1	6.14-1	5.34-1	4.85-1	4.54-1	4.38-1	4.21-1	4.13-1
2	He	1.02+2	5.18+1	2.86+1	1.53+1	9.24+0	5.82+0	3.64+0	2.51+0	1.73+0	1.24+0	9.33-1	7.73-1	6.04-1	5.13-1
3	Li	3.71+2	1.95+2	1.09+2	5.91+1	3.58+1	2.24+1	1.38+1	9.31+0	6.19+0	4.22+0	2.97+0	2.33+0	1.66+0	1.30+0
4	Be	9.29+2	5.09+2	2.97+2	1.64+2	1.01+2	6.41+1	3.99+1	2.70+1	1.80+1	1.22+1	8.53+0	6.62+0	4.61+0	3.54+0
5	B	1.88+3	1.03+3	6.15+2	3.44+2	2.13+2	1.36+2	8.55+1	5.82+1	3.90+1	2.66+1	1.86+1	1.44+1	1.00+1	7.68+0
6	C	3.33+3	1.86+3	1.11+3	6.32+2	3.98+2	2.57+2	1.63+2	1.12+2	7.56+1	5.19+1	3.65+1	2.84+1	1.98+1	1.52+1
7	N	4.99+3	2.85+3	1.74+3	1.01+3	6.37+2	4.15+2	2.65+2	1.83+2	1.24+2	8.59+1	6.07+1	4.73+1	3.31+1	2.54+1
8	O	6.75+3	3.93+3	2.45+3	1.44+3	9.23+2	6.08+2	3.93+2	2.73+2	1.87+2	1.30+2	9.24+1	7.22+1	5.09+1	3.92+1
9	F	8.30+3	4.95+3	3.16+3	1.86+3	1.20+3	7.95+2	5.17+2	3.61+2	2.48+2	1.73+2	1.24+2	9.67+1	6.84+1	5.28+1
10	Ne	7.31+2	6.70+3	4.20+3	2.51+3	1.64+3	1.09+3	7.17+2	5.04+2	3.49+2	2.45+2	1.76+2	1.38+2	9.83+1	7.61+1
11	Na	9.82+2	5.55+2	5.20+3	3.13+3	2.04+3	1.37+3	8.99+2	6.33+2	4.40+2	3.10+2	2.23+2	1.75+2	1.25+2	9.70+1
12	Mg	1.38+3	7.86+2	4.50+2	3.92+3	2.59+3	1.75+3	1.16+3	8.22+2	5.74+2	4.07+2	2.94+2	2.32+2	1.66+2	1.29+2
13	Al	1.75+3	1.00+3	6.10+2	3.55+2	3.04+3	2.08+3	1.39+3	9.95+2	7.01+2	5.00+2	3.63+2	2.87+2	2.07+2	1.61+2
14	Si	2.30+3	1.33+3	8.22+2	4.89+2	3.10+2	2.63+3	1.76+3	1.25+3	8.79+2	6.26+2	4.54+2	3.59+2	2.58+2	2.02+2
15	P	2.83+3	1.63+3	1.01+3	6.01+2	3.95+2	2.55+2	2.00+3	1.44+3	1.02+3	7.28+2	5.31+2	4.21+2	3.04+2	2.38+2
16	S	3.59+3	2.08+3	1.28+3	7.66+2	5.02+2	3.39+2	2.24+2	1.74+3	1.23+3	8.86+2	6.48+2	5.14+2	3.72+2	2.92+2
17	Cl	4.15+3	2.41+3	1.50+3	9.00+2	5.92+2	4.01+2	2.69+2	1.86+2	1.38+3	9.92+2	7.28+2	5.78+2	4.20+2	3.30+2
18	Ar	4.75+3	2.76+3	1.71+3	1.02+3	6.67+2	4.50+2	3.00+2	2.14+2	1.48+2	1.11+3	8.13+2	6.46+2	4.70+2	3.69+2
19	K	5.96+3	3.49+3	2.17+3	1.30+3	8.56+2	5.79+2	3.87+2	2.78+2	1.97+2	1.41+2	9.77+2	7.78+2	5.69+2	4.48+2
20	Ca	7.00+3	4.12+3	2.54+3	1.58+3	1.08+3	6.90+2	4.65+2	3.33+2	2.37+2	1.71+2	1.26+2	8.98+2	6.63+2	5.24+2
21	Sc	7.59+3	4.46+3	2.76+3	1.72+3	1.18+3	7.53+2	5.08+2	3.64+2	2.58+2	1.86+2	1.37+2	1.04+2	6.93+2	5.54+2
22	Ti	8.37+3	4.96+3	3.09+3	1.93+3	1.32+3	8.51+2	5.78+2	4.14+2	2.93+2	2.11+2	1.55+2	1.24+2	9.02+1	6.01+2
23	V	9.17+3	5.47+3	3.42+3	2.15+3	1.48+3	9.49+2	6.39+2	4.57+2	3.22+2	2.32+2	1.70+2	1.36+2	9.95+1	7.60+1
24	Cr	1.06+4	6.35+3	3.97+3	2.49+3	1.72+3	1.11+3	7.46+2	5.34+2	3.78+2	2.72+2	2.00+2	1.60+2	1.17+2	9.29+1
25	Mn	1.13+4	6.85+3	4.32+3	2.73+3	1.89+3	1.22+3	8.33+2	5.97+2	4.21+2	3.03+2	2.23+2	1.78+2	1.30+2	1.03+2
26	Fe	1.28+4	7.75+3	4.91+3	3.11+3	2.15+3	1.40+3	9.63+2	6.90+2	4.87+2	3.49+2	2.56+2	2.04+2	1.50+2	1.18+2
27	Co	1.19+4	8.34+3	5.31+3	3.38+3	2.35+3	1.53+3	1.06+3	7.58+2	5.35+2	3.84+2	2.82+2	2.25+2	1.65+2	1.31+2
28	Ni	1.74+3	9.61+3	6.09+3	3.88+3	2.70+3	1.77+3	1.22+3	8.76+2	6.17+2	4.43+2	3.25+2	2.59+2	1.89+2	1.50+2
29	Cu	1.94+3	8.71+3	6.52+3	4.12+3	2.88+3	1.88+3	1.28+3	9.11+2	6.48+2	4.75+2	3.49+2	2.78+2	2.04+2	1.61+2
30	Zn	2.19+3	7.14+3	6.79+3	4.54+3	3.17+3	2.07+3	1.40+3	1.01+3	7.19+2	5.22+2	3.84+2	3.07+2	2.26+2	1.79+2
31	Ga	2.40+3	1.42+3	7.25+3	4.79+3	3.35+3	2.27+3	1.75+3	1.18+3	7.86+2	5.99+2	4.04+2	3.25+2	2.41+2	1.91+2
32	Ge	2.68+3	1.59+3	6.78+3	5.18+3	3.62+3	2.46+3	1.89+3	1.28+3	8.58+2	6.54+2	4.41+2	3.53+2	2.61+2	2.06+2
33	As	3.01+3	1.86+3	1.15+3	5.44+3	3.73+3	2.67+3	2.06+3	1.39+3	9.37+2	7.15+2	4.83+2	3.88+2	2.88+2	2.28+2
34	Se	3.30+3	2.08+3	1.39+3	5.00+3	3.97+3	2.84+3	2.19+3	1.48+3	1.00+3	7.64+2	5.18+2	4.16+2	3.08+2	2.45+2
35	Br	3.79+3	2.33+3	1.51+3	9.00+2	4.21+3	3.13+3	2.41+3	1.64+3	1.11+3	8.45+2	5.74+2	4.61+2	3.41+2	2.71+2
36	Kr	4.12+3	2.51+3	1.58+3	1.01+3	4.35+3	3.57+3	2.37+3	1.69+3	1.19+3	8.54+2	6.26+2	4.99+2	3.65+2	2.89+2
37	Rb	4.51+3	2.76+3	1.74+3	1.12+3	3.47+3	3.92+3	2.64+3	1.88+3	1.32+3	9.45+2	6.91+2	5.49+2	4.00+2	3.16+2

TABLE 4 (continued)

Mass Attenuation Coefficients for $K\beta_1$ Lines

Emitter		Ne	Na	Mg	Al	St	P	S	Cl	Ar	K	Ca	Sc	Ti	V
Wavelength		1.45+1	1.16+1	9.52+0	7.96+0	6.75+0	5.80+0	5.03+0	4.40+0	3.89+0	3.45+0	3.09+0	2.78+0	2.51+0	2.28+0
Energy (keV)		8.58-1	1.07+0	1.30+0	1.56+0	1.84+0	2.14+0	2.46+0	2.82+0	3.19+0	3.59+0	4.01+0	4.46+0	4.93+0	5.43+0
Absorber															
38	Sr	4.92+3	3.02+3	1.91+3	1.23+3	8.17+2	3.51+3	2.85+3	2.05+3	1.44+3	1.03+3	7.50+2	5.97+2	4.35+2	3.43+2
39	Y	5.44+3	3.35+3	2.16+3	1.39+3	9.76+2	2.72+3	3.11+3	2.24+3	1.57+3	1.12+3	8.21+2	6.53+2	4.76+2	3.75+2
40	Zr	5.89+3	3.64+3	2.35+3	1.52+3	1.07+3	6.90+2	2.84+3	2.43+3	1.71+3	1.22+3	8.91+2	7.08+2	5.15+2	4.05+2
41	Nb	6.53+3	4.03+3	2.60+3	1.68+3	1.18+3	7.68+2	2.21+3	2.60+3	1.88+3	1.34+3	9.75+2	7.74+2	5.63+2	4.43+2
42	Mo	6.93+3	4.30+3	2.78+3	1.80+3	1.26+3	8.42+2	5.94+2	2.31+3	2.01+3	1.43+3	1.04+3	8.25+2	5.99+2	4.71+2
43	Tc	7.28+3	4.71+3	3.27+3	1.91+3	1.35+3	9.02+2	6.44+2	2.41+3	2.09+3	1.50+3	1.10+3	8.71+2	6.34+2	4.99+2
44	Ru	7.97+3	5.17+3	3.58+3	2.10+3	1.48+3	9.77+2	6.71+2	5.02+2	1.84+3	1.61+3	1.18+3	9.36+2	6.81+2	5.36+2
45	Rh	8.59+3	5.58+3	3.87+3	2.27+3	1.60+3	1.06+3	7.30+2	5.51+2	1.95+3	1.71+3	1.25+3	9.94+2	7.24+2	5.71+2
46	Pd	9.20+3	5.99+3	4.16+3	2.44+3	1.72+3	1.14+3	7.82+2	5.81+2	1.52+3	1.53+3	1.36+3	1.08+3	7.81+2	6.14+2
47	Ag	9.78+3	6.40+3	4.45+3	2.63+3	1.85+3	1.23+3	8.45+2	6.29+2	4.58+2	1.64+3	1.44+3	1.15+3	8.34+2	6.56+2
48	Cd	1.02+4	6.91+3	5.56+3	4.06+3	2.43+3	1.30+3	8.91+2	6.50+2	4.81+2	1.23+3	1.26+3	1.20+3	8.74+2	6.88+2
49	In	1.08+4	7.33+3	5.90+3	4.32+3	2.59+3	1.39+3	9.56+2	6.97+2	5.16+2	3.99+2	1.34+3	1.23+3	9.21+2	7.29+2
50	Sn	1.05+4	7.68+3	6.18+3	4.53+3	2.73+3	1.47+3	1.01+3	7.39+2	5.48+2	4.25+2	1.02+3	1.06+3	9.76+2	7.76+2
51	Sb	1.10+4	8.06+3	6.49+3	4.77+3	2.88+3	1.56+3	1.08+3	7.86+2	5.80+2	4.45+2	3.33+2	1.08+3	9.90+2	7.93+2
52	Te	1.11+4	8.14+3	6.57+3	4.84+3	2.95+3	1.62+3	1.12+3	8.17+2	6.04+2	4.64+2	3.47+2	8.08+2	8.57+2	8.25+2
53	I	9.93+3	7.73+3	6.61+3	4.92+3	3.09+3	1.83+3	1.41+3	9.70+2	6.59+2	5.05+2	3.78+2	2.93+2	9.33+2	8.80+2
54	Xe	1.06+4	8.24+3	6.45+3	4.86+3	3.13+3	1.93+3	1.49+3	1.02+3	6.88+2	5.15+2	3.88+2	3.08+2	6.80+2	7.33+2
55	Cs	1.13+4	9.23+3	6.38+3	4.87+3	3.23+3	2.06+3	1.60+3	1.10+3	7.42+2	5.61+2	4.19+2	3.38+2	2.52+2	7.96+2
56	Ba	1.13+4	7.03+3	6.25+3	4.82+3	3.26+3	2.14+3	1.66+3	1.14+3	7.74+2	5.86+2	4.38+2	3.53+2	2.64+2	5.95+2
57	La	5.39+3	7.43+3	6.08+3	4.84+3	3.35+3	2.25+3	1.75+3	1.21+3	8.33+2	6.42+2	4.44+2	3.64+2	2.79+2	2.18+2
58	Ce	2.40+3	8.33+3	6.64+3	5.05+3	3.56+3	2.44+3	1.90+3	1.31+3	8.99+2	6.93+2	4.78+2	3.90+2	2.97+2	2.36+2
59	Pr	2.54+3	9.01+3	6.92+3	5.15+3	3.70+3	2.60+3	2.02+3	1.39+3	9.58+2	7.39+2	5.11+2	4.15+2	3.14+2	2.52+2
60	Nd	2.63+3	8.00+3	5.71+3	4.90+3	3.77+3	2.69+3	2.10+3	1.45+3	1.00+3	7.71+2	5.34+2	4.36+2	3.32+2	2.68+2
61	Pm	2.74+3	3.41+3	5.99+3	5.18+3	3.88+3	2.82+3	2.19+3	1.52+3	1.05+3	8.10+2	5.61+2	4.57+2	3.49+2	2.80+2
62	Sm	2.87+3	1.90+3	6.31+3	5.35+3	3.99+3	2.94+3	2.29+3	1.59+3	1.10+3	8.48+2	5.88+2	4.80+2	3.66+2	2.94+2
63	Eu	3.02+3	2.02+3	6.67+3	5.54+3	4.13+3	3.09+3	2.41+3	1.67+3	1.16+3	8.95+2	6.21+2	5.06+2	3.85+2	3.09+2
64	Gd	3.06+3	2.07+3	6.72+3	4.45+3	3.91+3	3.13+3	2.44+3	1.70+3	1.18+3	9.16+2	6.37+2	5.19+2	3.96+2	3.18+2
65	Tb	3.32+3	2.23+3	7.26+3	4.91+3	4.24+3	3.35+3	2.61+3	1.82+3	1.26+3	9.76+2	6.77+2	5.51+2	4.18+2	3.35+2
66	Dy	3.49+3	2.37+3	1.56+3	5.04+3	4.32+3	3.39+3	2.66+3	1.87+3	1.31+3	1.01+3	7.05+2	5.73+2	4.35+2	3.49+2
67	Ho	3.68+3	2.50+3	1.70+3	5.20+3	4.52+3	3.40+3	2.69+3	1.92+3	1.37+3	1.06+3	7.38+2	6.00+2	4.55+2	3.65+2
68	Er	3.92+3	2.67+3	1.84+3	4.30+3	3.69+3	3.33+3	2.74+3	1.99+3	1.44+3	1.11+3	7.74+2	6.28+2	4.75+2	3.81+2
69	Tm	4.19+3	2.84+3	1.96+3	4.01+3	3.91+3	3.53+3	2.80+3	2.06+3	1.51+3	1.17+3	8.16+2	6.62+2	5.00+2	4.01+2
70	Yb	4.38+3	2.99+3	2.15+3	1.70+3	4.08+3	3.63+3	2.77+3	2.05+3	1.56+3	1.21+3	8.43+2	6.85+2	5.18+2	4.15+2
71	Lu	4.53+3	3.10+3	2.23+3	1.38+3	4.23+3	3.65+3	2.67+3	2.12+3	1.62+3	1.26+3	8.78+2	7.14+2	5.41+2	4.34+2
72	Hf	4.76+3	3.26+3	2.35+3	1.46+3	4.40+3	3.04+3	2.81+3	2.21+3	1.68+3	1.31+3	9.15+2	7.43+2	5.62+2	4.50+2
73	Ta	5.01+3	3.37+3	2.21+3	1.60+3	5.29+3	3.55+3	2.92+3	2.52+3	1.84+3	1.33+3	9.89+2	7.93+2	5.87+2	4.67+2
74	W	5.25+3	3.54+3	2.32+3	1.68+3	3.60+3	3.70+3	3.02+3	2.34+3	1.91+3	1.38+3	1.03+3	8.25+2	6.11+2	4.88+2

TABLE 4 (continued)

Mass Attenuation Coefficients for $K\beta_1$ Lines

Emitter		Ne	Na	Mg	Al	Si	P	S	Cl	Ar	K	Ca	Sc	Ti	V
Wavelength		1.45+1	1.16+1	9.52+0	7.96+0	6.75+0	5.80+0	5.03+0	4.40+0	3.89+0	3.45+0	3.09+0	2.78+0	2.51+0	2.28+0
Energy (keV)		8.58-1	1.07+0	1.30+0	1.56+0	1.84+0	2.14+0	2.46+0	2.82+0	3.19+0	3.59+0	4.01+0	4.46+0	4.93+0	5.43+0
Absorber															
75	Re	5.46+3	3.70+3	2.43+3	1.76+3	1.17+3	3.88+3	3.14+3	2.46+3	1.98+3	1.44+3	1.07+3	8.61+2	6.38+2	5.09+2
76	Os	5.63+3	3.86+3	2.67+3	1.84+3	1.27+3	4.01+3	3.23+3	2.52+3	2.04+3	1.49+3	1.11+3	8.89+2	6.59+2	5.26+2
77	Ir	5.98+3	4.10+3	2.84+3	1.96+3	1.34+3	4.08+3	2.84+3	2.42+3	2.09+3	1.55+3	1.16+3	9.28+2	6.88+2	5.49+2
78	Pt	6.31+3	4.33+3	3.00+3	2.07+3	1.42+3	2.87+3	3.00+3	2.56+3	2.01+3	1.63+3	1.21+3	9.68+2	7.16+2	5.70+2
79	Au	6.61+3	4.46+3	3.08+3	2.11+3	1.54+3	1.01+3	2.96+3	2.53+3	2.01+3	1.65+3	1.23+3	9.90+2	7.37+2	5.90+2
80	Hg	6.82+3	4.51+3	3.07+3	2.14+3	1.50+3	1.08+3	3.12+3	2.22+3	1.93+3	1.71+3	1.29+3	1.03+3	7.67+2	6.12+2
81	Tl	7.10+3	4.95+3	3.59+3	2.29+3	1.67+3	1.14+3	2.14+3	2.34+3	2.01+3	1.61+3	1.33+3	1.07+3	7.91+2	6.32+2
82	Pb	6.96+3	5.15+3	3.74+3	2.39+3	1.75+3	1.20+3	8.29+2	2.41+3	2.08+3	1.66+3	1.37+3	1.11+3	8.21+2	6.56+2
83	Bi	7.22+3	5.36+3	3.89+3	2.50+3	1.83+3	1.27+3	9.10+2	2.47+3	2.12+3	1.57+3	1.43+3	1.15+3	8.53+2	6.81+2
84	Po	7.58+3	5.62+3	4.10+3	2.65+3	1.93+3	1.35+3	9.62+2	2.54+3	1.86+3	1.64+3	1.35+3	1.17+3	8.85+2	7.10+2
85	At	8.00+3	5.77+3	4.25+3	2.80+3	2.05+3	1.43+3	1.02+3	1.78+3	1.97+3	1.73+3	1.41+3	1.20+3	9.24+2	7.44+2
86	Rn	8.10+3	5.43+3	4.17+3	2.81+3	2.05+3	1.43+3	1.02+3	7.41+2	1.95+3	1.70+3	1.27+3	1.07+3	9.13+2	7.37+2
87	Fr	7.38+3	5.70+3	4.28+3	2.94+3	2.15+3	1.50+3	1.07+3	8.05+2	1.99+3	1.46+3	1.32+3	1.11+3	9.45+2	7.65+2
88	Ra	7.61+3	5.94+3	4.39+3	3.05+3	2.24+3	1.56+3	1.12+3	8.33+2	1.36+3	1.52+3	1.36+3	1.04+3	9.73+2	7.89+2
89	Ac	7.75+3	6.09+3	4.44+3	3.15+3	2.31+3	1.67+3	1.32+3	9.34+2	6.25+2	1.58+3	1.42+3	1.10+3	9.23+2	8.21+2
90	Th	7.72+3	6.00+3	4.27+3	3.23+3	2.38+3	1.72+3	1.36+3	9.66+2	6.57+2	1.62+3	1.21+3	1.14+3	9.41+2	8.26+2
91	Pa	8.22+3	5.65+3	4.61+3	3.45+3	2.53+3	1.83+3	1.45+3	1.03+3	7.09+2	1.13+3	1.27+3	1.20+3	9.09+2	8.54+2
92	U	8.23+3	5.74+3	4.65+3	3.49+3	2.57+3	1.81+3	1.30+3	1.00+3	7.54+2	1.12+3	1.26+3	1.18+3	9.04+2	7.76+2
93	Np	8.47+3	6.05+3	4.90+3	3.69+3	2.72+3	1.97+3	1.55+3	1.11+3	7.89+2	6.18+2	1.36+3	1.24+3	9.64+2	8.26+2
94	Pu	8.26+3	6.37+3	5.09+3	3.53+3	2.79+3	2.04+3	1.61+3	1.14+3	8.11+2	6.25+2	1.42+3	1.08+3	1.10+3	9.07+2

TABLE 4 (continued)

Mass Attenuation Coefficients for $K\beta_1$ Lines

Emitter	Cr	Mn	Fe	Co	Ni	Cu	Zn	Ga	Ge	As	Se	Br	Kr	Rb
Wavelength	2.08+0	1.91+0	1.76+0	1.62+0	1.50+0	1.39+0	1.30+0	1.21+0	1.13+0	1.06+0	9.92-1	9.33-1	8.79-1	8.29-1
Energy (keV)	5.95+0	6.49+0	7.06+0	7.65+0	8.26+0	8.91+0	9.57+0	1.03+1	1.10+1	1.17+1	1.25+1	1.33+1	1.41+1	1.50+1
Absorber														
1 H	4.05-1	4.00-1	3.96-1	3.93-1	3.90-1	3.88-1	3.86-1	3.85-1	3.83-1	3.82-1	3.80-1	3.79-1	3.78-1	3.76-1
2 He	4.32-1	3.84-1	3.41-1	3.14-1	2.91-1	2.73-1	2.59-1	2.49-1	2.40-1	2.32-1	2.26-1	2.21-1	2.17-1	2.12-1
3 Li	9.90-1	8.12-1	6.51-1	5.54-1	4.71-1	4.08-1	3.64-1	3.28-1	3.02-1	2.76-1	2.59-1	2.46-1	2.33-1	2.19-1
4 Be	2.60+0	2.06+0	1.58+0	1.29+0	1.04+0	8.55-1	7.24-1	6.19-1	5.46-1	4.71-1	4.21-1	3.85-1	3.48-1	3.10-1
5 B	5.59+0	4.40+0	3.32+0	2.67+0	2.12+0	1.70+0	1.41+0	1.17+0	1.01+0	8.40-1	7.28-1	6.49-1	5.68-1	4.83-1
6 C	1.11+1	8.69+0	6.54+0	5.23+0	4.11+0	3.27+0	2.68+0	2.20+0	1.87+0	1.53+0	1.30+0	1.14+0	9.78-1	8.07-1
7 N	1.86+1	1.46+1	1.10+1	8.78+0	6.89+0	5.46+0	4.45+0	3.64+0	3.07+0	2.48+0	2.10+0	1.82+0	1.54+0	1.25+0
8 O	2.87+1	2.26+1	1.70+1	1.36+1	1.07+1	8.46+0	6.88+0	5.61+0	4.72+0	3.80+0	3.20+0	2.76+0	2.32+0	1.86+0
9 F	3.88+1	3.06+1	2.31+1	1.85+1	1.46+1	1.16+1	9.39+0	7.66+0	6.45+0	5.19+0	4.35+0	3.76+0	3.14+0	2.50+0
10 Ne	5.62+1	4.44+1	3.36+1	2.70+1	2.13+1	1.69+1	1.37+1	1.12+1	9.43+0	7.59+0	6.36+0	5.48+0	4.58+0	3.64+0
11 Na	7.18+1	5.68+1	4.32+1	3.47+1	2.73+1	2.18+1	1.77+1	1.45+1	1.22+1	9.80+0	8.22+0	7.08+0	5.91+0	4.69+0
12 Mg	9.57+1	7.59+1	5.78+1	4.65+1	3.67+1	2.92+1	2.38+1	1.95+1	1.64+1	1.32+1	1.10+1	9.51+0	7.93+0	6.29+0
13 Al	1.20+2	9.56+1	7.30+1	5.88+1	4.65+1	3.71+1	3.03+1	2.47+1	2.08+1	1.68+1	1.41+1	1.21+1	1.01+1	8.01+0
14 Si	1.50+2	1.19+2	9.11+1	7.34+1	5.81+1	4.64+1	3.79+1	3.10+1	2.61+1	2.10+1	1.76+1	1.52+1	1.27+1	1.01+1
15 P	1.78+2	1.42+2	1.09+2	8.78+1	6.97+1	5.57+1	4.56+1	3.74+1	3.15+1	2.54+1	2.14+1	1.84+1	1.54+1	1.22+1
16 S	2.19+2	1.75+2	1.34+2	1.08+2	8.62+1	6.90+1	5.65+1	4.64+1	3.91+1	3.16+1	2.66+1	2.29+1	1.91+1	1.52+1
17 Cl	2.48+2	1.98+2	1.53+2	1.24+2	9.84+1	7.89+1	6.47+1	5.31+1	4.49+1	3.63+1	3.06+1	2.64+1	2.20+1	1.76+1
18 Ar	2.77+2	2.22+2	1.71+2	1.38+2	1.10+2	8.84+1	7.24+1	5.95+1	5.03+1	4.07+1	3.42+1	2.95+1	2.47+1	1.97+1
19 K	3.38+2	2.71+2	2.09+2	1.70+2	1.36+2	1.09+2	8.96+1	7.38+1	6.24+1	5.06+1	4.27+1	3.69+1	3.09+1	2.46+1
20 Ca	3.97+2	3.19+2	2.47+2	2.01+2	1.60+2	1.29+2	1.06+2	8.76+1	7.42+1	6.03+1	5.08+1	4.39+1	3.68+1	2.94+1
21 Sc	4.21+2	3.39+2	2.63+2	2.14+2	1.72+2	1.39+2	1.14+2	9.42+1	7.98+1	6.49+1	5.48+1	4.74+1	3.97+1	3.18+1
22 Ti	4.61+2	3.73+2	2.91+2	2.38+2	1.92+2	1.55+2	1.28+2	1.06+2	9.01+1	7.34+1	6.21+1	5.38+1	4.51+1	3.62+1
23 V	5.07+2	4.11+2	3.21+2	2.62+2	2.11+2	1.71+2	1.41+2	1.17+2	9.91+1	8.08+1	6.83+1	5.91+1	4.97+1	3.99+1
24 Cr	7.07+1	4.76+2	3.71+2	3.04+2	2.45+2	1.98+2	1.64+2	1.36+2	1.15+2	9.40+1	7.95+1	6.89+1	5.79+1	4.65+1
25 Mn	7.85+1	6.19+1	4.00+2	3.28+2	2.64+2	2.14+2	1.77+2	1.47+2	1.25+2	1.02+2	8.63+1	7.48+1	6.29+1	5.06+1
26 Fe	9.01+1	7.28+1	5.66+1	3.66+2	2.97+2	2.42+2	2.00+2	1.66+2	1.42+2	1.16+2	9.85+1	8.54+1	7.19+1	5.80+1
27 Co	9.94+1	8.04+1	6.27+1	5.07+1	3.32+2	2.69+2	2.23+2	1.85+2	1.57+2	1.28+2	1.09+2	9.43+1	7.93+1	6.38+1
28 Ni	1.14+2	9.20+1	7.18+1	5.89+1	4.71+1	2.89+2	2.42+2	2.02+2	1.72+2	1.42+2	1.21+2	1.05+2	8.87+1	7.19+1
29 Cu	1.22+2	9.89+1	7.72+1	6.34+1	5.12+1	4.18+1	2.55+2	2.13+2	1.82+2	1.50+2	1.27+2	1.11+2	9.36+1	7.59+1
30 Zn	1.36+2	1.10+2	8.64+1	7.10+1	5.76+1	4.70+1	3.88+1	2.38+2	2.03+2	1.67+2	1.42+2	1.24+2	1.05+2	8.47+1
31 Ga	1.45+2	1.17+2	9.18+1	7.53+1	6.09+1	4.96+1	4.13+1	3.40+1	2.06+2	1.72+2	1.47+2	1.28+2	1.08+2	8.78+1
32 Ge	1.57+2	1.26+2	9.86+1	8.08+1	6.52+1	5.31+1	4.42+1	3.66+1	3.05+1	1.78+2	1.54+2	1.34+2	1.14+2	9.25+1
33 As	1.73+2	1.40+2	1.09+2	8.95+1	7.23+1	5.90+1	4.90+1	4.04+1	3.42+1	2.85+1	1.71+2	1.49+2	1.26+2	1.03+2
34 Se	1.86+2	1.50+2	1.17+2	9.59+1	7.75+1	6.31+1	5.25+1	4.38+1	3.75+1	3.10+1	2.58+1	1.53+2	1.32+2	1.09+2
35 Br	2.05+2	1.66+2	1.29+2	1.06+2	8.54+1	6.95+1	5.78+1	4.82+1	4.13+1	3.40+1	2.86+1	2.41+1	1.40+2	1.18+2
36 Kr	2.19+2	1.77+2	1.38+2	1.13+2	9.15+1	7.45+1	6.20+1	5.18+1	4.43+1	3.65+1	3.04+1	2.62+1	2.22+1	1.24+2
37 Rb	2.39+2	1.92+2	1.50+2	1.22+2	9.86+1	8.02+1	6.66+1	5.54+1	4.74+1	3.90+1	3.33+1	2.90+1	2.46+1	2.01+1

TABLE 4 (continued)

Mass Attenuation Coefficients for $K\beta_1$ Lines

Emitter	Cr	Mn	Fe	Co	Ni	Cu	Zn	Ga	Ge	As	Se	Br	Kr	Rb
Wavelength	2.08+0	1.91+0	1.76+0	1.62+0	1.50+0	1.39+0	1.30+0	1.21+0	1.13+0	1.06+0	9.92-1	9.33-1	8.79-1	8.29-1
Energy (keV)	5.95+0	6.49+0	7.06+0	7.65+0	8.26+0	8.91+0	9.57+0	1.03+1	1.10+1	1.17+1	1.25+1	1.33+1	1.41+1	1.50+1
Absorber														
38 Sr	2.59+2	2.09+2	1.62+2	1.33+2	1.07+2	8.70+1	7.22+1	6.01+1	5.13+1	4.23+1	3.60+1	3.14+1	2.67+1	2.18+1
39 Y	2.84+2	2.28+2	1.77+2	1.45+2	1.17+2	9.50+1	7.88+1	6.56+1	5.61+1	4.61+1	3.93+1	3.43+1	2.91+1	2.37+1
40 Zr	3.06+2	2.46+2	1.91+2	1.56+2	1.25+2	1.02+2	8.44+1	7.02+1	5.99+1	4.92+1	4.19+1	3.66+1	3.10+1	2.52+1
41 Nb	3.35+2	2.69+2	2.09+2	1.70+2	1.37+2	1.11+2	9.22+1	7.66+1	6.54+1	5.37+1	4.58+1	3.99+1	3.38+1	2.75+1
42 Mo	3.55+2	2.85+2	2.21+2	1.80+2	1.45+2	1.17+2	9.72+1	8.07+1	6.88+1	5.65+1	4.81+1	4.19+1	3.55+1	2.88+1
43 Tc	3.77+2	3.03+2	2.35+2	1.92+2	1.55+2	1.25+2	1.04+2	8.65+1	7.38+1	6.07+1	5.17+1	4.50+1	3.82+1	3.11+1
44 Ru	4.05+2	3.26+2	2.53+2	2.07+2	1.66+2	1.35+2	1.12+2	9.29+1	7.93+1	6.51+1	5.55+1	4.83+1	4.10+1	3.33+1
45 Rh	4.32+2	3.48+2	2.70+2	2.21+2	1.78+2	1.44+2	1.20+2	9.97+1	8.51+1	7.00+1	5.97+1	5.20+1	4.41+1	3.59+1
46 Pd	4.63+2	3.72+2	2.88+2	2.35+2	1.89+2	1.53+2	1.27+2	1.05+2	8.96+1	7.36+1	6.26+1	5.45+1	4.61+1	3.75+1
47 Ag	4.95+2	3.98+2	3.09+2	2.52+2	2.03+2	1.64+2	1.36+2	1.13+2	9.64+1	7.92+1	6.74+1	5.87+1	4.97+1	4.04+1
48 Cd	5.19+2	4.16+2	3.23+2	2.63+2	2.11+2	1.71+2	1.42+2	1.18+2	1.00+2	8.22+1	6.99+1	6.08+1	5.15+1	4.18+1
49 In	5.51+2	4.43+2	3.43+2	2.80+2	2.25+2	1.83+2	1.51+2	1.26+2	1.07+2	8.80+1	7.49+1	6.52+1	5.52+1	4.49+1
50 Sn	5.85+2	4.70+2	3.64+2	2.97+2	2.38+2	1.93+2	1.59+2	1.32+2	1.13+2	9.25+1	7.87+1	6.85+1	5.79+1	4.70+1
51 Sb	6.01+2	4.84+2	3.77+2	3.08+2	2.48+2	2.02+2	1.68+2	1.40+2	1.19+2	9.81+1	8.36+1	7.29+1	6.19+1	5.04+1
52 Te	6.25+2	5.04+2	3.92+2	3.21+2	2.58+2	2.10+2	1.74+2	1.45+2	1.24+2	1.02+2	8.69+1	7.57+1	6.42+1	5.23+1
53 I	6.77+2	5.46+2	4.25+2	3.47+2	2.79+2	2.27+2	1.88+2	1.56+2	1.33+2	1.10+2	9.35+1	8.14+1	6.90+1	5.62+1
54 Xe	6.88+2	5.57+2	4.33+2	3.54+2	2.86+2	2.32+2	1.92+2	1.60+2	1.37+2	1.13+2	9.59+1	8.36+1	7.09+1	5.77+1
55 Cs	7.44+2	6.04+2	4.69+2	3.84+2	3.09+2	2.51+2	2.08+2	1.73+2	1.48+2	1.21+2	1.03+2	9.01+1	7.64+1	6.21+1
56 Ba	6.46+2	6.28+2	4.89+2	3.99+2	3.21+2	2.61+2	2.16+2	1.80+2	1.54+2	1.26+2	1.08+2	9.37+1	7.94+1	6.46+1
57 La	6.91+2	6.60+2	5.21+2	4.26+2	3.42+2	2.77+2	2.30+2	1.91+2	1.63+2	1.33+2	1.14+2	9.89+1	8.37+1	6.80+1
58 Ce	5.25+2	5.78+2	5.54+2	4.52+2	3.64+2	2.95+2	2.45+2	2.04+2	1.74+2	1.43+2	1.21+2	1.06+2	8.96+1	7.28+1
59 Pr	1.94+2	6.13+2	5.87+2	4.80+2	3.86+2	3.13+2	2.59+2	2.16+2	1.84+2	1.51+2	1.29+2	1.12+2	9.49+1	7.71+1
60 Nd	2.07+2	4.66+2	5.14+2	5.03+2	4.06+2	3.29+2	2.72+2	2.26+2	1.93+2	1.58+2	1.35+2	1.17+2	9.93+1	8.06+1
61 Pm	2.17+2	4.83+2	5.37+2	5.20+2	4.24+2	3.44+2	2.85+2	2.37+2	2.02+2	1.66+2	1.41+2	1.23+2	1.04+2	8.46+1
62 Sm	2.27+2	1.83+2	4.04+2	4.53+2	4.45+2	3.61+2	2.99+2	2.48+2	2.12+2	1.74+2	1.48+2	1.29+2	1.09+2	8.85+1
63 Eu	2.39+2	1.95+2	4.26+2	4.76+2	4.67+2	3.79+2	3.14+2	2.61+2	2.23+2	1.83+2	1.56+2	1.35+2	1.15+2	9.31+1
64 Gd	2.45+2	2.00+2	1.58+2	3.55+2	3.98+2	3.90+2	3.24+2	2.69+2	2.29+2	1.88+2	1.60+2	1.39+2	1.18+2	9.56+1
65 Tb	2.59+2	2.11+2	1.67+2	3.72+2	4.19+2	4.10+2	3.41+2	2.83+2	2.42+2	1.98+2	1.69+2	1.47+2	1.24+2	1.01+2
66 Dy	2.69+2	2.19+2	1.73+2	1.42+2	3.13+2	3.55+2	3.54+2	2.94+2	2.51+2	2.06+2	1.75+2	1.52+2	1.29+2	1.05+2
67 Ho	2.81+2	2.29+2	1.81+2	1.50+2	3.27+2	2.65+2	3.65+2	3.06+2	2.61+2	2.14+2	1.82+2	1.59+2	1.34+2	1.09+2
68 Er	2.93+2	2.39+2	1.88+2	1.56+2	1.26+2	2.77+2	3.17+2	3.19+2	2.72+2	2.23+2	1.90+2	1.65+2	1.40+2	1.14+2
69 Tm	3.09+2	2.52+2	1.99+2	1.65+2	1.34+2	2.91+2	2.40+2	3.33+2	2.85+2	2.35+2	2.00+2	1.74+2	1.47+2	1.20+2
70 Yb	3.20+2	2.61+2	2.06+2	1.71+2	1.39+2	1.14+2	2.51+2	2.87+2	2.91+2	2.42+2	2.07+2	1.80+2	1.53+2	1.24+2
71 Lu	3.34+2	2.72+2	2.15+2	1.77+2	1.45+2	1.19+2	2.61+2	2.15+2	2.99+2	2.52+2	2.17+2	1.89+2	1.60+2	1.29+2
72 Hf	3.46+2	2.82+2	2.22+2	1.84+2	1.50+2	1.23+2	2.71+2	2.25+2	2.60+2	2.61+2	2.26+2	1.97+2	1.66+2	1.35+2
73 Ta	3.59+2	2.92+2	2.29+2	1.89+2	1.54+2	1.27+2	1.06+2	2.24+2	1.87+2	2.59+2	2.25+2	1.96+2	1.66+2	1.35+2
74 W	3.75+2	3.05+2	2.40+2	1.98+2	1.62+2	1.33+2	1.11+2	2.44+2	2.06+2	2.36+2	2.44+2	2.12+2	1.80+2	1.46+2

TABLE 4 (continued)

Mass Attenuation Coefficients for $K\beta_1$ Lines

Emitter	Cr	Mn	Fe	Co	Ni	Cu	Zn	Ga	Ge	As	Se	Br	Kr	Rb
Wavelength	2.08+0	1.91+0	1.76+0	1.62+0	1.50+0	1.39+0	1.30+0	1.21+0	1.13+0	1.06+0	9.92-1	9.33-1	8.79-1	8.29-1
Energy (keV)	5.95+0	6.49+0	7.06+0	7.65+0	8.26+0	8.91+0	9.57+0	1.03+1	1.10+1	1.17+1	1.25+1	1.33+1	1.41+1	1.50+1
Absorber														
75 Re	3.91+2	3.18+2	2.51+2	2.08+2	1.69+2	1.39+2	1.17+2	9.69+1	2.11+2	1.76+2	2.04+2	2.13+2	1.82+2	1.51+2
76 Os	4.04+2	3.29+2	2.60+2	2.14+2	1.75+2	1.44+2	1.21+2	1.00+2	2.14+2	1.80+2	2.10+2	2.15+2	1.86+2	1.55+2
77 Ir	4.22+2	3.43+2	2.71+2	2.24+2	1.83+2	1.50+2	1.26+2	1.05+2	8.87+1	1.87+2	1.58+2	1.85+2	1.91+2	1.61+2
78 Pt	4.37+2	3.55+2	2.79+2	2.30+2	1.87+2	1.54+2	1.29+2	1.08+2	9.16+1	1.93+2	1.64+2	1.91+2	1.96+2	1.67+2
79 Au	4.55+2	3.71+2	2.93+2	2.43+2	1.99+2	1.64+2	1.37+2	1.16+2	9.96+1	8.29+1	1.67+2	1.42+2	1.66+2	1.69+2
80 Hg	4.71+2	3.84+2	3.03+2	2.50+2	2.04+2	1.68+2	1.41+2	1.19+2	1.02+2	8.51+1	1.75+2	1.51+2	1.26+2	1.78+2
81 Tl	4.86+2	3.96+2	3.13+2	2.58+2	2.11+2	1.73+2	1.45+2	1.22+2	1.05+2	8.78+1	7.37+1	1.54+2	1.31+2	1.53+2
82 Pb	5.05+2	4.12+2	3.25+2	2.69+2	2.20+2	1.81+2	1.52+2	1.28+2	1.10+2	9.17+1	7.73+1	1.64+2	1.41+2	1.18+2
83 Bi	5.25+2	4.28+2	3.38+2	2.79+2	2.28+2	1.88+2	1.57+2	1.33+2	1.14+2	9.52+1	8.07+1	6.86+1	1.37+2	1.16+2
84 Po	5.46+2	4.45+2	3.52+2	2.91+2	2.38+2	1.95+2	1.64+2	1.38+2	1.19+2	9.91+1	8.44+1	7.24+1	1.42+2	1.21+2
85 At	5.73+2	4.67+2	3.69+2	3.05+2	2.49+2	2.05+2	1.72+2	1.45+2	1.25+2	1.04+2	8.88+1	7.69+1	6.46+1	1.27+2
86 Rn	5.68+2	4.63+2	3.65+2	3.02+2	2.47+2	2.03+2	1.70+2	1.43+2	1.23+2	1.03+2	8.83+1	7.71+1	6.55+1	1.26+2
87 Fr	5.90+2	4.81+2	3.81+2	3.15+2	2.57+2	2.12+2	1.78+2	1.50+2	1.29+2	1.08+2	9.28+1	8.16+1	7.00+1	5.79+1
88 Ra	6.09+2	4.97+2	3.93+2	3.25+2	2.66+2	2.19+2	1.84+2	1.55+2	1.33+2	1.11+2	9.58+1	8.42+1	7.22+1	5.98+1
89 Ac	6.33+2	5.17+2	4.09+2	3.38+2	2.76+2	2.28+2	1.91+2	1.61+2	1.39+2	1.16+2	9.97+1	8.76+1	7.52+1	6.22+1
90 Th	6.46+2	5.28+2	4.18+2	3.46+2	2.83+2	2.33+2	1.95+2	1.64+2	1.42+2	1.18+2	1.02+2	8.95+1	7.67+1	6.35+1
91 Pa	6.77+2	5.54+2	4.38+2	3.63+2	2.96+2	2.44+2	2.05+2	1.72+2	1.49+2	1.24+2	1.07+2	9.37+1	8.03+1	6.65+1
92 U	6.76+2	5.54+2	4.39+2	3.63+2	2.97+2	2.45+2	2.06+2	1.73+2	1.49+2	1.25+2	1.07+2	9.44+1	8.10+1	6.71+1
93 Np	7.18+2	5.89+2	4.66+2	3.85+2	3.14+2	2.58+2	2.17+2	1.82+2	1.57+2	1.31+2	1.13+2	9.89+1	8.47+1	7.00+1
94 Pu	7.75+2	6.38+2	5.01+2	4.12+2	3.32+2	2.65+2	2.21+2	1.86+2	1.60+2	1.33+2	1.15+2	1.01+2	8.62+1	7.12+1

TABLE 4 (continued)

Mass Attenuation Coefficients for $K\beta_1$ Lines

Emitter	Sr	Y	Zr
Wavelength	7.83-1	7.41-1	7.02-1
Energy (keV)	1.58+1	1.67+1	1.77+1
Absorber			
1 He	3.75-1	3.74-1	3.73-1
2 He	2.09-1	2.06-1	2.03-1
3 Li	2.11-1	2.04-1	1.98-1
4 Be	2.90-1	2.70-1	2.56-1
5 B	4.39-1	3.96-1	3.65-1
6 C	7.18-1	6.30-1	5.68-1
7 N	1.09+0	9.43-1	8.37-1
8 O	1.62+0	1.38+0	1.21+0
9 F	2.17+0	1.84+0	1.61+0
10 Ne	3.14+0	2.66+0	2.31+0
11 Na	4.05+0	3.41+0	2.97+0
12 Mg	5.43+0	4.57+0	3.96+0
13 Al	6.90+0	5.80+0	5.02+0
14 Si	8.66+0	7.28+0	6.30+0
15 P	1.05+1	8.87+0	7.68+0
16 S	1.31+1	1.11+1	9.57+0
17 Cl	1.51+1	1.27+1	1.10+1
18 Ar	1.70+1	1.43+1	1.24+1
19 K	2.13+1	1.79+1	1.56+1
20 Ca	2.54+1	2.14+1	1.86+1
21 Sc	2.75+1	2.32+1	2.01+1
22 Ti	3.13+1	2.65+1	2.30+1
23 V	3.45+1	2.92+1	2.53+1
24 Cr	4.02+1	3.40+1	2.95+1
25 Mn	4.38+1	3.70+1	3.22+1
26 Fe	5.03+1	4.26+1	3.71+1
27 Co	5.53+1	4.68+1	4.07+1
28 Ni	6.24+1	5.31+1	4.63+1
29 Cu	6.59+1	5.61+1	4.89+1
30 Zn	7.36+1	6.25+1	5.45+1
31 Ga	7.63+1	6.49+1	5.66+1
32 Ge	8.05+1	6.85+1	5.99+1
33 As	8.92+1	7.60+1	6.64+1
34 Se	9.50+1	8.10+1	7.07+1
35 Br	1.03+2	8.82+1	7.71+1
36 Kr	1.08+2	9.25+1	8.09+1
37 Rb	1.16+2	9.94+1	8.72+1
38 Sr	1.88+1	1.06+2	9.35+1
39 Y	2.07+1	1.78+1	1.01+2
40 Zr	2.20+1	1.88+1	1.62+1
41 Nb	2.40+1	2.05+1	1.79+1
42 Mo	2.51+1	2.15+1	1.85+1
43 Tc	2.71+1	2.32+1	2.03+1
44 Ru	2.91+1	2.49+1	2.18+1
45 Rh	3.14+1	2.68+1	2.35+1
46 Pd	3.27+1	2.79+1	2.44+1
47 Ag	3.53+1	3.01+1	2.64+1

Emitter	Sr	Y	Ar
Wavelength	7.83-1	7.41-1	7.02-1
Energy (keV)	1.58+1	1.67+1	1.77+1
Absorber			
48 Cd	3.64+1	3.11+1	2.73+1
49 In	3.91+1	3.34+1	2.93+1
50 Sn	4.09+1	3.50+1	3.06+1
51 Sb	4.40+1	3.77+1	3.31+1
52 Te	4.57+1	3.91+1	3.43+1
53 I	4.90+1	4.19+1	3.67+1
54 Xe	5.04+1	4.31+1	3.78+1
55 Cs	5.42+1	4.64+1	4.06+1
56 Ba	5.63+1	4.82+1	4.22+1
57 La	5.92+1	5.06+1	4.43+1
58 Ce	6.35+1	5.43+1	4.75+1
59 Pr	6.73+1	5.75+1	5.04+1
60 Nd	7.02+1	5.99+1	5.25+1
61 Pm	7.37+1	6.30+1	5.52+1
62 Sm	7.71+1	6.58+1	5.77+1
63 Eu	8.11+1	6.92+1	6.06+1
64 Gd	8.33+1	7.11+1	6.22+1
65 Tb	8.78+1	7.49+1	6.56+1
66 Dy	9.11+1	7.78+1	6.81+1
67 Ho	9.52+1	8.13+1	7.12+1
68 Er	9.91+1	8.46+1	7.41+1
69 Tm	1.04+2	8.90+1	7.79+1
70 Yb	1.08+2	9.21+1	8.06+1
71 Lu	1.13+2	9.62+1	8.42+1
72 Hf	1.17+2	1.00+2	8.76+1
73 Ta	1.18+2	1.01+2	8.84+1
74 W	1.27+2	1.09+2	9.50+1
75 Re	1.31+2	1.12+2	9.80+1
76 Os	1.35+2	1.15+2	1.01+2
77 Ir	1.41+2	1.20+2	1.05+2
78 Pt	1.46+2	1.24+2	1.09+2
79 Au	1.48+2	1.27+2	1.11+2
80 Hg	1.56+2	1.33+2	1.17+2
81 Tl	1.58+2	1.36+2	1.20+2
82 Pb	1.41+2	1.45+2	1.28+2
83 Bi	1.39+2	1.44+2	1.27+2
84 Po	1.05+2	1.26+2	1.33+2
85 At	1.11+2	9.48+1	1.37+2
86 Rn	1.10+2	9.46+1	1.13+2
87 Fr	1.15+2	9.84+1	8.49+1
88 Ra	1.17+2	1.01+2	8.81+1
89 Ac	5.39+1	1.05+2	9.23+1
90 Th	5.54+1	1.08+2	9.54+1
91 Pa	5.83+1	1.14+2	1.01+2
92 U	5.91+1	5.11+1	1.00+2
93 Np	6.16+1	5.33+1	1.05+2
94 Pu	6.26+1	5.41+1	4.71+1

V. TABLES OF EXPERIMENTAL VALUES OF X-RAY FLUORESCENCE AND COSTER-KRONIG YIELDS FOR THE K-, L-, AND M-SHELLS

R. W. Fink, Georgia Institute of Technology, and
P. Venugopala Rao, Emory University

The fluorescence yield[1] of an atomic shell or subshell is defined as the probability that a vacancy in that shell or subshell is filled through a radiative transition. Thus, for a sample of many atoms, the fluorescence yield of a shell of a singly ionized atom is equal to the number of photons emitted when vacancies in the shell are filled, divided by the number of primary vacancies in the shell. The application of this definition to the K-shell of an atom, normally containing two $s_{1/2}$ electrons, is straightforward. The K-shell fluorescence yield is

$$\omega_K = I_K/n_K, \qquad (1)$$

where I_K is the total number of characteristic K x-ray photons emitted from a sample, and n_K is the number of primary K-shell vacancies.

The definition of fluorescence yields of higher atomic shells[1] is more complicated for two reasons: (1) Shells above the K-shell consist of more than one subshell, so the average fluorescence yield depends, in general, on how the shells are ionized, since different methods of creating ionization give rise to different sets of subshell primary vacancy distributions. (2) Coster-Kronig transitions, which are transitions between the subshells of an atomic shell having the same principal quantum number, make it possible for a primary vacancy created in one of the subshells to shift to a higher subshell before the vacancy is filled by another transition.

Consequently, great care is required in formulating proper definitions of the quantities that are measured and in interpreting experimental results in a manner that is consistent with these definitions.

In shells higher than the K-shell, two alternative approaches can be taken[1] in accounting for the effect of Coster-Kronig transitions: (1) The average fluorescence yield $\bar{\omega}_X$ can be regarded as a linear combination of the subshell fluorescence yields ω_i^X with a vacancy distribution V_i^X that results from alteration of the primary vacancy distribution N_i^X by Coster-Kronig transitions. This method has the advantage that it leads to equations which contain the subshell fluorescence yields ω_i^X from the beginning and that it corresponds closely to the actual physical situation in the major X-shell. (2) The expression for the average fluorescence yield $\bar{\omega}_X$ can be regarded mathematically as a linear combination of the primary vacancy distribution N_i^X with a set of specially defined coefficients ν_i^X for the X-shell. The definition of the ν_i^X coefficients must be such as to account properly for the effect of Coster-Kronig transitions. This method has the advantage that it is more convenient from the experimental point of view if the primary vacancy distribution for a given experiment is known.

Both approaches have been widely used; the failure to distinguish properly between them in the literature has sometimes led to confusion. Below, equations according to each approach are formulated,[1] and transformation equations that relate the two alternative descriptions are given.

A. Description in Terms of the Altered Vacancy Distributions V_i^X

The mean fluorescence yield of the X-shell can be written as follows:

$$\bar{\omega}_X = \sum_{i=1}^{k} V_i^X \omega_i^X. \qquad (2)$$

Here the coefficients V_i^X denote the relative numbers of vacancies in the subshells X_i, *including* vacancies shifted to each subshell by Coster-Kronig transitions. The quantities V_i^X obey the relation

$$\sum_{i=1}^{k} V_i^X > 1: \qquad (3)$$

This condition applies because of the way in which the subshell fluorescence yields ω_i^X are defined. The sum of the V_i^X exceeds unity because some of the vacancies created in subshells below X_i must be counted more than once as Coster-Kronig transitions shift them to higher X-subshells.

The Coster-Kronig transition probability for shifting a vacancy from a subshell X_i to a higher subshell X_j is denoted by f^X_{ij}. Accordingly, the quantities V^X_i can be written in terms of the relative numbers N^X_i of primary vacancies as follows:

$$\begin{aligned}
&V_1{}^X = N_1{}^X,\\
&V_2{}^X = N_2{}^X + f_{12}{}^X N_1{}^X,\\
&V_3{}^X = N_3{}^X + f_{23}{}^X N_2{}^X + (f_{13}{}^X + f_{12}{}^X f_{23}{}^X) N_1{}^X, \cdots \\
&V_k{}^X = N_k{}^X + f_{k-1,k}{}^X N_{k-1}{}^X + (f_{k-2,k-1}{}^X f_{k-1,k}{}^X) N_{k-2}{}^X\\
&\quad + \cdots + (f_{1k}{}^X + f_{12}{}^X f_{2k}{}^X + f_{12}{}^X f_{23}{}^X f_{3k}{}^X + \cdots) N_1{}^X.
\end{aligned} \tag{4}$$

B. Description in Terms of the Primary Vacancy Distribution N^X_i

Under this alternative approach, the average fluorescence yield of the X-shell is expressed as

$$\varpi_X = \sum_{i=1}^{k} N^X_i \nu^X_i , \tag{5}$$

which is a linear combination of the relative numbers of primary vacancies N^X_i. The coefficients ν^X_i in Equation 5 are especially defined to be consistent with the defining equation (4). A coefficient ν^X_i represents the total number of characteristic X-shell x-rays (not necessarily from the radiative filling of a vacancy in the X_i-subshell) that result per primary vacancy in the X-subshell. This definition is quite different from that of the actual subshell fluorescence yield ω^X_i, in which it is required that characteristic x-rays observed must be due to transitions to the X_i-subshell. The products $V^X_i \omega^X_i$ and $N^X_i \nu^X_i$ are *not* equal; only the sums of the products are equal to the average fluorescence yield ϖ_X, as shown by Equations 2 and 5. From the physical definition of $V^X_i \omega^X_i$, it is seen that this quantity represents the number of radiative transitions from higher shells to the *i*th subshell per vacancy in any subshell of the entire X-shell. On the other hand, the quantity $N^X_i \nu^X_i$ is the number of x-rays emitted in transitions to *all* the subshells of the X-shell per vacancy in the *i*th subshell.

C. Transformation Equations Relating the Two Descriptions[1]

The transformation relations between the coefficients ν^X_i and the subshell fluorescence yields ω^X_i follow from Equations 2, 4, and 5:

$$\begin{aligned}
&\nu_1{}^X = \omega_1{}^X + f_{12}{}^X \omega_2{}^X + (f_{13}{}^X + f_{12}{}^X f_{23}{}^X)\omega_3{}^X + \cdots\\
&+(f_{1k}{}^X + f_{12}{}^X f_{2k}{}^X + f_{13}{}^X f_{3k}{}^X + \cdots + f_{1,k-1}{}^X f_{k-1,k}{}^X\\
&+ \text{products of 3, 4, } \cdots, (k-1)\ f_{ij}{}^X\text{'s ordered to take the}\\
&\text{vacancy from subshell 1 to subshell k})\ \omega_k{}^X, \cdots\\
&\nu_{k-1}{}^X = \omega_{k-1}{}^X + f_{k-1,k}{}^X \omega_k{}^X,\ \nu_k{}^X = \omega_k{}^X.
\end{aligned} \tag{6}$$

For clarity, we specialize the general relations between N^X_i and V^X_i and between ν^X_i and ω^X_i for the L-shell. The relations for the M-subshells can be found in Reference 1. In the L-shell, the initial and final vacancy distributions are related as follows:

$$\begin{aligned}
&V_1{}^L = N_1{}^L,\\
&V_2{}^L = N_2{}^L + f_{12}{}^L N_1{}^L\\
&V_3{}^L = N_3{}^L + f_{23}{}^L N_2{}^L + (f_{13}{}^L + f_{12}{}^L f_{23}{}^L) N_1{}^L
\end{aligned} \tag{7}$$

and between the coefficients ν^X_i and the subshell fluorescence yields ω^X_i, for the L-shell:

$$\begin{aligned}
&\nu_1{}^L = \omega_1{}^L + f_{12}{}^L \omega_2{}^L + (f_{13}{}^L + f_{12}{}^L f_{23}{}^L)\omega_3{}^L,\\
&\nu_2{}^L = \omega_2{}^L + f_{23}{}^L \omega_3{}^L,\\
&\nu_3{}^L = \omega_3{}^L,
\end{aligned} \tag{8}$$

where the quantities f_{12}, f_{13}, and f_{23} are the L-shell Coster-Kronig transition probabilities.

Methods for the experimental determination of the subshell fluorescence yields and Coster-Kronig transition probabilities and theoretical calculations of these quantities for the L-subshells are reviewed in References 1 and 2.

The notation[1] is unambiguous and has the following characteristics: (1) The symbols for all average fluorescence yields carry the designation of the major shell as a subscript. Thus, ω_K is the K-shell fluorescence yield for a singly ionized atom, ϖ_L is the mean L-shell fluorescence yield for a given subshell vacancy distribution, and similarly for higher shells. The notation ω_{KL} denotes a mean L-shell fluorescence yield for the particular distribution of primary vacancies that results from K_α x-ray emission and is a linear combination of L_2- and L_3-subshell fluorescence yields ω_2 and ω_3 (see Reference 1). (2) The symbols for individual subshell fluorescence yields carry a subscript denoting the subshell and a superscript denoting the major shell. The subscripts are ordered such that $i = 1$ denotes the most tightly bound subshell and $i = k$, the least tightly bound subshell. Thus, ω^M_3 denotes the fluorescence yield of the $2p_{3/2}$ level. (3) The symbols for Coster-Kronig transition probabilities carry two subscripts, indicating the subshells between which the transitions occur, and a superscript denoting the major shell. Thus, f_{14}^{M} is the Coster-Kronig transition probability for a shift of a vacancy from the M_1- to the M_4-subshell.

Comprehensive reviews of theory and experimental methods are given in References 1 and 2, and the latest experimental results are evaluated and tabulated in Reference 1. The following is a set of tables of K-shell x-ray fluorescence yields for singly ionized atoms and of L- and M-subshell and mean fluorescence and Coster-Kronig yields from Reference 1 updated to May 1973.

TABLE 5

Experimental Values of K-shell X-ray Fluorescence Yields*

Z Element	ω_K Selected "Most Reliable" Experimental Values[a]	ω_K Fitted Values[b]
13 Al	0.0380	0.0357 ± 0.0028
14 Si	0.043[c]	0.0470 ± 0.0082
15 P	0.058[d]	0.0604 ± 0.0100
16 S	0.080[c,d]	0.0761 ± 0.0100
17 Cl	0.098[d]	0.0942 ± 0.0051
18 Ar	0.122	0.115 ± 0.006
19 K		0.138 ± 0.013
20 Ca		0.163 ± 0.016
21 Sc	0.190	0.190 ± 0.016
22 Ti	0.221	0.219 ± 0.018
23 V	0.253	0.250 ± 0.007
24 Cr	0.280[e]	0.282 ± 0.007
25 Mn	0.313	0.314 ± 0.023
26 Fe	0.347[f]	0.347 ± 0.008
27 Co	0.366	0.381 ± 0.027
28 Ni		0.414 ± 0.028
29 Cu	0.443[g]	0.445 ± 0.009
30 Zn		0.479 ± 0.030
31 Ga	0.528	0.510 ± 0.008
32 Ge	0.554	0.540 ± 0.026
33 As	0.587	0.567 ± 0.031
34 Se		0.596 ± 0.032
35 Br		0.622 ± 0.032
36 Kr	0.656	0.646 ± 0.011
37 Rb	0.669	0.669 ± 0.008
38 Sr	0.702	0.691 ± 0.013
39 Y		0.711 ± 0.031
40 Zr		0.730 ± 0.032
41 Nb		0.748 ± 0.032
42 Mo		0.764 ± 0.032
43 Tc		0.779 ± 0.032
44 Ru		0.793 ± 0.031
45 Rh		0.807 ± 0.031
46 Pd		0.819 ± 0.030
47 Ag	0.834	0.830 ± 0.025
48 Cd		0.840 ± 0.029
49 In		0.850 ± 0.029
50 Sn		0.859 ± 0.028
51 Sb		0.867 ± 0.028
52 Te	0.873 ± 0.017[h]	0.875 ± 0.028

TABLE 5 (continued)

Experimental Values of K-shell X-ray Fluorescence Yields*

Z Element	ω_K Selected "Most Reliable" Experimental Values[a]	ω_K Fitted Values[b]
53 I		0.882 ± 0.028
54 Xe	0.894	0.889 ± 0.020
55 Cs	0.889	0.895 ± 0.012
56 Ba		0.901 ± 0.026
57 La		0.906 ± 0.026
58 Ce		0.911 ± 0.026
59 Pr		0.915 ± 0.025
60 Nd		0.920 ± 0.024
61 Pm		0.924 ± 0.024
62 Sm		0.928 ± 0.023
63 Eu	0.925	0.931 ± 0.015
64 Gd		0.934 ± 0.022
65 Tb		0.937 ± 0.022
66 Dy	0.943	0.940 ± 0.016
67 Ho		0.943 ± 0.021
68 Er		0.945 ± 0.021
69 Tm		0.948 ± 0.020
70 Yb		0.950 ± 0.020
71 In		0.952 ± 0.020
72 Hf		0.954 ± 0.019
73 Ta		0.956 ± 0.019
74 W		0.957 ± 0.019
75 Re		0.959 ± 0.018
76 Os		0.961 ± 0.018
77 Ir		0.962 ± 0.018
78 Pd	0.967	0.963 ± 0.013
79 Au		0.964 ± 0.017
80 Hg	0.958	0.966 ± 0.020
82 Pb	0.972	0.968 ± 0.013
92 U	0.970[c]	0.970 ± 0.013

*For low-Z elements, the K-shell fluorescence yield ω_K appears to depend significantly on the chemical state. Therefore, no experimental results are selected as most reliable, and no fitted values are recommended below Z = 13. (For values of ω_K below Z = 13 reported in the literature, see References 2 and 3.

[a]Weighted mean of best experimental values.
[b]The fitted values were calculated[1,3] from the equation $[\omega_K/(1-\omega_K)]^{1/4} = A + BZ + CZ^3$, with the constants A = 0.015 ± 0.010, B = 0.0327 ± 0.0005, and $C = -(0.64 \pm 0.07) \times 10^{-6}$ determined by fitting the selected "most reliable" experimental values to this equation. The total uncertainty takes into account the uncertainties in the constants A, B, and C and uncertainties due to systematic errors in the measurements. For further details, see References 1 and 3.
[c]Values communicated too late to be included in the fitted values of References 1 and 3.
[d]Recent values (Reference 4) of 0.056 for P and 0.077 for S have been averaged with values (Reference 5) of 0.060 and 0.082, respectively.
[e]Recent values for Cr of 0.267 (Reference 6) and 0.284 (Reference 7) have been included.
[f]A recent value for Fe of 0.357 (corrected for $P_K = 0.891$ in Co^{57} decay as discussed in References 1 and 3) reported by Reference 7 has been included.
[g]A value for Cu of 0.436 (corrected for $P_K = 0.8855$ in Zn^{65} decay as discussed in References 1 and 3) reported by Reference 7 has been included.
[h](Reference 8).

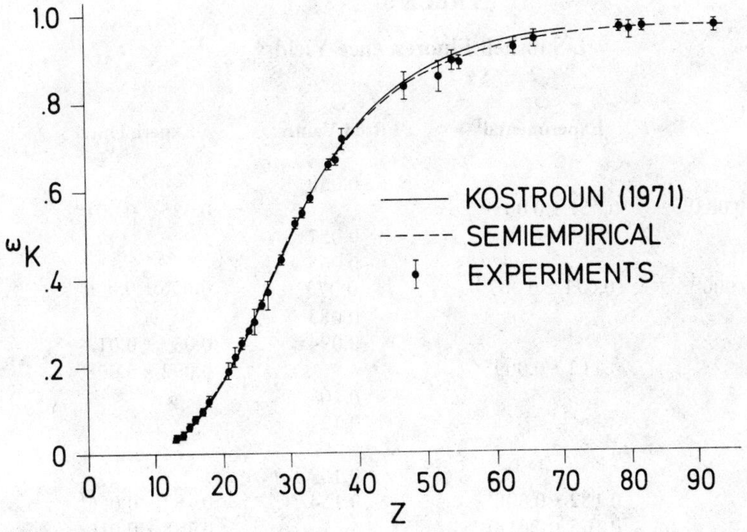

FIGURE 1. Plot of selected "most reliable" experimental values of the K-shell x-ray fluorescence yield ω_K for singly ionized atoms from References 1 and 3. The solid curve is the theoretical predication of Kostroun, Chen, and Crasemann.[9]

TABLE 6

L-Subshell Fluorescence Yields[a]

Z Element	ω_1	ω_2 Experimental[b]	ω_2 Fitted Values[c]	ω_3 Experimental[b]	ω_3 Fitted Values[c]
46 Pd			0.050		0.025
47 Ag	0.034 ± 0.003[d]	0.051 ± 0.005[d]		0.035 ± 0.004[d]	
48 Cd			0.057		0.034
50 Sn			0.065		0.044
52 Te	0.062 ± 0.006[d]	0.071 ± 0.007[d]	0.073	0.056 ± 0.006[d]	0.056
54 Xe			0.083		0.069
56 Ba	0.06		0.094	0.05 ± 0.01	0.084
57 La		0.112 ± 0.009[e]		0.092 ± 0.008[e]	
58 Ce			0.107		0.099
60 Nd			0.121		0.116
62 Sm			0.137		0.134
64 Gd		0.182 ± 0.008[f]	0.154	0.187 ± 0.006[f]	0.152
65 Tb		0.165 ± 0.018		0.188 ± 0.016	
66 Dy			0.173		0.172
67 Ho		0.170 ± 0.055		0.169 ± 0.030	
68 Er		0.185 ± 0.060	0.194	0.172 ± 0.032	0.190
70 Yb		0.188 ± 0.011	0.216	0.183 ± 0.011	0.213
71 Lu				0.236 ± 0.040 (av)	
72 Hf			0.239	0.224 ± 0.030 (av)	0.234
73 Ta		0.257 ± 0.013		0.228 ± 0.013	
74 W			0.264	0.24 ± 0.03 (av)	0.256
75 Re				0.284 ± 0.043	
76 Os		0.300 ± 0.022[g]	0.277	0.301 ± 0.020[g]	0.278
77 Ir				0.253 ± 0.040 (av)	
78 Pt		0.318 ± 0.022[g]	0.317	0.309 ± 0.020[g]	0.301
79 Au				0.301 ± 0.030 (av)	
80 Hg		0.317 ± 0.010	0.345	0.300 ± 0.010	0.324
81 Tl	0.07 ± 0.02	0.346 ± 0.025 (av)		0.318 ± 0.020 (av)	
82 Pb	0.08 ± 0.02	0.363 ± 0.015	0.373	0.315 ± 0.013	0.345
83 Bi	0.095 ± 0.05	0.38 ± 0.02		0.340 ± 0.018	
84 Po			0.401		0.372
86 Rn		0.459 ± 0.025[h]	0.429	0.384 ± 0.020[h]	0.396
88 Ra		0.493 ± 0.030[h]	0.458	0.408 ± 0.027[h]	0.421
90 Th		0.456 ± 0.040[i]	0.485	0.469 ± 0.042 (av)	0.446
91 Pa				0.46 ± 0.05	
92 U	0.21 ± 0.04[j]	0.560 ± 0.033[j]	0.513	0.481 ± 0.029[j]	0.472
94 Pu		0.513 ± 0.022[h]	0.539	0.509 ± 0.029[j]	0.497
96 Cm	0.25 ± 0.06[k]	0.552 ± 0.032	0.565	0.515 ± 0.034	0.523
98 Cf			0.589		0.549

[a] All values are from Reference 1 unless otherwise noted.
[b] These are selected best experimental values or in some cases are the average of the selected best experimental values.
[c] The fitted values were obtained by averaging all reported values (not just the selected best ones) for each element and then fitting them to the equation $[\omega_i/(1-\omega_i)]^{1/4} = A_i + B_iZ + C_iZ^2 + D_iZ^3$. The constants A_i, B_i, C_i, and D_i are 0.491, −0.010, 2.55×10^{-4}, and -9.20×10^{-7} for ω_2 and −0.910, 0.045, -4.37×10^{-4}, and 1.91×10^{-6} for ω_3.
[d] Reference 10, by assuming values of the mean L-fluorescence yield $\bar{\omega}_L$ in order to obtain these subshell yields.
[e] Reference 11.
[f] Reference 12.
[g] Reference 13.
[h] Reference 14.
[i] Reference 15.
[j] Reference 16.
[k] Reference 17.

TABLE 7

Coster-Kronig Transition Probabilities in the L-subshells[a]

Z Element	f_{12}	f_{13}	f_{23} (note b)
70 Yb			0.142 ± 0.009
73 Ta	<0.14	<0.36	0.148 ± 0.010
76 Os			0.106 ± 0.023[c]
78 Pt			0.126 ± 0.021[c]
80 Hg			0.189 ± 0.010
81 Tl	0.155 ± 0.050 (av)	0.56 ± 0.05 (av)	0.164 ± 0.013 (av)
82 Pb	0.16 ± 0.05 (av)	0.59 ± 0.06 (av)	0.160 ± 0.016 (av)
83 Bi	0.18 ± 0.02	0.58 ± 0.02	(0.164 assumed)
86 Rn			0.105 ± 0.011[d]
88 Ra			0.053 ± 0.026[d]
			0.01 ± 0.07[e]
90 Th			0.13 ± 0.10[e]
92 U	<0.07[f]	(assumed f_{13} = 0.67 to get f_{12})[f]	0.147 ± 0.010[f]
94 Pu			0.226 ± 0.016[d]
96 Cm	≤0.10[g]	0.69 ± 0.08[g]	0.188 ± 0.019

[a]All values are from Reference 1 unless otherwise noted.
[b]These are selected best experimental values.
[c]Reference 13.
[d]Reference 14.
[e]Reference 15.
[f]Reference 16.
[g]Reference 17.

TABLE 8

Average L-shell Fluorescence Yields[a]

Z Element	ν_1	ν_2	ω_{KL}	$\bar{\omega}_L$ (note b)
23 V				0.00235 ± 0.00025
25 Mn				0.00295 ± 0.0004
29 Cu				0.0056
31 Ga				0.0064 ± 0.0004
37 Rb			0.013 ± 0.002	0.010 ± 0.002[c]
39 Y				0.0315 ± 0.0028
40 Zr			0.034 ± 0.012	
41 Nb			0.029 ± 0.012	
46 Pd			0.047 ± 0.012	
47 Ag			0.0477 ± 0.020[c]	0.0518 ± 0.006[c]
48 Cd			0.055 ± 0.014	
49 In			0.065 ± 0.014	
50 Sn			0.064 ± 0.014	
51 Sb			0.070 ± 0.015	
52 Te			0.073 ± 0.007	
54 Xe			0.086 ± 0.010	0.107 ± 0.010[c]
55 Cs				0.089 ± 0.013[d]
56 Ba				0.093 ± 0.012[d]
57 La			0.137 ± 0.022[c]	0.101 ± 0.015[c]
58 Ce			0.16 ± 0.02	
59 Pr			0.125 ± 0.020[c]	0.123 ± 0.017[d]
60 Nd			0.16 ± 0.02	0.131 ± 0.017[d]
61 Pm			0.185 ± 0.013	
62 Sm			0.17 ± 0.01	
63 Eu			0.175 ± 0.015	0.142 ± 0.023[d]
64 Gd			0.18 ± 0.02	
65 Tb	0.29 ± 0.08	0.177 ± 0.019	0.19 ± 0.02[c]	0.194 ± 0.027[d]
66 Dy			0.21 ± 0.01	0.14 ± 0.02
67 Ho		0.22 ± 0.04	0.195 ± 0.015[c]	
68 Er		0.21 ± 0.04	0.21 ± 0.03	
69 Tm			0.23 ± 0.03	
70 Yb		0.28 ± 0.05[c]	0.217 ± 0.020[c]	
71 Lu		0.290 ± 0.040	0.26 ± 0.03	
72 Hf		0.35 ± 0.05	0.26 ± 0.03[c]	
73 Ta	0.22 ± 0.02[c]	0.33 ± 0.05[c]	0.28 ± 0.02[c]	0.225 ± 0.01[e]
74 W		0.33 ± 0.05	0.31 ± 0.04	
75 Re		0.347 ± 0.052	0.30 ± 0.04[c]	
76 Os		0.366 ± 0.038	0.32 ± 0.04[c]	
77 Ir		0.351 ± 0.048	0.301 ± 0.04[c]	0.30 ± 0.04
78 Pt		0.375 ± 0.035[c]	0.35 ± 0.02[c]	0.32 ± 0.02[e]
79 Au		0.395 ± 0.032	0.335 ± 0.04[c]	0.398 ± 0.020[c]
80 Hg		0.455 ± 0.062	0.38 ± 0.04[c]	0.38 ± 0.04[c]
81 Tl	0.280 ± 0.010	0.415 ± 0.025[c]	0.395 ± 0.050[c]	0.43 ± 0.07[c]
82 Pb	0.295 ± 0.010	0.414 ± 0.03[c]	0.384 ± 0.040[c]	0.36 ± 0.04[c]
83 Bi		0.469 ± 0.04[c]	0.399 ± 0.034[c]	0.400 ± 0.08[c]
88 Ra				0.451 ± 0.03[c]
90 Th		0.540 ± 0.043	0.525 ± 0.050	0.488 ± 0.008
91 Pa				0.51 ± 0.04[c]

TABLE 8(continued)

Average L-shell Fluorescence Yields[a]

Z Element	ν_1	ν_2	ω_{KL}	$\bar{\omega}_L$ (note b)
92 U		0.610 ± 0.049	0.473 ± 0.040[c]	0.51 ± 0.04[c]
93 Np				0.575 ± 0.08[c]
94 Pu				0.581 ± 0.020[c]
96 Cm	0.61 ± 0.06[c]	0.650 ± 0.036		0.531 ± 0.010

[a]All values are taken from Reference 1 unless otherwise noted.
[b]It should be remembered that $\bar{\omega}_L$ depends on the distribution of L-subshell vacancies (see text). The listed values serve only as a guide for estimation.
[c]Mean of reported values.
[d]From Reference 18.
[e]$\bar{\omega}_L = \omega_{LL}$ (see Reference 1): vacancies created by L-electron capture radioactive decay.

TABLE 9
M-Shell Fluorescence and Coster-Kronig Yields[a]

Z Element	$\bar{\omega}_M$	ω_{LM} (note b)	ω_{LM} (note c)	$(\omega_1^M + f_{12}^M \omega_2^M)$	ν_i^M	ω_i^M
76 Os		0.013 ± 0.0024	0.016 ± 0.003			
79 Au	0.023 ± 0.001	0.024 ± 0.005	0.030 ± 0.006			
82 Pb	0.029 ± 0.002	0.026 ± 0.005	0.032 ± 0.006			
83 Bi	0.036 ± 0.005[d]	0.030 ± 0.006	0.037 ± 0.005			
92 U	0.06					
93 Np				$0.002^{+0.003}_{-0.002}$	ν_1 = 0.065 ± 0.014	
					ν_2 = 0.080 ± 0.029	
					ν_4 = 0.062 ± 0.005	
					$\nu_{4,5}$ = 0.065 ± 0.012	ω_3 = 0.06 ± 0.012
96 Cm				$0.0075^{+0.0089}_{-0.0075}$	ν_1 = 0.081 ± 0.016	
					ν_2 = 0.068 ± 0.023	$\omega_2 = 0.0046^{+0.0051}_{-0.0046}$
					ν_3 = 0.062 ± 0.019	
					ν_4 = 0.080 ± 0.006	
					$\nu_{4,5}$ = 0.075 ± 0.012	$\omega_3 \approx 0.075 \pm 0.012$

[a] All values are from Reference 1.
[b] Corrected for a 20% contribution from double M-shell vacancies (see Reference 1).
[c] Uncorrected values (see Reference 1).
[d] Mean of reported values.

REFERENCES

1. **Bambynek, W., Crasemann, B., Fink, R. W., Freund, H. U., Mark, Hans, Swift, C. D., Price, R. E., and Rao, P. Venugopala,** *Rev. Mod. Phys.,* 44, 716, 1972.
2. **Burhop, E. H. S. and Asaad, W. N.,** *Adv. Atomic Mol. Phys.,* 8, 163, 1972.
3. **Bambynek, W.,** in *Inner Shell Ionization Phenomena and Future Applications,* Fink, R. W., Manson, S. T., Palms, J. M., and Rao, P. V., Eds., CONF-720404, USAEC, 1973, 80.
4. **Konstantinov, A. A. and Sazonova, T. E.,** in *Inner Shell Ionization Phenomena and Future Applications,* Fink, R. W., Manson, S. T., Palms, J. M., and Rao, P. V., Eds., CONf-720404, USAEC, 1973, 158.
5. **Moljk, A.,** in *Inner Shell Ionization Phenomena and Future Applications,* Fink, R. W., Manson, S. T., Palms, J. M., and Rao, P. V., Eds., CONF-720404, USAEC, 1973, 116.
6. **Konstantinov, A. A., Sazonova, T. E., and Konstantinov, A.,** in *Inner Shell Ionization Phenomena and Future Applications,* Fink, R. W., Manson, S. T., Palms, J. M., and Rao, P. V., Eds., CONF-720404, USAEC, 1973, 144.
7. **Mukerji, A. and Chin, L.,** in *Inner Shell Ionization Phenomena and Future Applications,* Fink, R. W., Manson, S. T., Palms, J. M., and Rao, P. V., Eds., CONF-720404, USAEC, 1973, 164.
8. **Tolea, F., Baker, K. R., and Fink, R. W.,** *Z. Phys.,* (in press, 1974).
9. **Kostroun, V. O., Chen, M. H., and Crasemann, B.,** *Phys. Rev.,* A3, 533, 1971.
10. **Budick, B. and Derman, S.,** *Phys. Rev. Lett.,* 29, 1055, 1972.
11. **Douglas, D. G.,** *Can. J. Phys.,* in press, 1973.
12. **Douglas, D. G.,** *Can. J. Phys.,* 50, 1697, 1972.
13. **Mohan, S., Schmidt-Ott, W. D., McGeorge, J. C., and Fink, R. W.,** in *Inner Shell Ionization Phenomena and Future Applications,* Fink, R. W., Manson, S. T., Palms, J. M., and Rao, P. V., Eds., CONF-720404, USAEC, 1973, 244.
14. **McGeorge, J. C., Nix, D. W., and Fink, R. W.,** *J. Phys. (Lond.),* B6, 573, 1973.
15. **Ferreira, J. G.,** in *Inner Shell Ionization Phenomena and Future Applications,* Fink, R. W., Manson, S. T., Palms, J. M., and Rao, P. V., Eds., CONF-720404, USAEC, 1973, 233.
16. **McGeorge, J. C., Nix, D. W., and Fink, R. W.,** *Z. Physik,* 255, 335, 1972.
17. **McGeorge, J. C. and Fink, R. W.,** *Z. Physik,* 250, 293, 1972.
18. **Nix, D. W., McGeorge, J. C., and Fink, R. W.,** in *Inner Shell Ionization Phenomena and Future Applications,* Fink, R. W., Manson, S. T., Palms, J. M., and Rao, P. V., Eds., CONF-720404, USAEC, 1973, 206; *Z. Physik,* 256, 131, 1972.

VI. APPROXIMATE JUMP FACTORS FOR K AND L ABSORPTION EDGES

L. S. Birks, Naval Research Laboratory

The tabulated *K*-edge jump values are from the curve of Figure 2, which shows the jump factors listed in McMaster, W. H., Kerr del Grande, N., Mallett, J. H., and Hubbell, J. H., Compilation of X-ray Cross Sections, Report UCRL-50174, Sect. II, Rev. 1, Lawrence Radiation Laboratory, University of California, Livermore, May 1969. The *L*-edge jump factors were obtained in a similar fashion. Errors of 5 to 10% may be present.

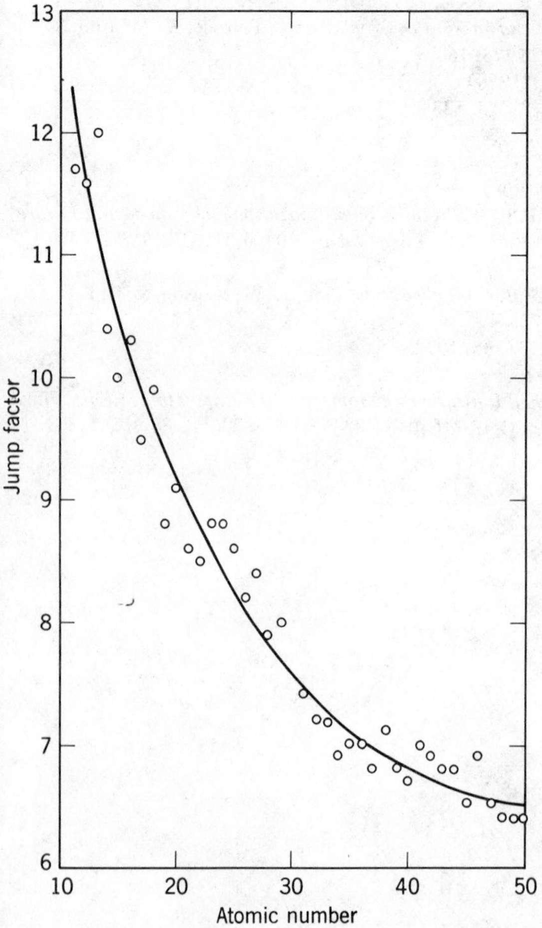

FIGURE 2. *K*-edge jump factor.

TABLE 10

***K*-Edge Jump Factors**

Element	*K* Jump Factor	Element	*K* Jump Factor
11 Na	12.3	31 Ga	7.5
12 Mg	11.8	32 Ge	7.4
13 Al	11.1	33 As	7.3
14 Si	10.8	34 Se	7.2
15 P	10.5	35 Br	7.1
16 S	10.2	36 Kr	7.0
17 Cl	9.8	37 Rb	7.0
18 Ar	9.6	38 Sr	6.9
19 K	9.3	39 Yt	6.9
20 Ca	9.1	40 Zr	6.8
21 Sc	8.9	41 Nb	6.8
22 Ti	8.8	42 Mo	6.7
23 V	8.6	43 Tc	6.7
24 Cr	8.4	44 Ru	6.6
25 Mn	8.3	45 Rh	6.6
26 Fe	8.1	46 Pd	6.6
27 Co	8.0	47 Ag	6.6
28 Ni	7.9	48 Cd	6.5
29 Cu	7.7	49 In	6.5
30 Zn	7.6	50 Sn	6.5

TABLE 11

***L*-Edge Jump Factors**

Element	*L* Jump Factor	Element	*L* Jump Factor
50 Sn	5.0	75 Re	3.8
51 Sb	4.9	76 Os	3.8
52 Te	4.8	77 Ir	3.8
53 I	4.7	78 Pt	3.7
54 Xe	4.6	79 Au	3.7
55 Cs	4.5	80 Hg	3.7
56 Ba	4.5	81 Tl	3.7
57 La	4.4	82 Pb	3.6
60 Nd	4.3	83 Bi	3.6
65 Tb	4.1	84 Po	3.6
70 Yb	4.0	85 At	3.6
72 Hf	3.9	90 Th	3.5
73 Ta	3.9	91 Pa	3.5
74 W	3.9	92 U	3.5

VII. SCHEMATIC ENERGY LEVEL DIAGRAM SHOWING THE X-RAY LINES

A. E. Sandström, Royal University of Uppsala

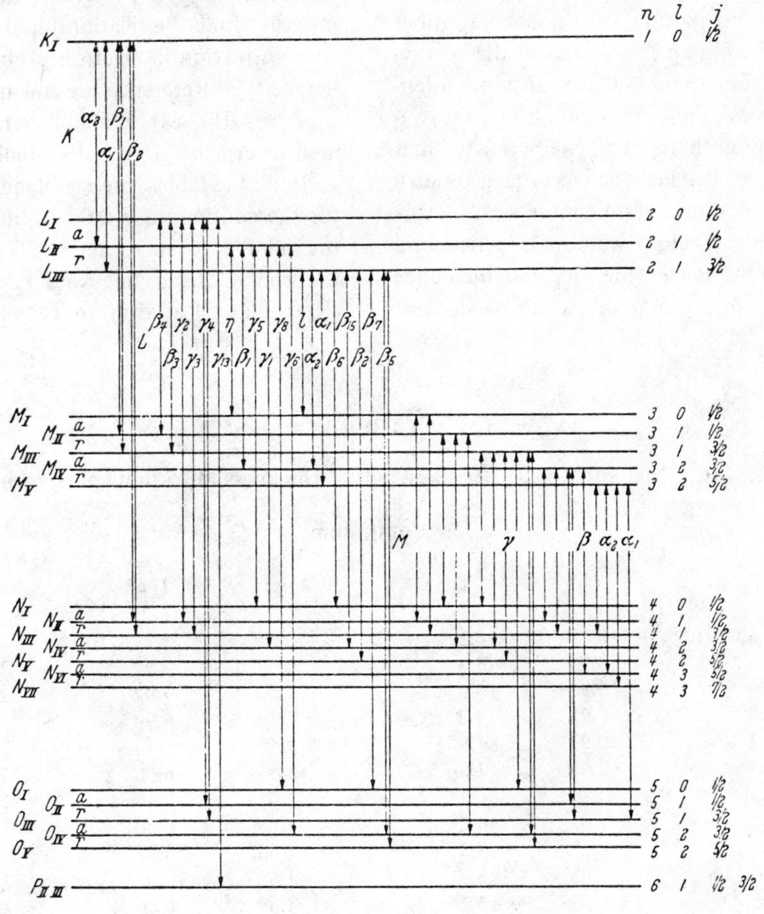

VIII. SPECTRAL DISTRIBUTION OF X-RAY TUBES

J. V. Gilfrich, Naval Research Laboratory

The spectral distributions of various x-ray tubes operated at 45 kV (c.p.) are given in the accompanying tables. They represent the absolute intensity in photons/s/sr/mA as a function of wavelength for both continuum and characteristic lines emitted by tubes having the specific geometry described. The two important geometrical factors as listed are the beryllium window thickness and the x-ray take-off angle (the electron incidence angle, in all cases, is normal to the emergent x-ray beam). The tabulated values may be corrected for other window thicknesses using the attenuation coefficients given in Table 4 of this chapter. Correction for different take-off angles, although not as straightforward as the window thickness correction, can be made following the intensity-function relationship used for the absorption correction in electron probe microanalysis as detailed in Reference 1a and modified in Reference 1b. The experimental details for the measured spectra are given in References 2, 3, and 4.

In all the tables, the wavelength increment (Δλ) for the continuum is 0.02 Å; the wavelength (λ) is the middle of this interval. The wavelengths for the characteristic lines are taken from Bearden (Reference 5) as given in Table 1 of this chapter.

TABLE 12

Cr Target; X-Ray Take-off Angle: 20°; Be Window Thickness; 0.25 mm [ph/s/sr/mA @ 45 kV (c.p.)]

Continuum

λ(Å)	$I_\lambda\Delta\lambda$	λ(Å)	$I_\lambda\Delta\lambda$	λ(Å)	$I_\lambda\Delta\lambda$	λ(Å)	$I_\lambda\Delta\lambda$
0.29	3.60 x 10^9	0.89	16.1 x 10^9	1.49	7.39 x 10^9	2.09	10.5 x 10^9
0.31	7.92	0.91	15.8	1.51	7.22	2.11	10.2
0.33	10.6	0.93	15.6	1.53	7.07	2.13	9.96
0.35	11.9	0.95	15.2	1.55	6.90	2.15	9.68
0.37	13.2	0.97	14.9	1.57	6.74	2.17	9.41
0.39	14.4	0.99	14.5	1.59	6.60	2.19	9.13
0.41	15.5	1.01	14.2	1.61	6.46	2.21	8.87
0.43	16.2	1.03	13.7	1.63	6.30	2.23	8.60
0.45	16.7	1.05	13.3	1.65	6.14	2.25	8.35
0.47	16.6	1.07	13.1	1.67	6.00	2.27	8.09
0.49	16.6	1.09	12.7	1.69	5.86	2.29	7.84
0.51	16.6	1.11	12.4	1.71	5.72	2.31	7.58
0.53	16.6	1.13	12.0	1.73	5.59	2.33	7.36
0.55	16.6	1.15	11.7	1.75	5.46	2.35	7.13
0.57	16.6	1.17	11.4	1.77	5.33	2.37	6.89
0.59	16.6	1.19	11.1	1.79	5.20	2.39	6.66
0.61	16.6	1.21	10.8	1.81	5.06	2.41	6.44
0.63	16.6	1.23	10.5	1.83	4.93	2.43	6.24
0.65	16.6	1.25	10.2	1.85	4.81	2.45	6.04
0.67	16.7	1.27	9.95	1.87	4.68	2.47	5.83
0.69	16.7	1.29	9.68	1.89	4.55	2.49	5.64
0.71	16.8	1.31	9.41	1.91	4.43	2.51	5.46
0.73	16.8	1.33	9.14	1.93	4.31	2.53	5.30
0.75	16.8	1.35	8.90	1.95	4.19	2.55	5.14
0.77	16.8	1.37	8.66	1.97	4.07	2.57	4.98
0.79	16.8	1.39	8.42	1.99	3.95	2.59	4.82
0.81	16.7	1.41	8.20	2.01	3.83	2.61	4.70
0.83	16.6	1.43	7.98	2.03	3.71	2.63	4.60
0.85	16.4	1.45	7.78	2.05	3.58	2.65	4.48
0.87	16.3	1.47	7.58	2.07*	7.10		

TABLE 12 (continued)

Continuum

λ(Å)	$I_\lambda \Delta\lambda$	λ(Å)	$I_\lambda \Delta\lambda$
2.67	4.37 x 10^9	2.83	3.62 x 10^9
2.69	4.27	2.85	3.54
2.71	4.16	2.87	3.47
2.73	4.06	2.89	3.38
2.75	3.97	2.91	3.30
2.77	3.89	2.93	3.22
		2.95	3.13
2.79	3.79	2.97	3.06
2.81	3.71	2.99	2.99

**K*-edge occurs at 2.070 Å ($I_\lambda \Delta\lambda$ is 1.74 x 10^9 from 2.06 to 2.07 Å and 5.36 x 10^9 from 2.07 to 2.08 Å).

Characteristic Lines

	λ (Å)	$I_\lambda \Delta\lambda$
$K\beta$	2.08478	498.0 x 10^9
$K\alpha$	2.29100	3,010.0 x 10^9

TABLE 13

Cu Target; X-Ray Take-off Angle: 20°; Be Window Thickness; 1.0 mm [ph/s/sr/mA @ 45 kV (c.p.)]

Continuum

λ (Å)	$I_\lambda \Delta\lambda$	λ (Å)	$I_\lambda \Delta\lambda$	λ (Å)	$I_\lambda \Delta\lambda$	λ (Å)	$I_\lambda \Delta\lambda$
0.29	2.76 x 10^9	0.97	17.9 x 10^9	1.63	10.5 x 10^9	2.11	4.43 x 10^9
0.31	6.83	0.99	17.4	1.65	10.2	2.13	4.28
0.33	10.8			1.67	9.85	2.15	4.12
0.35	14.8	1.01	16.7	1.69	9.54	2.17	3.96
0.37	18.7	1.03	15.9	1.71	9.24	2.19	3.81
0.39	22.0	1.05	15.2			2.21	3.67
0.41	23.9	1.07	14.4	1.73	8.93	2.23	3.56
0.43	24.4	1.09	13.7	1.75	8.63	2.25	3.44
0.45	24.5	1.11	13.0	1.77	8.35	2.27	3.29
0.47	24.5	1.13	12.3	1.79	8.07	2.29	3.16
0.49	24.5	1.15	11.7	1.81	7.78	2.31	3.06
0.51	24.5	1.17	11.2	1.83	7.52	2.33	2.94
		1.19	10.8	1.85	7.25	2.35	2.82
0.53	24.5	1.21	10.4	1.87	7.00	2.37	2.72
0.55	24.4	1.23	10.2	1.89	6.75		
0.57	24.4			1.91	6.50		
0.59	24.2	1.25	9.92	1.93	6.26	2.39	2.61
0.61	24.0	1.27	9.72			2.41	2.49
0.63	24.0	1.29	9.55			2.43	2.39
0.65	23.9	1.31	9.44	1.95	6.03	2.45	2.27
0.67	23.7	1.33	9.35	1.97	5.79	2.47	2.15
0.69	23.5	1.35	9.29	1.99	5.56	2.49	2.07
0.71	23.2	1.37*	9.20	2.01	5.34	2.51	1.99
0.73	22.9	1.39	14.6	2.03	5.14	2.53	1.89
0.75	22.4	1.41	14.2	2.05	4.94	2.55	1.79
		1.43	13.9	2.07	4.76	2.57	1.69
0.77	21.9	1.45	13.5	2.09	4.59	2.59	1.59
0.79	21.4	1.47	13.2				
0.81	20.7						
0.83	20.4	1.49	12.8				
0.85	20.0	1.51	12.5				
0.87	19.7	1.53	12.2				
0.89	19.4	1.55	11.8				
0.91	19.0	1.57	11.5				
0.93	18.7	1.59	11.2				
0.95	18.4	1.61	10.8				

**K*-edge occurs at 1.380 Å.

Characteristic Lines

	λ (Å)	$I_\lambda \Delta\lambda$
$K\beta$	1.392218	392.0 x 10^9
$K\alpha$	1.541841	2,154.0 x 10^9

TABLE 14

Mo Target; X-Ray Take-off Angle: 20° Be Window Thickness: 1.0 mm [ph/s/sr/mA @ 45 kV (c.p.)]

Continuum

λ (Å)	$I_\lambda \Delta\lambda$
0.29	3.28 x 10^9
0.31	7.81
0.33	11.9
0.35	15.7
0.37	19.4
0.39	22.9
0.41	26.1
0.43	28.2
0.45	29.5
0.47	30.5
0.49	31.3
0.51	32.1
0.53	32.7
0.55	32.9
0.57	32.8
0.59	32.6
0.61*	32.3
0.63	44.0
0.65	43.2
0.67	42.4
0.69	41.5
0.71	40.6
0.73	39.8
0.75	39.1
0.77	38.4
0.79	37.7
0.81	36.9
0.83	36.3
0.85	36.1
0.87	36.1
0.89	36.1
0.91	36.1
0.93	36.0
0.95	35.9

λ (Å)	$I_\lambda \Delta\lambda$
0.97	35.7 x 10^9
0.99	35.3
1.01	34.9
1.03	34.4
1.05	33.8
1.07	33.2
1.09	32.4
1.11	31.6
1.13	30.9
1.15	30.2
1.17	29.5
1.19	28.8
1.21	28.1
1.23	27.4
1.25	26.6
1.27	25.9
1.29	25.2
1.31	24.6
1.33	24.0
1.35	23.4
1.37	22.7
1.39	22.1
1.41	21.6
1.43	21.0
1.45	20.3
1.47	19.8
1.49	19.3
1.51	18.7
1.53	18.3
1.55	17.8
1.57	17.3
1.59	16.9
1.61	16.4

Continuum

λ (Å)	$I_\lambda \Delta\lambda$
1.63	16.0 x 10^9
1.65	15.6
1.67	15.2
1.69	14.7
1.71	14.3
1.73	13.9
1.75	13.5
1.77	13.1
1.79	12.8
1.81	12.4
1.83	12.1
1.85	11.7
1.87	11.4
1.89	11.0
1.91	10.7
1.93	10.3
1.95	9.95
1.97	9.59
1.99	9.24
2.01	8.88
2.03	8.52
2.05	8.17
2.07	7.81
2.09	7.46
2.11	7.19

λ (Å)	$I_\lambda \Delta\lambda$
2.13	6.93 x 10^9
2.15	6.57
2.17	6.30
2.19	6.04
2.21	5.77
2.23	5.59
2.25	5.42
2.27	5.15
2.29	4.88
2.31	4.71
2.33	4.53
2.35	4.35
2.37	4.17
2.39	4.00
2.41	3.82
2.43	3.64
2.45	3.46
2.47	3.29
2.49	3.20
2.51	3.11
2.53	2.93
2.55	2.75
2.57	2.66
2.59	2.58

*K-edge occurs at 0.620 Å.

Characteristic Lines

	λ (Å)	$I_\lambda \Delta\lambda$
$K\beta$	0.632288	105.0 x 10^9
$K\alpha$	0.710730	593.0 x 10^9

TABLE 15

Rh Target; X-Ray Take-off Angle: 20°; Be Window Thickness: 0.125 mm [ph/s/sr/mA @ 45 kV (c.p.)]

Continuum

λ*(Å)	$I_\lambda \Delta\lambda$	λ*(Å)	$I_\lambda \Delta\lambda$	λ*(Å)	$I_\lambda \Delta\lambda$	λ*(Å)	$I_\lambda \Delta\lambda$
0.29	6.08×10^9	1.29	26.9×10^9	2.29	7.68×10^9	3.29	1.78×10^9
0.31	19.0	1.31	26.3	2.31	7.45	3.31	1.73
0.33	25.5	1.33	25.8	2.33	7.20	3.33	1.69
0.35	29.0	1.35	25.2	2.35	6.99	3.35	1.64
0.37	31.3	1.37	24.6	2.37	6.78	3.37	1.60
0.39	33.0	1.39	24.2	2.39	6.54	3.39	1.55
0.41	33.7	1.41	23.7	2.41	6.34	3.41	1.52
0.43	34.0	1.43	23.1	2.43	6.13	3.43	1.47
0.45	34.4	1.45	22.6	2.45	5.93	3.45	1.44
0.47	34.0	1.47	22.3	2.47	5.78	3.47	1.40
0.49	33.7	1.49	21.9	2.49	5.58	3.49	1.37
0.51	33.1	1.51	21.6	2.51	5.40	3.51	1.34
0.53**	35.0	1.53	21.1	2.53	5.17	3.53	1.31
0.55	39.7	1.55	20.7	2.55	5.09	3.55	1.28
0.57	39.5	1.57	20.2	2.57	4.94	3.57	1.25
0.59	39.4	1.59	19.8	2.59	4.79	3.59	1.22
0.61	39.2	1.61	19.3	2.61	4.64	3.61	1.19
0.63	39.1	1.63	19.0	2.63	4.56	3.63**	1.28
0.65	38.8	1.65	18.2	2.65	4.41	3.65	1.35
0.67	38.6	1.67	18.2	2.67	4.26	3.67	1.32
0.69	38.3	1.69	17.9	2.69	4.10	3.69	1.30
0.71	38.2	1.71	17.5	2.71	4.00	3.71	1.28
0.73	38.0	1.73	17.0	2.73	3.88	3.73	1.25
0.75	37.8	1.75	16.7	2.75	3.80	3.75	1.23
0.77	37.7	1.77	16.4	2.77	3.65	3.77	1.22
0.79	37.4	1.79	16.0	2.79	3.57	3.79	1.19
0.81	37.1	1.81	15.5	2.81	3.45	3.81	1.17
0.83	36.9	1.83	15.2	2.83	3.34	3.83	1.15
0.85	36.6	1.85	14.7	2.85	3.27	3.85	1.12
0.87	36.3	1.87	14.3	2.87	3.16	3.87	1.11
0.89	36.2	1.89	14.0	2.89	3.07	3.89	1.08
0.91	35.9	1.91	13.7	2.91	2.99	3.91	1.07
0.93	35.6	1.93	13.2	2.93	2.89	3.93	1.05
0.95	35.3	1.95	12.9	2.95	2.81	3.95**	1.57
0.97	35.0	1.97	12.5	2.97	2.74	3.97	1.58
0.99	34.7	1.99	12.2	2.99	2.66	3.99	1.55
1.01	34.4	2.01	11.9	3.01	2.58	4.01	1.54
1.03	34.0	2.03	11.8	3.03	2.51	4.03	1.52
1.05	33.7	2.05	11.2	3.05	2.43	4.05	1.49
1.07	33.1	2.07	10.9	3.07	2.37	4.07	1.47
1.09	32.8	2.09	10.6	3.09	2.31	4.09	1.44
1.11	32.2	2.11	12.2	3.11	2.25	4.11	1.42
1.13	31.6	2.13	9.88	3.13	2.19	4.13**	2.98
1.15	31.0	2.15	9.58	3.15	2.13	4.15	4.47
1.17	30.4	2.17	9.27	3.17	2.08	4.17	4.38
1.19	29.8	2.19	8.97	3.19	2.02	4.19	4.26
1.21	29.2	2.21	8.66	3.21	1.98	4.21	4.16
1.23	28.6	2.23	8.44	3.23	1.92	4.23	4.06
1.25	28.0	2.25	8.21	3.25	1.87	4.25	3.95
1.27	27.4	2.27	7.90	3.27	1.82	4.27	3.85

TABLE 15 (continued)

Continuum

λ*(Å)	$I_\lambda\Delta\lambda$	λ*(Å)	$I_\lambda\Delta\lambda$	λ*(Å)	$I_\lambda\Delta\lambda$	λ*(Å)	$I_\lambda\Delta\lambda$
4.29	3.75 x 10^9	5.33	0.641 x 10^9	6.35	0.109 x 10^9	6.71	0.071 x 10^9
4.31	3.65	5.35	0.620	6.37	0.106	6.73	0.070
4.33	3.56	5.37	0.599	6.39	0.103	6.75	0.068
4.35	3.47	5.39	0.578	6.41	0.101	6.77	0.067
4.37	3.36	5.41	0.555	6.43	0.099	6.79	0.065
4.39	3.27	5.43	0.534	6.45	0.096	6.81	0.065
4.41	3.16	5.45	0.517	6.47	0.093	6.83	0.063
4.43	3.07	5.47	0.499	6.49	0.091	6.85	0.062
4.45	2.99	5.49	0.482	6.51	0.089	6.87	0.061
4.47	2.89	5.51	0.464	6.53	0.087	6.89	0.060
4.49	2.81	5.53	0.448	6.55	0.085	6.91	0.059
4.51	2.72	5.55	0.432	6.57	0.083	6.93	0.058
4.53	2.63	5.57	0.415	6.59	0.081	6.95	0.057
4.55	2.55	5.59	0.401	6.61	0.079	6.97	0.056
4.57	2.48	5.61	0.388	6.63	0.078	6.99	0.055
4.59	2.39	5.63	0.375	6.65	0.076	7.01	0.054
4.61	2.31	5.65	0.362	6.67	0.074	7.03	0.053
4.63	2.23	5.67	0.348	6.69	0.073	7.05	0.052
4.65	2.17	5.69	0.334			7.07	0.052
4.67	2.10	5.71	0.324			7.09	0.051
4.69	2.02	5.73	0.313				
4.71	1.96	5.75	0.301				
4.73	1.90	5.77	0.290				
4.75	1.84	5.79	0.280				
4.77	1.78	5.81	0.271				
4.79	1.72	5.83	0.260				
4.81	1.64	5.85	0.252				
4.83	1.58	5.87	0.243				
4.85	1.54	5.89	0.233				
4.87	1.47	5.91	0.225				
4.89	1.43	5.93	0.217				
4.91	1.37	5.95	0.210				
4.93	1.32	5.97	0.202				
4.95	1.28	5.99	0.195				
4.97	1.23	6.01	0.188				
4.99	1.19	6.03	0.182				
5.01	1.14	6.05	0.176				
5.03	1.10	6.07	0.170				
5.05	1.06	6.09	0.163				
5.07	1.03	6.11	0.158				
5.09	0.988	6.13	0.154				
5.11	0.958	6.15	0.149				
5.13	0.920	6.17	0.143				
5.15	0.889	6.19	0.138				
5.17	0.859	6.21	0.135				
5.19	0.821	6.23	0.131				
5.21	0.798	6.25	0.126				
5.23	0.768	6.27	0.123				
5.25	0.745	6.29	0.119				
5.27	0.702	6.31	0.116				
5.29	0.690	6.33	0.112				
5.31	0.666						

*λ for continuum is the middle of the Δλ interval.

**Edges: K @ 0.534 Å ($I_\lambda\Delta\lambda$ is 23.0 x 10^9 from 0.52 to 0.534 Å and 11.9 x 10^9 from 0.534 to 0.54 Å).

L_I @ 3.629 Å ($I_\lambda\Delta\lambda$ is 0.52 x 10^9 from 3.62 to 3.629 Å and 0.75 x 10^9 from 3.629 to 3.64 Å).

L_{II} @ 3.942 Å ($I_\lambda\Delta\lambda$ is 0.11 x 10^9 from 3.94 to 3.942 Å and 1.47 x 10^9 from 3.942 to 3.96 Å).

L_{III} @ 4.130 Å ($I_\lambda\Delta\lambda$ is 0.70 x 10^9 from 4.12 to 4.13 Å and 2.28 x 10^9 from 4.13 to 4.14 Å).

Characteristic Lines***

	λ(Å)	$I_\lambda\Delta\lambda$
K_α	0.61473	338.0 x 10^9
K_β	0.54397	79.8
$L_{\gamma 2,3}$	3.6855	3.44
$L_{\gamma 1}$	3.9437	9.50
$L_{\beta 2,15}$	4.1310	32.4
$L_{\beta 3}$	4.2522	57.8
$L_{\beta 4}$	4.2888	30.2
$L_{\beta 1}$	4.37414	358.0
$L_{\alpha 1,2}$	4.59835	600.0
L_η	4.9217	4.06
L_ℓ	5.2169	9.73

***λ for lines is from Bearden (weighted average for doublets).

Δλ for lines is natural line breadth (from Blokhin, *Physics of X-Rays,* AEC translation 4502).

TABLE 16

W Target; X-Ray Take-off Angle: 20°; Be Window Thickness: 1.0 mm [ph/s/sr/mA @ 45 kV (c.p.)]

Continuum

λ(Å)	$I_\lambda \Delta\lambda$	λ(Å)	$I_\lambda \Delta\lambda$	λ(Å)	$I_\lambda \Delta\lambda$	λ(Å)	$I_\lambda \Delta\lambda$
0.29	7.44×10^9	1.01	18.3×10^9	1.73	9.22×10^9	2.17	3.74×10^9
0.31	17.6	1.03	18.0	1.75	8.78	2.19	3.60
0.33	27.3	1.05	17.6	1.77	8.40	2.21	3.50
0.35	36.8	1.07	17.3	1.79	8.06	2.23	3.36
0.37	46.2	1.09	17.1	1.81	7.73	2.25	3.22
0.39	53.3	1.11	16.8	1.83	7.44	2.27	3.07
0.41	55.9	1.13	16.6	1.85	7.15	2.29	2.93
0.43	55.0	1.15	16.3	1.87	6.86	2.31	2.83
0.45	52.8	1.17	16.0	1.89	6.58	2.33	2.74
0.47	50.2	1.19	15.8	1.91	6.29	2.35	2.59
0.49	47.6	1.21*	16.0	1.93	6.05	2.37	2.45
0.51	45.1	1.23	17.4	1.95	5.86	2.39	2.35
0.53	42.7	1.25	17.2	1.97	5.62	2.41	2.26
0.55	40.5	1.27	17.0	1.99	5.38	2.43	2.16
0.57	38.5	1.29	16.8	2.01	5.18	2.45	2.02
0.59	36.8	1.31	16.6	2.03	4.99	2.47	1.87
0.61	35.2	1.33	16.4	2.05	4.80	2.49	1.78
0.63	33.6	1.35	16.1	2.07	4.66	2.51	1.68
0.65	32.2	1.37	15.8	2.09	4.51	2.53	1.58
0.67	30.8	1.39	15.6	2.11	4.32	2.55	1.49
0.69	29.4	1.41	15.4	2.13	4.13	2.57	1.39
0.71	28.1	1.43	15.1	2.15	3.94	2.59	1.30
0.73	27.0	1.45	14.8				
0.75	25.9	1.47	14.5				
0.77	24.9	1.49	14.3				
0.79	24.0	1.51	13.9				
0.81	23.1	1.53	13.6				
0.83	22.4	1.55	13.2				
0.85	21.7	1.57	12.9				
0.87	21.1	1.59	12.5				
0.89	20.6	1.61	12.1				
0.91	20.2	1.63	11.7				
0.93	19.8	1.65	11.1				
0.95	19.4	1.67	10.6				
0.97	19.0	1.69	10.1				
0.99	18.6	1.71	9.65				

*L_{III}-edge occurs at 1.216 Å ($I_\lambda \Delta\lambda$ is 12.5×10^9 from 1.2 to 1.216 Å and 3.5×10^9 from 1.216 to 1.22 Å).

Characteristic Lines

	λ(Å)	$I_\lambda \Delta\lambda$
$L_{\gamma 3}$	1.06200	2.45×10^9
$L_{\gamma 2}$	1.06806	9.74
$L_{\gamma 1}$	1.09855	26.0
$L_{\beta 2}$	1.24460	168.0
$L_{\beta 1}$	1.281809	381.0
L_{α}	1.47639	554.0
L_{ℓ}	1.6782	12.9

REFERENCES

1a. **Philibert, J.,** *X-Ray Optics and X-Ray Microanalysis,* Academic Press, New York, 1963, 379.

1b. **Duncumb, P., Shields-Mason, P. K., and da Casa, C.,** *Fifth International Congress on X-Ray Optics and Microanalysis, Tübingen,* Springer-Verlag, New York, 1969, 149.

2. **Gilfrich, J. V. and Birks, L. S.,** *Anal. Chem.,* 40, 1077, 1968.

3. **Gilfrich, J. V., Burkhalter, P. G., Whitlock, R. R., Warden, E. S., and Birks, L. S.,** *Anal. Chem.,* 43, 934, 1971.

4. **Brown, D. B. and Gilfrich, J. V.,** *J. Appl. Phys.,* 42, 4044, 1971.

5. **Bearden, J. A.,** Report NYO-10586, USAEC, 1964.

IX. CRYSTALS AND MULTILAYER LANGMUIR-BLODGETT FILMS USED AS ANALYZERS IN WAVELENGTH-DISPERSIVE X-RAY SPECTROMETERS

Eugene P. Bertin, RCA, Laboratories/David Sarnoff Research Center

The crystals and multilayer films are arranged in order of increasing 2d spacing (see below), that is, in order of increasing useful wavelength region.

A *crystal* analyzer is properly designated by its name or symbol *and* the Miller indexes (hkl), or perhaps the 2d spacing, of the diffracting planes – for example, quartz (502), quartz (2d 1.62), LiF (220), Si (111), ADP (101). However, some crystals are used in only one "cut," and the indexes or spacing are commonly omitted–for example, PET, EDDT, KHP (KAP). A multilayer-film analyzer need be designated only by its chemical name or letter symbol.

Column 1 is simply the serial number of the crystal in the table.

Column 2 gives common and chemical names and commonly used letter symbols, if any. Only Pb salts are given for the multilayer films. The Ba or other divalent heavy-metal salt usually has substantially the same 2d spacing as the Pb salt, but it usually has a lower diffracted intensity.

Column 3 gives the Miller indexes (hkl) of the diffracting planes parallel to the analyzer surface for crystals. (?) indicates that the crystal is developmental and the diffracting planes have not been indexed or that the indexes are not ascertainable by the compiler. An asterisk * following Miller indexes indicates that when reference is made in the literature to this crystal without specification of (hkl) or 2d, it is likely to be this "cut" that is indicated. LBF indicates that the analyzer is a multilayer Langmuir-Blodgett film.

Column 4 gives twice the interplanar spacing for crystals and twice the repeat interval between metal-atom layers for multilayer films, both in angstroms. The value 2d is also the longest wavelength that the analyzer can diffract.

Column 5 gives the chemical formula for the crystal substance. For organic compounds the formula is given in a form that indicates the molecular structure.

Column 6 gives the wavelength region lying in the 2θ interval 10 to 140°. Only in special cases should the crystal be used outside these limits, which are themselves a little generous.

Column 7 gives the principal application(s) of the analyzer.

No comprehensive compilation of inter-comparable relative diffracted intensities for analyzer crystals is known to the compiler. However, some relative intensities are given in column 7 (remarks). Secondary x-ray emission from the crystal ("crystal emission") is readily predictable from column 5 (chemical formula).

The applicability of a specified crystal to a specified x-ray spectral line is evaluated by comparison of the line wavelength with columns 4 (2d, longest wavelength diffracted) and 6 (practical wavelength region).

TABLE 17

Crystals and Multilayer Langmuir-Blodgett Films Used as Analyzers in Wavelength-Dispersive X-ray Spectrometers

No.	Crystal	(hkl)	2d, Å	Chemical Formula	Practical Useful Wavelength Region (10-145° 2θ) Å	Optimal Application Remarks
1	α-Quartz, silicon dioxide	(502)	1.624	SiO_2	0.142–1.55	Shortest 2d of any practical crystal. Good for high-Z *K*-lines excited by 100-kV generators.
2	Lithium fluoride	(422)	1.652	LiF	0.144–1.58	Better than quartz (502) for the same applications.
3	Corundum, aluminum oxide	(146)	1.660	Al_2O_3	0.145–1.58	Same applications as quartz (502).
4	Lithium fluoride	(420)	1.80	LiF	0.157–1.72	Similar to LiF (422).
5	Topaz	(303)*	2.712	$Al_2(F,OH)_2SiO_4$	0.236–2.59	Improves dispersion for V-Ni *K*-lines and rare earth *L*-lines.
6	Corundum, aluminum oxide	(030)	2.748	Al_2O_3	0.240–2.62	Diffracted intensity ~2–4X topaz (303) and quartz (203) with the same or better resolution.
7	α-Quartz, silicon dioxide	(203)	2.749	SiO_2	0.240–2.62	Same applications as topaz (303) and LiF (220).
8	Topaz	(006)	2.795	$Al_2(F,OH)_2SiO_4$	0.244–2.67	
9	Lithium fluoride	(220)	2.848	LiF	0.248–2.72	Same applications as topaz (303) and quartz (203), with 2–4X their diffracted intensity. Diffracted intensity ~0.4–0.8X LiF (200).
10	Mica	(331)	3.00	$K_2O \cdot 3Al_2O_3 \cdot 6SiO_2 \cdot 2H_2O$	0.262–2.86	Transmission-crystal optics.

TABLE 17 (continued)

Crystals and Multilayer Langmuir-Blodgett Films Used as Analyzers in Wavelength-Dispersive X-ray Spectrometers

No.	Crystal	(hkl)	2d, Å	Chemical Formula	Practical Useful Wavelength Region (10-145° 2θ) Å	Optimal Application Remarks
11	α-Quartz, silicon dioxide	(211)	3.082	SiO_2	0.269–2.94	
12	α-Quartz, silicon dioxide	(112)	3.636	SiO_2	0.317–3.47	
13	Silicon	(220)	3.84	Si	0.335–3.66	
14	Fluorite, calcium fluoride	(220)	3.862	CaF_2	0.337–3.68	
15	Germanium	(220)	4.00	Ge	0.349–3.82	
16	Lithium fluoride	(200)*	4.027	LiF	0.351–3.84	Best general crystal for K *K*- to Lr *L*-lines. Highest intensity–with high dispersion–for largest number of elements of any crystal.
17	Aluminum	(200)	4.048	Al	0.353–3.86	Curved, especially doubly curved, optics.
18	α-Quartz, silicon dioxide	(102)	4.564	SiO_2	0.398–4.35	Used in prototype Laue multichannel spectrometer.
19	Topaz	(200)	4.64	$Al_2(F,OH)_2SiO_4$	0.405–4.43	
20	Aluminum	(111)	4.676	Al	0.408–4.46	Curved, especially doubly curved, optics.
21	Gypsum, calcium sulfate dihydrate	(002)	4.990	$CaSO_4 \cdot 2H_2O$	0.435–4.76	

TABLE 17 (continued)

Crystals and Multilayer Langmuir-Blodgett Films Used as Analyzers in Wavelength-Dispersive X-ray Spectrometers

No.	Crystal	(hkl)	2d, Å	Chemical Formula	Practical Useful Wavelength Region (10-145° 2θ) Å	Optimal Application Remarks
22	Rock salt, sodium chloride	(200)	5.641	NaCl	0.492–5.38	S $K\alpha$ and Cl $K\alpha$ in light matrixes. Like LiF (200), good general crystal for S *K* to Lr *L*.
23	Calcite, calcium carbonate	(200)	6.071	$CaCO_3$	0.529–5.79	Very precise wavelength measurements.
24	Ammonium dihydrogen phosphate (ADP)	(112)	6.14	$NH_4H_2PO_4$	0.535–5.86	
25	Silicon	(111)*	6.271	Si	0.547–5.98	Eliminates second order. Useful for intermediate- and high-Z elements where Si $K\alpha$ crystal emission is absorbed by the air path.
26	Sylvite, potassium chloride	(200)	6.292	KCl	0.549–6.00	
27	Fluorite, calcium fluoride	(111)	6.306	CaF_2	0.550–6.02	Very weak second order, strong third order.
28	Germanium	(111)*	6.532	Ge	0.570–6.23	Eliminates second order. Useful for intermediate- and low-Z elements where Ge $K\alpha$ emission is eliminated by pulse-height selection.
29	Potassium bromide	(200)	6.584	KBr	0.574–6.28	

TABLE 17 (continued)

Crystals and Multilayer Langmuir-Blodgett Films Used as Analyzers in Wavelength-Dispersive X-ray Spectrometers

No.	Crystal	(hkl)	2d, Å	Chemical Formula	Practical Useful Wavelength Region (10-145° 2θ) Å	Optimal Application Remarks
30	α-Quartz, silicon dioxide	(101)	6.687	SiO_2	0.583–6.38	P $K\alpha$ in low-Z matrixes, especially in calcium. Intensity for P-K K-lines greater than EDDT, but less than PET.
31	Graphite	(002)	6.708	C	0.585–6.40	P, S, Cl K-lines. P $K\alpha$ intensity >5X EDDT. Relatively poor resolution.
32	Ammonium hydrogen citrate	(?)	7.38	$C(OH)(COOH)(CH_2COONH_4)_2$	0.644–7.04	
33	Ammonium dihydrogen phosphate (ADP)	(200)	7.5	$NH_4H_2PO_4$	0.654–7.16	Higher intensity than EDDT.
34	Topaz	(002)	8.374	$Al_2(F,OH)_2SiO_4$	0.730–7.99	
35	α-Quartz, silicon dioxide	(100)*	8.52	SiO_2	0.742–8.12	Same applications as EDDT and PET; higher resolution, but lower intensity.
36	Pentaerythritol (PET)	(002)	8.742	$C(CH_2OH)_4$	0.762–8.34	Al, Si, P, S, Cl $K\alpha$. Intensities ~1.5–2X EDDT, ~2.5X KHP. Good general crystal for Al–Sc $K\alpha$. Low background.
37	Ammonium tartrate	(?)	8.80	$(CHOH)_2(COONH_4)_2$	0.767–8.4	
38	Ethylenediamine-*d*-tartrate (EDDT, EDT)	(020)	8.808	$NH_2-CH_2-CH_2-NH_2$ / $COOH-(CHOH)_2-COOH$	0.768–8.40	Same applications as PET, but lower intensity.

TABLE 17 (continued)

Crystals and Multilayer Langmuir-Blodgett Films Used as Analyzers in Wavelength-Dispersive X-ray Spectrometers

No.	Crystal	(hkl)	2d, Å	Chemical Formula	Practical Useful Wavelength Region (10-145° 2θ) Å	Optimal Application Remarks
39	Ammonium dihydrogen phosphate (ADP)	(101)*	10.640	$NH_4H_2PO_4$	0.928–10.15	Mg $K\alpha$. Same applications as PET, EDDT, but lower intensity.
40	Oxalic acid dihydrate	(001)	11.92	$(COOH)_2 \cdot 2H_2O$	1.04–11.37	
41	Sorbitol hexaacetate (SHA)	(110)	13.98	$CHOH{-}CO{-}CH_3$ | $(COH{-}CO{-}CH_3)_4$ | $CHOH{-}CO{-}CH_3$	1.22–13.34	Applications similar to ADP (101) and gypsum (020).
42	Rock sugar, sucrose	(001)	15.12	$C_{12}H_{22}O_{11}$	1.32–14.42	
43	Gypsum, calcium sulfate dihydrate	(020)*	15.185	$CaSO_4 \cdot 2H_2O$	1.32–14.49	Na $K\alpha$. Inferior to KHP and RHP.
44	Beryl	(100)	15.954	$3BeO \cdot Al_2O_3 \cdot 6SiO_2$	1.39–15.22	
45	Bismuth titanate	(040)	16.40	$Bi_2(TiO_3)_3$	1.43–15.65	
46	Itaconic acid, methylenebutanedioic acid	(020)	18.50	$CH_2{:}C(COOH)CH_2COOH$	1.61–17.65	
47	Mica	(002)*	19.84	$K_2O \cdot 3Al_2O_3 \cdot 6SiO_2 \cdot 2H_2O$	1.73–18.93	Variable-radius curved-crystal spectrometers.
48	Silver acetate	(001)	20.0	CH_3COOAg	1.74–19.08	
49	Rock sugar, sucrose	(100)	20.12	$C_{12}H_{22}O_{11}$	1.75–19.19	
50	Thallium hydrogen phthalate	(100)	25.9	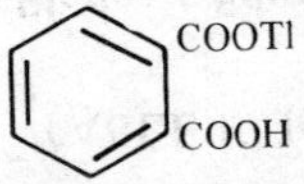	2.26–24.7	Same applications as KHP, RHP.

TABLE 17 (continued)

Crystals and Multilayer Langmuir-Blodgett Films Used as Analyzers in Wavelength-Dispersive X-ray Spectrometers

No.	Crystal	(hkl)	2d, Å	Chemical Formula	Practical Useful Wavelength Region (10-145° 2θ) Å	Optimal Application Remarks
51	Rubidium hydrogen phthalate (RHP, RbHP, RAP[a], RbAP[a])	(100)	26.12	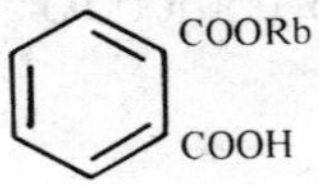	2.28–24.92	Diffracted intensity ~3X KHP for Na, Mg, Al $K\alpha$ and Cu $L\alpha_1$; ~4X KHP for F $K\alpha$; ~8X KHP for O $K\alpha$.
52	Potassium hydrogen phthalate (KHP, KAP[a])	(100)	26.632	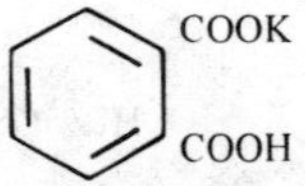	2.32–25.41	Good general crystal for all low-Z elements down to O.
53	Clinochlore (hydrated Mg Al Fe silicate aluminate)	(001)	28.39		2.48–27.09	O $K\alpha$ intensity ~4X KHP but only ~0.2X Pb stearate.
54	Penninite (similar to clinochlore)	(001)	28.4		2.48–27.1	Same applications as clinochlore.
55	Potassium hydrogen cyclo-hexane-1,2-diacetate	(?)	31.2	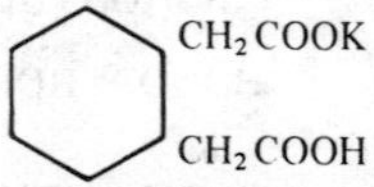	2.72–29.76	
56	Tetradecanoamide	(?)	~54	$CH_3(CH_2)_{12}CONH_2$	4.71–51.5	Ultralong-wavelength region down to C $K\alpha$.
57	Hexadecyl hydrogen maleate (HHM)	(?)	58.0	$CH_3(CH_2)_{15}OOC{-}CH{:}CH{-}COOH$	5.06–55.3	Ultralong-wavelength region down to C $K\alpha$.
58	Octadecyl hydrogen maleate (OHM)	(?)	63.5	$CH_3(CH_2)_{17}OOC{-}CH{:}CH{-}COOH$	5.54–60.6	Ultralong-wavelength region down to C $K\alpha$.
59	Lead laurate, lead dodecanoate	LBF	~70	$[CH_3(CH_2)_{10}COO]_2Pb$	6.10–66.8	Ultralong-wavelength region down to B $K\alpha$.
60	Behenyl hydrogen maleate (BHM)	(?)	~74	$CH_3(CH_2)_{21}OOC{-}CH{:}CH{-}COOH$	6.45–70.6	Ultralong-wavelength region down to B $K\alpha$.

TABLE 17 (continued)

Crystals and Multilayer Langmuir-Blodgett Films Used as Analyzers in Wavelength-Dispersive X-ray Spectrometers

No.	Crystal	(hkl)	2d, Å	Chemical Formula	Practical Useful Wavelength Region (10-145° 2θ) Å	Optimal Application Remarks
61	Lead myristate, lead tetradecanoate (LTD)	LBF	80.5	$[CH_3(CH_2)_{12}COO]_2Pb$	7.02–76.8	Ultralong-wavelength region down to B $K\alpha$.
62	Dioctadecyl terephthalate (OTO)	(?)	~84	$COO(CH_2)_{17}CH_3$ 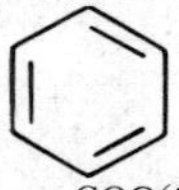 $COO(CH_2)_{17}CH_3$	7.32–80.1	Ultralong-wavelength region down to B $K\alpha$.
63	Lead palmitate, lead hexadecanoate	LBF	~90	$[CH_3(CH_2)_{14}COO]_2Pb$	7.85–85.9	Ultralong-wavelength region down to B $K\alpha$.
64	Dioctadecyl adipate (OAO)	(?)	~94	$(CH_2)_4[COO(CH_2)_{17}CH_3]_2$	8.20–89.7	Ultralong-wavelength region down to B $K\alpha$.
65	Octadecyl hydrogen succinate (OHS)	(?)	~97	$CH_3(CH_2)_{17}OOC\text{–}CH_2\text{–}CH_2COOH$	8.46–92.5	Ultralong-wavelength region down to B $K\alpha$.
66	Lead stearate decanoate, lead octadecanoate decanoate (LSD[b], LOD[c])	LBF	~100	$CH_3(CH_2)_{16}COOPbOOC(CH_2)_8CH_3$	8.72–95.4	Ultralong-wavelength region down to B $K\alpha$. Diffracted intensity ~2X Pb stearate at wavelengths <44 Å.
67	Lead stearate, lead octadecanoate (LOD[c])	LBF	100.4	$[CH_3(CH_2)_{16}COO]_2Pb$	8.75–95.8	Ultralong-wavelength region down to B $K\alpha$. LOD/KHP intensity ratios slightly <1 for Al $K\alpha$, ~1 for Mg $K\alpha$, ~1.5 for Na $K\alpha$, ~2.5 for F $K\alpha$.
68	Lead arachidate, lead eicosanoate	LBF	~110	$[CH_3(CH_2)_{18}COO]_2Pb$	9.6–105	Ultralong-wavelength region down to B $K\alpha$.

TABLE 17 (continued)

Crystals and Multilayer Langmuir-Blodgett Films Used as Analyzers in Wavelength-Dispersive X-ray Spectrometers

No.	Crystal	(hkl)	2d, Å	Chemical Formula	Practical Useful Wavelength Region (10-145° 2θ) Å	Optimal Application Remarks
69	Lead behenate, lead docosanoate	LBF	~120	$[CH_3(CH_2)_{20}COO]_2Pb$	10.5–114	Ultralong-wavelength region down to Be $K\alpha$.
70	Lead lignocerate, lead carnaubate, lead tetracosanoate (LTE)	LBF	~126	$[CH_3(CH_2)_{22}COO]_2Pb$	11.4–124	Ultralong-wavelength region down to Be $K\alpha$.
71	Lead cerotate, lead hexacosanoate	LBF	~140	$[CH_3(CH_2)_{24}COO]_2Pb$	12.2–134	Ultralong-wavelength region down to Be $K\alpha$.
72	Lead melissate, lead triacontanoate (LTC)	LBF	~156	$[CH_3(CH_2)_{28}COO]_2Pb$	14.0–156	Ultralong-wavelength region down to Be $K\alpha$.

*See under column 3 in explanation of table above.

[a] For rubidium or potassium *acid* phthalate, which is not preferred nomenclature.

[b] Not to be confused with the hallucinogenic drug, which is lysergic acid diethylamide.

[c] Unfortunately, the symbol LOD is used for both lead octadecanoate (stearate) and lead octadecanoate decanoate.

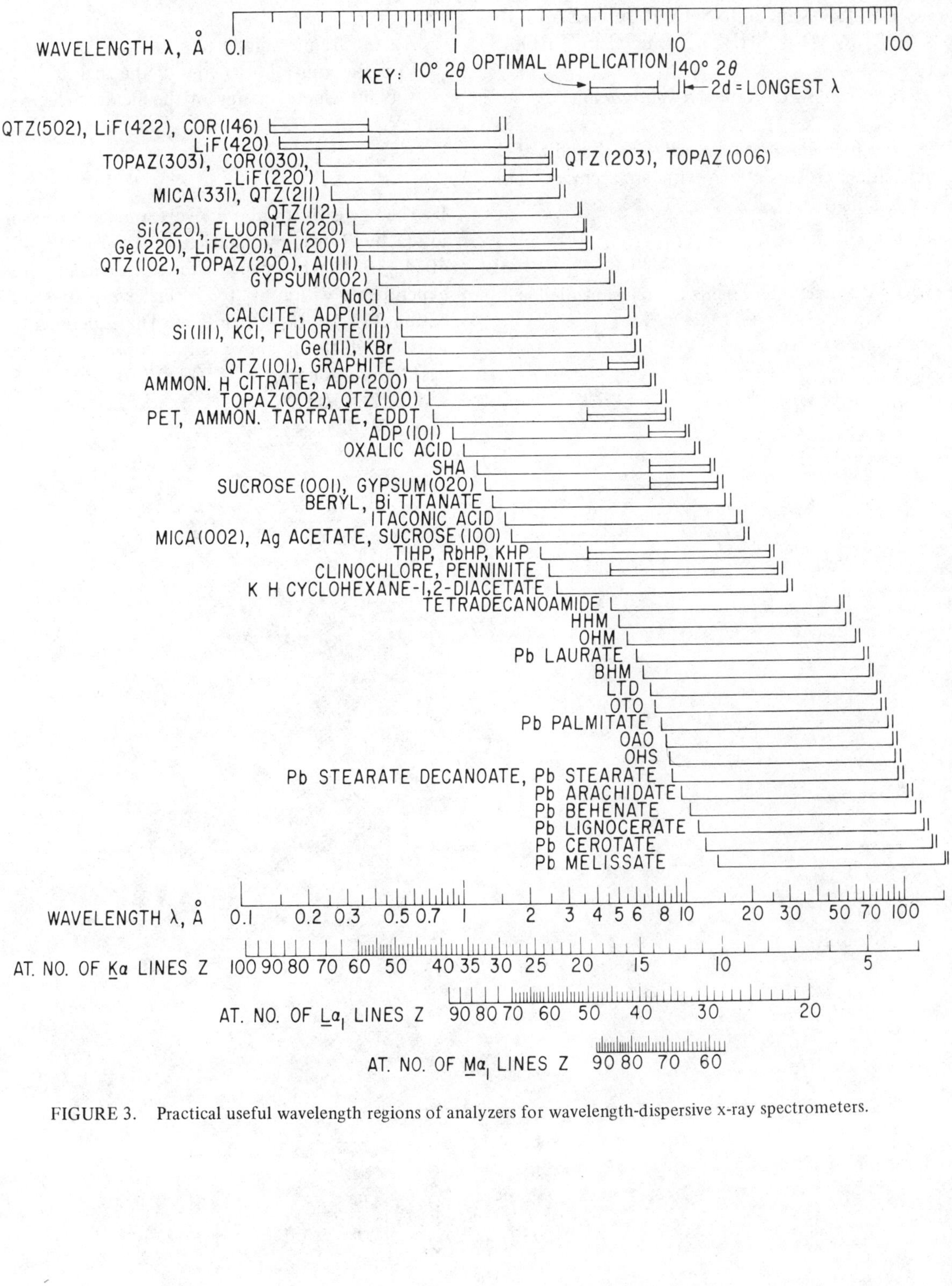

FIGURE 3. Practical useful wavelength regions of analyzers for wavelength-dispersive x-ray spectrometers.

X. CROSS SECTIONS FOR IONIZATION OF K- AND L-SHELLS BY ELECTRONS

D. B. Brown, Naval Research Laboratory

A. The following formulae will give K- and L-shell ionization cross sections with an accuracy indicated in Part B.

$$Q_i \text{ (in cm}^2\text{)} = 7.92 \times 10^{-20} \frac{C_i}{V_i V} \ln \frac{V}{V_i},$$

where the index i represents the relevant shell and

$$C_K = 0.85 + 0.0047\,Z$$
$$C_{LI} = C_{LII} = 0.61 + 0.0058\,Z$$
$$C_{LIII} = 2.19 + 0.0098\,Z.$$

Also

Z is the atomic number;

V_i is the ionization energy of the shell in keV;

V is the kinetic energy of the incident electron in keV.

B. The accuracy of the above formulae has been tested by Brown and Gilfrich, *J. Appl. Phys.*, 42, 4044, 1971. This paper shows agreement with experiments within 6% for K-shell x-ray lines and within 35% for L_{III}- shell lines. The experimental tests on which the above estimated accuracies are based were done for $V < 50$ keV, for $V/V_i < 25$, and for $Z > 10$.

XI. ELECTRON RANGE AND ELECTRON STOPPING POWER

D. B. Brown, Naval Research Laboratory

A. The electron stopping power of a homogeneous multielement material is defined as

$$\frac{1}{\rho}\frac{dV}{ds},$$

where
ρ is the density of the material in g/cm^2;
V is the electron energy in keV;
s is the path length of travel within the material.

The following formula will give the relativistic electron stopping power with an estimated accuracy stated in Section E.

$$\frac{1}{\rho}\frac{dV}{ds} = 3.076 \times 10^2 \frac{1}{\beta^2} \times \sum_i C_i \frac{Z_i}{A_i} \left\{ \ln \left[\frac{V}{I_i} \sqrt{\gamma + 1} \right] + 0.153 - \frac{1}{2}\beta^2 + \frac{1}{16}\left[\frac{\gamma - 1}{\gamma}\right]^2 - .693 \frac{2\gamma - 1}{2\gamma^2} \right\},$$

where the summation is over all the elements present in the material and

$$\beta = \sqrt{1 - \frac{1}{\gamma^2}}\,;$$

$$\gamma = \frac{V}{511} + 1\,;$$

C_i is the weight fraction of element i;
Z_i is the atomic number of element i;
A_i is the atomic weight of element i;
I_i is the ' average ionization energy" of element i (see Section B).

The above formulation is a modification of the work of Rohrlich, F. and Carlson, B. C., *Phys. Rev.*, 93, 38, 1954.

B. The average ionization energy values used here are given by the following table. The values tabulated are I/Z (in eV) for selected Z.

Z	3	4	6	7	8	10	13	17	22	26
I/Z	12.6	16.1	13.7	12.8	12.8	13.1	12.4	10.4	10.3	10.9

Z	29	40	47	50	54	74	79	82	92
I/Z	10.9	9.8	10.0	9.8	9.0	10.0	10.2	10.2	9.4

For further information on this parameter, see, for example,

1. **Chu, W. K. and Powers, D.**, *Phys. Lett.*, 40A, 23, 1972.
2. **Bichsel, H.**, Passage of Charged Particles Through Matter, University of Southern California, Report USC-136-150, July 1969.

C. In the following tables, each number is followed by the power of ten to which it is to be raised; i.e., 0.357 -2 should be read 0.357×10^{-2}.

TABLE 18A

The Stopping Power, $\frac{1}{\rho}\frac{dV}{ds}$ (keV cm^2 g^{-1}), for Electrons of Energy V in Targets of Atomic Number Z

V(keV) \ Z	3	4	6	7	8	10	13	17	22	26
1.0	0.117 + 6	0.101 + 6	0.104 + 6	0.101 + 6	0.958 + 5	0.853 + 5	0.751 + 5	0.712 + 5	0.592 + 5	0.518 + 8
1.5	0.872 + 5	0.771 + 5	0.803 + 5	0.791 + 5	0.746 + 5	0.675 + 5	0.604 + 5	0.578 + 5	0.493 + 5	0.445 + 5
2.0	0.704 + 5	0.629 + 5	0.660 + 5	0.643 + 5	0.617 + 5	0.563 + 5	0.508 + 5	0.488 + 5	0.423 + 5	0.387 + 5
2.5	0.594 + 5	0.535 + 5	0.564 + 5	0.550 + 5	0.530 + 5	0.486 + 5	0.441 + 5	0.425 + 5	0.371 + 5	0.343 + 5
3.0	0.517 + 5	0.468 + 5	0.495 + 5	0.483 + 5	0.466 + 5	0.429 + 5	0.391 + 5	0.378 + 5	0.332 + 5	0.309 + 5
3.5	0.459 + 5	0.417 + 5	0.442 + 5	0.432 + 5	0.417 + 5	0.386 + 5	0.353 + 5	0.341 + 5	0.301 + 5	0.281 + 5
4.0	0.413 + 5	0.377 + 5	0.400 + 5	0.392 + 5	0.379 + 5	0.351 + 5	0.322 + 5	0.311 + 5	0.276 + 5	0.259 + 5
4.5	0.377 + 5	0.345 + 5	0.367 + 5	0.359 + 5	0.348 + 5	0.323 + 5	0.296 + 5	0.287 + 5	0.255 + 5	0.240 + 5
5.0	0.347 + 5	0.318 + 5	0.339 + 5	0.332 + 5	0.322 + 5	0.299 + 5	0.275 + 5	0.267 + 5	0.237 + 5	0.224 + 5
6.0	0.300 + 5	0.277 + 5	0.295 + 5	0.290 + 5	0.281 + 5	0.262 + 5	0.242 + 5	0.235 + 5	0.209 + 5	0.198 + 5
7.0	0.266 + 5	0.246 + 5	0.263 + 5	0.258 + 5	0.250 + 5	0.234 + 5	0.216 + 5	0.210 + 5	0.188 + 5	0.179 + 5
8.0	0.239 + 5	0.222 + 5	0.237 + 5	0.233 + 5	0.226 + 5	0.212 + 5	0.196 + 5	0.191 + 5	0.171 + 5	0.163 + 5
9.0	0.218 + 5	0.202 + 5	0.217 + 5	0.213 + 5	0.207 + 5	0.194 + 5	0.180 + 5	0.175 + 5	0.157 + 5	0.150 + 5
10.0	0.200 + 5	0.186 + 5	0.200 + 5	0.196 + 5	0.191 + 5	0.179 + 5	0.166 + 5	0.162 + 5	0.146 + 5	0.139 + 5
15.0	0.145 + 5	0.136 + 5	0.146 + 5	0.144 + 5	0.140 + 5	0.132 + 5	0.123 + 5	0.120 + 5	0.109 + 5	0.104 + 5
20.0	0.115 + 5	0.108 + 5	0.117 + 5	0.115 + 5	0.112 + 5	0.106 + 5	0.992 + 4	0.969 + 4	0.881 + 4	0.849 + 4
25.0	0.996 + 4	0.911 + 4	0.985 + 4	0.970 + 4	0.948 + 4	0.899 + 4	0.840 + 4	0.821 + 4	0.748 + 4	0.723 + 4
30.0	0.838 + 4	0.792 + 4	0.857 + 4	0.845 + 4	0.827 + 4	0.784 + 4	0.734 + 4	0.718 + 4	0.655 + 4	0.634 + 4
35.0	0.744 + 4	0.705 + 4	0.763 + 4	0.753 + 4	0.737 + 4	0.700 + 4	0.656 + 4	0.642 + 4	0.586 + 4	0.568 + 4
40.0	0.672 + 4	0.638 + 4	0.691 + 4	0.682 + 4	0.667 + 4	0.635 + 4	0.595 + 4	0.583 + 4	0.533 + 4	0.517 + 4
45.0	0.615 + 4	0.584 + 4	0.634 + 4	0.625 + 4	0.612 + 4	0.583 + 4	0.547 + 4	0.536 + 4	0.490 + 4	0.476 + 4
50.0	0.569 + 4	0.541 + 4	0.587 + 4	0.579 + 4	0.568 + 4	0.540 + 4	0.508 + 4	0.497 + 4	0.456 + 4	0.443 + 4
60.0	0.498 + 4	0.475 + 4	0.515 + 4	0.509 + 4	0.499 + 4	0.476 + 4	0.447 + 4	0.438 + 4	0.402 + 4	0.391 + 4
70.0	0.446 + 4	0.426 + 4	0.463 + 4	0.458 + 4	0.449 + 4	0.428 + 4	0.403 + 4	0.395 + 4	0.363 + 4	0.353 + 4
80.0	0.407 + 4	0.389 + 4	0.423 + 4	0.418 + 4	0.410 + 4	0.392 + 4	0.369 + 4	0.362 + 4	0.332 + 4	0.324 + 4
90.0	0.376 + 4	0.360 + 4	0.392 + 4	0.387 + 4	0.380 + 4	0.363 + 4	0.342 + 4	0.335 + 4	0.308 + 4	0.301 + 4
100.0	0.351 + 4	0.337 + 4	0.366 + 4	0.362 + 4	0.355 + 4	0.340 + 4	0.320 + 4	0.314 + 4	0.289 + 4	0.282 + 4

TABLE 18B

The Stopping Power, $\frac{1}{\rho}\frac{dV}{ds}$ (keV cm^2 g^{-1}), for Electrons of Energy V in Targets of Atomic Number Z

V(keV) \ Z	29	40	47	50	54	74	79	82	92
1.0	0.469 + 5	0.376 + 5	0.311 + 5	0.287 + 5	0.283 + 5	0.144 + 5	0.116 + 5	0.103 + 5	0.904 + 4
1.5	0.410 + 5	0.344 + 5	0.301 + 5	0.281 + 5	0.277 + 5	0.182 + 5	0.163 + 5	0.193 + 5	0.143 + 5
2.0	0.360 + 5	0.308 + 5	0.275 + 5	0.259 + 5	0.254 + 5	0.182 + 5	0.168 + 5	0.160 + 5	0.151 + 5
2.5	0.320 + 5	0.278 + 5	0.251 + 5	0.237 + 5	0.233 + 5	0.174 + 5	0.163 + 5	0.156 + 5	0.148 + 5
3.0	0.289 + 5	0.253 + 5	0.231 + 5	0.218 + 5	0.214 + 5	0.165 + 5	0.155 + 5	0.149 + 5	0.142 + 5
3.5	0.264 + 5	0.233 + 5	0.213 + 5	0.202 + 5	0.198 + 5	0.155 + 5	0.147 + 5	0.142 + 5	0.136 + 5
4.0	0.244 + 5	0.215 + 5	0.198 + 5	0.188 + 5	0.184 + 5	0.147 + 5	0.139 + 5	0.135 + 5	0.129 + 5
4.5	0.226 + 5	0.201 + 5	0.185 + 5	0.176 + 5	0.173 + 5	0.139 + 5	0.132 + 5	0.128 + 5	0.123 + 5
5.0	0.212 + 5	0.188 + 5	0.174 + 5	0.166 + 5	0.162 + 5	0.132 + 5	0.126 + 5	0.122 + 5	0.117 + 5
6.0	0.188 + 5	0.168 + 5	0.156 + 5	0.149 + 5	0.146 + 5	0.120 + 5	0.115 + 5	0.112 + 5	0.107 + 5
7.0	0.169 + 5	0.152 + 5	0.142 + 5	0.135 + 5	0.132 + 5	0.110 + 5	0.106 + 5	0.103 + 5	0.990 + 4
8.0	0.155 + 5	0.139 + 5	0.130 + 5	0.124 + 5	0.122 + 5	0.102 + 5	0.983 + 4	0.955 + 4	0.920 + 4
9.0	0.143 + 5	0.129 + 5	0.121 + 5	0.115 + 5	0.113 + 5	0.952 + 4	0.918 + 4	0.893 + 4	0.860 + 4
10.0	0.133 + 5	0.120 + 5	0.113 + 5	0.108 + 5	0.105 + 5	0.893 + 4	0.862 + 4	0.839 + 4	0.809 + 4
15.0	0.997 + 4	0.906 + 4	0.857 + 4	0.819 + 4	0.802 + 5	0.692 + 4	0.671 + 4	0.654 + 4	0.631 + 4
20.0	0.812 + 4	0.741 + 4	0.703 + 4	0.672 + 4	0.658 + 5	0.573 + 4	0.557 + 4	0.544 + 4	0.526 + 4
25.0	0.692 + 4	0.633 + 4	0.602 + 4	0.576 + 4	0.564 + 5	0.495 + 4	0.481 + 4	0.470 + 4	0.455 + 4
30.0	0.608 + 4	0.557 + 4	0.531 + 4	0.508 + 4	0.497 + 4	0.438 + 4	0.427 + 4	0.417 + 4	0.404 + 4
35.0	0.545 + 4	0.500 + 4	0.477 + 4	0.457 + 4	0.447 + 4	0.396 + 4	0.386 + 4	0.377 + 4	0.365 + 4
40.0	0.496 + 4	0.456 + 4	0.436 + 4	0.417 + 4	0.408 + 4	0.362 + 4	0.354 + 4	0.346 + 4	0.335 + 4
45.0	0.457 + 4	0.421 + 4	0.402 + 4	0.385 + 4	0.377 + 4	0.335 + 4	0.327 + 4	0.320 + 4	0.310 + 4
50.0	0.425 + 4	0.392 + 4	0.375 + 4	0.359 + 4	0.351 + 4	0.313 + 4	0.306 + 4	0.299 + 4	0.290 + 4
60.0	0.376 + 4	0.347 + 4	0.332 + 4	0.319 + 4	0.311 + 4	0.279 + 4	0.272 + 4	0.267 + 4	0.258 + 4
70.0	0.340 + 4	0.314 + 4	0.301 + 4	0.288 + 4	0.282 + 4	0.253 + 4	0.248 + 4	0.242 + 4	0.235 + 4
80.0	0.312 + 4	0.288 + 4	0.277 + 4	0.265 + 4	0.259 + 4	0.233 + 4	0.228 + 4	0.223 + 4	0.217 + 4
90.0	0.290 + 4	0.268 + 4	0.257 + 4	0.247 + 4	0.241 + 4	0.217 + 4	0.213 + 4	0.208 + 4	0.202 + 4
100.0	0.272 + 4	0.251 + 4	0.242 + 4	0.232 + 4	0.227 + 4	0.205 + 4	0.200 + 4	0.196 + 4	0.190 + 4

TABLE 19

The Mass-range ρs (g/cm^2) at Which the Electron Energy Has Fallen from Its Initial Energy, V_O, to the K-shell Ionization Energy in Targets of Atomic Number Z

V_0 (keV) \ Z	6	7	8	10	13	17	22	26	29	40	47	50
1.0	0.529 – 5	0.483 – 5	0.421 – 5	0.143 – 5	–	–	–	–	–	–	–	–
1.5	0.108 – 4	0.105 – 4	0.102 – 4	0.807 – 5	–	–	–	–	–	–	–	–
2.0	0.177 – 4	0.176 – 4	0.176 – 4	0.162 – 4	0.808 – 5	–	–	–	–	–	–	–
2.5	0.259 – 4	0.260 – 4	0.264 – 4	0.258 – 4	0.187 – 4	–	–	–	–	–	–	–
3.0	0.354 – 4	0.358 – 4	0.365 – 4	0.368 – 4	0.307 – 4	0.467 – 5	–	–	–	–	–	–
3.5	0.462 – 4	0.467 – 4	0.478 – 4	0.491 – 4	0.442 – 4	0.186 – 4	–	–	–	–	–	–
4.0	0.581 – 4	0.589 – 4	0.604 – 4	0.627 – 4	0.591 – 4	0.340 – 4	–	–	–	–	–	–
4.5	0.711 – 4	0.722 – 4	0.742 – 4	0.775 – 4	0.753 – 4	0.507 – 4	–	–	–	–	–	–
5.0	0.853 – 4	0.867 – 4	0.892 – 4	0.936 – 4	0.928 – 4	0.688 – 4	0.147 – 5	–	–	–	–	–
6.0	0.117 – 4	0.119 – 3	0.123 – 3	0.129 – 4	0.132 – 3	0.109 – 3	0.464 – 4	–	–	–	–	–
7.0	0.153 – 4	0.156 – 3	0.160 – 3	0.170 – 3	0.176 – 3	0.154 – 3	0.969 – 4	–	–	–	–	–
8.0	0.193 – 3	0.197 – 3	0.202 – 3	0.215 – 3	0.224 – 3	0.204 – 3	0.153 – 3	0.524 – 4	–	–	–	–
9.0	0.237 – 3	0.242 – 3	0.249 – 3	0.264 – 3	0.278 – 3	0.259 – 3	0.214 – 3	0.116 – 3	0.712 – 5	–	–	–
10.0	0.285 – 3	0.291 – 3	0.299 – 3	0.318 – 3	0.335 – 3	0.318 – 3	0.280 – 3	0.186 – 3	0.798 – 4	–	–	–
15.0	0.583 – 3	0.593 – 3	0.609 – 3	0.647 – 3	0.690 – 3	0.682 – 3	0.682 – 3	0.605 – 3	0.520 – 3	–	–	–
20.0	0.968 – 3	0.984 – 3	0.101 – 2	0.107 – 2	0.115 – 2	0.115 – 2	0.120 – 3	0.114 – 2	0.108 – 2	0.260 – 3	–	–
25.0	0.144 – 2	0.146 – 2	0.150 – 2	0.159 – 2	0.170 – 2	0.171 – 2	0.182 – 2	0.178 – 2	0.175 – 2	0.993 – 3	–	–
30.0	0.198 – 2	0.201 – 2	0.206 – 2	0.218 – 2	0.233 – 2	0.237 – 2	0.253 – 2	0.252 – 2	0.252 – 2	0.184 – 2	–	–
35.0	0.260 – 2	0.264 – 2	0.271 – 2	0.286 – 2	0.306 – 2	0.310 – 2	0.334 – 2	0.335 – 2	0.339 – 2	0.279 – 2	0.799 – 3	0.155 – 3
40.0	0.329 – 2	0.334 – 2	0.342 – 2	0.361 – 2	0.386 – 2	0.392 – 2	0.424 – 2	0.428 – 2	0.463 – 2	0.384 – 2	0.179 – 2	0.119 – 2
45.0	0.405 – 2	0.411 – 2	0.420 – 2	0.443 – 2	0.474 – 2	0.482 – 2	0.522 – 2	0.529 – 2	0.541 – 2	0.498 – 2	0.289 – 2	0.243 – 2
50.0	0.487 – 2	0.494 – 2	0.505 – 2	0.533 – 2	0.569 – 2	0.579 – 2	0.627 – 2	0.638 – 2	0.654 – 2	0.621 – 2	0.409 – 2	0.359 – 2
60.0	0.669 – 2	0.679 – 2	0.649 – 2	0.730 – 2	0.779 – 2	0.794 – 2	0.862 – 2	0.878 – 2	0.905 – 2	0.873 – 2	0.538 – 2	0.493 – 2
70.0	0.874 – 2	0.886 – 2	0.905 – 2	0.953 – 2	0.102 – 1	0.103 – 1	0.112 – 1	0.115 – 1	0.119 – 1	0.120 – 1	0.822 – 2	0.790 – 2
80.0	0.110 – 1	0.112 – 1	0.114 – 1	0.120 – 2	0.128 – 1	0.130 – 1	0.141 – 1	0.144 – 1	0.149 – 1	0.153 – 1	0.114 – 1	0.112 – 1
90.0	0.135 – 1	0.136 – 1	0.139 – 1	0.146 – 2	0.156 – 1	0.159 – 1	0.173 – 1	0.176 – 1	0.183 – 1	0.189 – 1	0.149 – 1	0.148 – 1
100.0	0.161 – 1	0.163 – 1	0.166 – 1	0.175 – 1	0.186 – 1	0.190 – 1	0.206 – 1	0.211 – 1	0.218 – 1	0.228 – 1	0.186 – 1	0.187 – 1
											0.226 – 1	0.229 – 1

TABLE 20

The Mass-range, ρs (g/cm^2), at Which the Electron Energy Has Fallen from Its Initial Energy, V_o, to the L_{III}-shell Ionization Energy in Targets of Atomic Number Z

V_0 (keV) \ Z	29	40	47	50	54	74	79	82	92
1.0	0.142 – 5	–	–	–	–	–	–	–	–
1.5	0.128 – 4	–	–	–	–	–	–	–	–
2.0	0.258 – 4	–	–	–	–	–	–	–	–
2.5	0.406 – 4	0.976 – 5	–	–	–	–	–	–	–
3.0	0.570 – 4	0.286 – 4	–	–	–	–	–	–	–
3.5	0.751 – 4	0.493 – 4	0.687 – 5	–	–	–	–	–	–
4.0	0.949 – 4	0.716 – 4	0.312 – 4	0.375 – 5	–	–	–	–	–
4.5	0.116 – 3	0.957 – 4	0.573 – 4	0.312 – 4	–	–	–	–	–
5.0	0.139 – 3	0.121 – 3	0.851 – 4	0.605 – 4	0.132 – 4	–	–	–	–
6.0	0.189 – 3	0.178 – 3	0.146 – 3	0.124 – 3	0.783 – 4	–	–	–	–
7.0	0.245 – 3	0.240 – 3	0.213 – 3	0.195 – 3	0.150 – 3	–	–	–	–
8.0	0.307 – 3	0.309 – 3	0.287 – 3	0.272 – 3	0.229 – 3	–	–	–	–
9.0	0.375 – 3	0.384 – 3	0.366 – 3	0.356 – 3	0.315 – 3	–	–	–	–
10.0	0.447 – 3	0.465 – 3	0.452 – 3	0.446 – 3	0.407 – 3	–	–	–	–
15.0	0.888 – 3	0.950 – 3	0.967 – 3	0.984 – 3	0.957 – 3	0.620 – 3	0.428 – 3	0.286 – 3	–
20.0	0.145 – 2	0.156 – 2	0.161 – 2	0.166 – 2	0.165 – 2	0.142 – 2	0.125 – 2	0.113 – 2	0.513 – 3
25.0	0.212 – 2	0.230 – 2	0.239 – 2	0.247 – 2	0.247 – 2	0.236 – 2	0.222 – 2	0.212 – 2	0.154 – 2
30.0	0.289 – 2	0.314 – 2	0.327 – 2	0.339 – 2	0.342 – 2	0.344 – 2	0.332 – 2	0.325 – 2	0.271 – 2
35.0	0.376 – 2	0.409 – 2	0.427 – 2	0.443 – 2	0.448 – 2	0.464 – 2	0.456 – 2	0.452 – 2	0.401 – 2
40.0	0.472 – 2	0.514 – 2	0.537 – 2	0.558 – 2	0.556 – 2	0.596 – 2	0.591 – 2	0.590 – 2	0.545 – 2
45.0	0.577 – 2	0.628 – 2	0.656 – 2	0.683 – 2	0.693 – 2	0.740 – 2	0.739 – 2	0.741 – 2	0.700 – 2
50.0	0.691 – 2	0.752 – 2	0.785 – 2	0.817 – 2	0.831 – 2	0.894 – 2	0.897 – 2	0.902 – 2	0.867 – 2
60.0	0.942 – 2	0.102 – 1	0.107 – 1	0.111 – 1	0.113 – 1	0.123 – 1	0.124 – 1	0.126 – 1	0.123 – 1
70.0	0.122 – 1	0.133 – 1	0.139 – 1	0.114 – 1	0.147 – 1	0.161 – 1	0.163 – 1	0.165 – 1	0.164 – 1
80.0	0.153 – 1	0.166 – 1	0.173 – 1	0.181 – 1	0.184 – 1	0.202 – 1	0.205 – 1	0.208 – 1	0.208 – 1
90.0	0.186 – 1	0.202 – 1	0.211 – 1	0.220 – 1	0.224 – 1	0.247 – 1	0.251 – 1	0.255 – 1	0.256 – 1
100.0	0.222 – 1	0.241 – 1	0.251 – 1	0.262 – 1	0.267 – 1	0.249 – 1	0.299 – 1	0.304 – 1	0.307 – 1

D. It is difficult to test experimentally the above tabular values. This is because the process of electron energy loss is difficult to separate from accompanying processes such as electron scattering. On the basis of indirect evidence, it is estimated that the above values have an accuracy of 5% or better.

E. There are five corrections to the formulation of Section A which may be useful for special purposes.

1. A shell correction which reduces the stopping power when the electron energy is lower than the ionization energy of one or more shells. This is not a solved problem. See, however, Walske, M. C., *Phys. Rev.*, 101, 940, 1956.
2. An energy straggling correction. See the discussion by Birkhoff, R. D., in *Handbuch der Physik*, Vol. XXXIV, Flügge, S., Ed., Springer-Verlag, Berlin, 1958.
3. An increase in stopping power due to energy loss to bremsstrahlung. This is important only for energies above 100 keV. See Berger, M. J. and Seltzer, S. M., Tables of Energy Losses and Ranges of Electrons and Positrons, NASA Document SP-3012, Washington, D.C., 1964.
4. A reduction of stopping power due to the "density effect." This correction becomes important only for energies above 100 keV. For futher detail see, for example, the Berger and Seltzer reference given above.
5. A correction for the continuous slowing-down approximation which allows for the discrete nature of electron energy loss. See Spencer, L. V. and Fano, U., *Phys. Rev.*, 93, 1172, 1954.

F. For the purpose of interpolating between the selected energies in the tables of mass-range (Tables 19 and 20), the following approximate form is recommended:

$$\rho s \propto V_0^2 - V_c^2 ,$$

where V_c is the K-shell ionization energy (for Table 19) or the L_{III}-shell ionization energy (for Table 20).

Section B

ESCA Photoelectron Spectroscopy

UV Spectra

X-Ray Molecular Orbital Spectra

X-Ray Core Spectra

ESCA – PHOTOELECTRON SPECTROSCOPY

Kai Siegbahn, Uppsala University; David A. Allison, University of Alberta; and Juanita H. Allison, University of Alberta

The title of this section includes the two most commonly used names for the field. Although the term photoelectron spectroscopy may correctly be used to denote the whole field, it frequently is used more narrowly to specify the use of ultraviolet radiation as the ionizing source, while ESCA refers to the use of x-radiation. The use of this distinction has been continued in preparing this section for the following considerations: ESCA has a much greater energy range than photoelectron spectroscopy with a corresponding loss of resolution. Furthermore, while calibration in photoelectron spectroscopy is a routine procedure, a wide variety of methods and standards are used in ESCA so that reported ionizations are useful only when the calibration method used is known. Thus, Table 1 on photoelectron spectroscopy includes both vertical and adiabatic ionization as well as vibrational data, while Tables 2 and 3 on ESCA have only vertical ionizations that include the calibration method. Valence band ESCA has been put into a separate table since it covers the energy region of photoelectron spectroscopy but is limited by the lower resolution of ESCA. For more background on this field, a book such as *Photoelectron Spectroscopy,* by A. D. Baker and D. Betteridge, Pergamon Press, 1972, is recommended as well as References 7 and 151 of Tables 1 and 3, respectively.

Although the three tables have different formats, the following features are common to all:

1. The compounds are listed alphabetically following the Chemical Abstracts system to facilitate locating any given compound. This is followed by the molecular formula and, if necessary, the structure of the compound.
2. The peak assignments, when given, are listed next to the value. No effort has been made to evaluate either the assignments or the measurements.
3. Errors, when given, immediately follow each number in parentheses. It should be noted that the given errors range from estimates to rigorously determined limits of the absolute value given. It is therefore imperative to refer to the original article to get a proper interpretation of the errors given.
4. The primary literature source of each value is given in the last column as a number which refers to the reference lists. References for Table 2 have been included with those of Table 3.

TABLE 1: UV SPECTRA

The numerical data in this table have been listed in columns four, five, six, and seven of the table. Peak and band values are arranged by adiabatic (fourth column) and vertical (sixth column) ionization potentials. When it was not clear which ionization potentials were being reported, the numbers were listed in column five between the adiabatic and vertical columns. Column seven contains all vibrational and spin-orbit splitting parameters, the latter being denoted by sos. The units of the whole number values in column seven are cm^{-1}, while the decimal values are in eV.

When the peak origin is uncertain or the assignment given, if any, is only tentative, this value is followed by a ?. Values in parentheses denote questionable peaks. This table includes data obtained by He I and He II radiation as well as Ne and Ar. No attempt has been made to indicate the radiation used in any given situation.

TABLE I

	Compound	Orbital	Ionization Energy Adiabatic	Ionization Energy Vertical	Vibrational Bands	Reference
Ar	Ar	$^2P_{3/2}$		15.759		7
		$^2P_{1/2}$		15.937		
$AsCl_3$	$AsCl_3$	a_1		10.89	250	1
		e, a_2		11.75		
		e		12.59		
		a_1		13.80		
		e		14.64		
AsF_3	AsF_3	a_1		13.00	500	1
		e, a_2		15.24		
		e		16.21		
		a_1		17.22		
		e		17.82		
AsH_3	AsH_3	$^2A_1$	10.06 (3)	10.58 (2)	ν_2 400 (20)	2
		^2E	11.9 (1)	12.9 (1)		
AsH_3	AsH_3	$2a_1$	9.89 (1)	10.51 (1)	ν_2' 452 (25)	3
		1e		12.12 (3)	1,600	
AsH_9Si_3	$(SiH_3)_3As$	$1a_2''$		9.3 (1)		4
		$2e'$		10.2 (1)		
		SiH		11.5–13.2		
		$Si3s(a_1')$		14.5 (1)		
BBr_3	BBr_3	la_2'	10.51 (2)	10.65 (2)		5
		$3e'$	11.13 (3)	11.36 (3)	0.14 (2)	
		$1e''$		11.71 (4)		
		$1a_2''$	12.89 (4)	13.18 (1)		
		$2e'$	13.67 (3)	14.20 (1)	0.27 (2)	
				14.46 (3)		
		$2a_1'$	16.63 (5)	16.74 (1)		
				17.14 (4)		
BBr_3	BBr_3	$1a_2'$		10.68		1
		$3e'$		11.36		
				11.46		
		le''		11.70		
				11.75		

TABLE 1 (continued)

	Compound	Orbital	Ionization Energy: Adiabatic	Ionization Energy: Vertical	Vibrational Bands	Reference
		$1a_2''$		13.15	ν_1 260	
		$2e'$		14.17	sos 0.31	
				14.48		
		$2a_1'$		16.70		
BBr_3	BBr_3			10.72		6
				11.26		
				11.77		
				13.14		
				14.13		
BCl_3	BCl_3	$1a_2'$	11.64 (2)	11.73 (1)		5
		$3e'$		12.66 (1)		
		$1e''$	12.19 (4)	12.39 (2)		
		$1a_2''$	14.22 (2)	14.42 (1)	0.055 (3)	
		$2e'$	15.32 (2)	15.54 (2)	0.18 (2)	
				15.72 (4) (sh)		
		$2a_1'$	17.74 (5)		0.055 (6)	
BCl_3	BCl_3	$1a_2'$		11.73		1
		$3e'$		12.38		
		$1e''$		12.65		
		$1a_2''$		14.40	ν_1 440	
		$2e'$		15.52	ν_1 330	
				15.70		
		$2a_1'$		17.71		
				17.75		
BCl_3	BCl_3			11.97		6
				12.43		
				12.77		
				14.50		
				15.75		
				17.79		

TABLE 1 (continued)

	Compound	Orbital	Ionization Energy: Adiabatic		Ionization Energy: Vertical	Vibrational Bands	Reference
BF_3	BF_3	$1a_2'$	15.57 (2)		15.95 (2)		5
		$3e'$	16.92 (1)		17.14 (1)		
		$1e''$	16.30 (1)		16.67 (1)	0.095 (7)	
		$1a_2''$	18.98 (1)		19.13 (2)	0.096 (3)	
		$2e'$	19.94 (1)		20.09 (2)	0.090 (3)	
						0.082 (4)	
BF_3	BF_3	$1a_2'$			16.68		1
		$3e'$			15.95		
		$1e''$			17.13		
					17.21		
					17.30		
		$1a_2''$			19.06	ν_1 670	
		$2e'$			20.14	ν_1 700	
		$2a_1'$			21.4		
BF_3	BF_3	$1e''$			15.94 (2)		8
		$1a_2'$			16.67 (1)		
		$3e'$			17.14 (1)	ν_1 690 (90)	
		$1a_2''$			19.10 (3)		
		$2e'$			20.03 (3)	720 (20)	
						660 (30)	
BF_3	BF_3				15.95		6
				16.65			
				17.21			
				19.0			
				20.0			
BF_3H_3P	F_3PBH_3		11.02 (3)		12.04 (2)		9
					12.59 (3)		
		$1a_2+6e$	16.25 (3)		16.82 (1)		
		$2a_1$			17.58 (1)		
		$5e$			18.42 (4)		
		$4e$	19.75 (3)		20.22 (3)		

TABLE 1 (continued)

	Compound	Orbital	Ionization Energy Adiabatic	Ionization Energy Vertical	Vibrational Bands	Reference
BF_3H_3P	F_3PBH_3	7e		12.0		10
		$10a_1$		12.6		
		$1a_2$, 6e		16.8		
		$9a_1$		17.6		
		5e		18.4		
		4e		20.2		
BH_6N	NH_3BH_3	$e(BH_3)$	9.44 (2)	10.33 (4)		9
		2e		10.90 (10) (sh)		
		$3a_1$	12.98 (8)	13.92 (9)		
		$1e+2a_1$		17.75 (7)		
BH_6N	NH_3BH_3	e		10.33 (4)		11
				10.90 (10) (sh)		
				13.92 (9)		
				17.75 (7)		
		e				
BI_3	BI_3	$1a_2'$	9.25 (3)	9.36 (1)		5
		$3e'$	9.85 (2)	9.92 (2)	0.18(2)	
			10.03 (2)	10.10 (2)		
		$1e''$	10.28 (2)	10.36 (2)	0.10(2)	
			10.44 (2)	10.48 (2)		
		$1a_2''$	11.56 (2)	11.74 (2)		
			12.28 (3)	12.46 (1)	0.50(1)	
		$2e'$	12.83 (3)	12.96 (2)		
		$2a_1'$	15.10 (2)	15.39 (2)		
BI_3	BI_3	$1a_2'$		9.40		1
		$3e'$		9.90		
				10.11		
		$1e''$		10.40		
				10.50		
				11.72		
		$1a_2''$		12.44	sos .50	
		$2e'$		12.94		
		$2a_1'$		15.2?		

TABLE 1 (continued)

			Ionization Energy			
Compound		Orbital	Adiabatic	Vertical	Vibrational Bands	Reference
B_2Cl_4	Cl_2BBCl_2	$4a_1$	10.42 (2)	10.97 (1)		223
		4e	11.49 (1)	11.97 (1) (sh)		
		$1a_2$		12.25 (1)		
		$1b_1$		12.49 (1)		
		$3b_2$		13.02 (2)		
		3e	13.34 (2)	13.54 (2)		
				13.72 (2)		
		$2e,3a_1$	14.42 (2)	14.92 (1)		
				15.20 (1)		
		$2b_2$	16.60 (1)	16.72 (1)		
			17.90 (3)	18.10 (2)		
B_2D_6	B_2D_6	$1b_{3g}$			ν_3 800 (120)	12
		$3a_g$			ν_2 1,500 (300)	
		$2b_{1u}$			ν_1 1,500 (80)	
					ν_3 650 (160)	
B_2F_4	F_2BBF_2	$4a_1$	12.23 (6)	13.26 (1)		223
		$1a_2+1b_1+4e$	15.50 (3)	15.98 (3) (sh)		
				16.32 (1)		
		$3b_2$	17.20 (1)	17.38 (1)	600 (100)	
		3e	18.71 (3)	19.01 (1)		
		2e	20.52 (1)		600 (60)	
B_2H_6	B_2H_6	$1b_{3g}$	11.41 (2)	11.89 (2)	ν_3 900 (60)	12
		$3a_g$	12.83 (4)	13.30 (1)	ν_2 1,700 (300)	
		$1b_{2u}$	13.81 (6)	13.91 (2)		
		$1b_{3u}$	14.42 (4)	14.75 (3)		
		$2b_{1u}$	16.08 (1)	16.11 (2)	ν_1 2,200 (150)	
					ν_3 1,000 (140)	
B_2H_6	B_2H_6	$1b_{2g}$	11.38 (1)	11.81 (1)	850	13
		$3a_g$	<12.7	13.3		
		$1b_{3u}$	<13.6	13.9 (1)		
		$1b_{2u}$	<14.5	14.7 (1)		
		$2b_{1u}$	16.06 (1)	16.06 (1)	2,250	
		$2a_g$	20.2 (1)	21.4 (1)		

TABLE 1 (continued)

Compound		Orbital	Ionization Energy: Adiabatic	Ionization Energy: Vertical	Vibrational Bands	Reference
B_2H_6	B_2H_6	$1b_{3g}$	11.37	11.9 (1)		14
		$1b_{3u}$	12.728 (1)		0.075 (5)	
		$1b_{2u}$	13.5	13.9 (2)		
		$3a_g$	14.5	14.9 (2)		
		$2b_{1u}$	16.05	16.4 (1)		
$B_3Cl_3H_3N_3$	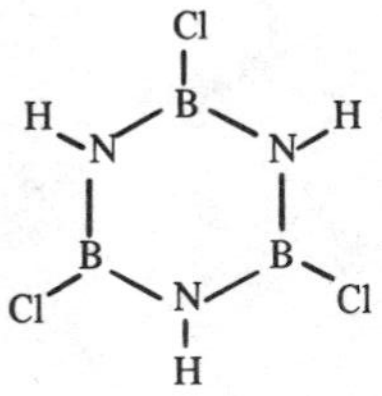	$2e''\pi$		10.55	1,100 (40)	15
				11.55		
				11.95		
				12.60		
				13.23		
				13.33		
				14.12		
				15.02		
				15.7		
				16.1		
				18.1		
				18.8		
$B_3F_3H_3N_3$	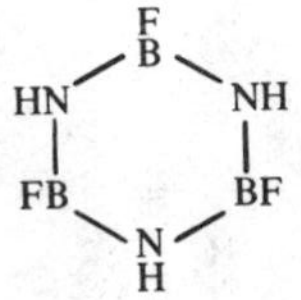	$2e''$	10.46 (1)	10.79 (2)	ν_2 1,050 (160)	12
			12.85 (1)	12.98 (1)	ν_2 1,500 (120)	
					ν_3 750 (100)	
		$2a_2''$	13.35 (1)	13.53 (3)		
		$1e''$	14.05 (1)	14.29 (2)	ν_2 1,200 (200)	
			15.42 (2)	15.85 (3)		
			16.11 (3)	16.20 (5)		
			16.69 (2)	16.87 (4)		
			17.67 (3)	17.73 (2)		
$B_3F_3H_3N_3$	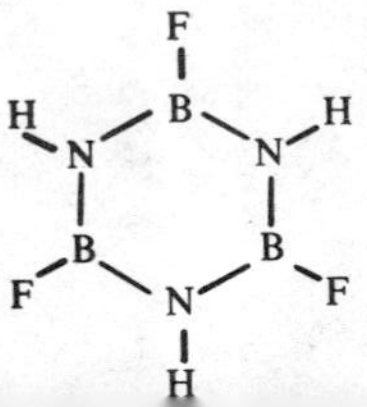	$2e''\pi$		10.66	1,400 (200)	15
					?500 (80)	
		$2a_2''\pi$		12.74		
		$6e'$		13.48		
		$5e'$		14.20		
		$1e''\pi$		15.8		
		$4e'$		16.2		
		$1a_2''\pi$		16.8		
		$4a_1'$		17.75		

TABLE 1 (continued)

Compound		Orbital	Ionization Energy: Adiabatic	Ionization Energy: Vertical	Vibrational Bands	Reference
$B_3H_6N_3$	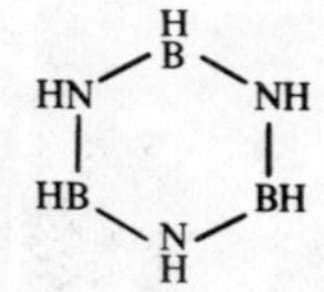	e′	10.01 (1)	10.09 (2)	640	16
		e″		11.42 (4)		
		a_1'		12.82 (4)		
		e′		13.98 (2)	2,100	
		a_2'		14.70 (5)		
		a_2''		17.10 (10)		
$B_3H_6N_3$	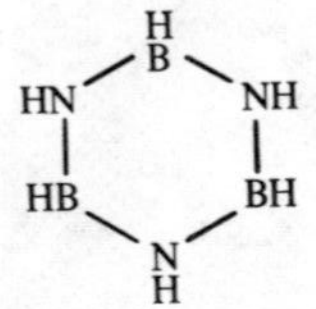	1e″	9.88 (2)	10.14 (1)	ν_4 700 (100)	12
				10.50 (3) (sh)		
		4e′	11.11 (6)	11.42 (2)		
				11.73 (6) (sh)		
		$1a_2''$	11.99 (3)	12.06 (3)		
		$1a_2'$	12.60 (9)	12.83 (2)		
		$3a_1'$	13.73 (1)	13.84 (3)	ν_2 1,900 (150)	
					ν_1 2,400 (250)	
		3e′		14.76 (3)		
		2e′	17.10 (5)	17.47 (3)		
				18.18 (7) (sh)		
B_4Cl_4	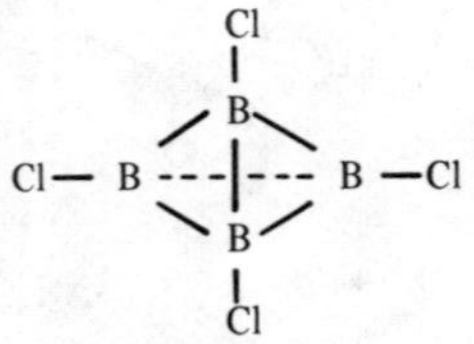			10.60 (1)		17
				12.44 (1)		
				13.00 (1)		
				13.57 (1)		
		(B-Cl)		15.36 (1)		
		(B-Cl)		15.96 (1)		
		a_1 (B2s-B2s)		19.51 (2)		
BrCN	BrCN	$^2\Pi_{3/2}$ (1)	11.85 (2) }		1,900	34
		$^2\Pi_{1/2}$ (1)	12.03 (2) }			
		$^2\Sigma^+$ (2)	13.54 (2)			
		$^2\Pi_{3/2}$ (3)		14.40 }	500	
		$^2\Pi_{1/2}$ (3)		14.49 (2) }		
		$^2\Sigma^+$ (4)		18.07 (2)		

TABLE 1 (continued)

			Ionization Energy			
Compound		Orbital	Adiabatic	Vertical	Vibrational Bands	Reference
BrCN	BrCN	$(\pi_2)^{-1}\ {}^2\Pi_{3/2}$	11.89	11.88	1,835, 580	19
		$(\pi_2)^{-1}\ {}^2\Pi_{1/2}$	12.07	12.07	1,835, 580	
		$(\sigma_N)^{-1}$	13.58	13.58		
		$(\pi_1)^{-1}\ {}^2\Pi_{3/2}$	14.19	~14.4	516	
		$(\pi_1)^{-1}\ {}^2\Pi_{1/2}$	14.34	~14.4	516	
		$(\sigma_{C\text{-}Br})^{-1}$		18.07		
BrC_5MnO_5	$Mn(CO)_5Br$	7e		8.76 (25)		20
		6e		10.04 (25)		
		$2b_2$		10.80 (25)		
		5σ		14.3		
		1π		15.4		
		4σ		18.6		
BrF	BrF	${}^2\Pi_{3/2}$	11.78 (1)	11.87 (1)	ν' 750 (40)	220
		${}^2\Pi_{1/2}$	12.09 (1)	12.19 (1)	ν' 750 (40)	
BrF_2P	PF_2Br	$P3p_z$		11.8 (1)		21
		$Br3p_\pi$		{10.86 (2), 11.51 (2)}		
		PBr		14.85 (2)		
		$F2p_\pi$		15.9 (1)		
		PF		{17.6 (1), 18.2 (1)}		
BrF_3	BrF_3	${}^2B_2, {}^2A_1$	12.15 (4)	12.38 (5)		220
		${}^2A_1$	13.58 (1)	13.94 (2)		
		${}^2B_1$		14.60 (4)		
		${}^2A_2$		15.05 (3)		
		${}^2B_2$		15.61 (3)		
		${}^2B_1$	16.26 (3)	16.67 (3)		
		${}^2A_1, {}^2B_2$		17.59 (2)		
		${}^2B_1$		18.76 (4)		

TABLE 1 (continued)

Compound		Orbital	Ionization Energy: Adiabatic	Ionization Energy: Vertical	Vibrational Bands	Reference
$BrGeH_3$	GeH_3Br			10.72 (5)	sos 0.22	22
$BrGeH_3$	GeH_3Br	2_e		10.61		23
				10.83		
		$3a_1$		12.51		
		1e		12.9		
BrH	HBr	$^2\Pi_{3/2}$	11.71 (1)			24
		$^2\Pi_{1/2}$	12.03 (1)			
		$^2\Sigma^+$	15.31 (1)			
BrH	HBr	$^2\Pi_{3/2,1/2}$	11.67 (1)			25
			12.00 (1)			
		$^2\Sigma^+$	15.29 (1)	15.6		
BrH	HBr	$^2\Pi_{1/2}$			2,420	7
		$^2\Sigma^+$	15.28 (9)		1,290	
BrH_3Si	SiH_3Br	2_e		10.96		23
				11.10		
		$3a_1$		12.85		
		1e		13.3		
		$2a_1$		18.1		
		$1a_1$		19.5		
BrH_3Si	SiH_3Br			11.03 (5)	sos 0.14	22
BrH_3Si	SiH_3Br	e(Br)		11.00		26
		a_1 (SiH_3Br)		12.96	ν(SiBr) 400	
		e(SiH_3)		13.63		
		a_1 (SiH_3Br)		18.04		
BrI	IBr	$(2\pi)^{-1}$		9.85 (2)		27
		$(1\pi)^{-1}$		11.99 (2)		
		$(3\sigma)^{-1}$		13.70 (2)		

TABLE 1 (continued)

Compound		Orbital	Ionization Energy: Adiabatic	Ionization Energy: Vertical	Vibrational Bands	Reference
BrTl	TlBr	$^2\Pi$		9.83		28
		$^2\Sigma$	13.57	13.66		
Br_2	Br_2	$^2\Pi_g$	10.51		sos 2,820 (40)	29
					ω_e 360 (40)	
		$^2\Pi_u$	12.5	13.08	sos ~2,000–2,200	
		$^2\Sigma_g^+$	14.3	14.60		
Br_2	Br_2	$(1\pi_g)^{-1}$	10.51 (1)	10.56 (1)	355 (20)	27
		$(1\pi_u)^{-1}$	12.41 (2)	12.77 (2)	187	
		$(2\sigma_g)^{-1}$	14.28 (2)	14.56 (3)		
Br_2	Br_2	$^2\Pi_{3/2g}$	10.51 (1)			24
		$^2\Pi_{1/2g}$	10.90 (1)			
		$^2\Pi_u$	12.52 (1)			
		$^2\Sigma_g^+$	14.44 (1)			
Br_2CO	Br_2CO			11.0		30
				11.5		
		n(O)		11.6		
				12.0		
				12.4		
		π(C=O)	14.8	15.5	~1,690	
		σ		16.2		
Br_2GeH_2	GeH_2Br_2			10.69		23
				10.85		
				11.28		
				12.93		
				13.17		
				13.71		
Br_2H_2Si	SiH_2Br_2			10.92		23
				11.12		
				11.61		
				13.35		
				13.7		

TABLE 1 (continued)

Compound		Orbital	Ionization Energy: Adiabatic	Ionization Energy: Vertical	Vibrational Bands	Reference
Br_2Hg	$HgBr_2$	$^2\Pi_{3/2g}$		10.62		31
		$^2\Pi_{1/2g}$		10.96		
		$^2\Pi_{3/2u}$		11.20		
		$^2\Pi_{1/2u}$		11.54		
		$^2\Sigma_u$		12.09		
		$^2\Sigma_g$		13.39		
		$^2D_{5/2}(\pm5/2)$		16.40		
		$(\pm3/2)$		16.69		
		$(\pm1/2)$		16.83		
		$^2D_{3/2}(\pm3/2,\pm1/2)$		18.34		
Br_2OS	$SOBr_2$	n(Br)	10.63			32
		n(Br)	10.92			
		n(Br)	11.24			
		n(Br)	11.68			
		n(S)	12.13			
		n(O)	12.37			
		S-Oπ	14.70			
		S-Brσ	15.81			
Br_4C	CBr_4			{10.40		33
		t_1		{10.49		
				{10.75		
				{11.05		
		$3t_2$		{11.23		
				{11.69		
		e		12.06		
		$2t_2$		15.04		
		$2a_1$		19.48		
Br_4C	CBr_4	t_1		10.39		1
				10.48		
				10.76		
		t_2		11.07		
				11.28		
				11.73		
		e		12.11		
				12.24		
		t_2		15.15		
		a_1		19.7		

TABLE 1 (continued)

	Compound	Orbital	Ionization Energy: Adiabatic	Ionization Energy: Vertical	Vibrational Bands	Reference
Br_4C	CBr_4		10.36			7
			10.72			
			11.02			
			11.65			
Br_4Ge	$GeBr_4$	t_1		10.75 (sh)		33
				10.85		
		$t_1,3t_2$		11.11		
				11.23		
		$3t_2,e$		11.89		
		$2t_2$		13.63		
				13.70		
				13.9 (sh)		
				14.0 (sh)		
		$2a_1$		17.6		
Br_4Si	$SiBr_4$	t_1		10.8 (sh)		33
				10.9		
				{ 11.17		
		$t_1,3t_2$		{ 11.52		
				{ 11.63 (sh)		
				{ 12.05		
		$3t_2,e$		{ 12.14 (sh)		
				{ 12.33 (sh)		
		$2t_2$		13.92		
				14.06 (sh)		
				14.19		
				14.23 (sh)		
		$2a_1$		17.31		
		$1t_2$?		~20		
Br_4Sn	$SnBr_4$	t_1		11.0		33
		$t_1,3t_2$		11.25		
		$3t_2,e$		11.75		
		$2t_2$		13.2		
		$2a_1$		16.7		
		$1t_2$?		18.2–19.7?		

TABLE 1 (continued)

Compound		Orbital	Ionization Energy: Adiabatic	Ionization Energy: Vertical	Vibrational Bands	Reference
Br_4Ti	$TiBr_4$	t_1		10.56		33
				10.80		
		$3t_2,1e,2t_2$		11.7		
				11.8 (sh)		
				12.0		
				12.25 (sh)		
				12.4		
		$2a_1$		13.08		
		$1t_2,1a_1$?		18.9–19.7		
CClN	ClCN	$(\pi_2)^{-1}\,{}^2\Pi_{3/2}$	12.34	12.34	1,890, 770	19
		$(\pi_2)^{-1}\,{}^2\Pi_{1/2}$	12.37	12.37	1,890, 770	
		$(\sigma_N)^{-1}$	13.80	13.80	~750	
		$(\pi_1)^{-1}$	15.13	15.38	508	
		$(\sigma_{C\text{-}Cl})^{-1}$		19.03		
CClN	ClCN	${}^2\Pi_{3/2}$ (1)	12.37 (2)		1,800	34
		${}^2\Sigma^+$ (2)	13.80 (2)			
		${}^2\Pi_{3/2}$ (3)		15.37 (2)	500	
		${}^2\Sigma^+$ (4)		19.0 (1)		
CCl_2O	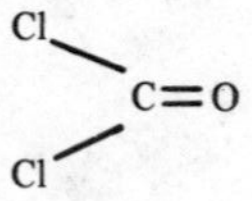	n(Cl)	~11.2	11.84	ν_3 280 (20)	30
				~12.3		
		n(O)		12.6		
				~13.0		
		n(Cl)	13.31	13.5	ν_3 275 (20)	
		π(C=O)	16.75	15.9	1,460 (20)	
					605 (20)	
					290 (20)	
		σ	16.63	16.7	ν_3 275 (20)	
		σ		17.0		
				19.5		

TABLE 1 (continued)

Compound		Orbital	Ionization Energy: Adiabatic	Ionization Energy: Vertical	Vibrational Bands	Reference
CCl_2O	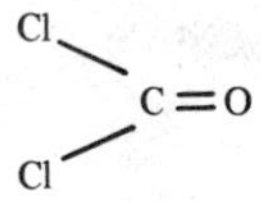	$8b_2$	11.55 (2)	11.83 (2)	ν_3 285 (40)	35
		$3b_1, 7b_2$		12.6 (1)		
		$11a_1$		13.05 (5)		
		$2a_2$	13.39 (2)	13.50 (2)	ν_3 290 (40)	
		$10a_1$	15.80 (2)	16.15 (10)	ν_2 540 (40)	
					ν_3 260 (40)	
		$2b_1$	16.66 (2)	16.73 (2)	ν_3 280 (40)	
		$6b_2$		17.11 (2)	ν_1 ~1,000	
		$9a_1$	19.29 (2)	19.48 (2)		
CCl_2S	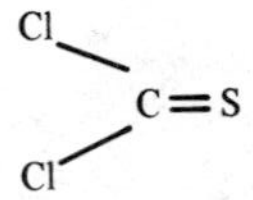	$9b_2$	9.61 (2)	9.84 (2)	ν_1 1,060 (40)	35
					ν_3 265 (40)	
		$4b_1$	10.65 (2)	10.88 (2)	ν_1 905 (40)	
		$8b_2$	11.67 (2)	11.96 (2)		
		$13a_1$		12.38 (2)		
		$2a_2$		12.69 (2)	ν_3 260 (40)	
		$12a_1$	14.23 (2)	14.47 (2)	ν_2 380 (40)	
		$3b_1$	14.99 (2)	15.11 (2)		
		$7b_2$	15.99 (2)	16.19 (2)		
		$11a_1$	18.09 (2)	18.25 (2)		
CCl_4	CCl_4	t_1		11.69		1
		t_2		12.44		
				12.65		
				12.78		
		e		13.37		
				13.50		
		t_2		16.58		
		a_1		20.0		
CCl_4	CCl_4		12.06			7
		^2E	13.5			
CCl_4	CCl_4	$1t_1$	11.47 (8)	11.64 (1)		36
		$3t_2$	12.27 (3)	12.51 (2)		
		1e		13.37 (2)		
		$2t_2$	16.34 (10)	16.68 (4)		

TABLE 1 (continued)

Compound		Orbital	Ionization Energy: Adiabatic	Ionization Energy: Vertical	Vibrational Bands	Reference
CCl_4	CCl_4		11.47 (1)			37
			12.24			
			13.29			
			16.47			
			(17.47)			
			(18.66)			
CCl_4	CCl_4	t_1		11.60		33
		$3t_2$		{12.40, 12.60, 12.75}		
		e		13.40		
		$2t_2$		16.60		
CDF_3	CDF_3	4e	17.11	17.24	ν_2 1,050	38
					ν_3 500	
CDHO	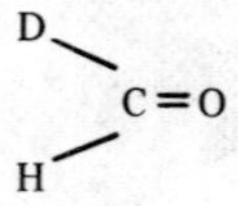	$^2B_2$	10.89 (5)		ν_1 1,940	7
					ν_2 1,610	
					ν_3 1,120	
		$^2B_1$	14.09 (2)		ν_2 1,210	
		$^2B_2$	15.83 (6)		ν_2 1,270	
					ν_3 940?	
		$^2A_1$			ν_1 1,060	
CDN	CDN	C≡Nπ		13.60 (1)	ν_3 1,760 (40)	39
				19.10 (1)	ν_1 1,450 (40)	
CD_2F_2	CD_2F_2	$2b_2$	12.79	13.36		38
		$4b_1$	≥14.5	15.4		
		$1a_2$		15.68	ν_3 970	
					ν_4 500	
		$5a_1$	≥18.20	18.9		

TABLE 1 (continued)

	Compound	Orbital	Ionization Energy: Adiabatic	Ionization Energy: Vertical	Vibrational Bands	Reference
CD_2O	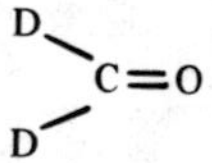	$^2B_2$	10.90 (4)		ν_1 1,910	7
					ν_2 1,560	
					ν_3 870	
		$^2B_1$	14.09 (5)		ν_2 1,210	
		$^2B_2$	15.84 (6)		ν_2 1,270	
					ν_3 940?	
CD_3Br	CD_3Br	$^2E_{3/2}$; $^2E_{1/2}$			sos 2,646 (30)	40
					ν_2 947	
					ν_4 2,165	
					ν_5 947	
CD_3F	CD_3F	2e	12.67	13.16	ν_6 800	38
CD_3NO_2	CD_3NO_2	$^2A_1\,(5a_1^{-1})$	11.08		558	41
		$^2A_2\,(1a_2^{-1})\,(\pi)$	11.73		560	
CD_4	CD_4	$1t_2$	12.83	14.0		38
		$2a_1$	22.48	22.8	ν_1 1,460	
CD_4	CD_4	a_1	22.50	22.95	1,460	42
CF_2NOP	F_2PNCO	$P3p_z$		12.2 (1)		21
		2π(NCO)		11.05 (2)		
		1π(NCO)		13.2 (1)		
		PN		15.8 (1)		
		$F2p_\pi$		16.6 (1)		
		PF		{ 17.7 (1), 19.4 (1) }		

TABLE 1 (continued)

Compound		Orbital	Ionization Energy: Adiabatic	Ionization Energy: Vertical	Vibrational Bands	Reference
CF_2NP	F_2PCN	$P3p_z$		11.9 (1)		21
		π(CN)		13.5 (1) 14.0 (1)		
		$F2p_\pi$		16.6 (1)		
		PF		18.2 (1) 19.2 (1)		
CF_2NPS	F_2PNCS	$P3p_z$		11.9 (1)		21
		2π(NCS)		10.2 (1)		
		1π(NCS)		13.9 (1)		
		PN		15.5 (1)		
		$F2p_\pi$		16.4 (1)		
		PF		18.0 (1)		
CF_2N_2	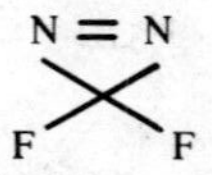	$4b_1$	11.2	11.78		50
		$5b_2,9a_1$	15.00	15.16	ν_1' 1,330	
		$4b_2,8a_1$		16.75		
		$1a_2$		17.8		
		$3b_1$	19.0	19.8		
		$7a_1,3b_2$		20.9		
		$6a_1,2b_1$		23.4		
CF_2O	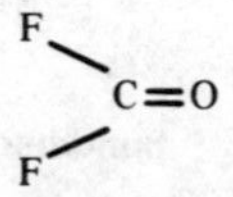	n(o)	13.04	13.62	ν_1 1,580 (20) ν_3 540 (20)	30
			14.26	14.62	1,430 (20) 505 (20)	
				16.6		
		$b_1\ \pi$(F)	16.90	17.0	ν_1 1,500 (20) ν_3 555 (20)	
			19.06	19.06	ν_3 490 (20)	
			19.46	19.66	ν_2 760 (20)	

TABLE 1 (continued)

Compound		Orbital	Ionization Energy: Adiabatic	Ionization Energy: Vertical	Vibrational Bands	Reference
CF_2O		$5b_1$	13.02	13.6	ν_1' 1,550	137
					ν_3' 530	
	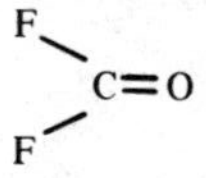	$2b_2$	14.09	14.6	ν_1' 1,450	
		$1a_2 4b_1, 8a_1$	1.61	16.6		
			16.91	17.2		
		$7a_1$	19.15	19.15		
		$1b_2$		19.8		
		$3b_1$		21.1		
		$6a_1$	~22.7	23.4	ν_2' 730	
CF_2S		S $3p(b_2)$	10.45 (1)		ν_1 1,380	228
	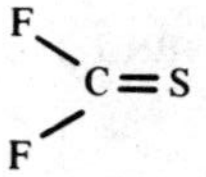				ν_3 450	
		C=S$\pi(b_1)$	11.34 (1)		ν_1 1,320–1,430	
					ν_2 710	
		C=S$\sigma(a_1)$	14.87		ν_1 1,160–1,280	
					ν_3 530	
		C-F bonding	17.65		734–661	
CF_4	CF_4	$1t_1$		16.25 (4)		43
		$3t_2$		17.46 (4)		
		1e		18.58 (4)		
CF_4	CF_4	t_2	15.9			44
		t_1	17.2			
		e	18.5			
CF_4	CF_4	$1t_1$		16.30 (4)		45, 46
		$3t_2$		17.49 (4)		
		1e		18.57 (4)		
CF_4	CF_4	t_1		16.20		33
				{17.36		
		$3t_2$		17.56		
				17.69}		
		e		18.46		

TABLE 1 (continued)

Compound		Orbital	Ionization Energy: Adiabatic	Ionization Energy: Vertical	Vibrational Bands	Reference
CF_4	CF_4	$1t_1$	⩾15.35	16.20		38
		$4t_2$	17.1	17.40		
		1e	18.3	18.50	ν_1 810	
					ν_2 400	
		$3t_2$	21.70	22.12	ν_1 645	
		$4a_1$	25.12	25.12	ν_1 730	
CF_4	CF_4	$1t_1$	15.84 (2)	16.30 (4)		36
		$3t_2$	17.17 (2)	17.49 (2)		
		1e		18.57 (2)		
CF_4	CF_4	t_1		16.23		1
		t_2		17.47		
		e		18.50		
		t_2		21.95	ν_1 640	
		a_1		25.1		
$CHBr_3$	$CHBr_3$	a_2		10.47		1
		e′		10.81		
				10.95		
		a_1		11.28		
		e″		11.72		
				11.88		
		e′		14.71		
		a_1		15.81		
		a_1		19.8		
$CHBr_3$	$CHBr_3$		10.44			7
			10.79			
			11.25			
			11.66			
$CHCl_3$	$CHCl_3$	a_2		11.48		1
		a_1		11.91		
		e′		12.01		
		e″		12.85		
		e′		15.99		
		a_1		16.96		
		a_1		19.8		

TABLE 1 (continued)

Compound		Orbital	Ionization Energy: Adiabatic	Ionization Energy: Vertical	Vibrational Bands	Reference
$CHCl_3$	$CHCl_3$		11.40 (1)			37
			12.73			
			15.86			
			(18.63)			
CHF_3	CHF_3		17.08		ν_2 1,030	7
					ν_3 570	
		$\tilde{D}$	20.00		ν_3 480	
CHF_3	CHF_3	$6a_1$	⩾13.8	14.80		38
		$1a_2$		15.5		
		5e		16.2		
		4e	17.11	17.24	ν_2 1,050	
					ν_3 550	
		$3e,5a_1$	20.6	19.84		
		$4a_1$	⩾24.34	24.44		
CHF_3	CHF_3	$\sigma\ a_1$	(13.86)	14.77		47
		π e		15.46		
		a_2 (1p)		16.16		
		e(1p)	17.13	17.26	0.13–.14	
		e	(20.05)	~21		
CHF_3	CHF_3	a_1		14.80		1
		a_2		15.50		
		e′		16.16		
		e″		17.25	ν_2 1,040	
					ν_3 560	
		a_1 + e		20.50	ν_6 480	
		a_1		24.4		
CHI_3	CHI_3		10.29			7

TABLE 1 (continued)

Compound		Orbital	Ionization Energy: Adiabatic	Ionization Energy: Vertical	Vibrational Bands	Reference
CHN	HCN	C≡Nπ	13.60 (1)		ν_3 1,800 (40)	39
		4σ	19.06 (1)		ν_1 1,690 (40)	
CHNO	HNCO	2π(a″)	11.62 (2)		ν_s 1,080 (50)	48
					ν_{as} 1,980 (50)	
					$\nu_s+\nu_{as}$ 3,200 (50)	
		2π(a′)		12.30 (2)	610 (50)	
		1π		15.8 (1)	1,120 (50)	
		4σ		17.50 (2)	460 (50)	
		3σ		19.24 (2)	1,020 (50)	
CHNO	HNCO	a″(πnb)	11.60 (1)		ν_3 1,050	49
					ν_2 2,020	
					ν_1 3,222	
		a′(πnb)		12.39 (1)	ν_4 565	
		a″(πb)	15.54 (5)		ν_3 1,113	
		pσ		12.39 (10)	ν_4 450	
CHNS	HNCS	2π(a″)		9.94 (2)		48
		2π(a′)		10.3 (1)	600 (50)	
		1π		13.31 (2)	850 (50)	
		4σ		15.12 (2)		
CHNS	HNCS	a″(πnb)	10.05 (10)			49
		a′(πnb)		10.35 (10)	ν_4 655	
		a″ (πb)	13.33 (3)		ν_3 856	
		pσ		10.35 (10)		
CH_2Br_2	CH_2Br_2		10.63			7
			10.83			
		a_2	11.25			

TABLE 1 (continued)

	Compound	Orbital	Ionization Energy: Adiabatic	Ionization Energy: Vertical	Vibrational Bands	Reference
CH_2Br_2	CH_2Br_2	b_2		10.61		1
		a_2		10.82		
		b_1,a_1		11.28		
		b_2		14.12		
		a_1		14.75		
		b_1		16.25		
		a_1		19.7		
CH_2Cl_2	CH_2Cl_2	b_2,a_2		11.40	ν_1 640	1
		a_1,b_1		12.22		
		b_2		15.30		
		a_1		15.94		
		b_1		16.77		
		a_1		20.3		
CH_2Cl_2	CH_2Cl_2		11.31		ν'_3 650	7
		a_2	12.18			
CH_2Cl_2	CH_2Cl_2		11.33 (1)			37
			12.12			
			15.07			
			(18.23)			
CH_2F_2	CH_2F_2	$2b_2$	12.72	13.27	ν_2? 1,010	38
		$4b_1$	$\geqslant$14.5	15.3		
		$1a_2$		15.71	ν_3 970	
		$3b_1$			ν_3 645	
		$5a_1$	18.20	18.9		
		$4a_1$	23.1	23.9		
CH_2F_2	CH_2F_2	πb_1	12.70	13.29	0.15–.13	47
		σb_2	(14.53)	15.2		
		a_2(1p)		15.71	0.13–.12	
		σb_2	18.17	19.13	0.10–.07	
CH_2F_2	CH_2F_2	$\tilde{X}$	12.74		ν_2 1,120	7
		$\tilde{B}$	15.58		ν_3 980	
					ν_4 480	
		$\tilde{C}$	18.31		ν_3 680	

TABLE 1 (continued)

	Compound	Orbital	Ionization Energy: Adiabatic	Ionization Energy: Vertical	Vibrational Bands	Reference
CH_2F_2	CH_2F_2	b_1		13.29	1,120	1
		a_1		15.25		
		b_2		15.40		
		a_2		15.58	980	
					500	
		b_2, a_1, b_1		18.97	ν_1 670	
		a_1		23.9		
CH_2I_2	CH_2I_2		9.52			7
			9.83			
			10.29			
			10.63			
CH_2I_2	CH_2I_2	b_2		9.46		1
		a_2		9.76		
		b_1		10.21		
		a_1		10.56		
		b_2		12.75	160	
		a_1		13.67	160	
		b_1		15.46	160	
		a_1		19.5	160	
CH_2N_2	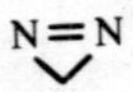	$3b_1$	10.3	10.75		50
		$2b_2$	12.8	13.25	ν'_2 1,300	
					ν'_4 890	
		$6a_1$	14.15	14.15	ν'_3 1,300	
		$5a_1$	16	16.5		
		$1b_2$		17.5		
		$2b_1$	21	21.5		
		$4a_1$		22.5		
CH_2O	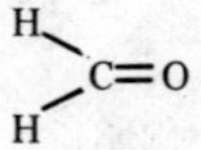			10.89	ν_2 0.216	51
					ν_3 0.186	
				14.4	~0.15	
				16.0	~0.15	
				16.9		
				~21		

TABLE 1 (continued)

Compound		Orbital	Ionization Energy: Adiabatic	Ionization Energy: Vertical	Vibrational Bands	Reference
CH_2O	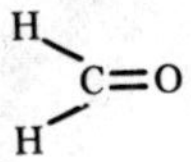	$^2B_2$	10.88 (4)	14.38 (7)	ν_1 2,560	7
					ν_2 1,590	
					ν_3 1,210	
		$^2B_1$	14.09 (5)	14.38 (8)	ν_2 1,210	
		$^2B_2$	15.85 (4)		ν_2 1,270	
					ν_3 1,270?	
		$^2A_1$	16.25 (4)		ν_1 1,400?	
CH_2O_2	HCOOH	10a′	11.33	11.51	1,460 (30)	52
		2a″	12.37	12.51	1,120 (30)	
		9a′	14.2	14.74	940 (30)	
		1a″	15.4	15.72	940 (30)	
		8a′	16.97	17.13	1,290 (30)	
		7a′		17.7?		
CH_2S	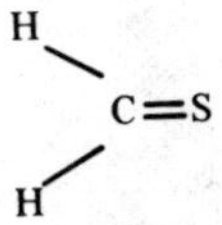			9.338 (10)	ν_2 1,000	53
			11.78 (1)	11.90 (1)	880 (50)	
CH_3BO	BH_3CO	e(BH_3)	11.14 (2)	11.92 (2)		9
				12.51 (2)		
		$6a_1$	13.73 (1)	14.13 (2)		
		1e	16.09 (2)	16.98 (3)		
		$5a_1$	18.48 (2)		1,660 (30)	
CH_3BO	BH_3CO	e		11.92 (2)		11
				12.51 (2) (sh)		
				14.13 (2)		
		π		16.98 (3)		
		σ		18.68 (2)	1,660 (30)	
CH_3Br	CH_3Br	$^2E_{3/2}$	10.54		ν_2 1,210	7
					810	
		$^2E_{1/2}$	10.85		ν_2 1,290	
					ν_3 560	

TABLE 1 (continued)

	Compound	Orbital	Ionization Energy		Vibrational Bands	Reference
			Adiabatic	Vertical		
CH_3Br	CH_3Br	n	10.53 (1)			54
		n	10.85 (1)			
CH_3Br	CH_3Br	$^2E_{3/2}$, $^2E_{1/2}$	10.53 (3)		sos 2,560 (30)	40
					ν_6 871	
					ν_5 1,287	
					ν_4 3,112	
					ν_2 3,832	
				13.52 (3)		
				15.14 (3)		
				15.85 (3)		
CH_3Br	CH_3Br	e($^2E_{3/2}$)		10.54	ν_2 1,240	1
					ν_6 800	
		($^2E_{1/2}$)		10.86	ν_3 560	
					ν_2 1,240	
		a_1		13.49		
		e		15.08		
		a_1		19.9		
CH_3BrHg	H_3CHgBr	$^2E_{3/2}$		10.16		31
		$^2E_{1/2}$		10.43		
		$^2A_1$		10.66		
		$^2A_1$		12.52		
		^2E		13.9		
		$^2D_{5/2}$(±5/2)		15.68		
		(±3/2,±1/2)		16.11		
		$^2D_{3/2}$(±3/2,±1/2)		17.64		
CH_3Cl	CH_3Cl	$^2E_{3/2}$	11.28			7
CH_3Cl	CH_3Cl		11.26 (1)			37
			14.08			
			(18.88)			

TABLE 1 (continued)

Compound		Orbital	Ionization Energy: Adiabatic	Ionization Energy: Vertical	Vibrational Bands	Reference
CH_3Cl	CH_3Cl	$^2E_{3/2}, ^2E_{1/2}$	11.29 (3)		sos 630 (40)	40
					ν_3 871	
					ν_5 1,550	
				14.45 (3)		
				15.47 (3)		
				16.25 (3)		
CH_3Cl	CH_3Cl	$e(^2E_{3/2})$		11.30		1
		$(^2E_{1/2})$		11.32	ν_2 1,000	
					ν_3 500	
		a_1		14.42		
		e		15.40		
		a_1		21.5		
CH_3ClHg	H_3CHgCl	$^2E_{1/2}$		10.88		31
		$^2A_1$		12.70		
		^2E		14.1		
		$^2D_{5/2}(\pm 5/2)$		15.79		
		$(\pm 3/2, \pm 1/2)$		16.24		
		$^2D_{3/2}(\pm 3/2, \pm 1/2)$		17.71		
CH_3ClO_2S	$SO_2Cl(CH_3)$			11.74		32
				12.02		
				12.51		
				13.46		
				15.62		
				16.84		
CH_3ClO_2S	$(CH_3)ClSO_2$			11.6		218
				11.94		
				12.36		
				12.6		
				13.32		
CH_3F	CH_3F	$\tilde{X}$	12.74		ν_2 1,468	7

TABLE 1 (continued)

	Compound	Orbital	Ionization Energy Adiabatic	Ionization Energy Vertical	Vibrational Bands	Reference
CH_3F	CH_3F	2e	12.54	13.05	ν_6 1,050, 950	38
		$5a_1$,1e	>15.8	~17.0		
		$4a_1$	22.7	23.4		
CH_3F	CH_3F	π e	12.54	13.07	0.13–0.14	47
		π e	(16.03)	17.14		
CH_3F	CH_3F	e		13.04	ν_2 1,120	1
					1,600	
		a_1,e		17.06		
		a_1		23.4		
CH_3FO_2S	$SO_2F(CH_3)$			12.61		32
				14.02		
				15.18		
				15.66		
				16.25		
				17.95		
CH_3FO_2S	$(CH_3)FSO_2$	$4b_1$,$4b_2$,$2a_2$		12.53		218
		$6a_1$		13.91		
				15.57		
CH_3GeNO	GeH_3NCO	$2\pi(a')$		10.76 (2)		48
		Ge p		12.8 (1)		
		1π		15.3 (1)		
		4σ		16.9 (1)		
CH_3GeNS	GeH_3NCS	$2\pi(a'')$		9.14 (2)		48
		Ge p		12.3 (1)		
		1π		13.4 (1)		
		4σ		14.1 (1)		
		3σ		15.5 (1)		

TABLE 1 (continued)

Compound		Orbital	Ionization Energy: Adiabatic	Ionization Energy: Vertical	Vibrational Bands	Reference
CH_3HgI	H_3CHgI	$^2E_{3/2}$		9.25		31
		$^2E_{1/2}$		9.68		
		$^2A_1$		10.29		
		$^2A_1$		12.21		
		^2E		13.6		
		$^2D_{5/2}(\pm5/2)$		15.48		
		$(\pm3/2,\pm1/2)$		15.83		
		$^2D_{3/2}(\pm3/2,\pm1/2)$		17.41		
CH_3I	CH_3I	e		9.54		1
				10.16		
		a_1		12.50	ν_3 480	
		e		14.80	ν_6 750	
		a_1		19.6	ν_2 1,260	
CH_3I	CH_3I	$^2E_{3/2}$, $^2E_{1/2}$	9.50 (3)		ν_2 1,225 (30)	40
					ν_1 3,030 (30)	
					sos 5,050 (40)	
				12.50 (3)		
				14.79 (3)		
				15.44 (3)		
CH_3I	CH_3I	$^2E_{3/2}$	9.55		ν_2 1,290	7
		$^2E_{1/2}$	10.16		ν_2 1,290	
CH_3NO	$HCONH_2$	10a′	10.13	10.32	1,600 (30)	52
		2a″	⩽10.52	10.52	640 (30)	
		9a′	13.76	14.18	1,090 (30)	
		1a″	14.62	14.75	1,050 (30)	
		8a′	16.16	16.30	1,100 (30)	
		7a′		19		
CH_3NOSi	SiH_3NCO	2π(a″)		11.10 (2)		48
		Si p		13.1 (1)		
		1π		15.7	790 (50)	
		4σ		17.1 (1)		

TABLE 1 (continued)

	Compound	Orbital	Ionization Energy Adiabatic	Ionization Energy Vertical	Vibrational Bands	Reference
CH_3NO_2	CH_3NO_2	$^2A_1(5a_1^{-1})$	11.07 (1)	11.32 (1)	565	41
		$^2A_2(1a_2^{-1})(\pi)$	11.73 (1)	11.73 (1)	565	
		$^2B_2(4b_2^{-1})$	13.85 (1)	14.73 (1)		
		$^2B_1(2b_1^{-1})(\pi)$		15.75 (1)		
		$^2B_2(3b_2^{-1})$	~16.7	17.45 (1)		
		$^2A_1(4a_1^{-1})$		19.1 (1)		
CH_3NO_2	CH_3NO_2		11.23 (1)			55
			(11.80)			
			14.22			
			(14.67)			
			15.42			
			17.23			
			(17.49)			
			(19.55)			
CH_3NO_2	CH_3ONO		10.53 (1)			55
			12.52			
			(12.83)			
			(14.43)			
			(15.61)			
			(16.78)			
			(19.26)			
CH_3NO_3	CH_3ONO_2		11.53 (1)			55
			(11.79)			
			(12.44)			
			14.20			
			15.58			
			(15.94)			
			18.08			

TABLE 1 (continued)

			Ionization Energy			
Compound		Orbital	Adiabatic	Vertical	Vibrational Bands	Reference
CH_3NSSi	SiH_3NCS	$2\pi(a'')$		9.54 (2)		48
		Si p		12.5 (1)		
		1π		13.9 (1)	490 (50)	
		4σ		14.7 (1)		
		3σ		15.9 (1)	740 (50)	
CH_3N_3	CH_3N_3	$2\pi(a'')$	9.81 (2)		ν_s 910 (50)	48
					ν_{as} 1,820 (50)	
		$2\pi(a')$		11.32 (2)		
		C p		14.4 (1)		
		4σ		15.2 (1)		
		1π		16.6 (1)		
		3σ		17.9 (1)		
CH_4	CH_4		12.99			56
CH_4	CH_4	σ	12.98 (1)			37
CH_4	CH_4		12.99			57
CH_4	CH_4	It_2	12.75	14.0	ν_4? 1,200	38
		$2a_1$	22.39	23.0	ν_1 2,020	
CH_4	CH_4	t_2	12.51		ν_2 0.152	58
					ν_3 0.22	
					ν_1 0.21	
					0.14	
CH_4	CH_4	$t_2\,{}^2B_2$	12.64	13.6	900 (20)	42
				14.4	2,500 (30)	
				15.0		
		a_1	22.39	22.91	ν_1 2,190 (80)	
CH_4	CH_4		12.78	13.62	ν_4 0.15–0.09	47
				14.32		

TABLE 1 (continued)

Compound		Orbital	Ionization Energy Adiabatic	Ionization Energy Vertical	Vibrational Bands	Reference
CH_4O	CH_3OH		10.83 (1)			37
			12.37			
			14.70			
			17.23			
			(19.27)			
CH_4O	CH_3OH		10.83			57
			12.33			
			14.64			
			17.23			
CH_4O	CH_3OH	O	10.83			56
		CH_3	12.33			
		CH_3,OH	14.64			
		CO	17.23			
		CH_3,O	21			
CH_4O	CH_3OH		10.85 (2)			59
CH_4O	CH_3OH		10.85	10.96		60
				12.72		
				15.15		
				15.55		
				17.50		
CH_4S	CH_3SH			9.44		61
CH_4S	CH_3SH	$S3p_x$		9.44		62
		CH		15.1		
		CS		12.0		
		SH		13.7		
CH_4S	CH_3SH			9.41	650	53
				11.90		
				13.50		
				14.90		
				15.5		

TABLE 1 (continued)

Compound		Orbital	Ionization Energy: Adiabatic	Ionization Energy: Vertical	Vibrational Bands	Reference
CH_5N	CH_3NH_2		9.18			57
			12.16			
			13.94			
			15.07			
			16.57			
			19.89			
CH_5N	CH_3NH_2		9.18			63
CH_5P	CH_3PH_2	$P3p_z$		9.6 (1)		4
		CP		12.4 (1)		
		CH		13.7–16.0		
		PH		13?		
CH_6N_2	$CH_3N(H)NH_2$		8.67			64
			(9.04)			
			9.88			
			12.81			
			(13.16)			
			15.50			
			(19.61)			
CH_8BN	$CH_3NH_2BH_3$	$e(BH_3)$	9.66 (1)	10.29 (3)	1,070 (60)	9
		7a′+3a″		10.82 (2) (sh)		
		6a′	11.76 (2)	12.47 (2)		
			13.47 (2)	14.39 (6)		
		2a″+5a′		14.90 (9) (sh)		
		4a′	16.02 (3)	16.54 (3)		
			17.39 (1)	17.83 (2)		
		1a″+3a′		18.40 (5) (sh)		
CH_9NSi_2	$(SiH_3)_2NCH_3$	$N2p_z$		9.2 (1)		4
		NC		14.4 (1)		
		SiH,CH,SiN		11.0–13.5		
		Si3s		17.0 (1)		

TABLE 1 (continued)

Compound		Orbital	Ionization Energy: Adiabatic	Ionization Energy: Vertical	Vibrational Bands˙	Reference
CIN	ICN	$^2\Pi_{3/2}$ (1)	10.91 (2)			34
					2,000	
		$^2\Pi_{1/2}$ (1)	11.14 (2)			
		$^2\Sigma^+$ (2)	13.15 (2)			
		$^2\Pi_{3/2}$ (3)		13.41 (2)		
					500	
		$^2\Pi_{1/2}$ (3)		13.56 (2)		
		$^2\Sigma^+$ (4)		16.69 (2)		
CIN	ICN	$(\pi_2)^{-1}\ ^2\Pi_{3/2}$	10.91	10.91	1,940, 420	19
		$(\pi_2)^{-1}\ ^2\Pi_{1/2}$	11.45	11.45	1,940, 420	
		$(\sigma_N)^{-1}$	13.17	13.17		
		$(\pi_1)^{-1}\ ^2\Pi_{3/2}$	13.35		~440	
		$(\sigma_{C\text{-}I})^{-1}$		16.71		
CO	CO		13.98			65
		$A^2\Pi$	16.58		0.17	
		$B^2\Sigma^+$	19.67		0.23	
CO	CO	$X^2\Sigma^+$	14.00	14.00		66
		$A^2\Pi$	16.54	16.91	~.18	
		$B^2\Sigma^+$	19.65	19.65	~.2	
CO	CO	nb	14.01			57
			16.51			
			19.72			
CO	CO	$\tilde{X}\ ^2\Sigma_g^+$	14.01 (8)	14.01	2,160	7
		$\tilde{A}\ ^2\Pi_u$	16.53 (6)	16.91	1,610	
		$\tilde{B}\ ^2\Sigma_u$	19.68 (8)	19.72	1,690	
COS	COS	$\tilde{X}^2\Pi$	11.18 (9)		ν_1 650 (50)	7
					ν_2 2,000 (50)	
		$\tilde{A}^2\Pi$	15.08 (0)	15.52 (8)	ν_1 790 (50)	
					ν_3 2,050 (50)	

TABLE 1 (continued)

Compound		Orbital	Ionization Energy: Adiabatic	Ionization Energy: Vertical	Vibrational Bands	Reference
COS (cont.)		$\tilde{B}^2\Sigma^+$	16.04 (2)			
		$\tilde{C}^2\Sigma^+$	17.96 (0)		ν_1 970 (50)	
					ν_3 2,170 (50)	
CO_2	CO_2	$\tilde{X}^2\Pi_g$	13.78 (8)		ν_1 1,210 (50)	7
					ν_3 1,420 (50)	
		$\tilde{A}^2\Pi_\mu$	17.32 (3)	17.59 (5)	ν_1 1,100 (50)	
		$\tilde{B}^2\Sigma_u^+$	18.08 (2)		ν_1 1,270 (50)	
					ν_3 1,400? (50)	
		$\tilde{C}^2\Sigma_g^+$	19.40 (0)		ν_1 1,390 (50)	
					ν_3 1,470 (50)	
CO_2	CO_2		13.68			57
			17.23			
			18.08			
		nb	19.29			
CS	CS	$X^2\Sigma$	11.34 (2)	11.34 (2)	1,384	229
		$A^2\Pi$	12.78 (2)	12.90 (2)	972	
		$B^2\Sigma$	15.83 (2)	16.06 (2)	868	
		$C^2\Sigma$	18.03 (2)	18.03 (2)	1,055	
CS	CS	$X^2\Sigma_g^+$	11.33 (2)	11.33 (2)		67
		$A^2\Pi_u$	12.79 (2)	12.92 (2)	ν_1 1,272	
CS	CS		11.33 (2)	11.33 (2)	1,290 (50)	68
			12.56 (2)		980 (50)	
CS_2	CS_2			10.06		53
				12.83	550	
CS_2	CS_2	nb	10.07			57
			12.62			
		nb	14.52			
			16.17			
			16.82			
			18.42			
			19.31			

TABLE 1 (continued)

	Compound	Orbital	Ionization Energy: Adiabatic	Ionization Energy: Vertical	Vibrational Bands	Reference
CS_2	CS_2	$\tilde{X}^2\Pi_g$	10.60 (8)		ν_3 1,170 (50) sos 0.055	7
		$\tilde{A}^2\Pi_g$	12.69 (4)	12.83 (8)	ν_1 560 (50)	
		$\tilde{B}^2\Sigma_u$	14.47 (8)		ν_1 600 (50)	
		$\tilde{C}^2\Sigma_g$	16.19 (6)		ν_1 600 (50)	
		$\tilde{D}^2\Sigma_u$	~16.6		ν_3 800? (50)	
C_2BrCl	Cl-C≡C-Br	$^2\Pi_{3/2}(1)$		9.98		69
		$^2\Pi_{3/2}(2)$		12.54		
		$^2\Pi_{1/2}(2)$		12.73		
		$^2\Pi_{3/2}(3)$		14.08		
		$^2\Sigma^+$		16.07		
		$^2\Sigma^+$		17.47		
C_2BrI	Br-C≡C-I	$^2\Pi_{3/2}(1)$		9.34 }	1,900	69
		$^2\Pi_{1/2}(1)$		9.68 }		
		$^2\Pi_{3/2}(2)$		11.24		
		$^2\Pi_{1/2}(2)$		11.67		
		$^2\Pi_{3/2}(3)$		13.03		
		$^2\Sigma^+$		14.71		
		$^2\Sigma^+$		16.35		
C_2Br_2	Br-C≡C-Br	$^2\Pi_{3/2}(1)$		9.67 }	1,800	69
		$^2\Pi_{1/2}(1)$		9.87 }		
		$^2\Pi_{3/2}(2)$		12.11		
		$^2\Pi_{1/2}(2)$		12.40		
		$^2\Pi_{3/2}(3)$		13.31		
		$^2\Pi_{1/2}(3)$		13.45		
		$^2\Sigma^+(g)$		15.64		
		$^2\Sigma^+(u)$		16.90		

TABLE 1 (continued)

Compound		Orbital	Ionization Energy: Adiabatic	Ionization Energy: Vertical	Vibrational Bands	Reference
C_2ClF_3	CF_2=CFCl	π(CC)	9.84 (1)	10.24 (1)	1,610 (40)	70
					1,090 (40)	
					660 (40)	
				13.01 (1)		
				13.66 (1)		
				15.11 (1)		
				~16.26		
				16.96 (1)		
				17.82 (1)		
C_2ClI	Cl-C≡C-I	$^2\Pi_{3/2}(1)$		9.44 }	2,000	69
		$^2\Pi_{1/2}(1)$		9.75 }		
		$^2\Pi_{3/2}(2)$		11.48		
		$^2\Pi_{1/2}(2)$		11.84		
		$^2\Pi_{3/2}(3)$		13.85		
		$^2\Sigma^+$		14.88		
		$^2\Sigma^+$		17.21		
C_2Cl_2	Cl-C≡C-Cl	$^2\Pi_{3/2}(1)$		10.09	2,000	69
		$^2\Pi_{3/2}(2)$		13.44		
		$^2\Pi_{3/2}(3)$		14.45		
		$^2\Sigma^+(g)$		16.76		
		$^2\Sigma^+(u)$		17.81		
$C_2Cl_2F_2$	CF_2=CCl_2		9.65 (1)	9.84 (1)	1,500 (40)	70
					1,060 (40)	
					440 (40)	
		(C13p)		12.14 (1)		
		(C13p)	12.53 (1)	12.53 (1)	190 (40)	
		(C13p)		12.67 (1)		
		(C13p)	12.83 (1)	12.92 (1)	250 (40)	
				14.43 (1)		
				15.49 (1)		
				16.22 (1)		
				18.15 (1)		

TABLE 1 (continued)

	Compound	Orbital	Ionization Energy: Adiabatic	Ionization Energy: Vertical	Vibrational Bands	Reference
C_2Cl_3N	Cl_3CCN			11.96		19
				12.22		
				12.70		
				13.03		
				13.18		
				13.88		
				~16.9		
				~18.3		
C_2Cl_4	$Cl_2=CCl_2$			9.58		219
				11.59		
				12.37		
				12.85		
				13.62		
				15.14		
C_2Cl_4	$CCl_2=CCl_2$	π(CC)	9.34 (1)	9.51 (1)	1,320 (40)	70
					480–350	
		n(Cl)		11.38 (1)		
		n(Cl)		12.18 (1)		
		n(Cl)		12.44 (1)		
		n(Cl)		12.54 (1)		
		n(Cl)		12.67 (1)		
		n(Cl)		12.77 (1)		
		n(Cl)		12.91 (1)		
				13.48 (1)	460 (40)	
				14.68 (1)		
				15.10 (1)		
				16.73 (1)		
				18.31 (1)		
$C_2Cl_4S_2$	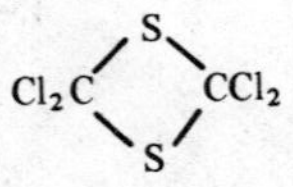			9.69		61
				10.16		

TABLE 1 (continued)

Compound		Orbital	Ionization Energy		Vibrational Bands	Reference
			Adiabatic	Vertical		
C_2D_2	C_2D_2		11.40 (1)		ν_2 1,610 (40)	39
			16.53 (1)		ν_1 2,500 (40)	
					ν_2 1,370 (40)	
			18.44 (1)		ν_2 2,290 (40)	
					ν_1 1,420 (40)	
C_2D_2	C_2D_2		11.40		ν_2 1,614	71
			16.54			
			18.42			
C_2D_3N	CD_3CN	$\tilde{X}$			ν_2 1,990	7
					ν_3 1,070	
					ν_4 810	
		$\tilde{B}$			970	
C_2D_3N	CD_3CN	C≡Nπ		12.23	2,000	19
					900	
		n(N)		13.14		
			15.17	15.64		
C_2D_4	$D_2C{=}CD_2$		10.53		ν_2 1,370 (30)	72
					ν_3 960	
					$2\nu_4$ 280 (30)	
					$4\nu_4$ 770 (30)	
			12.47		ν_1 2,640 (100)	
					ν_2 900 (100)	
			14.43		ν_2 1,000 (100)	
			15.74		ν_3 930 (40)	
			≃ 18.8			
			≃ 22.8			
C_2D_4	$D_2C{=}CD_2$	$^2B_{3u}$		10.52	ν_2 1,200 (30)	73
					ν_3 1,100 (100)	
					$2\nu_4$ 230 (30)	

TABLE 1 (continued)

			Ionization Energy			
	Compound	Orbital	Adiabatic	Vertical	Vibrational Bands	Reference
C_2D_4 (cont.)						
		$^2B_{3g}$		12.48		
		^2A_g		14.45		
		$^2B_{2u}$		15.83	ν_2 1,110	
					ν_3 930	
		$^2B_{1u}$		18.90		
C_2D_4	$D_2C{=}CD_2$	$^2B_{3u}$	10.52		ν_2 1,200 (30)	74
					$2\nu_4$ 230 (30)	
					ν_3 1,100 (100)	
		$^2B_{3g}$	12.48			
		^2A_g	14.45			
		$^2B_{2u}$	15.83		ν_2 1,100	
					ν_3 930	
		$^2B_{1u}$	18.90			
C_2D_6	CD_3CD_3				1,070	7
C_2F_4	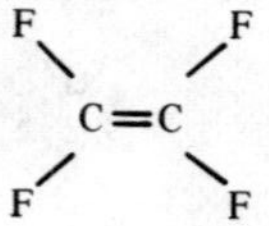	$2b_{2u}$	10.10 (8)	10.52 (0)	ν_2' 1,660	137
					ν_1' 790	
					ν_3' 370	
		$6a_g$	~15.6	15.95 (5)		
		$4b_{2g}$		16.4 (0)		
		$4b_{1u}$		16.6 (3)		
		$1a_u$		16.9 (5)		
		$1b_{3g}$	17.50 (9)	17.60 (0)		
		$5b_{3u}$	18.0	18.21		
		$3b_{1u}$	19.19 (1)	19.46		
		$5a_g$	~20.6	21.0		
		$4b_{3u}$	~22.3	22.5		

TABLE 1 (continued)

Compound		Orbital	Ionization Energy: Adiabatic	Ionization Energy: Vertical	Vibrational Bands	Reference
C_2F_4	$CF_2{=}CF_2$		10.11 (1)	10.54 (1)	1,690 (40)	70
					740 (40)	
				15.93 (1)		
				16.42 (1)		
				16.57 (1)		
				16.64 (1)		
				16.94 (1)		
			17.57 (1)	17.57 (1)	740 (40)	
					330 (40)	
				18.45 (1)		
			19.24 (1)	19.41 (1)	660 (40)	
$C_2F_6N_2$	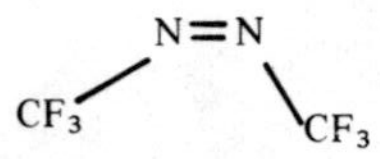		~10.5	11.35		137
			~14.6	15.3		
				15.9		
				16.8		
				17.7		
			20.3	21.4		
			22.7	23.1		
			~26.2	27.1		
C_2HBr	Br-C≡C-H	$^2\Pi_{3/2}(1)$	10.24		ν(C≡C) 1,880	75
		$^2\Pi_{1/2}(1)$	10.38		ν(C-Br) 640	
		$^2\Pi_{3/2}(2)$		12.93	ν(C-Br) 560	
		$^2\Pi_{1/2}(2)$		13.06		
		$^2\Sigma^+(3)$		15.99		
		$^2\Sigma^+(4)$		17.6		
$C_2HBrClF_3$	$CF_3CHBrCl$				sos 0.26	7
					520	
					560	
					1,170	

TABLE 1 (continued)

Compound		Orbital	Ionization Energy		Vibrational Bands	Reference
			Adiabatic	Vertical		
C_2HCl	Cl–C≡C–H	$^2\Pi_{3/2,1/2}(1)$	10.63		ν(C≡C) 2,040	75
					ν(C-Cl) 900	
		$^2\Pi_{3/2}(2)$		14.08	ν(C-Cl) 560	
		$^2\Sigma^+(3)$		16.76		
		$^2\Sigma^+(4)$		18.1		
C_2HCl_2N	Cl_2CHCN			12.21		19
				12.59		
				12.75		
				12.91		
				13.39		
				13.99		
				16.35		
				16.98		
				17.39		
C_2HCl_3	Cl_2C=CHCl	π(CC)	9.48 (1)	9.65 (1)	1,390 (40)	70
					330 (40)	
				11.73 (1)		
				12.18 (1)		
				12.72 (1)		
				12.96 (1)		
				14.40 (1)		
				14.68 (1)		
				16.30 (1)		
				16.77 (1)		
				18.70 (1)		
C_2HCl_3	Cl_2C=CHCl			9.75		219
				11.71		
				12.24		
				12.91		
				14.59		
C_2HF	F–C≡C–H	$^2\Pi_{3/2,1/2}(1)$	11.26		ν(C≡C) 2,180	75
					ν(C-F) 1,210	
		$^2\Pi_{3/2}(2)$		?17.8		
		$^2\Sigma^+(4)$		?18		

TABLE 1 (continued)

	Compound	Orbital	Ionization Energy: Adiabatic	Ionization Energy: Vertical	Vibrational Bands	Reference
C_2HF_2Cl	$CF_2{=}CHCl$	$\pi(CC)$	9.84 (1)	10.04 (1)	1,570 (40)	70
					940 (40)	
					410 (40)	
			12.15 (1)	12.15 (1)		
				12.29 (1)	590 (40)	
				13.50 (1)		
				15.25 (1)		
				15.94 (1)		
				16.38 (1)		
				18.18 (1)		
C_2HF_3	$F_2C{=}CHF$			10.53 (6)		137
				14.64 (8)		
$C_2HF_3O_2$	CF_3COOH	n_O	11.46	11.77	1,250 (100)	76
		π_2		12.92		
C_2HI	$I{-}C{\equiv}C{-}H$	$^2\Pi_{3/2}(1)$	9.73		{ $\nu(C{\equiv}C)$ 1,850	75
		$^2\Pi_{1/2}(1)$	10.14		{ $\nu(C{-}I)$ 560	
		$^2\Pi_{3/2}(2)$		11.96		
					$\nu(C{-}I)$ 420	
		$^2\Pi_{1/2}(2)$		12.19		
		$^2\Sigma^+(3)$		14.86		
		$^2\Sigma^+(4)$		17.4		
C_2H_2	C_2H_2		11.63		0.20	65
			16.27			
			18.33			
C_2H_2	C_2H_2			11.40 (1)	ν_2 1,830 (40)	39
				16.36 (1)		
				18.38 (1)	ν_2 2,510 (40)	
					ν_1 1,900 (40)	
C_2H_2	C_2H_2		11.40		ν_2 1,774	71
				16.44	ν_2 1,774	
			18.42			

TABLE 1 (continued)

Compound		Orbital	Ionization Energy: Adiabatic	Ionization Energy: Vertical	Vibrational Bands	Reference
C_2H_2	C_2H_2		11.41			57
			16.41			
			18.56			
			20.51			
C_2H_2ClN	$ClCH_2CN$		12.05			19
			12.30			
			13.06			
			13.34			
			13.72			
			15.76			
			17.01			
			17.98			
			19.20?			
$C_2H_2Cl_2$	$Cl_2C{=}CH_2$		9.74	10.00	ν_2 1,320	77
					ν_4 730	
			11.38	11.66		
			12.16			
			12.24			
			12.50	12.55		
			13.47	13.84		
				14.25		
			15.49	15.89		
				(17.29)		
				~18.42		
$C_2H_2Cl_2$	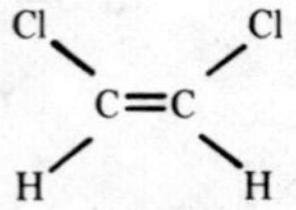		9.68	9.93	ν_2 1,270	77
					ν_4 820	
			11.56	11.90		
			12.00			
			12.09			
			12.38	12.58		
			13.52	14.31		
				13.89		

TABLE 1 (continued)

Compound		Orbital	Ionization Energy: Adiabatic	Ionization Energy: Vertical	Vibrational Bands	Reference
$C_2H_2Cl_2$ (cont.)			15.46	15.70		
				16.94		
				19.01		
$C_2H_2Cl_2$	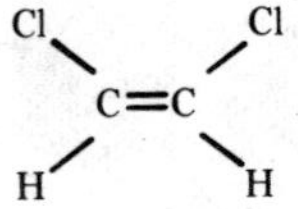			9.93		219
				11.70		
				12.11		
				12.62		
				14.11		
$C_2H_2Cl_2$	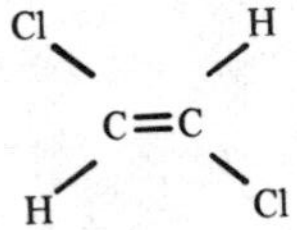			9.91		219
				11.80		
				12.05		
				12.78		
				14.00		
			9.69	9.93	ν_2 1,230; ν_4 870	77
			11.68	12.14		
			11.94			
			12.03			
			12.57	12.66		
				14.20		
			13.59	13.88		
			15.62	16.15		
				(17.41)		
				19.10		
$C_2H_2Cl_2$	$CH_2{=}CCl_2$	π(CC)	9.83 (1)	10.00 (1)	1,320 (40)	70
					650 (40)	
		n(Cl3p)	11.46 (1)	11.67 (1)	270 (40)	
		n(Cl3p)	12.06 (1)	12.17 (1)	270 (40)	
		b_1		12.51 (1)	320 (40)	
				~13.7		

TABLE 1 (continued)

Compound		Orbital	Ionization Energy: Adiabatic	Ionization Energy: Vertical	Vibrational Bands	Reference
$C_2H_2Cl_2$ (cont.)				14.24 (1)	1,010 (40)	
				16.27 (1)	1,940 (40)	
				18.47 (1)	1,290 (40)	
$C_2H_2Cl_2$	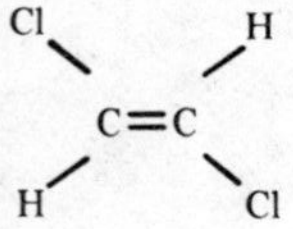		9.64 (1)	9.81 (1)	1,410 (40)	70
					900 (40)	
					360 (40)	
		b_u(Cl3p)	11.86 (1)	11.86 (1)		
		b_g(Cl3p)	11.93 (1)	11.93 (1)		
		a_g(Cl3p)		12.06 (1)		
		a_u(Cl3p)	12.61 (1)	12.61 (1)	770 (40)	
					270 (40)	
				13.85 (1)		
				14.20 (1)		
				16.23 (1)		
				~19.00		
$C_2H_2Cl_2$	$Cl_2C{=}CH_2$			10.16		219
				11.65		
				12.17		
				12.60		
				14.00		
$C_2H_2Cl_2$	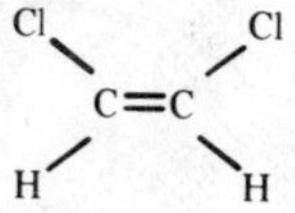	π(CC)	9.65 (1)	9.83 (1)	1,400 (40)	70
					840 (40)	
		b_2 (Cl3p)		11.71 (1)		
		a_2 (Cl3p)		11.85 (1)		
		a_1 (Cl3p)		12.09 (1)	770 (40)	
				12.51 (1)	660 (40)	
				13.72 (1)	640 (40)	
				~14.1		
				15.66 (1)	600 (40)	
				16.72 (1)	1,940 (40)	
				~18.8		

TABLE 1 (continued)

	Compound	Orbital	Ionization Energy: Adiabatic	Ionization Energy: Vertical	Vibrational Bands	Reference
$C_2H_2F_2$	$CH_2=CF_2$		10.31 (1)	10.72 (1)	1,600 (40)	70
					720 (40)	
			14.06 (1)	14.79 (1)	1,180 (40)	
				15.73 (1)	1,290 (40)	
				18.22 (1)	1,270 (40)	
				19.68 (1)		
$C_2H_2F_2$	$CH_2=CF_2$		10.48	10.84	0.18	7
			14.19		0.15	
			15.64			
$C_2H_2F_2$	*trans*-FHC=CHF			10.38		137
				13.90		
$C_2H_2F_2$	*cis*-FHC=CHF			10.43		137
				13.97		
$C_2H_2F_3I$	CF_3CH_2I		9.99	9.99		7
			10.61	10.61		
$C_2H_2N_4$		b_{2g} $(2b_1)$	11.6	11.9		78
		b_{1g} $(1a_2)$	12.5	12.8		
		b_{3u} $(1b_1)$	15.51	15.8	ν_1 0.107	
		b_{3g} $(7b_2)$	9.24	9.7	ν_{6a} 0.087	
					ν_1 0.108	
		a_g $(11a_1)$		12.1		
		b_{2u} $(6b_2)$		~17.5		
		b_{2u} $(5b_2)$	18.9	19.3		
		b_{1u} $(10a_1)$	13.2	13.3		
		a_g $(8a_1)$	18.9	19.3		
		b_{1u} $(9a_1)$	16.5	17.1		
		a_g $(7a_1)$	22.0	22.4		
		b_{3g} $(4b_2)$	~24	24.5		

TABLE 1 (continued)

	Compound	Orbital	Ionization Energy: Adiabatic	Ionization Energy: Vertical	Vibrational Bands	Reference
C_2H_2O	H_2CCO		9.64		ν_2 2,140	79
					ν_4 1,020	
			13.84		1,130?	
				14.62	940	
			16.08		ν_3 1,020	
$C_2H_2O_2$	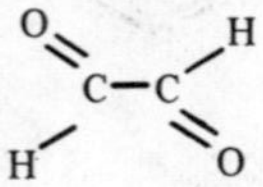	n_+		10.59		80
		n_-		12.19		
			12.19		ν_2 1,610	7
					ν_5 400	
		1bg	13.85		ν_2 1,360	
					1,410	
					990	
C_2H_3Cl	CH_2=CHCl			10.29		219
				11.73		
				11.83		
				13.54		
				15.45		
C_2H_3Cl	CH_2=CHCl	π(CC)	10.00 (1)	10.18 (1)	1,400 (40)	70
					860 (40)	
					350 (40)	
		a′(Cl3p)	11.72 (1)	11.72 (1)		
		a″(Cl3p)	11.79 (1)	11.87 (1)	600 (40)	
				13.14 (1)		
				~13.56 (1)		
				15.39 (1)		
				16.31 (1)		
				18.76 (1)		
C_2H_3ClO	$ClCH_2CHO$		10.48 (3)			59

TABLE 1 (continued)

Compound		Orbital	Ionization Energy: Adiabatic	Ionization Energy: Vertical	Vibrational Bands	Reference
C_2H_3ClO	$CH_3C(O)Cl$			11.1 (4)		7
				12.0 (2)		
C_2H_3F	$CH_2{=}CHF$		10.31			7
C_2H_3F	$CH_2{=}CHF$		10.37 (1)	10.58 (1)	1,530 (40)	70
					1,330 (40)	
					510 (40)	
				13.79 (1)		
				14.51 (1)		
				16.77 (1)		
				17.97 (1)		
C_2H_3N	CH_3NC		11.27		ν_2 2,280	7
					ν_3 1,410	
		π	12.24		ν_2 1,770	
					ν_3 1,130	
			15.59		ν_4 750	
C_2H_3N	CH_3CN	$C{\equiv}N\pi$		12.20	2,010	19
					800	
		n(N)		13.14		
			15.11	15.50		
C_2H_3N	CH_3CN	e	12.12	12.18		81
		a_1	13.11	13.11		
		a_1	15.12	15.15		
		e	16.98	17.4		
C_2H_3N	CH_3CN	$\tilde{X}$	12.21		ν_2 2,010	7
					ν_3 1,430	
					ν_4 810	
		$\tilde{B}$	13.14		ν_3 1,290	
		$\tilde{C}$	15.13		ν_3 1,440	
					ν_4 860	

TABLE 1 (continued)

Compound		Orbital	Ionization Energy Adiabatic	Ionization Energy Vertical	Vibrational Bands	Reference
C_2H_3NO	CH_3NCO	$2\pi(a'')$	10.67 (2)		ν_s 1,150 (50)	48
					ν_{as} 2,180 (50)	
					$\nu_s+\nu_{as}$ 3,260 (50)	
		$2\pi(a')$		11.20 (2)		
		1π		14.7 (1)		
		4σ		16.1 (1)	700 (50)	
		C p		16.7 (1)		
		3σ		18.0 (1)		
C_2H_3NS	CH_3NCS	$2\pi(a'')$		9.37 (2)		48
		1π		12.6 (1)		
		4σ		14.6 (1)		
		C p		15.6 (1)		
		3σ		17.5 (1)		
C_2H_4	$H_2C{=}CH_2$	$1b_{2u}$	10.51 (4)	10.51 (4)		137
		$1b_{2g}$	12.45 (3)	12.85		
		$3a_g$	14.43	14.66		
		$1b_{1u}$	15.74	15.87		
		$2b_{3u}$	~18.8	~19.1		
		$2a_g$	~22.8	~23.5		
C_2H_4	$H_2C{=}CH_2$	$^2B_{3u}$	10.51 (2)		ν_2 1,250 (30)	74
					$2\nu_4$ 400 (30)	
					ν_3 1,450 (100)	
		$^2B_{3g}$	12.46			
		^2A_g	14.46			
		$^2B_{2u}$	15.78		ν_2,ν_3 1,200	
		$^2B_{1u}$	18.87			
C_2H_4	$H_2C{=}CH_2$			10.86		219
				13.06		

TABLE 1 (continued)

Compound		Orbital	Ionization Energy: Adiabatic	Ionization Energy: Vertical	Vibrational Bands	Reference
C_2H_4	$H_2C{=}CH_2$	$1b_{3u}(\pi)$	10.51 (5)	10.51 (5)		82
		$3a_g(\sigma)$	12.40	12.78		
		$1b_{1g}(\sigma)$	(14.35)	14.73		
		$1b_{2u}(\sigma)$	15.76	15.91		
		$2b_{1u}(\sigma)$	18.46			
C_2H_4	$H_2C{=}CH_2$	$^2B_{3u}$		10.51 (2)	ν_2 1,230 (30)	73
					ν_3 1,450 (100)	
					$2\nu_4$ 400 (30)	
		$^2B_{3g}$		12.46 (2)		
		^2A_g		14.46 (2)		
		$^2B_{2u}$		15.78 (2)	ν_2, ν_3 1,200	
		$^2B_{1u}$		18.87 (2)		
C_2H_4	$H_2C{=}CH_2$		10.51		ν_2 1,290 (30)	72
					ν_3 1,470 (80)	
					$2\nu_4$ 405 (30)	
			12.45		ν_1 3,000 (100)	
					ν_2 1,150 (100)	
					ν_3 800 (100)	
			14.43		ν_1 1,900 (100)	
			15.74		ν_3 1,240 (40)	
			$\simeq$18.85			
			$\simeq$22.8			
C_2H_4	$H_2C{=}CH_2$		10.48			57
			12.50			
			14.39			
			15.63			
			19.13			
C_2H_4	$H_2C{=}CH_2$	$2p_x+2p_x$	10.56	10.86		83
		$2p_y-2p_y$	12.56	13.06		
		$2p_\sigma+2p_\sigma$	14.46			
		$2p_y+2p_y$	15.96			
		$2s-2s$	18.91			

TABLE 1 (continued)

Compound		Orbital	Ionization Energy: Adiabatic	Ionization Energy: Vertical	Vibrational Bands	Reference
C_2H_4	$H_2C{=}CH_2$	π	10.50 (1)			37
			12.44			
			14.37			
			15.68			
			(18.03)			
C_2H_4O			10.49			57
			11.48			
			13.48			
			16.16			
			20.16			
C_2H_4O		$^2B_2$		10.57		84
		$^2A_1$		11.7		
		$^2B_1$		13.7		
		$^2A_2$		~14.2		
		$^2A_1$		16.6		
		$^2B_2$		17.4	1,080	
C_2H_4O	CH_3CHO		10.20 (1)			37
			12.71			
			13.97			
			15.06			
			16.36			
			(18.87)			
C_2H_4O	CH_3CHO		10.22 (1)			59
$C_2H_4O_2$	$HCOOCH_3$	n_O	10.85	11.02	1,370 (50)	76
		π_2		11.55		
$C_2H_4O_2$	CH_3COOH	n_O	10.70	10.87	1,310 (50)	76
		π_2		12.05	~1,050	
C_2H_5Br	CH_3CH_2Br	n	10.30 (1)			54
		n	10.61 (1)			

TABLE 1 (continued)

Compound		Orbital	Ionization Energy: Adiabatic	Ionization Energy: Vertical	Vibrational Bands	Reference
C_2H_5Br	CH_3CH_2Br	$^2E_{3/2}$		10.28		235
		$^2E_{1/2}$		10.60		
				12.44		
				13.20		
				14.25		
				15.40		
				16.25		
C_2H_5BrO	$HOCH_2CH_2Br$		10.63			60
				10.91		
				11.29		
				12.50		
				13.32		
				14.48		
				16.09		
				17.50		
C_2H_5Cl	CH_3CH_2Cl			11.01		235
				13.07		
				13.4 (sh)		
				14.50		
				16.60		
C_2H_5ClO	$HOCH_2CH_2Cl$		10.90			60
				11.45		
				11.71		
				12.62		
				13.90		
				14.62		
				15.78		
				16.18		
				17.60		

TABLE 1 (continued)

	Compound	Orbital	Ionization Energy Adiabatic	Ionization Energy Vertical	Vibrational Bands	Reference
C_2H_5FO	$HOCH_2CH_2F$		11.05			60
				12.65		
				13.09		
				14.00		
				15.00		
				16.00		
				17.35		
				18.08		
C_2H_5I	CH_3CH_2I	$^2E_{3/2}$		9.34		235
		$^2E_{1/2}$		9.93		
				11.66		
				12.90		
				13.85		
				15.05		
				15.90		
C_2H_5I	CH_3CH_2I		9.37			60
				9.93		
				11.68		
				12.92		
				13.80		
				15.00		
				15.90		
C_2H_5IO	$HOCH_2CH_2I$		9.62			60
				10.18		
				10.87		
				11.85		
				12.65		
				14.00		
				15.78		
				17.34		
C_2H_5N			9.52			64
			(9.78)			
			11.51			
			(11.79)			
			15.56			
			16.97			
			17.29			
			(19.51)			

TABLE 1 (continued)

	Compound	Orbital	Ionization Energy: Adiabatic	Ionization Energy: Vertical	Vibrational Bands	Reference
C_2H_5N	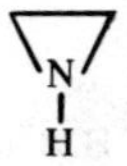	$^2A'$	9.8		700	84
C_2H_5NO	CH_3CONH_2	n_O π_2	9.80	9.96 10.32	~1,350 (100)	76
C_2H_5NO	$HCONHCH_3$	2a″ 10a′	9.79 10.05 12.6	9.87 10.05 13.2 14.3 15.7 18.3 20?	≈700 1,500 (30)	52
$C_2H_5NO_2$	$CH_3CH_2NO_2$		10.92 (1) (11.55) 12.93 (13.70) 16.78 (17.34) 17.91 (19.41)			55
C_2H_6	CH_3CH_3	σ	11.51 (1) 14.77			37
C_2H_6	CH_3CH_3		11.49 14.74 20.13			56
C_2H_6	CH_3CH_3		11.49 14.74 20.13			57
C_2H_6	CH_3CH_3		11.56		1,170	7

TABLE 1 (continued)

Compound		Orbital	Ionization Energy Adiabatic	Ionization Energy Vertical	Vibrational Bands	Reference
$C_2H_6BBr_2N$	$(CH_3)_2NBBr_2$	π		9.60		85
				10.27		
				10.80		
				11.21		
				12.12		
				12.65		
				15.3		
				16.0		
				17.7		
$C_2H_6BCl_2N$	$(CH_3)_2NBCl_2$	π		9.56		85
				11.04		
				11.55		
				11.94		
				12.88		
				13.60		
				15.54		
				16.35		
$C_2H_6BF_2N$	$(CH_3)_2NBF_2$	π		9.71		85
$C_2H_6F_2NP$	$F_2PN(CH_3)_2$	N2p		9.6		21
		P3p		10.5		
C_2H_6Hg	$Hg(CH_3)_2$	$^2D_{5/2}(\pm5/2)$		14.95		31
		$(\pm3/2,\pm1/2)$		15.44		
		$^2D_{3/2}(\pm3/2,\pm1/2)$		16.90		
$C_2H_6N_2$	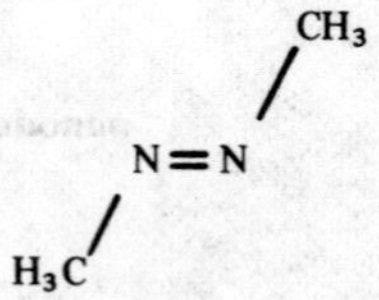		~8.20	8.98		137
			11.35	11.81		
				12.3		
			~13.1	13.6		
				14.5		
			~15.3	15.8		
			~17.8	18.6		
			~21.6	22.4		

TABLE 1 (continued)

Compound		Orbital	Ionization Energy: Adiabatic	Ionization Energy: Vertical	Vibrational Bands	Reference
$C_2H_6N_2$	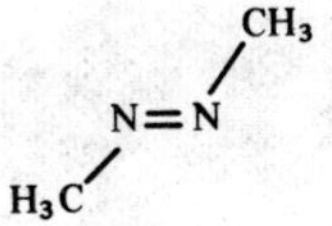	n_+		8.98		86
		π		11.84	0.15	
		n_-		12.3 (2)		
$C_2H_6N_2$	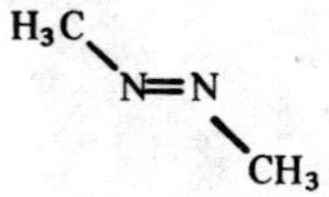	n_+	8.7	8.98		87
		π		11.38, 11.53,		
				11.84, 12.00		
		n_-		12.3		
		σ		13.5		
		σ		14.6		
		σ		15.8		
C_2H_6O	CH_3OCH_3		9.94 (1)			37
			11.65			
			13.09			
			15.72			
C_2H_6O	CH_3OCH_3			10.04		88
C_2H_6O	CH_3OCH_3		9.94 (1)			59
C_2H_6O	CH_3OCH_3	$O2p_x$		10.04		62
		CH		14.2		
		CH		16.5		
		$3a_1$		11.91		
		$2b_2$		13.43		
C_2H_6O	CH_3CH_2OH		10.63			57
			11.81			
			12.80			
			15.69			
			17.38			
			20.12			

TABLE 1 (continued)

			Ionization Energy			
Compound		Orbital	Adiabatic	Vertical	Vibrational Bands	Reference
C_2H_6O	CH_3CH_2OH		10.46 (1)			37
			11.76			
			12.76			
			15.68			
			17.25			
			(19.75)			
			(20.15)			
C_2H_6O	CH_3CH_2OH		10.46 (2)			59
C_2H_6O	CH_3CH_2OH		10.65			60
				12.20		
				13.31		
				13.82		
				15.85		
				17.35		
C_2H_6OS	$SO(CH_3)_2$	n(S)		9.11		32
		n(O)		10.26		
		S-Oπ		12.58		
		σ		13.42		
		σ		13.94		
		σ		14.66		
		σ		15.43		
$C_2H_6O_2S$	$SO_2(CH_3)_2$			10.97		32
				11.31		
				11.89		
				12.23		
				14.74		
				16.50		
$C_2H_6O_2S$	$(CH_3)_2SO_2$	$4b_1$		10.65		218
		$4b_2$		11.18		
		$2a_2$		11.65		
		$6a_1$		12.0		
C_2H_6S	CH_3SCH_3			8.67		88

TABLE 1 (continued)

	Compound	Orbital	Ionization Energy: Adiabatic	Ionization Energy: Vertical	Vibrational Bands	Reference
C_2H_6S	CH_3SCH_3			8.67		61
C_2H_6S	CH_3SCH_3	$S3p_x$		8.71		62
		CH		14.5		
		$3a_1$		11.28		
		$2b_2$		12.68		
$C_2H_6S_2$	CH_3SSCH_3			8.97		61
				9.21		
$C_2H_6S_2$	CH_3SSCH_3			8.82		89
				9.13		
				11.15		
				12.28		
				13.38		
				14.67		
C_2H_6Se	$(CH_3)_2Se$	$Se4p_x$		8.40		62
		CH		14.0		
		$3a_1$		11.0		
		$2b_2$		12.0		
C_2H_6Si	$CH_2=CHSiH_3$	π_1		10.4		90
		$\sigma_1 (H_3Si\text{-}C)$		11.5	(Si-C) 645	
		$\sigma_2 (SiH_3)$		12.4	(SiH) 2,036	
		π_2, σ_3		13.9		
				15.4		
C_2H_6Te	$(CH_3)_2Te$	$Te5p_x$		7.89		62
		CH		14.0		
		$3a_1$		10.35		
		$2b_2$		11.32		
C_2H_6Zn	$Zn(CH_3)_2$	$^2D_{5/2}(\pm 5/2)$		16.96		31

TABLE 1 (continued)

	Compound	Orbital	Ionization Energy: Adiabatic	Ionization Energy: Vertical	Vibrational Bands	Reference
C_2H_7N	$CH_3CH_2NH_2$		9.19			57
			11.86			
			12.66			
			14.65			
			15.55			
			16.81			
			19.71			
C_2H_7N	$(CH_3)_2NH$		8.36			57
			12.88			
			14.63			
			16.35			
			19.62			
C_2H_7N	$(CH_3)_2NH$		8.36			63
C_2H_7NOS	$(CH_3)_2S(NH)O$			9.5		218
				10.29		
				10.94		
				12.0		
C_2H_8BN	$(CH_3)_2NBH_2$	π		9.51		85
$C_2H_8N_2$	$(CH_3)_2NNH_2$		8.28			64
			(8.60)			
			9.77			
			12.35			
			(12.72)			
			16.45			
			(19.13)			

TABLE 1 (continued)

Compound		Orbital	Ionization Energy: Adiabatic	Ionization Energy: Vertical	Vibrational Bands	Reference
$C_2H_8N_2$	$CH_3N(H)N(H)CH_3$		8.22			64
			(8.70)			
			(11.57)			
			12.04			
			(12.45)			
			(13.23)			
			15.53			
			(16.97)			
			(19.03)			
$C_2H_8N_2S$	$(CH_3)_2S(NH)_2$			8.87		218
				9.4		
				10.0		
				12.06		
C_2H_9NSi	$(CH_3)_2NSiH_3$	$N2p_z$		8.5 (1)		4
		NC		15.2 (1)		
		CH, SiH, SiN		11.1–14.5		
		Si3s		17.5 (1)		
$C_2H_{10}BN$	$(CH_3)_2NHBH_3$	$e(BH_3)$	9.39 (1)	10.12 (1)	980 (50)	9
		5a″+8a′		10.74 (3) (sh)		
		7a′	11.56 (2)	11.89 (1)		
			12.99 (3)	{13.65 (2)		
		4a″+6a′+3a″+5a′		{14.19 (6)		
				{14.81 (4)		
			16.04 (3)	16.28 (1)		
		2a″+4a′+3a	17.22 (3)	17.56 (2)		
				18.11 (3) (sh)		

TABLE 1 (continued)

Compound		Orbital	Ionization Energy: Adiabatic	Ionization Energy	Ionization Energy: Vertical	Vibrational Bands	Reference
C_2I_2	I-C≡C-I	$^2\Pi_{3/2}(1)$			9.03	1,800	69
		$^2\Pi_{1/2}(1)$			9.47		
		$^2\Pi_{3/2}(2)$			10.63		
		$^2\Pi_{1/2}(2)$			11.23		
		$^2\Pi_{3/2}(3)$			12.17		
		$^2\Pi_{1/2}(3)$			12.38		
		$^2\Sigma^+(g)$			14.22		
		$^2\Sigma^+(u)$			15.48		
C_2N_2	$(CN)_2$	$1\pi g$		13.36 (1)		ν_1 2,120 (40)	39
		n(N)		14.49 (1)		ν_1 1,860 (40)	
		n(N)		14.86			
		π		15.47 (1)		570 (40)	
						ν_2 710 (40)	
$C_3Cl_2F_4O$	$ClF_2C(=O)CF_2Cl$		10.71 (1)				59
$C_3Cl_3F_3O$	$CF_3C(=O)CCl_3$		10.80 (1)				59
C_3D_6O	$(CD_3)_2C=O$		9.68 (8)		9.68 (8)	ν_4' 880	137
				10–17			
			17.77 (7)		17.90 (5)	1,050	
$C_3F_3N_3$	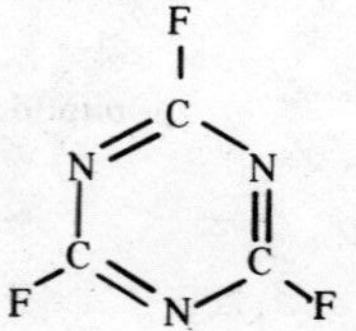		11.5		12.0		160
					12.34	ν_1' 1,370	
			14.87		15.12	ν_1' 1,000	
			15.4		15.53	ν_1' 1,000	
			16.25		16.25	ν_1' 1,000	

TABLE 1 (continued)

Compound		Orbital	Ionization Energy: Adiabatic	Ionization Energy: Vertical	Vibrational Bands	Reference
C_3F_6O	$CF_3C(=O)CF_3$		11.68 (1)			37
			15.09			
			17.60			
			(20.54)			
C_3F_6O	$(CF_3)_2C{=}O$		11.44	12.09		137
				16.0		
				16.5		
				17.1		
				17.75		
				18.4		
			~20.3	21.2		
			~22.5	22.9		
				26.0		
C_3F_8	$CF_3CF_2CF_3$		13.38 (1)			37
			15.21			
			(17.13)			
			19.99			
			20.72			
C_3HN	$H{-}C{\equiv}C{-}C{\equiv}N$	π		11.60 (1)	ν_2 2,180 (40)	39
		n(N)		13.54 (1)	ν_4 860 (40)	
		π		14.03 (1)	ν_4 810 (40)	
					ν_2 1,940 (40)	
				17.62 (1)	ν_1 1,320 (40)	
$C_3H_3F_3O$	$CF_3C(=O)CH_3$		10.67 (1)			59
$C_3H_3F_3O_2$	$HCOOCH_2CF_3$	n_O	11.31	11.65	1,370 (50)	76
		π_2		12.09		

TABLE 1 (continued)

Compound		Orbital	Ionization Energy		Vibrational Bands	Reference
			Adiabatic	Vertical		
C_3H_3N	$CH_2=CHCN$	C=Cπ		10.91	1,450	19
					~2,000	
		C≡Nπ		12.36	2,000	
					1,100	
		n(N)		13.04		
				13.56		
				14.43		
				16.17		
				17.62		
C_3H_3NO				10.2		94
				11.3		
C_3H_3NO	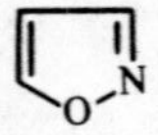		9.99 (5)	10.17 (5)	1,370, 565	91
			11.13 (5)	11.29 (5)	1,210	
			13.31	13.85		
				14.61		
				15.64		
				17.81		
$C_3H_3N_3$	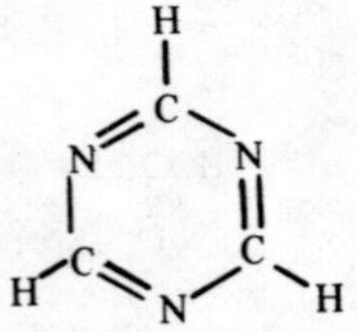		10.1	10.41	ν_2' 970	160
			11.71	11.71	ν_2' 1,050	
				12.2		
			13.25	13.25	ν_2' 1,190	
			14.4	14.65		
				14.85		
			17.7	17.94	ν_1' 2,900	
				22.3		
C_3H_4	H_2CCCH_2		9.69	10.0	ν_3 720	79
				10.6		
			14.10	14.9	ν_2 1,090	
				15.4?		
				17.4		
				19.5?		

TABLE 1 (continued)

Compound		Orbital	Ionization Energy: Adiabatic	Ionization Energy: Vertical	Vibrational Bands	Reference
C_3H_4	$H_2C{=}C{=}CH_2$	π	9.83 (1)			37
			(12.19)			
			14.29			
			17.13			
C_3H_4	$H_3C\text{-}C{\equiv}CH$	1π		10.37 (1)	ν_5 940 (40)	39
					ν_3 1,940 (40)	
				13.69 (1)	ν_4 1,290 (40)	
				15.2		
				17.2		
C_3H_4	$CH_3C{\equiv}CH$	e	10.37	10.37		81
		a_1	13.93	14.4		
		e	15.13	15.5		
		a_1	16.79	17.2		
C_3H_4		π		9.86	≈1,250	92
		b_2 (σ)		11.02		
		a_1 (σ)		12.7	≈1,100	
C_3H_4	*cis*- 	π	9.70	9.86	1,240	93
		σ	10.5 (1)	11.0 (1)		
C_3H_4		$2b_2$	9.97	9.86	ν'_3 1,300	50
		$3b_1$	10.57	10.89		
		$6a_1$	12.38	12.7		
		$1b_2$	14.5	15.09		
		$5a_1$	16.2	16.68		
		$2b_1$	17.8	18.3		
		$4a_1$	19.2	19.6		
$C_3H_4Cl_2O$	$ClCH_2C(=O)CH_2Cl$		10.03 (2)			59

TABLE 1 (continued)

Compound		Orbital	Ionization Energy Adiabatic	Ionization Energy Vertical	Vibrational Bands	Reference
$C_3H_4N_2$	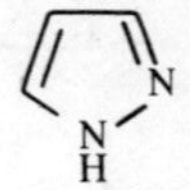			9.5 10.1 10.8		94
$C_3H_4N_2$	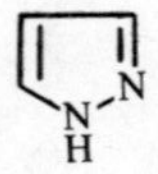		9.27 (5) 10.00 (5) 10.53 (5)	9.39 (5) 10.00 (5) 10.73 (5) 13.60 14.62 17.50	870 1,535	91
C_3H_4O	CH_2=CHCHO		10.11 10.93		1,050 1,370 970 500	7
$C_3H_4O_3$	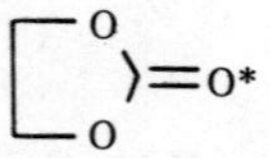	n(O*)	10.70		1,500	76
$C_3H_4S_3$	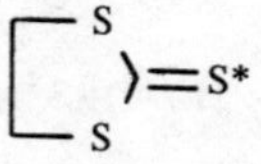	n(S*) n(ring S) n(ring S)		8.47 8.92 9.46	810 ~800 (100)	76
C_3H_5Br	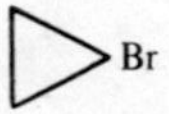		9.32 10.26	10.26		7

TABLE 1 (continued)

	Compound	Orbital	Ionization Energy		Vibrational Bands	Reference
			Adiabatic	Vertical		
C_3H_5BrO	O / \ $H_2C - CHCH_2Br$		10.46	10.70 10.99 11.50 13.34 13.72 14.65 15.15 16.20 17.20		60
C_3H_5ClO	O ‖ $ClCH_2CCH_3$		9.98 (1)			59
C_3H_5ClO	O / \ $H_2C - CHCH_2Cl$		10.64	11.33 11.52 13.78 15.04 15.45 16.47 17.40 19.65		60
C_3H_5FO	O / \ $H_2C - CHCH_2F$		10.74	11.80 13.17 14.22 15.10 16.32 17.05		60

TABLE 1 (continued)

	Compound	Orbital	Ionization Energy: Adiabatic	Ionization Energy: Vertical	Vibrational Bands	Reference
C_3H_5N	C_2H_5CN	C≡Nπ	11.85	12.11	2,100	19
					810	
		n(N)		12.91		
				13.64		
				13.86		
				15.07		
				16.59		
				17.47		
C_3H_6	$CH_3CH{=}CH_2$	$2p_x+2p_x$	9.74	10.01		83
		$2p_y-2p_y$	11.82	12.07		
		$2p_\sigma+2p_\sigma$	13.07	13.27		
		$\pi(CH_3)$	14.13	14.58		
		$2p_y+2p_y$	15.71			
		2s-2s	17.93			
C_3H_6	$CH_3CH{=}CH_2$		10.0		ν_2 1,370 (50)	95
					ν_4 438 (50)	
C_3H_6	$CH_3CH{=}CH_2$	π_1		9.9		90
		σ_1 (H_3C-C)		12.3		
		σ_2		13.2		
		σ_3, π_2		14.5		
				15.9		
C_3H_6	$CH_3CH{=}CH_2$	π	9.69 (1)			37
			11.76			
			13.01			
			14.14			
			15.78			
			(18.03)			
C_3H_6			10.06 (1)			37
			11.07			
			12.44			
			15.34			
			(18.95)			

TABLE 1 (continued)

	Compound	Orbital	Ionization Energy: Adiabatic	Ionization Energy: Vertical	Vibrational Bands	Reference
C_3H_6		2E′		10.53	480	84
		2E″		13.2		
		$3A'_1$		15.7		
		$2A''_2$		16.5	1,130	
C_3H_6	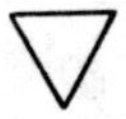	$1a''_2$		15.7		96
		$3a'_1$		~16.5	ν_2 1,130	
		2e′		19.3 (1)		
$C_3H_6Cl_2$	$ClCH_2CH_2CH_2Cl$		10.93			60
				11.16		
				11.36		
				11.55		
				12.72		
				13.41		
				14.60		
				15.07		
				16.35		
$C_3H_6Cl_2$	$ClCH_2CH(Cl)-CH_3$		10.73	11.06		60
				11.29		
				11.73		
				12.93		
				13.45		
				14.57		
				15.30		
				15.86		
				16.55		
$C_3H_6N_2$	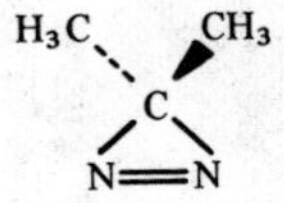			9.76		92
				12.11		
				13.31		
C_3H_6O	CH_3CH_2CHO		9.97 (1)			59

TABLE 1 (continued)

	Compound	Orbital	Ionization Energy: Adiabatic	Ionization Energy: Vertical	Vibrational Bands	Reference
C_3H_6O	CH_3CH_2CHO		9.94 (1)			37
			11.98			
			(13.21)			
			(14.68)			
			15.18			
			(16.16)			
			(18.59)			
C_3H_6O	$CH_3\overset{\overset{\displaystyle O}{\|}}{C}CH_3$		9.71 (1)			59
C_3H_6O	$CH_3\overset{\overset{\displaystyle O}{\|}}{C}CH_3$		9.68 (1)			37
			12.16			
			(13.94)			
			15.47			
			(18.02)			
			19.90			
C_3H_6O	$CH_3\overset{\overset{\displaystyle O}{\|}}{C}CH_3$		9.67			57
			12.16			
			14.15			
			15.55			
			17.92			
			19.88			
C_3H_6O	$CH_3\overset{\overset{\displaystyle O}{\|}}{C}CH_3$		9.72 (3)	9.72 (3)	ν_4' 1,210 360	137
			~11.8	12.6		
				13.4		
				13.9		
				14.5		
				15.55		
			17.73 (3)	17.73 (3)	1,370	
			~21	23.2		

TABLE 1 (continued)

	Compound	Orbital	Ionization Energy Adiabatic	Ionization Energy Vertical	Vibrational Bands	Reference
$C_3H_6O_2$	CH_3COOCH_3	n_O π_2	10.33	10.48 11.16	1,200 (50)	76
$C_3H_6O_2$	$HCOOCH_2CH_3$	n_O π_2	10.62	10.96 11.28	1,370 (50)	76
$C_3H_6O_2$		n n		10.1 10.65		97
$C_3H_6O_3$	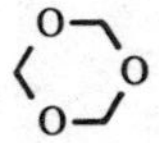	n n		~10.8 11.15		97
C_3H_6S	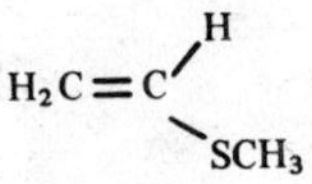			8.45		61
$C_3H_6S_3$	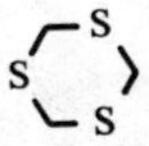	n n		8.76 9.27		97
C_3H_7Br	$CH_3CH_2CH_2Br$	n n	10.18 10.49			54
C_3H_7Br	$(CH_3)_2CHBr$	n n	10.12 10.41			54

TABLE 1 (continued)

	Compound	Orbital	Ionization Energy: Adiabatic	Ionization Energy: Vertical	Vibrational Bands	Reference
C_3H_7Br	$CH_3CH_2CH_2Br$	$^2E_{3/2}$		10.18		235
		$^2E_{1/2}$		10.50		
				11.81		
				12.45		
				12.9_5 (sh)		
				13.8 (sh)		
				14.40		
				15.50		
				16.05		
C_3H_7Cl	$CH_3CH_2CH_2Cl$			10.88		235
				12.06		
				12.68		
				13.2 (sh)		
				14.10		
				14.60		
				15.90		
				16.30		
C_3H_7I	$CH_3CH_2CH_2I$	$^2E_{3/2}$		9.27		235
		$^2E_{1/2}$		9.82		
				11.43		
				12.22		
				12.78		
				13.5 (sh)		
				14.25		
				15.25		
				15.90		
C_3H_7I	$CH_3CH_2CH_2I$		9.27			60
				9.84		
				11.46		
				12.25		
				12.80		
				14.25		
				15.30		
				15.95		

TABLE 1 (continued)

	Compound	Orbital	Ionization Energy: Adiabatic	Ionization Energy: Vertical	Vibrational Bands	Reference
C_3H_7I	$CH_3CH_2CH_2I$	$p_{3/2,1/2}$	9.26, 9.84 (05)			59
C_3H_7I	$(CH_3)_2CHI$		9.19	9.74 11.18 12.35 12.80 13.95 14.50 15.40		60
C_3H_7I	$(CH_3)_2CHI$	$p_{3/2,1/2}$	9.18,9.69 (05)			59
C_3H_7N	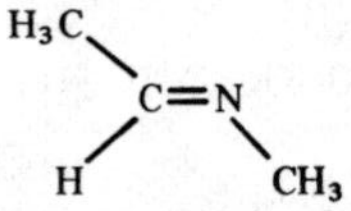	n π		9.49 10.66		86
C_3H_7N	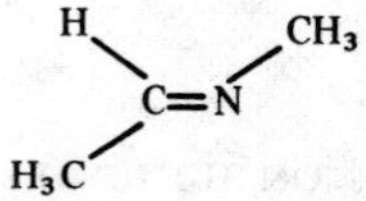	n π σ	9.1 10.4 12.2	9.5 10.67 12.9		87
C_3H_7NO	$HCON(CH_3)_2$	2a″ 10a′	9.14 ⩾9.40 12.3	9.25 9.77 13.4 14.2 15.9 17.4 18.9 20.4	650–750 1,600 (30)	52

TABLE 1 (continued)

Compound		Orbital	Ionization Energy Adiabatic	Ionization Energy Vertical	Vibrational Bands	Reference
C_3H_7NO	$CH_3CONHCH_3$	n_O		~9.85		76
		π_2		9.68		
$C_3H_7NO_2$	$CH_3CH_2CH_2NO_2$		10.75 (1)			55
			(10.95)			
			12.23			
			14.44			
			16.75			
			(17.06)			
			(19.44)			
$C_3H_7NO_2$	$CH_3CH_2CH_2ONO$		10.34 (1)			55
			(10.60)			
			11.86			
			(12.24)			
			14.28			
			(16.55)			
			(19.28)			
			(19.74)			
$C_3H_7NO_2$	$CH_3CH(NO_2)CH_3$		10.77 (1)			55
			(10.94)			
			12.44			
			(14.41)			
			16.42			
			(19.15)			
$C_3H_7NO_2$	$CH_3CH(ONO)CH_3$		10.23 (1)			55
			(10.50)			
			12.04			
			(12.40)			
			(14.74)			
			(15.63)			
			(19.24)			

TABLE 1 (continued)

Compound		Orbital	Ionization Energy: Adiabatic	Ionization Energy: Vertical	Vibrational Bands	Reference
C_3H_8	$CH_3CH_2CH_3$	$4b_1$		11.5		215
		$6a_1$		12.1		
		$2b_2$		12.7		
		$1a_2$		13.5		
		$3b_1$		14.1		
		$5a_1$		15.3		
		$1b_2$		16.0		
C_3H_8	$CH_3CH_2CH_3$	σ	11.06 (1)			37
			13.22			
			15.19			
C_3H_8	$CH_3CH_2CH_3$		11.07			57
			13.17			
			15.17			
			19.8			
C_3H_8O	$CH_3CH_2CH_2OH$		10.25 (1)			37
			11.36			
			14.19			
			(15.99)			
			(17.29)			
			(19.21)			
C_3H_8O	$CH_3CH_2CH_2OH$		10.32 (2)			59
C_3H_8O	$CH_3CH_2CH_2OH$		10.48			60
				11.73		
				12.34		
				13.04		
				14.60		
				16.00		
				17.14		
C_3H_8O	$(CH_3)_2CHOH$		10.29 (2)			59

TABLE 1 (continued)

	Compound	Orbital	Ionization Energy		Vibrational Bands	Reference
			Adiabatic	Vertical		
C_3H_8O	$(CH_3)_2CHOH$		10.42			60
				11.71		
				12.68		
				13.08		
				13.75		
				15.14		
				15.80		
				17.20		
C_3H_8O	$(CH_3)_2CHOH$		10.18 (1)			37
			11.30			
			12.32			
			15.07			
			(17.25)			
			(19.26)			
$C_3H_8S_2$	$CH_3SCH_2SCH_3$			8.65		61
				8.90		
C_3H_9B	$B(CH_3)_3$		10.4	10.9		95
				11.5		
			12.6	13.3		
				14.5		
$C_3H_9B_3Cl_3N_3$	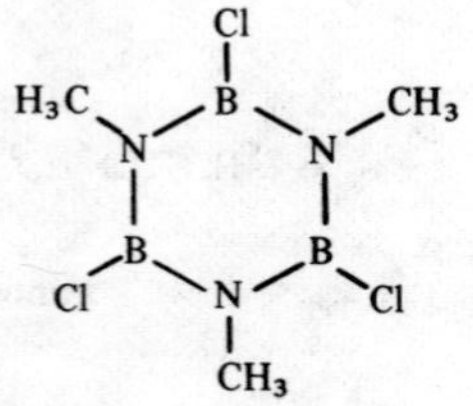	$3e''\pi$		9.45	1,050 (100)	15
				11.11		
				11.58		
				12.30		
				14.1		
				14.7		
				16.7		
				18.0		

TABLE 1 (continued)

	Compound	Orbital	Ionization Energy: Adiabatic	Ionization Energy: Vertical	Vibrational Bands	Reference
$C_3H_9B_3F_3N_3$	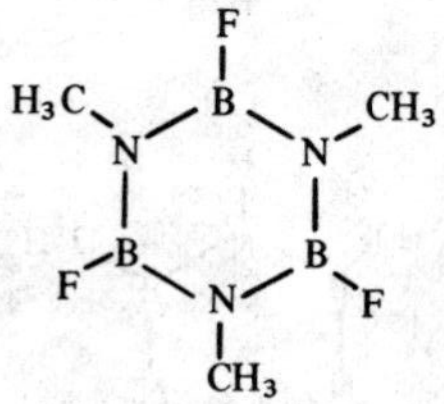	$3e''\pi$		9.48	1,400 (100)	15
		$3a_2''\pi$		11.51		
		$3a_2'$		12.72		
		$2a_2'$		13.8		
		$6e'$		15.0		
		$2a_2''\pi$		16.5		
		$5e'$		18.0		
		$1e''\pi$		19.0		
C_3H_9N	$(CH_3)_2CHNH_2$		8.86			57
			11.23			
			14.87			
			16.41			
			19.09			
C_3H_9N	$(CH_3)_3N$	$1a_2''$		8.5 (1)		4
		$2e'$		15.7 (1)		
		CH		11.6–15		
		$C2s(a_1')$		19.4 (1)		
C_3H_9N	$(CH_3)_3N$	$4a_1$		8.45 (1)		9
		$4e, 1a_2$		12.36 (4) (sh)		
				12.88 (3)		
		3e		13.81 (2)		
		$2e + 3a_1$		15.88 (2)		
C_3H_9N	$(CH_3)_3N$		8.12			57
			11.63			
			13.52			
			15.31			
			19.34			
$C_3H_9N_3Si$	$(CH_3)_3SiN_3$			9.7 (1)		48
				10.3 (1)		
		$[(CH_3)_3Si]$		11.2 (1)		
				12.5–16		

TABLE 1 (continued)

Compound		Orbital	Ionization Energy: Adiabatic	Ionization Energy: Vertical	Vibrational Bands	Reference
$C_3H_{12}BN$	$(CH_3)_3NBH_3$	$e(BH_3)$	9.28 (2)	10.01 (2)	1,000 (30)	9
		5e		10.63 (2) (sh)		
		$5a_1$	11.24 (2)	11.51 (2)		
			12.59 (1)			
		$1e + 4a_2$		13.25 (4) (sh)		
				13.60 (2)		
		$3e + 4a_1$	14.44 (1)	14.71 (2)		
		2e	16.36 (3)	16.78 (2)		
		$3a_1$	17.79 (2)	18.04 (2)		
$C_3H_{12}B_3N_3$	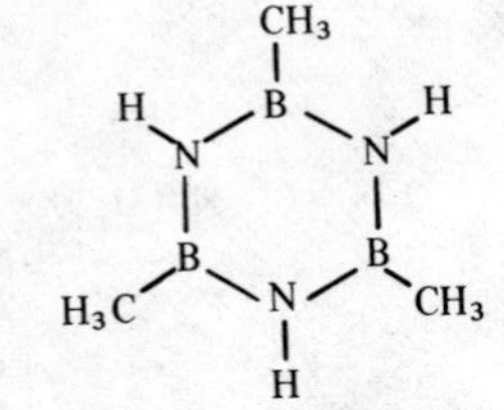	e″		9.64 (3)		98
				10.90 (3)		
				11.87 (1)		
				12.46 (4)		
				14.07 (5)		
				15.24 (1)		
				16.68 (1)		
				17.65 (2)		
$C_3H_{12}B_3N_3$	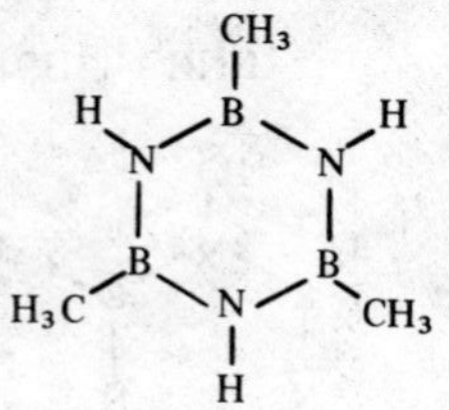	$2e''\pi$		9.50	1,100 (200)	15
		$6e'$		10.60		
		$2a_2''\pi$		11.15		
		$2a_2'$		11.90		
		$4a_1'$		12.50		
		$5e'$		14.0		
		$4e'$		15.2		
		$1e''\pi$		16.75		
		$1a_2''\pi$		18.0		
$C_3H_{12}B_3N_3$	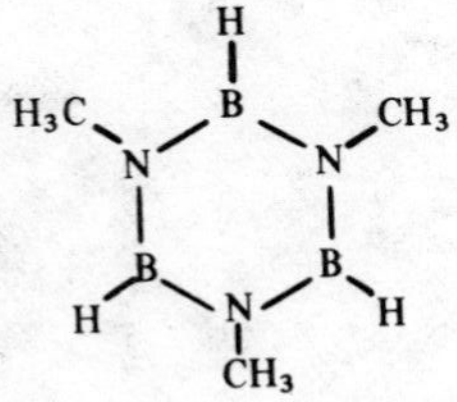	$2e''\pi$		8.99	800 (200)	15
		$2a_2''\pi$		11.1		
		$6e'$		11.45		
		$2a_2'$		12.38		
		$5e'$		13.00		
		$4a_1'$		14.1		
		$1e''\pi$		16.00		
		$1a_2''\pi$		17.6		

TABLE 1 (continued)

Compound		Orbital	Ionization Energy		Vibrational Bands	Reference
			Adiabatic	Vertical		
$C_3H_{12}B_3N_3$	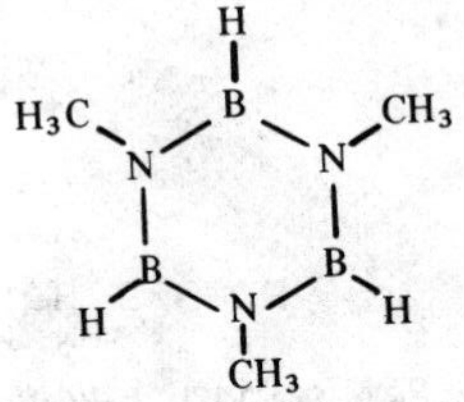	e″		9.28 (2)		98
				11.14 (9)		
				11.48 (10)		
				12.41 (1)		
				12.96 (10)		
				14.05 (20)		
				15.93 (2)		
				17.51 (2)		
C_3N_2O	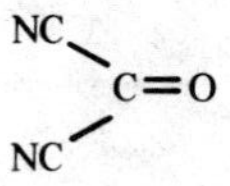	n(O)		12.56		30
				13.76		
				14.41		
				14.79		
		π(C=O)		16.7	1,580	
					700	
				17.9		
C_3O_2	OCCCO	$2\pi_u$	10.60		ν_1 1,950	7
					ν_2 660	
					ν_2 700	
			16.98			
			17.25			
C_4D_2	D–C≡C–C≡C–D		10.18		ν_2 2,041	71
					ν_4 2,219	
					ν_3, 823	
			12.62			
			16.77			
			19.8			
C_4D_2	D–C≡C–C≡C–D		10.18 (1)		ν_4 2,180 (40)	39
					ν_2 1,980 (40)	
			12.62 (1)		ν_3 800 (40)	
					ν_2 1,770 (40)	
			16.74 (1)			
			19.8			

TABLE 1 (continued)

			Ionization Energy			
	Compound	Orbital	Adiabatic	Vertical	Vibrational Bands	Reference
C_4F_6	CF_2=CF–CF=CF_2 (*cis*-bent)		≃9.5	10.4		99
				11.4		
			14.0	14.45		
			15.3	15.75		
				16.3		
				16.6		
			≃18.0	18.8		
				19.4		
				20.7		
			21.5	21.9		
				22.8		
C_4F_8	$CF_3CFCFCF_3$		11.25 (1)			37
			13.75			
			15.14			
			(17.21)			
			19.38			
			20.53			
C_4F_8	*trans*-F_3CFC=$CFCF_3$			11.55		137
				14.16		
C_4H_2	CH≡C–C≡CH		10.17		ν_2 2,121	71
					ν_4 2,703	
				12.62	ν_3 887	
				16.61		
				19.8		
C_4H_2	CH≡C–C≡CH	$1\pi_g$		10.17 (1)	ν_4 2,820 (39)	39
					ν_2 2,120 (40)	
		π		12.62 (1)	ν_3 810 (40)	
					ν_2 1,860 (40)	
				16.61 (1)		
				19.8		

TABLE 1 (continued)

Compound	Orbital	Ionization Energy: Adiabatic	Ionization Energy: Vertical	Vibrational Bands	Reference
$C_4H_2Cl_2S$		8.60 (5)	8.80 (5)	1,615, 325	91
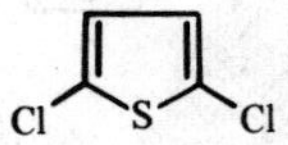		9.71 (5)	9.78 (5)	970	
	(Cl)		11.58		
			12.8		
			13.1		
			14.1		
			14.4		
			16.7		
			17.9		
$C_4H_2F_4$	(π)	8.98	9.38	1,600	99
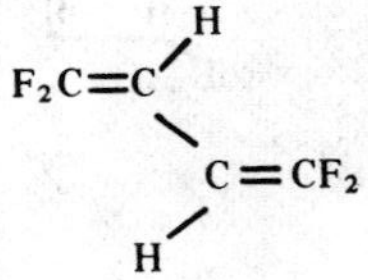		11.55	12.04		
		≃13.5	14.5		
			15.3		
			16.0		
		17.4	18.0		
		19.2	19.6		
		20.7	21.0		
			21.9		
C_4H_3BrS	a″($1a_2$)	8.664	8.664	ν_{14} 0.039	100
				ν_6 0.157	
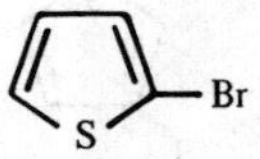	a″($3b_1$)	9.558	9.558	ν_{11} 0.113	
	a′(n)	10.870	10.870	ν_{14} 0.037	
				ν_{13} 0.081	
	a″(n)	11.385	11.385	ν_{14} 0.033	
				ν_{13} 0.074	
	a″($2b_1$)	≃11.93	12.27		
	a′($11a_1$)		≈13.1		
	a′($7b_2$)		≈13.3		
	a ($10a_1$)		≈13.9		
	a′($6b_2$)		≈14.3		
	a′($9a_1$)	16.341	16.341	ν_{11} 0.099	
				CH 0.331	

TABLE 1 (continued)

Compound		Orbital	Ionization Energy: Adiabatic	Ionization Energy: Vertical	Vibrational Bands	Reference
C_4H_3BrS	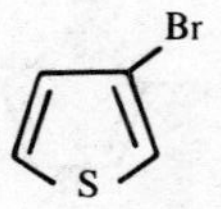	a″($1a_2$)	8.812	8.812	ν_{14} 0.038	100
					ν_6 0.160	
		a″($3b_1$)	9.490	9.490	ν_{11} 0.107	
		a′(n)	10.728	10.728	ν_{14} 0.037	
					ν_{11} 0.102	
		a″(n)	11.265	11.265	ν_{14} 0.036	
					ν_{12} 0.089	
		a″($2b_1$)	≈11.93	12.235	ν_{11} 0.101	
		a′($11a_1$)		≈13.0		
		a′($7b_2$)		≈13.4		
		a($10a_1$)		≈14.0		
		a′($6b_2$)		≈14.4		
		a′($9a_1$)		≈16.36		
C_4H_3BrS	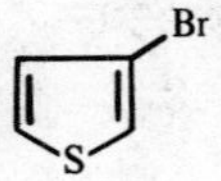		8.90 (5)	9.00 (5)	970	91
			9.51 (5)	9.51 (5)		
		(Br)	10.67 (5)	10.67 (5)		
		(Br)		11.47 (5)		
				12.3		
				13.43 (5)		
				14.1		
				14.4		
				16.4		
				17.75 (5)		
C_4H_3BrS	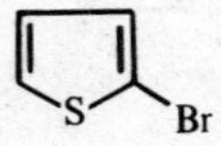		8.50	8.50		91
			9.41	9.41		
		(Br)	10.71	10.74		
		(Br)		11.28		
				12.18		
				13.25		
				13.85		
				16.4		
C_4H_3ClO	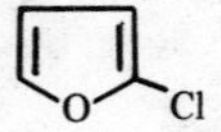		8.75			7
			10.52			
			12.0(2)			

TABLE 1 (continued)

Compound		Orbital	Ionization Energy: Adiabatic	Ionization Energy: Vertical	Vibrational Bands	Reference
C_4H_3ClS	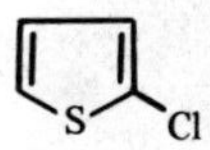		8.70 (5)	8.87 (5)	1,290, 435	91
			9.62	9.62	970	
		(Cl)	11.55	11.55		
		(Cl)		12.02		
				12.36		
				13.88		
				14.37		
				16.64		
				17.6		
C_4H_3IS	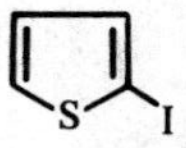		8.55 (5)	8.55 (5)	970	91
			9.47 (5)	9.47 (5)	805	
		(I)	10.00	10.00		
		(I)		10.65		
				12.17		
				12.59		
				13.5		
				16.0		
$C_4H_4N_2$	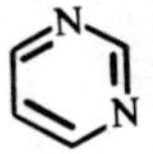	nb	9.42			101·
		π	(9.64)			
			10.39			
			11.06			
			13.62			
			(13.82)			
			15.56			
			(15.84)			
			16.75			
			(19.20)			
$C_4H_4N_2$		$7b_2$	9.32	9.7	ν_{6a} 0.081	53
					ν_1 0.122	
		$2b_1$	10.40	10.5	ν_1 0.120	
					ν_{8a} 0.200	
		$1a_2$	11.1	11.2	ν_1 0.120	

TABLE 1 (continued)

Compound		Orbital	Ionization Energy Adiabatic	Ionization Energy Vertical	Vibrational Bands	Reference
$C_4H_4N_2$ (cont.)		$11a_1$	11.3	11.5		
		$1b_1$	13.6	13.9	ν_{16a} 0.050	
		$6b_2, 10a_1$	~14	~14.5		
		$9a_1$	15.3	15.8		
		$5b_2$	16.6	16.9		
		$8a_1$	17.2	17.4		
		$7a_1, 4b_2$	20.0	20.5		
		$6a_1$	23.4	24.4		
$C_4H_4N_2$		$b_2(n_-)$		9.73		102
		$b_1(\pi)$		10.41		
		$a_1(n_+)$		11.23		
		$a_2(\pi)$		11.39		
$C_4H_4N_2$	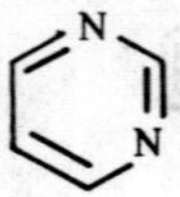		9.44			7
			10.52			
			13.60			
$C_4H_4N_2$	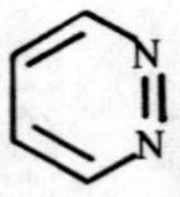	$b_2(n_-)$		9.31		102
		$a_2(\pi)$		10.61		
		$b_1(\pi)$		10.9		
		$a_1(n_+)$		11.31		
		nb	8.90			101
			(9.22)			
			10.53			
			11.16			
			13.63			
			(13.83)			
			15.70			
			16.64			
			(19.25)			
			(19.71)			

TABLE 1 (continued)

	Compound	Orbital	Ionization Energy Adiabatic	Ionization Energy Vertical	Vibrational Bands	Reference
$C_4H_4N_2$	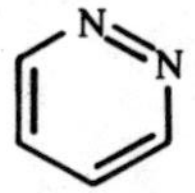	$2b_1$	~11.1	11.3		103
		$1a_2$	10.483 (1)	10.5	ν_{6a} 0.079	
					ν_1 0.117	
					ν_{9a} 0.148	
		$1b_1$	13.504 (3)	13.8	ν_{16a} or ν_{16b} 0.048	
					ν_{6a} 0.080	
					ν_1 0.120	
					ν_{9a} 0.150	
		$7b_2$	8.706 (1)	9.3	ν_{6a} 0.080	
					ν_1 0.130	
		$11a_1$	~11.1	11.3		
		$5b_2$	~16.5	17		
		$6b_2$	~14.5	14.8		
		$10a_1$	~13.8	14.2		
		$8a_1$	~17.0	17.4		
		$9a_1$	15.88	15.9	ν_2 0.320	
		$7a_1,4b_2$	20.0	20.7		
$C_4H_4N_2$			9.29			7
			10.15			
			11.62			
$C_4H_4N_2$		π	9.36			101
			(9.51)			
		nb	10.15			
			11.14			
			11.73			
			13.13			
			(13.38)			
			14.78			
			16.00			
			16.60			
			(19.04)			
			(20.20)			

TABLE 1 (continued)

Compound		Orbital	Ionization Energy		Vibrational Bands	Reference
			Adiabatic	Vertical		
$C_4H_4N_2$	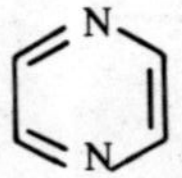	π	9.29		615	104
					ν_4 1,015	
		n	11.2			
		n	11.6			
$C_4H_4N_2$	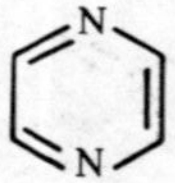	$a_{1g}(n_+)$		9.63		102
		$b_{2g}(\pi)$		10.18		
		$b_{2u}(n_-)$		11.35		
		$b_{1g}(\pi)$		11.77		
$C_4H_4N_2$	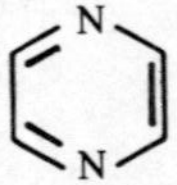	$1b_{1g}$	9.216		ν_{18} 75 meV	105
					ν_2 132 meV	
					ν_{17} 170 meV	
		$5b_{1u}$	11.659		ν_{18} 71 meV	
					ν_2 117 meV	
					ν_{16} 191 meV	
$C_4H_4N_2$	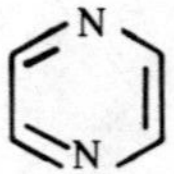	π	9.28 (5)	9.62 (5)	670	82
		n	10.16	10.16		
		π		11.38		
		(π)		11.83		
		(π)	13.1	13.6		
		σ	14.71	14.91		
		σ		16.1		
		σ		16.9		
C_4H_4O			8.89		ν_3 1,300	7
			10.25		1,000	
			17.17		ν_7~900	
					970 (50)	
C_4H_4O			9.42			7

TABLE 1 (continued)

Compound		Orbital	Ionization Energy: Adiabatic	Ionization Energy: Vertical	Vibrational Bands		Reference
C_4H_4O		$1a_2$	8.883		0	0	106
					ν_1	839	
					ν_4	1,073	
					ν_6	1,420	
					$\nu_1+\nu_4$	1,944	
					$\nu_1+\nu_6, 2\nu_4$	2,194	
					$\nu_4+\nu_6$	2,500	
					$2\nu_6$	2,823	
		$2b_1$	10.308		0	0	
					ν_1	871	
					ν_3	952	
					ν_5	1,355	
					$2\nu_1, \nu_1+\nu_3, 2\nu_3$	1,855	
					$3\nu_1, 2\nu_1+\nu_3$, $\nu_1+2\nu_3, 3\nu_3$	2,799	
		$7a_1$	17.4		0	0	
					ν_3	1,024	
					$2\nu_3$	2,048	
					$\nu_8, 3\nu_3$	2,920	
					$\nu_8+\nu_3, 4\nu_3$	3,847	
C_4H_4O			8.89 (5)	8.89 (5)	1,370, 1,050		91
			10.30 (5)	10.42 (5)	970		
			12.63	12.87			
				13.70			
				14.35			
				15.02			
				17.32	100, 354 meV		
C_4H_4O				9.0			94
				10.4			

TABLE 1 (continued)

Compound	Orbital	Ionization Energy: Adiabatic	Ionization Energy: Vertical	Vibrational Bands	Reference
C_4H_4O	$1a_2$	8.883	8.883	ν_1 0.104	107
				ν_4 0.133	
				ν_6 0.196	
	$2b_1$	10.308	10.308	ν_1 0.108	
				ν_5 0.168	
				ν_3 0.118	
	$1b_1$	~13.9	14.4		
	$9a_1$	12.6	13.0		
	$5b_2$	~14.7	15.6		
	$6b_2$	~13.3	13.8		
	$8a_1$	~14.6	15.1		
	$7a_1$	17.4	17.5	ν_3 0.127	
				ν_8 0.360	
	$6a_1$	~18	19.0		
	$4b_2$	~19	19.5		
	$3b_2$	~21.5	~23		
	$5a_1$	~23	~25		
C_4H_4O	π	8.90 (5)	8.90 (5)	1,100	82
				1,330	
	π	10.32	10.32	887	
	σ	12.66	13.06		
	σ	(13.4)	13.8		
	σ	14.2	14.4		
	σ	14.9	15.2		
	π	17.4	(17.5)	887	
				952	
C_4H_4S	π	8.87 (5)	8.87 (5)		82
	π		9.49		
	π?		11.94		
	π?		(12.39)		
	π?		(12.57)		
	π?		13.07		

TABLE 1 (continued)

Compound		Orbital	Ionization Energy: Adiabatic	Ionization Energy: Vertical	Vibrational Bands		Reference
C_4H_4S (cont.)				14.14			
				(15.4)			
			16.26	16.4			
				17.4			
C_4H_4S		$1a_2$	8.872		0	0	106
					ν_1	645	
					ν_4	1,137	
					$2\nu_1$	1,290	
					ν_6	1,395	
					$\nu_1+\nu_4$	1,760	
					$3\nu_1$	1,879	
					$\nu_1+\nu_6$	2,017	
					$2\nu_4$	2,230	
					$\nu_4+\nu_6$	2,492	
		$2b_1$	9.3				
C_4H_4S			8.80 (5)	8.80 (5)	ν_3	1,290	91
						565	
			9.44 (5)	9.44 (5)			
			11.46 (5)	11.86 (5)			
				12.4			
				13.1			
				14.2			
				16.4			
				17.5			
C_4H_4S		$1a_2$	8.872	8.872	ν_1 0.080		108
					ν_4 0.141		
					ν_6 0.173		
		$2b_1$	~9.3	9.52			
		$1b_1$	11.5	12.1	ν_1 0.070		
					ν_3 0.100		
					ν_6 0.168		

TABLE 1 (continued)

			Ionization Energy			
Compound		Orbital	Adiabatic	Vertical	Vibrational Bands	Reference
C_4H_4S (cont.)		$8a_1$	~12.2	12.7		
		$5b_2$	~12.9	13.3		
		$9a_1$	~13.3	~13.9		
		$6b_2$	~13.8	14.3		
		$7a_1$	16.3	16.6	ν_3 0.110	
					ν_6 0.165	
					ν_8 0.365	
		$4b_2$	~17.3	17.6		
		$6a_1$	~17.7	~18.3		
		$3b_2$	~20.9	~22.1		
		$5a_1$	~21.1	~22.3		
$C_4H_5F_3O_2$	$CH_3COOCH_2CF_3$	n_O	10.84	11.15	~1,250 (100)	76
		π_2		11.79		
$C_4H_5F_3O_2$	$CF_3COOC_2H_5$	n_O		~11.6		76
		π_2		11.81		
C_4H_5N	$CH_2{=}CHCH_2CN$	$C{=}C\pi$	10.18	10.56	1,450	19
		$C{\equiv}N\pi$		12.13		
		n(N)		12.95		
				13.34		
				14.63		
				15.93		
				~17.1		
				~19.1		
C_4H_5N		$1a_2$	8.209	8.209	ν_1 0.108	109
					ν_4 0.132	
					ν_5 0.170	
					ν_6 0.182	
		$2b_1$	9.20	9.20	ν_1 0.108	
		$9a_1$	~12.0	12.6		
		$1b_1$	~12.6	~13.0		
		$6b_2$	~13.3	~13.7		

TABLE 1 (continued)

Compound		Orbital	Ionization Energy: Adiabatic	Ionization Energy: Vertical	Vibrational Bands		Reference
C_4H_5N (cont.)		$8a_1$	~13.8	~14.3			
		$5b_2$	~14.3	~14.8			
		$7a_1$	~16.9	~17.5			
		$4b_2$	~17	~18.1			
		$6a_1$	~18	~18.8			
		$3b_2$	~21	~22.3			
		$5a_1$	~22.5	~23.8			
C_4H_5N				8.2			94
				9.2			
C_4H_5N		π	8.20 (5)	8.20 (5)			82
		π	9.16	9.16			
		π	12.09	12.8			
		σ		13.5			
		σ		14.3			
		σ		14.8			
		σ	17.0				
C_4H_5N	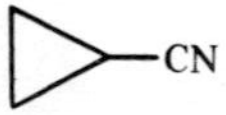			12.62			7
				13.00			
C_4H_5N		$1a_2$	8.209		0	0	106
					ν_1	871	
					ν_4	1,065	
					ν_5	1,371	
					ν_6	1,468	
					$2\nu_1$	1,742	
					$\nu_1+\nu_4$	1,936	
					$2\nu_4$	2,129	
					$\nu_4+\nu_5$	2,460	
					$\nu_4+\nu_6$	2,541	
					$\nu_5+\nu_6$	2,839	
		$2b_1$	9.2		0	0	
					ν_1	871	

TABLE 1 (continued)

	Compound	Orbital	Ionization Energy: Adiabatic	Ionization Energy: Vertical	Vibrational Bands	Reference
C_4H_5N			8.22 (5)	8.22 (5)	1,450, 1,050	91
			9.22 (5)	9.22 (5)	970	
				12.70		
				12.95		
				13.6		
				14.4		
				14.95		
				17.8		
C_4H_6	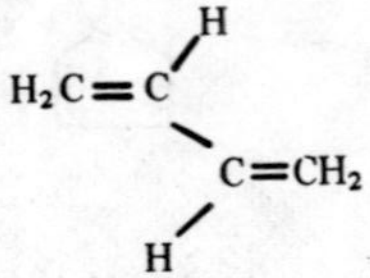	$1b_g(\pi)$	9.06	9.06	520	99
					1,200	
					1,500	
		$1a_u(\pi)$				
		$7a_g(\sigma)$	11.22	11.47,12.23		
		$6b_u(\sigma)$	12.99	13.5		
		$6a_g(\sigma)$		13.9		
		$5b_u(\sigma)$	$\simeq 15.0$	15.28		
		$5a_g(\sigma)$		16.1(?)		
		$4b_u(\sigma)$	17.5	18.0		
		$4a_g(\sigma)$		19.1		
		$3b_u(\sigma)$	21.2	22.4		
C_4H_6	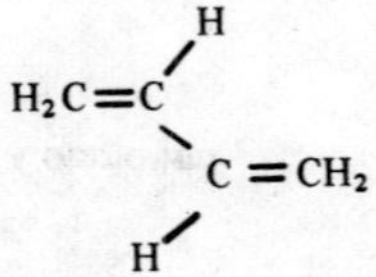	π	9.09 (5)	9.09 (5)	ν_4 1,400	82
		π	(11.2)	11.55		
			(12.0)	12.35		
			13.05	(13.7)		
			15.1	15.31		
				(17.7)		
C_4H_6	*trans*-$CH_2CHCHCH_2$		9.07			110

TABLE 1 (continued)

	Compound	Orbital	Ionization Energy: Adiabatic	Ionization Energy: Vertical	Vibrational Bands	Reference
C_4H_6	$CH_2CHCHCH_2$		9.08 11.25 12.14 13.23 15.14 18.78 20.57			57
C_4H_6	$H_2CCHCHCH_2$		9.08		1,520 1,180 500	7
C_4H_6	*trans*-$CH_2CHCHCH_2$	π	9.07 (1) 11.27 12.17 13.11 15.16 (17.78) (19.02) (20.56)			37
C_4H_6	*cis*- 	π σ	9.43 10.6 (1)	9.43 11.3 (1)	1,320	93
C_4H_6O	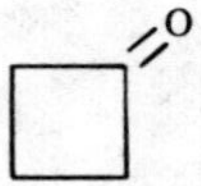	n σ onset	 11.4	9.61 (2)		111
C_4H_6O	$CH_3CH{=}CHCHO$		9.77 10.21			7

TABLE 1 (continued)

	Compound	Orbital	Ionization Energy: Adiabatic	Ionization Energy: Vertical	Vibrational Bands	Reference
$C_4H_6O_2$	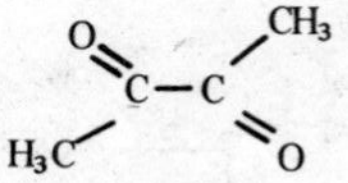	n_+ n_-		9.55 11.43		80
$C_4H_6O_2S$	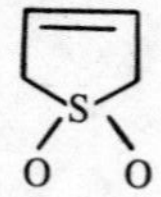	π		10.44 10.66 11.25 11.63 11.99	ν_2 1,200 (100) ν_3 560 (100)	218
C_4H_8	$CH_2CHCH_2CH_3$	π	9.59 (1) 11.30 14.46			37
C_4H_8	*trans*-$H_3CHC{=}CHCH_3$			9.11 11.90		137
C_4H_8	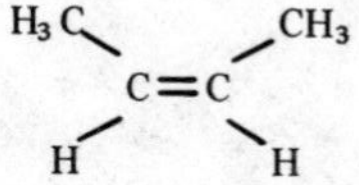		9.07 11.27 12.42 13.19 17.40 19.10	9.32 11.52 12.52 13.89		83
C_4H_8	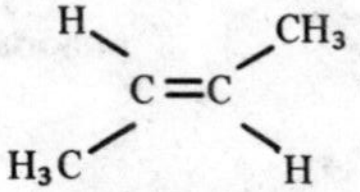	π	9.12 (1) 11.28 12.40 (13.74) (14.75) 16.07 (18.84)			37

TABLE 1 (continued)

	Compound	Orbital	Ionization Energy: Adiabatic	Ionization Energy: Vertical	Vibrational Bands	Reference
C_4H_8	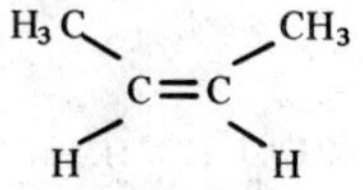	π		9.11	0.17	86
C_4H_8	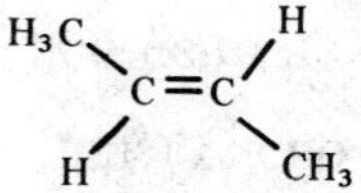	$a_u(\pi)$		9.11, 9.28		87
				9.47, 9.63		
		σ	11.4	11.9		
		σ		12.7		
		σ	15.1			
C_4H_8	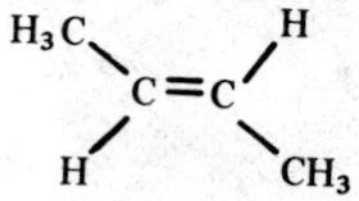		9.09	9.35		83
			11.43	11.62		
			12.49	12.84		
			14.14	14.79		
			17.64			
			19.17			
C_4H_8	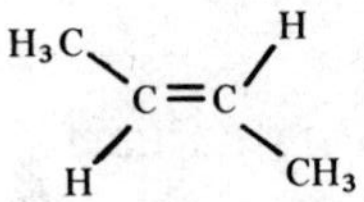	π	9.12 (1)			37
			11.46			
			12.58			
			13.99			
C_4H_8		4e		10.7, 11.3		112
		$4a_1$		11.7		
		$1b_1$		12.5		
		3e		13.4, 13.6		
		$3a_1$		15.9		
		$3b_2$		18.2		
C_4H_8	$(H_3C)_2C{=}CH_2$		9.21	9.44		83
			11.35	11.59		
			12.58	13.21		
			14.71	15.32		
			17.09			
			[illegible]			

TABLE 1 (continued)

	Compound	Orbital	Ionization Energy: Adiabatic	Ionization Energy: Vertical	Vibrational Bands	Reference
C_4H_8	$CH_2=C(CH_3)_2$		9.17 (1) 11.36 12.65 14.73 17.28			37
$C_4H_8Cl_2$	$ClCH_2CH_2CH_2CH_2Cl$		11.03	11.18 12.24 12.90 14.90 15.60 16.20		60
C_4H_8O	$CH_3CH_2CH_2CHO$		9.73 (3)			59
C_4H_8O	$(CH_3)_2CHCHO$		9.69 (1)			59
C_4H_8O	$CH_3C(=O)CH_2CH_3$		9.51 (1) 11.74 14.11 (15.92)			37
C_4H_8O	$CH_3CH_2C(=O)CH_3$		9.54 (1)			59
C_4H_8OS	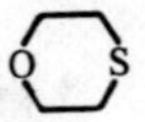	n(S) n(O)		8.67 10.00		97
$C_4H_8O_2$	$CH_3COOCH_2CH_3$	n_O π_2	10.24	10.39 10.99	1,200 (50)	76

TABLE 1 (continued)

	Compound	Orbital	Ionization Energy: Adiabatic	Ionization Energy: Vertical	Vibrational Bands	Reference
$C_4H_8O_2$	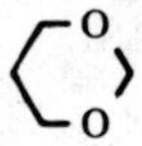	n n		10.1 10.35		97
$C_4H_8O_2$	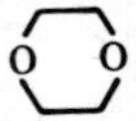	n n		9.43 10.65		97
$C_4H_8O_2$	$HCOOCH_2CH_2CH_3$	n_O π_2	10.62	10.95 11.19	1,370 (50)	76
$C_4H_8S_2$	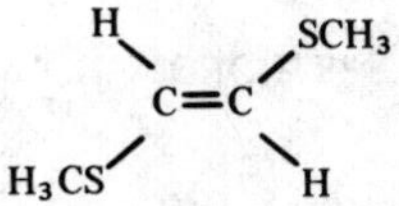			7.96		61
$C_4H_8S_2$	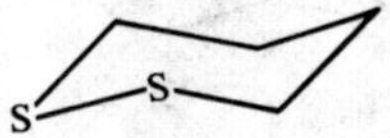			8.36 9.31		61
$C_4H_8S_2$	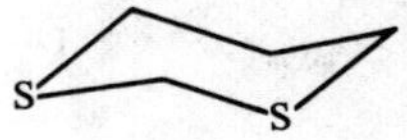			8.33 8.76		61
$C_4H_8S_2$	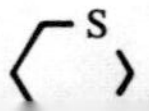	n n		8.54 8.95		97

TABLE 1 (continued)

			Ionization Energy			
	Compound	Orbital	Adiabatic	Vertical	Vibrational Bands	Reference
$C_4H_8S_2$		n n		8.58 9.03		97
$C_4H_8S_2$				8.46 8.95		61
C_4H_9Br	$CH_3CH_2CH_2CH_2Br$	n n	10.13 10.44			54
C_4H_9Br	$(CH_3)_2CHCH_2Br$	n n	10.10 10.41			54
C_4H_9Br	$(CH_3)_3CBr$	n n	9.95 10.24			54
C_4H_9Br	$CH_3CH_2CH_2CH_2Br$	$^2E_{3/2}$ $^2E_{1/2}$		10.15 10.44 11.38 12.03 12.45 12.9 (sh) 13.30 14.25 14.85 16.00		235
C_4H_9Cl	$CH_3CH_2CH_2CH_2Cl$			10.84 11.61 12.13 12.6 (sh) 13.14 13.60 14.45 15.1_5 (sh) 16.25		235

TABLE 1 (continued)

			Ionization Energy			
Compound		Orbital	Adiabatic	Vertical	Vibrational Bands	Reference
C_4H_9I	$CH_3CH_2CH_2CH_2I$	$^2E_{3/2}$ $^2E_{1/2}$		9.24 9.79 11.22 11.90 12.3 (sh) 12.50 12.8_5 (sh) 14.1 (sh) 14.70 15.75		235
C_4H_9I	$CH_3CH_2CH_2CH_2I$	$p_{3/2,1/2}$	9.23, 9.78 (05)			59
C_4H_9I	$(CH_3)_2CHCH_2I$	$p_{3/2,1/2}$	9.18, 9.73 (05)			59
C_4H_9I	$(CH_3)_3CI$	$p_{3/2,1/2}$	9.02, 9.52 (1)			59
C_4H_9N	$CH_3CH{=}NCH_2CH_3$		9.29 10.57 11.63 12.55 14.36 15.63 19.73			57
C_4H_9N	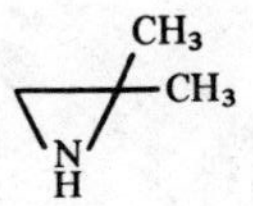		8.94 (9.24) 10.71 (10.98) 12.89 16.59 (18.62)			64

TABLE 1 (continued)

	Compound	Orbital	Ionization Energy: Adiabatic	Ionization Energy: Vertical	Vibrational Bands	Reference
C_4H_9N	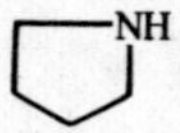		8.41			57
			11.10			
			14.13			
			16.64			
			18.62			
C_4H_9NO	$CH_3CON(CH_3)_2$	n_O		9.43	~1,400 (100)	76
		π_2		9.09		
C_4H_9NOSi	$(CH_3)_3SiNCO$			10.3 (1)		48
		$[(CH_3)_3Si]$		11.5 (1)		
				12.5–16		
$C_4H_9NO_2$	$CH_3CH_2CH_2CH_2NO_2$		10.71 (1)			55
			(11.02)			
			13.51			
			(13.79)			
			16.80			
			18.14			
			(19.42)			
$C_4H_9NO_2$	$CH_3CH_2CH(NO_2)CH_3$		10.71 (1)			55
			11.87			
			13.74			
			(14.34)			
			(14.78)			
			16.71			
			17.51			
			18.08			
C_4H_9NSSi	$(CH_3)_3SiNCS$			9.31 (1)		48
		$[(CH_3)_3Si]$		11.0 (1)		
				12.5–16		

TABLE 1 (continued)

Compound		Orbital	Ionization Energy: Adiabatic	Ionization Energy: Vertical	Vibrational Bands	Reference
C_4H_{10}	$CH_3CH_2CH_2CH_3$		10.50 12.36 14.13 15.70 18.57 20.16			57
C_4H_{10}	$CH_3CH_2CH_2CH_3$	σ	10.67 (1) 14.14			37
C_4H_{10}	$CH_3CH(CH_3)CH_3$		10.78 12.54 14.51 15.69 19.96			57
C_4H_{10}	$CH_3-CH(CH_3)-CH_3$	5e $6a_1$ $1a_2$ 4e 3e $5a_1$ $4a_1$		11.4 12.1 12.8 13.4 14.9 16.0	1,360 (30)	215
C_4H_{10}	$CH_3CH(CH_3)CH_3$	σ	10.69 (1) 12.47 14.73			37
$C_4H_{10}Hg$	$Hg(CH_2CH_3)_2$	$^2D_{5/2}(\pm5/2)$ $^2D_{3/2}(\pm3/2,\pm1/2)$		14.68 16.61		31
$C_4H_{10}O$	$CH_3CH_2CH_2CH_2OH$		10.09 (2)			59

TABLE 1 (continued)

	Compound	Orbital	Ionization Energy		Vibrational Bands	Reference
			Adiabatic	Vertical		
$C_4H_{10}O$	$CH_3CH_2CH_2CH_2OH$		10.37			60
				11.48		
				11.95		
				12.25		
				12.55		
				13.55		
				15.10		
$C_4H_{10}O$	$(CH_3)_2CHCH_2OH$		10.09 (2)			59
$C_4H_{10}O$	$(CH_3)_3COH$		9.97 (2)			59
$C_4H_{10}O$	$(CH_3)_3COH$		10.23			60
				11.48		
				12.35		
				12.78		
				15.42		
				16.50		
$C_4H_{10}O$	$(CH_2CH_3)_2O$		9.61			57
			11.08			
			11.92			
			16.23			
			19.67			
$C_4H_{10}O$	$(CH_3CH_2)_2O$		9.51 (1)			37
			11.03			
			(11.92)			
			16.22			
$C_4H_{10}O$	$(CH_3CH_2)_2O$		9.50 (1)			59
$C_4H_{10}S$	$(C_2H_5)_2S$			8.44		61

TABLE 1 (continued)

Compound		Orbital	Ionization Energy Adiabatic	Ionization Energy Vertical	Vibrational Bands	Reference
$C_4H_{10}S_2$	$C_2H_5SSC_2H_5$			8.70		61
				8.97		
$C_4H_{10}S_2$	$CH_3S(CH_2)_2SCH_3$			8.64		61
				8.90		
$C_4H_{11}ClSi$	$(CH_3)_3SiCH_2Cl$	Si-C		10.17 (10)		222
		Cl lone pairs		11.0 (1)		
		C-Cl		12.24 (10)		
		C-H		14.3 (1)		
				16.0 (1) (sh)		
$C_4H_{11}N$	n-$C_4H_9NH_2$		8.79			57
			10.75			
			14.11			
			15.28			
			19.35			
$C_4H_{11}N$	t-$C_4H_9NH_2$		8.83			57
			9.81			
			12.46			
			15.11			
			19.46			
$C_4H_{11}N$	$(CH_3CH_2)_2NH$		8.51			57
			11.08			
			14.45			
			19.18			
$C_4H_{12}BBrN_2$	$[(CH_3)_2N]_2BBr$	π(nb)		8.13		85
		π		9.30		
				10.10		
				10.92		
				12.1		
				12.7		
				17.1		

TABLE 1 (continued)

Compound		Orbital	Ionization Energy		Vibrational Bands	Reference
			Adiabatic	Vertical		
$C_4H_{12}BClN_2$	$[(CH_3)_2N]_2BCl$	π(nb)		8.08		85
		π		9.42		
				10.90		
				11.68		
				12.3		
				13.1		
				15.7		
				17.5		
$C_4H_{12}BFN_2$	$[(CH_3)_2N]_2BF$	π(nb)		8.04		85
		π		9.53		
				12.2		
				13.6		
				14.9		
				16.8		
				17.8		
$C_4H_{12}BN$	$(CH_3)_2NB(CH_3)_2$	π		8.92		85
				10.40		
				11.9		
				12.4		
				13.2		
				15.3		
				16.7		
$C_4H_{12}Ge$	$Ge(CH_3)_4$	Onset	9.33			43
		$3t_2(b_2)$		9.89		
		(e)		10.21,10.5		
		$1t_1$		~13.0		
		1e		15.8		
		$2t_2$		~14.0		
		$2a_1$		~14.0		

TABLE 1 (continued)

	Compound	Orbital	Ionization Energy: Adiabatic	Ionization Energy: Vertical	Vibrational Bands	Reference
$C_4H_{12}Ge$	$(CH_3)_4Ge$		9.38 (10)			113
		$3t_2$		10.23 (10)		
		t_1, e, $2t_2$ }		~13.0 (sh)		
				13.85 (10)		
		$2a_1$		~15.9		
$C_4H_{12}N_2$	$(CH_3)_2NN(CH_3)_2$		7.93			64
			(8.24)			
			11.91			
			(18.69)			
$C_4H_{12}Pb$	$Pb(CH_3)_4$	Onset	8.50			43
		$3t_2$ $(g_{3/2})$		9.10		
		$(e_{5/2})$		9.75		
		$1t_1$ (a_2)		12.9		
		(e)		13.1		
		$1e(a_1)$		15.0		
		(b_1)		15.2		
		$2t_2$		13.7		
		$2a_1$		11.5		
		$1a_1$		16.4	ν_2 0.1	
$C_4H_{12}Pb$	$(CH_3)_4Pb$	(Threshold)	8.38 (10)			113
		$3t_2$		{ 8.81 (10), 9.09 (10), 9.86 (10)		
		t_1, e, $2t_2$ }		~13.3 (1)		
		$2a_1$		~15.3 (1)		

TABLE 1 (continued)

	Compound	Orbital	Ionization Energy: Adiabatic	Ionization Energy: Vertical	Vibrational Bands	Reference
$C_4H_{12}Si$	$Si(CH_3)_4$	Onset	9.79			43
		(b_2)		10.29		
		$3t_2$ (e)		10.62, 10.9		
		$1t_1$ (a_2)		12.7		
		(e)		12.9		
		1e		15.6		
		$2t_2$ (b_2)		13.8		
		(e)		14.1		
		$2a_1$		14.5		
$C_4H_{12}Si$	$(CH_3)_4Si$		9.42 (10)			113
		$3t_2$		10.57 (10)		
		t_1, e, $2t_2$		13.06 (10), 14.08 (10)		
		$2a_1$		15.58 (10)		
$C_4H_{12}Sn$	$Sn(CH_3)_4$	Onset	8.93			43
		$3t_2$ (b_2)		9.36		
		(e)		9.65, 9.85		
		$1t_1$ (a_2)		12.8		
		(e)		13.0		
		1e		14.8		
		$2t_2$		~13.8		
		$2a_1$		12.1		
$C_4H_{12}Sn$	$(CH_3)_4Sn$		8.85 (10)			113
		$3t_2$		9.70 (10)		
		t_1,e,$2t_2$		~13.4 (1)		
$C_4H_{13}BN_2$	$[(CH_3)_2N]_2BH$	π(nb)		7.76		85
		π		8.66		
				11.7		
				12.9		
				13.7		
				15.7		
				17.25		

TABLE 1 (continued)

Compound		Orbital	Ionization Energy: Adiabatic	Ionization Energy: Vertical	Vibrational Bands	Reference
C_4N_2	N≡C–C≡C–C≡N	$2\pi_u$	11.81 (1)		ν_1 2,200 (40)	39
			13.89 (1)			
		$1\pi_u$	14.95 (1)		ν_2 2,100 (40)	
					ν_3 590 (40)	
C_4NiO_4	$Ni(CO)_4$	t_2	8.24 (14)	8.93 (5)		114
		e	9.58 (5)	9.76 (6)		
C_5ClMnO_5	$Mn(CO)_5Cl$	7e		8.80 (25)		20
		6e		10.43 (25)		
		$2b_2$		11.00 (25)		
		5σ		14.4		
		1π		15.2		
		4σ		18.7		
C_5F_5N	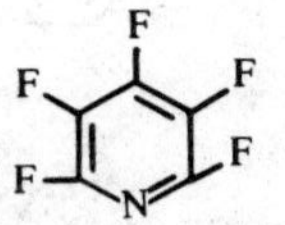		10.08	10.27	ν'_1 1,450	160
			11.17	11.37	ν'_1 1,530	
				12.08		
			13.46	13.62	ν'_1 or ν'_3 1,330	
					ν'_6 650 (?)	
			14.20	14.38	ν'_1 1,370	
					980 (?)	
			15.32	15.45	ν'_1 1,200	
			~16.04	16.27		
			~17.3	17.6		
			~18.0	18.6		
			~19.8	20.5		
			~21.7	22.2		
				22.7		
C_5FeO_5	$Fe(CO)_5$	e′	8.00 (8)	8.60 (4)		114
		e″	9.50 (6)	9.86 (4)		

TABLE 1 (continued)

	Compound	Orbital	Ionization Energy: Adiabatic	Ionization Energy: Vertical	Vibrational Bands	Reference
C_5HMnO_5	$Mn(CO)_5H$	6e		9.00 (25)		20
		$2b_2$		10.60 (25)		
		5σ		13.80 (25)		
		1π		14.6		
		4σ		17.97 (25)		
C_5H_4BrN	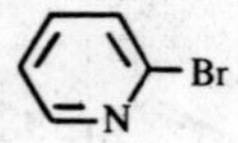		9.2			7
			10.48			
C_5H_4ClN	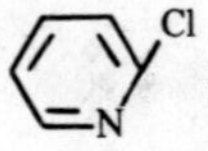		9.69			7
			11.46			
			12.08			
C_5H_4ClN	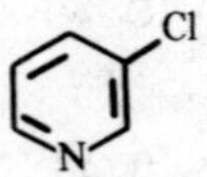		9.38			7
			10.48			
			11.70			
			12.31			
C_5H_4ClN	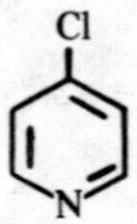		11.8(0)			7

TABLE 1 (continued)

Compound		Orbital	Ionization Energy: Adiabatic	Ionization Energy: Vertical	Vibrational Bands	Reference
$C_5H_4O_2$	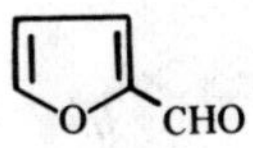		9.22 (1)			37
			9.79			
			10.71			
			(12.61)			
			13.24			
			(17.17)			
			(18.24)			
			(21.06)			
$C_5H_4S_3$	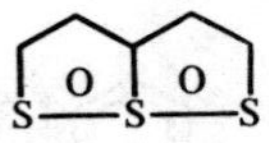	π_1		8.11		115
		n_1		8.27		
		π_2		9.58		
		π_3		10.01		
				10.64		
				11.10		
$C_5H_5F_2P$	$F_2PC_5H_5$	P3p		11.4		21
		PC		15.2		
		CH,CCσ		12–14.5		
C_5H_5N	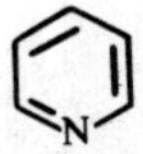	a_1 (n)		9.59		102
		a_2 (π)		9.73		
		b_1 (π)		10.50		
C_5H_5N	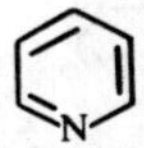		9.28			57
		nb	10.54			
			12.22			
			13.43			
			14.44			
			15.49			
			16.94			
			19.39			
			20.14			

TABLE 1 (continued)

Compound		Orbital	Ionization Energy: Adiabatic	Ionization Energy: Vertical	Vibrational Bands	Reference
C_5H_5N			9.26		ν_5 560	7
		n(N)	10.5			
			12.27		560	
					1,650	
			13.0			
			13.8			
			14.2			
			15.6			
			16.9			
C_5H_5N	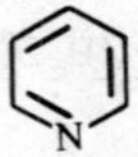	π	9.3		ν_5 560	104
		n	9.6			
		π	10.5			
C_5H_5N	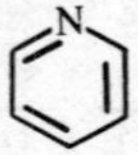	π	9.31			101
		nb	(9.51)			
			10.45			
			12.30			
			(13.83)			
			(14.54)			
			15.51			
			17.19			
			(19.21)			
C_5H_6			8.55			110
C_5H_6		$1a_2$	8.566	8.566	ν_1 0.100	116
					ν_4 0.138	
					ν_6 0.178	
		$2b_1$	10.620	10.724	ν_1 0.104	
		$8a_1$	11.7	~12.2		
		$1b_1$	~12.3	~12.6		
		$9a_1$ or $5b_2$	~12.7	13.2		
		$6b_2$	~13.3	13.8		
		$9a_1$ or $5b_2$	~13.9	14.8		

TABLE 1 (continued)

Compound		Orbital	Ionization Energy: Adiabatic	Ionization Energy: Vertical	Vibrational Bands	Reference
C_5H_6 (cont.)		$7a_1$	16.1	16.4	ν_3 0.110; ν_6 or ν_{10} 0.175	
		$4b_2$	~17	17.5		
		$6a_1$	~17.5	18.4		
		$5a_1$	~21	22.0		
		$3b_2$	~21.5	22.3		
C_5H_6		π	8.55 (1)			37
			10.57			
			11.84			
			14.64			
			16.30			
			(18.70)			
C_5H_6			8.61 (5)	8.61 (5)	1,460, 810	91
			10.60 (5)	10.70 (5)	805	
			11.78	12.59		
				14.75		
				16.35		
C_5H_6		$1a_2$	8.566		0 — 0	106
					ν_1 — 807	
					ν_4 — 1,113	
					ν_6 — 1,436	
					$\nu_1+\nu_6$ — 2,218	
					$\nu_4+\nu_6$ — 2,525	
					$2\nu_6$ — 2,871	
					$\nu_1+2\nu_6$ — 3,622	
		$2b_1$	10.620		0 — 0	
					ν_1 — 839	
					$2\nu_1$ — 1,614	

TABLE 1 (continued)

Compound		Orbital	Ionization Energy: Adiabatic	Ionization Energy: Vertical	Vibrational Bands	Reference
C_5H_6O	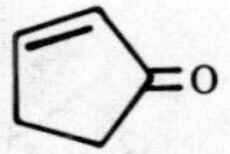	n π		9.34 (2) 10.10 (2) 11.9–15.3 16.23 (2)	663 (40) 1,089 (40) 1,417 (40)	117
C_5H_6O	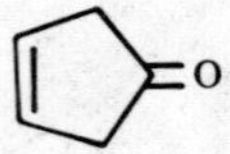	n π		9.44 (2) 9.98 (2) 12.0–15.1 16.22 (2)	1,423 (40) 1,204 (40)	117
C_5H_6S	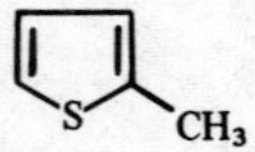		8.14 8.96	8.32 8.96 11.8 12.4 13.0 13.7 16.1		91
C_5H_6S	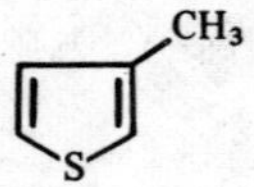		8.40 9.11	8.54 9.11 11.94 12.5 13.1 13.8 15.9 17.2		91
C_5H_7N			7.95 (5) 8.80 (5) 11.92	7.95 (5) 8.80 (5) 12.67 13.8 17.1		91

TABLE 1 (continued)

	Compound	Orbital	Ionization Energy: Adiabatic	Ionization Energy: Vertical	Vibrational Bands	Reference
C_5H_8	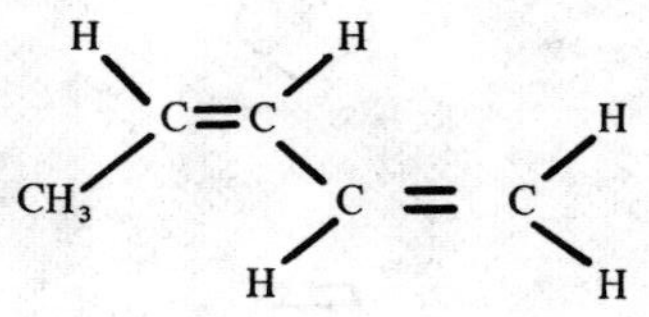	π	8.59 (1) 10.89 11.69 12.52 13.67 (15.75) (17.72) (18.40) (18.92) (20.51)			37
C_5H_8	*cis*-$CH_2CHCHCHCH_3$		8.59			110
C_5H_8	*trans*-$CH_2CHCHCHCH_3$		8.56			110
C_5H_8	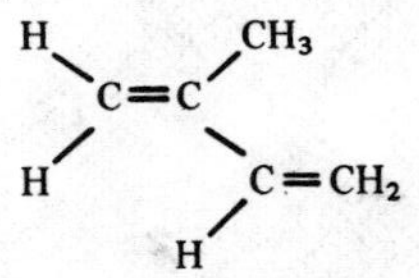			9.04 11.0 11.8		118
C_5H_8	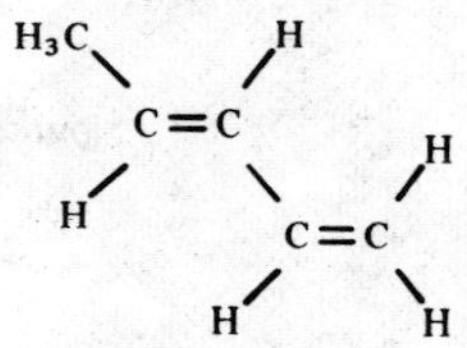	π	8.56 (1) 10.95 11.65 (12.53) (13.63) (15.68) (17.76) (20.47)			37

TABLE 1 (continued)

Compound		Orbital	Ionization Energy: Adiabatic	Ionization Energy: Vertical	Vibrational Bands	Reference
C_5H_8	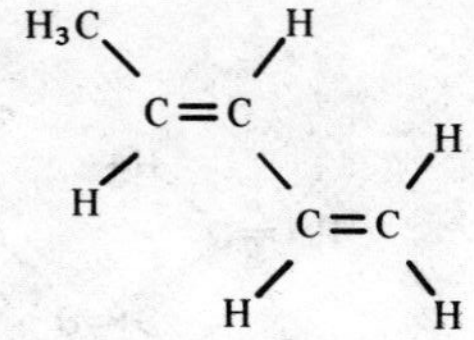		8.58	8.78 11.2 12.1		118
C_5H_8		π	9.00 (1) 11.10 (15.51) (18.33)			37
C_5H_8	 *cis*	π σ σ	9.01 10.9 (1)	9.18 11.7 (1) (sh) 12.1 (1)	1,320	93
C_5H_8			9.01 (1)			119
C_5H_8	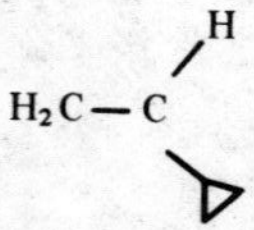	5a″(π) 14a′(σ) 4a″(π)		9.2 10.7 11.7		120

TABLE 1 (continued)

	Compound	Orbital	Ionization Energy: Adiabatic	Ionization Energy: Vertical	Vibrational Bands	Reference
C_5H_8	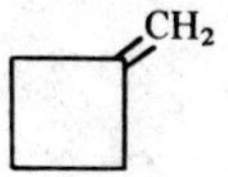	π	9.12 10.44 11.6 14.4 15.6 16.9 18.7 19.4	10.06 (11.3) 12.6 15.1 16.6		121
C_5H_8	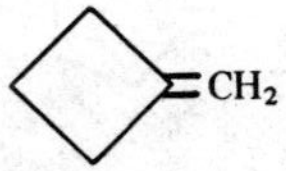		9.19		1,320	7
C_5H_8			9.45 (1) 11.89 15.50 18.04 (18.69) (19.17)			37
			9.45 11.89 15.50 18.04 (18.69) (19.17)			122
C_5H_8O	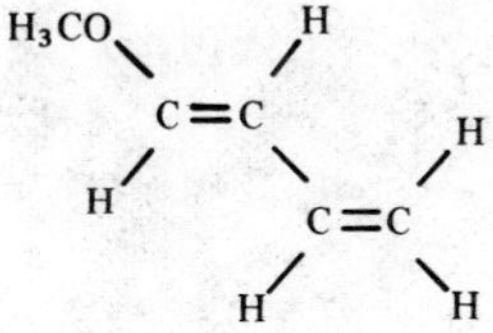		8.03	8.21 10.7 12.2		118

TABLE 1 (continued)

			Ionization Energy			
Compound		Orbital	Adiabatic	Vertical	Vibrational Bands	Reference
C_5H_8O	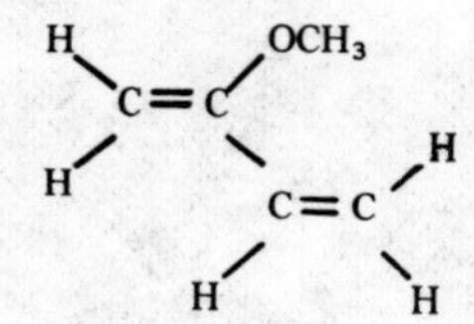		8.43	8.62		118
				10.1		
				12.2		
C_5H_8O	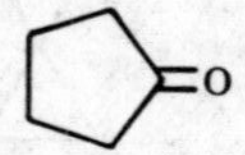		9.28 (1)			59
C_5H_8O	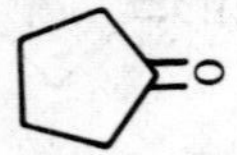	n		9.25	710 (40)	111
					1,220 (40)	
		σ onset	11.3			
C_5H_8O	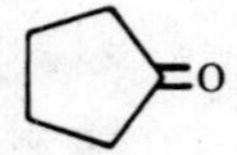	n		9.25 (2)	710 (40)	117
					1,220 (40)	
				11.3–15.3		
				15.94 (2)		
				16.56 (2)		
C_5H_9BrSi	$(CH_3)_3Si{-}C{\equiv}CBr$	12e	9.4 (1)	9.6 (1)		123
		11e	10.5 (1)	10.8 (1)		
		$19a_1$	11.8 (1)	12.1 (1)		
		10e	12.3 (1)	12.6 (1)		
		$1a_2$,9e, 8e, $18a_1$	13.0–15.0			
		$17a_1$	15.6 (1)	15.8 (1)		
		$16a_1$		16.7 (1)		

TABLE 1 (continued)

	Compound	Orbital	Ionization Energy: Adiabatic	Ionization Energy: Vertical	Vibrational Bands	Reference
C_5H_9ClSi	$(CH_3)_3Si{-}C{\equiv}CCl$	9e	9.4 (1)	9.7 (1)		123
		8e	10.6 (1)	10.9 (1)		
		$16a_1$	11.9 (1)	12.1 (1)		
		$1a_2$, 7e, 6e, $15a_1$		12.9–15.0		
		5e		13.6 (1)		
		$14a_1$	16.1 (1)	16.2 (1)		
		$13a_1$	17.0 (1)	17.2 (1)		
C_5H_9FSi	$(CH_3)_3Si{-}C{\equiv}CF$	8e	9.8 (1)	10.2 (1)		123
		7e	10.9 (1)	11.1 (1)		
		$14a_1$	12.0 (1)	12.3 (1)		
		$1a_2$, 6e, 5e, $13a_1$		12.9–15.0		
		$12a_1$	16.4 (1)	16.7 (1)		
		4e		17.4 (1)		
C_5H_9ISi	$(CH_3)_3Si{-}C{\equiv}CI$	15e	9.1 (1)	9.4 (1)		123
		14e	10.4 (1)			
		13e	11.5 (1)	11.8 (1)		
		$1a_2$, 12e, 11e, $21a_1$		13.1–15.1		
		$19a_1$		16.6 (1)		
C_5H_{10}	$H(H_3C)C{=}C(CH_3)_2$	$2p_x+2p_x$	8.72	8.92		83
		$2p_y-2p_y$	11.08	11.23		
		$2p_\sigma+2p_\sigma$	12.23	13.03		
		$\pi(CH_3)$	14.65	15.10		
		$2p_y+2p_y$	16.83	16.83		
		2s-2s	18.90			
C_5H_{10}	$CH_2{=}CHCH(CH_3)_2$		9.52 (1)			37
			11.00			
			13.11			
			(14.74)			
C_5H_{10}			10.49 (1)			37
			13.89			
			15.91			
			(18.27)			

TABLE 1 (continued)

	Compound	Orbital	Ionization Energy: Adiabatic	Ionization Energy: Vertical	Vibrational Bands	Reference
C_5H_{10}	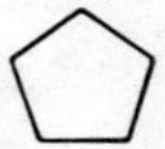		10.50 (1)			119
$C_5H_{10}O$	$CH_3CH_2CH_2CH_2CHO$		9.77 (1)			59
$C_5H_{10}O$	$(CH_3)_2CHCH_2CHO$		9.68 (2)			59
$C_5H_{10}O$	$(CH_3)_3CCHO$		9.51 (1)			59
$C_5H_{10}O$	$CH_3CH_2CH_2\overset{O}{\overset{\Vert}{C}}CH_3$		9.40 (1)			59
$C_5H_{10}O$	$(CH_3)_2CH\overset{O}{\overset{\Vert}{C}}CH_3$		9.30 (1)			59
$C_5H_{10}O$	$CH_3CH_2\overset{O}{\overset{\Vert}{C}}CH_2CH_3$		9.31 (2)			59
$C_5H_{10}O$	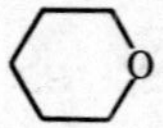	n		9.50		97
$C_5H_{10}O_2$	$HCOOCH_2CH_2CH_2CH_3$	n_O π_2	10.54	10.88 11.06	1,370 (50)	76
$C_5H_{10}O_2$	$CH_3COOC(H)(CH_3)_2$	n_O π_2	10.08	10.38 10.77	1,200 (50)	76
$C_5H_{10}O_2$	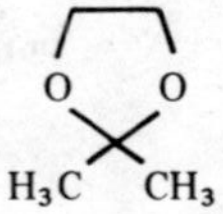	n n		9.71 10.20		97

TABLE 1 (continued)

	Compound	Orbital	Ionization Energy: Adiabatic	Ionization Energy: Vertical	Vibrational Bands	Reference
$C_5H_{10}S$	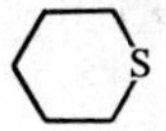	n		8.45		97
$C_5H_{10}Si$	$(CH_3)_3Si{-}C{\equiv}CH$	7e	9.9 (1)	10.2 (1)		123
		6e	10.9 (1)	11.0 (1)		
		$12a_1$	11.9 (1)	12.1 (1)		
		$1a_2$, 5e, 4e, $11a_1$		12.9–14.9		
		$10a_1$	16.0 (1)	16.1 (1)		
$C_5H_{11}Br$	$(CH_3)_3CCH_2Br$	n	10.04			54
		n	10.34			
$C_5H_{11}I$	n-$C_5H_{11}I$		9.21			60
				9.77		
				11.06		
				11.60		
				13.00		
				14.50		
				16.10		
$C_5H_{11}I$	n-$C_5H_{11}I$	$p_{3/2,1/2}$	9.18,9.72 (1)			59
$C_5H_{11}I$	i-$C_5H_{11}I$	$p_{3/2,1/2}$	9.17,9.72 (1)			59
$C_5H_{11}I$	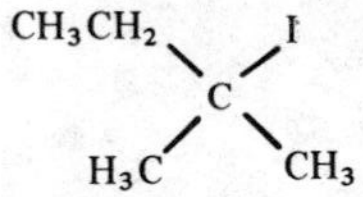	$p_{3/2,1/2}$	8.93,9.50 (1)			59

TABLE 1 (continued)

Compound		Orbital	Ionization Energy Adiabatic	Ionization Energy Vertical	Vibrational Bands	Reference
$C_5H_{11}N$	$(CH_3)_2CNCH_2CH_3$		8.83			57
			9.79			
			11.63			
			14.08			
			15.16			
			19.50			
C_5H_{12}	$CH_3CH_2CH_2CH_2CH_3$	σ	10.37 (1)			37
			14.84			
C_5H_{12}	$(CH_3)_2CHCH_2CH_3$		10.32 (1)			37
			(13.99)			
			(14.77)			
			(18.20)			
C_5H_{12}	$C(CH_3)_4$		10.40 (1)			37
			12.40			
			13.87			
			15.04			
			(17.97)			
C_5H_{12}	$(CH_3)_4C$	$4t_2$		11.3		215
		$1t_1$		12.7		
		1e		14.1		
		$3t_2$		15.4		
C_5H_{12}	$(CH_3)_4C$		10.25 (10)			113
		$3t_2$		{ 10.96 (10)		
				{ 11.44 (10)		
		t_1 }		{ 12.58 (10)		
		e }		{ 13.91 (10)		
		$2t_2$ }		{ 15.24 (10)		

TABLE 1 (continued)

Compound		Orbital	Ionization Energy: Adiabatic	Ionization Energy: Vertical	Vibrational Bands	Reference
C_5H_{12} (cont.)		$2a_1$		17.68 (10)	ν_2	
				17.84 (10)		
				18.01 (10)		
				18.18 (10)		
				18.34 (10)		
				17.74 (10)	$\nu_2 + \nu_3$	
				17.91 (10)		
				18.08 (10)		
				18.24 (10)		
C_5H_{12}	$C(CH_3)_4$	onset	10.21			43
		$3t_2$ (b_2)		10.89		
		$3t_2$ (e)		11.39, 11.86		
		$1t_1$ (a_2)		12.61		
		(e)		12.88, 13.14		
		$1e(a_1)$		13.94		
		(b_1)		14.29		
		$2t_2$ (b_2)		15.21		
		(e)		15.55, 15.83		
		$2a_1$		17.77	ν_2 0.17	
					ν_3 0.09	
$C_5H_{12}O$	$(CH_3)_3COCH_3$		9.4			7
$C_5H_{12}Si$	$CH_2{=}CHSi(CH_3)_3$	π_1		9.8		90
		σ_1 (Me_3 Si-C)		10.3		
		σ_2		10.6		
		π_2		11.0		
$C_5H_{12}Si$	$H_2C{=}CHSi(CH_3)_3$	π		9.8		124
		(Me_3 Si-C)σ, (Me_3 Si)σ		10.8		

TABLE 1 (continued)

	Compound	Orbital	Ionization Energy Adiabatic	Ionization Energy Vertical	Vibrational Bands	Reference
$C_5H_{15}BN_2$	$[(CH_3)_2N]_2BCH_3$	π(nb)		7.63		85
		π		9.15		
				11.1		
				11.8		
				15.2		
				16.9		
C_5IMnO_5	$Mn(CO)_5I$	7e		8.35 (25)		20
				8.65 (25)		
		6e		9.57 (25)		
		$2b_2$		10.37 (25)		
				14.1		
		5σ		15.0		
		1π		15.6		
				16.4		
		4σ		18.6		
$C_{10}Mn_2O_{10}$	$Mn_2(CO)_{10}$	6e		8.02 (25)		20
		$2b_2$		8.34 (25)		
				8.97		
				17.7		
C_6BrF_5	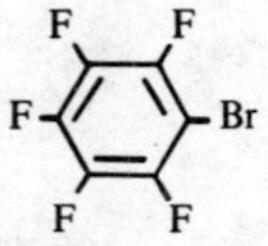		10.0			7
			11.5			
			11.9			

TABLE 1 (continued)

Compound		Orbital	Ionization Energy: Adiabatic	Ionization Energy: Vertical	Vibrational Bands	Reference
C_6ClF_5			10.1			7
			12.5			
	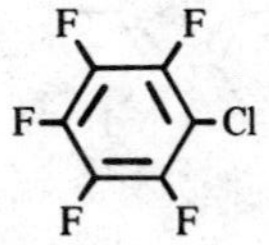					
$C_6D_5NO_2$		$^2B_1(b_1^{-1})$ (ring π)			845	41
	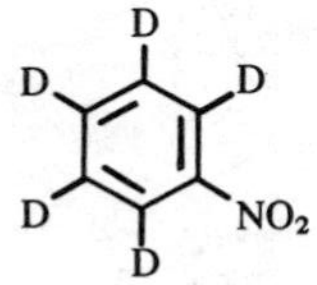					
C_6D_6	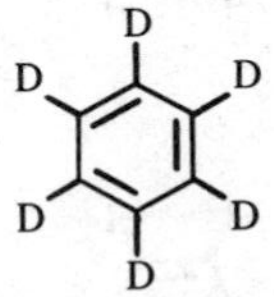	$1e_{1g}$	9.2		ν_{18} 0.078	105
					ν_{16} 0.194	
					ν_1 0.289	
		$3e_{2g}$	11.5		ν_{18} 0.074	
					ν_{17} 0.108	
					ν_{16} 0.194	
					ν_1 0.265	
		$2b_{1u}$	15.4		ν_1 ≈0.200	
		$3a_{1g}$	16.9		ν_2 0.114	
					ν_1 0.278	
$C_6F_3MnO_5$	$Mn(CO)_5CF_3$	6e		9.20 (25)		20
		$2b_2$		10.30 (25)		
		5σ }		{ 14.0		
		1π }		{ 14.5		
				{ 15.4		
		4σ		18.5		

TABLE 1 (continued)

Compound		Orbital	Ionization Energy: Adiabatic	Ionization Energy: Vertical	Vibrational Bands	Reference
C_6F_6	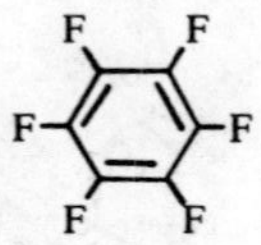		9.97			7
			12.62			
			13.88			
			14.79			
C_6F_6	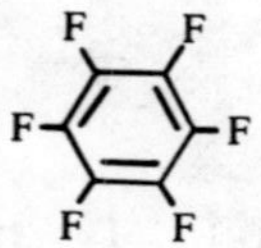		9.93 (6)	10.12 (0)	ν_1' 1,450	160
					ν_2' 400	
			12.58 (1)	12.77 (1)	ν_1' 1,550	
					ν_2' 530	
			13.84 (4)	14.02 (4)	ν_1' 1,450	
			14.75 (1)	14.75 (1)	ν_1' 1,550	
					ν_2' 480	
			15.82	15.82		
				16.3		
				16.6 (?)		
				17.6		
				18.6		
			~19.8	20.3		
			~21.8	22.4		
				25.5		
C_6F_6	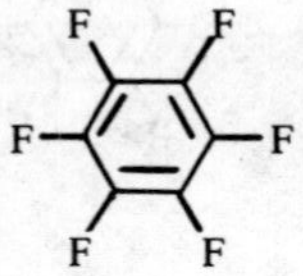			9.88 (5)		125
				11.12 (6)		
				11.64 (6)		
				12.71 (6)		
				13.75 (7)		
				13.93 (7)		
				14.64 (5)		
				15.73 (7)		
				16.16 (10)		
				17.42 (7)		
				18.15 (8)		
				19.5 (30)		

TABLE 1 (continued)

Compound		Orbital	Ionization Energy: Adiabatic	Ionization Energy: Vertical	Vibrational Bands	Reference
C_6HF_5	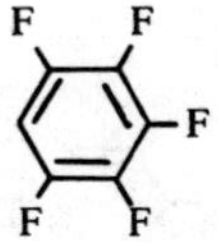		10.1 12.8			7
$C_6H_2F_5N$	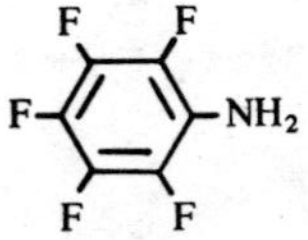		8.9 9.7 11.7			7
$C_6H_3F_3$	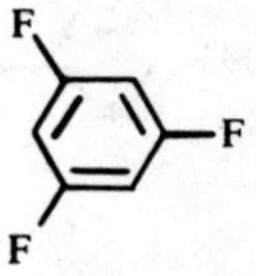	e″	9.64		a_1' 565 968 1,452	226
		$a_2''(\pi)$	12.35		565 968 1,452	
		σ		13.58		
$C_6H_3F_3$	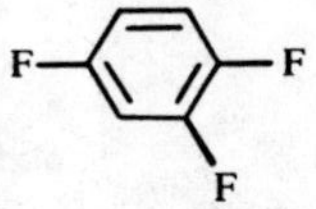			9.30 (5) 10.05 (4) 12.26 (4) 12.93 (5) 13.64 (5) 14.35 (6) 15.26 (8) 15.93 (10) 16.92 (10) 17.07 (8) 17.92 (8) 20.5 (20)		125

TABLE 1 (continued)

	Compound	Orbital	Ionization Energy: Adiabatic	Ionization Energy: Vertical	Vibrational Bands	Reference
$C_6H_3MnO_5$	$Mn(CO)_5CH_3$	6e		8.46 (25)		20
		$2b_2$		9.10 (25)		
		5σ		12.6		
		1π		13.8		
		4σ		18.0		
C_6H_4BrCl				9.04		63
				9.96		
				10.79		
				11.07		
				11.54		
C_6H_4BrCl			12.3			7
			~16.7			
$C_6H_4Br_2$			8.97			7
			9.95			
			10.66			
			10.91			
$C_6H_4Br_2$				8.97		63
				9.95		
				10.66		
				10.91		
C_6H_4ClF				9.26		63
				10.07		
				11.77		
			12.3 (1)			

TABLE 1 (continued)

Compound		Orbital	Ionization Energy: Adiabatic	Ionization Energy: Vertical	Vibrational Bands	Reference
C_6H_4ClF			12.3			7
			17.4			
C_6H_4ClNO	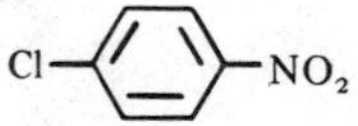			9.02		63
				9.74		
				10.27		
				11.8		
				12.0		
$C_6H_4ClNO_2$	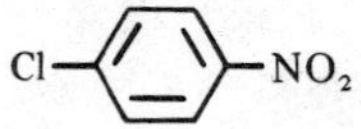			9.99		63
				10.46		
				11.41		
				11.97		
				12.48		
$C_6H_4Cl_2$	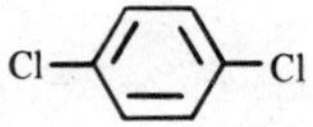			9.17		63
				10.01		
				11.57		
			12.7 (1)			
			12.6			7
			16.9			
$C_6H_4Cl_2$	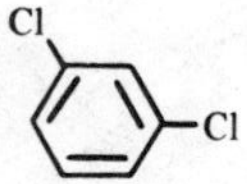		11.73			7
$C_6H_4F_2$	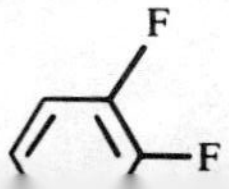	a_2 (S)		9.6		126
		b_1 (A)		9.9_5		
		b_1		12.4_5		

TABLE 1 (continued)

Compound		Orbital	Ionization Energy: Adiabatic	Ionization Energy: Vertical	Vibrational Bands	Reference
$C_6H_4F_2$	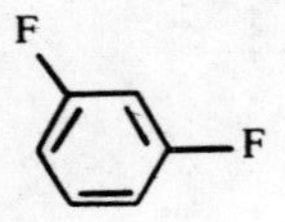	b_1 (S) a_2 (A) b_1		9.6 10.0 12.4_5		126
$C_6H_4F_2$	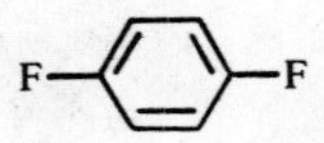	b_{3g}(A) b_{1g}(S) b_{2u}	9.33 10.10 12.2 17.09	9.4 10.2 12.6		7, 126
$C_6H_4F_2$			12.1 (1)	9.50 10.24 12.72 13.84		63
$C_6H_4F_2$				9.15 (6) 10.04 (8) 12.16 (6) 13.55 (6) 14.24 (6) 15.01 (10) 15.44 (10) 16.79 (10) 17.12 (10) 17.93 (10) 19.74 (10) 20.3 (10)		125
$C_6H_4O_2$	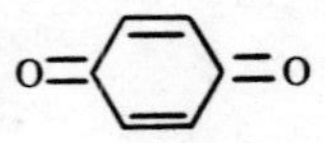	π	9.95 (1) 10.88 13.26 14.05 16.44 (18.65) (19.19)			37

TABLE 1 (continued)

	Compound	Orbital	Ionization Energy: Adiabatic	Ionization Energy: Vertical	Vibrational Bands	Reference
$C_6H_4O_2$	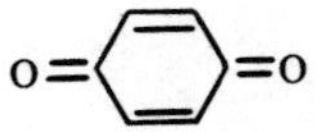	n_+ n_-		10.03 10.93		80
C_6H_5Br	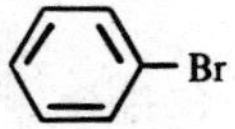		11.8	9.25 9.78 10.65 11.20		63
C_6H_5Br	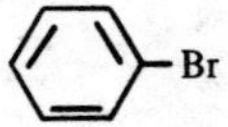		9.05 9.67 10.61 11.1(8) 11.8 16.7(7)			7
C_6H_5BrO	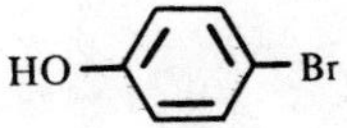			8.52 9.60 10.52 10.75		63
C_6H_5Cl	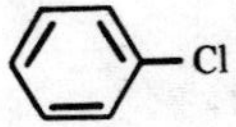		12.2	9.31 9.71 11.42 11.76 12.35		63
			9.0 (6) 9.6 (9) 11.32 11.6 (9) 12.2 16.9 (2)			7

TABLE 1 (continued)

Compound		Orbital	Ionization Energy Adiabatic	Ionization Energy Vertical	Vibrational Bands	Reference
C_6H_5Cl	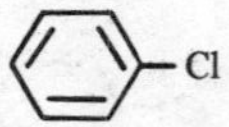	π_3 π_2 $Cl_{3p_{x,y}}$ $Cl_{3p_{x,y}}$ π_1	8.99 9.51	9.35 9.68 11.44 11.79 12.02		127
C_6H_5ClO	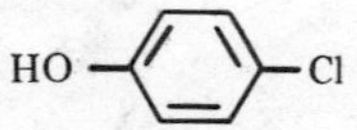			8.69 9.76 11.32		63
C_6H_5F	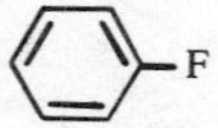	a_2 (A) b_1 (S) b_1		9.3_5 9.7_5 12.1_5		126
C_6H_5F	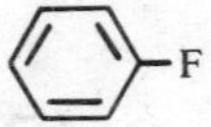			9.21 (4) 9.87 (7) 11.83 (7) 12.98 (8) 13.89 (7) 14.55 (9) 16.24 (8) 17.77 (9) 19.02 (9) 19.55 (20) 20.69 (10)		125
C_6H_5F	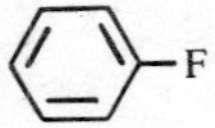		9.19 9.8 (2) 11.7 (7) 13.6 (8) 17.3			7
C_6H_5F	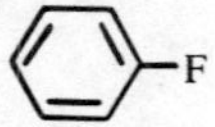		11.8	9.5 9.86 ~14.1		63

TABLE 1 (continued)

Compound		Orbital	Ionization Energy: Adiabatic	Ionization Energy: Vertical	Vibrational Bands	Reference
C_6H_5I	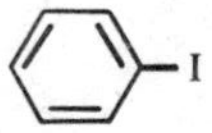			8.78		63
				9.75		
				10.78		
				11.36		
				12.44		
C_6H_5I			8.67			7
			9.38			
			9.64			
			10.45			
			11.3			
			16.4			
C_6H_5NO	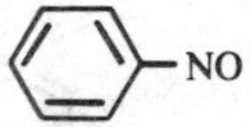			9.87		63
				9.97		
C_6H_5NO	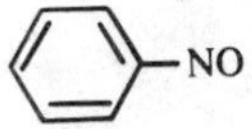	NO nonbonding	8.09	8.51		128
		Ring π	9.49	9.49	846	
		Ring π		9.90		
$C_6H_5NO_2$		$^2B_1(b_1^{-1})$(ring π)	9.99 (1)	9.99 (1)	850	41
		$^2A_2(a_2^{-1})$(ring π)		10.35 (1)		
		$^2A_1(a_1^{-1})(NO_2-\sigma)$	10.6	11.15 (1)		
		$^2A_2(a_2^{-1})(NO_2-\pi)$		11.30 (1)		
			12.3	12.7		
				13.5		
			14.5	14.95		
				15.55		
			~16.3	16.8		
				18.9		
$C_6H_5NO_2$	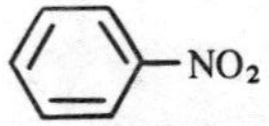			10.26		63
				11.28		
				12.86		

TABLE 1 (continued)

Compound		Orbital	Ionization Energy: Adiabatic	Ionization Energy: Vertical	Vibrational Bands	Reference
C_6H_6		π	9.24			101
		π	11.50			
			13.87			
			(15.46)			
			16.84			
			(18.43)			
			(18.75)			
			(20.17)			
C_6H_6		π	9.24 (1)			37
			11.50			
			13.87			
			(15.46)			
			16.84			
			(18.43)			
			(18.75)			
			(20.17)			
C_6H_6		$1b_{3g}$, $1b_{2g}$		9.24		129
		$1b_{1u}$		12.25		
C_6H_6		$1e_{1g}$	9.241 (1)		ν_{18} 0.085	105
					ν_2 0.122	
					ν_{17} 0.160	
					ν_{16} 0.197	
					ν_1 0.367	
		$3e_{2g}$	11.490		ν_{18} 0.080	
					ν_{17} 0.160	
					ν_{16} 0.188	
					ν_1 0.353	
		$2b_{1u}$	15.4		ν_1 0.290	
		$3a_{1g}$	16.9		ν_2 0.115	
					ν_1 0.346	

TABLE 1 (continued)

Compound		Orbital	Ionization Energy: Adiabatic	Ionization Energy: Vertical	Vibrational Bands		Reference
C_6H_6	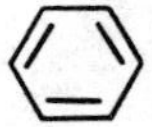			9.25 (2) 11.51 (4) 13.88 (4) 14.87 (6) 15.54 (6) 16.84 (5) 18.22 (8) 18.82 (10) 20.26 (8)			125
C_6H_6		$e_{1g}(\pi)$		9.24			102
C_6H_6		$3a_{1g}$	16.9		0 v′ 2v′ 3v′, v″ 4v′, v″+v′	0 928 1,839 2,791 3,718	106
C_6H_6				11.49 16.84	0.11 0.11		130
C_6H_6		$2e_{2g}$ $2e_{1u}$		19.0 22.5			2
C_6H_6	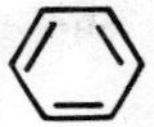	e_{1g} a_{2u}		9.2_5 11.6			126
C_6H_6				9.25 11.5			131

TABLE 1 (continued)

Compound		Orbital	Ionization Energy: Adiabatic	Ionization Energy: Vertical	Vibrational Bands	Reference
C_6H_6	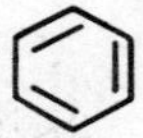		9.24 (7) 11.49 16.84		ν_2 930 610	7
C_6H_6				9.24		61
C_6H_6	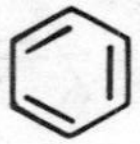			9.24 (1) 11.50 (1) 13.87 (1) 15.46 (1) 16.84 (1) 18.43 (1) 18.75 (1) 20.17 (1)		132
C_6H_6		e_{2g} b_{2x}	9.25 11.49 12.19 13.67 14.44 16.73 18.75 19.82			57
C_6H_6		e_{1g}	11.5	9.40 (3)		63
C_6H_6	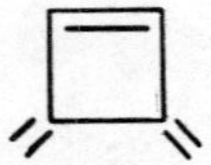	$2b_1 (\pi)$ $1a_2 (\pi)$ $10a_1 (\sigma)$ $8b_2 (\sigma)$		8.80 9.44 11.5 12.3		133

TABLE 1 (continued)

Compound	Orbital	Ionization Energy: Adiabatic	Ionization Energy: Vertical	Vibrational Bands	Reference
C_6H_6 (cont.)	$1b_1\,(\pi)$		13.3		
	σ		14.1		
C_6H_6 	$1a_2\,(\pi)$		8.55	1,400, 1,200	133
	$2b_1\,(\pi)$		9.54	1,700, 1,000	
	$7b_2\,(\sigma)$		12.1		
	$1b_1\,(\pi)$		12.8		
	σ		13.6		
	σ		14.6 (sh)		
C_6H_6ClN 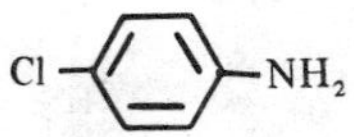			8.18		63
			9.51		
			10.64		
			11.14		
C_6H_6O 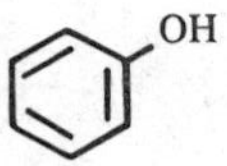	π	8.52 (1)			37
		9.36			
		11.32			
		14.00			
		15.44			
		(17.40)			
		(18.94)			
C_6H_6O 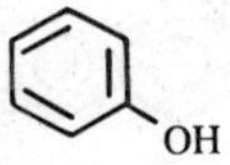			8.75		63
			9.45		
			~11.3		
C_6H_6O 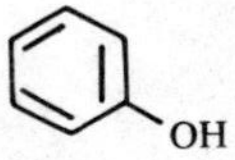	π	8.48 (5)	8.74 (5)		82
	π	9.3	9.44		
	π	11.2	11.58		
	σ		11.95		
	σ		12.6		
	σ		13.3		
	σ		14.1		
	σ		15.6		
	(π)		16.4		
			17.5		

TABLE 1 (continued)

			Ionization Energy			
Compound		Orbital	Adiabatic	Vertical	Vibrational Bands	Reference
$C_6H_6S_3$	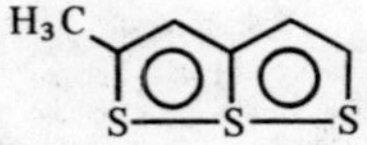	π_1		7.83		115
		n_1		8.10		
		π_2		9.32		
		π_3		9.68		
				10.82		
				11.20		
C_6H_7N	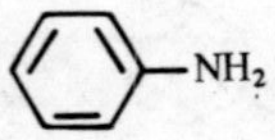	b_1		8.00		230
		a_2		9.15		
		b_1		10.76		
C_6H_7N	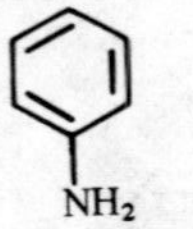	π	(7.68)	8.08		82
		π	(8.94)	9.19		
		π	(10.51)	10.81		
		σ		11.72		
		π		12.5		
		σ	13.58	13.93		
		σ		15.5		
		σ		16.7		
C_6H_7N	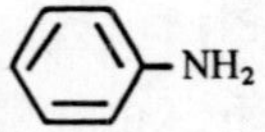			8.04		63
				9.11		
			10.50	10.70		
			11.5 (1)			
C_6H_8	$C_5H_5CH_3$ (includes 1,2, and 5-$CH_3C_5H_5$)					224
				8.28 (5)	152 (15)	
				10.45		
				11.8 (sh)		
				12.4		
				13.3		
				14.5		
				15.9		

TABLE 1 (continued)

Compound		Orbital	Ionization Energy: Adiabatic	Ionization Energy: Vertical	Vibrational Bands	Reference
$C_6H_8N_2$	$C_6H_5NHNH_2$		7.74			64
			9.12			
			10.52			
			11.52			
			(11.84)			
			13.71			
			15.38			
			16.58			
$C_6H_8N_2$	$C_6H_5NHNH_2$	a_2		7.86		230
		b_1		9.19		
		a_2		10.09		
		b_1		10.64		
$C_6H_8N_2$	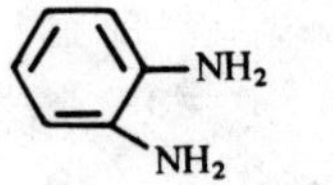	b_1		7.69		230
		a_2		8.59		
		b_1		10.55		
		a_2		11.01		
$C_6H_8N_2$	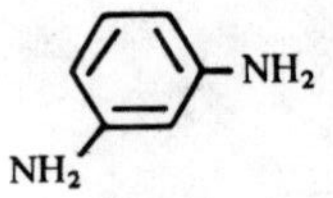	a_2		7.60		230
		b_1		8.26		
		b_1		10.05		
		a_2		11.44		
$C_6H_8N_2$		$b_{1g}(a_2)$		7.34		230
		$b_{2g}(b_1)$		9.10		
		$b_{3u}(b_1)$		9.71		
		$b_{1g}(a_2)$		11.54		
$C_6H_8O_2$	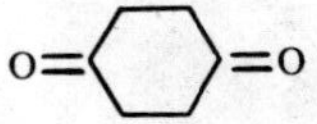	n_+		9.65		80
		n_-		9.80		

TABLE 1 (continued)

	Compound	Orbital	Ionization Energy: Adiabatic	Ionization Energy: Vertical	Vibrational Bands	Reference
C_6H_9B	$B(CHCH_2)_3$		9.7	10.0		95
				10.2		
			10.7		ν_2 1,210 (50)	
					ν_4 430 (50)	
			12.7			
			~14.5			
C_6H_{10}	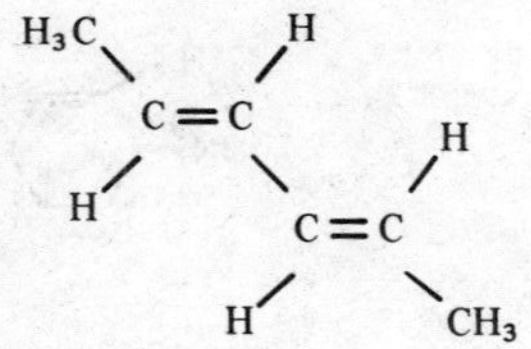			8.39		118
				10.8		
				11.8 (sh)		
C_6H_{10}	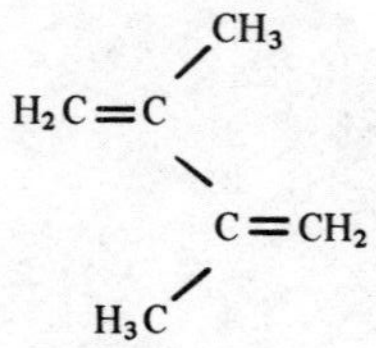			8.76		118
				10.3		
				11.5		
C_6H_{10}		π	8.92	9.97		121
			10.43			
				12.40		
			12.81	13.6		
			14.96	15.7		
			16.3			
			19.1			

TABLE 1 (continued)

	Compound	Orbital	Ionization Energy: Adiabatic	Ionization Energy: Vertical	Vibrational Bands	Reference
C_6H_{10}			8.72 10.29 10.98 12.47 16.25 18.48			57
C_6H_{10}	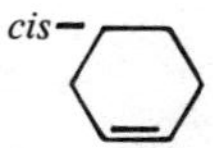	π σ	8.94 10.1 (1)	9.12 10.7 (1)	1,420	93
C_6H_{10}				9.12 10.66 11.27 12.88–13.36 15.21 16.35 16.98 19.49		134
C_6H_{10}	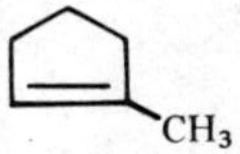			8.54 (1)		119
C_6H_{10}	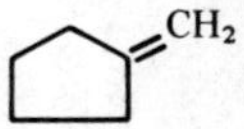			8.51 (1)		119
C_6H_{10}	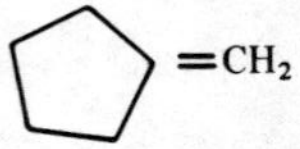		8.96		1,120	7

TABLE 1 (continued)

Compound		Orbital	Ionization Energy: Adiabatic	Ionization Energy: Vertical	Vibrational Bands	Reference
C_6H_{10}	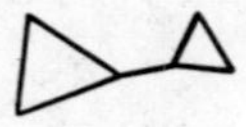		9.04 11.72 12.43 13.97 15.32 15.59 (19.05) (19.51)			122
$C_6H_{10}O$	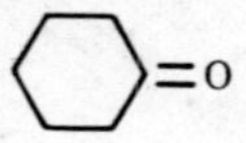		9.16 (1)			59
$C_6H_{10}O$	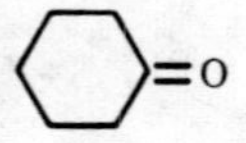	n		9.14 (2)	627 (40) 1,229 (40)	111
		σ onset		10.9		
$C_6H_{10}S_2$	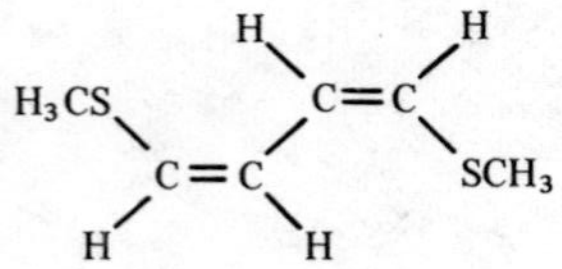			7.48		61
C_6H_{12}	$(CH_3)_2C{=}C(CH_3)_2$		8.26 10.69 11.85 14.54 15.80 18.67	8.41 10.83 12.75 14.68 15.80		83

TABLE 1 (continued)

	Compound	Orbital	Ionization Energy: Adiabatic	Ionization Energy: Vertical	Vibrational Bands	Reference
C_6H_{12}	$CH_2{=}CHC(CH_3)_3$	π_1		9.7		90
		σ_1 (Me_3 C-C)		11.2		
		σ_2		11.6		
		π_2		12.0		
C_6H_{12}			9.81 (1)			37
			(11.88)			
			(12.74)			
			14.50			
			(18.04)			
			(19.34)			
C_6H_{12}	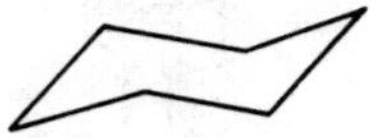			10.32		134
				10.98		
				11.85		
				12.87		
				14.69		
				16.15		
				18.07		
				19.48		
C_6H_{12}	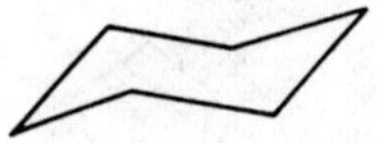		9.79			57
			11.33			
			12.22			
			14.37			
			19.43			
			9.89			121
			11.9	(12.2)		
			12.8	13.6		
			14.4	15.6		
			16.0	16.3		
			16.8	17.4		
			18.0	18.7		
			18.8			
			19.4			

TABLE 1 (continued)

Compound		Orbital	Ionization Energy: Adiabatic	Ionization Energy: Vertical	Vibrational Bands	Reference
$C_6H_{12}BN$		π		8.06 10.1 11.2 12.1 15.9		85
$C_6H_{12}Ge$	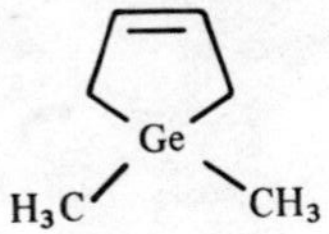	π_1 σ_1 π_2 σ_2		9.0 9.7 10.15 10.4 12.0		135
$C_6H_{12}N_2$	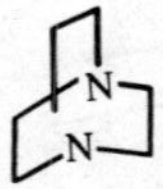	a_1' a_2''		7.52 9.65 11.50 13.26 14.05 16.56	0.093 0.082	136
$C_6H_{12}N_2$		$a_1'(n_+)$ $a_2''(n_-)$	7.52 9.65		$765 \leqslant \nu \leqslant 815$ $510 \leqslant \nu \leqslant 555$	138
$C_6H_{12}N_4$	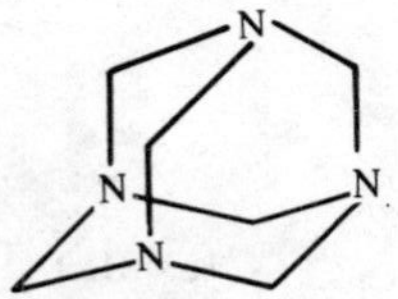		8.26 (1) 11.80 (12.54) 15.19 (15.51) (16.55) (18.25) (18.71)			37
$C_6H_{12}O$	$CH_3CH_2CH_2CH_2C(=O)CH_3$		9.36 (2)			59

TABLE 1 (continued)

	Compound	Orbital	Ionization Energy: Adiabatic	Ionization Energy: Vertical	Vibrational Bands	Reference
$C_6H_{12}O$	$(CH_3)_2CHCH_2C(=O)CH_3$		9.34 (1)			59
$C_6H_{12}O$	$(CH_3)_3CC(=O)CH_3$		9.14 (1)			59
$C_6H_{12}O_2$	$CH_3COO(CH_2)_3CH_3$	n_O	10.17	~10.5	~1,200 (100)	76
		π_2		10.83		
$C_6H_{12}Si$	$(H_3C)_2Si(CH{=}CH_2)_2$	π_1 (b_1)		9.8		139
		π_2 (a_2)		10.0		
		σ_1 (b_2)		10.6		
		σ_2 (a_1)		11.0		
		π_3 (b_1)		11.2		
$C_6H_{12}Si$	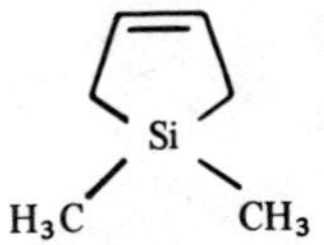	π_1		9.0		135
		σ_1		10.0		
		π_2		10.5		
		σ_2		10.9		
				12.0		
$C_6H_{13}N$	$CH_3CH_2CH_2CHNCH_2CH_3$		9.00			57
			10.15			
			11.15			
			12.59			
			13.37			
			15.34			
			19.17			
$C_6H_{13}N$	$(CH_3)_2CHCHNCH_2CH_3$		8.94			57
			10.12			
			11.08			
			12.54			
			13.28			
			14.59			
			19.17			

TABLE 1 (continued)

	Compound	Orbital	Ionization Energy: Adiabatic	Ionization Energy: Vertical	Vibrational Bands	Reference
$C_6H_{13}N$	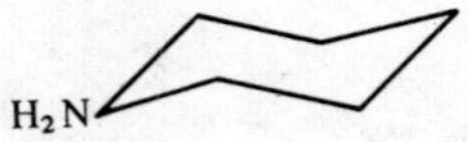		8.86 10.25 14.56 18.17			57
C_6H_{14}	$CH_3(CH_2)_4CH_3$	σ	10.27 (1)			37
$C_6H_{14}BN_3$	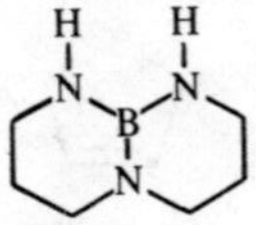	π(nb) π		7.90 10.10 11.2 11.9 13.7 15.8 17.0		85
$C_6H_{14}O$	$(CH_3CH_2CH_2)_2O$		9.32 (1)			59
$C_6H_{14}S$	$(C_3H_7)_2S$			8.34		61
$C_6H_{14}S$	$(CH_3)_2CHSCH(CH_3)_2$			8.26		61
$C_6H_{14}S_2$	$C_3H_7SSC_3H_7$			8.62 8.87		61
$C_6H_{14}S_2$	$(CH_3)_2CHSSCH(CH_3)_2$			8.54 8.76		61
$C_6H_{14}Si$	$CH_2{=}CHCH_2Si(CH_3)_3$	$(\pi+CH_2\text{-}Si)_1$ σ_1 σ_2 σ_3		9.0 10.5 10.8 11.2		90
$C_6H_{14}Si$	$H_2C{=}CHCH_2Si(CH_3)_3$	π,Si-CH $(Me_3SiCH_2)\sigma$		9.0 10.9		124

TABLE 1 (continued)

	Compound	Orbital	Ionization Energy: Adiabatic	Ionization Energy: Vertical	Vibrational Bands	Reference
$C_6H_{15}B$	$B(CH_2CH_3)_3$		9.6	10.2		95
				10.6		
			11.5		1,170 (50)	
			~14			
$C_6H_{15}N$	$(CH_3CH_2)_3N$		7.84			57
			10.79			
			14.36			
			15.37			
			19.92			
$C_6H_{18}BN_3$	$[(CH_3)_2N]_3B$	π(nb)		7.58		85
		π		9.20		
				11.6		
				12.5		
				14.6		
				16.0		
$C_6H_{18}B_3N_3$	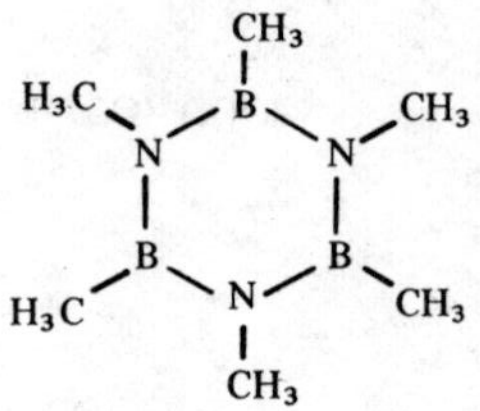	$3e''\pi$		8.53	1,100 (200)	15
		$3a_2''\pi$		10.30		
		$8e'$		10.88		
		$2a_2'$		12.7		
$C_6H_{18}W$	$W(CH_3)_6$	e_g	9.8	10.00 (5)		140
		t_{1u}		10.35 (5)		
		a_{1g}		10.8 (1)		
		$t_{1g}, t_{2g}, t_{1u}, t_{2u}$(CH$\sigma$)	11.5–16			

TABLE 1 (continued)

	Compound	Orbital	Ionization Energy: Adiabatic	Ionization Energy: Vertical	Vibrational Bands	Reference
C_6O_6V	$V(CO)_6$	Metal t_{2g}		7.52		141
		Metal t_{2g}		7.88		
		Carbonyl 5σ, 1π		12.95		
		Carbonyl 5σ, 1π		13.64		
		Carbonyl 4σ		17.3		
$C_7F_3MnO_6$	$Mn(CO)_5COCF_3$	6e		9.0		20
		5σ }		{ 13.3		
		1π }		{ 14.5		
		4σ		{ 15.0		
				18.5		
				19.9		
C_7HF_5O	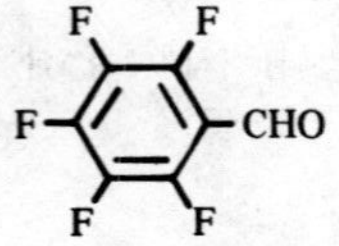		10.5			7
			12.9			
$C_7H_3F_5O$	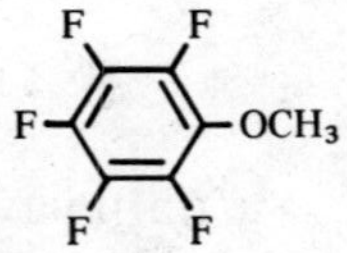		10.0			7
			11.5			
$C_7H_4BrF_3$	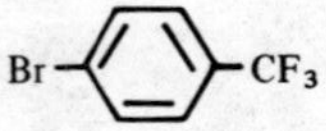		9.55			7
			10.02			
			10.92			
			11.60			

TABLE 1 (continued)

Compound		Orbital	Ionization Energy: Adiabatic	Ionization Energy: Vertical	Vibrational Bands	Reference
$C_7H_4BrF_3$	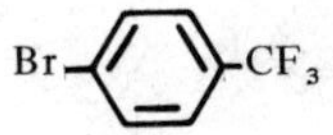			9.55		63
				10.02		
				10.92		
				11.60		
C_7H_4BrN	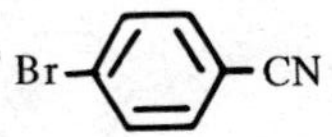			9.54		63
				10.41		
				11.07		
				11.47		
				11.99		
$C_7H_4ClF_3$	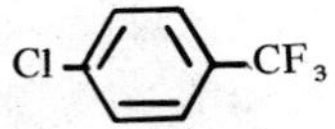			9.80		63
				10.19		
				11.73		
				12.16		
			12.5 (1)			
$C_7H_4ClF_3$	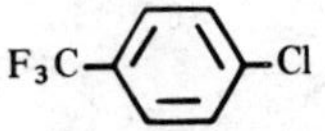		12.4			7
$C_7H_4FeO_3$	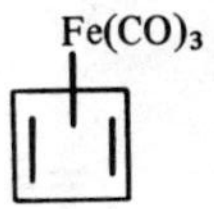		8.04 (1)			37
			9.02			
			(10.89)			
			11.64			
			(11.99)			
			12.25			
			(13.59)			
			16.71			
			(21.10)			
C_7H_5ClO	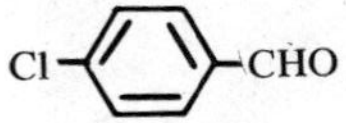			9.59		63
				9.88		
				11.77		
			12.4 (1)			

TABLE 1 (continued)

	Compound	Orbital	Ionization Energy: Adiabatic	Ionization Energy: Vertical	Vibrational Bands	Reference
$C_7H_5F_3$	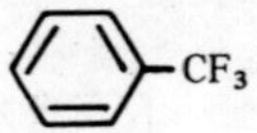		11.9 (1)	9.90		63
			9.7 (0) 11.9 18.1			7
$C_7H_5F_3O$	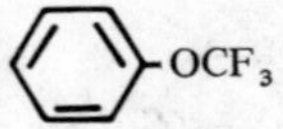			10.00		63
$C_7H_5FeNO_3$	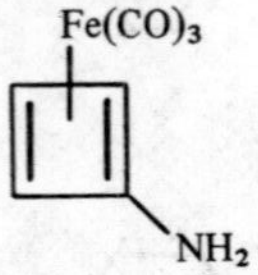		7.77 (1) 8.91 10.71 11.72 12.30 (12.58) (15.58) (16.66) (21.10)			37
C_7H_5N	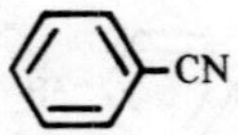		11.8 (1)	10.02 12.18		63
C_7H_5N	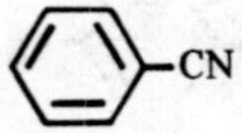		9.6 (8) 11.8 (0)			7
C_7H_5N	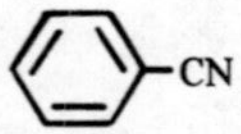	Ring π	9.62	9.73		128
		Ring π		10.15		
		In-plane C≡Nπ	11.93	11.93		
		Out-of-plane C≡Nπ	12.18	12.18		

TABLE 1 (continued)

Compound		Orbital	Ionization Energy: Adiabatic	Ionization Energy: Vertical	Vibrational Bands	Reference
C_7H_5NS	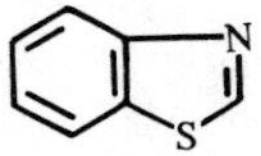	π	8.72 (5)	8.72 (5)		82
		π		9.1		
		π		10.05		
		π	10.65	10.65		
		σ	11.40	11.60		
		(π)		12.6		
		(π)		13.35		
		σ		(14.5)		
		σ		15.55		
$C_7H_6FeO_3$	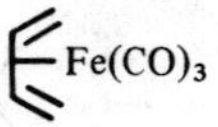		8.04 (1)			37
			9.73			
			(10.92)			
			11.23			
			12.29			
			(12.53)			
			(13.60)			
			16.64			
			(21.11)			
C_7H_6O	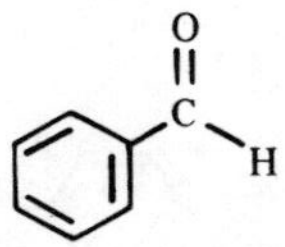			9.80		63
				10.0		
C_7H_6O	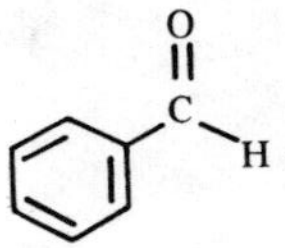	Ring π	9.40	9.59		128
		Oxygen n, ring σ		9.69		
		Ring π		9.81		

TABLE 1 (continued)

Compound		Orbital	Ionization Energy: Adiabatic	Ionization Energy: Vertical	Vibrational Bands	Reference
C_7H_7Br	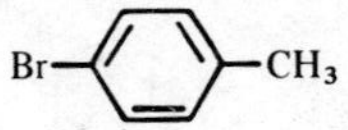			8.71 9.45 10.50 10.88 11.9		63
			11.5 ~16.5			7
C_7H_7Br	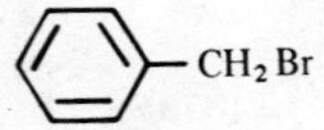	$\pi_1(b_1)$ $\pi_2(a_2)$ n_1 n_2		9.23 9.50 10.22 10.50		232
C_7H_7BrO	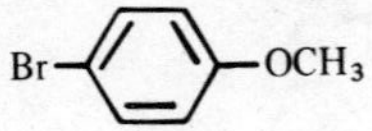		10.68			7
				8.49 9.65 10.68		63
C_7H_7Cl	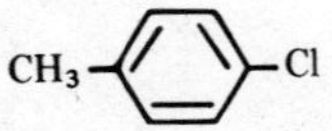			8.90 9.57 11.39		63
			11.7 (1)			
			~11.5 ~16.5			7

TABLE 1 (continued)

Compound		Orbital	Ionization Energy Adiabatic	Ionization Energy Vertical	Vibrational Bands	Reference
C_7H_7Cl	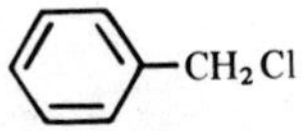	$\pi_1 (b_1)$		9.30		232
		$\pi_2 (a_2)$		9.60		
		n_1, n_2		10.90		
C_7H_7F	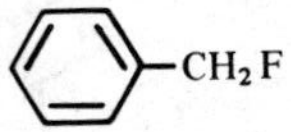	$\pi_1 (b_1)$		9.55		232
		$\pi_2 (a_2)$		9.80		
C_7H_7I	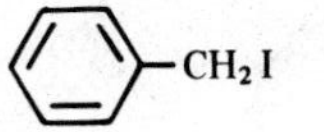	$\pi_1 (b_1)$		8.91		232
		n_1		9.28		
		n_2		9.98		
C_7H_8	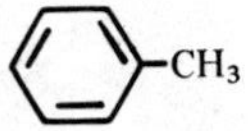		8.82			7
			11.2			
			16.3 (8)			
				8.78		236
				9.00		
			11.0	11.3		
C_7H_8	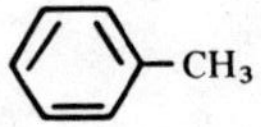	b_1 (S)		9.0		126
		a_2 (A)		9.3		
		b_1		11.4		
				8.9		63
				9.13		

TABLE 1 (continued)

Compound		Orbital	Ionization Energy Adiabatic	Ionization Energy Vertical	Vibrational Bands	Reference
C_7H_8	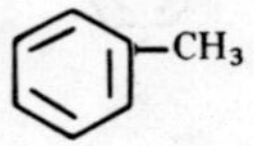	π	8.82 (1)			37
			11.20			
			(12.70)			
			13.04			
			13.52			
			15.01			
			16.33			
			(18.31)			
C_7H_8			8.40			122
			9.31			
			10.73			
			11.51			
			(12.27)			
			14.00			
			14.65			
			16.52			
C_7H_8			8.62			122
			9.42			
			11.11			
			12.38			
			14.01			
			(15.41)			
			(16.73)			
C_7H_8		π	8.42	8.95		121
		π	9.52	9.78		
			10.90	11.60		
			12.2	12.8		
			14.0	14.4		
			15.5	15.8		
			16.4	17.0		
			(17.7)			
			(18.7)			

TABLE 1 (continued)

Compound		Orbital	Ionization Energy: Adiabatic	Ionization Energy: Vertical	Vibrational Bands	Reference
C_7H_8	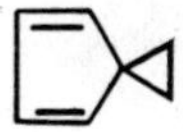	$2a_2$ (π)		8.14		120
		$4b_1$ (π)		9.46		
		$12a_1$ (σ)		10.9		
		$7b_2$ (σ)		11.89		
		$3b_1$ (π)		12.7		
C_7H_8	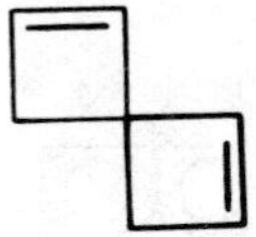		9.02			122
			10.30			
			11.26			
			12.41			
			14.18			
			(14.50)			
			16.23			
			19.26			
C_7H_8O	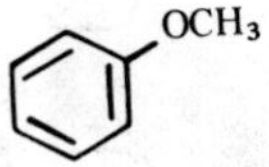	π_1		8.42		142
		π_2		9.23		
		π_3 ?		11.02		
C_7H_8O	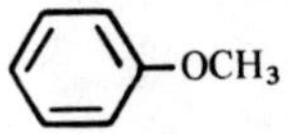			8.54		63
				9.37		
				11.2		
C_7H_8O	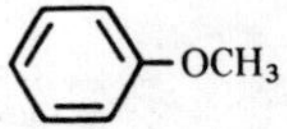		8.21 (1)			37
			9.17			
			10.76			
			12.14			
			13.67			
			15.37			
			17.11			
			(18.26)			

TABLE 1 (continued)

	Compound	Orbital	Ionization Energy: Adiabatic	Ionization Energy: Vertical	Vibrational Bands	Reference
C_7H_8O	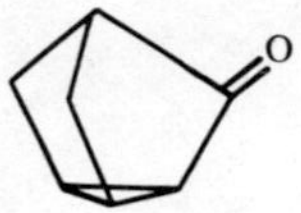		9.01			122
			9.98			
			(10.33)			
			12.60			
			14.90			
			(16.93)			
C_7H_8S	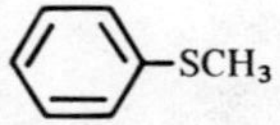			8.07		61
C_7H_8S	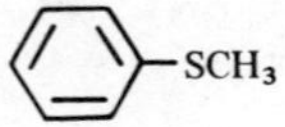	π_1		8.07		142
		π_2		9.28		
		π_3		10.15		
$C_7H_8S_3$	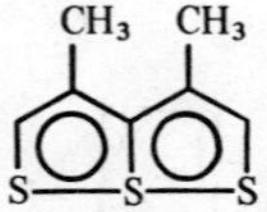	π_1		7.63		115
		n_1		7.92		
		π_2		9.14		
		π_3		9.47		
				10.67		
				11.15		
$C_7H_8S_3$	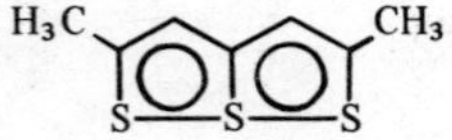	π_1		7.73		115
		n_1		7.90		
		π_2		9.08		
		π_3		9.53		
				10.40		
				10.70		
C_7H_9N				7.78		63
				9.02		
				10.47		
C_7H_9N	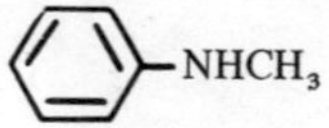			7.73		63
				9.03		
			10.05	10.24		

TABLE 1 (continued)

Compound		Orbital	Ionization Energy Adiabatic	Ionization Energy Vertical	Vibrational Bands	Reference
C_7H_9N	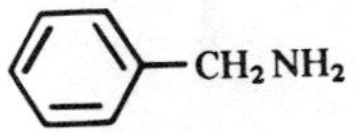		8.73			64
			11.22			
			(11.55)			
			12.82			
			13.66			
			(14.87)			
			16.57			
C_7H_{10}	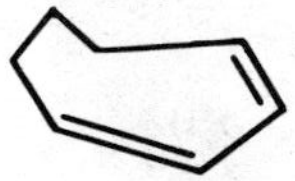	a″(π)		8.30		143
		a′(π)		10.60		
		σ		(beg) 11.16		
C_7H_{10}			8.83			122
			10.32			
			11.47			
			13.08			
			(19.04)			
				8.97		134
				10.55		
				11.85		
				13.22		
				14.79		
				15.81		
				16.71		
				18.22		
		π	8.82	9.20		121
			10.26	10.75		
			11.4	12.0		
			13.0	13.4		
			14.5	14.9		
			15.6	15.9		
			16.5	16.8		
			17.8			
			19.2			

TABLE 1 (continued)

Compound		Orbital	Ionization Energy Adiabatic	Ionization Energy Vertical	Vibrational Bands	Reference
C_7H_{10}	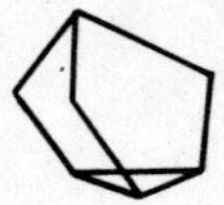		9.02 10.71 12.06 14.14 15.08 16.96 (19.35)			122
$C_7H_{10}N_2$	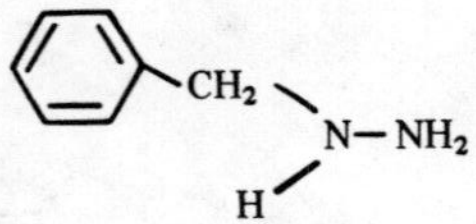		8.64 (8.91) 11.31 12.92 13.59 16.49 (18.61)			64
$C_7H_{10}N_2$	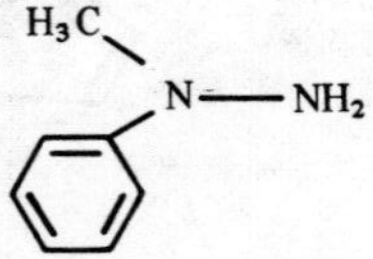		7.43 8.97 9.79 11.22 (11.53) (13.20) 13.68 16.59 (18.58)			64
C_7H_{12}	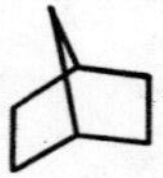		9.80 (10.15) (11.26) 13.36 15.42 (19.13)			122

TABLE 1 (continued)

Compound		Orbital	Ionization Energy: Adiabatic	Ionization Energy: Vertical	Vibrational Bands	Reference
C_7H_{12}	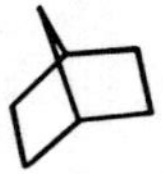		9.74			121
			11.0	(11.8)		
			12.0	(12.7)		
			13.4	14.1		
			15.3	15.9		
			16.4	17.1		
			17.5			
			18.8			
C_7H_{12}				10.17		134
				10.70		
				11.43–12.12		
				13.37		
				15.48		
				16.43		
				17.46		
C_7H_{12}	*cis-* 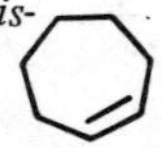	π	8.87	9.04	1,250	93
		σ	10.3 (1)	10.8 (1) (sh)		
		σ		11.3 (1)		
C_7H_{12}	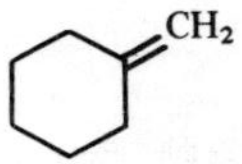	π	8.94	9.83		121
			10.3	(11.3)		
			11.9	12.6		
			12.9	13.8		
			14.0	14.6		
				15.7		
			15.8	16.3		
			17.0			
			18.7			
C_7H_{12}	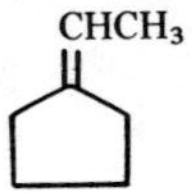	π	8.46	9.41		121
			(9.8)	9.99		
			10.5	(11.5)		
			11.7	12.6		
			13.0	13.6		

TABLE 1 (continued)

	Compound	Orbital	Ionization Energy: Adiabatic	Ionization Energy: Vertical	Vibrational Bands	Reference
C_7H_{12} (cont.)			14.0 15.7 16.9 18.6	15.0 16.6 17.6		
C_7H_{12}	$(H_2C{=}CH)_2C(CH_3)_2$	b_1 a_2		9.55 9.95		231
$C_7H_{12}O$	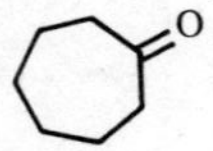		9.49 (1)			59
$C_7H_{12}O$	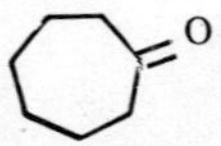	n σ onset	10.6	9.17 (2)	665 (40) 1,233 (40)	111
$C_7H_{13}N$		a_1		8.02 10.45 11.41 12.66 13.70 16.10		136
C_7H_{14}	$CH_2{=}CHCH_2C(CH_3)_3$	$(\pi{+}CH_2{-}C)_1$ σ_1 σ_2 σ_3		9.6 11.0 11.4 11.8		90
C_7H_{14}	$CH_3CHC(CH_2CH_3)_2$		8.53 10.16			121
$C_7H_{14}O$	$CH_3CH_2CH_2C(=O)CH_2CH_2CH_3$		9.15 (2)			59
$C_7H_{14}O$	$(CH_3)_2CHC(=O)CH(CH_3)_2$		8.96 (1)			59

TABLE 1 (continued)

Compound		Orbital	Ionization Energy: Adiabatic	Ionization Energy: Vertical	Vibrational Bands	Reference
$C_7H_{14}O$	$CH_3CH_2CH_2CH_2C(=O)CH_2CH_3$		9.15 (2)			59
C_7H_{16}	n-C_7H_{16}		10.20			57
			14.38			
			15.18			
			18.63			
			19.86			
$C_8H_3F_5$	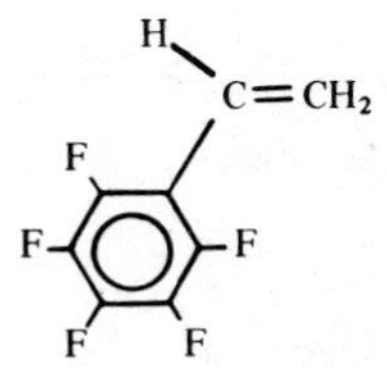	π_4	9.18 (2)	9.36 (2)		236
		π_3		9.73 (5)		
		π_2		11.15 (2)		
			12.2	12.60 (5)		
$C_8H_4F_6$	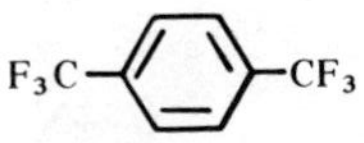		12.4			7
			18.6			
$C_8H_4FeO_4$	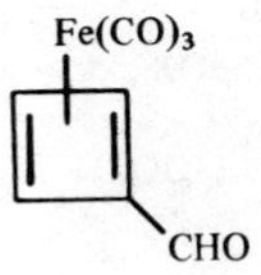		8.32 (1)			37
			9.27			
			(9.70)			
			(10.86)			
			11.73			
			12.29			
			(13.56)			
			(15.62)			
			(16.78)			
			(17.72)			
			(19.72)			
			(21.09)			

TABLE 1 (continued)

Compound		Orbital	Ionization Energy: Adiabatic	Ionization Energy: Vertical	Vibrational Bands	Reference
$C_8H_5F_5O$	$C_6H_5OC_2F_5$			9.97		63
$C_8H_5F_6N$				10.00 11.32		63
C_8H_6	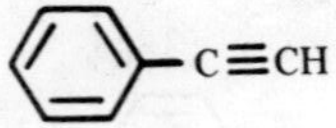	Ring π Ring π In-plane C≡Cπ Out-of-plane C≡Cπ	8.75 9.34 10.36 11.03	8.82 9.51 10.36 11.03	484 C≡C, 2,050 484 ϕ-C 1,049 645	128
		π_4 π_3 π(C≡C) π_2		8.88 (2) 9.57 (5) 10.38 (2) 11.05 (5)		236
C_8H_6	CH_3-(C≡C)$_3$-CH_3	$2\pi_u$ $1\pi_g$ $1\pi_u$	8.60 (1) 10.63 (1) 12.10 (1) 13.77 (1) 15.2 17.52 (1) 19.3		2,180 (40) 1,090 (40) 2,020 (40) 970 (40) 850 (40) ~300	39
$C_8H_6Cl_2$	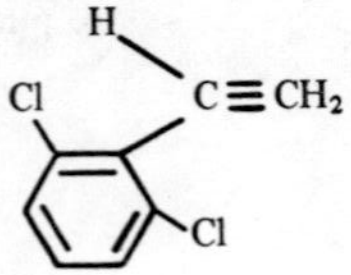	π_4 π_3 π_2 n(Cl)	8.70 10.05 (2) 11.1	9.05 (2) 9.30 (5) 10.50 (2) 11.35 (5)		236

TABLE 1 (continued)

Compound		Orbital	Ionization Energy: Adiabatic	Ionization Energy: Vertical	Vibrational Bands	Reference
$C_8H_6N_2$	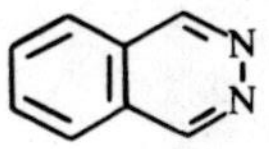	nb	8.68			101
		π	9.17			
			9.68			
			10.77			
			12.07			
			(12.58)			
			14.09			
			15.23			
			(18.83)			
$C_8H_6N_2$	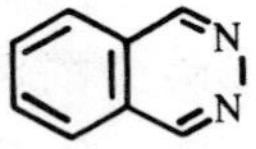	n_1		8.70		144
		π_1		9.07		
		π_2		9.95		
		n_2		10.60		
		π_3		11.00		
$C_8H_6N_2$	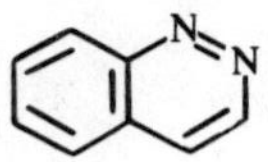	n_1		8.90		144
		π_1		9.10		
		π_2		9.83		
		π_3		11.00		
		n_2		11.05		
		nb	8.51			101
		π	9.03			
			9.75			
			10.83			
			12.04			
			(12.46)			
			13.85			
			16.16			
			(17.11)			
			(18.96)			
$C_8H_6N_2$	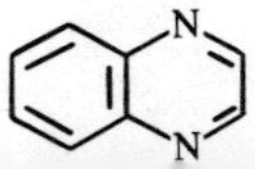	π_1		9.00		144
		n_1, π_2		9.30		

TABLE 1 (continued)

Compound		Orbital	Ionization Energy Adiabatic	Ionization Energy Vertical	Vibrational Bands	Reference
$C_8H_6N_2$ (cont.)		n_2		10.90		
		π_3		11.56		
$C_8H_6N_2$	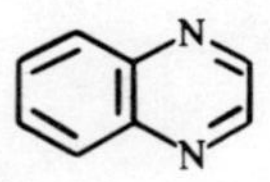	π	8.99			101
		π	10.72			
			11.58			
			(12.32)			
			13.98			
			15.30			
			16.21			
			17.07			
			(18.26)			
$C_8H_6N_2$	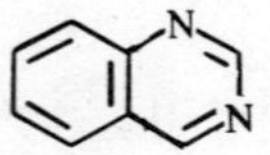	π_1		9.08		144
		n_1		9.50		
		π_2		9.80		
		n_2		10.70		
		π_3		11.30		
		π	9.02			101
		π	9.74			
			10.72			
			11.26			
			12.02			
			(13.78)			
			(14.41)			
			16.28			
			17.23			
			(18.80)			
$C_8H_6N_2$	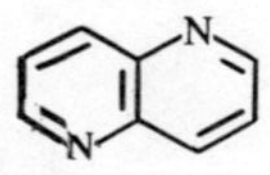	n_1, π_1		9.20		144
		π_2		9.30		
		n_2		10.40		
		π_3		11.05		

TABLE 1 (continued)

Compound		Orbital	Ionization Energy Adiabatic	Ionization Energy Vertical	Vibrational Bands	Reference
$C_8H_6N_2$	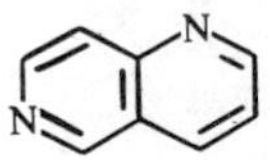	π_1		9.07		144
		n_1		9.50		
		n_2		9.90		
		π_2		10.00		
		π_3		11.10		
$C_8H_6N_2$	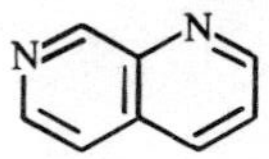	π_1		8.99		144
		n_1		9.30		
		n_2, π_2		10.00		
		π_3		11.14		
$C_8H_6N_2$	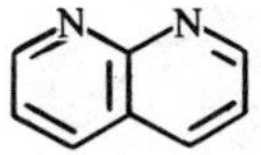	n_1		9.20		144
		π_1, π_2		9.40		
		n_2		10.10		
		π_3		11.33		
$C_8H_6N_2$	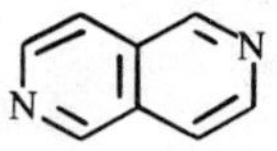	π_1		8.87		144
		n_1		9.40		
		n_2		10.00		
		π_2		10.35		
		π_3		10.85		
$C_8H_6N_2$	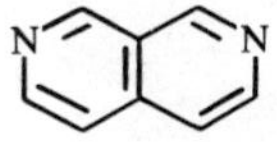	π_1		8.98		144
		n_1		9.35		
		π_2		9.90		
		n_2		10.10		
		π_3		10.98		
C_8H_6O	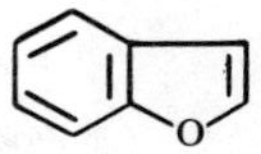	π	8.29 (5)	8.36 (5)		82
		π		8.89		
		π	10.48	10.48		
		$\pi+\sigma$	11.25	11.7		
				12.5		
				13.25		
				14.2		

TABLE 1 (continued)

Compound		Orbital	Ionization Energy: Adiabatic	Ionization Energy: Vertical	Vibrational Bands	Reference
C_8H_6O (cont.)				15.65		
				(16.05)		
		π?		16.7		
				18.8		
C_8H_6S	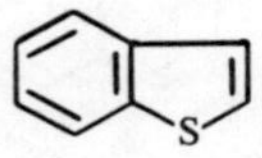	π	8.17 (5)	8.17 (5)		82
		π		8.73		
		π	10.00	10.05		
		π	11.02	11.02		
		σ		11.45		
		σ		12.15		
		π?		13.0		
		σ		13.95		
		σ		15.0		
C_8H_7N	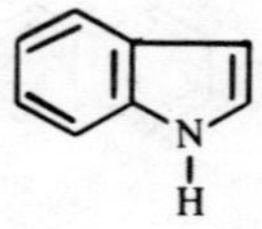	π	7.75 (5)	7.90 (5)		82
		π		(8.35)		
		π	9.75	9.75		
		π	10.75	(11.05)		
		σ		11.45		
		σ		12.25		
		π		13.0		
		σ	(13.55)	(14.1)		
		σ		15.1		
		σ		16.6		
C_8H_8	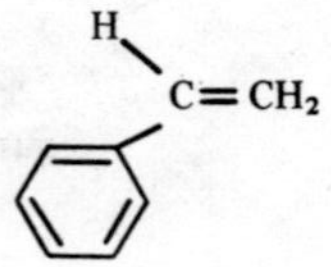	π	8.43 (1)			37
			9.18			
			10.42			
			11.31			
			13.56			
			(16.65)			
			(18.24)			
		π_4	8.40 (2)	8.50 (2)		236
		π_3		9.30 (5)		
		π_2	10.30 (2)	10.55 (2)		
			11.2	11.5 (05)		

TABLE 1 (continued)

	Compound	Orbital	Ionization Energy: Adiabatic	Ionization Energy: Vertical	Vibrational Bands	Reference
C_8H_8	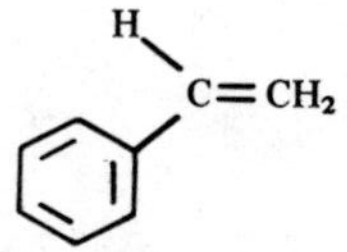			8.55		61
C_8H_8	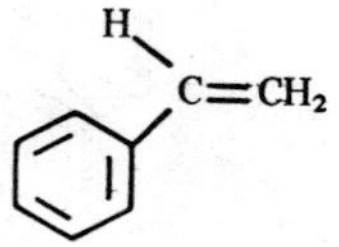	Ring π + Ethylenic π	8.42	8.48	ring C-C 1,533	128
		Ring π	9.13	9.28		
		Ethylenic π + Ring π	10.55	10.55	ϕ-C 969	
C_8H_8	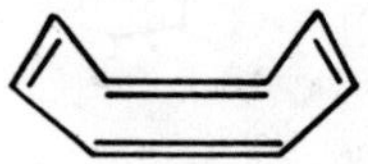		8.21			122
			9.62			
			10.91			
			12.22			
			14.28			
			14.50			
			16.46			
			(17.79)			
			(19.29)			
C_8H_8		π		8.5		82
		π		9.8		
		π		11.2		
		σ		11.6		
		σ	12.15	12.3		
		σ		14.5		
		σ		16.3		
		σ		17.9		
C_8H_8	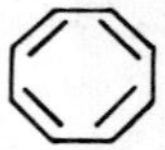		8.04			57
			9.49			
			10.84			
			11.49			
			12.09			

TABLE 1 (continued)

Compound		Orbital	Ionization Energy: Adiabatic	Ionization Energy: Vertical	Vibrational Bands	Reference
C_8H_8 (cont.)			14.49			
			16.44			
			17.69			
			18.56			
C_8H_8	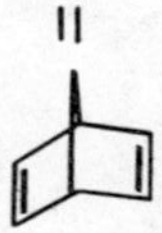	π_1 (a)		8.5_0		145
		π_2 (s)		9.6_5		
		π_3 (a)		9.9_0		
C_8H_8		$a_2'(\pi)$	8.23	8.23	570	146
		$e'(\pi)$	9.45	9.65,10.02	420	
		$e''(\sigma)$	10.96	11.25		
		$a'(\sigma)$		11.9–12.0		
			13.0	13.2		
				13.9		
			14.5	14.7		
C_8H_8			8.24			122
			? 9.22			
			9.63			
			11.11			
			?11.49			
			13.05			
			?13.79			
			14.51			
			?16.89			
			(18.11)			
			(19.24)			
			?(20.20)			
C_8H_8	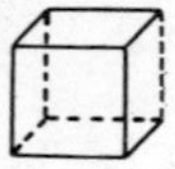		8.74			122
			13.62			
			15.34			
			(16.87)			
			(17.26)			

TABLE 1 (continued)

Compound		Orbital	Ionization Energy Adiabatic	Ionization Energy Vertical	Vibrational Bands	Reference
C_8H_8	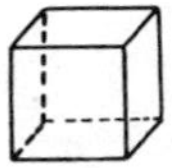		8.74 (1)			37
			13.62			
			15.34			
			(16.87)			
			(17.26)			
C_8H_8BN	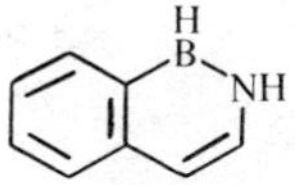		8.24 (1)			37
			10.07			
			10.95			
			12.23			
			13.07			
			14.05			
			15.53			
			16.47			
			(18.43)			
			(19.35)			
			(21.01)			
$C_8H_8FeO_3$	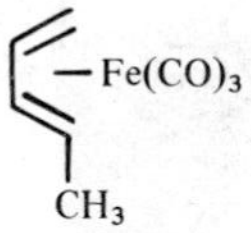		7.84 (1)			37
			9.58			
			(10.75)			
			11.13			
			12.06			
			(13.60)			
			(15.59)			
			(17.73)			
			(19.73)			
			(21.08)			
C_8H_8O	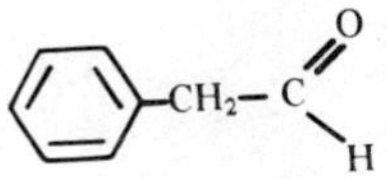	Ring π	8.80	9.15		128
		Ring π		9.56		
		Oxygen n		10.08		

TABLE 1 (continued)

Compound		Orbital	Ionization Energy: Adiabatic	Ionization Energy: Vertical	Vibrational Bands	Reference
$C_8H_8O_2$				8.87		63
				9.77		
				11.51		
				11.87		
C_8H_{10}	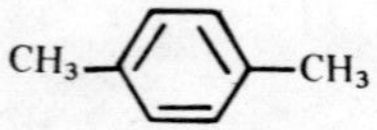			8.71		63
				9.21		
C_8H_{10}				8.37		236
				9.05		
			10.8	11.1		
C_8H_{10}	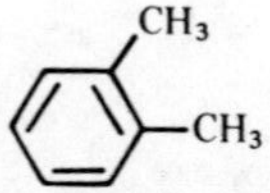			8.45		236
				8.90		
			10.8	11.0		
		b_1 (A)		8.7_5		126
		a_2 (S)		9.0		
		b_1		11.2_5		
C_8H_{10}	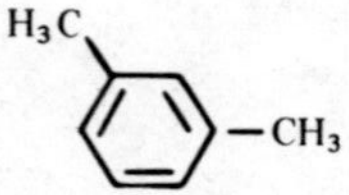	a_2 (A)		8.7_5		126
		b_1 (S)		9.0_5		
		b_1		11.2		
				8.50		236
				9.00		
			10.8	11.0		
C_8H_{10}	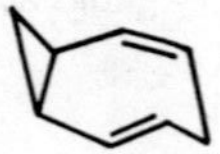		8.43	8.79		147
				9.46		
			10.00	10.5		
				10.9		
			11.68	12.0		
				12.4		

TABLE 1 (continued)

Compound		Orbital	Ionization Energy: Adiabatic	Ionization Energy: Vertical	Vibrational Bands	Reference
C_8H_{10}		π_S e_S e_A σ		9.0_5 9.5 10.3 {11.3 {12.2		148
C_8H_{10}	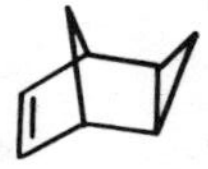	π_S e_S e_A σ		8.9 9.6 10.2 {11.5_5 {11.9 {12.5_5		148
$C_8H_{10}O$		$b_{1g}(S)$ $b_{3g}(A)$ b_{2u}		8.6 9.1_5 11.2_5		126
$C_8H_{10}O_2$		π_1 π_2 π_3		7.90 9.25 10.25		142
$C_8H_{10}O_2$				7.90 9.19 10.18		63
$C_8H_{10}S_2$		π_1 π_2 π_3 π_4		7.93 8.80 9.28 10.10		142
$C_8H_{11}N$	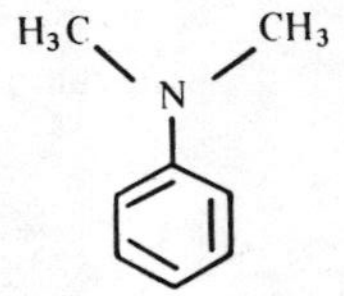			7.51 9.03 9.79		63

TABLE 1 (continued)

	Compound	Orbital	Ionization Energy: Adiabatic	Ionization Energy: Vertical	Vibrational Bands	Reference
$C_8H_{11}N$	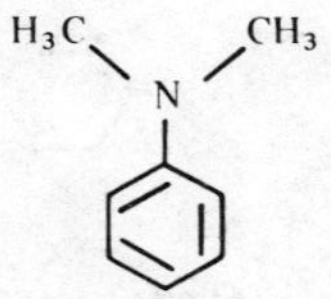		7.6 9.2 10.0			149
$C_8H_{11}P$	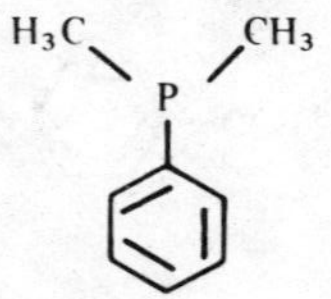		8.45 9.2			149
C_8H_{12}		π(a)		9.4_0		145
C_8H_{12}	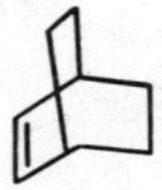			9.05 10.03 12.64 14.90 15.73 16.68 18.50		134
C_8H_{12}	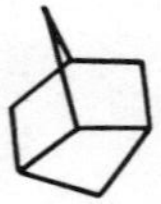			8.75 9.40 (10.05) 15.00 16.75		122

TABLE 1 (continued)

Compound		Orbital	Ionization Energy: Adiabatic	Ionization Energy: Vertical	Vibrational Bands	Reference
C_8H_{12}	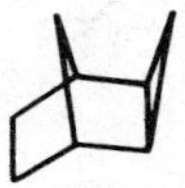	e_S		9.4		148
		e_A		10.0		
		σ		{10.8		
				11.5		
				11.8}		
C_8H_{12}		e_S		9.4		148
		e_A		10.2		
		σ		{10.7		
				11.4		
				12.0}		
C_8H_{12}			8.92			122
			9.87			
			11.93			
			(18.75)			
$C_8H_{12}O_2$	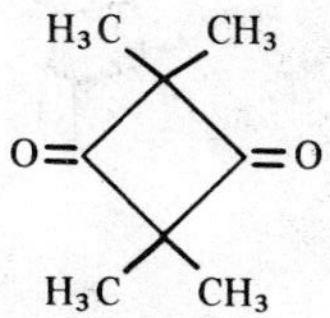	n_+		8.80		80
		n_-		9.53		
$C_8H_{12}Si$	$Si(CH{=}CH_2)_4$	π_1 (e)		9.8		150
		π_2 (a_2)		10.1		
		π_3 (b_1)		10.35		
		σ_1 (b_2)		≈10.8		
		π_4 (e)		≈11.2		
C_8H_{14}	cis— 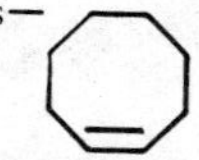	π	8.82	8.98	1,290	93
		σ	10.0 (1)	10.5 (1)		

TABLE 1 (continued)

	Compound	Orbital	Ionization Energy: Adiabatic	Ionization Energy	Ionization Energy: Vertical	Vibrational Bands	Reference
C_8H_{14}	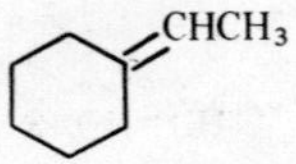	π	8.41		9.21		121
			10.01		(10.7)		
			13.0		13.6		
			15.0		15.6		
			15.8		16.3		
			16.9		17.6		
			18.0				
			19.3				
C_8H_{14}	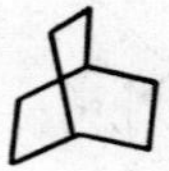				9.71		136
					11.20		
					12.61		
					15.77		
					18.79		
C_8H_{14}				9.71			134
				11.20			
				12.61			
				15.77			
				18.79			
			9.53				122
			11.08				
			11.98				
			(12.60)				
			15.65				
			(18.80)				
$C_8H_{14}O$	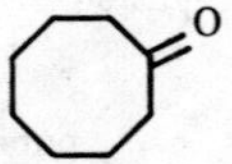	n			9.09 (2)	740 (40)	111
						1,267 (40)	
				10.3			
C_8H_{18}	$(CH_3)_3CCH_2CH(CH_3)_2$	σ onset	9.91				57
			11.95				
			14.09				
			19.74				

TABLE 1 (continued)

Compound		Orbital	Ionization Energy: Adiabatic	Ionization Energy: Vertical	Vibrational Bands	Reference
$C_8H_{18}NO$	$((H_3C)_3C)_2N{-}O\cdot$	e^- in π^* n (O) n (O) (N-O)π	6.77 8.62 9.15 10.09	7.20 (2) 8.85 (2) 9.26 (2)	1,370 (80)	156
$C_8H_{18}O$	$(CH_3)_3COC(CH_3)_3$		8.94 (1)			59
$C_8H_{18}S$	$(CH_3)_3CSC(CH_3)_3$			8.07		61
$C_8H_{18}S_2$	$(CH_3)_3CSSC(CH_3)_3$			8.17 8.82		61
C_9F_7N	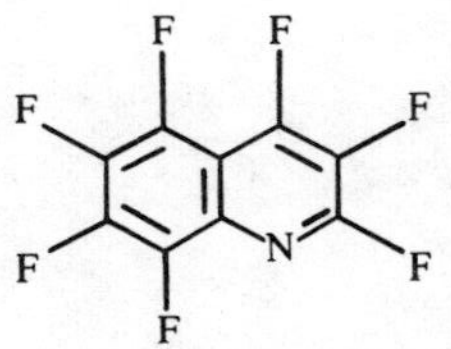	π_1 π_2 π_3 π_4 n		9.51 10.19 (11.45) 12.22 (11.4)		151
C_9F_7N	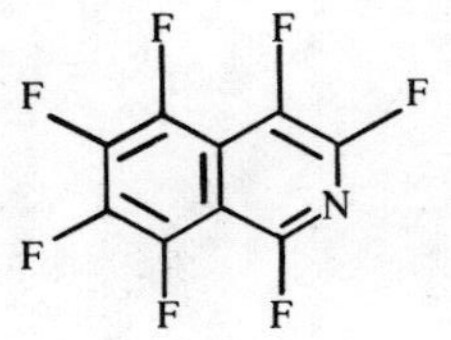	π_1 π_2 π_3 π_4 n		9.29 10.61 11.23 12.57 (11.6)		151

TABLE 1 (continued)

	Compound	Orbital	Ionization Energy Adiabatic	Ionization Energy Vertical	Vibrational Bands	Reference
$C_9H_6FeO_4$	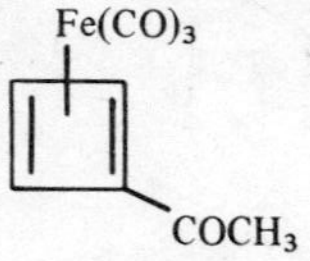		8.27 (1)			37
			9.23			
			(10.86)			
			11.73			
			12.28			
			(12.50)			
			(13.72)			
			(15.66)			
			(16.97)			
			(17.73)			
			(19.73)			
			(21.09)			
C_9H_7N	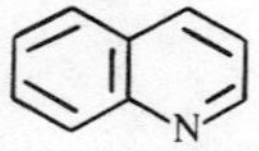			8.67 (5)		152
				9.00		
				10.63 (5)		
				11.37 (5)		
C_9H_7N	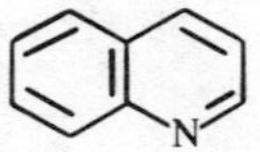	π_1		8.62		151
		π_2		(9.16)		
		π_3		10.58		
		n		(9.2)		
		π	8.62			101
		nb	9.07			
			10.64			
			11.42			
			13.07			
			(13.65)			
			(14.22)			
			15.05			
			16.20			
			(18.36)			
C_9H_7N	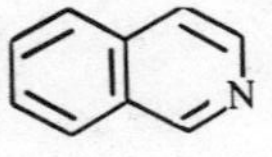	π_1		8.54		151
		π_2		(9.40)		
		π_3		10.42		
		n		(9.40)		

TABLE 1 (continued)

Compound		Orbital	Ionization Energy Adiabatic	Ionization Energy Vertical	Vibrational Bands	Reference
C_9H_7N		π	8.54			101
		nb	9.24			
			10.50			
			11.60			
			(12.54)			
			(13.26)			
	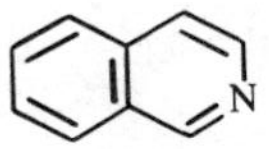		14.03			
			(14.67)			
			15.98			
			16.69			
			(18.29)			
			(18.78)			
				8.53 (5)		152
				9.16 (5)		
				10.32 (5)		
				11.43 (5)		
C_9H_8	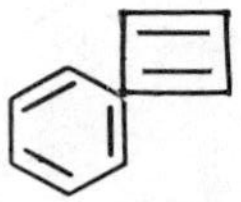	π	7.43 (1)			37
			8.48			
			10.00			
			10.76			
			11.94			
			(12.49)			
			14.39			
			15.43			
			(18.23)			
			(21.09)			
C_9H_8	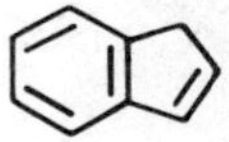			8.14 (1)		132
				8.82 (1)		
				10.25 (1)		
				11.14 (1)		
				11.74 (1)		
				12.83 (1)		
				13.62 (1)		
				14.76 (1)		
				16.33 (1)		
				17.50 (1)		

TABLE 1 (continued)

Compound		Orbital	Ionization Energy: Adiabatic	Ionization Energy: Vertical	Vibrational Bands	Reference
C_9H_8	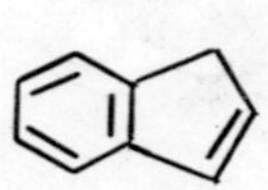			8.13 (5) 8.95 (5) 10.29 (5) 11.58 (5)		152
C_9H_{10}	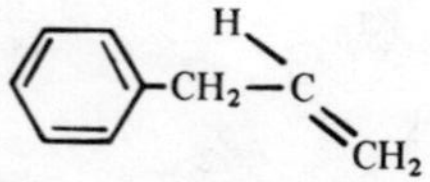	Ring π Ring π Ethylenic π	8.60	8.85 9.27 9.71		128
C_9H_{10}	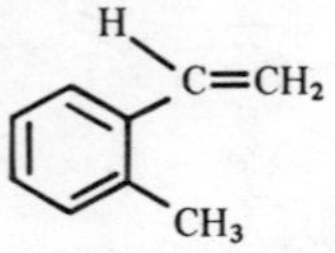	π_4 π_3 π_2	8.20 (2) 9.90 (2) 11.0	8.50 (2) 9.00 (5) 10.40 (2) 11.3 (05)		236
C_9H_{10}	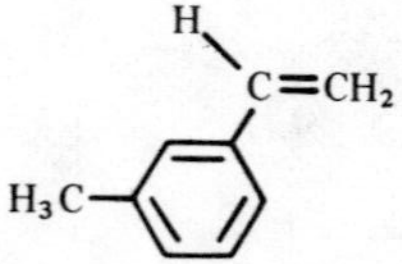	π_4 π_3 π_2	8.15 (2) 10.10 (2) 11.0	8.36 (2) 8.97 (5) 10.33 (2) 11.3 (05)		236
C_9H_{10}	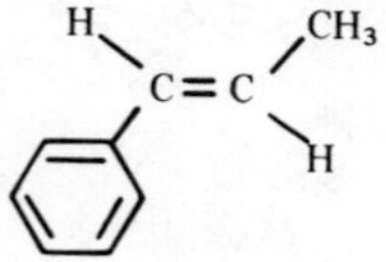	π_4 π_3 π_2	8.20 (2) 9.95 (2) 10.9	8.37 (2) 9.14 (5) 10.25 (2) 11.4 (05)		236
C_9H_{10}	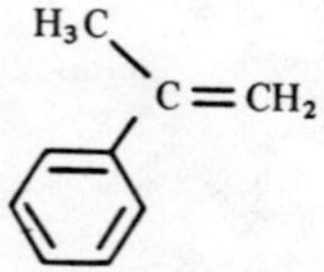	π_4 π_3 π_2	8.20 (2) 8.90 (5) 9.70 (2) 10.8	8.50 (2) 9.13 (5) 10.00 (2) 11.2 (05)		236

TABLE 1 (continued)

Compound		Orbital	Ionization Energy: Adiabatic	Ionization Energy: Vertical	Vibrational Bands	Reference
C_9H_{10}	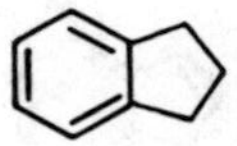			8.45		236
				9.05		
			10.8	11.1		
C_9H_{10}	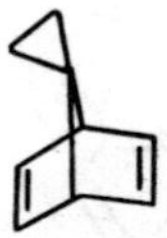	b_2		8.37		217
		a_1		9.26		
		b_2		10.05		
				10.8		
				11.1		
				12.5		
C_9H_{10}		$a''(\pi)$		8.36		143
		$a'(\pi)$		9.02		
		$a'(\pi)$		10.55		
		σ		(beg) 11.28		
C_9H_{10}		$\pi_1(a')$		8.8		153
		$e_S(a')$		9.5		
		$e_A(a'')$		10.0		
		σ		10.5		
$C_9H_{10}S$	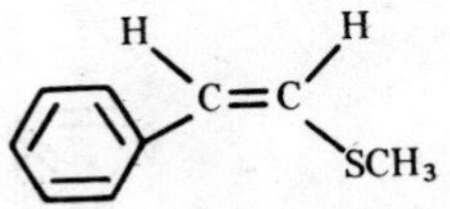			8.75		61
C_9H_{12}		$\pi_1(a')$		8.6_5		153
		$\pi_2(a')$		9.5		
		$e_S(a')$		9.8		
		$e_A(a'')$		10.1_5		
		σ		11.3		

TABLE 1 (continued)

	Compound	Orbital	Ionization Energy: Adiabatic	Ionization Energy: Vertical	Vibrational Bands	Reference
C_9H_{12}		e(π)	8.45	8.77		143
		e(π)		8.9–9.0		
		a_1 (π)		9.80		
		σ		(beg) 11.32		
C_9H_{12}	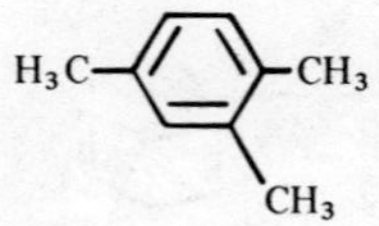	a″(A)		8.5		126
		a″(S)		8.9_5		
		a″		11.0		
C_9H_{12}	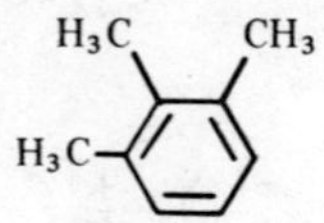	a_2 (A)		8.6		126
		b_1 (S)		8.6		
		b_1		10.9_5		
C_9H_{12}	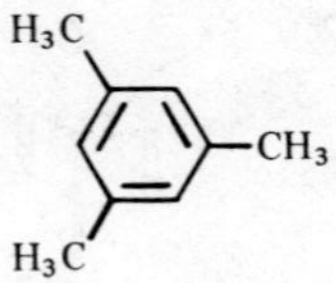	e″(A)		8.6_5		126
		e″(S)		8.6_5		
		a_2''		11.0		
C_9H_{12}	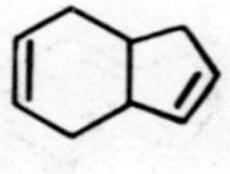		8.78			122
			10.39			
			12.28			
			15.79			
			(18.45)			
			(19.56)			
C_9H_{12}	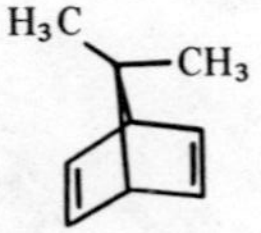	b_2 (π)	7.97	7.97		154
		b_2 (π)	8.9	9.25		
		a_1 (π)		9.54		
		σ onset	10.4			

TABLE 1 (continued)

	Compound	Orbital	Ionization Energy: Adiabatic	Ionization Energy: Vertical	Vibrational Bands	Reference
C_9H_{12}				9.0_0 9.2_0		155
C_9H_{12}	$(H_2C{=}CH)_4C$	e a_2 e b_1		9.52 9.67 10.06 10.40		231
$C_9H_{13}N$	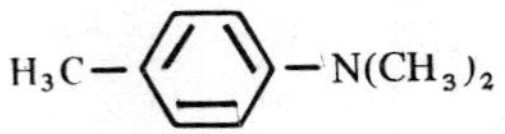			7.48 9.06 9.65		63
C_9H_{14}	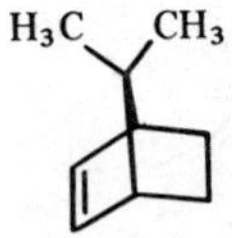	a′(π) a′(π) σ onset	8.27 9.9	8.43 8.9 (5) 10.15		154
C_9H_{14}	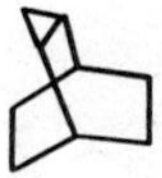	$e_s(a')$ $e_a(a'')$ σ		9.3 10.0 10.4_5		153
C_9H_{16}	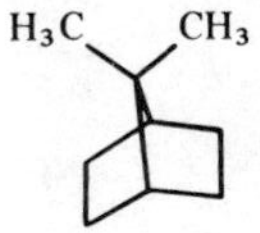	b_2(π) σ onset	8.30 9.6	8.49 10.0		154

TABLE 1 (continued)

	Compound	Orbital	Ionization Energy: Adiabatic	Ionization Energy: Vertical	Vibrational Bands	Reference
$C_9H_{17}B$	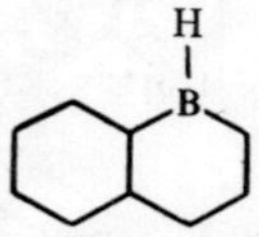			8.47 (1)		37
				(9.28)		
				10.22		
				14.60		
				(15.53)		
				17.84		
				(18.23)		
$C_9H_{18}NO$	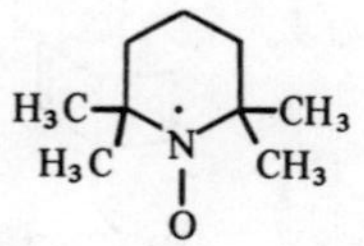	e^- in π^*	6.73	7.31 (2)	1,370 (80)	156
		n(O)	8.63	8.94 (2)		
		n(O)	9.21	9.27 (2)		
		(N-O)π	9.93			
$C_9H_{18}O$	*n*-$C_7H_{15}C(=O)CH_3$		9.32 (2)			59
$C_9H_{18}O$	$(CH_3)_3CC(=O)C(CH_3)_3$		8.71 (2)			59
$C_{10}F_8$	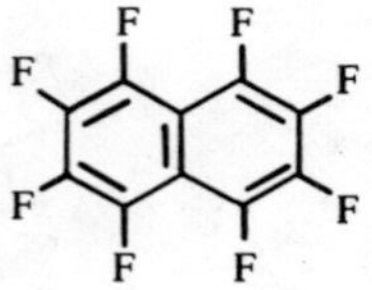		8.85 (3)	9.05 (3)	1,530	160
			9.90 (8)	10.08 (5)	1,450	
			10.78 (2)	10.96	1,400	
			11.57	11.76	1,450	
			~13.0	13.71	1,200	
			14.20	14.20	1,450	
				14.9		
				15.4		
				16.1		
				17.0		
				17.5		
				18.3		

TABLE 1 (continued)

Compound		Orbital	Ionization Energy: Adiabatic	Ionization Energy: Vertical	Vibrational Bands	Reference
$C_{10}F_8$ (cont.)				18.9 20.1 ~22.2 ~24.5		
$C_{10}H_8$	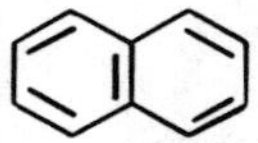	$1a_u$ $2b_{1u}$ $1b_{2g}$ $1b_{3g}$		8.15 8.88 10.10 10.86		129
$C_{10}H_8$	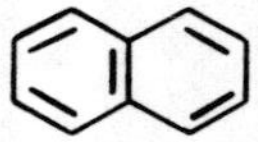			8.15		61
$C_{10}H_8$	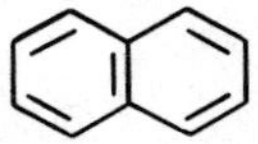			8.12 (5) 8.90 (5) 10.00 (5) 10.85 (5)		152
$C_{10}H_8$	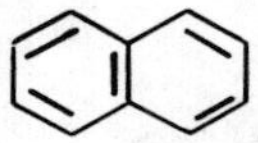			8.11 (1) 8.79 (1) 9.96 (1) 10.90 (1) 12.26 (1) 13.22 (1) 15.73 (1) 18.65 (1) 21.03 (1)		132
$C_{10}H_8$	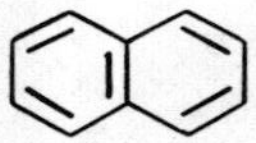		8.15 10.00			7

TABLE 1 (continued)

	Compound	Orbital	Ionization Energy: Adiabatic	Ionization Energy: Vertical	Vibrational Bands	Reference
$C_{10}H_8$	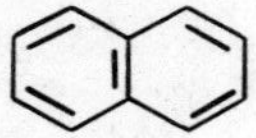		8.13 (3)	8.13 (3)	ν'_3 1,450	160
			~8.7	8.88 (4)		
			10.01 (1)	10.01 (1)	1,050	
					ν'_9 400	
			10.90	10.90		
				11.08		
				11.37		
				11.89		
				12.50		
				13.8		
				14.5		
				16.0		
				16.5		
				19.0		
				22.3		
$C_{10}H_8$	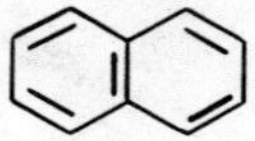	π	8.11 (1)			37
			8.79			
			9.96			
			10.90			
			12.26			
			13.22			
			15.73			
			(18.65)			
			(21.03)			
$C_{10}H_8$	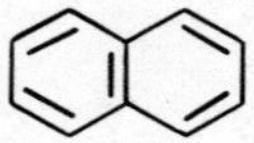		8.11			101
			8.79			
			9.96			
			10.90			
			12.26			
			13.22			
			15.73			
			(18.65)			
			21.03			

TABLE 1 (continued)

Compound		Orbital	Ionization Energy Adiabatic	Ionization Energy Vertical	Vibrational Bands	Reference
$C_{10}H_8$	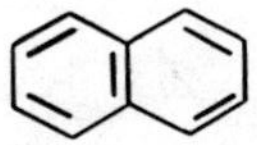	π	8.12	8.12		157
		π	8.91	8.91		
		π	10.08	10.08		
		π	10.85	10.85		
				11.05		
				11.35		
				11.90		
		π		12.5		
			13.5	13.5		
				13.7		
				14.45		
			(17.5)	15.9		
				16.25		
$C_{10}H_8$	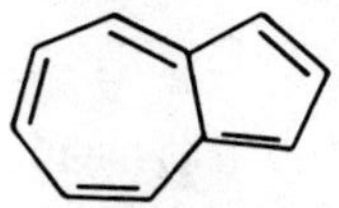			7.42 (5)		152
				8.49 (5)		
				9.91 (5)		
				10.81 (5)		
		π	7.42	7.42		157
		π	8.52	8.52		
		π	9.90	10.0		
		π	10.80	11.0		
				11.35		
			11.8	12.5		
				13.2		
			14.4	14.5		
			15.6	15.7		

TABLE 1 (continued)

Compound		Orbital	Ionization Energy Adiabatic	Ionization Energy Vertical	Vibrational Bands	Reference
$C_{10}H_8$	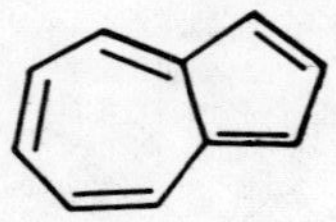			7.43 (1)		132
				8.48 (1)		
				10.00 (1)		
				10.76 (1)		
				11.94 (1)		
				12.49 (1)		
				14.39 (1)		
				15.43 (1)		
				18.23 (1)		
				21.09 (1)		
$C_{10}H_8Cl_2Fe$	$Fe(\pi\text{-}C_5H_4Cl)_2$	$e_{2g}(d)$		7.03		224
		$a_{1g}(d)$		7.37		
		$e_{1u}(\pi)$		8.71		
				9.09		
		$e_{1g}(\pi)$		9.49		
		Cl pπ		10.98		
		Cl pπ		11.44		
		Ligand σ, π		12.4 (sh)		
		Ligand σ, π		13.58		
		Ligand σ		16.63		
$C_{10}H_{10}$	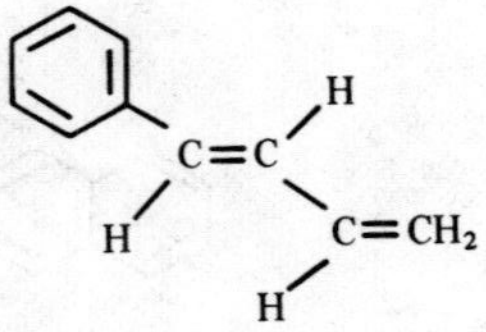		7.95	8.16		118
				9.27		
				9.8		
$C_{10}H_{10}$	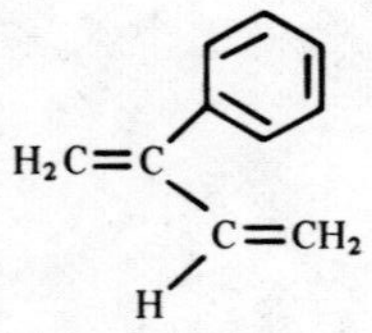		8.57	8.77		118
				9.3		
				11.2 (sh)		

TABLE 1 (continued)

Compound		Orbital	Ionization Energy: Adiabatic	Ionization Energy: Vertical	Vibrational Bands	Reference
$C_{10}H_{10}$	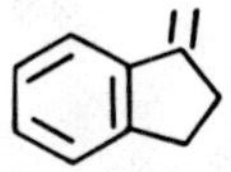	π_4		8.00 (2)		236
		π_3		8.86 (5)		
		π_2		9.91 (2)		
			10.7	10.9 (05)		
$C_{10}H_{10}$	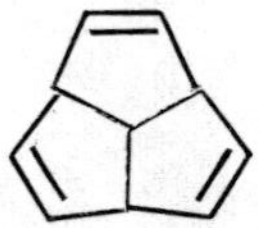	e(π)		9.0		234
				9.2–9.3		
		a_1 (π)		9.5		
		σ onset		10.4		
$C_{10}H_{10}$			8.05	8.34		147
				8.7		
			9.03	9.2		
			11.10	11.4		
				11.7		
$C_{10}H_{10}$			8.13			122
			(9.16)			
			11.12			
			(11.33)			
			12.87			
			14.68			
			16.32			
			16.65			
			(18.51)			
$C_{10}H_{10}Cr$	Cr (π-C_5H_5)$_2$	$a_{1g}(^2E_{2g})$	5.50	5.69		158
		$e_{2g}(^4A_{2g})$		7.02		
		$(^2E_{1g})$		~7.3		
		$(^2A_{2g}, ^2A_{1g})$		~7.4–7.9		
				8.9–10.4		
				12.6		
				13.7		
				17.2		

TABLE 1 (continued)

Compound		Orbital	Ionization Energy: Adiabatic	Ionization Energy: Vertical	Vibrational Bands	Reference
$C_{10}H_{10}Fe$	$Fe(\pi\text{-}C_5H_5)_2$	$e_{2g}(^2E_{2g})$	6.72	6.858	ν_4 282	158
		$a_{1g}(^2A_{1g})$		7.234	ν_4 274	
		$e_{1g}(^2E_{1g})$		8.715	ν_4 274	
		$e_{1u}(^2E_{1u})$		9.38		
				12.2		
				13.6		
				16.4		
$C_{10}H_{10}Fe$	$Fe(\pi\text{-}C_5H_5)_2$	$e_{2g}(d)$		6.88		224
		$a_{1g}(d)$		7.23		
		$e_{1u}(\pi)$		8.72		
				8.87 (sh)		
		$e_{1g}(\pi)$		9.14		
				9.39		
		Ligand σ, π		12.3		
		Ligand σ, π		13.0		
		Ligand σ, π		13.46		
		Ligand σ		16.5		
$C_{10}H_{10}Mg$	$Mg(C_5H_5)_2$			8.06		7
				8.98		
$C_{10}H_{10}Mg$	$Mg(\pi\text{-}C_5H_5)_2$	$e_{1g}(\pi)$		8.11, 8.23, 8.44		224
		$e_{1u}(\pi)$		9.03, 9.26 (sh)		
		$a_{1g}(\pi)$		12.2 (sh)		
		$a_{2u}(\pi)$		12.5		
		C-H σ		13.5		
		σ		16.65		
		σ		17.28 (sh)		
$C_{10}H_{10}Mn$	$Mn(\pi\text{-}C_5H_5)_2$	$a_{1g}(^1A_{1g})$	6.55	6.70		158
		$e_{2g}(^3E_{2g})$		6.85		
		$(^1E_{2g})$		7.10		
				7.9–9.3		
				12.2		
				13.3		
				16.6		

TABLE 1 (continued)

Compound		Orbital	Ionization Energy: Adiabatic	Ionization Energy: Vertical	Vibrational Bands	Reference
$C_{10}H_{10}Ni$	π-$(C_5H_5)_2Ni$	$e_{1g}(^2E_{1g})$	6.2	6.4		158
				8.2–10.9		
				12.4		
				13.6		
				17.2		
$C_{10}H_{10}O$	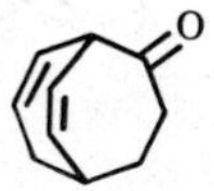		8.72			122
			10.85			
			(12.46)			
			(14.49)			
			(15.32)			
			16.98			
$C_{10}H_{10}Ru$	$Ru(\pi$-$C_5H_5)_2$	Metal d		7.45		224
		Metal d		7.63 (sh)		
		$e_{1u}(\pi)$		8.51		
				8.80 (sh)		
		$e_{1g}(\pi)$		9.93		
		$e_{1g}(\pi)$		10.23 (sh)		
		Ligand σ, π		11.8 (sh)		
		Ligand σ, π		12.3		
		Ligand σ, π		13.4		
		Ligand σ		16.75		
$C_{10}H_{12}$	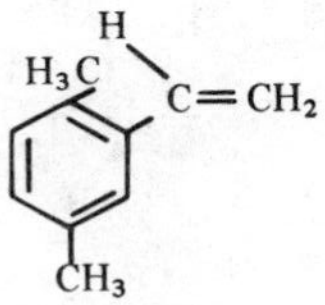	π_4	8.00 (2)	8.30 (2)		236
		π_3		8.76 (5)		
		π_2	9.90 (2)	10.23 (2)		
			10.8	11.1 (05)		

TABLE 1 (continued)

Compound		Orbital	Ionization Energy: Adiabatic	Ionization Energy: Vertical	Vibrational Bands	Reference
$C_{10}H_{12}$	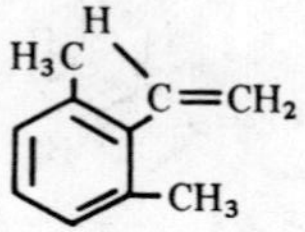	π_3	8.10 (2)	8.45 (2)		236
		π_4		8.65 (5)		
		π_2	9.60 (2)	9.95 (2)		
			10.65 (5)	11.0 (05)		
$C_{10}H_{12}$	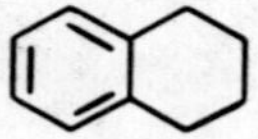			8.45		236
				8.95		
			10.1	10.6		
$C_{10}H_{12}$	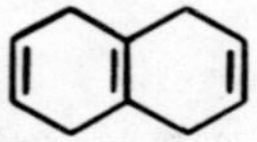		8.2	8.29		159
			9.0	9.05		
			9.5	9.59		
$C_{10}H_{12}$	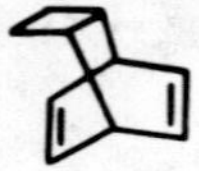	π_1(a′)		8.8		153
		π_2(a′)		9.4_5		
		e_S(a′)		9.8		
		e_A(a″)		10.3		
		a_1(a′)		10.7		
		σ		11.5		
$C_{10}H_{12}$			8.02	8.32		147
			8.43	8.73		
			10.15	10.4		
				10.9		
				11.4		
				12.3		
$C_{10}H_{12}$	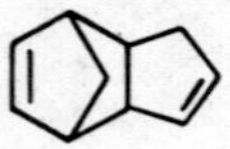		8.79 (5)	8.93 (5)		91
				11.82		
				15.90		
				17.3		

TABLE 1 (continued)

			Ionization Energy			
Compound		Orbital	Adiabatic	Vertical	Vibrational Bands	Reference
$C_{10}H_{12}S_3$	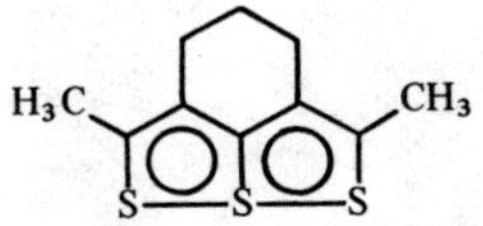	π_1		7.34		115
		n_1		7.73		
		π_2		8.92		
		π_3		9.09		
				10.26		
				11.00		
$C_{10}H_{13}ClO$	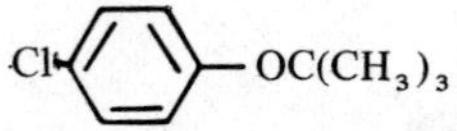			8.72		63
				9.76		
				11.38		
$C_{10}H_{14}$	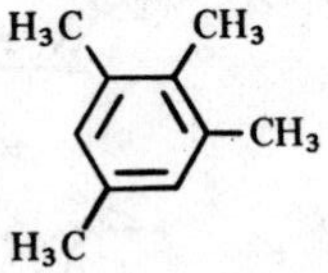	b_1 (S)		8.3		126
		a_2 (A)		8.6		
		b_1		10.9		
$C_{10}H_{14}$	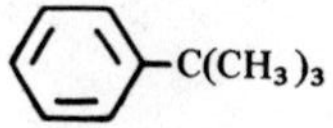		10.5			7
			16.5			
$C_{10}H_{14}$				8.9_5		155
				9.3_0		
$C_{10}H_{14}$	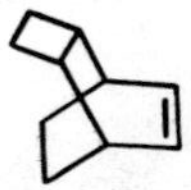	π_1 (a')		9.0		153
		e_S(a')		9.5_5		
		e_A(a'')		9.9_5		
		a_1 (a')		10.3		
		σ		11.3		

TABLE 1 (continued)

Compound		Orbital	Ionization Energy: Adiabatic	Ionization Energy: Vertical	Vibrational Bands	Reference
$C_{10}H_{14}$	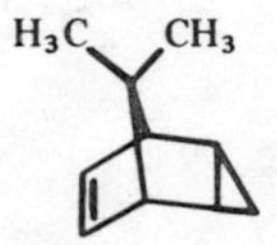	a′(π), a′(π) a′(Δ) a″(Δ) σ	7.9 8.8 10.7	8.14 9.11 9.46 10.06 10.98		154
$C_{10}H_{14}$			7.95 9.14 10.19	8.26 9.50 10.5 10.9 11.9 13.2		147
$C_{10}H_{14}O$	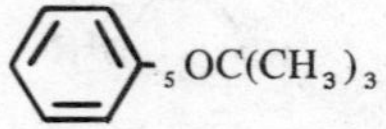			8.75 9.33 9.80		63
$C_{10}H_{14}O$	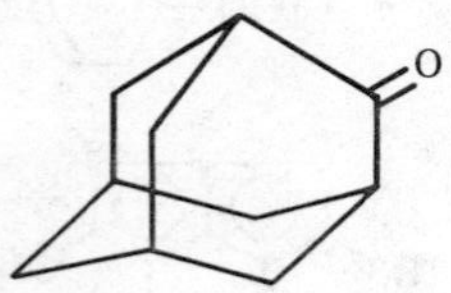		8.76 9.99 11.50 13.41 15.16 (18.20)			122
$C_{10}H_{14}O_2$	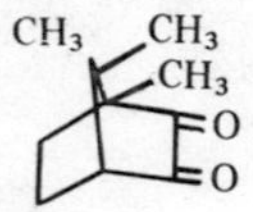	n_+ n_-		8.80 10.40		80
$C_{10}H_{15}N$	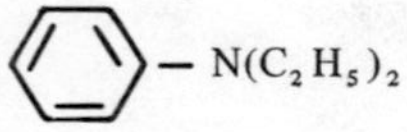			7.51 9.11 9.79		63

TABLE 1 (continued)

	Compound	Orbital	Ionization Energy: Adiabatic	Ionization Energy: Vertical	Vibrational Bands	Reference
$C_{10}H_{16}$	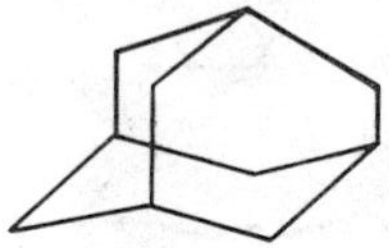		9.25 (1) 10.69 12.90 14.94 16.79 (18.01)			37
$C_{10}H_{16}$	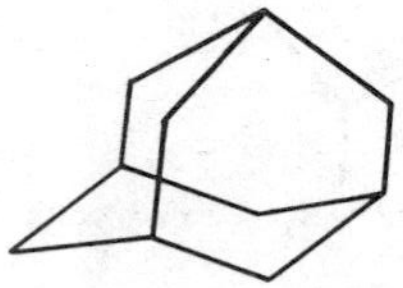		9.25 10.69 12.90 14.94 16.79 (18.01)			122
$C_{10}H_{16}$	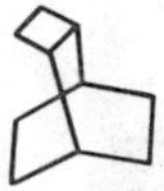	$e_S(a')$ $e_A(a'')$ $a_1(a')$ σ		9.4_5 9.9 10.2 10.8		153
$C_{10}H_{16}$	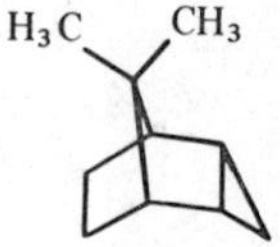	$a'(\pi)$ $a'(\Delta)$ $a''(\Delta)$ σ	8.18 8.9 9.7	8.28 9.31 9.97 10.38		154
$C_{10}H_{16}$			8.71	9.05 9.62 10.25 10.7 11.1 11.9		147

TABLE 1 (continued)

Compound		Orbital	Ionization Energy: Adiabatic	Ionization Energy: Vertical	Vibrational Bands	Reference
$C_{10}H_{16}$			8.07 9.25 11.43 13.12 14.53 15.74 18.57			57
$C_{10}H_{16}O$	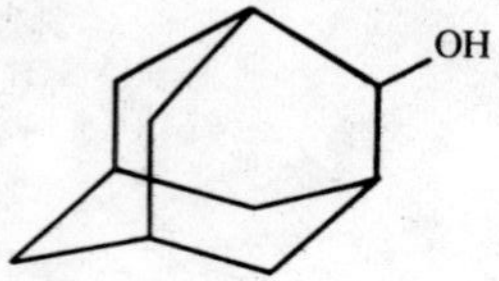		9.25 10.88 12.90 (13.97) (15.35) (18.68)			122
$C_{10}H_{16}O$	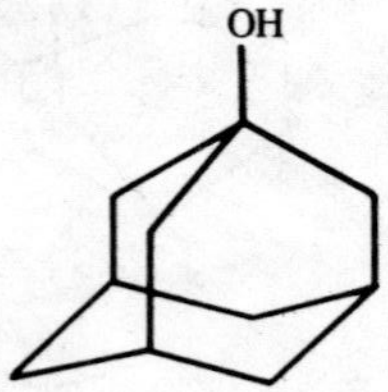		9.23 (12.62) 13.13 14.60 (15.18) (18.27)			122
$C_{10}H_{18}$	*cis*- 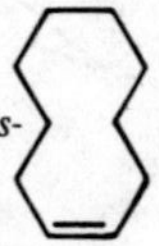	π σ	8.80 9.9 (1)	8.98 10.4 (1)	1,340	93
$C_{10}H_{18}$	*cis*– 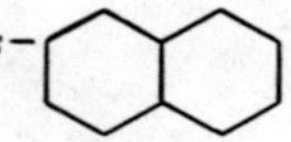		9.40 (1) (10.93) 13.68 (18.30)			37

TABLE 1 (continued)

Compound		Orbital	Ionization Energy: Adiabatic	Ionization Energy: Vertical	Vibrational Bands	Reference
$C_{10}H_{18}$	trans- 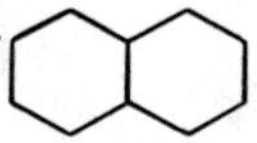		9.35 (1)			37
			10.67			
			13.84			
			15.21			
			(17.89)			
$C_{11}H_{10}S$	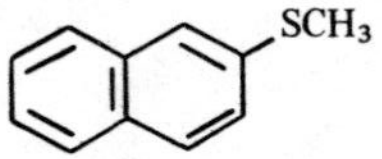			7.71		61
$C_{11}H_{11}Cr$	$(\pi{-}C_6H_6)(\pi{-}C_5H_5)Cr$	$^1A_1 + ^3E_2$		6.20		161
		$^1E_2$		7.15		
		$1e_1 + 2e_1$		{8.76, 9.17, 9.68		
		$1a_1 + 2a_1$ $+\sigma$ Orbitals		{11.5, 12.2, 13.8, 17.2		
$C_{11}H_{11}Mn$	$(\pi{-}C_6H_6)(\pi{-}C_5H_5)Mn$	$3a_1$		6.36		161
		$1e_2$		6.72		
		$1e_1 + 2e_1$		{8.75, 9.25, 9.79		
		$1a_1 + 2a_1$ $+\sigma$ Orbitals		{11.4, 12.2, 14.1, 16.8		
$C_{11}H_{12}$	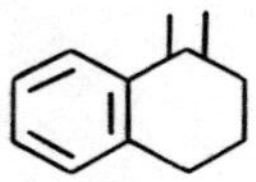	π_4		7.90 (2)		236
		π_3		8.80 (5)		
		π_2		9.80 (2)		
			10.4	10.7 (05)		

TABLE 1 (continued)

	Compound	Orbital	Ionization Energy: Adiabatic	Ionization Energy: Vertical	Vibrational Bands	Reference
$C_{11}H_{14}$	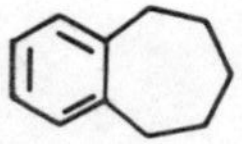		10.1	8.40 8.95 10.5		236
$C_{11}H_{18}$	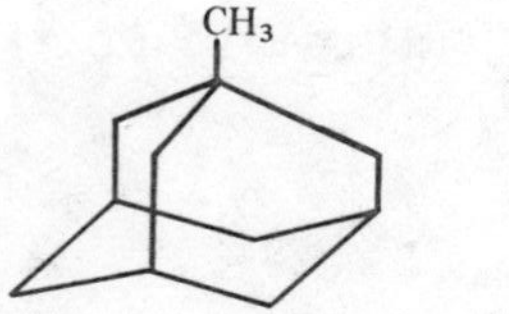		9.24 10.68 12.37 14.44 (16.95) (18.02)			122
$C_{11}H_{18}$	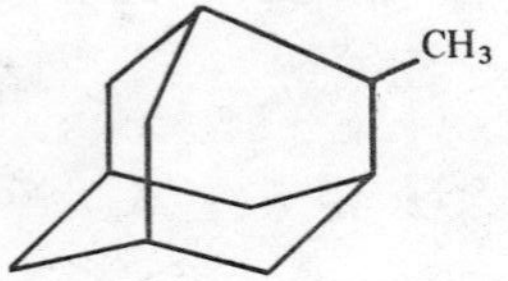		9.24 10.51 12.42 12.97 14.78 (18.26)			122
$C_{11}H_{18}O$	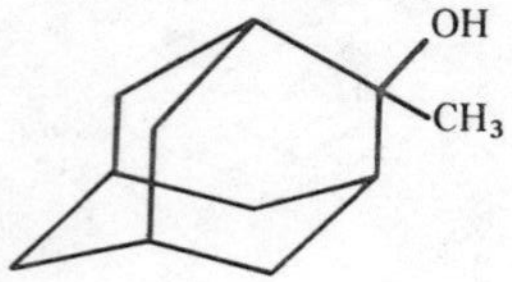		9.22 10.75 12.52 (18.36)			122
$C_{11}H_{22}O$	$n\text{-}C_9H_{19}C(=O)CH_3$		9.29 (1)			59

TABLE 1 (continued)

Compound		Orbital	Ionization Energy: Adiabatic	Ionization Energy: Vertical	Vibrational Bands	Reference
$C_{12}H_8$	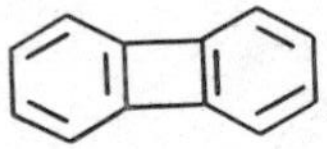	π	7.56 (5)	7.66 (5)		82
		π	8.82	8.82		
		π	9.65	9.65		
		π	(9.95)	10.15		
		(π)	(10.7)			
		(π)		11.17		
$C_{12}H_8$	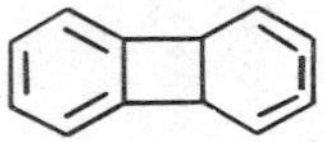	π	7.53	7.62		157
		π	8.89	8.89		
		π	9.68	9.68		
		π	(9.9)	10.10		
			10.75	11.04		
		π	(11.35)	11.50		
				(11.9)		
			12.4	12.9		
		π?		13.35		
				13.65		
				14.1		
				15.0		
			16.5	16.6		
$C_{12}H_8$	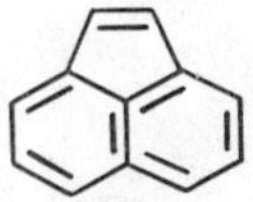			8.02 (1)		132
				10.70 (1)		
				12.86 (1)		
				14.73 (1)		
				16.44 (1)		
				17.76 (1)		
				19.02 (1)		
				20.52 (1)		
$C_{12}H_8O$	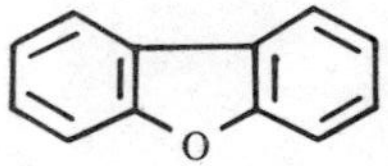	$\pi+\pi$	7.9	8.4		82
		π	9.2	9.25		
		π	(9.9)	9.90		
		$\pi(+\sigma)$	(10.8)	11.6		
		(π)		12.4		

TABLE 1 (continued)

Compound		Orbital	Ionization Energy: Adiabatic	Ionization Energy: Vertical	Vibrational Bands	Reference
$C_{12}H_{10}$	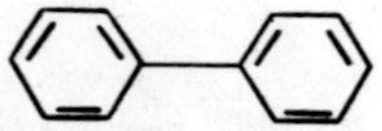	π	8.2	8.41		157
		π	9.08	9.22		
		π	(9.7)	9.87		
			11.05	11.25		
				12.10		
			13.6	14.1		
				14.85		
				16.2		
				17.0		
$C_{12}H_{10}$	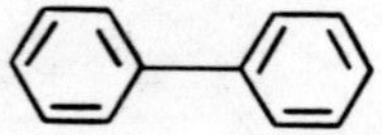			8.20 (5)		152
				9.08 (5)		
				9.70 (5)		
				11.02 (5)		
$C_{12}H_{10}$	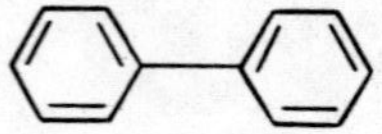			8.3		162
				9.1		
				9.75		
				11.8		
				14.05		
				16.9		
$C_{12}H_{10}$	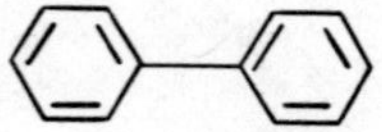			8.23 (1)		132
				9.08 (1)		
				9.76 (1)		
				11.02 (1)		
				13.55 (1)		
				13.82 (1)		
				16.73 (1)		
				18.21 (1)		
$C_{12}H_{10}$	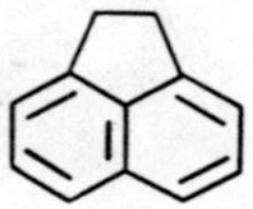			7.73 (1)		132
				8.66 (1)		
				9.60 (1)		
				10.50 (1)		
				13.03 (1)		

TABLE 1 (continued)

Compound		Orbital	Ionization Energy: Adiabatic	Ionization Energy: Vertical	Vibrational Bands	Reference
$C_{12}H_{10}$ (cont.)				13.50 (1)		
				15.46 (1)		
				18.49 (1)		
				19.41 (1)		
$C_{12}H_{10}O$	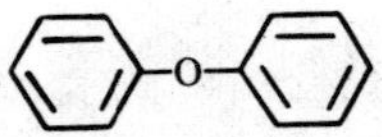	π	(8.10)	8.35		82
		π^2	9.10	9.10		
		π		(9.4)		
		(π)	10.65	11.1		
		(π)		(11.6)		
		σ		12.1		
		σ		13.45		
		σ		14.1		
		σ		15.25		
$C_{12}H_{12}$	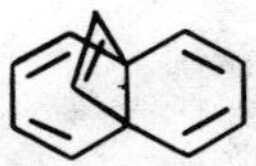	$a_2(\pi_4)$		8.1		233
		$b_1(\pi_3)$		8.5		
		$b_2(\pi_b)$		9.2		
		$b_2(\pi_2)$		10.3		
		$a_1(\pi_1)$		~10.8		
		σ onset		10.5		
$C_{12}H_{12}Cr$	$(\pi\text{–}C_6H_6)_2Cr$	a_{1g}		5.4		161
		e_{2g}		6.4		
		$e_{1u}+e_{1g}$		9.6		
		$a_{2u}+a_{1g}+\sigma$ orbitals		{11.5 – 13.8}		
$C_{12}H_{14}$	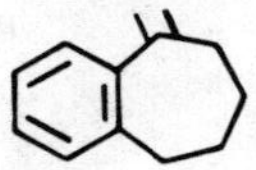	π_4		8.45 (2)		236
		π_3		8.90 (5)		
		π_2		9.55 (2)		
			10.4	10.9 (05)		

TABLE 1 (continued)

Compound		Orbital	Ionization Energy Adiabatic	Ionization Energy Vertical	Vibrational Bands	Reference
$C_{12}H_{14}$	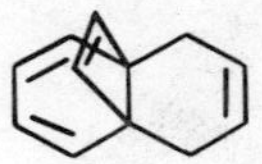	$a''(\pi'_-)$		8.0		233
		$a'(\pi_-)$		9.0_5		
		$a'(\pi_+)$		9.2		
		$a'(\pi'_+)$		10.5		
		σ onset		10.0		
$C_{12}H_{14}Fe$	$Fe(\pi-C_5H_4CH_3)_2$	$e_{2g}(d)$		6.72		224
		$a_{1g}(d)$		7.06		
		$e_{1u}(\pi)$		8.53		
				8.73 (sh)		
		$e_{1g}(\pi)$		9.17		
		Ligand σ,π		11.81		
		Ligand σ,π		12.58		
		Ligand σ,π		13.23		
		Ligand σ		16.02		
		Ligand σ		16.89		
$C_{12}H_{14}Mg$	$Mg(\pi-C_5H_4CH_3)_2$	$e_{1g}(\pi)$		7.78, 7.90 (sh), 8.10 (sh)		224
		$e_{1u}(\pi)$		8.62, 8.86 (sh)		
		$a_{1g}(\pi)$		11.7 (sh)		
		$a_{2u}(\pi)$		12.4 (sh)		
		C–H σ		13.0		
		σ		15.9		
		σ		~16.8 (sh)		
$C_{12}H_{14}Os$	$Os(\pi-C_5H_4CH_3)_2$	Metal d		6.93		224
		Metal d		7.21		
		Metal d		7.55		
		$e_{1u}(\pi)$		8.26		
				8.68		
		$e_{1g}(\pi)$		9.90		
		Ligand σ,π		11.42		
		Ligand σ,π		11.81		
		Ligand σ,π		13.51		
		Ligand σ		15.98		
		Ligand σ		16.75		

TABLE 1 (continued)

Compound		Orbital	Ionization Energy: Adiabatic	Ionization Energy: Vertical	Vibrational Bands	Reference
$C_{12}H_{14}Ru$	$Ru(\pi-C_5H_4CH_3)_2$	Metal d		7.25		224
		$e_{1u}(\pi)$		8.24		
				8.40 (sh)		
		$e_{1g}(\pi)$		9.76		
		Ligand σ,π		11.72		
		Ligand σ,π		12.33		
		Ligand σ,π		13.26		
		Ligand σ		15.95		
		Ligand σ		17.69		
$C_{12}H_{16}$	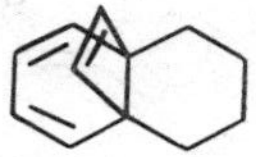	$a''(\pi'_-)$		8.0		233
		$a'(\pi_b)$		9.0_5		
		$a'(\pi'_+)$		10.5		
		σ onset		10.0		
$C_{12}H_{16}$	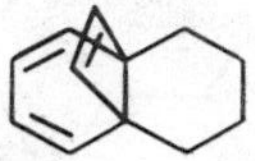	$b_2(\pi_1)$		8.7		233
		$a_1(\pi_2)$		8.9		
		$b_2(\pi_3)$		9.1_5		
		σ onset		10.0		
$C_{12}H_{16}S_3$	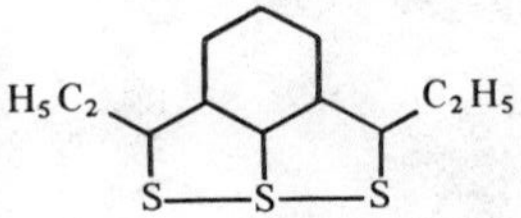	π_1		7.33		115
		n_1		7.70		
		π_2		8.80		
		π_3		9.10		
				10.10		
				10.70		
$C_{12}H_{18}$	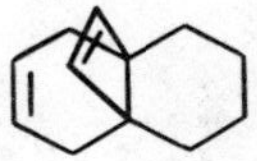	$a'(\pi_-)$		8.9		233
		$a'(\pi_+)$		9.0_5		
		σ onset		9.8		
$C_{12}H_{20}$	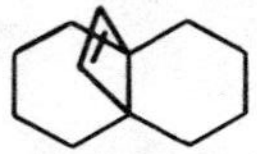	$b_2(\pi_b)$		9.0_5		233
		σ onset		9.6		

TABLE 1 (continued)

Compound		Orbital	Ionization Energy: Adiabatic	Ionization Energy: Vertical	Vibrational Bands	Reference
$C_{12}H_{22}$	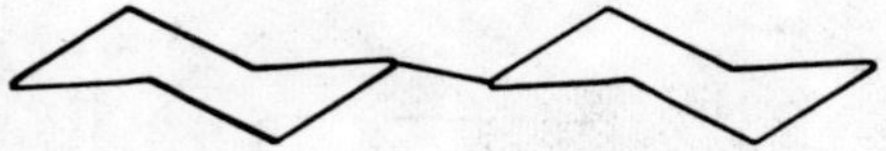		9.41			122
			10.73			
			(12.46)			
			14.04			
			14.53			
			(18.72)			
$C_{13}H_{10}$	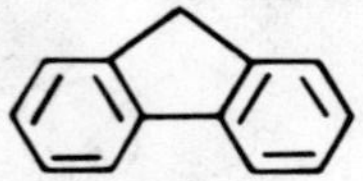			7.93 (1)		132
				8.74 (1)		
				9.72 (1)		
				10.90 (1)		
				13.09 (1)		
$C_{13}H_{12}$	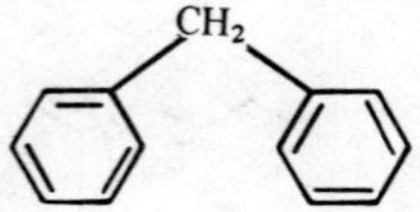			8.80		236
				9.25		
			10.9	11.3		
				9.1		162
				11.8		
				13.85		
				15.05		
				16.4		
$C_{14}H_{10}$	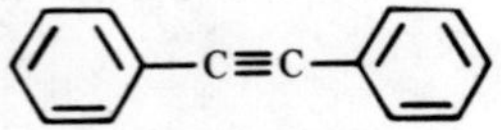	π	8.0	8.1		157
		π	9.05	9.28		
		π?	(9.5)	(10.2)		
		π	10.84	10.84		
			11.4	11.8		
				12.4		

TABLE 1 (continued)

Compound		Orbital	Ionization Energy: Adiabatic	Ionization Energy: Vertical	Vibrational Bands	Reference
$C_{14}H_{10}$ (cont.)			13.6	13.8		
				14.4		
				14.8		
				15.4		
				16.8		
$C_{14}H_{10}$	> 150°C < 300°C 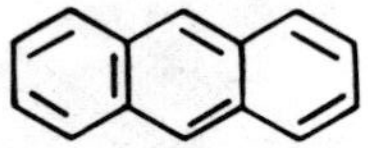		7.47			221
			8.59			
			9.20			
			10.21			
			11.98			
			12.58			
$C_{14}H_{10}$	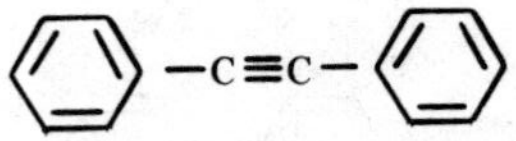	π'_7	7.90 (2)	8.06 (2)		236
		π_3		9.30 (5)		
				9.55 (5)		
		π'_3		10.87 (2)		
			11.5	11.7		
$C_{14}H_{10}$	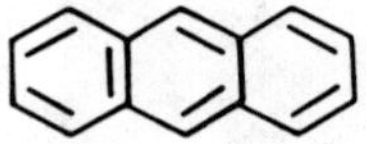	$2b_{2g}$		7.40		129
		$2b_{3g}$		8.52		
		$1a_u$		9.16		
		$1b_{2g}$		10.13		
		$2b_{1u}$		10.21		
		$1b_{3g}$		11.9		
		$1b_{1u}$		12.64		
$C_{14}H_{10}$	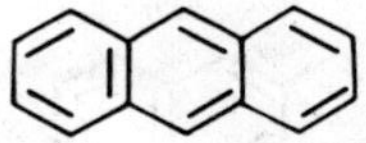	π	7.41	7.41		157
		π	8.55	8.55		
		π	9.16	9.16		
		π	10.16	10.16		
			10.8	10.95		
		π?		11.7		
		π?	12.4	12.55		
				12.9		
				13.9		
				14.8		
				15.7		

TABLE 1 (continued)

Compound		Orbital	Ionization Energy Adiabatic	Ionization Energy Vertical	Vibrational Bands	Reference
$C_{14}H_{10}$	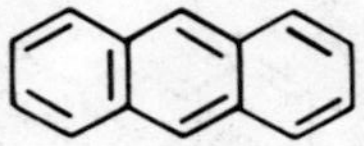			7.40		163
				8.55		
				9.15		
				10.30		
$C_{14}H_{10}$	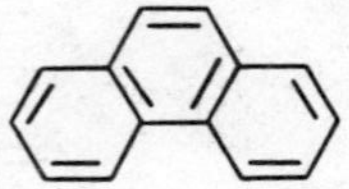			7.91 (1)		132
				9.18 (1)		
				9.74 (1)		
				10.71 (1)		
				12.07 (1)		
				13.03 (1)		
				13.63 (1)		
				15.18 (1)		
				15.57 (1)		
				18.23 (1)		
		π	7.92	7.92		157
		π		(8.12)		
		π	9.28	9.28		
		π	9.98	9.98		
		π	10.5	10.64		
			10.95	11.05		
		π?		11.6		
				12.1		
				12.4		
		π?		13.05		
				13.8		
			15.1	15.25		
				16.6		
$C_{14}H_{12}$	> 150°C < 300°C 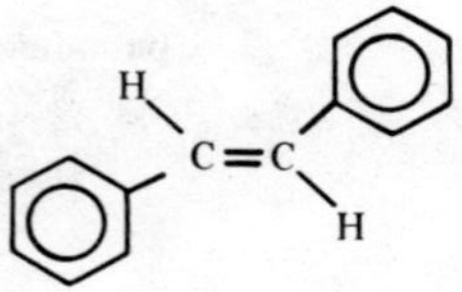		7.76			221
			9.04			
			10.53			
			(11.15)			
			13.70			
			(16.57)			

TABLE 1 (continued)

Compound		Orbital	Ionization Energy: Adiabatic	Ionization Energy: Vertical	Vibrational Bands	Reference
$C_{14}H_{12}$	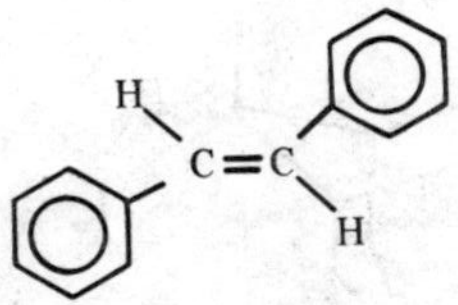	π'_7	7.70 (2)	8.00 (2)		236
		π_3		9.25 (5)		
				9.55 (5)		
		π'_3	10.30 (2)	10.60 (2)		
			11.0	11.35 (5)		
$C_{14}H_{12}$	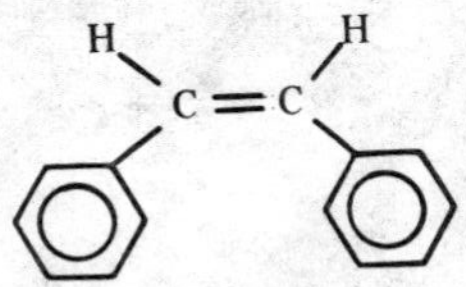	π'_7	7.80 (2)	8.20 (2)		236
		π_3		9.08 (5)		
				9.40 (5)		
		π'_3	10.10 (2)	10.35 (2)		
			10.9	11.3		
$C_{14}H_{12}$	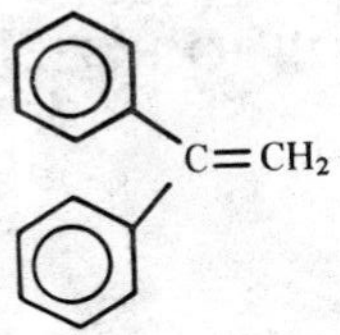	π'_7	8.00 (2)	8.25 (2)		236
		π_3		9.05 (5)		
				9.20 (5)		
		π_3	9.95 (2)	10.25 (2)		
			10.8	11.2		
$C_{14}H_{14}$	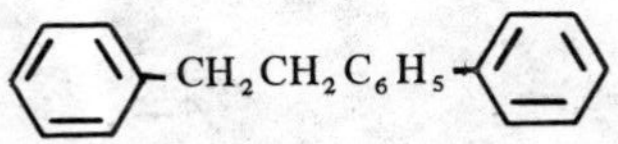			9.1		162
				11.9		
				13.95		
				14.75		
				16.35		

TABLE 1 (continued)

Compound		Orbital	Ionization Energy: Adiabatic	Ionization Energy: Vertical	Vibrational Bands	Reference
$C_{14}H_{15}N$	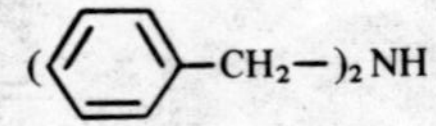		8.22			64
			8.73			
			11.01			
			(11.43)			
			12.84			
			13.62			
			14.79			
			16.53			
			(18.32)			
$C_{14}H_{16}Cr$	$(\pi\text{-}C_6H_5CH_3)_2Cr$	a_{1g}		5.24		161
		e_{2g}		6.19		
		$e_{1u}+e_{1g}$		9.16		
				9.53		
				11.1		
				11.6		
		$a_{2u}+a_{1g}+$		13.8		
		σ orbitals		14.7		
				16.2		
$C_{14}H_{20}$	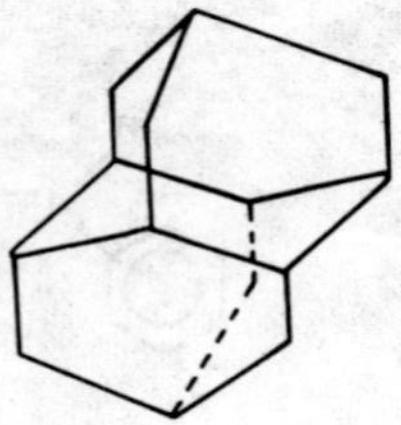		8.93 (1)			37
			10.20			
			11.59			
			(12.50)			
			(14.30)			
			14.84			
			(15.52)			
			(18.20)			
$C_{14}H_{20}$	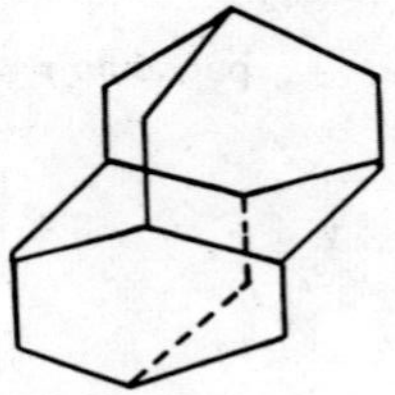		8.93			122
			10.20			
			11.59			
			(12.50)			
			(14.30)			
			14.84			
			15.52			
			(18.20)			

TABLE 1 (continued)

Compound		Orbital	Ionization Energy: Adiabatic	Ionization Energy: Vertical	Vibrational Bands	Reference
$C_{14}H_{20}S_3$	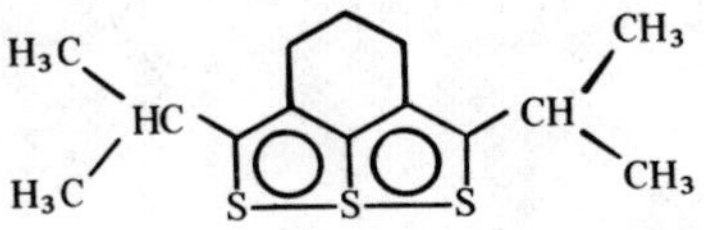	π_1		7.19		115
		n_1		7.56		
		π_2		8.70		
		π_3		8.90		
				10.07		
				10.70		
$C_{14}H_{24}$	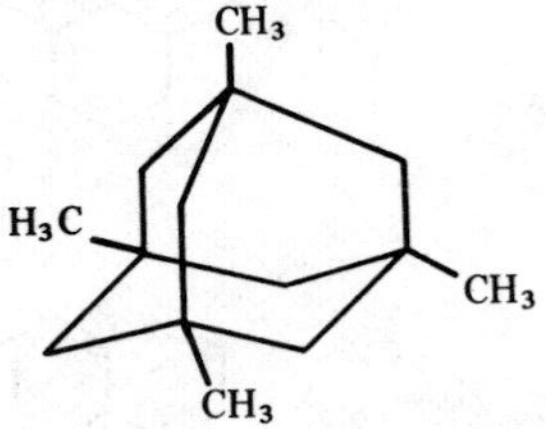		9.23			122
			10.34			
			12.07			
			14.51			
			(17.67)			
$C_{15}H_3CoF_{18}O_6$	$Co(CF_3COCHCOCF_3)_3$			9.95 (3)		164
				10.62 (3)		
$C_{15}H_3CrF_{18}O_6$	$Cr(CF_3COCHCOCF_3)_3$			9.54 (3)		164
				10.62 (3)		
$C_{15}H_3F_{18}FeO_6$	$Fe(CF_3COCHCOCF_3)_3$			10.13 (3)		165
$C_{15}H_3F_{18}FeO_6$	$Fe(CF_3COCHCOCF_3)_3$			8.28 (3)		164
				10.14 (3)		
$C_{15}H_3F_{18}O_6Ti$	$Ti(CF_3COCHCOCF_3)_3$		7.98			225

TABLE 1 (continued)

Compound		Orbital	Ionization Energy: Adiabatic	Ionization Energy: Vertical	Vibrational Bands	Reference
$C_{15}H_{17}N$	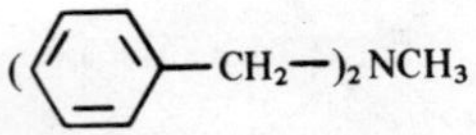		7.85 8.74 10.89 (11.24) (12.40) (16.53) (18.57)			64
$C_{16}H_{10}$	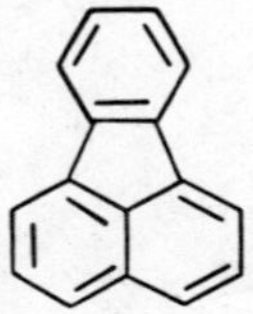			7.80 (1) 8.78 (1) 9.70 (1) 10.74 (1) 12.06 (1)		132
$C_{16}H_{10}$	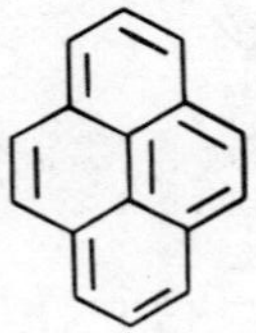	$2b_{3g}$ $2b_{2g}$ $3b_{1u}$ $1a_u$ $2b_{1u}$		7.41 8.2_6 9.0_0 9.2_9 9.9_6 10.7 11.2 12.0	1,390 (30) 1,130 (40)	166
$C_{16}H_{10}$	>150°C < 300°C 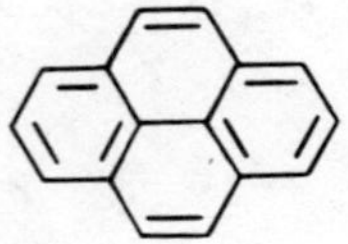		7.45 8.30 9.44 10.07 10.70 11.88 (15.14)			221

TABLE 1 (continued)

	Compound	Orbital	Ionization Energy		Vibrational Bands	Reference
			Adiabatic	Vertical		
$C_{16}H_{16}$	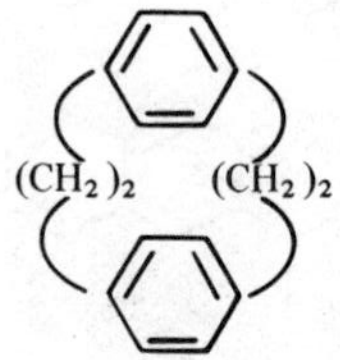			8.4		162
				9.7		
				10.3		
				11.7		
$C_{16}H_{44}CrSi_4$	$[(CH_3)_3SiCH_2]_4Cr$	Cr d electrons		7.26 (10)		222
		t_2 ($\sigma_{Cr\text{-}C}$)		8.69 (10)		
		Si-C		10.4 (1)		
		C-H		13.6 (1)		
$C_{16}H_{44}PbSi_4$	$[(CH_3)_3SiCH_2]_4Pb$	t_2 ($\sigma_{Pb\text{-}C}$)		8.14 (10)		222
				8.86 (10)		
		Si-C		10.3 (1)		
		C-H		13.2 (1)		
$C_{16}H_{44}Si_4Sn$	$[(CH_3)_3SiCH_2]_4Sn$	t_2 ($\sigma_{Sn\text{-}C}$)		8.71 (10)		222
		Si-C		10.3 (1)		
		C-H		13.2 (1)		
$C_{17}H_{12}S_3$	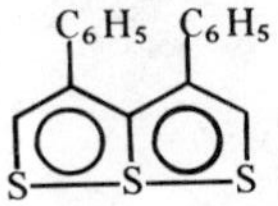	π_1		7.57		115
		n_1		7.93		
		π_2		8.60		
		π_3		9.15		
				9.44		
				10.70		
$C_{18}H_{12}$	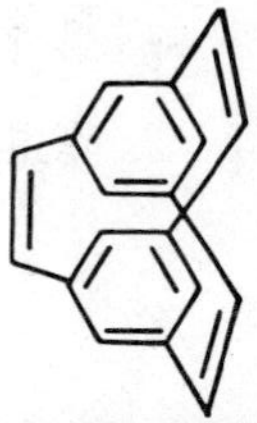	e″(benzene)		8.06		227
		e′(benzene)		9.24		
		a_2'(ethylene)		9.4		
		e′(ethylene)		9.95		
			11.1			
			12.1			

TABLE 1 (continued)

Compound		Orbital	Ionization Energy Adiabatic	Ionization Energy Vertical	Vibrational Bands	Reference
$C_{18}H_{12}$	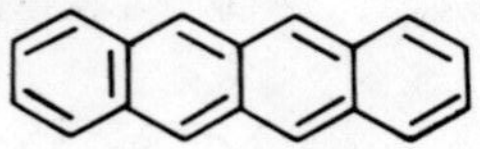	$2a_u$		7.01		129
		$2b_{2g}$		8.41		
		$3b_{1u}$		8.6		
		$1a_u$		9.56		
		$2b_{3g}$		9.7		
		$1b_{2g}$		10.25		
		$1b_{3g}$		12.0		
$C_{18}H_{12}$	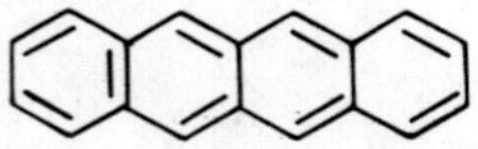	a_u		7.01		168
		b_{1g}		8.41		
		b_{3u}		8.6 (sh)		
		a_u		9.56		
		b_{2g}		9.7 (sh)		
		b_{1g}		10.25		
$C_{18}H_{12}$	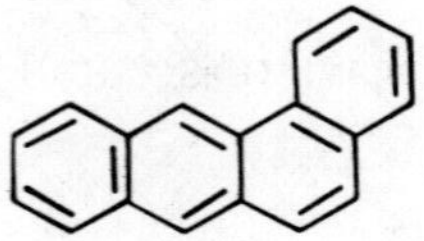	a″		7.42		168
		a″		8.03		
		a″		8.82		
		a″		9.34		
		a″		9.90		
		a″		10.40		
$C_{18}H_{12}$	> 150°C < 300°C 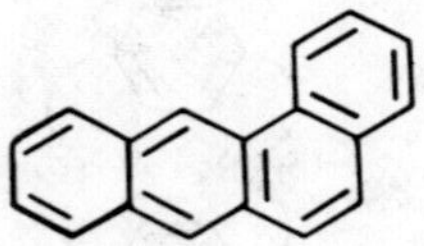		7.56			221
			7.95			
			8.79			
			9.29			
			9.85			
			10.77			
			(12.44)			
$C_{18}H_{12}$	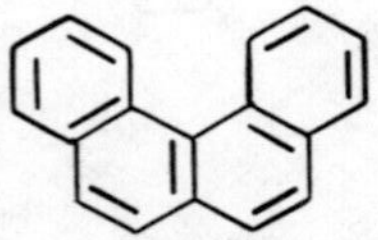	b_1		7.62		168
		a_2		8.00		
		a_2		8.96		
		b_1		9.1 (sh)		
		b_1		9.95		
		a_2		10.26		

TABLE 1 (continued)

	Compound	Orbital	Ionization Energy: Adiabatic	Ionization Energy: Vertical	Vibrational Bands	Reference
$C_{18}H_{12}$	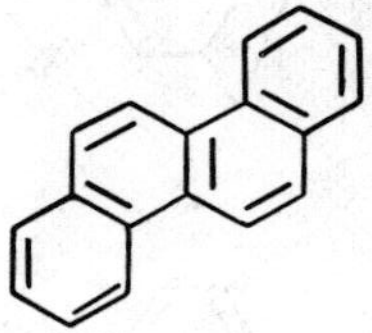	a_u		7.61		168
		a_u		8.10		
		b_g		8.68		
		b_g		9.44		
		a_u		9.73		
		b_g		10.52		
$C_{18}H_{12}$	> 150°C < 300°C 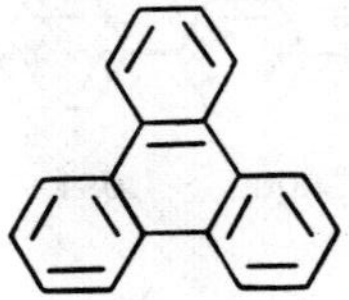		7.84			221
			8.59			
			9.60			
			10.60			
			11.98			
			13.29			
			15.01			
			16.66			
$C_{18}H_{12}$	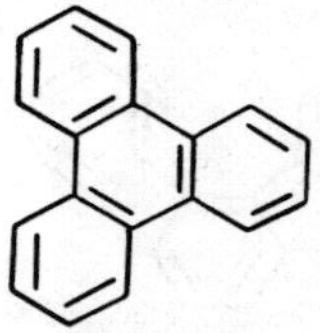	e''		7.86		168
		a_1''		8.63		
		e''		9.66		
		a_2''		10.05		
$C_{18}H_{14}$	> 150°C < 300°C 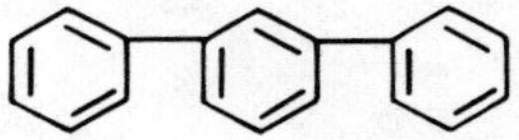		8.01			221
			8.97			
			10.89			
			13.43			
			(16.45)			
			(16.88)			
			(18.04)			

TABLE 1 (continued)

			Ionization Energy			
	Compound	Orbital	Adiabatic	Vertical	Vibrational Bands	Reference
$C_{18}H_{14}$	> 150°C < 300°C 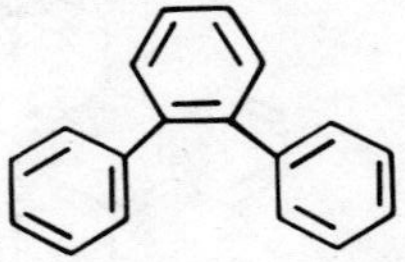		7.99 8.46 (8.85) 10.42 (10.80) (13.41) (14.37) (18.23)			221
$C_{18}H_{14}$	> 150°C < 300°C 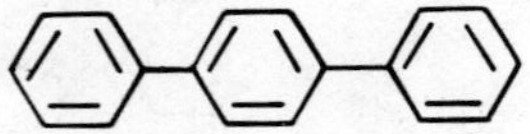		7.78 8.83 10.82 13.31 (16.87)			221
$C_{18}H_{16}$	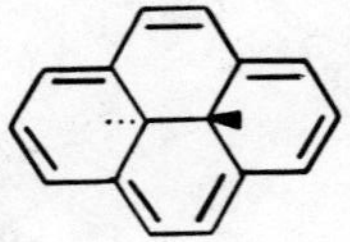	20ag, 12bg		6.7–7.5	1,150 (150)	167
$C_{18}H_{18}$	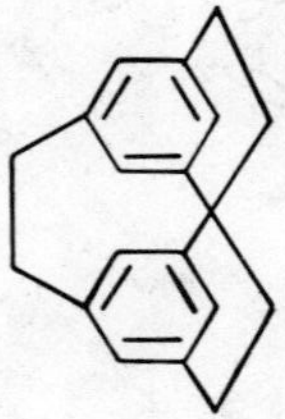	e″ e′		7.70 8.75		227

TABLE 1 (continued)

	Compound	Orbital	Ionization Energy: Adiabatic	Ionization Energy: Vertical	Vibrational Bands	Reference
$C_{19}H_{13}As$	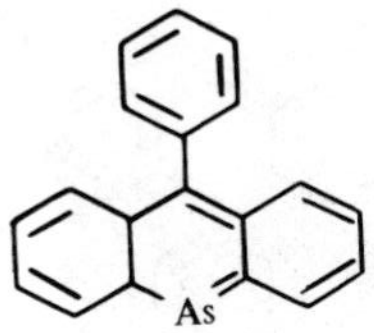			7.05 8.60 8.95 9.25 9.70 10.10		163
$C_{19}H_{13}N$	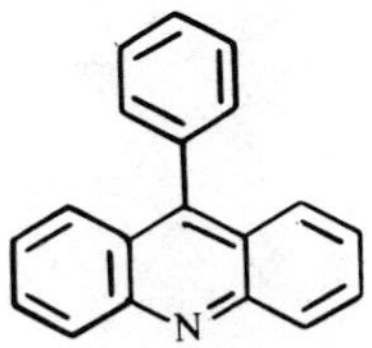			7.80 8.65 9.15 10.40 10.85		163
$C_{19}H_{13}P$	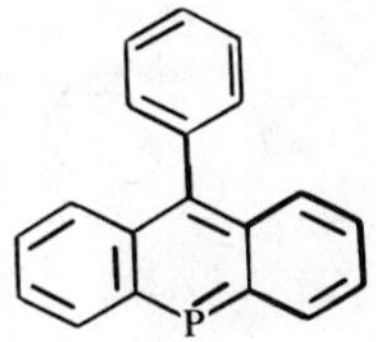			7.25 8.65 9.00 9.30 9.90		163
$C_{19}H_{35}O_2P$	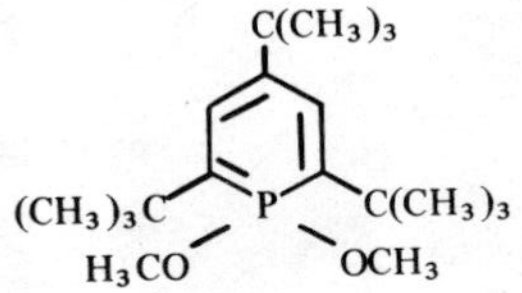	π_1 (S)		6.7 8.4		169

TABLE 1 (continued)

	Compound	Orbital	Ionization Energy Adiabatic	Ionization Energy Vertical	Vibrational Bands	Reference
$C_{20}H_{12}$	> 150°C < 300°C 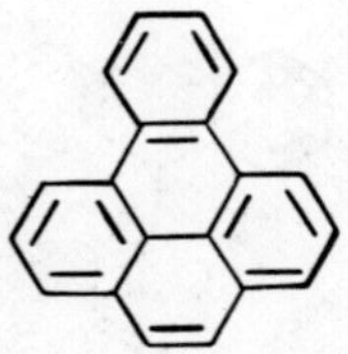		7.39 7.85 8.67 9.71 10.46 11.46 (11.91) (15.21)			221
$C_{20}H_{12}$	> 150°C < 300°C 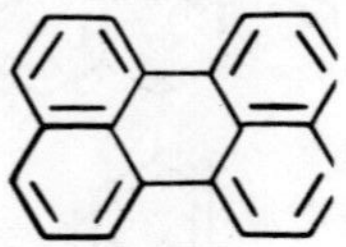		6.90 8.50 10.29 (15.52) (16.75)			221
$C_{20}H_{14}$	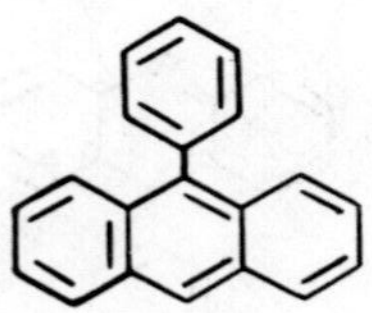			7.25 8.45 9.00 9.25 10.05 10.80		163
$C_{20}H_{44}Cr$	$[(CH_3)_3CCH_2]_4Cr$	Cr d electrons $t_2(\sigma_{Cr\text{-}C})$ C-C C-H		7.25 (10) 8.37 (10) 11.0 (1) 12.2 (1) 13.2 (1) 14.5 (1) 17.0 (1)		222

TABLE 1 (continued)

Compound		Orbital	Ionization Energy: Adiabatic	Ionization Energy: Vertical	Vibrational Bands	Reference
$C_{22}H_{14}$	> 150°C < 300°C 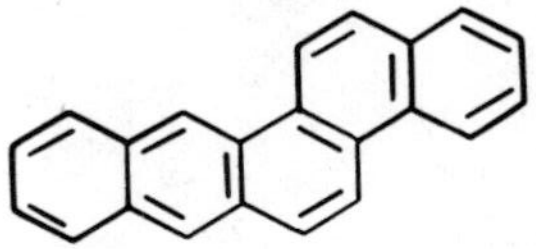		7.35			221
			7.89			
			8.67			
			9.69			
			10.48			
			11.64			
			13.41			
			15.07			
$C_{22}H_{14}$	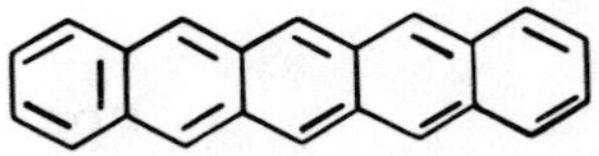	$3b_{2g}$		6.64		129
		$2a_u$		7.93		
		$3b_{3g}$		8.35		
		$2b_{2g}$		9.00		
		$3b_{1u}$		9.39		
		$1a_u$		9.80		
		$1b_{2g}$		10.26		
$C_{24}H_{12}$	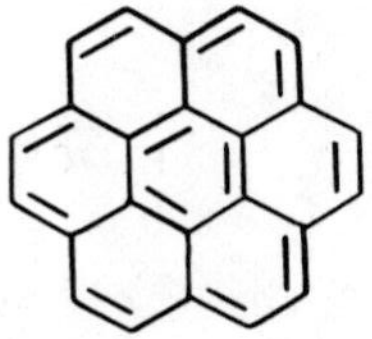			7.3_4		166
				8.6_4		
				9.1_5		
				10.4		
				10.5_5		
				11.6		
ClD	DCl	$X^2\Pi_{3/2}$	12.756 (5)		1←0 1,856 (20)	170
		$A^2\Sigma^+$	16.271 (5)		1←0 1,138 (20)	
ClD_3Si	SiD_3Cl			~18.2	ν_1 1,320	26
ClF	ClF	$^2\Pi_{3/2}$	12.66 (1)		0.11	171
		$^2\Pi_{1/2}$	12.74 (1)		0.11	
		$^2\Pi$	16.39 (1)	17.01 (1)		
		$^2\Sigma^+$	17.80 (1)	18.36 (1)		

TABLE 1 (continued)

	Compound	Orbital	Ionization Energy: Adiabatic	Ionization Energy: Vertical	Vibrational Bands	Reference
ClF	ClF	$^2\Pi_{3/2}$	12.66 (1)		ν' 870	220
		$^2\Pi_{1/2}$	12.74 (1)		ν' 870	
		$^2\Pi_{3/2,1/2}$	16.25 (8)	17.06 (2)		
		$^2\Sigma^+$	17.81 (8)	18.41 (2)		
$ClFO_2S$	SO_2FCl			12.61		32
				13.36		
				14.14		
				14.63		
				15.04		
				16.58		
				16.8		
				18.8		
$ClFO_3$	ClO_3F	$1a_2$	12.945 (5)		ν_3 520 (40)	172
					ν_1 900 (40)	
		7e	13.68 (2)	14.06 (2)		
				14.29 (2) (sh)		
		$10a_1$				
		6e	15.385 (8)	15.786 (7)	ν_1 790 (40)	
		5e		17.13 (2)		
		4e	19.70 (1)	19.83 (1)		
				19.91 (1)		
		$9a_1$		21.3 (1)		
		$8a_1$		23.8 (1)		
ClF_2P	PF_2Cl	$P3p_z$		12.8 (1)		21
		$Cl2p_\pi$		11.5 (1)		
		PCl		15.7 (1)		
		$F2p_\pi$		16.4 (1)		
		PF		{18.0 (1) {18.8 (1)		

TABLE 1 (continued)

Compound		Orbital	Ionization Energy: Adiabatic	Ionization Energy: Vertical	Vibrational Bands	Reference
ClF_3	ClF_3	$^2B_2, ^2A_1$	12.65 (5)	12.88 (1)		220
		$^2A_1$	13.76 (6)	14.07 (4)		
		$^2B_1$		14.83 (3)		
		$^2A_2$		15.36 (3)		
		$^2B_2$		16.07 (1)		
		$^2B_1$	16.82 (6)	17.27 (2)		
		$^2A_1, ^2B_2$		~19		
		$^2B_1$		~19.5		
$ClGeH_3$	GeH_3Cl			11.34 (5)		22
$ClGeH_3$	GeH_3Cl	2e		11.30	~400	23
		$3a_1$		13.05		
		1e		13.3		
ClH	HCl	$^2\Pi_{3/2}$	12.75 (1)			24
		$^2\Pi_{1/2}$	12.85 (1)			
		$^2\Sigma^+$	16.28 (1)			
ClH	HCl	$^2\Pi_{3/2}$			2,660	7
		$^2\Pi_{1/2}$	16.25		2,660	
		$^2\Sigma^+$			1,610	
ClH	HCl	$X^2\Pi_{3/2}$	12.748 (5)		1←0 2,570 (20)	170
		$A^2\Sigma^+$	16.254 (5)		1←0 1,520 (20)	
ClH	HCl	$^2\Pi_{3/2,1/2}$	12.74 (1)			25
			12.82 (1)			
		$^2\Sigma^+$	16.23 (1)	16.6	1,500	
ClH_3Si	SiH_3Cl			11.61 (5)	520 (40)	22
ClH_3Si	SiH_3Cl	2e		11.61	520 (40)	23
		$3a_1$		13.4	480 (40)	
		1e		13.7		
		$2a_1$		18.04	1,760	

TABLE 1 (continued)

			Ionization Energy				
Compound		Orbital	Adiabatic		Vertical	Vibrational Bands	Reference
ClH_3Si	SiH_3Cl	e		11.65			173
ClH_3Si	SiH_3Cl	e,n(Cl)σ* (SiH)			11.65	500	26
		a_1,σ(SiCl)			13.51		
		e,σ(SiH), π(SiCl)			13.99		
		a_1, σ(SiH_3Cl)	18.13		18.23	ν_1 1,800	
ClI	ICl	$(2\pi)^{-1}$		10.10 (2)		390 (30)	27
		$(1\pi)^{-1}$		12.88 (2)			
		$(3\sigma)^{-1}$		14.26 (2)			
ClNS	NSCl	16a′(σ)			10.96		216
		15a′(σ),4a″(π)			11.80		
		14a′(σ)			13.77		
		13a′(σ)			14.46		
ClO_2	ClO_2		10.36 (2)		10.48 (2)	ν_1 980	174
		$^3B_2$	12.32 (2)		12.94 (2)		
		$^1B_2$	15.27 (2)		15.45 (2)	725	
			16.25 (2)		17.50 (2)	1,170	
			17.69 (2)		17.95 (2)	725	
					19.36 (2)		
					20.89 (2)		
ClTl	TlCl	$^2\Sigma_{1/2}$,$^2\Pi_{3/2}$			9.89		28
		$^2\Pi$			10.38		
		$^2\Sigma$	13.79		13.89		
Cl_2	Cl_2	$^2\Pi_g$	11.49			sos 645 (40)	29
						ω_e 645 (40)	
		$^2\Pi_u$	14.0		14.43		
		$^2\Sigma_g^+$	15.8		16.10		

TABLE 1 (continued)

Compound		Orbital	Ionization Energy: Adiabatic	Ionization Energy: Vertical	Vibrational Bands	Reference
Cl_2	Cl_2	$^2\Pi_g$	11.50 (1)			24
		$^2\Pi_u$	14.11 (1)			
		$^2\Sigma_g^+$	15.94 (1)			
Cl_2	Cl_2	$(1\pi_g)^{-1}$	11.51 (1)	11.59 (1)	645 (20)	27
		$(1\pi_u)^{-1}$	13.96 (2)	14.40 (2)	323 (20)	
		$(2\sigma_g)^{-1}$	15.72 (2)	16.08 (2)		
Cl_2GeH_2	GeH_2Cl_2			11.42		23
				11.72		
				12.08		
				13.76		
Cl_2H_2Si	SiH_2Cl_2	b_2, n(Cl)		11.70		26
		b_1, n(Cl), σ^*(SiH)		12.09		
		a_2, n(Cl)		12.53		
		a_1, n(Cl), σ^*(SiH)		12.76 (sh)		
		b_2, σ(SiCl)		14.20		
		a_1, σ(SiCl)		14.45		
		b_1, σ(SiH)		14.60		
		a_1, $\sigma(H_2SiCl_2)$		18.32		
Cl_2H_2Si	SiH_2Cl_2	b_2	11.70			88
		b_1	12.09			
		a_2	12.53			
		a_1	12.76			
Cl_2H_2Si	SiH_2Cl_2			11.64		23
				12.06		
				12.50		
				14.3		
				18.12		

TABLE 1 (continued)

			Ionization Energy			
Compound		Orbital	Adiabatic	Vertical	Vibrational Bands	Reference
Cl_2Hg	$HgCl_2$	$^2\Pi_{3/2g}$		11.37		31
		$2\Pi_{1/2g}$		11.50		
		$^2\Pi_{3/2u}, ^2\Pi_{1/2u}$		12.13		
		$^2\Sigma_u$		12.74		
		$^2\Sigma_g$		13.74		
		$^2D_{5/2}(\pm5/2)$		16.71		
		$(\pm3/2)$		17.05		
		$(\pm1/2)$		17.27		
		$^2D_{3/2}(\pm3/2,\pm1/2)$		18.65		
Cl_2O	Cl_2O	b_1	10.94	11.02	ν_1 670 (40)	175
					ν_2 300 (40)	
				12.37		
				12.65		
		a_2		12.79		
				15.90		
				16.65		
				17.68		
				20.64		
Cl_2OS	$SOCl_2$	n(Cl)		11.12		32
		n(Cl)		11.89		
		n(S)		12.15		
		n(Cl)		12.55		
		n(Cl)		13.15		
		n(O)		13.25		
		S-Oπ		15.69		
		S-Clσ		16.32		
Cl_2O_2S	Cl_2SO_2			12.41		218
				13.17		
				13.67		
				14.06		

TABLE 1 (continued)

	Compound	Orbital	Ionization Energy: Adiabatic	Ionization Energy: Vertical	Vibrational Bands	Reference
Cl_2O_2S	SO_2Cl_2			12.42		32
				13.26		
				13.81		
				14.20		
				16.98	1,040	
				17.70		
				18.20		
Cl_3HSi	$SiHCl_3$	a_2, n(Cl)		11.94		26
		a_1, n(Cl), σ^*(SiH)		12.41		
		e, n(Cl)		12.41		
		e, n(Cl)		13.07		
		e, σ(SiCl)		14.75		
		a_1, σ(SiH)		14.98 (sh)		
		a_1, σ($SiHCl_3$)		18.14	2,000	
Cl_3HSi	$SiHCl_3$	a_2		11.94		173
		e		12.41		
		a_1		12.41		
		e		13.07		
Cl_3P	PCl_3	a_1		10.52	250	1
		e		11.71		
		a_2		12.01		
		e		12.97		
		a_1		14.24		
		e		15.22		
		a_1		18.85		
Cl_4Ge	$GeCl_4$	$1t_1$	11.88 (2)	12.17 (1)		36
		$3t_2$		12.64 (2)		
		1e		13.05 (1)		
		$2t_2$	14.56 (1)	14.88 (1)		
		$2a_1$	18.21 (3)	18.38 (2)		

TABLE 1 (continued)

	Compound	Orbital	Ionization Energy: Adiabatic	Ionization Energy: Vertical	Vibrational Bands	Reference
Cl_4Ge	$GeCl_4$	t_1		12.12		33
		$3t_2$		12.60		
				12.75 (sh)		
		e		13.08		
				14.7		
		$2t_2$		14.8		
				14.9		
		$2a_1$		18.0		
Cl_4Si	$SiCl_4$	t_1		12.03		33
				12.12 (sh)		
		$3t_2$		12.85		
				13.05 (sh)		
		e		13.35		
				13.44		
		$2t_2$		15.05 (sh)		
				15.13		
				15.25		
				15.31 (sh)		
		$2a_1$		17.98		
Cl_4Si	$SiCl_4$	$1t_1$	11.79 (1)	12.12 (2)		36
		$3t_2$	12.75 (1)	13.03 (3)		
		1e		13.51 (4)		
		$2t_2$	15.09 (1)	15.27 (1)		
		$2a_1$	17:85 (4)	18.10 (2)		
Cl_4Si	$SiCl_4$	t_1		12.06		173
		t_2		12.95		
		e		13.44		
Cl_4Sn	$SnCl_4$	$1t_1$	11.88 (5)	12.13 (2)		36
		$3t_2$		12.42 (3)		
		1e		12.74 (2)		
		$2t_2$	13.95 (1)	14.29 (1)		
		$2a_1$	17.07 (4)	17.36 (5)		

TABLE 1 (continued)

	Compound	Orbital	Ionization Energy: Adiabatic	Ionization Energy: Vertical	Vibrational Bands	Reference
Cl_4Sn	$SnCl_4$	t_1		12.10		33
		$3t_2$		12.38		
				12.50		
		e		12.71		
		$2t_2$		14.0		
		$2a_1$		17.0		
Cl_4Ti	$TiCl_4$	t_1		11.7		33
				11.8 (sh)		
		$3t_2$, 1e, $2t_2$		12.66		
				13.3		
		$2a_1$		13.88		
		$1t_2$, $1a_1$?		16.4–19.4		
Cl_4Ti	$TiCl_4$	t_1		11.78		176
				12.78		
				13.23		
		a_1		13.97		
Cl_4V	VCl_4	$^1A_1$(e)		9.41 (4)		176
		t_1		11.75 (4)		
				12.88 (4)		
				13.54 (4)		
		a_1		15.26 (4)		
DH	HD				1,987 (3)	177
D_2	D_2				1,625 (3)	177
D_2	D_2				0.17	178
D_2O	D_2O	$1b_1$	12.633			179
		$3a_1$	13.930 (10)			

TABLE 1 (continued)

	Compound	Orbital	Ionization Energy Adiabatic	Vertical	Vibrational Bands	Reference
D_2O	D_2O		12.69			57
			14.28			
			18.07			
D_2O	D_2O	$^1B_1$	12.62		ν_1 2,310 (50)	180
					ν_2 980 (50)	
		$3a_1$	13.7		ν_2 715 (20)	
		$1b_2$	17.26		ν_1 2,170 (100)	
					ν_2 1,210 (100)	
D_3N	ND_3	$^2A_2''$ $3a_1$	10.17		ν_2 720	44
		^2E 1e	15.15			
D_3N	ND_3	$^2A_1$	10.180 (10)		ν_2 .09	181
		^2E	14.94		.14	
D_3N	ND_3	$2a_1$	10.21 (1)	10.95 (1)	ν_2' 725 (25)	3
		1e		15.10 (3)		
D_3N	ND_3	$^2A_1$			.09	73
		$^2E_1$	15.15			
$FGeH_3$	GeH_3F			15.0 (1)		22
$FGeH_3$	GeH_3F	2e		12.3		23
		$3a_1$		15		
		1e		15.0		
FH	HF	$^2\Pi$	16.06 (1)			24
		$^2\Sigma^+$	16.48 (1)		~.33	
FH	HF	$^2\Pi$	16.05 (1)		2,950	25
		$^2\Sigma^+$	18.6	20.0		

TABLE 1 (continued)

	Compound	Orbital	Ionization Energy: Adiabatic	Ionization Energy: Vertical	Vibrational Bands	Reference
FH_3Si	SiH_3F	2e		12.6		23
		$3a_1$		16		
		1e		16.2		
FH_3Si	SiH_3F			16.1 (1)		22
FH_3Si	H_3SiF	e, σ(SiH), π^*(SiF)		12.80		26
		a_1, σ(SiH)		≈16.13		
		e, n(F), π(SiF)		16.38 (sh)		
		a_1, σ (SiH_3F)		19.29	800	
FNS	NSF	$13a'(\sigma)$		11.82		182
		$12a'(\sigma)$		13.50	ν_1 (N-S) 1,334 (64)	
					ν_2 (S-F) 889	
					ν_3 (N-S-F) 422 (51)	
		$3a''(\pi)$		13.87	ν_1 1,058 (48)	
					ν_2 707 (54)	
					ν_3 476 (110)	
		$11a'(\sigma)$		15.61	ν_2 746 (86)	
		$10a'(\sigma)$		16.47		
				17.2 (sh)		
FNS	NSF	$13a'(\sigma)$		11.82		216
		$12a'(\sigma)$		13.50		
		$3a''(\pi)$		13.87		
		$11a'(\sigma)$		15.61		
FNS	NSF	7a′	11.49 (2)	11.98 (2)		183
		6a′	13.39 (2)	13.53 (2)	ν_2 780 (80)	
					ν_3 460 (80)	
		2a″	13.78 (2)	13.9	ν_1 1,030 (80)	
					ν_2 690 (80)	
					ν_3 360 (80)	
		5a′	15.35 (2)	15.62 (2)	ν_1 800 (80)	
		1a″, 4a′	16.3	16.6		

TABLE 1 (continued)

Compound		Orbital	Ionization Energy: Adiabatic	Ionization Energy: Vertical	Vibrational Bands	Reference
FNS	NSF	13a′	11.54 (1)	11.89 (3)	ν_3 300 (50)	184
		12a′	13.382 (4)	13.543 (4)	ν_2 820 (40)	
					ν_3 460 (50)	
		3a″	13.775 (5)	13.906 (2)	ν_1 1,060 (40)	
					ν_2 695 (40)	
					ν_3 365 (40)	
		11a′	14.93 (1)	15.639 (5)	895 (30)	
		2a″		16.56 (3)		
		10a′		17.24 (8) (sh)		
		9a′		21.1 (1)		
F_2	F_2	$^2\Pi_g$	15.63 (1)			24
		$^2\Sigma_g^+$	17.35 (1)		1,202	
		$^2\Pi_u$	18.46 (1)			
F_2	F_2	$(1\pi_g)^{-1}$	15.70 (1)	15.83 (1)	1,065 (20)	27
		$(1\pi_u)^{-1}$	18.39 (3)	18.80 (3)	500	
F_2	F_2	$^2\Pi_g$	15.70		sos ξ 337 (40)	29
					ω_e 1,050 (40)	
		$^2\Pi_u$	18.4	18.98		
F_2GeH_2	GeH_2F_2			13.0		23
				14.6		
				16.3		
F_2HP	PF_2H	$P3p_z$		11.0 (1)		21
		PH		15.1 (1)		
		$F2p_\pi$		15.8 (1)		
		PF		17.6, 18.3 (1)		
F_2H_2NP	F_2PNH_2	N2p		10.9		21
		P3p		11.5		
		NH, PN		~15.4		

TABLE 1 (continued)

Compound		Orbital	Ionization Energy: Adiabatic	Ionization Energy: Vertical	Vibrational Bands	Reference
F_2H_2Si	SiH_2F_2	b_1, σ(SiH)		12.85		26
		a_1, σ(SiH)		15.20		
		b_2, n(F)		16.07		
		a_2, n(F)		16.37		
		b_1, n(F), π(SiF)		17.60		
		a_1, n(F), π(SiF)		17.93		
		b_1, σ(SiF)		18.30		
		a_1, σ(SiF)		20.19		
F_2H_2Si	SiH_2F_2			12.9		23
				15.2		
				16.0		
				17.5		
F_2H_4NPSi	$F_2PNHSiH_3$	P3p		11.0		21
				11.2 (1)		
F_2IP	PF_2I	$P3p_z$		{ 10.1 (1)		21
		$I4p_\pi$		{ 10.5 (1)		
		PI		14.2 (1)		
		$F2p_\pi$		15.9 (1)		
				{ 17.7 (1)		
		PF		{ 18.5 (1)		
F_2Kr	KrF_2	$4\pi_u$	⩽13.16	13.34		185
				13.47		
		$8\sigma_g$	13.75	13.90		
		$2\pi_g$	14.0	14.37		
		$3\pi_u$	16.25	16.92		
		$5\sigma_u$		17.7		
		$7\sigma_g$	22.0	23.0		

TABLE 1 (continued)

Compound		Orbital	Ionization Energy: Adiabatic	Ionization Energy: Vertical	Vibrational Bands	Reference
F_2N_2	FN=NF	$4a_g$	12.8	13.4		137
		$2a_u$	13.65	14.1	980	
		$1a_u$	18.0	18.70		
		$5b_u$		19.80		
		$5a_g$		21.0		
		$4b_u$	22.3	22.7		
F_2O	OF_2	$2b_2$	13.11 (5)	13.25 (2)	ν_1' 1,010	137
		$6a_1$	15.74	16.10		
		$4b_1$		16.44		
		$1a_2$	~17.9	18.50		
		$3b_1$, $5a_1$		19.55		
		$1b_2$		20.7		
F_2O	F_2O	b_1	13.13	13.26	ν_1 1,032 (40)	175
		a_1		16.17		
		b_2		16.47		
		a_2		18.68		
		a_1		19.50		
		b_2		20.9		
F_2OS	SOF_2	a′(S)	12.19	12.62	420 (20)	32
		a″(O)		14.04		
		Bonding (S-O)	14.54	14.80	1,208	
					832	
					368	
		n(F)		16.4		
		n(F)		16.97		
			18.03	18.21	704	
					388	
F_2O_2S	F_2SO_2	$4b_2$		13.75		218
		$2a_2$		13.92		
		$4b_1$		15.16		
		$6a_1$		15.29		
				16.68		

TABLE 1 (continued)

	Compound	Orbital	Ionization Energy: Adiabatic	Ionization Energy: Vertical	Vibrational Bands	Reference
F_2O_2S	SO_2F_2	$6b_2$	13.04 (1)		ν_3 or ν_4 370 (40)	172
		$2a_2$	13.57 (2)		ν_3 475 (60)	
		$6b_1$	14.85 (1)	15.181 (6)	ν_4 340 (16)	
		$11a_1$	15.181 (6)	15.307 (6)	ν_1 1,025 (30)	
		$5b_2$	16.676 (5)	16.676 (5)	ν_1 1,135 (16)	
					ν_2 805 (30)	
					ν_3 510 (20)	
		$5b_1$	18.07 (3)	18.31 (2)		
		$4b_2$	19.175 (7)	19.390 (4)	ν_2 850 (30)	
					ν_3 485 (40)	
		$9a_1$	19.699 (7)	19.807 (7)	ν_2 855 (30)	
					ν_3 500 (20)	
		$4b_1$		21.7 (1)		
		$8a_1$		24.2 (1)		
F_2O_2S	SO_2F_2	a_2 (O)		13.43		32
		b_2 (O)		13.78	450	
		a_1 (S-Oπ)	14.8	15.15	360	
		b_1 (S-Oπ)		15.30	1,040	
		n(F)	16.68	16.68	1,120	
					800	
					520	
				18.29		
				19.80		
F_2Xe	XeF_2	$5\pi_u$	12.35 (1)	12.42 (1)	520	186
			12.89 (1)	12.89 (1)		
		$10\sigma_g$	≈13.5	13.65 (5)		
		$3\pi_g$	14.00 (5)	14.35 (5)		
		$4\pi_u$	15.25 (5)	15.60 (5)		
				16.00 (5)		
		$6\sigma_u$	16.80 (5)	17.35 (5)		
		$9\sigma_g$		≈22.5		

TABLE 1 (continued)

	Compound	Orbital	Ionization Energy: Adiabatic	Ionization Energy: Vertical	Vibrational Bands	Reference
F_3N	NF_3	a_1		13.73	500	1
		e, a_2		15.95		
		e		17.40		
		a_1		19.73		
F_3N	NF_3	$4a_1$		13.73 (3)		45
		4e		16.15 (5)		
		$1a_2$		16.55 (5) (sh)		
		3e		17.52 (3)		
		$3a_1$		19.71 (3)		
F_3NO	F_3NO		13.51	14.26	1,010	187
			15.1	15.63		
			16.5	17.33		
			20.0	20.33		
F_3NO	ONF_3	5e		14.11 (5)	970 (50)	45
		$4a_1$		15.54 (5)		
		$4e, 1a_2$		16.88 (8)		
		3e		20.17 (1)		
				21.04 (4) (sh)		
F_3NS	NSF_3	$7e(\pi)$		12.50		216
		$10a_1 (\sigma)$		14.15		
		$6e(\pi)$		16.65		
		$1a_2$		18.35		
F_3OP	F_3PO		12.75	13.53		187
			15.25	15.70		
			16.70	17.11		
			17.3	17.84		
			18.45	18.91	740	
			19.3	19.68	740	

TABLE 1 (continued)

Compound		Orbital	Ionization Energy: Adiabatic	Ionization Energy: Vertical	Vibrational Bands	Reference
F_3OP	OPF_3	7e		13.5		190
		$10a_1$		15.7		
		$1a_2$		17.1		
		6e		17.7		
		5e		18.8		
		$9a_1$		19.5		
		4e		20.8		
F_3P	PF_3	$8a_1$	11.57 (1)	12.27 (1)	ν_2 470 (80)	188
		6e		15.88 (2)		
		$1a_2$		16.30 (5)		
		5e		17.46 (2)		
		$7a_1$		18.60 (5)		
		4e		19.50 (5)		
		$6a_1$		22.55 (5)		
F_3P	PF_3	a_1		12.28	500	1
		e		15.89		
		a_2		16.29		
		e		17.35		
		a_1		18.51		
		e		19.31		
F_3P	PF_3	$P3p_z$		12.23 (2)		21
		$F2p_\pi$		{15.9 (1), 17.45 (2)}		
		PF		{18.57 (2), 19.44 (2)}		
F_3P	PF_3	a_1		12.3		189
		e, a_2		15.9		
		e		17.4		
		a_1		18.5		
		e		19.4		

TABLE 1 (continued)

Compound		Orbital	Ionization Energy: Adiabatic	Ionization Energy: Vertical	Vibrational Bands	Reference
F_3P	PF_3	$8a_1$		12.3		190
		$1a_2$		15.8		
		6e		16.3		
		5e		17.5		
		$7a_1$		18.6		
		4e		19.4		
F_3P	PF_3	$8a_1$		12.3		10
		$1a_2$		15.8		
		6e		16.3		
		5e		17.5		
		$7a_1$		18.6		
		4e		19.4		
F_4Ge	GeF_4	$1t_1$		16.06 (4)		43
		$3t_2$		16.55 (4)		
		$2a_1$		17.06 (4)		
		$2t_2$		18.55 (4)		
F_4Ge	GeF_4	$1t_1$	15.69 (2)	16.03 (1)		36
		$3t_2$		16.56 (2)		
		1e		17.08 (2)		
		$2t_2$	18.21 (1)	18.54 (1)		
F_4Ge	GeF_4			16.08		191
				16.50		
				17.04		
				18.60		
		a_1		21.3		
F_4Ge	GeF_4	$1t_1$		16.17 (4)		45, 46
		$3t_2$		16.56 (4)		
		1e		16.95 (4)		
		$2t_2$		18.54 (4)		

TABLE 1 (continued)

	Compound	Orbital	Ionization Energy: Adiabatic	Ionization Energy: Vertical	Vibrational Bands	Reference
F_4OP_2	F_2POPF_2	O2p		11.2		21
		P3p		12.4		
				~14.2 (br)		
F_4P_2	F_2PPF_2	P3p		9.64		21
		P3p		12.45		
		PP		14.4		
F_4Si	SiF_4	$1t_1$		16.46 (4)		45, 46
		$3t_2$		17.54 (4)		
		1e		18.12 (4)		
		$2t_2$		19.52 (4)		
F_4Si	SiF_4	$1t_1$		16.46 (4)		43
		$3t_2$		17.55 (4)		
		$2a_1$		18.09 (4)		
		1e		19.51 (4)		
F_4Si	SiF_4	$1t_1$	15.81 (2)	16.45 (1)		36
		$3t_2$	17.33 (2)	17.53 (2)		
		1e		18.11 (2)		
		$2t_2$	19.22 (4)	19.51 (4)		
F_4Xe	XeF_4	$10a_{1g}$	⩽12.72	13.06		192
		$5a_{2u}$	13.38	13.38	ν_1 490	
		$5b_{1g}$	~14.0	14.46		
		$1a_{2g}$, $7e_u$		15.14		
		$1b_{2u}$		15.78		
		$3e_g$, $3b_{2g}$		16.30		
		$4a_{2u}$	~17.4	17.94		
		$6e_u$		18.40		
		$9a_{1g}$	~19.2	19.75		

TABLE 1 (continued)

			Ionization Energy			
	Compound	Orbital	Adiabatic	Vertical	Vibrational Bands	Reference
$F_6N_3P_3$	$(NPF_2)_3$			11.4 (1)		193
				13.1 (1)		
				15.4 (1)		
				16.6 (1)		
				17.2 (1)		
				18.2 (1)		
				19.6 (1)		
				20.1 (1)		
F_6S	SF_6	t_{1u}		15.69		1
		t_{1g}		16.96		
		e_{1g}		18.40		
		t_{2u}		18.71		
		t_{2g}		19.68		
		t_{1u}		22.5		
		a_1		26.8		
F_6U	UF_6	t_{1u}		14.4		1
		t_{1g}		15.25		
		e_{1g}		16.02		
		t_{2u}		16.52		
		t_{2g}		17.42		
		t_{1u}		19.46		
		a_1		23.5?		
F_6Xe	XeF_6	$8a_{1g}$	≥11.96	12.51		192
		$5e_g$	14.0	15.2		
		$1t_{1g}$, $7t_{2u}$ }		{16.0		
		$1t_{2u}$, $3t_{2g}$ }		{17.65		
		$6t_{1u}$	~19	~20.0		
		$7a_{1g}$		21.0		

TABLE 1 (continued)

Compound		Orbital	Ionization Energy: Adiabatic	Ionization Energy: Vertical	Vibrational Bands	Reference
$F_8N_4P_4$	$(NPF_2)_4$			10.7 (1)		193
				11.5 (1)		
				12.5 (1)		
				13.6 (1)		
				14.9 (1)		
				15.9 (1)		
				16.7 (1)		
				17.4 (1)		
				18.2 (1)		
				19.4 (1)		
				19.9 (1)		
$F_{10}N_5P_5$	$(NPF_2)_5$			11.4 (1)		193
				12.5 (1)		
				13.3 (1)		
				14.3 (1)		
				15.8 (1)		
				16.5 (1)		
				17.2 (1)		
				18.1 (1)		
				20.0 (1)		
$F_{12}N_6P_6$	$(NPF_2)_6$			10.9		193
				11.7		
				12.7		
				13.4		
				14.1		
				15.8		
				16.3		
				17.2		
				18.0		
				20.0		

TABLE 1 (continued)

	Compound	Orbital	Ionization Energy: Adiabatic	Ionization Energy: Vertical	Vibrational Bands	Reference
$F_{12}NiP_4$	$Ni(PF_3)_4$	t_2		9.6		189
		e		10.6		
		t_2		13.1		
				15.8		
				17.4		
				19.3		
$F_{12}NiP_4$	$Ni(PF_3)_4$			9.69		194
				10.74		
				13.17		
				14.65		
				15.97		
				17.48		
				19.42		
$F_{12}P_4Pt$	$Pt(PF_3)_4$			9.83		194
				12.45		
				14.54		
				15.87		
				17.53		
				19.40		
$F_{12}P_4Pt$	$Pt(PF_3)_4$	t_2, e		9.8		189
		t_2		12.3		
		a_1		14.5		
				15.8		
				17.4		
				19.5		
$F_{14}N_7P_7$	$(NPF_2)_7$			11.3 (1)		193
				12.3 (3)		
				13.0 (2)		
				13.5 (2)		
				15.8 (1)		
				16.2 (2)		
				17.2 (1)		
				17.9 (1)		
				19.9 (1)		

TABLE 1 (continued)

Compound		Orbital	Ionization Energy: Adiabatic	Ionization Energy: Vertical	Vibrational Bands	Reference
$F_{16}N_8P_8$	$(NPF_2)_8$			10.9 (1)		193
				15.7 (1)		
				17.2 (1)		
				18.0 (1)		
				19.8 (1)		
GeH_2I_2	GeH_2I_2			9.56		23
				9.82		
				10.18		
				10.53		
				11.89		
				12.32		
				13.02		
GeH_3I	GeH_3I			9.84 (5)	sos 0.55	22
GeH_3I	GeH_3I	2e		9.59		23
				10.14		
		$3a_1$		11.71		
		1e		12.6		
GeH_3N_3	GeH_3N_3	$2\pi(a'')$		10.01 (2)		48
		$2\pi(a')$		10.77 (2)		
		Ge p		12.8 (1)		
		4σ		14.7 (1)		
		1π		16.2 (1)		
GeH_4	GeH_4	t_2	11.34	12.46	ν_2 670 (20)	42
		a_1	18.21	18.4	1,534 (30)	
GeH_4	GeH_4		11.31	11.98	.09	47
				12.46		

TABLE 1 (continued)

Compound		Orbital	Ionization Energy Adiabatic	Ionization Energy Vertical	Vibrational Bands	Reference
GeH_4	GeH_4	a_1		18.65	ν_1 1,610 (40)	191
		t_2		12		
		4s		34.21		
		3d		26.9		
		3d		27.4		
GeH_4S	GeH_3SH	$S3p_x$		9.69		62
		GeH		12.5		
		GeS		11.39		
		SH		14.08		
GeH_5P	GeH_3PH_2	$P3p_z$		9.7 (1)		4
		GeP		11.4 (1)		
		GeH		11.7–12.8		
		PH		13.5 (1)		
		Ge4s		16.8 (1)		
Ge_2H_6O	$(GeH_3)_2O$	$O2p_x$		10.40		62
		GeH		12.2		
		$3a_1$		10.9		
		$2b_2$		13.5		
Ge_2H_6S	$(GeH_3)_2S$	$S3p_x$		9.25		62
		GeH		12.3		
		$3a_1$		10.66		
		$2b_2$		11.30		
Ge_2H_6Se	$(GeH_3)_2Se$	$Se4p_x$		8.84		62
		GeH		12.2		
		$3a_1$		10.44		
		$2b_2$		10.88		
Ge_2H_6Te	$(GeH_3)_2Te$	$Te5p_x$		8.34		62
		GeH		12.0		
		$3a_1$		9.93		
		$2b_2$		10.56		

TABLE 1 (continued)

Compound		Orbital	Ionization Energy: Adiabatic	Ionization Energy: Vertical	Vibrational Bands	Reference
Ge_3H_9N	$(GeH_3)_3N$	$1a_2''$		9.2 (1)		4
Ge_3H_9P	$(GeH_3)_3P$	$1a_2''$		9.0 (1)		4
		$2e'$		10.4 (1)		
		GeH		11.2–13.2		
H	H	^1S	13.61	13.61		195
HI	HI	$^2\Pi_{3/2}$	10.42 (1)			24
		$^2\Pi_{1/2}$	11.08 (1)			
		$^2\Sigma^+$	14.03 (1)			
HI	HI	$^2\Pi_{3/2,1/2}$	10.38 (1)			25
			11.05 (1)			
			13.85 (1)	14.25 (1)		
HI	HI	$^2\Pi_{3/2}$			2,020	7
		$^2\Pi_{1/2}$			2,100	
		$^2\Sigma^+$			1,300	
HN_3	HN_3	$a''(\pi nb)$	10.740 (5)		ν_3 1,073	49
		$a'(n\pi b)$		12.2 (1)	ν_4 445	
		$p\sigma$	15.47 (1)			
		πb		16.8		
HN_3	HN_3	$2\pi(a'')$	10.72 (2)		ν_s 840 (50)	48
					ν_{as} 1,780 (50)	
					3,000 (50)	
		$2\pi(a')$		12.24 (2)	570 (50)	
		4σ	15.37 (2)		δ 560 (50)	
					ν_s 900 (50)	
					ν_{as} 2,340 (50)	
					$\nu_{as}+\delta$ 2,800 (50)	
		1π		16.8 (1)		

TABLE 1 (continued)

	Compound	Orbital	Ionization Energy Adiabatic	Ionization Energy Vertical	Vibrational Bands	Reference
H_2	H_2				2,319 (3)	177
H_2	H_2		15.45	15.98	~0.20	66
H_2	H_2	$\sigma_g 1s$	15.41	15.95	0.26	178
H_2	H_2	$\tilde{X}\ ^2\Sigma_g^+$	15.45		2,260	7
H_2I_2Si	SiH_2I_2			9.69		23
				9.99		
				10.35		
				10.73		
				12.13		
				12.63		
				13.24		
H_2O	H_2O		12.61		ν 0.4 (1)	56
			14.23			
			18.02			
H_2O	H_2O		12.61			57
			14.23			
			18.02			
H_2O	H_2O	$1b_1$	12.614			179
		$3a_1$	13.930 (10)		ν_1 3,680	
					ν_2 935	
		$1b_2$	17.390			
H_2O	H_2O	$1b_1$	12.62		ν_1 3,220 (40)	3
					ν_2 1,370 (40)	
		$2a_1$	13.78	14.74	ν_2 887 (40)	
		$1b_2$	17.02	18.51	ν_1 2,985 (80)	
		$1a_1$		32.2		

TABLE 1 (continued)

Compound		Orbital	Ionization Energy: Adiabatic		Ionization Energy: Vertical	Vibrational Bands	Reference
H_2O	H_2O	$^1B_1$	12.61		12.61	ν_1 3,200 (50)	180
						ν_2 1,380 (50)	
		$3a_1$	13.7		14.73	ν_2 975 (20)	
		$1b_2$	17.22		18.55	ν_1 2,990 (100)	
						ν_2 1,610 (100)	
H_2S	H_2S				10.48	2,380	89
					13.21	940	
H_2S	H_2S	$1b_1$	10.48 (4)			ν_1 2,380 (50)	7
			12.76 (2)		13.25 (4)	ν_1 2,040 (50)?	
						ν_2 940 (50)	
			14.56		15.35	ν_1 1,900 (100)?	
						ν_2 1,470 (100)?	
H_2S	H_2S	$^2B_1$	10.43			ν_1 2,516	196
						ν_2 ~1,000	
		$^2A_1$	12.81			ν_2 855	
		$^2B_2$	14.79			ν_1 2,025	
H_2S	H_2S	$1b_1$		10.47		ν_1 2,485 (40)	3
		$2a_1$	12.78		13.33	ν_2 910 (20)	
						540 (20)	
		$1b_2$	14.78		15.47	ν_1 2,730	
		$1a_1$			22.2		
H_2S	H_2S	$^2B_1$	10.43			ν_1 2,476	197
		$^2A_1$	12.76			ν_2 1,113	
		$^2B_2$	14.91			2,000	
H_2S	H_2S	mb	10.42				57
			12.62				
			14.82				
			18.00				
			20.12				

TABLE 1 (continued)

	Compound	Orbital	Ionization Energy Adiabatic		Ionization Energy Vertical	Vibrational Bands	Reference
H_2Se	H_2Se	$1b_1$		9.88		ν_1 2,260 (40)	3
		$2a_1$	12.40		12.93	ν_2 830 (20)	
		$1b_2$	14.11		14.62	ν_1 2,180	
		$1a_1$			21.0		
H_2Se	H_2Se	$^2B_1$	9.93			ν_1 2,280	196
						ν_2 1,017	
		$^2A_1$	12.17			ν_2 750	
		$^2B_2$	13.61			ν_1 1,726	
H_2Te	H_2Te	$1b_1$		9.14		ν_1 2,100 (200)	3
		$2a_1$	11.63		12.00	ν_2 702 (20)	
		$1b_2$	13.04		13.25	ν_1 1,694 (100)	
		$1a_1$			18.6		
H_3ISi	SiH_3I				10.05 (5)	sos 0.55	22
H_3ISi	SiH_3I	2e			$\left\{\begin{matrix}9.78\\10.33\end{matrix}\right.$		23
		$3a_1$			12.04		
		1e			12.8		
H_3N	NH_3	$^2A_2''3a_1$	10.15		10.8	ν_2 950	44
		^2E 1e	14.92		15.5		
H_3N	NH_3	$^2A_1$	10.175 (10)			ν_2 970	181
		^2E	14.94 (3)			ν_1 2,000	
						0.25 and 0.18	
H_3N	NH_3		10.16 (0)		10.85	900	7
			14.8 (7)		15.8	1,800?	
H_3N	NH_3	$2a_1$	10.15 (1)		10.88 (1)	ν_2' 900 (40)	3
		1e		14.98 (2)		1,800	
		$1a_1$			27.0		

TABLE 1 (continued)

Compound		Orbital	Ionization Energy: Adiabatic		Ionization Energy: Vertical	Vibrational Bands	Reference
H_3N	NH_3	$^2A_1'$ $^2E_1'$	10.14 14.92			0.13	73
H_3N	NH_3		10.16 15.02				57
H_3N	NH_3			10.16			63
H_3N_3Si	SiH_3N_3	$2\pi(a'')$ $2\pi(a'')$ Si p 4σ 1π			10.33 (2) 11.00 (2) 13.0 (1) 15.0 (1) 16.2 (1)		48
H_3P	PH_3	$^2A_1$ ^2E	10.13 (2) 12.5 (1)		10.59 (2) 13.6 (1)	ν_2 500 (20)	2
H_3P	PH_3	$2a_1$ le $1a_1$	9.96 (1)	12.64 (2)	10.60 (1) 19.0	ν_2' 489 (25) 1,600	3
H_3P	PH_3	$5a_1$	9.27 12.19		9.9 13.0	ν_2 420 1,600	7
H_3P	PH_3	$^2A_1'(5a_1)$ $^2E(2e)$	9.96 (1) 12.40 (2)		10.58 (1) 13.50 (5)	ν_2 (a_1) 530 (80) ν_1 (a_1) 1,610 (80) ν_4 (e) 810 (80)	188
H_3Sb	SbH_3	$2a_1$ 1e	9.51 (1)	11.39 (2)	10.02 (1)	ν_2' 387 (25) 1,370	3
H_4N_2	H_2NNH_2		8.93 (9.32) 14.80 16.44 (19.65)				64

TABLE 1 (continued)

	Compound	Orbital	Ionization Energy: Adiabatic	Ionization Energy: Vertical	Vibrational Bands	Reference
H_4SSi	SiH_3SH	$S3p_x$		9.97		62
		SiH		12.5		
		SiS		11.75		
		SH		14.41		
H_4Si	SiH_4		11.66	12.36	0.10	47
				12.85		
H_4Si	SiH_4	$3a_1$	17.94		ν_1 1,770 (40)	198
H_4Si	SiH_4	t_2	11.60	12.82	ν_2 750 (20)	42
		a_1	17.95	18.17	1,690 (30)	
H_4Sn	SnH_4	t_2	10.75	11.27	600 (30)	42
		a_1	16.68	16.88	1,476 (30)	
H_5PSi	SiH_3PH_2	$P3p_z$		9.9 (1)		4
		SiP		11.6 (1)		
		SiH		12.0–13.3		
		PH		13.6 (1)		
		Si3s		16.8		
H_6OSi_2	$(SiH_3)_2O$	$O2p_x$		11.17		62
		SiH		12.5		
		$3a_1$		11.2		
		$2b_2$		14.5		
		Si3s		17.2		
H_6SSi_2	$(SiH_3)_2S$	$S3p_x$		9.70		62
		SiH		12.5		
		$3a_1$		11.15		
		$2b_2$		11.71		
		Si3s		16.9		

TABLE 1 (continued)

Compound		Orbital	Ionization Energy: Adiabatic	Ionization Energy: Vertical	Vibrational Bands	Reference
H_6SeSi_2	$(SiH_3)_2Se$	$Se4p_x$		9.18		62
		SiH		12.5		
		$3a_1$		10.85		
		$2b_2$		11.29		
		Si3s		16.75		
H_6Si_2Te	$(SiH_3)_2Te$	$Te5p_x$		8.63		62
		SiH		12.3		
		$3a_1$		10.23		
		$2b_2$		10.83		
H_9NSi_3	$(SiH_3)_3N$	$1a_2''$		9.7 (1)		4
		$2e'$		13.7 (1)		
		CH		10.8–13		
		$Si3s(a_1')$		16.6 (1)		
		$Si3s(e')$		18.2 (1)		
H_9PSi_3	$(SiH_3)_3P$	$1a_2''$		9.3 (1)		4
		$2e'$		10.6 (1)		
		SiH		11.5–13.7		
		$Si3s(a_1)$		15.6 (1)		
		$Si3s(e')$		17.4 (1)		
Hg	Hg	$^2D_{5/2}$		14.84		31
		$^2D_{3/2}$		16.71		
Hg	Hg	$^2S_{1/2}$	10.443 (9)			199
		$^2D_{5/2}$	14.842			
		$^2D_{3/2}$	16.715 (4)			
		$^2P_{3/2}$	20.725 (4)			
HgI_2	HgI_2					31
		$^2\Pi_{3/2g}$		9.50		
		$^2\Pi_{1/2g}$		10.16		
		$^2\Pi_{3/2u}$		10.00		

TABLE 1 (continued)

Compound		Orbital	Ionization Energy: Adiabatic	Ionization Energy: Vertical	Vibrational Bands	Reference
HgI_2 (cont.)		$^2\Pi_{1/2u}$		10.40		
		$^2\Sigma_u$		11.29		
		$^2\Sigma_g$		12.85		
		$^2D_{5/2}(\pm5/2)$		15.99		
		$(\pm3/2,\pm1/2)$		16.17		
		$^2D_{3/2}(\pm3/2,\pm1/2)$		17.91		
IT1	T1I	$^2\Sigma_{1/2}, ^2\Pi_{3/2}$	8.47 (2)	8.91		28
		$^2\Pi$	9.39	9.72		
		$^2\Sigma$	13.0	{13.14		
				{13.52		
I_2	I_2	$^2\Pi_{3/2g}$	9.33 (1)			24
		$^2\Pi_{1/2g}$	9.96 (1)			
		$^2\Pi_{3/2u}$	10.87 (1)			
		$^2\Pi_{1/2u}$	11.68 (1)			
		$^2\Sigma_g^+$	12.79 (1)			
I_2	I_2	$^2\Pi_g$		9.34	sos 5,125 (40)	29
				9.97	$\omega_e \sim 220$	
		$^2\Pi_u$	10.8	11.03		
			11.6	11.82	sos ~6,400	
		$^2\Sigma_g^+$	12.7	12.95		
I_2	I_2	$(1\pi_g)^{-1}$	9.22 (1)	9.35 (1)	236	27
		$(1\pi_u)^{-1}$	10.74 (2)	11.01 (2)	125	
		$(2\sigma_g)^{-1}$	12.66 (2)	12.95 (2)		
Kr	Kr	$^2P_{3/2}$		14.000		7
		$^2P_{1/2}$		14.665		
N	N	^3P	14.55	14.55		195
NO	NO		9.26		0.28	200

TABLE 1 (continued)

	Compound	Orbital	Ionization Energy: Adiabatic	Ionization Energy: Vertical	Vibrational Bands	Reference
NO	NO		9.23		0.29	65
		$^1\Sigma^+$	15.4		0.16	
			16.53			
			18.34		0.17 (2)	
NO	NO		9.34			57
			15.23			
		nb	16.5			
			18.27			
NO	NO	$\tilde{X}\ ^1\Sigma^+$	9.26		2,260	7
		$^3\Sigma^+$	15.65		1,200	
		$^3\Pi$	16.54		1,610	
		$^3\Delta$	16.84		1,200	
		$^3\Sigma^-$	17.55		1,200	
		$^1\Pi$	18.30		1,450	
		$^1\Sigma^-$	18.39		1,100	
		$^1\Delta$	19.28		1,000	
NO	NO	$X^1\Sigma^+$	9.262			201
		$a^3\Sigma^+$	14.0			
		$^3\Delta$	15.68			
		$^3\Sigma^-$	16.56			
		$^3\Pi$	17.17_2			
		$^1\Sigma^-$	17.31_5			
		$A^1\Pi$	18.33			
		$^1\Delta$	18.90			
NO	NO	$X^2\Pi$	9.24	9.80	~0.28	66
		$?^1\Sigma^+$	15.65		~0.14	
		$^1\Pi$	16.52	16.52		
		$^1\Pi$	18.26	18.26	0.18	

TABLE 1 (continued)

	Compound	Orbital	Ionization Energy: Adiabatic	Ionization Energy: Vertical	Vibrational Bands	Reference
NO	NO	$2\pi(^1\Sigma^+)$	9.267			202
		$1\pi^4(^3\Sigma^+)$	15.649		0.147	
		$(^3\Delta)$	16.860		0.153	
		$(^3\Sigma^-)$	17.585		0.151	
		$(^1\Sigma^-)$	17.820		0.141	
		$(^1\Delta)$	18.07		0.120	
		$(^1\Sigma^+)$		23.3		
		$5\sigma^2(^3\Pi)$	16.558		0.210	
		$(^1\Pi)$	18.322		0.191	
		$4\sigma^2(^3\Pi)$	20.41			
		$(^1\Pi)$	21.72			
NO_2	NO_2		9.75			203
NO_2	NO_2		10.2		650	200
NO_2	NO_2			18.84		204
			16.9	14.56,14.66		
				14.15,14.11		
				13.69,13.81		
				13.09,13.25		
			10.9, 10.75, 10.8			
			9.29, 8.8		$\nu_3$0.25	
NO_2	NO_2		10.97			57
			12.82			
			13.48			
			14.01			
			14.37			
			16.79			
			18.86			

TABLE 1 (continued)

	Compound	Orbital	Ionization Energy: Adiabatic	Ionization Energy: Vertical	Vibrational Bands	Reference
NO_2	NO_2	$^1A_1$ 6a		11.25		205
		$^3B_2$ $4b_2$	12.863		0.081	
		$^3A_2$ $1a_2$	13.60		0.082	
		$^1A_2$ $1a_2$	14.070		0.086	
					0.117	
		$^1B_2$ $4b_2$	14.446		0.072	
					0.125	
		$^3B_1$ $1b_1$	17.069		0.125	
		$^1B_1$ $1b_1$	17.13		0.125	
		$^3A_1$ $5a_1$	~17.5	~18		
		B_2 $3b_2$	18.864		0.019	
		$^1A_1$ $5a_1$	~20.7	21.2		
		A_1 $4a_1$	21.26			
			23.2	23.7		
NO_2	NO_2	$^1A_1(6a_1)^{-1}$	⩾9.75	11.23	ν_2 650	206
		$^3B_2(4b_2)^{-1}$	12.85	13.01	ν_2 650	
		$^3A_2(1a_2)^{-1}$	13.60	13.60	ν_2 650	
		$^1A_2(1a_2)^{-1}$	14.07	14.06	ν_1 970	
					ν_2 600	
		$^1B_2(4b_2)^{-1}$	14.37	14.51	ν_2 520	
		$^3A_1(5a_1)^{-1}$	16.99	17.64	ν_1 1,100	
		$^3B_1(1b_1)^{-1}$	17.06	17.45	ν_1 1,100	
		$^3B_2(3b_2)^{-1}$	18.86	18.86	ν_1 1,100	
					ν_2 700	
		$^1B_2(3b_2)^{-1}$?	~20.8	~21.0		
		$^3A_1(4a_1)^{-1}$	21.26	21.26		
N_2	N_2	$X^2\Sigma_g^+$	15.58 (1)			18
		$A^2\Pi_u$	16.70 (1)			
		$B^2\Sigma_u^+$	18.80 (1)			
N_2	N_2	$\tilde{X}\ ^2\Sigma_g$	15.57	15.60	2,100	7
		$\tilde{A}\ ^2\Pi_u$	16.69 (1)	16.98	1,810	
		$\tilde{B}^2\Sigma_u^+$	18.75 (9)	18.78	2,340	

TABLE 1 (continued)

	Compound	Orbital	Ionization Energy		Vibrational Bands	Reference
			Adiabatic	Vertical		
N_2	N_2	$X^2\Sigma_g^+$	15.59	15.59		66
		$A^2\Pi_u$	16.73	16.96	~0.23	
		$B^2\Sigma_u^+$	18.78	18.78	~0.27	
N_2	N_2		15.58 (1)			37
			16.70			
			18.75			
N_2	N_2	$^2\Sigma_g^+$	15.57		0.29	178
		$^2\Pi_u$	16.72		0.22	
		$^2\Sigma_u^+$	18.72		0.3	
N_2O	N_2O			18.2		207
				19.5		
				22.5		
				24.3		
N_2O	N_2O	nb	12.82			57
			15.37			
			16.37			
			17.67			
			20.10			
N_2O	N_2O	$\tilde{X}\,^2\Pi$	12.89 (3)		ν_1 1,140 (50)	7
					ν_3 1,750 (50)	
		$\tilde{A}\,^2S^+$	16.38 (9)		ν_1 1,350 (50)	
					ν_3 2,460 (50)	
		$\tilde{B}\,^2\Pi$	17.65	18.2		
		$\tilde{C}\,^2\Sigma^+$	20.11 (3)		ν_1 1,280 (50)	
					ν_3 2,300 (50)	
O	O	^4S	13.62	13.62		195
		^2D	16.96	16.96		
OS	SO		10.34 (2)		10.34 (2) 1,210	208
			14.96 (2)		14.96 (2) 970	
O_2	O_2	$^2\Pi_g$			0.25–0.16	73

TABLE 1 (continued)

	Compound	Orbital	Ionization Energy Adiabatic	Ionization Energy Vertical	Vibrational Bands	Reference
O_2	O_2	$\tilde{X}\ ^2\Pi_g$	12.07 (0)		1,780	7
		$\tilde{a}\ ^4\Pi_u$	16.12		1,010	
		$\tilde{b}\ ^4\Sigma_g$	18.7		1,090	
		$^4\Sigma_u$ or $^2\Sigma_g^-$	20.29		1,130	
O_2	O_2		12.070 (5)			209
O_2	$O_2\ ^1\delta g$	$?^2\Delta_g$	18.81		~920	210
		$?^2\Phi_u$	~17.45		~900	
O_2	O_2	$X^3\Sigma_g^-$	12.08	12.54	~0.22	66
		$^4\Pi_u$	16.12	16.72	~0.11	
		$^4\Sigma_g^-$	18.17	18.17	~0.13	
		$?^4\Sigma$	20.29	20.42	~0.13	
O_2	O_2		12.07			57
			16.42			
			17.99			
			20.12			
O_2	O_2	$^2\Pi_g$	12.10	12.32	0.21	65
		$^4\Pi_u$	16.11	16.6	0.11 (3)	
		$^4\Sigma_g^-$	18.18		0.13 (7)	
			20.31		0.12 (3)	
O_2	$O_2(^1\Delta_g)$	$^2\Pi_g$	11.09 (0.005)		0.22	211
O_2	O_2	$X^2\Pi_{g1/2}$	12.071 (5)		1,905 (7)	212
		$X^2\Pi_{g3/2}$	12.095 (5)			
		$a^4\Pi_u$	16.101 (2)		1,036 (4)	
		$A^2\Pi_u$	17.045 (4)		896 (4)	
		$b^4\Sigma_g^-$	18.171 (3)		1,193 (4)	
		$B^2\Sigma_g^-$	20.296 (4)		1,155 (8)	
		$^2\Pi_u$		24.0		
		$c^4\Sigma_u^-$	24.577 (12)		1,549 (20)	
O_2S	SO_2		12.32			57
			13.17			
			16.42			

TABLE 1 (continued)

	Compound	Orbital	Ionization Energy: Adiabatic	Ionization Energy: Vertical	Vibrational Bands	Reference
O_2S	SO_2	$6a_1$	12.29 (0)	12.50 (2)	ν_2 400	7
			12.98 (0)	13.2	ν_2 380	
		$1a_2$, $4b_2$			ν_3 930?	
				13.5	ν_2 500	
			15.97 (2)	16.6	ν_1 850	
					ν_3 1,240?	
			16.33, 16.44	16.6	ν_1 900	
O_3	O_3		12.3 (1)			213
			12.52 (5)			
			13.52 (5)			
			16.4–17.4			
			19.24 (1)			
P_4	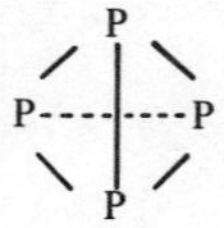	2e	9.20	9.56		214
				9.92		
		$6t_2$	10.20	10.42		
				10.61		
		$5a_1$	11.807	11.874	~560	
		$5t_2$	~14.2	15.25		
				16.35		
				~17.5		
P_4	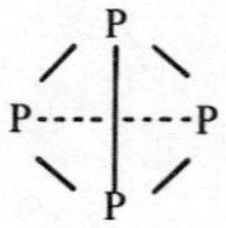	Onset	9.10 (5)			96
		$6t_2$		9.54 (5)		
		$6t_2$		9.90 (5)		
				10.40 (5)		
		2e		10.54 (5)		
				10.74 (5) (sh)		
		$5a_1$		11.85 (5)	a_1 508 (10)	
		$5t_2$		15.39 (5)		
		$5t_2$		16.60 (5)		
Xe	Xe	$^2P_{3/2}$		12.130		7
		$^2P_{1/2}$		13.436		
Zn	Zn	$^2D_{5/2}$		17.17		31
		$^2D_{3/2}$		17.51		

REFERENCES FOR TABLE 1

1. **Potts, A. W., Lempka, H. J., Streets, D. G., and Price, W. C.,** *Philos. Trans. R. Soc. Lond.*, A268, 59, 1970.
2. **Branton, G. R., Frost, D. C., McDowell, C. A., and Stenhouse, I. A.,** *Chem. Phys. Lett.*, 5, 1, 1970.
3. **Potts, A. W. and Price, W. C.,** *Proc. R. Soc. Lond. [A]*, 326, 181, 1972.
4. **Cradock, S., Ebsworth, E. A. V., Savage, W. J., and Whiteford, R. A.,** *J. Chem. Soc. Faraday Trans. II*, 68, 934, 1972.
5. **Bassett, P. J. and Lloyd, D. R.,** *J. Chem. Soc. A*, p. 1551, 1971.
6. **Boyd, R. J. and Frost, D. C.,** *Chem. Phys. Lett.*, 1, 649, 1968.
7. **Turner, D. W., Baker, C., Baker, A. D., and Brundle, C. R.,** *Molecular Photoelectron Spectroscopy*, Interscience, London, 1970.
8. **Bassett, P. J. and Lloyd, D. R.,** *J. Chem. Soc. D*, p. 36, 1970.
9. **Lloyd, D. R. and Lynaugh, N.,** *J. Chem. Soc. Faraday Trans. II*, 68, 947, 1972.
10. **Hillier, I. H., Marriott, J. C., Saunders, V. R., Ware, M. J., Lloyd, D. R., and Lynaugh, N.,** *J. Chem. Soc. D*, p. 1586, 1970.
11. **Lloyd, D. R. and Lynaugh, N.,** *J. Chem. Soc. D*, p. 1545, 1970.
12. **Lloyd, D. R. and Lynaugh, N.,** *Philos. Trans. R. Soc. Lond.*, A268, 97, 1970.
13. **Brundle, C. R., Robin, M. B., Basch, H., Pinsky, M., and Bond, A.,** *J. Am. Chem. Soc.*, 92, 3863, 1970.
14. **Rose, T., Frey, R., and Brehm, B.,** *J. Chem. Soc. D*, p. 1519, 1969.
15. **Kroner, J., Proch, D., Fuss, W., and Bock, H.,** *Tetrahedron*, 28, 1585, 1972.
16. **Frost, D. C., Herring, F. G., McDowell, C. A., and Stenhouse, I. A.,** *Chem. Phys. Lett.*, 5, 291, 1970.
17. **Lloyd, D. R. and Lynaugh, N.,** *J. Chem. Soc. D*, p. 627, 1971.
18. **Frost, D. C., McDowell, C. A., and Vroom, D. A.,** *Proc. R. Soc. Lond. [A]*, 296, 566, 1967.
19. **Lake, R. F. and Thompson, H.,** *Proc. R. Soc. Lond. [A]*, 317, 187, 1970.
20. **Evans, S., Green, J. C., Green, M. L. H., Orchard, A. F., and Turner, D. W.,** *Discuss. Faraday Soc.*, 47, 112, 1969.
21. **Cradock, S. and Rankin, D. W. H.,** *J. Chem. Soc. Faraday Trans. II*, 68, 940, 1972.
22. **Cradock, S. and Ebsworth, E. A. V.,** *J. Chem. Soc. D*, p. 57, 1971.
23. **Cradock, S. and Whiteford, R. A.,** *Trans. Faraday Soc.*, 67, 3425, 1971.
24. **Frost, D. C., McDowell, C. A., and Vroom, D. A.,** *J. Chem. Phys.*, 46, 4255, 1967.
25. **Lempka, H. J., Passmore, T. R., and Price, W. C.,** *Proc. R. Soc. Lond. [A]*, 304, 53, 1968.
26. **Frost, D. C., Herring, F. G., Katrib, A., McLean, R. A. N., Drake, J. E., and Westwood, N. P. C.,** *Can. J. Chem.*, 49, 4033, 1971.
27. **Potts, A. W. and Price, W. C.,** *Trans. Faraday Soc.*, 67, 1242, 1971.
28. **Berkowitz, J.,** *J. Chem. Phys.*, 56, 2766, 1972.
29. **Cornford, A. B., Frost, D. C., McDowell, C. A., Ragle, J. L., and Stenhouse, I. A.,** *J. Chem. Phys.*, 54, 2651, 1971.
30. **Thomas, R. K. and Thompson, H.,** *Proc. R. Soc. Lond. [A]*, 327, 13, 1972.
31. **Eland, J. H. D.,** *Int. J. Mass Spectrom. Ion Phys.*, 4, 37, 1970.
32. **Mines, G. W., Thomas, R. K., and Thompson, H.,** *Proc. R. Soc. Lond. [A]*, 329, 275, 1972.
33. **Green, J. C., Green, M. L. H., Joachim, P. J., Orchard, A. F., and Turner, D. W.,** *Philos. Trans. R. Soc. Lond.*, A268, 111, 1970.
34. **Heilbronner, E., Hornung, V., and Muszkat, K. A.,** *Helv. Chim. Acta*, 53, 347, 1970.
35. **Chadwick, D.,** *Can. J. Chem.*, 50, 737, 1972.
36. **Bassett, P. J. and Lloyd, D. R.,** *J. Chem. Soc. A*, p. 641, 1971.
37. **Dewar, M. J. S. and Worley, S. D.,** *J. Chem. Phys.*, 50, 654, 1969.
38. **Brundle, C. R., Robin, M. B., and Basch, H.,** *J. Chem. Phys.*, 53, 2196, 1970.
39. **Baker, C. and Turner, D. W.,** *Proc. R. Soc. Lond. [A]*, 308, 19, 1968.
40. **Ragle, J. L., Stenhouse, I. A., Frost, D. C., and McDowell, C. A.,** *J. Chem. Phys.*, 53, 178, 1970.
41. **Rabalais, J. W.,** *J. Chem. Phys.*, 57, 960, 1972.
42. **Potts, A. W. and Price, W. C.,** *Proc. R. Soc. Lond. [A]*, 326, 165, 1972.
43. **Jonas, A. E., Schweitzer, G. K., Grimm, F. A., and Carlson, T. A.,** *J. Electron Spectrosc.*, 1, 29, 1972.
44. **Frost, D. C., Herring, F. G., McDowell, C. A., Mustafa, M. R., and Sandhu, J. S.,** *Chem. Phys. Lett.*, 2, 663, 1968.
45. **Bassett, P. J. and Lloyd, D. R.,** *Chem. Phys. Lett.*, 6, 166, 1970.
46. **Bassett, P. J. and Lloyd, D. R.,** *Chem. Phys. Lett.*, 3, 22, 1969.
47. **Pullen, B. P., Carlson, T. A., Moddeman, W. E., Schweitzer, G. K., Bull, W. E., and Grimm, F. A.,** *J. Chem. Phys.*, 53, 768, 1970.
48. **Cradock, S., Ebsworth, E. A. V., and Murdoch, J. D.,** *J. Chem. Soc. Faraday Trans. II*, 68, 86, 1972.
49. **Eland, J. H. D.,** *Philos. Trans. R. Soc. Lond.*, A268, 87, 1970.
50. **Robin, M. B., Brundle, C. R., Kuebler, N. A., Ellison, G. B., and Wiberg, K. B.,** *J. Chem. Phys.*, 57, 1758, 1972.
51. **Brundle, C. R. and Turner, D. W.,** *Chem. Commun. (J. Chem. Soc. Sect. D)*, p. 314, 1967.
52. **Brundle, C. R., Turner, D. W., Robin, M. B., and Basch, H.,** *Chem. Phys. Lett.*, 3, 292, 1969.

53. Åsbrink, L., Fridh, C., Jonsson, B. Ö., and Lindholm, E., *Int. J. Mass Spectrom. Ion Phys.*, 8, 215, 1972.
54. Hashmall, J. A. and Heilbronner, E., *Angew. Chem. [Engl.]*, 82, 320, 1970.
55. Dewar, M. J. S., Shanshal, M., and Worley, S. D., *J. Am. Chem. Soc.*, 91, 3590, 1969.
56. Al-Joboury, M. I. and Turner, D. W., *J. Chem. Soc. B*, p. 373, 1967.
57. Al-Joboury, M. I. and Turner, D. W., *J. Chem. Soc.*, p. 4434, 1964.
58. Malmsten, G., Thorén, I., Högberg, S., Bergmark, J.-E., and Karlsson, S.-E., *Physica Scr.*, 3, 96, 1971.
59. Cocksey, B. J., Eland, J. H. D., and Danby, C. J., *J. Chem. Soc. B*, p. 790, 1971.
60. Baker, A. D., Betteridge, D., Kemp, N. R., and Kirby, R. E., *Anal. Chem.*, 43, 375, 1971.
61. Bock, H. and Wagner, G., *Angew. Chem. [Engl.]*, 84, 119, 1972.
62. Cradock, S. and Whiteford, R. A., *J. Chem. Soc. Faraday Trans. II*, 68, 281, 1972.
63. Baker, A. D., May, D. P., and Turner, D. W., *J. Chem. Soc. B*, p. 22, 1968.
64. Bodor, N., Dewar, M. J. S., Jennings, W. B., and Worley, S. D., *Tetrahedron*, 26, 4109, 1970.
65. Al-Joboury, M. I., May, D. P., and Turner, D. W., *J. Chem. Soc.*, p. 616, 1965.
66. Turner, D. W. and May, D. P., *J. Chem. Phys.*, 45, 471, 1966.
67. Jonathan, N., Morris, A., Okuda, M., Smith, D. J., and Ross, K. J., *Chem. Phys. Lett.*, 13, 334, 1972.
68. King, G. H., Kroto, H. W., and Suffolk, R. J., *Chem. Phys. Lett.*, 13, 457, 1972.
69. Heilbronner, E., Hornung, V., and Kloster-Jensen, E., *Helv. Chim. Acta*, 53, 331, 1970.
70. Lake, R. F. and Thompson, H., *Proc. R. Soc. Lond. [A]*, 315, 323, 1970.
71. Baker, C. and Turner, D. W., *Chem. Commun. (J. Chem. Soc. Sect. D)*, p. 797, 1967.
72. Brundle, C. R. and Brown, D. B., *Spectrochim. Acta*, 27A, 2491, 1971.
73. Branton, G. R., Frost, D. C., Makita, T., McDowell, C. A., and Stenhouse, I. A., *Philos. Trans. R. Soc. Lond.*, A268, 77, 1970.
74. Branton, G. R., Frost, D. C., Makita, T., McDowell, C. A., and Stenhouse, I. A., *J. Chem. Phys.*, 52, 802, 1970.
75. Haink, H. J., Heilbronner, E., Hornung, V., and Kloster-Jensen, E., *Helv. Chim. Acta*, 53, 1073, 1970.
76. Sweigart, D. A. and Turner, D. W., *J. Am. Chem. Soc.*, 94, 5592, 1972.
77. Jonathan, N., Ross, K., and Tomlinson, V., *Int. J. Mass Spectrom. Ion Phys.*, 4, 51, 1970.
78. Fridh, C., Åsbrink, L., Jonsson, B. Ö., and Lindholm, E., *Int. J. Mass Spectrom. Ion Phys.*, 9, 485, 1972.
79. Baker, C. and Turner, D. W., *J. Chem. Soc. D*, p. 480, 1969.
80. Cowan, D. O., Gleiter, R., Hashmall, J. A., Heilbronner, E., and Hornung, V., *Angew. Chem. [Engl.]*, 83, 405, 1971.
81. Frost, D. C., Herring, F. G., McDowell, C. A., and Stenhouse, I. A., *Chem. Phys. Lett.*, 4, 533, 1970.
82. Eland, J. H. D., *Int. J. Mass Spectrom. Ion Phys.*, 2, 471, 1969.
83. Frost, D. C. and Sandhu, J. S., *Indian J. Chem.*, 9, 1105, 1971.
84. Basch, H., Robin, M. B., Kuebler, N. A., Baker, C., and Turner, D. W., *J. Chem. Phys.*, 51, 52, 1969.
85. Bock, H. and Fuss, W., *Chem. Ber.*, 104, 1687, 1971.
86. Haselbach, E., Hashmall, J. A., Heilbronner, E., and Hornung, V., *Angew. Chem. [Engl.]*, 81, 897, 1969.
87. Haselbach, E. and Heilbronner, E., *Helv. Chim. Acta*, 53, 684, 1970.
88. Wagner, G., Ph.D., Dissertation, University of Frankfurt, Germany, as cited in Bock, H., Wagner, G., and Kroner, J., *Tetrahedron Lett.*, p. 3713, 1971.
89. Kroto, H. W. and Suffolk, R. J., *Chem. Phys. Lett.*, 15, 545, 1972.
90. Weidner, U. and Schweig, A., *J. Organometal. Chem.*, 39, 261, 1972.
91. Baker, A. D., Betteridge, D., Kemp, N. R., and Kirby, R. E., *Anal. Chem.*, 42, 1064, 1970.
92. Haselbach, E., Heilbronner, E., Mannschreck, A., and Seitz, W., *Angew. Chem. [Engl.]*, 82, 879, 1970.
93. Bischof, P. and Heilbronner, E., *Helv. Chim. Acta*, 53, 1677, 1970.
94. Baker, A. D., Betteridge, D., Kemp, N. R., and Kirby, R. E., *J. Chem. Soc. D*, p. 286, 1970.
95. Holliday, A. K., Reade, W., Johnstone, R. A. W., and Neville, A. F., *J. Chem. Soc. D*, p. 51, 1971.
96. Evans, S., Joachim, P. J., Orchard, A. F., and Turner, D. W., *Int. J. Mass Spectrom. Ion Phys.*, 9, 41, 1972.
97. Sweigart, D. A. and Turner, D. W., *J. Am. Chem. Soc.*, 94, 5599, 1972.
98. Lloyd, D. R. and Lynaugh, N., *J. Chem. Soc. D*, p. 125, 1971.
99. Brundle, C. R. and Robin, M. B., *J. Am. Chem. Soc.*, 92, 5550, 1970.
100. Rabalais, J. W., Werme, L. O., Bergmark, T., Karlsson, L., and Siegbahn, K., *Int. J. Mass Spectrom. Ion Phys.*, 9, 185, 1972.
101. Dewar, M. J. S. and Worley, S. D., *J. Chem. Phys.*, 51, 263, 1969.
102. Gleiter, R., Heilbronner, E., and Hornung, V., *Angew. Chem. [Engl.]*, 82, 878, 1970.
103. Åsbrink, L., Fridh, C., Jonsson, B. Ö., and Lindholm, E., *Int. J. Mass Spectrom. Ion Phys.*, 8, 229, 1972.
104. Baker, A. D. and Turner, D. W., *Philos. Trans. R. Soc. Lond.*, A268, 131, 1970.
105. Åsbrink, L., Lindholm, E., and Edqvist, O., *Chem. Phys. Lett.*, 5, 609, 1970.
106. Derrick, P. J., Åsbrink, L., Edqvist, O., and Lindholm, E., *Spectrochim. Acta*, 27A, 2525, 1971.
107. Derrick, P. J., Åsbrink, L., Edqvist, O., Jonsson, B. Ö., and Lindholm, E., *Int. J. Mass Spectrom. Ion Phys.*, 6, 161, 1971.
108. Derrick, P. J., Åsbrink, L., Edqvist, O., Jonsson, B. Ö., and Lindholm, E., *Int. J. Mass Spectrom. Ion Phys.*, 6, 177, 1971.
109. Derrick, P. J., Åsbrink, L., Edqvist, O., Jonsson, B. Ö., and Lindholm, E., *Int. J. Mass Spectrom. Ion Phys.*, 6, 191, 1971.

110. Dewar, M. J. S. and Worley, S. D., *J. Chem. Phys.*, 49, 2454, 1968.
111. Chadwick, D., Frost, D. C., and Weiler, L., *Tetrahedron Lett.*, p. 4543, 1971.
112. Bischof, P., Haselbach, E., and Heilbronner, E., *Angew. Chem. [Engl.]*, 82, 952, 1970.
113. Evans, S., Green, J. C., Joachim, P. J., Orchard, A. F., Turner, D. W., and Maier, J. P., *J. Chem. Soc. Faraday Trans. II*, 68, 905, 1972.
114. Lloyd, D. R. and Schlag, E. W., *Inorg. Chem.*, 8, 2544, 1969.
115. Gleiter, R., Hornung, V., Lindberg, B., Högberg, S., and Lozac'h, N., *Chem Phys. Lett.*, 11, 401, 1971.
116. Derrick, P. J., Åsbrink, L., Edqvist, O., Jonsson, B. Ö., and Lindholm, E., *Int. J. Mass Spectrom. Ion Phys.*, 6, 203, 1971.
117. Chadwick, D., Frost, D. C., and Weiler, L., *J. Am. Chem. Soc.*, 93, 4320, 1971.
118. Sustmann, R. and Schubert, R., *Tetrahedron Lett.*, p. 2739, 1972.
119. Praet, M.-Th. and Delwiche, J., *Chem. Phys. Lett.*, 5, 546, 1970.
120. Gleiter, R., Heilbronner, E., and de Meijere, A., *Helv. Chim. Acta*, 54, 1029, 1971.
121. Demeo, D. A. and Yencha, A. J., *J. Chem. Phys.*, 53, 4536, 1970.
122. Bodor, N., Dewar, M. J. S., and Worley, S. D., *J. Am. Chem. Soc.*, 92, 19, 1970.
123. Bieri, G., Brogli, F., Heilbronner, E., and Kloster-Jensen, E., *J. Electron Spectrosc.*, 1, 67, 1972.
124. Weidner, U. and Schweig, A., *Angew. Chem. [Engl.]*, 84, 167, 1972.
125. Clark, I. D. and Frost, D. C., *J. Am. Chem. Soc.*, 89, 244, 1967.
126. Klessinger, M., *Angew. Chem. [Engl.]*, 84, 544, 1972.
127. May, D. P. and Turner, D. W., *Chem. Commun. (J. Chem. Soc. Sect. D)*, p. 199, 1966.
128. Rabalais, J. W. and Colton, R. J., *J. Electron Spectrosc.*, 1, 83, 1972.
129. Clark, P. A., Brogli, F., and Heilbronner, E., *Helv. Chim. Acta*, 55, 1415, 1972.
130. Turner, D. W., *Tetrahedron Lett.*, p. 3419, 1967.
131. Samson, J. A. R., *Chem. Phys. Lett.*, 4, 257, 1969.
132. Dewar, M. J. S., Haselbach, E., and Worley, S. D., *Proc. R. Soc. Lond. [A]*, 315, 431, 1970.
133. Heilbronner, E., Gleiter, R., Hopf, H., Hornung, V., and de Meijere, A., *Helv. Chim. Acta*, 54, 783, 1971.
134. Bischof, P., Hashmall, J. A., Heilbronner, E., and Hornung, V., *Helv. Chim. Acta*, 52, 1745, 1969.
135. Schweig, A., Weidner, U., and Manuel, G., *Angew. Chem. [Engl.]*, 84, 899, 1972.
136. Bischof, P., Hashmall, J. A., Heilbronner, E., and Hornung, V., *Tetrahedron Lett.*, p. 4025, 1969.
137. Brundle, C. R., Robin, M. B., Kuebler, N. A., and Basch, H., *J. Am. Chem. Soc.*, 94, 1451, 1972.
138. Heilbronner, E. and Muszkat, K. A., *J. Am. Chem. Soc.*, 92, 3818, 1970.
139. Weidner, U. and Schweig, A., *Angew. Chem. [Engl.]*, 84, 550, 1972.
140. Cradock, S. and Savage, W., *Inorg. Nucl. Chem. Lett.*, 8, 753, 1972.
141. Evans, S., Green, J. C., Orchard, A. F., Saito, T., and Turner, D. W., *Chem. Phys. Lett.*, 4, 361, 1969.
142. Bock, H., Wagner, G., and Kroner, J., *Tetrahedron Lett.*, p. 3713, 1971.
143. Bischof, P., Gleiter, R., and Heilbronner, E., *Helv. Chim. Acta*, 53, 1425, 1970.
144. van den Ham, D. M. W. and van der Meer, D., *Chem. Phys. Lett.*, 12, 447, 1972.
145. Hoffmann, R. W., Schüttler, R., Schäfer, W., and Schweig, A., *Angew. Chem. [Engl.]*, 84, 533, 1972.
146. Haselbach, E., Heilbronner, E., and Schröder, G., *Helv. Chim. Acta*, 54, 153, 1971.
147. Bischof, P., Gleiter, R., Heilbronner, E., Hornung, V., and Schröder, G., *Helv. Chim. Acta*, 53, 1645, 1970.
148. Bischof, P., Heilbronner, E., Prinzbach, H., and Martin, H.-D , *Helv. Chim. Acta*, 54, 1072, 1971.
149. Schäfer, W. and Schweig, A., *Angew. Chem. [Engl.]*, 84, 898, 1972.
150. Weidner, U. and Schweig, A., *Angew. Chem. [Engl.]*, 84, 551, 1972.
151. van den Ham, D. M. W. and van der Meer, D., *Chem. Phys. Lett.*, 15, 549, 1972.
152. Eland, J. H. D. and Danby, C. J., *Z. Naturforsch.*, 23A, 355, 1968.
153. Bruckman, P. and Klessinger, M., *Angew. Chem. [Engl.]*, 84, 543, 1972.
154. Heilbronner, E. and Martin, H.-D., *Helv. Chim. Acta*, 55, 1490, 1972.
155. Heilbronner, E., *Isr. J. Chem.*, 10, 143, 1972.
156. Morishima, I., Yoshikawa, K., Yonezawa, T., and Matsumoto, H., *Chem. Phys. Lett.*, 26, 336, 1972.
157. Eland, J. H. D., *Int. J. Mass Spectrom. Ion Phys.*, 9, 214, 1972.
158. Rabalais, J. W., Werme, L. O., Bergmark, T., Karlsson, L., Hussain, M., and Siegbahn, K., *J. Chem. Phys.*, 57, 1185, 1972.
159. Bischof, P., Hashmall, J. A., Heilbronner, E., and Hornung, V., *Tetrahedron Lett.*, p. 1033, 1970.
160. Brundle, C. R., Robin, M. B., and Kuebler, N. A., *J. Am. Chem. Soc.*, 94, 1466, 1972.
161. Evans, S., Green, J. C., and Jackson, S. E., *J. Chem. Soc. Faraday Trans. II*, 68, 249, 1972.
162. Pignataro, S., Mancini, V., Ridyard, J. N. A., and Lempka, H. J., *J. Chem. Soc. D*, p. 142, 1971.
163. Schäfer, W., Schweig, A., Bickelhaupt, F., and Vermeer, H., *Angew. Chem. [Engl.]*, 84, 993, 1972.
164. Lloyd, D. R., *J. Chem. Soc. D*, p. 868, 1970.
165. Evans, S., Hamnett, A., and Orchard, A. F., *J. Chem. Soc. D*, p. 1282, 1970.
166. Boschi, R. and Schmidt, W., *Tetrahedron Lett.*, p. 2577, 1972.
167. Boekelheide, V., Murrell, J. N., and Schmidt, W., *Tetrahedron Lett.*, p. 575, 1972.
168. Brogli, F. and Heilbronner, E., *Angew. Chem.*, 84, 551, 1972.

169. Schweig, A., Schäfer, W., and Dimroth, K., *Angew. Chem. [Engl.]*, 84, 636, 1972.
170. Weiss, M. J., Lawrence, G. M., and Young, R. A., *J. Chem. Phys.*, 52, 2867, 1970.
171. Anderson, C. P., Mamantor, G., Bull, W. E., Grimm, F. A., Carver, J. C., and Carlson, T. A., *Chem. Phys. Lett.*, 12, 137, 1971.
172. De Kock, R. L., Lloyd, D. R., Hillier, I. H., and Saunders, V. R., *Proc. R. Soc. Lond. [A]*, 328, 401, 1972.
173. Frost, D. C., Herring, F. G., Katrib, A., McLean, R. A. N., Drake, J. E., and Westwood, N. P. C., *Chem. Phys. Lett.*, 10, 347, 1971.
174. Cornford, A. B., Frost, D. C., Herring, F. G., and McDowell, C. A., *Chem. Phys. Lett.*, 10, 345, 1971.
175. Cornford, A. B., Frost, D. C., Herring, F. G., and McDowell, C. A., *J. Chem. Phys.*, 55, 2820, 1971.
176. Cox, P. A., Evans, S., Hamnett, A., and Orchard, A. F., *Chem Phys. Lett.*, 7, 414, 1970.
177. Cornford, A. B., Frost, D. C., McDowell, C. A., Ragle, J. L., and Stenhouse, I. A., *Chem. Phys. Lett.*, 5, 486, 1970.
178. Al-Joboury, M. I. and Turner, D. W., J. *Chem. Soc.*, p. 5141, 1963.
179. Åsbrink, L. and Rabalais, J. W., *Chem. Phys. Lett.*, 12, 182, 1971.
180. Brundle, C. R. and Turner, D. W., *Proc. Roy. Soc. Lond. [A]*, 307, 27, 1968.
181. Weiss, M. J. and Lawrence, G. M., *J. Chem. Phys.*, 53, 214, 1970.
182. Cowan, D. O., Gleiter, R., Glemser, O., Heilbronner, E., and Schaublin, J., *Helv. Chim. Acta*, 54, 1559, 1971.
183. Dixon, R. N., Duxbury, G., Fleming, G. R., and Hugo, J. M. V., *Chem. Phys. Lett.*, 14, 60, 1972.
184. De Kock, R. L., Lloyd, D. R., Breeze, A., Collins, G. A. D., Cruickshank, D. W. J., and Lempka, H. J., *Chem. Phys. Lett.*, 14, 525, 1972.
185. Brundle, C. R. and Jones, G. R., *J. Chem. Soc. Faraday Trans. II*, 68, 959, 1972.
186. Brundle, C. R., Robin, M. B., and Jones, G. R., *J. Chem. Phys.*, 52, 3383, 1970.
187. Frost, D. C., Herring, F. G., Mitchell, K. A. R., and Stenhouse, I. A., *J. Am. Chem. Soc.*, 93, 1596, 1971.
188. Maier, J. P. and Turner, D. W., *J. Chem. Soc. Faraday Trans. II*, 68, 711, 1972.
189. Green, J. C. and King, D. I., *J. Chem. Soc. D*, p. 1121, 1970.
190. Bassett, P. J., Lloyd, D. R., Hillier, I. H., and Saunders, V. R., *Chem. Phys. Lett.*, 6, 253, 1970.
191. Cradock, S., *Chem. Phys. Lett.*, 10, 291, 1971.
192. Brundle, C. R., Jones, G. R., and Basch, H., *J. Chem. Phys.*, 55, 1098, 1971.
193. Branton, G. R., Brion, C. E., Frost, D. C., Mitchell, K. A. R., and Paddock, N. L., *J. Chem. Soc. A*, p. 151, 1970.
194. Hillier, I. H., Saunders, V. R., Ware, M. J., Bassett, P. J., Lloyd, D. R., and Lynaugh, N., *J. Chem. Soc. D*, p. 1316, 1970.
195. Jonathan, N., Morris, A., Smith, D. J., and Ross, K. J., *Chem. Phys. Lett.*, 7, 497, 1970.
196. Delwiche, J., Natalis, P., and Collin, J. E., *Int. J. Mass Spectrom. Ion Phys.*, 5, 443, 1970.
197. Delwiche, J. and Natalis, P., *Chem. Phys. Lett.*, 5, 564, 1970.
198. Cradock, S., *J. Chem. Phys.*, 55, 980, 1971.
199. Frost, D. C., McDowell, C. A., and Vroom, D. A., *Chem. Phys. Lett.*, 1, 93, 1967.
200. Brundle, C. R., *Chem. Phys. Lett.*, 5, 410, 1970.
201. Collin, J. E. and Natalis, P., *Chem. Phys. Lett.*, 2, 194, 1968.
202. Edqvist, O., Lindholm, E., Selin, L. E., Sjögren, H., and Åsbrink, L., *Ark. Fysik*, 40, 439, 1970.
203. Natalis, P., Delwiche, J., and Collin, J. E., *Chem. Phys. Lett.*, 9, 139, 1971.
204. Natalis, P. and Collin, J. E., *Chem. Phys. Lett.*, 2, 79, 1968.
205. Edqvist, O., Lindholm, E., Selin, L. E., Åsbrink, L., Kuyatt, C. E., Mielczarek, S. R., Simpson, J. A., and Fischer-Hjalmers, I., *Physica Scr.*, 1, 172, 1970.
206. Brundle, C. R., Neumann, D., Price, W. C., Evans, D., Potts, A. W., and Streets, D. G., *J. Chem. Phys.*, 53, 705, 1970.
207. Lorquet, J. C. and Cadet, C., *Chem. Phys. Lett.*, 6, 198, 1970.
208. Jonathan, N., Smith, D. J., and Ross, K. J., *Chem. Phys. Lett.*, 9, 217, 1971.
209. Turner, D. W., *Proc. R. Soc. Lond. [A]*, 307, 15, 1968.
210. Jonathan, N., Morris, A., Ross, K. J., and Smith, D. J., *J. Chem. Phys.*, 54, 4954, 1971.
211. Jonathan, N., Smith, D. J., and Ross, K. J., *J. Chem. Phys.*, 53, 3758, 1970.
212. Edqvist, O., Lindholm, E., Selin, L. E., and Åsbrink, L., *Physica Scr.*, 1, 25, 1970.
213. Radwan, T. N. and Turner, D. W., *J. Chem. Soc.*, 85, 1966.
214. Brundle, C. R., Kuebler, N. A., Robin, M. B., and Basch, H., *Inorg. Chem.*, 11, 20, 1972.
215. Murrell, J. N. and Schmidt, W., *J. Chem. Soc. Faraday Trans. II*, 68, 1709, 1972.
216. Cowan, D. O., Gleiter, R., Glemser, O., and Heilbronner, E., *Helv. Chim. Acta*, 55, 2418, 1972.
217. Brogli, F., Heilbronner, E., and Ipaktschi, J., *Helv. Chim. Acta*, 55, 2447, 1972.
218. Solouki, B., Bock, H., and Appel, R., *Angew. Chem. [Engl.]*, 84, 944, 1972; *Int. Ed.*, 11, 927, 1972.
219. Sandhu, J. S., *Indian J. Chem.*, 10, 667, 1972.
220. De Kock, R. L., Higginson, B. R., Lloyd, D. R., Breeze, A., Cruickshank, D. W. J., and Armstrong, D. R., *Mol. Phys.*, 24, 1059, 1972.
221. Dewar, M. J. S. and Goodman, D. W., *J. Chem. Soc. Faraday Trans. II*, 68, 1784, 1972.
222. Evans, S., Green, J. C., and Jackson, S. E., *J. Chem. Soc. Faraday Trans. II*, 69, 191, 1973.
223. Lynaugh, N., Lloyd, D. R., Guest, M. F., Hall, M. B., and Hillier, I. H., *J. Chem. Soc. Faraday Trans. II*, 68, 2192, 1972.

224. Evans, S., Green, M. L. H., Jewitt, B., Orchard, A. F., and Pygall, C. F., *J. Chem. Soc. Faraday Trans. II,* 68, 1847, 1972.
225. Evans, S., Hamnett, A., and Orchard, A. F., *J. Coord. Chem.*, 2, 57, 1972.
226. Gilbert, R., Sauvageau, P., and Sandorfy, C., *Chem. Phys. Lett.,* 17, 465, 1972.
227. Boekelheide, V. and Schmidt, W., *Chem. Phys. Lett.,* 17, 410, 1972.
228. Kroto, H. W. and Suffolk, R. J., *Chem. Phys. Lett.,* 17, 213, 1972.
229. Frost, D. C., Lee, S. T., and McDowell, C. A., *Chem. Phys. Lett.,* 17, 153, 1972.
230. Streets, D. G., Hall, W. E., and Ceasar, G. P., *Chem. Phys. Lett.,* 17, 90, 1972.
231. Schweig, A., Weidner, U., Berger, J. G., and Grahn, W., *Tetrahedron Lett.,* p. 557, 1973.
232. Schmidt, H. and Schweig, A., *Tetrahedron Lett.,* p. 981, 1973.
233. Gleiter, R., Heilbronner, E., Paquette, L. A., Thompson, G. L., and Wingard, R. E., Jr., *Tetrahedron,* 29, 565, 1973.
234. Bünzli, J. C., Frost, D. C., and Weiler, L., *Tetrahedron Lett.,* p. 1159, 1973.
235. Kimura, K., Katsumata, S., Achiba, Y., Matsumoto, H., and Nagakura, S., *Bull. Chem. Soc. Jap.,* 46, 373, 1973.
236. Maier, J. P. and Turner, D. W., *J. Chem. Soc. Faraday Trans. II,* 69, 196, 1973.

TABLE 2: X-RAY MOLECULAR ORBITAL SPECTRA

A calibration column has been included in this table as calibration procedures have not yet been standardized. Also, the third column indicates whether the spectra were obtained on the solid or gas.

TABLE 2

Compound		Phase	Orbital	E_B(eV)	Calibrant	Exciting Radiation	Reference
AsGa	GaAs	cryst	X_4	2.4	Au E_{Fermi}	AlK_α	135
			W_2	3.9			
			V	5.1			
			L_1	6.8			
			W_1	8.9			
			L_2	11.5			
			T_1	13.8			
BN	BN	s		3.9	b 285.0	MgK_α	71
				9.0			
				11.4			
BeO	BeO	s		7.6	b 285.0	MgK_α	71
				11.0			
CF_4	CF_4	g	$3t_2$	16.1		MgK_α	151
			$1t_1$	17.4			
			1e	18.5			
			$2t_2$	22.2			
			$2a_1$	25.1			
			$1t_2$	40.3			
			$1a_1$	43.8			
CH_4	CH_4	g	$1t_2$	13.6 (1)	N_2, Ne, He, Ar	AlK_α	39
			$2a_1$	23.1 (1)			
CH_4O	CH_3OH	g	2a″	11.1		MgK_α	151
			5a′	12.9			
			4a′	15.2			
			1a″	17.5			
			3a′	18.7			
			2a′	22.9			
			1a′	32.2			
CNNa	NaCN	s	Na2p	30.52	b 285.0	MgK_α	131
			1σ	24.67			
			K^+ imp.	16.98			
			2σ	12.76			
			π	8.96			
			3σ	5.28			
CO	CO	g	5σ	14.0	CO Cls 206.2	MgK_α	60
			1π	17.2			
			4σ	19.8			
			3σ	38.9			

TABLE 2 (continued)

Compound		Phase	Orbital	E_B(eV)	Calibrant	Exciting Radiation	Reference
CO	CO	g	3σ	14.5		MgK_α	151
			1π	17.2			
			2σ	20.1			
			1σ	38.3			
COS	COS	g	6σ	35.8 (4)		MgK_α	38
			7σ	27.4 (4)			
			8σ	18.0			
			9σ	16.0			
			2π	15.5			
			3π	11.2			
CO_2	CO_2	g	$3\sigma_g$, $2\sigma_u$	37.6 (2)		MgK_α	38
			$4\sigma_g$	19.4			
			$3\sigma_u$	18.1			
			$1\pi_u$	17.6			
			$1\pi_g$	13.8			
CS_2	CS_2	g	$5\sigma_g$, $4\sigma_u$	26.5 (8)		MgK_α	38
			$6\sigma_g$	16.2			
			$5\sigma_u$	14.5			
			$2\pi_u$	12.9			
			$2\pi_g$	10.1			
C_2H_2	HCCH	g	$2\sigma_g$	23.5 (2)	CHF_3 Cls 299.1	MgK_α	6
			$2\sigma_u$	18.5 (2)			
C_2H_4	$H_2C{=}CH_2$	g	$2a_g$	24.5 (1)	CHF_3 Cls 299.1	MgK_α	6
			$2a_u$	19.5 (1)			
C_2H_6	H_3CCH_3	g	$2a_{1g}$	24.2 (2)	CHF_3 Cls 299.1	MgK_α	6
			$2a_{2u}$	20.6 (2)			
C_2H_6	C_2H_6	g	$3a_{1g}$	10.7 (1)	N_2, Ne, He, Ar	AlK_α	39
			$1e_g$	10.7 (1)			
			$1e_u$	14.7 (1)			
			$2a_{2u}$	20.3 (1)			
			$2a_{1g}$	23.9 (1)			
C_3O_2	OCCCO	g	$4\sigma_g$	35.5	Ne 2s	MgK_α	19
			$3\sigma_u$	35.5			
			$5\sigma_g$	25.6 (1)			
			$4\sigma_u$	21.9 (2)			
			$6\sigma_g$	17.5			
			$5\sigma_u$	17.3			
			$1\pi_u$	16.0			
			$1\pi_g$	15.0			
			$2\pi_u$	10.8 (2)			
C_4H_4O		g	$4a_1$	34.1 (2)	Ne2s 48.42	MgK_α	69
			$5a_1$	25.2 (2)	Ne2p 21.59		
			$3b_2$	23.5 (2)			
			$4b_2$	19.2 (2)			
			$6a_1$	18.6 (2)			
			$7a_1$	17.5 (2)			

TABLE 2 (continued)

Compound		Phase	Orbital	E_B(eV)	Calibrant	Exciting Radiation	Reference
C_4H_4O (cont.)			$1b_1$	15.6 (2)			
			$5b_2$	15.1 (2)			
			$6b_2$	14.4 (2)			
			$8a_1$	13.8 (2)			
			$9a_1$	13.0 (2)			
			$2b_1$	10.3 (2)			
			$1a_2$	8.9 (2)			
C_4H_4S		g	$6a_1$	26.1 (2)	Ne2s 48.42	MgK_α	69
			$4b_2$	22.3 (2)	Ne2p 21.59		
			$7a_1$	22.1 (2)			
			$8a_1$	18.8 (2)			
			$5b_2$	17.8 (2)			
			$9a_1$	16.6 (2)			
			$6b_2$	14.3 (2)			
			$10a_1$	13.9 (2)			
			$2b_1$	13.3 (2)			
			$7b_2$	12.7 (2)			
			$11a_1$	12.1 (2)			
			$3b_1$	9.5 (2)			
			$1a_2$	8.9 (2)			
C_4H_5N	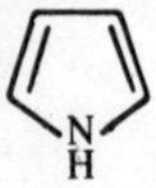	g	$4a_1$	29.5 (2)	Ne2s 48.42	MgK_α	69
			$5a_1$	23.8 (2)	Ne2p 21.59		
			$3b_2$	22.3 (2)			
			$6a_1$	18.8 (2)			
			$4b_2$	18.1 (2)			
			$7a_1$	17.5 (2)			
			$8a_1$	14.8 (2)			
			$1b_1$	14.3 (2)			
			$5b_2$	13.7 (2)			
			$6b_2$	13.0 (2)			
			$9a_1$	12.6 (2)			
			$2b_1$	9.2 (2)			
			$1a_2$	8.2 (2)			
C_6H_6		g	$2a_{1g}$	25.9 (2)	Ne2s 48.42	MgK_α	69
			$2e_{1u}$	22.7 (2)	Ne2p 21.59		
			$2e_{2g}$	19.0 (2)			
			$3a_{1g}$	17.0 (2)			
			$2b_{1u}$	15.7 (2)			
			$1b_{2u}$	14.9 (2)			
			$3e_{1u}$	14.2 (2)			
			$1a_{2u}$	12.3 (2)			
			$3e_{2g}$	11.8 (2)			
			$1e_{1g}$	9.4 (2)			
$ClLiO_4$	$LiClO_4$	s	t_1	6.3	b 285.0	AlK_α	43
			e, t_2	9.0			
			t_2	13.4			
			a_1	16.5			
			t_2	27.0			
			a_1	34.4			
FLi	LiF	s		9.4	b 285.0	MgK_α	71

TABLE 2 (continued)

Compound		Phase	Orbital	E_B(eV)	Calibrant	Exciting Radiation	Reference
F_6S	SF_6	g	$2e_g$	≈16		MgK_α	151
			$3t_{1u}$	17.3			
			$1t_{1g}$				
			$1t_{2u}$	18.7			
			$1t_{2g}$	19.9			
			$2t_{1u}$	22.9			
			$2a_{1g}$	27.0			
			$1e_g$	39.3			
			$1t_{1u}$	41.2			
			$1a_{1g}$	44.2			
GaSe	GaSe	s		2.5	Ga3d 18.7	AlK_α	42
				7			
				13			
H_2O	H_2O	g	$1b_1$	12.6		MgK_α	151
			$2a_1$	14.7			
			$1b_2$	18.4			
			$1a_1$	32.2			
H_2S	H_2S	g	$1b_1$	10.3		MgK_α	151
			$2a_1$	13.2			
			$1b_2$	15.1			
			$1a_1$	22			
KNO_3	KNO_3	s	K3s	33.40	b 285.0	MgK_α	131
			$1e'$	26.27			
			K3p	17.37			
			a_2''	14.59			
			$2e'$	11.56			
			a_2'	7.46			
Li_2O_4S	Li_2SO_4	s	t_1	5.8	b 285.0	AlK_α	43
			e, t_2	7.7			
			t_2	11.4			
			a_1	14.3			
			t_2	25.3			
			a_1	29.0			
NO	NO	g	2π	10		MgK_α	151
			1π	14			
			3σ	16.7			
			3σ	18.5			
			2σ	21.7			
			2σ	23.3			
			1σ	40.6			
			1σ	43.8			
N_2	N_2	g	σ_g 2p	15.5		MgK_α	151
			π_u 2p	16.8			
			σ_u 2s	18.6			
			σ_g 2s	37.3			

TABLE 2 (continued)

Compound		Phase	Orbital	E_B(eV)	Calibrant	Exciting Radiation	Reference
O_2	O_2	g	π_g 2p	13.1	Ar $2p_{3/2}$	MgK_α	151
			π_u 2p	17.0			
			σ_g 2p	18.8			
			σ_g 2p	21.1			
			σ_u 2s	25.3			
			σ_u 2s	27.9			
			σ_g 2s	39.6			
			σ_g 2s	41.6			
Sb_2Se_3	Sb_2Se_3	s		~14			138
SeZn	ZnSe	cryst	X_4	3.0	Au E_{Fermi}	AlK_α	135
			V	5.2			
			L_1	6.3			
			L_2	13.8			
			T_1	14.5			

TABLE 3: X-RAY CORE SPECTRA

The data have been arranged by element in this table so that all compounds are listed alphabetically under each element, and a given compound will be listed under each element whose binding energies were measured. Column three indicates whether the samples studied were solids or gases. Calibration of spectra is far from standardized, and the methods used, when given, are listed along with the reference value. For a number of the most commonly used standards, a letter has been used along with the value of the line. The letters and corresponding standards are

a Scotch tape Cls
b Pump oil – contaminant – residual Cls
c Au $4f_{7/2}$
d Compound – internal Cls
e Cu KL_{II} L_{III} Auger line
f Graphite Cls
g PbO Pb $4f_{7/2}$
h $Na_4P_2O_7$ P2p
i Mg K(Cr K_a, Cu K_a)
j KNO_3 Nls
k Deposited C layer Cls

TABLE 3 (continued)

Compound		Phase	Orbital	E_B(eV)	Calibrant	Exciting Radiation	Reference
Ag							
Ag	Ag	s	$2p_{3/2}$ $3d_{5/2}$	3,352.5 (5) 368.2 (1)	Pd $2p_{3/2}$	CrK_α MgK_α	70
Ag	Ag	s	d band	−4.7 (2)	Pd fermi level 0.0	MgK_α	51
Ag	Ag	s	L_{III} L_{II}	3,350.8 3,523.5	CuA6	$CuK_{\alpha 1}$	123
Ag	Ag	s	L_I L_{II}	3,806.2 3,523.7	$AgL_{III}(CuK_{\alpha 1})$	$CuK_{\alpha 1}$	45
Ag	Ag(fcc)	s	3d	368 (0.5)		MgK_α	122
$Ag_{0.71}Pd_{0.29}$	$Ag_{0.71}Pd_{0.29}$	s	$2p_{3/2}$ $3d_{5/2}$	3,352.3 (5) 368.1 (1)	Au, Pt $4f_{7/2}$	CrK_α MgK_α	70
Al							
Al	Al	s	L_I	117.7	$MgOMgK(CrK_{\alpha 1})$	$CrK_{\alpha 1}$	67
AlF_6Na_3	Na_3AlF_6	s	2p 2s	78.8 124.6	Au4f(N_7 82.8) (N_6 86.4)	AlK_α	133
$AlNaO_8Si_3$	Albite $NaAlSi_3O_8$	s	2p	73.8 (5)	Internal Si2p 102.0	Al, MgK_α	57
$Al_2Fe_3Mg_3O_{12}Si_3$	Garnet $(MgFe)_3Al_2(SiO_4)_3$	s	2p	74.5 (5)	Internal Si2p 102.0	Al, MgK_α	57
$Al_2K_2O_{16}Si_6$	Microcline $K_2O \cdot Al_2O_3 \cdot 6SiO_2$	s	2p 2s	75.0 119.9	Au4f(N_7 82.8) (N_6 86.4)	AlK_α	133
Al_2O_3	Al_2O_3	s	2p 2s	76.4 121.0	Au4f(N_7 82.8) (N_6 86.4)	AlK_α	133
Al_2O_3	Al_2O_3	s	L_I	117.4		$CrK_{\alpha 1}$	65

TABLE 3 (continued)

Compound		Phase	Orbital	E_B(eV)	Calibrant	Exciting Radiation	Reference
Al_2O_3	Al_2O_3	s	K	1,559.6 (4)	e, i	CrK_α	76
Ar							
Ar	Ar	g	ls 2s $2p_{1/2}$ $2p_{3/2}$ 3s 3p	3,205.9 (5) 326.3 (1) 250.56 (7) 248.45 (7) 29.3 (1) 15.81	Ar 3p 15.81	CrK_α Al, MgK_α	151
As							
AlAs	AlAs	s	$3p_{1/2}$ $3p_{3/2}$	149.0 (2) 144.1 (1)	b 285.0	AlK_α	9
As	As	s	$3p_{3/2}$ 3d	141.1 42.0 (2)	b 285.0	AlK_α	9
$AsBr_3$	$AsBr_3$	s	$3p_{1/2}$ $3p_{3/2}$	150.4 145.9	b 285.0	AlK_α	9
AsF_6K	$KAsF_6$	s	$3p_{1/2}$ $3p_{3/2}$ 3d	151.3 (2) 146.8 (3) 47.9 (5)	b 285.0	AlK_α	9
AsF_6Li	$LiAsF_6$	s	$3p_{1/2}$ $3p_{3/2}$ 3d	151.7 (2) 147.6 (4) 49.3 (3)	b 285.0	AlK_α	9
$AsHNa_2O_4 \cdot 7H_2O$	$Na_2HAsO_4 \cdot 7H_2O$	s	$3p_{1/2}$ $3p_{3/2}$ 3d	148.9 (2) 144.2 (2) 45.1 (2)	b 285.0	AlK_α	9
AsH_2KO_4	KH_2AsO_4	s	$3p_{1/2}$ $3p_{3/2}$ 3d	149.3 (2) 144.8 (2) 46.9 (2)	b 285.0	AlK_α	9

TABLE 3 (continued)

Compound		Phase	Orbital	E_B(eV)	Calibrant	Exciting Radiation	Reference
AsIn	InAs	s	3d	41.3 (2)	b, KCl Cl2p	AlK_{α}	13
AsK_3O_4	K_3AsO_4	s	$3p_{1/2}$	148.4 (2)	b 285.0	AlK_{α}	9
			$3p_{3/2}$	144.0 (1)			
			3d	45.2 (8)			
$AsNaO_2$	$NaAsO_2$	s	$3p_{1/2}$	148.6	b 285.0	AlK_{α}	9
			$3p_{3/2}$	143.6			
$AsNa_3O_4$	Na_3AsO_4	s	$3p_{1/2}$	148.2 (2)	b 285.0	AlK_{α}	9
			$3p_{3/2}$	143.5 (3)			
			3d	44.6 (8)			
$As_2Na_4O_7$	$Na_4As_2O_7$	s	$3p_{1/2}$	149.3 (1)	b 285.0	AlK_{α}	9
			$3p_{3/2}$	144.5 (1)			
			3d	45.6 (1)			
As_2O_3	As_2O_3	s	$3p_{1/2}$	150.0 (2)	b 285.0	AlK_{α}	9
			$3p_{3/2}$	145.6 (2)			
			3d	46.0 (6)			
As_2O_3	As_2O_3	s	3d	45.6		AlK_{α}	102
As_2O_3	As_2O_3	s	3d	45.2 (2)	b KCl Cl2p	AlK_{α}	13
As_2O_5	As_2O_5	s	$3p_{1/2}$	150.1 (6)	b 285.0	AlK_{α}	9
			$3p_{3/2}$	145.5 (3)			
			3d	46.4 (5)			
As_2O_5	As_2O_5	s	3d	46.6 (4)	b, KC Cl2p	AlK_{α}	13
As_2O_5	As_2O_5	s	3d	46.8		AlK_{α}	102
As_2S_3	As_2S_3	s	3d	43.7 (2)	b KCl Cl2p	AlK_{α}	13
As_2S_3	As_3O_3	s	$3p_{1/2}$	148.0	b 285.0	AlK_{α}	9
			$3p_{3/2}$	142.9			
			3d	43.7 (2)			

TABLE 3 (continued)

Compound		Phase	Orbital	E_B(eV)	Calibrant	Exciting Radiation	Reference
As_2S_5	As_2S_5	s	$3p_{1/2}$ $3p_{3/2}$ 3d	148.9 144.2 44.3 (5)	b 285.0	AlK_α	9
As_2Zn_3	Zn_3As_2	s	$3p_{1/2}$ $3p_{3/2}$	143.6 140.4	b 285.0	AlK_α	9
As_4S_4	As_4S_4	s	$3p_{1/2}$ $3p_{3/2}$	147.8 143.2	b 285.0	AlK_α	9
$C_2H_7AsO_2$	$(CH_3)_2AsO(OH)$	s	$3p_{1/2}$ $3p_{3/2}$ 3d	148.9 (6) 144.3 (4) 45.1 (2)	b 285.0	AlK_α	9
$C_2H_7AsO_2$	$(CH_3)_2AsO(OH)$	s	3d	44.7 (7)	b KCl Cl2p	AlK_α	13
$C_6H_7AsO_3$	$(C_6H_5)AsO(OH)_2$	s	$3p_{1/2}$ $3p_{3/2}$ 3d	150.3 (2) 145.4 (2) 46.3 (2)	b 285.0	AlK_α	9
$C_6H_7AsO_3$	$C_6H_5AsO(OH_2)_2$	s	3d	46.1 (2)	b, KCl Cl2p	AlK_α	13
$C_6H_7AsO_4$	$(p\text{-}OHC_6H_4)AsO(OH)_2$	s	$3p_{1/2}$ 3d	149.6 (2) 144.6 (2)	b 285.0	AlK_α	9
$C_6H_8AsNO_3$	$(p\text{-}NH_2C_6H_4)AsO(OH)_2$	s	$3p_{1/2}$ $3p_{3/2}$ 3d	148.5 (2) 144.3 (2) 45.3 (2)	b 285.0	AlK_α	9
$C_6H_8AsNO_3$	$(o\text{-}NH_2C_6H_4)AsO(OH)_2$	s	$3p_{1/2}$ $3p_{3/2}$ 3d	149.6 (2) 144.8 (2) 46.1 (2)	b 285.0	AlK_α	9
$C_6H_{18}As_4N_6$	$As_4(NCH_3)_6$	s	$3p_{1/2}$ $3p_{3/2}$	148.8 (2) 144.1 (2)	b 285.0	AlK_α	9
$C_{18}H_{15}As$	$(C_6H_5)_3As$	s	$3p_{1/2}$ $3p_{3/2}$ 3d	146.7 (1) 142.1 (1) 43.2 (2)	b 285.0	AlK_α	9

TABLE 3 (continued)

Compound		Phase	Orbital	E_B(eV)	Calibrant	Exciting Radiation	Reference
$C_{18}H_{15}AsCl_2Hg$	$((C_6H_5)_3As)HgCl_2$	s	$3p_{1/2}$ $3p_{3/2}$ 3d	148.7 143.0 44.1	b 285.0	AlK_α	9
$C_{18}H_{15}AsO$	$(C_6H_5)_3AsO$	s	$3p_{1/2}$ $3p_{3/2}$ 3d	148.2 (3) 143.3 (3) 44.5 (2)	b 285.0	AlK_α	9
$C_{18}H_{17}AsO_2$	$(C_6H_5)_3As(OH)_2$	s	$3p_{1/2}$ $3p_{3/2}$ 3d	148.7 143.7 44.7	b 285.0	AlK_α	9
$C_{19}H_{15}AsF_6$	$(C_6H_5)_3CAsF_6$	s	$3p_{1/2}$ $3p_{3/2}$ 3d	151.5 (1.2) 146.5 (5) 48.5 (2)	b 285.0	AlK_α	9
$C_{24}H_{20}AsBr$	$[(C_6H_5)_4As]Br$	s	$3p_{1/2}$ $3p_{3/2}$ 3d	148.9 143.8 44.9	b 285.0	AlK_α	9
$C_{24}H_{20}AsCl$	$[(C_6H_5)_4As]Cl$	s	$3p_{1/2}$ $3p_{3/2}$	148.3 143.8	b 285.0	AlK_α	9
$C_{36}H_{30}As_2Cl_2HgO_2$	$((C_6H_5)_3AsO)_2HgCl_2$	s	$3p_{1/2}$ $3p_{3/2}$ 3d	148.2 144.0 45.0	b 285.0	AlK_α	9
$C_{36}H_{30}As_2HgI_2$	$((C_6H_5)_3As)_2HgI_2$	s	$3p_{1/2}$ $3p_{3/2}$ 3d	147.8 142.7 43.6	b 285.0	AlK_α	9
Au							
Au	Au	s	d band	−3.2 (2) −6.0 (2)	Pd Fermi level 0.0	MgK_α	51
Au	Au	s	L_{III} L_{II}	11,919.3 13,734.0	CuK($MoK_{\alpha l}$)	$MoK_{\alpha l}$	119

TABLE 3 (continued)

Compound		Phase	Orbital	E_B(eV)	Calibrant	Exciting Radiation	Reference
Au	Au	s	L_{II}	13,733.2 (4)	e	MoK_a	77
			L_{III}	11,918.2 (4)			
			M_I	3,424.7 (4)		CuK_a	
			M_{II}	3,149.4 (5)			
			M_{III}	2,743.0 (5)			
			M_{IV}	2,291.2 (4)		CrK_a	
			M_V	2,206.1 (4)			
Au	Au	s	$4f_{7/2}$	83.8 (1)	Pd $2p_{3/2}$	MgK_a	70
Au	Au		$4f_{5/2}$	92.2	a 290.0	AlK_a	107
			$4f_{7/2}$	88.85			
Au	Au(fcc)	s	4f	84(0.5)		MgK_a	122
AuC_2KN_2	$KAu(CN)_2$		$4f_{5/2}$	94.85	a 290.0	AlK_a	107
			$4f_{7/2}$	91.15			
$AuCl_4K$	$KAuCl_4$		$4f_{5/2}$	97.4	a 290.0	AlK_a	107
			$4f_{7/2}$	93.85			
$Au_{0.45}Pd_{0.55}$	$Au_{0.45}Pd_{0.55}$	s	$4f_{7/2}$	83.6 (1)	Au, Pt $4f_{7/2}$	MgK_a	70
$C_2H_3AuO_2S$	$AuSCH_2CO_2H$		$4f_{5/2}$	94.45	a 290.0	AlK_a	107
			$4f_{7/2}$	90.8			
B							
B	B	s	ls	183.8	LiF Fls 685.4		114
B	B amor	s	ls	187.5 (2)	b	MgK_a	8
BCl_3	BCl_3	g	ls	−2.3 (1)	BF_3 Bls 0.0	MgK_a	113
BF_3	BF_3	g	ls	0.0	BF_3 Bls 0.0	MgK_a	113
BF_4K	KBF_4	s	ls	195.9	LiF Fls 685.4		114
BF_4Na	$NaBF_4$	s	ls	195.1 (2)	b	MgK_a	8

TABLE 3 (continued)

Compound		Phase	Orbital	E_B(eV)	Calibrant	Exciting Radiation	Reference
BH_3O_3	$B(OH)_3$	s	ls	193.2 (2)	b	MgK_a	8
BH_3O_3	H_3BO_3	s	ls	191.8	LiF Fls 685.4		114
BH_4Na	$NaBH_4$	s	ls	185.7	LiF Fls 685.4		114
BH_4Na	$NaBH_4$	s	ls	187.4 (2)	b	MgK_a	8
BN	BN	s	ls	190.6	b 285.0	MgK_a	71
BN	BN	s	ls	190.2 (2)	b	MgK_a	8
BN	BN	s	ls	188.6	LiF Fls 685.4		114
BP	BP	s	ls	192.5	LiF Fls 685.4		114
B_2H_6	B_2H_6	g	ls	−6.3 (1)	BF_3 Bls 0.0	MgK_a	113
B_2O_3	B_2O_3	s	K	188.0 (6)	e, i	CrK_a	76
B_2O_3	B_2O_3	s	ls	191.4	LiF Fls 685.4		114
$B_3Na_3O_6$	$Na_3B_3O_6$	s	ls	192.2 (2)	b	MgK_a	8
B_4C	B_4C	s	ls	186.7 (2)	b	MgK_a	8
B_4C	B_4C	s	ls	184.0	LiF Fls 685.4		114
$B_4Na_2O_7 \cdot 10H_2O$	$Na_2B_4O_7 \cdot 10H_2O$	s	ls	192.8 (2)	b	MgK_a	8
$B_4Na_2O_7$	$Na_2B_4O_7$	s	ls	190.7	LiF Fls 685.4		114
B_4Si	B_4Si	s	ls	188.8	LiF Fls 685.4		114
$B_{10}Cs_2H_{10}$	$Cs_2B_{10}H_{10}$	s	ls	187.6 (2)	b	MgK_a	8
$B_{10}H_{14}$	$B_{10}H_{14}$	s	ls	188.0 (2)	b	MgK_a	8
$B_{12}H_{12}Na_2 \cdot XH_2O$	$Na_2B_{12}H_{12} \cdot XH_2O$	s	ls	187.7 (2)	b	MgK_a	8

TABLE 3 (continued)

Compound		Phase	Orbital	E_B(eV)	Calibrant	Exciting Radiation	Reference
$CH_3BK_2O_2$	$K_2BH_3CO_2$	s	ls	187.5 (2)	b	MgK_a	8
CH_3BO	BH_3CO	g	ls	−7.6 (1)	BF_3 Bls 0.0	MgK_a	113
C_3H_9B	$B(CH_3)_3$	g	ls	−6.4 (1)	BF_3 Bls 0.0	MgK_a	113
$C_3H_9BF_3N$	$(CH_3)_3NBF_3$	s	ls	193.8 (2)	b	MgK_a	8
$C_3H_9BO_3$	$B(OCH_3)_3$	g	ls	−4.4 (1)	BF_3 Bls 0.0	MgK_a	113
$C_3H_{10}BO_3Na$	$NaBH(OCH_3)_3$	s	ls	192.3 (2)	b	MgK_a	8
$C_3H_{12}BN$	$BH_3N(CH_3)_3$	g	ls	−9.1 (1)	BF_3 Bls 0.0	MgK_a	113
$C_4H_{20}B_3N$	$[(CH_3)_4N]B_3H_8$	s	ls	187.4 (2)	b	MgK_a	8
$C_4H_{20}B_{18}CoCsS_2$	$Cs[Co(1,2\text{-}B_9C_2H_{10}\text{-}8\text{-}S)_2]$	s	ls	188.9 (2)	b	MgK_a	8
$C_4H_{21}B_{17}CoRb$	$Rb[Co(1,2\text{-}B_9C_2H_{11})(B_8C_2H_{10})]$	s	ls	188.4 (2)	b	MgK_a	8
$C_4H_{22}B_{18}CoCs$	$Cs[Co(1,2\text{-}B_9C_2H_{11})_2]$	s	ls	188.2 (2)	b	MgK_a	8
$C_6H_6BClO_2$	*p*-$ClC_6H_4B(OH)_2$	s	ls	191.9 (2)	b	MgK_a	8
$C_6H_6BFO_2$	*p*-$FC_6H_4B(OH)_2$	s	ls	191.9 (2)	b	MgK_a	8
$C_7H_{16}B_9N$	$C_2B_9H_{11}\cdot C_5H_5N$	s	ls	188.4 (2)	b	MgK_a	8
$C_8H_{28}B_{18}Br_6CoN$	$[(CH_3)_4N]$ $[(8,9,12\text{-}Br_3\text{-}1,2\text{-}B_9C_2H_8)_2Co]$	s	ls	189.5 (2)	b	MgK_a	8
$C_{12}H_{37}B_3P_2Pt$	$((C_2H_5)_3P)_2PtB_3H_7$	s	ls	188.9	d 285.0	AlK_a	87
$C_{12}H_{42}B_8P_2Pt$	$((C_2H_5)_3P)_2PtB_8H_{12}$	s	ls	189.0 (1)	d 285.0	AlK_a	87
$C_{12}H_{42}B_{10}P_2Pt$	$((C_2H_5)_3P)_2PtB_{10}N_{12}$	s	ls	189.1 (1)	d 285.0	AlK_a	87
$C_{13}H_{19}B_2F_6N_6P$	$[C_2H_5B($$)_3BC_2H_5]PF_6$	s	ls	191.9 (2)	b	MgK_a	8

TABLE 3 (continued)

Compound		Phase	Orbital	E_B(eV)	Calibrant	Exciting Radiation	Reference
$C_{14}H_{12}BN_9O_3^-W$	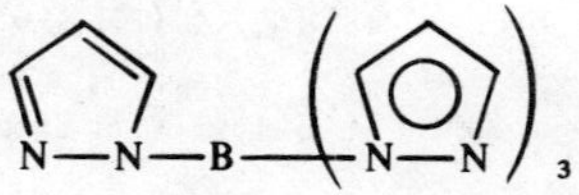 W(CO)$_2$NO	s	ls	191.9 (2)	b	MgK_α	8
$C_{16}H_{64}B_{20}N_2Pt$	$[(C_2H_5)_4N]_2Pt(B_{10}H_{12})_2$	s	ls	187.8 (1)	d 285.0	AlK_α	87
$C_{24}H_{20}BNa$	$NaB(C_6H_5)_4$	s	ls	187.7 (2)	b	MgK_α	8
$C_{36}H_{42}B_{10}P_2Pt$	$((C_6H_5)_3P)_2PtB_{10}H_{12}$	s	ls	188.7 (1)	d 285.0	AlK_α	87
$C_{38}H_{44}B_9NP_2Pt$	$((C_6H_5)_3P)_2PtB_9H_{11}(CH_3CN)$	s	ls	188.6 (1)	d 285.0	AlK_α	87
Ba							
BaF_2	BaF_2	s	5p	23.6	a 290	AlK_α	30
BaO	BaO	s	L_I L_{II} L_{III}	5,987.0 (1.2) 5,623.5 (5) 5,247.2 (5)	e	MoK_α CuK_α	78
Be							
BeO	BeO	s	ls	114.2	b 285.0	MgK_α	71
Bi							
Bi	Bi	s	L_{III}	13,419.0	CuK($MoK_{\alpha l}$)	$MoK_{\alpha 1}$	119
Bi	Bi	s	L_{II} L_{III} M_I M_{II} M_{III} M_{IV} M_V N_I N_{II} N_{III} N_{IV}	15,708.7 (4) 13,418.3 (4) 3,999.0 (4) 3,696.3 (4) 3,176.7 (4) 2,687.3 (4) 2,579.4 (4) 938.7 (5) 805.3 (4) 678.9 (4) 463.6 (4)	e	AgK_α MoK_α CuK_α CrK_α	77

TABLE 3 (continued)

Compound		Phase	Orbital	E_B(eV)	Calibrant	Exciting Radiation	Reference
Bi (continued)			N_V	440.1 (4)			
$BiCl_6CoH_{18}N_6$	$[Co(NH_3)_6]BiCl_6$	s	$4f_{5/2}$ $4f_{7/2}$	170.2 164.2	a 290.0	AlK_α	107
$BiCsI_4$	$CsBiI_4$	s	$4f_{5/2}$ $4f_{7/2}$	171.6 166.3	a 290	AlK_α	107
BiIO	BiOI	s	$4f_{5/2}$ $4f_{7/2}$	171.4 166.1	a 290.0	AlK_α	107
BiI_3	BiI_3	s	$4f_{5/2}$ $4f_{7/2}$	171.8 166.5	a 290.0	AlK_α	107
$BiNaO_3$	$NaBiO_3$	s	$4f_{5/2}$ $4f_{7/2}$	171.8 166.5	a 290.0	AlK_α	107
Bi_2O_3	Bi_2O_3	s	$4f_{5/2}$ $4f_{7/2}$	172.2 166.85	a 290.0	AlK_α	107
Br							
$BrCCl_3$	CCl_3Br	s	3s $3p_{1/2}$ $3p_{3/2}$ $3d_{3/2,5/2}$	259.1 193.1 186.1 72.1	c 84	MgK_α	28
$BrC_4ClK_2N_4Pt$	$K_2Pt(CN)_4ClBr$	s	3p	184.0	g	MgK_α	129
BrCs	CsBr	s	4p	12.0	a 290	AlK_α	30
BrCu	CuBr	s	$3d_{3/2,5/2}$	79.6	a 285.5	AlK_α	46
BrK	KBr	s	3d	70.0	KBr-KCl	AlK_α	13
BrK	KBr	s	3p	184.1	g	MgK_α	129
BrK	KBr	s	4p	10.7	a 290	AlK_α	30

TABLE 3 (continued)

Compound		Phase	Orbital	E_B(eV)	Calibrant	Exciting Radiation	Reference
$BrKO_3$	$KBrO_3$	s	3d	77.6	KBr-KCl	AlK_α	13
$BrKO_4$	$KBrO_4$	s	3d	76.0	KBr-KCl	AlK_α	13
BrLi	LiBr	s	L_{III}	1,594.7 (7)	e	CrK_α	78
BrNa	NaBr	s	L_I L_{II}	1,781.9 (7) 1,596.1 (1.0)	MgK	CuK_α	78
$Br_2C_4K_2N_4Pt$	$K_2Pt(CN)_4Br_2$	s	3p	183.6	g	MgK_α	129
Br_2Cu	$CuBr_2$	s	$3d_{3/2,5/2}$	71.5	a 285.5	AlK_α	46
Br_2Pd	$PdBr_2$	s	$3p_{3/2}$	182.6 (1)	b 285.0		86
Br_4K_2Pd	$K_2[PdBr_4]$	s	$3p_{3/2}$	182.1 (2)	b 285.0		86
Br_4K_2Pt	K_2PtBr_4	s	3p	183.8	g	MgK_α	129
Br_6K_2Pt	K_2PtBr_6	s	3p	183.5	g	MgK_α	129
$CHBrCl_2$	$CHBrCl_2$	s	3s $3p_{1/2}$ $3p_{3/2}$ $3d_{3/2,5/2}$	259.1 193.0 185.9 72.0	c 84	MgK_α	28
$C_2H_8Br_2CuN_2 \cdot H_2O$	$CuBr_2 \cdot H_2NCH_2CH_2NH_2 \cdot H_2O$	s	$3d_{3/2,5/2}$	71.0	a 285.5	AlK_α	46
$C_4H_{16}Br_2CuN_4 \cdot H_2O$	$CuBr_2 \cdot 2(H_2NCH_2CH_2NH_2) \cdot H_2O$	s	$3d_{3/2,5/2}$	69.7	a 285.5	AlK_α	46
$C_6H_{24}Br_2CuN_6 \cdot 5H_2O$	$CuBr_2 \cdot 3(H_2NCH_2CH_2NH_2) \cdot 5H_2O$	s	$3d_{3/2,5/2}$	70.0	a 285.5	AlK_α	46
$C_{10}H_8Br_2CuN_2$	$CuBr_2 \cdot$ 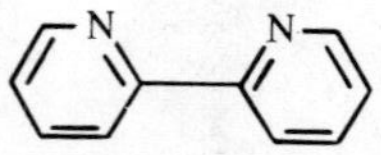	s	$3d_{3/2,5/2}$	70.1	a 285.5	AlK_α	46
$C_{20}H_{16}Br_2CuN_4 \cdot 2H_2O$	$CuBr_2 \cdot 2$ 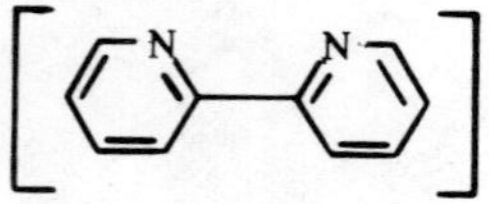 $\cdot 2H_2O$	s	$3d_{3/2,5/2}$	69.2	a 285.5	AlK_α	46

TABLE 3 (continued)

Compound		Phase	Orbital	E_B(eV)	Calibrant	Exciting Radiation	Reference
$C_{36}H_{30}Br_2P_2Pd$	$Pd(P(C_6H_5)_3)_2Br_2$	s	$3p_{3/2}$	182.1 (1)	b 285.0		86
C							
$AlNaO_8Si_3$	Albite $NaAlSi_3O_8$	s	ls	284.3 (5)	Internal Si 2p 102.0	Al, MgK_{α}	57
$Al_2Fe_3Mg_3O_{12}Si_3$	Garnet $(MgFe)_3Al_2(SiO_4)_3$	s	ls	284.7 (5)	Internal Si 2p 102.0	Al, MgK_{α}	57
$Al_6Ca_4Fe_6H_2O_{22}Si_6$	Epidote 13575 86% Fe^{3+} $4CaO \cdot 3(AlFe)_2O_3 \cdot 6SiO_2 \cdot H_2O$	s	ls	284.5 (4)	c 84.0 (3)	Al, MgK_{α}	57
$BrCCl_3$	CCl_3Br	s	ls	291.7	c 84	MgK_{α}	28
C	Graphite	s	ls	284.1		MgK_{α}	34
C	Amorphous	s	K	283.8 (5)	e, i	CrK_{α}	76
C	Diamond	s	ls	287	Varian IEE-15	MgK_{α}	90
C	Graphite	s	ls	284.3	b 285.0	MgK_{α}	71
CCl_3F	CCl_3F	s	ls	293.3	c 84	MgK_{α}	28
CCl_4	CCl_4	s	ls	292.1	c 84	MgK_{α}	28
CCl_4	CCl_4	s	ls	292.6 (2)	b 285.0	Mg, AlK_{α}	48
CCl_4	CCl_4	g	ls	296.3	CHF_3, CH_4, or C_6H_6 from Ref. 6	MgK_{α}	6
CCl_4	CCl_4	g	ls	296.23	Ar $2p_{3/2}$ 248.457		85
CCuN	CuCN	s	ls	286.8	a 285.5	AlK_{α}	46
CCuNS	CuSCN	s	ls	287.0	a 285.5	AlK_{α}	46

TABLE 3 (continued)

Compound		Phase	Orbital	E_B(eV)	Calibrant	Exciting Radiation	Reference
$CCuO_3$	$CuCO_3$	s	ls	287.5	a 285.5	AlK_α	46
CF_2O	F_2CO	s	ls	294.1 (2)	b 285.0	Mg, AlK_α	48
CF_4	CF_4	g	ls	301.8	CHF_3, CH_4, or C_6H_6 from Ref. 6	MgK_α	121
CF_4	CF_4	s	ls	296.9 (2)	b 285.0	Mg, AlK_α	48
CF_4	CF_4	s	ls	296.1 (2)	b	MgK_α	8
CF_4	CF_4	g	ls	301.68	Ar $2p_{3/2}$ 248.457		85
CF_4	CF_4	g	ls	301.8	CH_4 Cls 290.7	MgK_α	151
$CHBrCl_2$	$CHBrCl_2$	s	ls	289.8	c 84	MgK_α	28
$CHCl_3$	$CHCl_3$	s	ls	290.5	c 84	MgK_α	28
$CHCl_3$	$CHCl_3$	g	ls	295.1	CHF_3, CH_4, or C_6H_6 from Ref. 6	MgK_α	121
$CHCl_3$	$CHCl_3$	s	ls	289.8 (2)	b 285.0	Mg, AlK_α	48
CHF_3	CHF_3	g	ls	299.1 (1)	Absolute	MgK_α	6
CHF_3	CHF_3	g	ls	299.1	CHF_3, CH_4, or C_6H_6 from Ref. 6	MgK_α	121
CHF_3	CHF_3	g	ls	298.8	CH_4 Cls 290.7	MgK_α	151
CHF_3	CHF_3	s	ls	293.5 (2)	b	MgK_α	8
CHF_3	CHF_3	g	ls	299.1 (1)	Nels, 2s 869.7 (1) 48.5	MgK_α	119
CHF_3	CHF_3	s	ls	294.9 (2)	b 285.0	Mg, AlK_α	48

TABLE 3 (continued)

Compound		Phase	Orbital	E_B(eV)	Calibrant	Exciting Radiation	Reference
$CHNaO_3$	$NaHCO_3$	s	ls	290.2 (2)	b 285.0	Mg, AlK_α	48
CH_2Br_2	CH_2Br_2	s	ls	287.3 (2)	b 285.0	Mg, AlK_α	48
CH_2Cl_2	CH_2Cl_2	s	ls	288.7	c 84	MgK_α	28
CH_2Cl_2	CH_2Cl_2	s	ls	288.0 (2)	b 285.0	Mg, AlK_α	48
CH_2Cl_2	CH_2Cl_2	g	ls	293.9	CHF_3, CH_4, or C_6H_6 from Ref. 6	MgK_α	121
CH_2O	H_2CO	s	ls	287.9 (2)	b 285.0	Mg, AlK_α	48
CH_2O_2	HCO_2H	g	ls	4.99 (10)	CH_4 Cls 0.0	$MgK_{\bar{\alpha}}$	61
CH_3Br	CH_3Br	g	ls	291.8	CHF_3, CH_4, or C_6H_6 from Ref. 6	MgK_α	121
CH_3Br	CH_3Br	g	ls	291.95	Ar $2p_{3/2}$ 248.457		85
CH_3Cl	CH_3Cl	g	ls	292.31	Ar $2p_{3/2}$ 248.457		85
CH_3Cl	CH_3Cl	g	ls	292.4	CHF_3, CH_4 or C_6H_6 from Ref. 6	MgK_α	121
CH_3F	CH_3F	g	ls	293.6	CHF_3, CH_4, or C_6H_6 from Ref. 6	MgK_α	121
CH_3NO_2	$HC(O)ONH_2$	s	ls	288.6 (2)	b 285.0	Mg, AlK_α	48
CH_4	CH_4	g	ls	290.8 (2)	CHF_3 (g) Cls 299.1	MgK_α	6
CH_4	CH_4	g	ls	290.74	Ar $2p_{3/2}$ 248.457		85
CH_4	CH_4	g	ls	290.7	CH_4 Cls 290.7	MgK_α	151
CH_4N_2O	$(NH_2)_2CO$	s	ls	288.9 (2)	b 285.0	Mg, AlK_α	48

TABLE 3 (continued)

Compound		Phase	Orbital	E_B(eV)	Calibrant	Exciting Radiation	Reference
CH_4O	CH_3OH	g	ls	1.9 (2)	CH_4 Cls 0.0	MgK_α	61
CH_4O	CH_3OH	s	ls	287.2 (2)	b 285.0	Mg, AlK_α	48
CH_4O	CH_3OH	g	ls	292.3	CH_4 Cls 290.7	MgK_α	151
CHf	HfC	s	ls	−4.0	b 0.0	Mg, AlK_α	72
CKN	KCN	s	ls	285.0 (2)	b 285.0	Mg, AlK_α	48
CMo_2	Mo_2C	s	ls	−2.1	b 0.0	Mg, AlK_α	72
$CNaO_3$	Na_2CO_3	s	ls	289.7 (2)	b 285.0	Mg, AlK_α	48
CNb	NbC	s	ls	−2.9	b 0.0	Mg, AlK_α	72
CO	CO	g	ls	296.2	Ne2s, 2p	MgK_α	60
CO	CO	s	ls	290.5		MgK_α	23
CO	CO	g	ls	295.9	CH_4 Cls 290.7	MgK_α	151
CO	CO	g	ls	296.2		MgK_α	88
COS	COS	g	ls	295.2 (1)		MgK_α	38
			Shake-up	−8.3 (2) −12.2 (2) −17.8 (2)	COS Cls 0.0		
CO_2	CO_2	g	ls	297.5 (1)		MgK_α	38
			Shake-up	−10.8 (2) −12.4 (2) −15.0 (2) −18.0 (2)	CO_2 Cls 0.0		
CO_2	CO_2	g	ls	297.5	CH_4 Cls 290.7	MgK_α	151
CO_2	CO_2	g	ls	6.84 (5)	CH_4 Cls 0.0	MgK_α	61

TABLE 3 (continued)

Compound		Phase	Orbital	E_B(eV)	Calibrant	Exciting Radiation	Reference
CO_2	CO_2	s	ls	292.1 (2)	b 285.0	Mg, AlK_a	48
CS_2	CS_2	s	ls	287.2 (2)	b 285.0	Mg, AlK_a	48
CS_2	CS_2	g	ls	293.1	CH_4 Cls 290.7	MgK_a	151
CS_2	CS_2	g	ls Shake-up	293.1 (1) −6.5 (2) −9.1 (2) −12.2 (5) −15.8 (4) −17.7 (3) −19.7 (3)	 CS_2 Cls 0.0	MgK_a	38
CTa	TaC	s	ls	−2.9	b 0.0	Mg, AlK_a	72
CTi	TiC	s	ls	−3.3	b 0.0	Mg, AlK_a	72
CV	VC	s	ls	−2.6	b 0.0	Mg, AlK_a	72
CW	WC	s	ls	−2.1	b 0.0	Mg, AlK_a	72
CZr	ZrC	s	ls	−3.7	b 0.0	Mg, AlK_a	72
C_2ClF_3	$-[CF_2-CFCl]-_n$	s	ls(CF_2) (CFCl)	291.9 (3) 290.8 (3)	b 285.0	MgK_a	130
$C_2Cl_3F_3$	$Cl_2F\overset{a}{C}\overset{b}{C}ClF_2$	s	^{a}ls ^{b}ls	291.9 (2) 293.1 (2)	b 285.0	Mg, AlK_a	48
$C_2Cl_3F_3$	$Cl_3\overset{a}{C}\overset{b}{C}F_3$	s	^{a}ls ^{b}ls	291.5 295.2	c 84	MgK_a	28
$C_2Cl_3NaO_2$	$[Cl_3\overset{a}{C}\overset{b}{C}OO]Na$	s	^{a}ls ^{b}ls	289.7 (2) 288.5 (2)	b 285.0	Mg, AlK_a	48
C_2Cl_6	Cl_3CCCl_3	s	ls	291.0	c 84	MgK_a	28

TABLE 3 (continued)

Compound		Phase	Orbital	E_B(eV)	Calibrant	Exciting Radiation	Reference
C_2Cr_3	Cr_3C_2	s	1s	−2.0	b 0.0	Mg, AlK$_\alpha$	72
$C_2F_3NaO_2$	$[F_3CCOO]Na$	s	^{a}1s ^{b}1s	292.3 (2) 289.1 (2)	b 285.0	Mg, AlK$_\alpha$	48
C_2F_4	$-(CF_2-CF_2)_n$	s	1s	290.3 (15)	c 83.3	AlK$_\alpha$	95
C_2F_4	$-(CF_2-CF_2)_n$	s	1s	292.2 (3)	b 285.0	MgK$_\alpha$	130
$C_2HCl_2F_3$	$Cl_2H\overset{ab}{C}CF_3$	s	^{a}1s ^{b}1s	290.0 294.8	c 84	MgK$_\alpha$	28
C_2HCl_5	$Cl_3\overset{ab}{C}CHCl_2$	s	^{a}1s ^{b}1s	290.6 289.3	c 84	MgK$_\alpha$	28
C_2HF_3	$-(CF_2-CHF)_n$	s	1s	289.6 (15) 287.4 (15)	c 83.3	AlK$_\alpha$	95
C_2HF_3	$-(\overset{a}{C}F_2-\overset{b}{C}FH)_n$	s	^{a}1s ^{b}1s	291.6 (3) 289.3 (3)	b 285.0	MgK$_\alpha$	130
C_2H_2	C_2H_2	g	1s	291.2 (2)	CHF_3 Cls 299.1	MgK$_\alpha$	6
$C_2H_2Cl_4$	$Cl_2HCCHCl_2$	s	1s	288.8	c 84	MgK$_\alpha$	28
$C_2H_2F_2$	$-(CFH-CFH)_n$	s	1s	288.4 (3)	b 285.0	MgK$_\alpha$	130
$C_2H_2F_2$	$-(CF_2-CH_2)_n$	s	1s	289.2 (15) 283.7 (15)	c 83.3	AlK$_\alpha$	95
$C_2H_2F_2$	$-(\overset{a}{C}F_2-\overset{b}{C}H_2)_n$	s	^{a}1s ^{b}1s	290.8 (3) 286.3 (3)	b 285.0	MgK$_\alpha$	130
$C_2H_2O_4$	HOOCCOOH	s	1s	290.1 (2)	b 285.0	Mg, AlK$_\alpha$	48
$C_2H_3Cl_3$	$Cl_3\overset{ab}{C}CH_3$	s	^{a}1s ^{b}1s	289.9 285.9	c 84	MgK$_\alpha$	28

TABLE 3 (continued)

Compound		Phase	Orbital	E_B(eV)	Calibrant	Exciting Radiation	Reference
C_2H_3F	$\lbrack\overset{a}{C}FH-\overset{b}{C}H_2\rbrack_n$	s	^{a}1s ^{b}1s	288.0 (3) 285.9 (3)	b 285.0	MgK_α	130
C_2H_3F	$(CHF-CH_2)_n$	s	1s	285.5 (15) 283.4 (15)	c 83.3	AlK_α	95
$C_2H_3F_6OSb$	$[CH_3CO][SbF_6]$	s	(+)1s	291.8			141
$C_2H_3N_3$	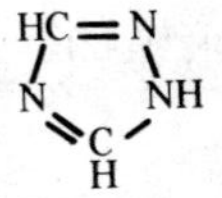	s	1s	286.5 (2)	b 285.0	Mg, AlK_α	48
$C_2H_3NaO_2$	$[\overset{a}{C}H_3\overset{b}{C}OO]Na$	s	^{a}1s ^{b}1s	285.3 (2) 289.0 (2)	b 285.0	Mg, AlK_α	48
C_2H_4	C_2H_4	g	1s	290.7 (2)	CHF_3 (g) C1s 299.1	MgK_α	6
C_2H_4	$(CH_2-CH_2)_n$	s	1s	283.1 (15)	c 83.3	AlK_α	95
C_2H_4	$\lbrack CH_2-CH_2\rbrack_n$ (1 CH_3/1000 C atoms)	s	1s	285.0 (3)	b 285.0	MgK_α	130
C_2H_4	$\lbrack CH_2-CH_2\rbrack_n$ (31 CH_3/1000 C atoms)	s	1s	285.0 (3)	b 285.0	MgK_α	130
$C_2H_4Cl_2$	Cl_2HCCH_3	s	^{a}1s ^{b}1s	288.1 285.4	c 84	MgK_α	28
$C_2H_4NNaO_2$	$[NH_2CH_2COO]Na$	s	1s	288.1 (2)	b 285.0	Mg, AlK_α	48
C_2H_4O	$\overset{a}{C}H_3\overset{b}{C}HO$	g	^{a}1s ^{b}1s	291.3 293.9	CH_4 C1s 290.7	MgK_α	151
C_2H_4O	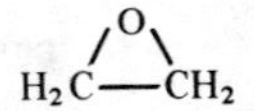	g	1s	1.6 (2)	C1s CH_4 (290.7) 0.0	MgK_α	149
C_2H_4O	C_2H_4O	g	1s	2.01 (5)	CH_4 C1s 0.0	MgK_α	61

TABLE 3 (continued)

Compound		Phase	Orbital	E_B(eV)	Calibrant	Exciting Radiation	Reference
$C_2H_4O_2$	$\overset{a}{C}H_3\overset{b}{C}OOH$	s	^{a}1s ^{b}1s	285.0 (2) 289.5 (2)	b 285.0	Mg, AlK_a	48
$C_2H_4O_2$	$\overset{a}{C}H_3\overset{b}{C}OOH$	g	^{a}1s ^{b}1s	291.4 295.4	CH_4 Cls 290.7	MgK_a	151
C_2H_5Cl	$\overset{a}{C}H_3\overset{b}{C}H_2Cl$	s	^{a}1s ^{b}1s	285.2 (2) 286.3 (2)	b 285.0	Mg, AlK_a	48
C_2H_6	CH_3CH_3	g	1s	290.6 (2)	CHF_3 (g) Cls 299.1	MgK_a	6
C_2H_6	CH_3CH_3	g	1s	290.58	Ar $2p_{3/2}$ 248.457		85
C_2H_6O	$\overset{a}{C}H_3\overset{b}{C}H_2OH$	g	^{a}1s ^{b}1s	290.9 292.3	CH_4 Cls 290.7	MgK_a	151
C_2H_6O	$\overset{a}{C}H_3\overset{b}{C}H_2OH$	s	^{a}1s ^{b}1s	285.1 (2) 286.5 (2)	b 285.0	Mg, AlK_a	48
C_2H_6O	$(CH_3)_2O$	g	1s	292.14	Ar $2p_{3/2}$ 248.457		85
C_2H_7N	$\overset{a}{C}H_3\overset{b}{C}H_2NH_2$	s	^{a}1s ^{b}1s	285.0 (2) 285.7 (2)	b 285.0	Mg, AlK_a	48
$C_2H_8Br_2CuN_2 \cdot H_2O$	$CuBr_2 \cdot H_2NCH_2CH_2NH_2 \cdot H_2O$	s	1s	287.0	a 285.5	AlK_a	46
$C_2H_8Cl_2CuN_2 \cdot H_2O$	$CuCl_2 \cdot H_2NCH_2CH_2NH_2 \cdot H_2O$	s	1s	286.8	a 285.5	AlK_a	46
$C_2H_8CuN_2O_3S \cdot H_2O$	$CuSO_3 \cdot H_2NCH_2CH_2NH_2 \cdot H_2O$	s	1s	286.0	a 285.5	AlK_a	46
$C_2Na_2O_4$	Na[OOCCOO]Na	s	1s	289.2 (2)	b 285.0	Mg, AlK_a	48
C_3F_6	$[CF(CF_3)-CF_2]_n$	s	1s(CF_3) (CF_2) (CF)	293.7 (3) 291.8 (3) 289.8 (3)	b 285.0	MgK_a	130
$C_3H_3F_3O$	$\overset{a}{C}H_3\overset{b}{C}(O)\overset{c}{C}F_3$	s	^{a}1s ^{b}1s ^{c}1s	285.4 (2) 288.7 (2) 292.8 (2)	b 285.0	Mg, AlK_a	48

TABLE 3 (continued)

Compound		Phase	Orbital	E_B(eV)	Calibrant	Exciting Radiation	Reference
C_3H_3NO	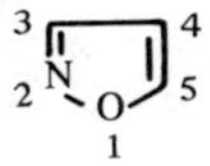	s	(3) 1s (4) 1s (5) 1s	286.9 (3) 285.9 (3) 287.4 (3)	c 84	MgK_α	25
C_3H_3NS	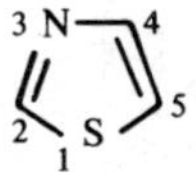	s	(2) 1s (4) 1s (5) 1s	286.8 (3) 287.2 (3) 286.1 (3)	c 84	MgK_α	25
$C_3H_4N_2$	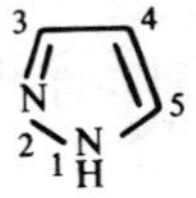	s	(3) 1s (4) 1s (5) 1s	286.3 (3) 285.5 (3) 287.1 (3)	c84	MgK_α	25
$C_3H_4N_2$	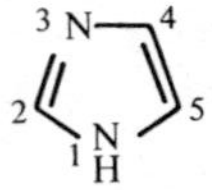	s	(2) 1s (4) 1s (5) 1s	287.2 (3) 285.7 (3) 286.5 (3)	c 84	MgK_α	25
$C_3H_5ClO_2$	$Cl\overset{a}{C}(O)O\overset{b}{C}H_2\overset{c}{C}H_3$	s	^{a}1s ^{b}1s ^{c}1s	291.0 (2) 287.3 (2) 285.6 (2)	b 285.0	Mg, AlK_α	48
C_3H_6		g	1s	−0.23 (5)	CH_4 Cls 0.0	MgK_α	61
C_3H_6	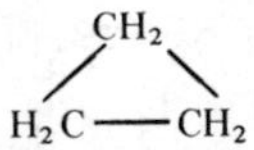	g	1s	−0.3 (2)	Cls CH_4 (290.7) 0.0	MgK_α	149
C_3H_6O	$(\overset{a}{C}H_3)_2\overset{b}{C}O$	g	^{a}1s ^{b}1s	291.2 293.8	CH_4 Cls 290.7	MgK_α	151
C_3H_6O	$(\overset{a}{C}H_3)_2\overset{b}{C}O$	s	^{a}1s ^{b}1s	285.6 (2) 288.1 (2)	b 285.0	Mg, AlK_α	48
$C_3H_6O_3$	$(\overset{a}{C}H_3O)_2\overset{b}{C}O$	s	^{a}1s ^{b}1s	287.7 (2) 291.4 (2)	b 285.0	Mg, AlK_α	48

TABLE 3 (continued)

Compound		Phase	Orbital	E_B(eV)	Calibrant	Exciting Radiation	Reference
C_3O_2	OCCCO (aba)	g	^{a}1s ^{b}1s	294.9 (1) 291.5 (1)	CO_2 C1s	MgK_α	19
$C_4Cl_4N_2$	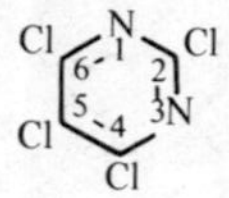	s	(2) 1s (4) 1s (5) 1s	289.4 289.2 288.0	c 84 eV	MgK_α	96
$C_4Cl_4N_2$	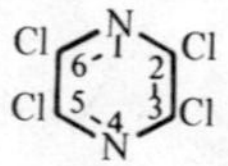	s	(2) 1s	288.6	c 84 eV	MgK_α	96
$C_4Cl_4N_2$	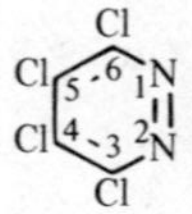	s	(3) 1s (4) 1s	288.2 288.2	c 84 eV	MgK_α	96
$C_4CuK_2O_8$	$K_2Cu(C_2O_4)_2$	s	1s	286.2, 289.9	a 285.5	AlK_α	46
$C_4F_4N_2$	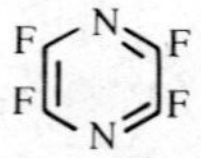	s	1s	290.6 (3)	c 84	MgK_α	96
$C_4F_4N_2$	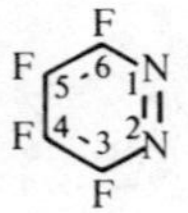	s	(3) 1s (4) 1s	289.9 289.7	c 84 eV	MgK_α	96
$C_4F_4N_2$	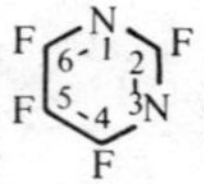	s	(2) 1s (4) 1s (3) 1s	290.4 290.2 289.1	c 84 eV	MgK_α	96
$C_4H_4N_2$	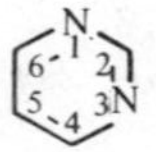	s	(2) 1s (4) 1s (5) 1s	287.4 286.7 285.6	c 84 eV	MgK_α	96

TABLE 3 (continued)

	Compound	Phase	Orbital	E_B(eV)	Calibrant	Exciting Radiation	Reference
$C_4H_4N_2$		s	(3) ls (4) ls	286.7 286.1	c 84 eV	MgK_α	96
$C_4H_4N_2$	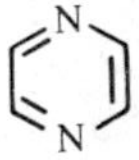	s	(2) ls	286.9	c 84 eV	MgK_α	96
C_4H_4O	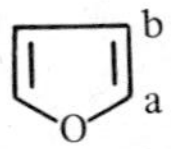	g	a_{ls} b_{ls}	291.5 (1) 290.3 (1)	CO_2 CO Cls 297.5, 295.9	MgK_α	69
C_4H_4O	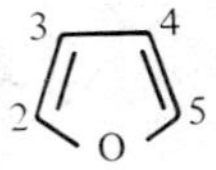	s	(2,5) ls (3,4) ls	286.7 (3) 285.6 (3)	c 84	MgK_α	25
C_4H_4S		s	ls	285.0 (3)	c 84	MgK_α	25
C_4H_4S		g	a_{ls} b_{ls}	290.5 (2) 290.2 (2)	CO_2, CO Cls 297.5,295.9	MgK_α	69
$C_4H_5F_3O_2$	$\overset{a}{C}F_3\overset{b}{C}(O)O\overset{c}{C}H_2\overset{d}{C}H_3$	s	a_{ls} b_{ls} c_{ls} d_{ls}	293.1 (2) 290.6 (2) 287.1 (2) 285.6 (2)	b 285.0	Mg, AlK_α	48
$C_4H_5KO_6$	$K[OO\overset{ab}{C}CH(OH)\overset{b}{C}H(OH)\overset{c}{C}OOH]$	s	a_{ls} b_{ls} c_{ls}	288.5 (2) 286.7 (2) 288.5 (2)	b 285.0	Mg, AlK_α	48
C_4H_5N	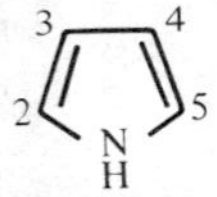	s	(2,5) ls (3,4) ls	285.7 (3) 284.8 (3)	c 84	MgK_α	25

TABLE 3 (continued)

Compound		Phase	Orbital	E_B(eV)	Calibrant	Exciting Radiation	Reference
C_4H_5N	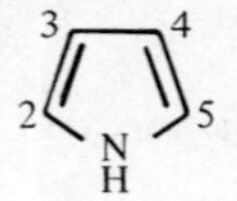	g	(2) ls (3) ls	290.8 (1) 289.8 (1)	CO_2 Cls 297.5	MgK_α	69
$C_4H_5N_3O$	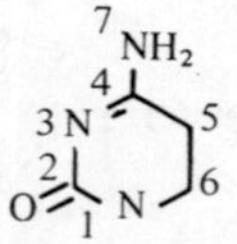	s	(5) ls (6) ls (4) ls (2) ls	285.4 (3) 286.5 (3) 287.9 (3) 289.4 (3)		AlK_α	18
$C_4H_6CuO_4 \cdot H_2O$	$Cu[CH_3C(O)O]_2 \cdot H_2O$	s	ls	287.0	a 285.5	AlK_α	46
$C_4H_6O_5$	$O(\overset{a}{C}H_2\overset{b}{C}OOH)_2$	s	^{a}ls ^{b}ls	286.9 (2) 289.7 (2)	b 285.0	Mg, AlK_α	48
$C_4H_7F_6OSb$	$[(CH_3)_2CHCO][SbF_6]$	s	(+)ls	290.0			141
C_4H_8O	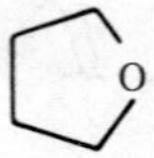	s	ls	960.9 (E_{kin})		MgK_α	132
$C_4H_8O_2$	$\overset{a}{C}H_3\overset{b}{C}(O)O\overset{c}{C}H_2\overset{d}{C}H_3$	s	^{a}ls ^{b}ls ^{c}ls ^{d}ls	285.6 (2) 289.4 (2) 287.1 (2) 285.6 (2)	b 285.0	Mg, AlK_α	48
C_4H_8S	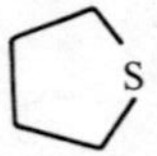	s	ls	960.6 (E_{kin})		MgK_α	132
C_4H_9Cl	$(CH_3)_3CCl$	s	ls	284.1 (1)	f 284	AlK_α	123
$C_4H_9F_6Sb$	$[(\overset{a}{C}H_3)_3\overset{b}{C}][SbF_6]$	s	^{a}ls ^{b}ls	288.6 285.0	f 284	AlK_α	111
C_4H_9N	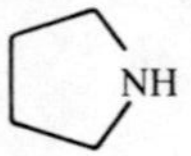	s	ls	962.1 (E_{kin})		MgK_α	132

TABLE 3 (continued)

Compound		Phase	Orbital	E_B(eV)	Calibrant	Exciting Radiation	Reference
C_4H_{10}	$(CH_3)_3CH$	s	1s	283.9	f 284	AlK_α	16
$C_4H_{10}O$	$(\overset{a}{C}H_3\overset{b}{C}H_2)_2O$	s	^{a}1s ^{b}1s	285.4 (2) 286.8 (2)	b 285.0	Mg, AlK_α	48
$C_4H_{10}O_3$	$H\overset{a}{C}(O\overset{b}{C}H_3)_3$	s	^{a}1s ^{b}1s	289.9 (2) 287.2 (2)	b 285.0	Mg, AlK_α	48
$C_4H_{16}Br_2CuN_4\cdot H_2O$	$CuBr_2\cdot 2(H_2NCH_2CH_2NH_2)\cdot H_2O$	s	1s	286.7	a 285.5	AlK_α	46
$C_4H_{16}Cl_2CuN_4\cdot H_2O$	$CuCl_2\cdot 2(H_2NCH_2CH_2NH_2)\cdot H_2O$	s	1s	286.4	a 285.5	AlK_α	46
$C_4H_{16}CuN_4O_4S\cdot H_2O$	$CuSO_4\cdot 2(H_2NCH_2CH_2NH_2)\cdot H_2O$	s	1s	286.8	a 285.5	AlK_α	46
$C_4N_4K_2Pt$	$K_2Pt(CN)_4$	s	1s	285.5 (1)	K_2PtCl_4 $K2p_{3/2}$ 293.4	AlK_α	87
C_4NiO_4	$Ni(CO)_4$	s	1s	3.4	Hexane C1s 0.0	Al, MgK_α	22
C_4NiO_4	$Ni(CO)_4$	s	1s	288.8 (3)		MgK_α	23
C_5Cl_5N	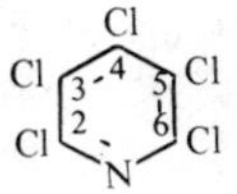	s	(2) 1s (3) 1s (4) 1s	288.3 287.8 288.2	c 84	MgK_α	96
C_5F_5N	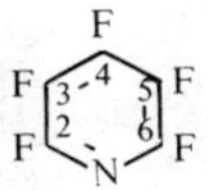	s	(2) 1s (3) 1s (4) 1s	290.1 289.5 290.5	c 84	MgK_α	96
$C_5FeN_6Na_2O\cdot 2H_2O$	$Na_2[Fe(CN)_5NO]\cdot 2H_2O$	s	1s	283.7 (2)	c 84.0 (3)	AlK_α	89
C_5FeO_5	$Fe(CO)_5$	s	1s	289.0 (3)		MgK_α	23
C_5FeO_5	$Fe(CO)_5$	s	1s	3.2	Hexane C1s 0.0	Al, MgK_α	22
$C_5H_3CrNO_5$	$Cr(CO)_5NH_3$	s	1s	287.3	Hexane C1s 285.0		40
C_5H_5	C_5H_5	s	1s	284.9		MgK_α	23

TABLE 3 (continued)

Compound		Phase	Orbital	E_B(eV)	Calibrant	Exciting Radiation	Reference
C_5H_5N		s	(2) ls	286.3	c 84	MgK_α	96
			(3) ls	285.5			
			(4) ls	285.9			
$C_5H_5N_5$	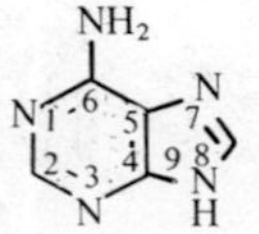	s	(5) ls	284.7 (3)		AlK_α	17
			(2) ls	285.7 (3)			
			(8) ls	286.2 (3)			
			(4) ls	286.6 (3)			
			(6) ls	287.8 (3)			
$C_5H_6N_2O_2$	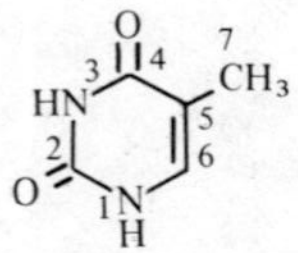	s	(7) ls	285.1 (3)		AlK_α	18
			(5) ls	285.8 (3)			
			(6) ls	286.6 (3)			
			(4) ls	288.5 (3)			
			(2) ls	289.9 (3)			
C_5H_{10}		s	ls	963.5 (E_{kin})		MgK_α	132
$C_5H_{10}O_2$	$\overset{a}{C}H_3\overset{b}{C}H_2\overset{c}{C}(O)OCH_2CH_3$	g	^{a}ls	290.8	CH_4 Cls 290.7	MgK_α	151
			^{b}ls	292.4			
			^{c}ls	294.5			
C_5H_{12}	$C(CH_3)_4$	g	ls	290.32	Ar $2p_{3/2}$ 248.457		85
C_5H_{12}	$C(CH_3)_4$	g	ls	290.4 (2)	CHF_3 (g) Cls 299.1	MgK_α	6
C_6Cl_6	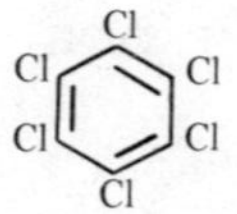	s	ls	287.6	c 84	MgK_α	96
$C_6CrK_3N_6$	$K_3Cr(CN)_6$	s	ls	283.4	Au		33
C_6CrO_6	$Cr(CO)_6$	s	ls	288.1	Hexane Cls 285.0		40
C_6CrO_6	$Cr(CO)_6$	s	ls	289.1	c 84	MgK_α	26

TABLE 3 (continued)

Compound		Phase	Orbital	E_B(eV)	Calibrant	Exciting Radiation	Reference
C_6CrO_6	$Cr(CO)_6$	s	ls	289.1 (3)		MgK_α	23
C_6CrO_6	$Cr(CO)_6$	s	Cls	3.1	Hexane Cls 0.0	Al, MgK_α	22
C_6F_6		s	ls	288.9 (2)	b 285.0	Mg, AlK_α	48
C_6F_6		g	ls	3.57 (9)	C_6H_6 Cls 0.0 (290.4)	MgK_α	151
C_6F_6		s	ls	289.5	c 84	MgK_α	96
C_6F_6		s	ls	289.5 (3)	c 84	MgK_α	27
$C_6FeK_3N_6$	$K_3Fe(CN)_6$	s	ls	286.3		MgK_α	34
$C_6FeK_4N_6$	$K_4Fe(CN)_6$	s	ls	286.4		MgK_α	34
$C_6Fe_2KN_6$	$KFe^{2+}Fe^{3+}(CN)_6$	s	ls	286.1		MgK_α	34
C_6HF_5	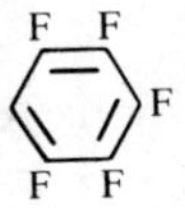	g	(F) ls (H) ls	3.38 (14) 1.32 (17)	C_6H_6 Cls 0.0	MgK_α	142
$C_6H_2F_4$	1,2,3,4–$C_6H_2F_4$	g	$C_H$ls $C_F$ls	0.96 (10) 3.20 (10)	C_6H_6 Cls 0.0	MgK_α	142
$C_6H_2F_4$	1,2,4,5–$C_6H_2F_4$	g	$C_H$ls $C_F$ls	1.12 (10) 3.20 (10)	C_6H_6 Cls 0.0	MgK_α	142
$C_6H_2F_4$	1,2,3,5–$C_6H_2F_4$	g	$C_H$ls $C_F$ls	0.86 (12) 3.05 (12)	C_6H_6 Cls 0.0	MgK_α	142

TABLE 3 (continued)

Compound		Phase	Orbital	E_B(eV)	Calibrant	Exciting Radiation	Reference
$C_6H_3F_3$	1,3,5–$C_6H_3F_3$	g	$C_H$ls $C_F$ls	0.56 (13) 3.02 (9)	C_6H_6 Cls 0.0	MgK_a	142
$C_6H_4F_2$	o-$C_6H_4F_2$	g	$C_H$ls $C_F$ls	0.72 (4) 2.87 (6)	C_6H_6 Cls 0.0	MgK_a	142
$C_6H_4F_2$	m-$C_6H_4F_2$	g	$C_H$ls $C_F$ls	0.70 (5) 2.92 (6)	C_6H_6 Cls 0.0 (290.4)	MgK_a	142
$C_6H_4F_2$	p-$C_6H_4F_2$	g	$C_H$ls $C_F$ls	0.76 (4) 2.74 (6)	C_6H_6 Cls 0.0	MgK_a	142
C_6H_5Cl	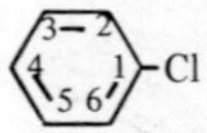	s	(1) ls (2) ls (3) ls (4) ls	287.1 (3) 286.0 (3) 285.5 (3) 285.3 (3)	c 84	MgK_a	118
C_6H_5F	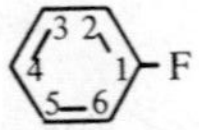	s	(1) ls (2) ls (3) ls (4) ls	287.8 (3) 285.4 (3) 285.9 (3) 285.2 (3)	c 84	MgK_a	118
C_6H_5F	C_6H_5F	g	$C_H$ls $C_F$ls	0.39 (3) 2.43 (4)	C_6H_6 Cls 0.0	MgK_a	142
C_6H_6	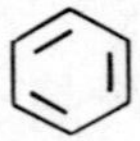	s	(1) ls (2) ls (3) ls (4) ls	284.9 (3) 284.9 (3) 284.9 (3) 284.9 (3)	c 84	MgK_a	118
C_6H_6		s	ls	284.9	c 84	MgK_a	96
C_6H_6		g	ls	290.2 (1)	CO_2 Cls 297.5	MgK_a	69
C_6H_6		s	ls	284.9 (3)	c	MgK_a	27

TABLE 3 (continued)

	Compound	Phase	Orbital	E_B(eV)	Calibrant	Exciting Radiation	Reference
C_6H_6		g	ls	290.4 (2)	CHF_3 (g) Cls 299.1	MgK_α	6
C_6H_6		s	ls	285.0 (2)	b 285.0	Mg, AlK_α	48
$C_6H_6Cl_4Pd_2$	$(\overset{a}{C}H_3\overset{b}{C}H{=}\overset{b}{C}H_2)ClPdCl_2PdCl(\overset{a}{C}H_3\overset{b}{C}H{=}\overset{b}{C}H_2)$	s	^{a}ls ^{b}ls	285.0 284.2	c 84	MgK_α	20
$C_6H_6Cl_4Pt_2$	$(\overset{a}{C}H_3\overset{b}{C}H{=}\overset{b}{C}H_2)ClPtCl_2PtCl(\overset{a}{C}H_3\overset{b}{C}H{=}\overset{b}{C}H_2)$	s	^{a}ls ^{b}ls	285.0 284.2	c 84	MgK_α	20
$C_6H_6O_3$	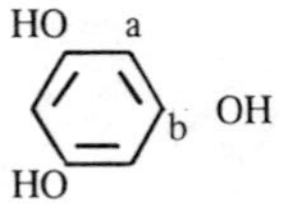	s	^{a}ls ^{b}ls	285.0 (2) 286.8 (2)	b 285.0	Mg, AlK_α	48
C_6H_{12}	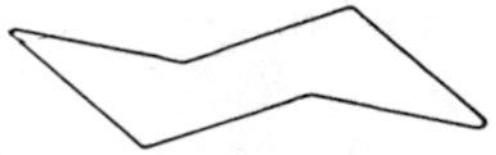	g	ls	290.3 (2)	CHF_3 (g) Cls 299.1	MgK_α	6
C_6H_{12}	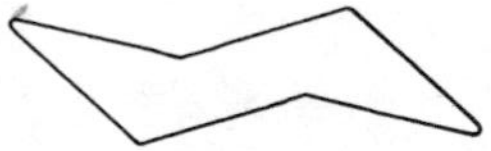	s	ls	285.4 (2)	b 285.0	Mg, AlK_α	48
$C_6H_{12}N_4$	$(CH_2)_6N_4$	s	ls	287.1 (2)	b 285.0	Mg, AlK_α	48
$C_6H_{12}O_3$	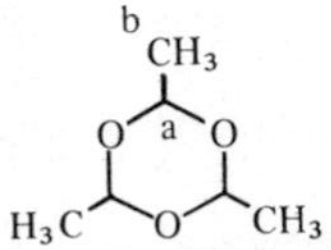	s	^{a}ls ^{b}ls	287.8 (2) 285.0 (2)	b 285.0	Mg, AlK_α	48
$C_6H_{12}O_6$	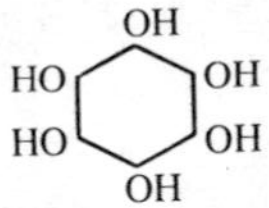	s	ls	286.9 (2)	b 285.0	Mg, AlK_α	48

TABLE 3 (continued)

Compound		Phase	Orbital	E_B(eV)	Calibrant	Exciting Radiation	Reference
$C_6H_{14}O$	$((\overset{a}{C}H_3)_2\overset{b}{C}H)_2O$	s	^{a}ls ^{b}ls	285.0 (2) 286.4 (2)	b 285.0	Mg, AlK_α	48
$C_6H_{18}I_2P_2Pt$	*trans*-$((CH_3)_3P)_2PtI_2$	s	ls	285.1	c 84	MgK_α	20
$C_6H_{18}I_2P_2Pt$	*cis*-$((CH_3)_3P)_2PtI_2$	s	ls	285.1	c 84	MgK_α	20
$C_6H_{24}Br_2CuN_6\cdot 5H_2O$	$CuBr_2\cdot 3(H_2NCH_2CH_2NH_2)\cdot 5H_2O$	s	ls	286.7	a 285.5	AlK_α	46
C_6N_4	$(NC)_2\overset{1}{C}=\overset{2}{C}(CN)_2$	g	(1) ls (2) ls	4.0 (2) 3.1 (2)	Cls CH_4 (290.7) 0.0	MgK_α	149
C_6N_4O	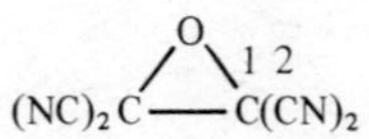	g g	(1) ls (2) ls	6.0 (2) 3.4 (2)	Cls CH_4 (290.7) 0.0	MgK_α	149
$C_6N_6O_6$	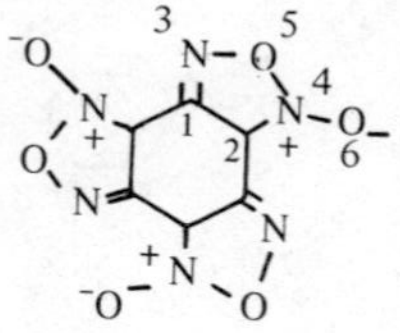	s	(2) ls (1) ls	287.5 285.6	f 284.2	MgK_α	115
C_6O_6	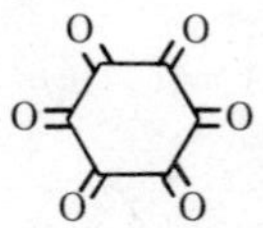	s	ls	288.5 (2)	b 285.0	Mg, AlK_α	48
C_6O_6W	$W(CO)_6$	s	ls	3.1	Hexane Cls 0.0	Al, MgK_α	22
$C_7H_2N_4$	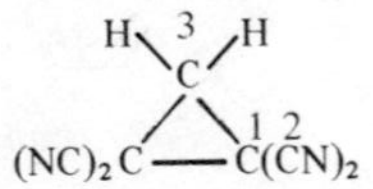	s	(1) ls (2) ls (3) ls	4.1 (2) 3.1 (2) 1.4 (2)	Cls CH_4 (290.7) 0.0	MgK_α	149

TABLE 3 (continued)

Compound		Phase	Orbital	E_B(eV)	Calibrant	Exciting Radiation	Reference
$C_7H_5Cl_3$	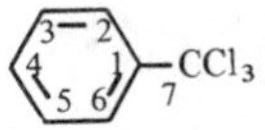	s	(1) ls (2) ls (3) ls (4) ls (7) ls	286.6 (3) 285.8 (3) 285.7 (3) 285.2 (3) 290.0 (3)	c 84	MgK_α	118
$C_7H_5Cl_3$	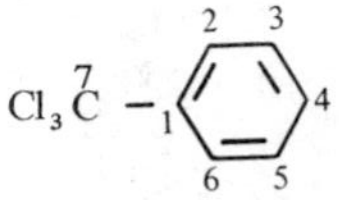	s	(7) ls (1) ls (2,6) ls (3,5) ls (4) ls	290.0 286.6 285.8 285.7 285.2	c 84	MgK_α	28
$C_7H_5CrNO_5$	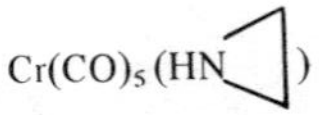	s	ls	287.3	Hexane Cls 285.0		40
$C_7H_5F_3$	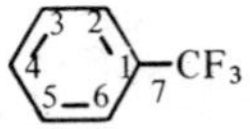	s	(1) ls (2) ls (3) ls (4) ls (7) ls	286.9 (3) 286.5 (3) 286.0 (3) 285.5 (3) 293.8 (3)	c 84	MgK_α	118
$C_7H_5F_6OSb$	$[C_6H_5CO][SbF_6]$	s	(+) ls	289.9			141
$C_7H_6Cl_2$	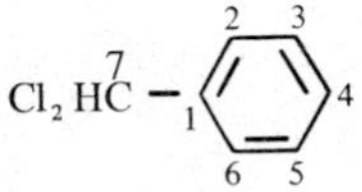	s	(7) ls (1) ls (2,6) ls (3,5) ls (4) ls	288.2 286.2 285.5 285.1 284.7	c 84	MgK_α	28
$C_7H_7F_6Sb$	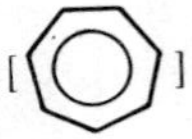 $[SbF_6]$	s	ls	284.7	f 284	AlK_α	16
C_7H_8	$C_6H_5CH_3$	s	(1) ls (2) ls (3) ls (4) ls (Me) ls	286.4 (3) 285.1 (3) 285.2 (3) 284.5 (3) 284.7 (3)	c 84	MgK_α	118

TABLE 3 (continued)

Compound		Phase	Orbital	E_B(eV)	Calibrant	Exciting Radiation	Reference
$C_8H_5MnO_3$	$Mn(\overset{a}{C}O)_3(\pi-\overset{b}{C}_5H_5)$	s	(a) ls (b) ls	288.4 (3) 286.4 (3)		MgK_α	23
$C_8H_7F_6OSb$	[p-$CH_3C_6H_4CO$] [SbF_6]	s	(+) ls	288.8			141
$C_8H_7F_6O_2Sb$	[p-$CH_3OC_6H_4CO$] [SbF_6]	s	(+) ls	289.4			141
$C_8H_9CrO_5P$	$Cr(CO)_5P(CH_3)_3$	s	ls	286.8	Hexane Cls 285.0		40
C_9H_7NO	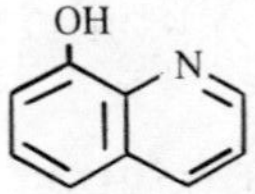	s	ls	285.7	c 84	MgK_α	36
C_9H_8ClNO	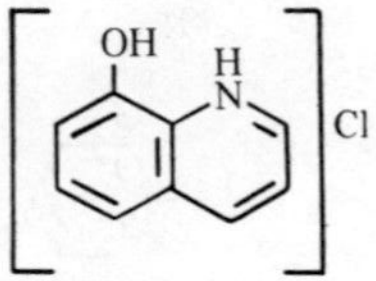	s	ls	285.7	c 84	MgK_α	36
$C_{10}F_8$	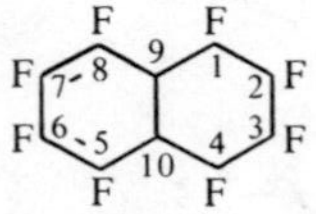	s	(1,4,5,8), ls (2,3,6,7), ls (9,10) ls	289.3 (3) 288.7 (3) 287.4 (3)	c 84	MgK_α	27
$C_{10}H_2Cl_4F_{14}$	$+CF_2-CFCl+_m$ $+CF_2-CH_2+_n$ m:n, 4:1	s	ls (CF_2) (CFCl) (CH_2)	291.7 (3) 290.5 (3) 286.8 (3)	b 285.0	MgK_α	130
$C_{10}H_8$	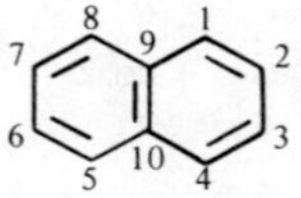	s	(1,4,5,8) ls (2,3,6,7) ls (9,10) ls	284.8 (3) 284.5 (3) 285.3 (3)	c 84	MgK_α	27
$C_{10}H_8Br_2CuN_2$	$CuBr_2\cdot$ 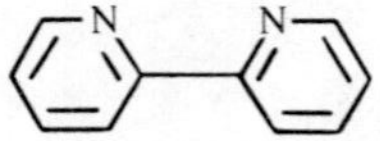	s	ls	286.5	a 285.5	AlK_α	46

TABLE 3 (continued)

Compound		Phase	Orbital	E_B(eV)	Calibrant	Exciting Radiation	Reference
$C_{10}H_8Cl_2CuN_2$	$CuCl_2\cdot$ 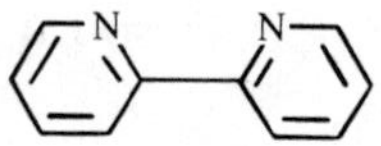	s	1s	286.3	a 285.5	AlK_α	46
$C_{10}H_8CuN_2O_4S\cdot 2H_2O$	$CuSO_4\cdot$ 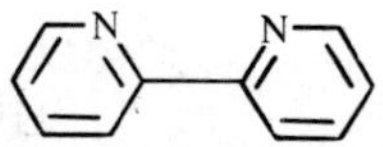 $\cdot 2H_2O$	s	1s	286.0	a 285.5	AlK_α	46
$C_{10}H_{10}Co$	$Co(\pi{-}C_5H_5)_2$	s	1s	285.7 (3)		MgK_α	23
$C_{10}H_{10}Cr$	$Cr(\pi{-}C_5H_5)_2$	s	1s	285.4	c 84	MgK_α	26
$C_{10}H_{10}Cr$	$Cr(\pi{-}C_5H_5)_2$	s	1s	285.4 (3)		MgK_α	23
$C_{10}H_{10}Fe$	$Fe(\pi{-}C_5H_5)_2$	s	1s	285.7 (3)		MgK_α	23
$C_{10}H_{10}Ni$	$Ni(\pi{-}C_5H_5)_2$	s	1s	285.6 (3)		MgK_α	23
$C_{10}H_{11}F_6OSb$	$[2,4,6{-}(CH_3)_3C_6H_2CO][SbF_6]$	s	(+) 1s	288.5			141
$C_{10}H_{14}CuO_4$	$Cu(H_3CC(O)CHC(O)CH_3)_2$	s	1s	285.9 287.8	a 285.5	AlK_α	46
$C_{11}F_{12}$	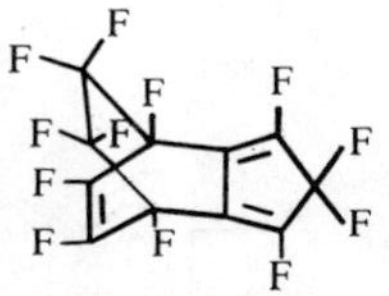	s	$(-CF_2-)$ 1s (−CF) 1s (=CF) 1s (=C) 1s	292.3 290.9 289.9 289.4 288.0	c 84	MgK_α	52
$C_{12}F_8$	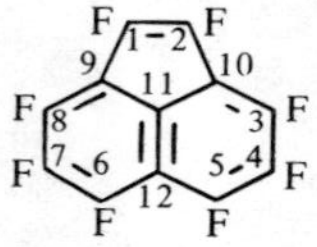	s	(1,2) 1s (3,8) 1s (4,7) 1s (5,6) 1s (9,10) 1s (11,12) 1s	288.3 (3) 289.5 (3) 288.8 (3) 289.0 (3) 286.4 (3) 287.2 (3)	c 84	MgK_α	27

TABLE 3 (continued)

Compound		Phase	Orbital	E_B(eV)	Calibrant	Exciting Radiation	Reference
$C_{12}F_8$	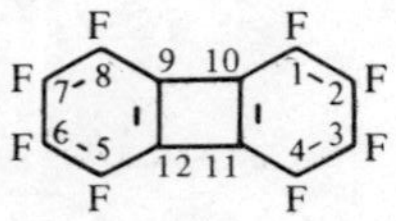	s	(1,4,5,8) ls (2,3,6,7) ls (9,10,11,12) ls	288.7 (3) 289.0 (3) 286.8 (3)	c 84	MgK_α	27
$C_{12}F_{14}$	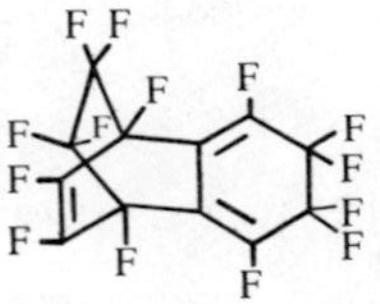	s	($-CF_2-$) ls ($-CF$) ls ($=CF$) ls ($=C$) ls	292.3 290.6 289.4 287.8	c 84	MgK_α	52
$C_{12}H_6F_{18}$	$\left[CF(CF_3)-CF_2\right]_m \left[CF_2-CH_2\right]_n$ m:n, 2:3	s	ls (CF_3) (CF_2) (CF) (CH_2)	293.3 (3) 291.1 (3) 289.4 (3) 286.6 (3)	b 285.0	MgK_α	130
$C_{12}H_8$	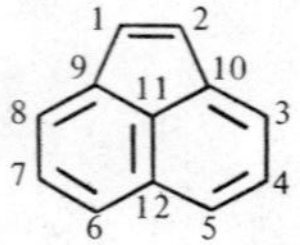	s	(1,2) ls (3,5,6,8,11,12) ls (4,7,9,10) ls	283.9 (3) 284.9 (3) 284.5 (3)	c 84	MgK_α	27
$C_{12}H_8$	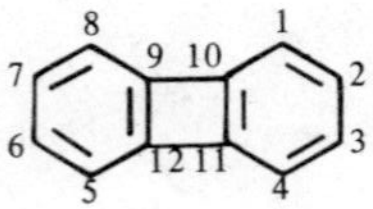	s	(1,4,5,8) ls (2,3,6,7) ls (9,10,11,12) ls	284.8 (3) 285.3 (3) 285.6 (3)	c 84	MgK_α	27
$C_{14}H_{10}CuO_4$	$Cu(C_6H_5COO)_2$	s	ls	285.6, 289.7	a 285.5	AlK_α	46
$C_{15}H_3CrF_6O_2$	$Cr(\overset{a}{C}F_3\overset{b}{C}O\overset{c}{C}HCOCF_3)_3$	s	[a]ls [b]ls [c]ls	293.8 288.9 286.0	c 84	MgK_α	26

TABLE 3 (continued)

Compound		Phase	Orbital	E_B(eV)	Calibrant	Exciting Radiation	Reference
$C_{16}H_{12}OS$	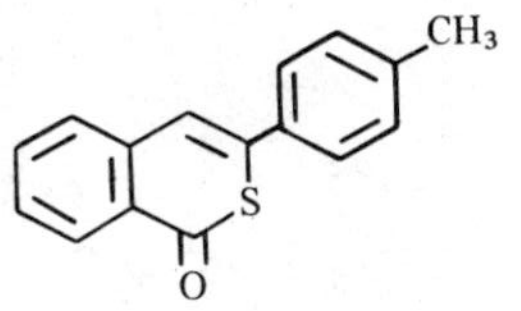	s	1s	282.6		Al	147
$C_{16}H_{12}OS$	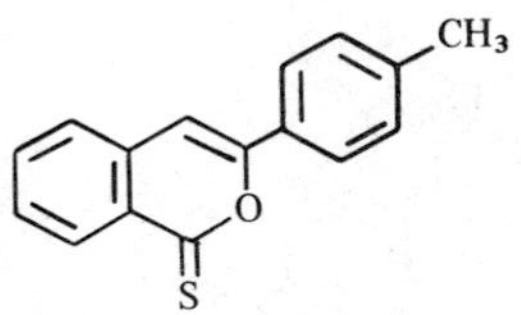	s	1s	282.9		Al	147
$C_{16}H_{12}S_2$	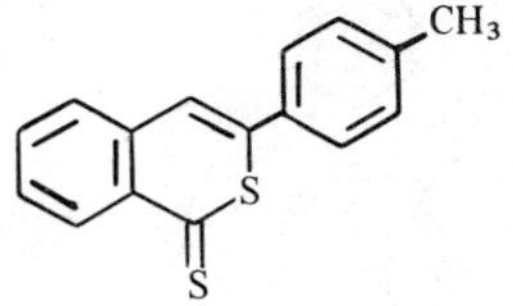	s	1s	282.9		Al	147
$C_{18}H_{12}N_2O_4U$	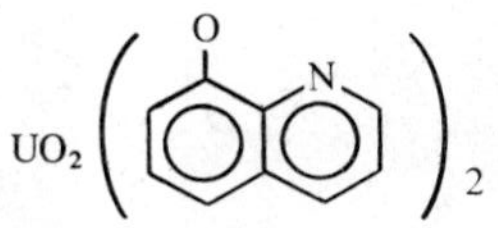	s	1s	285	c 84	MgK_{α}	36
$C_{18}H_{12}N_2O_4U\cdot C_9H_7NO$	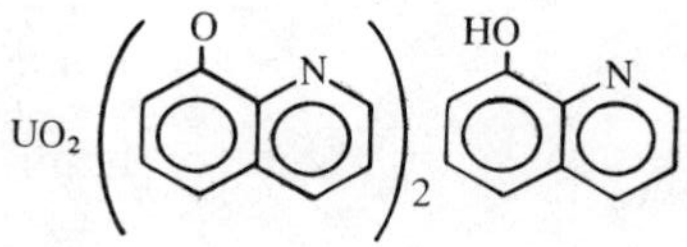	s	1s	285.7	c 84	MgK_{α}	36
$C_{18}H_{15}ClCuP$	$CuCl\cdot(C_6H_5)_3P$	s	1s	285.6	a 285.5	AlK_{α}	46
$C_{18}H_{42}Cl_4P_2Pt_2$	$(n\text{-}C_3H_7)_3PClPtCl_2PtClP(n\text{-}C_3H_7)_3$	s	1s	284.7	c 84	MgK_{α}	20
$C_{18}H_{54}Cl_2P_2Pd$	*cis*-$((C_6H_5CH_2CH_2)_3P)_2PdCl_2$	s	1s	284.7	c 84	MgK_{α}	20

TABLE 3 (continued)

Compound		Phase	Orbital	E_B(eV)	Calibrant	Exciting Radiation	Reference
$C_{18}H_{54}Cl_2P_2Pd$	*trans*-$((C_6H_5CH_2CH_2)_3P)_2PdCl_2$	s	ls	284.7	c 84	MgK_α	20
$C_{19}H_{15}F_6Sb$	$[(C_6H_5)_3C]SbF_6$	s	ls	284.7	f 284	AlK_α	16
$C_{20}H_{14}Cl_3F_{23}$	$\lbrack CF_2-CFCl \rbrack_m$ $\lbrack CF_2-CH_2 \rbrack_n$ m:n, 3:7	s	ls(CF_2) (CFCl) (CH_2)	291.5 (3) 290.6 (3) 286.9 (3)	b 285.0	MgK_α	130
$C_{20}H_{16}Br_2CuN_4\cdot 2H_2O$	$CuBr_2\cdot 2$ 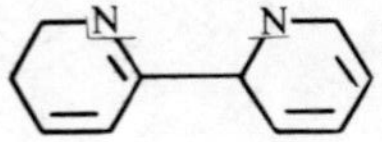 $\cdot 2H_2O$	s	ls	286.2	a 285.5	AlK_α	46
$C_{20}H_{16}Cl_2CuN_4\cdot 3H_2O$	$CuCl_2\cdot 2$ 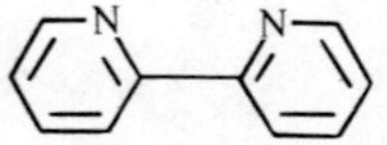 $\cdot 3H_2O$	s	ls	286.0	a 285.5	AlK_α	46
$C_{22}H_{17}NO$	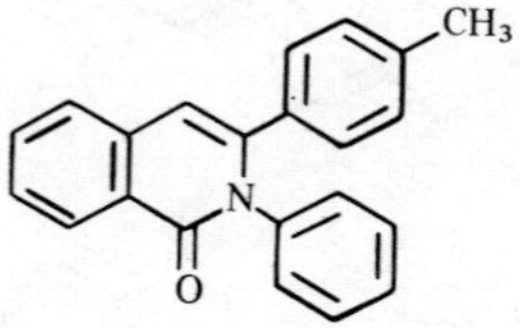	s	ls	283.2		Al	147
$C_{22}H_{17}NS$	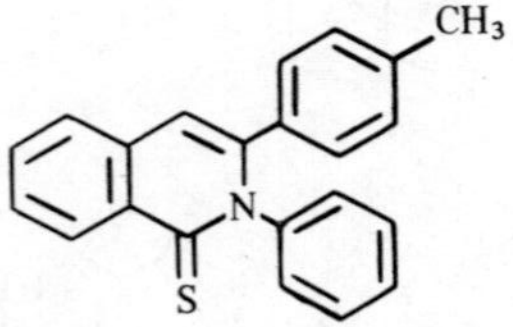	s	ls	282.7		Al	147
$C_{23}H_{14}F_{32}$	$\lbrack CF(CF_3)-CF_2 \rbrack_m$ $\lbrack CF_2-CH_2 \rbrack_n$ m:n, 3:7	s	ls(CF_3) (CF_2) (CF) (CH_2)	293.4 (3) 290.9 (3) 289.3 (3) 284.6 (3)	b 285.0	MgK_α	130

TABLE 3 (continued)

Compound		Phase	Orbital	E_B(eV)	Calibrant	Exciting Radiation	Reference
$C_{24}H_{54}Cl_2P_2Pt$	*cis*-$((n\text{-}C_4H_9)_3P)_2PtCl_2$	s	1s	284.7	c 84	MgK_α	20
$C_{24}H_{54}Cl_2P_2Pt$	*trans*-$((n\text{-}C_4H_9)_3P)_2PtCl_2$	s	1s	284.7	c 84	MgK_α	20
$C_{24}H_{54}Cl_4P_2Pd_2$	$(n\text{-}C_4H_9)_3PClPdCl_2PdClP(n\text{-}C_4H_9)_3$	s	1s	284.7	c 84	MgK_α	20
$C_{25}H_{20}AsNO$	$[(C_6H_5)_4As]NCO$	s	1s	291.2	c 84	MgK_α	145
$C_{25}H_{20}AsNS$	$[(C_6H_5)_4As]NCS$	s	1s	291.3	c 84	MgK_α	145
$C_{25}H_{20}AsNSe$	$[(C_6H_5)_4As]NCSe$	s	1s	291.3	c 84	MgK_α	145
$C_{26}H_{24}Cl_2P_2Pt$	$(C_6H_5)_2PCH_2CH_2P(C_6H_5)_2PtCl_2$	s	1s	284.7	c 84	MgK_α	20
$C_{28}H_{22}NO$	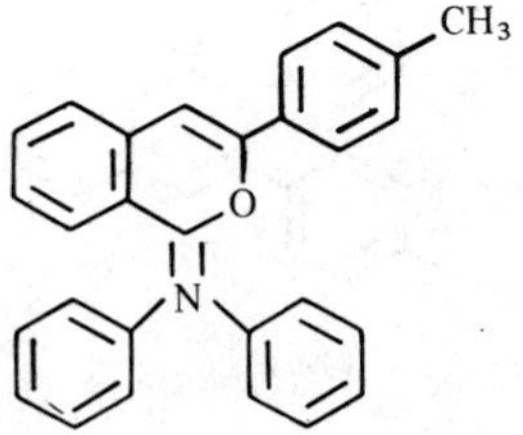	s	1s	282.9		Al	147
$C_{28}H_{22}NS$	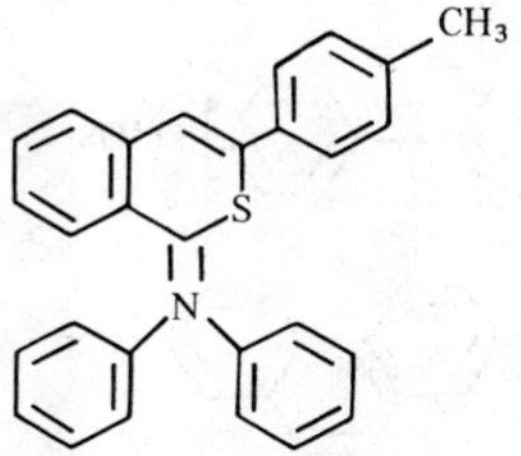	s	1s	282.5		Al	147
$C_{28}H_{30}P_2Pt$	$(C_6H_5)_2PCH_2CH_2P(C_6H_5)_2Pt(CH_3)_2$	s	1s	284.7	c 84	MgK_α	20

TABLE 3 (continued)

Compound		Phase	Orbital	E_B(eV)	Calibrant	Exciting Radiation	Reference
$C_{30}H_{23}ClCuN_2P$	CuCl· 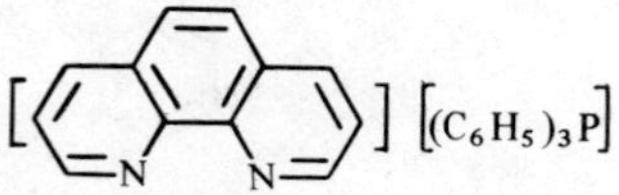	s	ls	285.6	a 285.5	AlK_α	46
$C_{30}H_{24}CuN_6O_4S·7H_2O$	$CuSO_4$·3 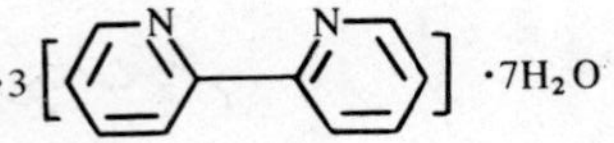	s	ls	285.9	a 285.5	AlK_α	46
$C_{32}H_{28}Cl_2FeN_4O_4$	*trans*-$FeCl_2(p-CNC_6H_4OCH_3)_4$	s	ls	284.2 (2)	c 84.0 (3)	AlK_α	89
$C_{32}H_{28}Cl_6FeN_4O_4Sn_2$	*trans*-$Fe(SnCl_3)_2(p-CNC_6H_4OCH_3)_4$	s	ls	284.2 (2)	c 84.0 (3)	AlK_α	89
$C_{34}H_{27}N_2$	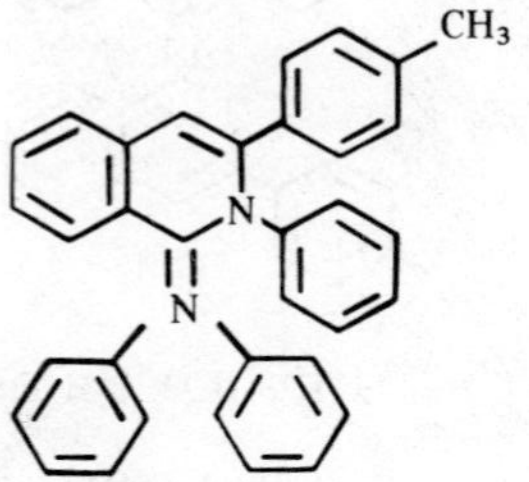	s	ls	283.2		Al	147
$C_{36}H_{24}Cl_2FeN_6O_8$	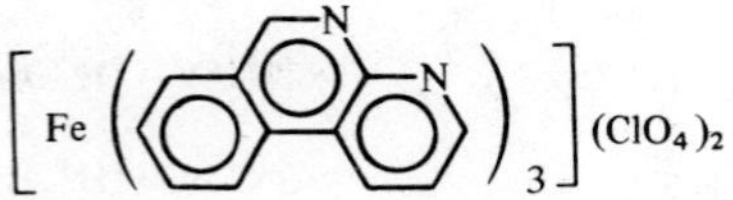	s	ls	284.2 (2)	c 84.0 (3)	AlK_α	89
$C_{36}H_{30}Cl_2P_2Pt$	*cis*-$((C_6H_5)_3P)_2PtCl_2$	s	ls	284.7	c 84	MgK_α	20
$C_{38}H_{30}Cl_4P_2Pt$	$((C_6H_5)_3P)_2PtCl(CCl{=}CCl_2)$	s	ls	284.6 (2)		MgK_α	93
$C_{38}H_{30}Cl_4P_2Pt$	$((C_6H_5)_3P)_2Pt(Cl_2C{=}CCl_2)$	s	ls	284.6 (2)		MgK_α	93
$C_{36}H_{33}ClCuP_3$	CuCl·$[(C_6H_5)_2PH]_3$	s	ls	285.6	a 285.5	AlK_α	46

TABLE 3 (continued)

Compound		Phase	Orbital	E_B(eV)	Calibrant	Exciting Radiation	Reference
$C_{38}H_{32}P_2Pt$	*cis*-$((\overset{a}{C}_6H_5)_3P)_2Pt\overset{b}{C}_2H_2$	s	^{a}1s ^{b}1s	284.7 283.3	c 84	MgK_α	30
$C_{38}H_{34}P_2Pt$	*cis*-$((\overset{a}{C}_6H_5)_3P)_2Pt\overset{b}{C}_2H_4$	s	^{a}1s ^{b}1s	284.7 283.2	c 84	MgK_α	30
$C_{38}H_{36}P_2Pt$	*trans*-$((C_6H_5)_3P)_2Pt(CH_3)_2$	s	1s	284.7	c 84	MgK_α	20
$C_{39}H_{34}P_2Pt$	*cis*-$((\overset{a}{C}_6H_5)_3P)_2Pt(\overset{a}{C}H_3\overset{bb}{CC}H)$	s	^{a}1s ^{b}1s	284.7 283.3	c 84	MgK_α	30
$C_{40}H_{40}Cl_4FeN_5O_4Sn$	$[Fe(SnCl_3)(p\text{-}CNC_6H_4OCH_3)_5]ClO_4$	s	1s	284.1 (2)	c 84.0 (3)	AlK_α	89
$C_{43}H_{36}P_2Pt$	*cis*-$((\overset{a}{C}_6H_5)_3P)_2Pt(\overset{a}{C}_6H_5\overset{bb}{CC}H)$	s	^{a}1s ^{b}1s	284.7 283.3	c 84	MgK_α	30
$C_{54}H_{45}ClCuP_3$	$CuCl\cdot[(C_6H_5)_3P]_3$	s	1s	285.6	a 285.5	AlK_α	46
$CaFeO_6Si_2$	Hedenbergite R6955 54% Fe^{2+} $CaFeSi_2O_6$	s	1s	284.4 (4)	c 84.0 (3)	Al, MgK_α	57
$CaFeO_6Si_2$	Hedenbergite 2B 85% Fe^{2+} $CaFeSi_2O_6$	s	1s	284.6 (4)	Internal O1s 530.8 (7)	Al, MgK_α	57
$Fe_5H_2Na_2O_{24}Si_8$	Crocidolite 93720 55% Fe^{2+}, 40% Fe^{3+} $Na_2Fe_3{}^{(+2)}Fe_2{}^{(+3)}(Si_4O_{11})_2(OH)_2$	s	1s	284.8 (4)	Internal O1s 530.8 (7)	Al, MgK_α	57
Ca							
CaF_2	CaF_2	s	3p	33.4	a 290	AlK_α	30
CaO	CaO	s	K	4,038.0 (5)	e, i	CuK_α	76
CaO	CaO	s	L_I	437.8	MgOMgK($CuK_{\alpha 1}$)	$CuK_{\alpha 1}$	67

Compound		Phase	Orbital	E_B(eV)	Calibrant	Exciting Radiation	Reference
Cd							
$C_{36}H_{30}CdCl_2P_2$	$Cd(P(C_6H_5)_3)_2Cl_2$	s	$3d_{3/2}$	413.0 (2)	d 285.0	Mg, AlK_{α}	116
			$3d_{5/2}$	406.1 (2)			
Cd	Cd	s	$4d_{3/2}$	11.46 (9)	Au E_{Fermi}	AlK_{α}	137
			$4d_{5/2}$	10.47 (9)			
			5s	2.2 (5)			
Cd	Cd	s	L_I	4,018.1	$CdL_{III}(CuK_{\alpha1})$	$CuK_{\alpha1}$	45
			L_{II}	3,727.1			
Cd	Cd	s	L_{III}	3,537.3	CuA6	$CuK_{\alpha1}$	123
$CdCl_2$	$CdCl_2$	s	3d	408 (0.5)		MgK_{α}	122
CdF_2	CdF_2	s	4d	19.15	a 290	AlK_{α}	30
CdO	CdO	s	4d	19.4	a 290	AlK_{α}	30
CdO	CdO	s	$4d_{5/2}$	12.20 (20)	k 283.8	AlK_{α}	109
			$4d_{3/2}$	13.06 (31)			
			4p	70.21 (20)			
			4s	110.94 (20)			
			$3d_{5/2}$	406.30 (23)			
			$3d_{3/2}$	413.08 (20)			
			$3p_{3/2}$	619.45 (20)			
			$3p_{1/2}$	653.81 (20)			
			3s	772.91 (20)			
CdS	CdS	s	4d	18.3	a 290	AlK_{α}	30
CdS	CdS	s	$4d_{5/2}$	11.05 (20)	k 283.8	AlK_{α}	109
			$4d_{3/2}$	11.81 (20)			
			4p	68.76 (20)			
			4s	109.65 (20)			
			$3d_{5/2}$	405.00 (20)			
			$3d_{3/2}$	411.80 (20)			
			$3p_{3/2}$	618.00 (20)			
			$3p_{1/2}$	652.20 (20)			
			3s	771.63 (20)			

TABLE 3 (continued)

	Compound	Phase	Orbital	E_B(eV)	Calibrant	Exciting Radiation	Reference
CdSe	CdSe	s	$4d_{5/2}$	11.13 (20)	k 283.8	AlK_a	109
			$4d_{3/2}$	12.00 (28)			
			4p	68.86 (20)			
			4s	109.78 (20)			
			$3d_{5/2}$	405.13 (20)			
			$3d_{3/2}$	411.93 (20)			
			$3p_{3/2}$	617.96 (20)			
			$3p_{1/2}$	652.10 (20)			
			3s	771.63 (58)			
CdTe	CdTe	s	$4d_{5/2}$	10.76 (43)	k 283.8	AlK_a	109
			$4d_{3/2}$	11.59 (57)			
			4p	68.29 (20)			
			4s	109.40 (20)			
			$3d_{5/2}$	404.74 (20)			
			$3d_{3/2}$	411.57 (20)			
			$3p_{3/2}$	617.75 (25)			
			$3p_{1/2}$	651.90 (20)			
			3s	771.36 (20)			
Ce							
Ce	Ce	s	$3dM_4$	904.8		AlK_a	58
				901.2			
			M_5	886.3			
				882.6			
			$4pN_2$	222.9			
			N_3	207.4			
			$4dN_{4,5}$	111.7			
				110.0			
			$5sO_1$	37.5			
			$5pO_{2,3}$	18.4			
CeO_2	CeO_2	s	L_I	6,548.9	e	MoK_{a1}	56
			L_{II}	6,164.7			
			L_{III}	5,724.0			

TABLE 3 (continued)

Compound		Phase	Orbital	E_B(eV)	Calibrant	Exciting Radiation	Reference
Cl							
$BrCCl_3$	CCl_3Br	s	2s $2p_{3/2}$	273.6 202.4	c 84	MgK_α	28
$BrC_4ClK_2N_4Pt$	$K_2Pt(CN)_4ClBr$	s	2p	200.4	g	MgK_α	129
CCl_3F	CCl_3F	s	2s $2p_{3/2}$	274.2 203.0	c 84	MgK_α	28
CCl_4	CCl_4	s	2s $2p_{3/2}$	273.9 202.7	c 84	MgK_α	28
CCl_4	CCl_4	g	2s	278.0	CHF_3, CH_4, or C_6H_6 from Ref. 6	MgK_α	121
$CHBrCl_2$	$CHBrCl_2$	s	2s $2p_{3/2}$	273.3 202.0	c 84	MgK_α	28
$CHCl_3$	$CHCl_3$	s	2s $2p_{3/2}$	273.5 202.3	c 84	MgK_α	28
$CHCl_3$	$CHCl_3$	g	2s	277.7	CHF_3, CH_4, or C_6H_6 from Ref. 6	MgK_α	121
CH_2Cl_2	CH_2Cl_2	g	2s	277.6	CHF_3, CH_4, or C_6H_6 from Ref. 6	MgK_α	121
CH_2Cl_2	CH_2Cl_2	s	2s $2p_{3/2}$	272.8 201.3	c 84	MgK_α	28
CH_3Cl	CH_3Cl	g	2s	277.2	CHF_3, CH_4, or C_6H_6 from Ref. 6	MgK_α	121
C_2ClF_3	$\text{+}CF_2-CFCl\text{+}_n$	s	$2p_{3/2}$ 2s	201.1 (3) 272.2 (3)	b 285.0	MgK_α	130
$C_2Cl_3F_3$	Cl_3CCF_3	s	2s $2p_{3/2}$	274.0 202.8	c 84	MgK_α	28

TABLE 3 (continued)

Compound		Phase	Orbital	E_B(eV)	Calibrant	Exciting Radiation	Reference
C_2Cl_6	Cl_3CCCl_3	s	2s	273.3	c 84	MgK_α	28
			$2p_{3/2}$	202.3			
$C_2HCl_2F_3$	Cl_2HCCF_3	s	2s	273.6	c 84	MgK_α	28
			$2p_{3/2}$	202.1			
C_2HCl_5	$\overset{a}{Cl_3}CCH\overset{b}{Cl_2}$	s	^a2s	273.2	c 84	MgK_α	28
			$^a2p_{3/2}$	201.9			
			^b2s	273.0			
			$^b2p_{3/2}$	201.6			
$C_2H_2Cl_4$	$Cl_2HCCHCl_2$	s	2s	272.8	c 84	MgK_α	28
			$2p_{3/2}$	201.3			
$C_2H_3Cl_3$	Cl_3CCH_3	s	2s	272.1	c 84	MgK_α	28
			$2p_{3/2}$	201.0			
$C_2H_4Cl_2$	Cl_2HCCH_3	s	2s	271.9	c 84	MgK_α	28
			$2p_{3/2}$	200.9			
$C_2H_4Cl_3K_2Pt$	$K_2PtCl_3(C_2H_4)$	s	2p	200.5	g	MgK_α	129
$C_2H_8Cl_2CuN_2 \cdot H_2O$	$CuCl_2 \cdot H_2NCH_2CH_2NH_2 \cdot H_2O$	s	2p	200.7	a 285.5	AlK_α	46
$C_4Cl_2K_2N_4Pt$	$K_2Pt(CN)_4Cl_2$	s	2p	200.4	g	MgK_α	129
$C_4Cl_4N_2$	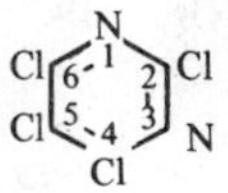	s	(2) 2s	272.9	c 84	MgK_α	96
			(4) 2s	272.9			
			(5) 2s	272.9			
			(2) $2p_{3/2}$	201.6			
			(4) $2p_{3/2}$	201.6			
			(5) $2p_{3/2}$	201.6			
$C_4Cl_4N_2$	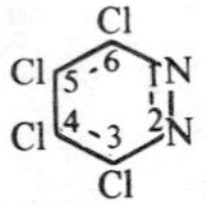	s	(3) 2s	272.7	c 84	MgK_α	96
			(3) $2p_{3/2}$	201.5			
			(4) 2s	272.7			
			(4) $2p_{3/2}$	201.5			

TABLE 3 (continued)

Compound		Phase	Orbital	E_B(eV)	Calibrant	Exciting Radiation	Reference
$C_4Cl_4N_2$	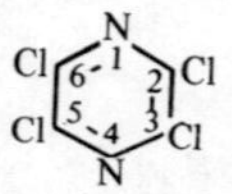	s	2s $2p_{3/2}$	272.7 201.2	c 84	MgK_α	96
$C_4H_{16}Cl_2CuN_4 \cdot H_2O$	$CuCl_2 \cdot 2(H_2NCH_2CH_2NH_2) \cdot H_2O$	s	2p	199.1	a 285.5	AlK_α	46
C_5Cl_5N	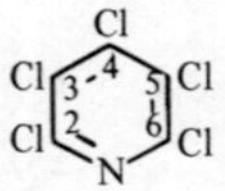	s	(2) 2s (3) 2s (4) 2s (2) $2p_{3/2}$ (3) $2p_{3/2}$ (4) $2p_{3/2}$	272.7 272.7 272.7 201.5 201.5 201.5	c 84	MgK_α	96
C_6Cl_6	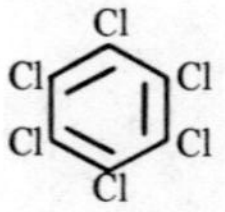	s	2s $2p_{3/2}$	272.5 201.4	c 84	MgK_α	96
C_6H_5Cl	C_6H_5Cl (chlorobenzene)		2s $2p_{3/2}$ $2p_{1/2}$	271.8 (3) 201.0 (3) 202.8 (3)	c 84	MgK_α	118
$C_6H_6Cl_4Pd_2$	$(CH_3CH{=}CH_2)\overset{a}{Cl}Pd\overset{b}{Cl_2}Pd\overset{a}{Cl}(CH_3CH{=}CH_2)$	s	$^a2p_{3/2}$ $^b2p_{3/2}$	199.3 198.3	c 84	MgK_α	20
$C_6H_6Cl_4Pt_2$	$(CH_3CH{=}CH_2)\overset{a}{Cl}Pt\overset{b}{Cl_2}Pt\overset{a}{Cl}(CH_3CH{=}CH_2)$	s	$^a2p_{3/2}$ $^b2p_{3/2}$	199.4 198.4	c 84	MgK_α	20
$C_7H_5Cl_3$	$C_6H_5CCl_3$		2s $2p_{3/2}$ $2p_{1/2}$	271.7 (3) 201.0 (3) 202.8 (3)	c 84	MgK_α	118
$C_7H_5Cl_3$	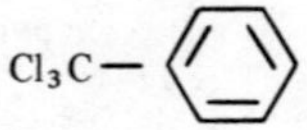	s	2s $2p_{3/2}$	271.7 201.0	c 84	MgK_α	28

TABLE 3 (continued)

Compound		Phase	Orbital	E_B(eV)	Calibrant	Exciting Radiation	Reference
$C_7H_6Cl_2$	Cl_2HC— 	s	2s $2p_{3/2}$	271.3 200.1	c 84	MgK_α	28
$C_8H_{12}Cl_2Pt$	$C_8H_{12}PtCl_2$	s	2p	198.7 (1)	d 285.0	AlK_α	87
C_9H_8ClNO	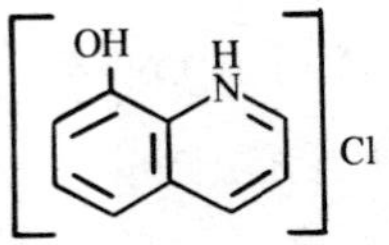	s	$2p_{3/2}$	197.7	c 84	MgK_α	36
$C_{10}H_2Cl_4F_{14}$	$\text{+}CF_2-CFCl\text{+}_m \text{+}CF_2-CH_2\text{+}_n$ m:n, 4:1	s	$2p_{3/2}$ 2s	201.4 (3) 272.8 (3)	b 285.0	MgK_α	130
$C_{12}H_{30}Cl_2P_2Pt$	$((C_2H_5)_3P)_2PtCl_2$	s	2p	198.3 (1)	d 285.0	AlK_α	87
$C_{12}H_{30}Cl_4IrP_2$	*trans*-$IrCl_4(P(CH_2CH_3)_3)_2$	s	$2p_{3/2}$	199.3 (3)	d 285	Al, MgK_α	97
$C_{12}H_{30}Cl_4OsP_2$	*trans*-$OsCl_4(P(CH_2CH_3)_3)_2$	s	$2p_{3/2}$	199.1 (3)	d 285	Mg, AlK_α	97
$C_{12}H_{30}Cl_4P_2Pt$	*trans*-$PtCl_4(P(CH_2CH_3)_3)_2$	s	$2p_{3/2}$	199.3 (3)	d 285	Al, MgK_α	97
$C_{12}H_{30}Cl_4P_2Pt$	$((C_2H_5)_3P)_2PtCl_4$	s	2p	199.4 (1)	d 285.0	AlK_α	87
$C_{12}H_{30}Cl_4P_2Re$	*trans*-$ReCl_4(P(C_2H_5)_3)_2$	s	$2p_{3/2}$	199.4 (3)	d 285	Mg, AlK_α	97
$C_{12}H_{30}Cl_4P_2W$	*trans*-$WCl_4(P(C_2H_5)_3)_2$	s	$2p_{3/2}$	199.5 (3)	d 285	Mg, AlK_α	97
$C_{12}H_{31}ClP_2Pt$	$((C_2H_5)_3P)_2PtHCl$	s	2p	198.2 (1)	d 285.0	AlK_α	87
$C_{13}H_{33}ClP_2Pt$	$((C_2H_5)_3P)_2Pt(CH_3)Cl$	s	2p	198.2 (1)	d 285.0	AlK_α	87
$C_{14}H_{16}Cl_4P_2W$	*trans*-$WCl_4(P(CH_3)_2C_6H_5)_2$	s	$2p_{3/2}$	199.3 (3)	d 285	Mg, AlK_α	97
$C_{16}H_{22}Cl_4IrP_2$	*trans*-$IrCl_4(P(CH_3)_2C_6H_5)_2$	s	$2p_{3/2}$	199.0 (3)	d 285	Mg, AlK_α	97
$C_{16}H_{22}Cl_4OsP_2$	*trans*-$OsCl_4(P(CH_3)_2C_6H_5)_2$	s	$2p_{3/2}$	199.1 (3)	d 285	Mg, AlK_α	97

TABLE 3 (continued)

Compound		Phase	Orbital	E_B(eV)	Calibrant	Exciting Radiation	Reference
$C_{16}H_{22}Cl_4P_2Pt$	*trans*-$PtCl_4(P(CH_3)_2C_6H_5)_2$	s	$2p_{3/2}$	198.5 (3)	d 285	Mg, AlK_α	97
$C_{16}H_{22}Cl_4P_2Re$	*trans*-$ReCl_4(P(CH_3)_2C_6H_5)_2$	s	$2p_{3/2}$	199.4 (3)	d 285	Mg, AlK_α	97
$C_{18}H_{15}ClCuP$	$CuCl\cdot(C_6H_5)_3P$	s	2p	199.1	a 285.5	AlK_α	46
$C_{18}H_{42}Cl_4P_2Pt_2$	$(n-C_3H_7)_3P\overset{a}{Cl}Pt\overset{b}{Cl_2}Pt\overset{a}{Cl}P(n-C_3H_7)_3$	s	$^a2p_{3/2}$ $^b2p_{3/2}$	199.1 198.1	c 84	MgK_α	20
$C_{18}H_{54}Cl_2P_2Pd$	*cis*-$((C_6H_5CH_2CH_2)_3P)_2PdCl_2$	s	$2p_{3/2}$	197.4	c 84	MgK_α	20
$C_{18}H_{54}Cl_2P_2Pd$	*trans*-$((C_6H_5CH_2CH_2)_3P)_2PdCl_2$	s	$2p_{3/2}$	198.2	c 84	MgK_α	20
$C_{20}H_{14}Cl_3F_{23}$	$[CF_2-CFCl]_m[CF_2-CH_2]_n$ m:n, 3:7	s	$2p_{3/2}$ 2s	201.6 (3) 272.5 (3)	b 285.0	MgK_α	130
$C_{20}H_{16}Cl_2CuN_4\cdot3H_2O$	$CuCl_2\cdot2$ 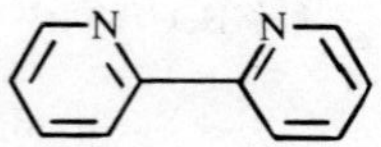 $\cdot3H_2O$	s	2p	199.4	a 285.5	AlK_α	46
$C_{24}H_{33}Cl_3IrP_3$	*mer*-$IrCl_3(P(CH_3)_2C_6H_5)_3$	s	$2p_{3/2}$	198.0	d 285	Mg, AlK_α	97
$C_{24}H_{33}Cl_3IrP_3$	*fac*-$IrCl_3(P(CH_3)_2C_6H_5)_3$	s	$2p_{3/2}$	198.8	d 285	Mg, AlK_α	97
$C_{24}H_{33}Cl_3MoP_3$	*mer*-$MoCl_3(P(CH_3)_2C_6H_5)_3$	s	$2p_{3/2}$	198.2 (3)	d 285	Mg, AlK_α	97
$C_{24}H_{33}Cl_3OsP_3$	*mer*-$OsCl_3(P(CH_3)_2C_6H_5)_3$	s	$2p_{3/2}$	198.4	d 285	Mg, AlK_α	97
$C_{24}H_{33}Cl_3P_3Re$	*mer*-$ReCl_3(P(CH_3)_2C_6H_5)_3$	s	$2p_{3/2}$	198.8	d 285	Mg, AlK_α	97
$C_{24}H_{33}Cl_3P_3Rh$	*fac*-$RhCl_3(P(CH_3)_2C_6H_5)_3$	s	$2p_{3/2}$	197.9	d 285	Mg, AlK_α	97
$C_{24}H_{33}Cl_3P_3Ru$	*mer*-$RuCl_3(P(CH_3)_2C_6H_5)_3$	s	$2p_{3/2}$	198.2	d 285	Mg, AlK_α	97
$C_{24}H_{36}Cl_6Pt_3Sn_2$	$(C_8H_{12})_3Pt_3Sn_2Cl_6$	s	2p	199.1 (1)	d 285.0	AlK_α	87
$C_{24}H_{54}Cl_2P_2Pt$	*cis*-$((n\text{-}C_4H_9)_3P)_2PtCl_2$	s	$2p_{3/2}$	198.1	c 84	MgK_α	20

TABLE 3 (continued)

Compound		Phase	Orbital	E_B(eV)	Calibrant	Exciting Radiation	Reference
$C_{24}H_{54}Cl_2P_2Pt$	*trans*-$((n\text{-}C_4H_9)_3P)_2PtCl_2$	s	$2p_{3/2}$	199.3	c 84	MgK_α	20
$C_{24}H_{54}Cl_4P_2Pd_2$	$(n\text{-}C_4H_9)_3P\overset{a}{Cl}Pd\overset{b}{Cl_2}Pd\overset{a}{Cl}P\ (n\text{-}C_4H_9)_3$	s	${}^a2p_{3/2}$ ${}^b2p_{3/2}$	198.7 197.7	c 84	MgK_α	20
$C_{24}H_{60}Cl_{15}N_3PtSn_5$	$[(C_2H_5)_4N]_3Pt(SnCl_3)_5$	s	2p	198.8 (1)	d 285.0	AlK_α	87
$C_{26}H_{24}Cl_2P_2Pt$	$(C_6H_5)_2PCH_2CH_2P(C_6H_5)_2Cl_2$	s	$2p_{3/2}$	198.0	c 84	MgK_α	20
$C_{30}H_{23}ClCuN_2P$	CuCl· 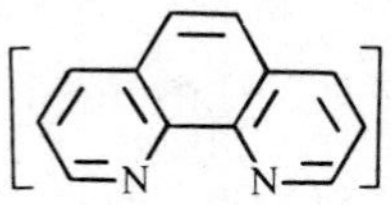 $[(C_6H_5)_3P]$	s	2p	198.4	a 285.5	AlK_α	46
$C_{32}H_{44}ClN_2P_4Re$	*trans*-$[ReCl(N_2)(P(CH_3)_2C_6H_5)_4]$	s	$2p_{3/2}$	198.7 (0.3)	d 285	Mg, AlK_α	97
$C_{32}H_{44}Cl_2OsP_4$	*trans*-$OsCl_2(P(CH_3)_2C_6H_5)_4$	s	$2p_{3/2}$	198.3	d 285	Mg, AlK_α	97
$C_{32}H_{44}Cl_2P_4Re$	*trans*-$ReCl_2(P(CH_3)_2C_6H_5)_4$	s	$2p_{3/2}$	198.4	d 285	Mg, AlK_α	97
$C_{32}H_{80}Cl_{20}N_4Pt_3Sn_8$	$[(C_2H_5)_4N]_4Pt_3Sn_8Cl_{20}$	s	2p	199.2	d 285.0	AlK_α	87
$C_{36}H_{30}Cl_2NiP_2$	$Ni(P(C_6H_5)_3)_2Cl_2$	s	2p	199.1 (2)	d 285.0	Mg, AlK_α	116
$C_{36}H_{30}CdCl_2P_2$	$Cd(P(C_6H_5)_3)_2Cl_2$	s	2p	198.9 (6)	d 285.0	Mg, AlK_α	116
$C_{36}H_{30}Cl_2P_2Pd$	$Pd(P(C_6H_5)_3)_2Cl_2$	s	2p	198.8 (5)	d 285.0	Mg, AlK_α	116
$C_{36}H_{30}Cl_2P_2Pt$	*cis*-$((C_6H_5)_3P)_2PtCl_2$	s	$2p_{3/2}$	198.0	c 84	MgK_α	20
$C_{36}H_{30}Cl_2P_2Pt$	*cis*-$((C_6H_5)_3P)_2PtCl_2$	s	2p	198.2 (1)	d 285.0	AlK_α	87
$C_{36}H_{33}ClCuP_3$	$CuCl\cdot[(C_6H_5)_2PH]_3$	s	2p	199.7	a 285.5	AlK_α	46
$C_{37}H_{30}BClF_4IrNO_2P_2$	$[Ir(CO)(P(C_6H_5)_3)_2Cl(NO^+)]BF_4$	s	2p	198.9 (3)	d 285.0	AlK_α	82
$C_{37}H_{30}ClIrO_3P_2$	$Ir(CO)(P(C_6H_5)_3)_2(Cl)O_2$	s	2p	198.5 (3)	d 285.0	MgK_α	82

TABLE 3 (continued)

Compound		Phase	Orbital	E_B(eV)	Calibrant	Exciting Radiation	Reference
$C_{38}H_{30}ClF_4P_2Rh$	$((C_6H_5)_3P)_2Rh(C_2F_4)Cl$	s	2p	198.9 (3)	d 285.0	MgK_α	82
$C_{38}H_{30}ClIrO_2P_2$	$Ir(CO)_2(P(C_6H_5)_3)_2Cl$	s	2p	198.5 (3)	d 285.0	MgK_α	82
$C_{38}H_{34}ClP_2Rh$	$((C_6H_5)_3P)_2Rh(C_2H_4)Cl$	s	2p	199.0 (3)	d 285.0	MgK_α	82
$C_{38}H_{30}Cl_4P_2Pt$	$((C_6H_5)_3P)_2Pt\overset{a}{Cl}(C\overset{b}{Cl}=C\overset{b}{Cl_2})$	s	$^a2p_{3/2}$ $^b2p_{3/2}$	197.3 (2) 199.5 (2)		AlK_α	93
$C_{38}H_{30}Cl_4P_2Pt$	$((C_6H_5)_3P)_2Pt(Cl_2C=CCl_2)$	s	$2p_{3/2}$	199.8 (2)		AlK_α	93
$C_{38}H_{30}Cl_4P_2Pt$	$((C_6H_5)_3P)_2PtC_2Cl_4$	s	2p	199.4 (3)(br)	d 285.0	MgK_α	82
$C_{39}H_{30}ClF_4IrOP_2$	$Ir(CO)(P(C_6H_5)_3)_2)(Cl)C_2F_4$	s	2p	198.2 (3)	d 285.0	MgK_α	82
$C_{42}H_{30}ClIrN_4P_2$	$Ir(P(C_6H_5)_3)_2Cl(C_2(CN)_4)$	s	2p	198.3 (3)	d 285.0	MgK_α	82
$C_{43}H_{30}ClIrN_4OP_2$	$Ir(CO)(P(C_6H_5)_3)_2Cl(C_2(CN)_4)$	s	2p	198.4 (3)	d 285.0	MgK_α	82
$C_{43}H_{30}ClN_4OP_2Rh$	$((C_6H_5)_3P)_2RhCl(CO)(C_2(CN)_4)$	s	2p	198.5 (3)	d 285.0	MgK_α	82
$C_{54}H_{45}ClCuP_3$	$CuCl\cdot[(C_6H_5)_3P]_3$	s	2p	199.4	a 285.5	AlK_α	46
$C_{54}H_{45}ClP_3Rh$	$((C_6H_5)_3P)_3RhCl$	s	2p	198.3 (3)	d 285.0	MgK_α	82
ClCs	CsCl	s	3p	13.4	a 290	AlK_α	30
ClCu	CuCl	s	2p	201.3	a 285.5	AlK_α	46
ClK	KCl	s	3p	11.9	a 290	AlK_α	30
ClK	KCl	s	2p	201.2	g	MgK_α	129
ClN_3S_4	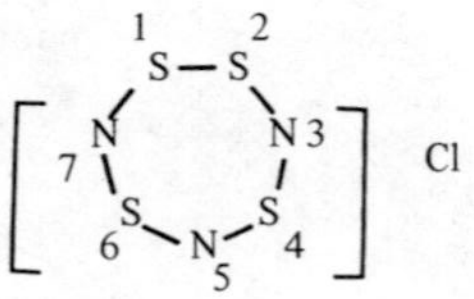	s	$2p_{3/2}$	197.5	a	MgK_α	106

TABLE 3 (continued)

Compound		Phase	Orbital	E_B(eV)	Calibrant	Exciting Radiation	Reference
ClNa	NaCl	s	L_I	270.2	e	$CrK_{\alpha 1}$	67
ClNa	NaCl	s	$2p_{1/2}$	200.1 (3)		MgK_α	53
			$2p_{3/2}$	198.5 (3)			
			3s	61.0 (3)			
			3p	5.0 (3)			
			2s	269.5 (4)		AlK_α	
			$2p_{3/2}$	198.5 (3)		AlK_α	
ClNa	NaCl	s	K	2,822.4 (4)	e, i	CrK_α	76
Cl_2Cu	$CuCl_2$	s	2p	201.2	a 285.5	AlK_α	46
$Cl_2Cu \cdot 2H_2O$	$CuCl_2 \cdot 2H_2O$	s	2p	200.8	a 285.5	AlK_α	46
$Cl_2CuO_8 \cdot 2H_2O$	$Cu(ClO_4)_2 \cdot 2H_2O$	s	2p	210.2	a 285.5	AlK_α	46
$Cl_2CuO_8 \cdot 4H_2O$	$Cu(ClO_4)_2 \cdot 4H_2O$	s	2p	209.8	a 285.5	AlK_α	46
$Cl_2CuO_8 \cdot 6H_2O$	$Cu(ClO_4)_2 \cdot 6H_2O$	s	2p	210.1	a 285.5	AlK_α	46
$Cl_2K_2N_4O_8Pt$	$K_2Pt(NO_2)_4Cl_2$	s	2p	200.2	g	MgK_α	129
Cl_2Pt	$PtCl_2$	s	2p	201.1	g	MgK_α	129
Cl_3OP	$POCl_3$	s	2p	0.9	PCl_3 Cl2p 0		24
Cl_3P	PCl_3	s	2p	0	PCl_3 Cl2p 0		24
$Cl_4FeN_5S_5$	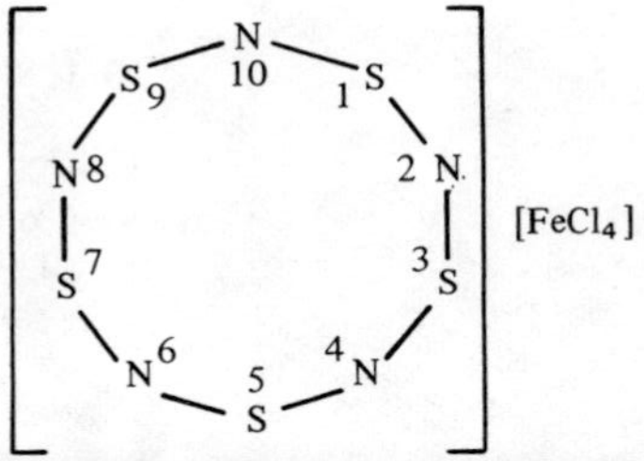		$2p_{3/2}$	199.1	a	MgK_α	106

TABLE 3 (continued)

Compound		Phase	Orbital	E_B(eV)	Calibrant	Exciting Radiation	Reference
Cl_4K_2Pt	K_2PtCl_4	s	2p	200.7	g	MgK_α	129
Cl_4K_2Pt	K_2PtCl_4	s	2p	199.4 (1)	$((C_2H_5)_3P)_2PtCl_4$ Cl2p 199.4	AlK_α	87
$Cl_5FeN_2S_3$	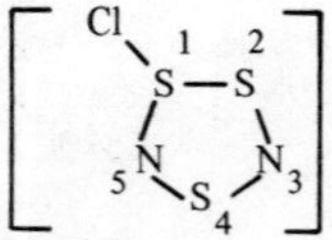 $[FeCl_4]$		$2p_{3/2}$	198.8	a	MgK_α	106
Cl_6IrK_2	K_2IrCl_6	s	$2p_{3/2}$	198.8 (3)	a 285	Mg, AlK_α	97
Cl_6IrK_2	K_2IrCl_6	s	$2p_{1/2,3/2}$	198.4 (2)	c 83.8	AlK_α	41
Cl_6K_2Mo	K_2MoCl_6	s	$2p_{1/2,3/2}$	198.2 (2)	c 83.8	AlK_α	41
Cl_6K_2Os	K_2OsCl_6	s	$2p_{1/2,3/2}$	198.4 (2)	c 83.8	AlK_α	41
Cl_6K_2Os	K_2OsCl_6	s	$2p_{3/2}$	198.9 (3)	a 285	Mg, AlK_α	97
Cl_6K_2Pt	K_2PtCl_6	s	2p	201.0	g	MgK_α	129
Cl_6K_2Pt	K_2PtCl_6	s	$2p_{3/2}$	199.1 (3)	a 285	Mg, AlK_α	97
Cl_6K_2Pt	K_2PtCl_6	s	$2p_{1/2,3/2}$	198.5 (2)	c 83.8	AlK_α	41
Cl_6K_2Pt	K_2PtCl_6	s	2p	199.4 (1)	$((C_2H_5)_3P)_2PtCl_4$ Cl2p 199.4	AlK_α	87
Cl_6K_2Re	K_2ReCl_6	s	$2p_{3/2}$	199.5 (3)	a 285	Mg, AlK_α	97
Cl_6K_2Re	K_2ReCl_6	s	$2p_{1/2,3/2}$	198.2 (2)	c 83.8	AlK_α	41
Cl_6K_2Sn	K_2SnCl_6	s	$2p_{1/2,3/2}$	198.2 (2)	c 83.8	AlK_α	41
Cl_6K_2W	K_2WCl_6	s	$2p_{3/2}$	199.2 (3)	a 285	Mg, AlK_α	97

TABLE 3 (continued)

	Compound	Phase	Orbital	E_B(eV)	Calibrant	Exciting Radiation	Reference
Co							
Br_2Co	$CoBr_2$	s	$2p_{1/2}$ $2p_{3/2}$	803.8 (3) 788.0 (3)	a 290.0	AlK_α	29
$C_6CoK_3N_6$	$K_3Co(CN)_6$	s	$2p_{1/2}$ $2p_{3/2}$	803.4 (3) 788.4 (3)	a 290.0	AlK_α	29
$C_6CoK_3N_6$	$K_3Co(CN)_6$	s	$2p_{3/2}$ 3s	778.8 (3) 103.7 (3)	b 285.0	Al, MgK_α	112
$C_6CoK_3O_{12}$	$K_3Co(C_2O_4)_3$	s	$2p_{3/2}$ 3s	781.1 (3) 103.8 (3)	b 285.0	Al, MgK_α	112
$C_6H_{24}Cl_3CoN_6$	$Co(H_2NCH_2CH_2NH_2)_3Cl_3$	s	$2p_{1/2}$ $2p_{3/2}$	802.5 (3) 787.5 (3)	a 290.0	AlK_α	29
$C_{10}H_{10}Co$	$Co(\pi{-}C_5H_5)_2$	s	$2p_{1/2}$ $2p_{3/2}$	797.5 (3) 782.2 (3)		MgK_α	23
$C_{22}H_{24}CoN_2O_2$	$Co^{II}\langle(C_6H_5C(O)CH_2C(CH_3){=}NCH_2)_2\rangle$	s	$2p_{3/2}$	780.0 (1)	d 285.0	AlK_α	127
$C_{22}H_{24}CoN_3O_3$	$Co^{III}\langle(C_6H_5C(O)CH_2C(CH_3){=}NCH_2)_2\rangle(NO)$	s	$2p_{3/2}$	780.9 (1)	d 285.0	AlK_α	127
$C_{27}H_{29}CoN_3O_4$	$Co^{III}\langle\langle(C_6H_5C(O)CH_2C(CH_3){=}NCH_2)_2\rangle\rangle(O_2)($$)$	s	$2p_{3/2}$	781.4 (1)	d 285.0	AlK_α	127
$C_{27}H_{29}CoN_3O_4$	$Co^{III}\langle\langle(C_6H_5C(O)CH_2C(CH_3){=}NCH_2)_2\rangle\rangle(NO_2)($$)$	s	$2p_{3/2}$	781.4 (1)	d 285.0	AlK_α	127
Cl_2Co	$CoCl_2$	s	$2p_{1/2}$ $2p_{3/2}$	805.2 (3) 789.1 (3)	a 290.0	AlK_α	29

TABLE 3 (continued)

Compound		Phase	Orbital	E_B(eV)	Calibrant	Exciting Radiation	Reference
$Cl_3CoH_{18}N_6$	$Co(NH_3)_6Cl_3$	s	$2p_{1/2}$ $2p_{3/2}$	803.0 (3) 788.0 (3)	a 290.0	$AlK_α$	29
$Cl_3CoH_{18}N_6$	$Co(NH_3)_6Cl_3$	s	$2p_{3/2}$ 3s	781.3 (3) 103.6 (3)	b 285.0	Al, $MgK_α$	112
$Cl_3CoH_{18}N_6$	$[Co(NH_3)_6]Cl_3$	s	$2p_{3/2}$ $2p_{1/2}$	785.2 800.3	a 290	$AlK_α$	30
Co	Co(fcc)	s	3p	57 (0.5)		$MgK_α$	122
Co	Co	s	K	7,709.5	CuK($MoK_{α1}$)	$MoK_{α1}$	119
Co	Co	s	L_I	925.6	MgO MgK($CuK_{α1}$)	$CuK_{α1}$	67
Co	Co	s	d band	−0.8 (2) −2 (sh)	Pd Fermi level 0.0	$MgK_α$	51
CoF_2	CoF_2	s	$2p_{1/2}$ $2p_{3/2}$	806.9 (3) 790.9 (3)	a 290.0	$AlK_α$	29
CoF_2	CoF_2	s	$2p_{3/2}$ 3s	783.2 (3) 107.2 (3)	b 285.0	Al, $MgK_α$	112
CoF_3	CoF_3	s	$2p_{3/2}$ 3s	782.6 (3) 105.5 (3)	b 285.0	Al, $MgK_α$	112
CoH_2O_2	$Co(OH)_2$	s	$2p_{1/2}$ $2p_{3/2}$	803.9 (3) 787.9 (3)	a 290.0	$AlK_α$	29
$CoN_6Na_3O_{12}$	$Na_3Co(NO_2)_6$	s	$2p_{1/2}$ $2p_{3/2}$	802.5 (3) 787.5 (3)	a 290.0	$AlK_α$	29
CoO_4S	$CoSO_4$	s	$2p_{1/2}$ $2p_{3/2}$	804.9 (3) 789.0 (3)	a 290.0	$AlK_α$	29
Cr							
$C_5CrK_3N_6O$	$K_3[Cr(CN)_5NO]$	s	3p	44.8 (2)	b	$MgK_α$	8

TABLE 3 (continued)

Compound		Phase	Orbital	E_B(eV)	Calibrant	Exciting Radiation	Reference
$C_5H_3CrNO_5$	$Cr(CO)_5NH_3$	s	$2p_{3/2}$	575.7	Hexane Cls 285.0		40
$C_6CrK_3N_6$	$K_3[Cr(CN)_6]$	s	3p	575.8	c		33
$C_6CrK_3N_6$	$K_3[Cr(CN)_6]$	s	3p	44.8 (2)	b	MgK_a	8
C_6CrO_6	$Cr(CO)_6$	s	$2p_{1/2}$ $2p_{3/2}$	587.5 (3) 578.5 (3)		MgK_a	23
C_6CrO_6	$Cr(CO)_6$	s	$2p_{1/2}$ $2p_{3/2}$ 3s	587.5 578,5 77.4	c 84	MgK_a	26
C_6CrO_6	$Cr(CO)_6$	s	3p	45.8 (2)	b	MgK_a	8
C_6CrO_6	$Cr(CO)_6$	s	$2p_{3/2}$	576.5	Hexane Cls 285.0		40
$C_7H_5CrNO_5$	$Cr(CO)_5$(HN)	s	$2p_{3/2}$	575.4	Hexane Cls 285.0		40
$C_8H_9CrO_5P$	$Cr(CO)_5P(CH_3)_3$	s	$2p_{3/2}$	575.4	Hexane Cls 285.0		40
$C_8H_{16}Cr_2O_{10}$	$Cr_2(CH_3COO)_4(H_2O)_2$	s	3p	44.5 (2)	b	MgK_a	8
$C_{10}H_{10}Cr$	$Cr(\pi-C_5H_5)_2$	s	$2p_{1/2}$ $2p_{3/2}$	585.9 (3) 576.9 (3)		MgK_a	23
$C_{10}H_{10}Cr$	$Cr(\pi-C_5H_5)_2$	s	$2p_{1/2}$ $2p_{3/2}$ 3s	585.9 576.9 77.2, 74.1	c 84	MgK_a	26
$C_{15}H_3CrF_{18}O_6$	$Cr(CF_3COCHCOCF_3)_3$	s	$2p_{1/2}$ $2p_{3/2}$ 3s	589.6 580.6 81.6, 77.1	c 84	MgK_a	26
Cl_3Cr	$CrCl_3$	s	$2p_{3/2}$ 3s	577.6 (3) 78.2 (3)	b 285.0	Al, MgK_a	112

TABLE 3 (continued)

Compound		Phase	Orbital	E_B(eV)	Calibrant	Exciting Radiation	Reference
$Cl_3Cr \cdot 6H_2O$	$CrCl_3$ $6H_2O$	s	3p	45.4 (2)	b	MgK_α	8
$Cl_3CrH_8O_4$	*trans*-$[Cr(H_2O)_4Cl_2]Cl$	s	3p	44.5 (2)	b	MgK_α	8
$Cl_3CrH_{10}O_5$	$[Cr(H_2O)_5Cl]Cl_2$	s	3p	45.2 (2)	b	MgK_α	8
$Cl_3CrH_{18}N_6$	$[Cr(NH_3)_6]Cl_3$	s	3p	44.7 (2)	b	MgK_α	8
Cr	Cr foil (reduced)	s	3p	43.2 (2)	b	MgK_α	8
Cr	Cr foil (unreduced)	s	3p	43.9 (2)	b	MgK_α	8
Cr	Cr	s	L_I	694.6	MgO $MgK(CuK_{\alpha1})$	$CuK_{\alpha1}$	67
CrF_3	CrF_3	s	$2p_{3/2}$	580.5 (3)	b 285.0	Al, MgK_α	112
			3s	80.5 (3)			
CrF_6K_3	K_3CrF_6	s	3p	578.0	c		33
$CrH_{12}N_3O_{15} \cdot 3H_2O$	$[Cr(H_2O)_6](NO_3)_3 \cdot 3H_2O$	s	3p	45.4 (2)	b	MgK_α	8
CrN	CrN	s	3p	43.2 (2)	b	MgK_α	8
$CrNa_2O_4 \cdot 4H_2O$	$Na_2CrO_4 \cdot 4H_2O$	s	3p	47.9 (2)	b	MgK_α	8
CrO_3	CrO_3	s	3p	48.2 (2)	b	MgK_α	8
CrO_3	CrO_3	s	3p	48.4		AlK_α	102
$Cr_2K_2O_7$	$K_2Cr_2O_7$	s	3p	48.7 (2)	b	MgK_α	8
$Cr_2K_2O_7$	$K_2Cr_2O_7$	s	$2p_{3/2}$	581.6 (3)	b 285.0	Al, MgK_α	112
			3s	75.9 (3)			
Cr_2O_3	Cr_2O_3	s	$2p_{3/2}$	577.0 (3)	b 285.0	Al, MgK_α	112
			3s	77.5 (3)			
Cr_2O_3	Cr_2O_3	s	K	5,989.1 (4)	e, i	CuK_α	112

TABLE 3 (continued)

Compound		Phase	Orbital	E_B(eV)	Calibrant	Exciting Radiation	Reference
Cr_2O_3	Cr_2O_3	s	3p	43.5 (2)	b	MgK_α	8
Cr_2O_3	Cr_2O_3	s	3p	45.6		AlK_α	102
$Cr_2O_3 \cdot XH_2O$	$Cr_2O_3 \cdot XH_2O$	s	3p	44.6 (2)	b	MgK_α	8
$Cr_2O_{12}S_3 \cdot XH_2O$	$Cr_2(SO_4)_3 \cdot XH_2O$	s	3p	46.9 (2)	b	MgK_α	8
Cr_2S_3	Cr_2S_3	s	$2p_{3/2}$	575.0 (3)	b 285.0	Al, MgK_α	112
			3s	75.9 (3)			
Cs							
BrCs	CsBr	s	5p	18.3	a 290	AlK_α	30
CCs_2O_3	Cs_2CO_3	s	$3d_{3/2}$	746.0 (3)	a 290.0	AlK_α	62
			$3d_{5/2}$	732.0 (3)			
			$4d_{3/2}$	84.9 (3)			
			$4d_{5/2}$	82.7 (3)			
ClCs	CsCl	s	$3d_{3/2}$	747.5 (3)	a 290.0	AlK_α	62
			$3d_{5/2}$	733.4 (3)			
			$4d_{3/2}$	87.5 (3)			
			$4d_{5/2}$	85.1 (3)			
ClCs	CsCl	s	5p	19.6	a 290	AlK_α	30
Cl_6Cs_2Os	Cs_2OsCl_6	s	$3d_{3/2}$	744.05	a 290.0	AlK_α	62
			$3d_{5/2}$	730.1 (3)			
			$4d_{3/2}$	83.5 (3)			
			$4d_{5/2}$	81.3 (3)			
Cl_6CsSb	$CsSbCl_6$	s	$3d_{3/2}$	745.6 (3)	a 290.0	AlK_α	62
			$3d_{5/2}$	731.7 (3)			
			$4d_{3/2}$	85.2 (3)			
			$4d_{5/2}$	83.1 (3)			
CsF	CsF	s	5p	16.3	a 290	AlK_α	30

TABLE 3 (continued)

Compound		Phase	Orbital	E_B(eV)	Calibrant	Exciting Radiation	Reference
CsI	CsI	s	5p	18.75	a 290	AlK_α	30
Cs_2I_6Os	Cs_2OsI_6	s	$3d_{3/2}$	743.15	a 290.0	AlK_α	62
			$3d_{5/2}$	729.1 (3)			
			$4d_{3/2}$	82.7 (3)			
			$4d_{5/2}$	80.7 (3)			
Cs_2MoS_4	Cs_2MoS_4	s	$3d_{3/2}$	743.3 (3)	a 290.0	AlK_α	62
			$3d_{5/2}$	729.3 (3)			
			$4d_{3/2}$	83.3 (3)			
			$4d_{5/2}$	81.0 (3)			
CsN_3	CsN_3	s	$3d_{5/2}$	723.83	b 285.0	Al, MgK_α	66
			4d	75.79			
			5s	23.78			
			5p	10.48			
CsO_4Re	$CsReO_4$	s	$3d_{3/2}$	746.3 (3)	a 290.0	AlK_α	62
			$3d_{5/2}$	732.2 (3)			
			$4d_{3/2}$	83.7 (3)			
Cs_2O_4S	Cs_2SO_4	s	L_I	5,712.9 (1.4)	e	MoK_α	78
			L_{II}	5,359.4 (5)		CuK_α	
			L_{III}	5,011.9 (5)			
Cs_2S_4W	Cs_2WS_4	s	$4d_{3/2}$	84.4 (3)	a 290.0	AlK_α	62
			$4d_{5/2}$	82.4 (3)			
			$3d_{3/2}$	744.6 (3)			
			$3d_{5/2}$	730.6 (3)			
Cs_2Se_4W	Cs_2WSe_4	s	$3d_{3/2}$	745.1 (3)	a 290.0	AlK_α	62
			$3d_{5/2}$	733.1 (3)			
Cu							
BrCu	CuBr	s	$2p_{3/2}$	932.5		AlK_α	54

TABLE 3 (continued)

Compound		Phase	Orbital	E_B(eV)	Calibrant	Exciting Radiation	Reference
BrCu	CuBr	s	$2p_{1/2}$	954.0	a 285.5	AlK_α	46
			$2p_{3/2}$	934.2			
			3s	124.4			
			$3p_{1/2,3/2}$	77.5			
Br_2Cu	$CuBr_2$	s	$2p_{1/2}$	955.6	a 285.5	AlK_α	46
			$2p_{3/2}$	935.8			
			3s	126.1			
			$3p_{1/2,3/2}$	79.4			
CCuN	CuCN	s	$2p_{1/2}$	955.0	a 285.5	AlK_α	46
			$2p_{3/2}$	935.2			
			3s	125.3			
			$3p_{1/2,3/2}$	78.0			
CCuNS	CuSCN	s	$2p_{1/2}$	954.4	a 285.5	AlK_α	46
			$2p_{3/2}$	934.6			
			3s	124.7			
			$3p_{1/2,3/2}$	77.9			
$CCuO_3$	$CuCO_3$	s	$2p_{1/2}$	957.1	a 285.5	AlK_α	46
			$2p_{3/2}$	937.2			
			3s	127.7			
			$3p_{1/2,3/2}$	80.5			
$C_2H_8Br_2CuN_2 \cdot H_2O$	$CuBr_2 \cdot H_2NCH_2CH_2NH_2 \cdot H_2O$	s	$2p_{1/2}$	956.2	a 285.5	AlK_α	46
			$2p_{3/2}$	936.3			
			3s	126.3			
			$3p_{1/2,3/2}$	79.4			
$C_2H_8Cl_2CuN_2 \cdot H_2O$	$CuCl_2 \cdot H_2NCH_2CH_2NH_2 \cdot H_2O$	s	$2p_{1/2}$	956.4	a 285.5	AlK_α	46
			$2p_{3/2}$	936.5			
			3s	126.8			
			$3p_{1/2,3/2}$	78.8			

TABLE 3 (continued)

Compound		Phase	Orbital	E_B(eV)	Calibrant	Exciting Radiation	Reference
$C_2H_8CuN_2O_3S \cdot H_2O$	$CuSO_3 \cdot H_2NCH_2CH_2NH_2 \cdot H_2O$	s	$2p_{1/2}$	956.6	a 285.5	AlK_a	46
			$2p_{3/2}$	936.6			
			3s	126.9			
			$3p_{1/2,3/2}$	80.8			
$C_4CuK_2O_8$	$K_2Cu(C_2O_4)_2$	s	$2p_{1/2}$	956.1	a 285.5	AlK_a	46
			$2p_{3/2}$	935.8			
			3s	126.8			
			$3p_{1/2,3/2}$	79.6			
$C_4H_6CuO_4 \cdot H_2O$	$Cu(CH_3COO)_2 \cdot H_2O$	s	$2p_{1/2}$	956.6	a 285.5	AlK_a	46
			$2p_{3/2}$	936.7			
			3s	127.4			
			$3p_{1/2,3/2}$	80.4			
$C_4H_{16}Br_2CuN_4 \cdot H_2O$	$CuBr_2 \cdot 2(H_2NCH_2CH_2NH_2) \cdot H_2O$	s	$2p_{1/2}$	955.7	a 285.5	AlK_a	46
			$2p_{3/2}$	936.0			
			3s	125.6			
			$3p_{1/2,3/2}$	79			
$C_4H_{16}Cl_2CuN_4 \cdot H_2O$	$CuCl_2 \cdot 2(H_2NCH_2CH_2NH_2) \cdot H_2O$	s	$2p_{1/2}$	955.9	a 285.5	AlK_a	46
			$2p_{3/2}$	935.7			
			3s	125.9			
			$3p_{1/2,3/2}$	78.9			
$C_4H_{16}CuN_4O_4S \cdot H_2O$	$CuSO_4 \cdot 2(H_2NCH_2CH_2NH_2) \cdot H_2O$	s	$2p_{1/2}$	956.3	a 285.5	AlK_a	46
			$2p_{3/2}$	936.1			
			3s	125.9			
			$3p_{1/2,3/2}$	80.0			
$C_6H_{24}Br_2CuN_6 \cdot 5H_2O$	$CuBr_2 \cdot 3(H_2NCH_2CH_2NH_2) \cdot 5H_2O$	s	$2p_{1/2}$	955.9	a 285.5	AlK_a	46
			$2p_{3/2}$	936.0			
			3s	125.9			
$C_8H_{22}CuN_4O_4 \cdot H_2O$	$Cu(CH_3COO)_2 \cdot 2(H_2NCH_2CH_2NH_2) \cdot H_2O$	s	$2p_{1/2}$	956.0	a 285.5	AlK_a	46
			$2p_{3/2}$	936.2			
			3s	125.7			
			$3p_{1/2,3/2}$	78.9			

TABLE 3 (continued)

Compound		Phase	Orbital	E_B(eV)	Calibrant	Exciting Radiation	Reference
$C_{10}H_8Br_2CuN_2$	$CuBr_2\cdot$ 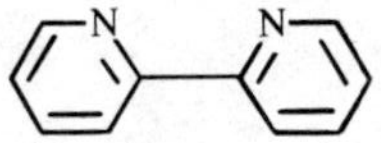	s	$2p_{1/2}$	954.9	a 285.5	AlK_α	46
			$2p_{3/2}$	935.1			
			3s	125.5			
			$3p_{1/2,3/2}$	78.7			
$C_{10}H_8Cl_2CuN_2$	$CuCl_2\cdot$ 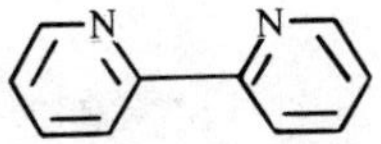	s	$2p_{1/2}$	955.2	a 285.5	AlK_α	46
			$2p_{3/2}$	935.4			
			3s	125.5			
			$3p_{1/2,3/2}$	79.3			
$C_{10}H_8CuN_2O_4S\cdot 2H_2O$	$CuSO_4\cdot$ 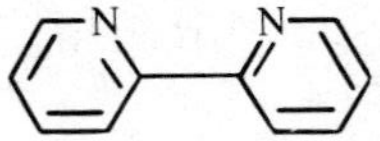 $\cdot 2H_2O$	s	$2p_{1/2}$	955.7	a 285.5	AlK_α	46
			$2p_{3/2}$	935.5			
			3s	125.9			
			$3p_{1/2,3/2}$	78.9			
$C_{10}H_{14}CuO_4$	$Cu(H_3C\overset{O}{\overset{\|\|}{C}}CH\overset{O}{\overset{\|\|}{C}}CH_3)_2$	s	$2p_{1/2}$	955.3	a 285.5	AlK_α	46
			$2p_{3/2}$	935.4			
		s	3s	125.5			
			$3p_{1/2,3/2}$	79.3			
$C_{14}H_{10}CuO_4$	$Cu(C_6H_5COO)_2$	s	$2p_{1/2}$	955.9	a 285.5	AlK_α	46
			$2p_{3/2}$	935.7			
			3s	126.5			
			$3p_{1/2,3/2}$	80.5			
$C_{18}H_{15}ClCuP$	$CuCl\cdot(C_6H_5)_3P$	s	$2p_{1/2}$	953.8	a 285.5	AlK_α	46
			$2p_{3/2}$	934.1			
			3s	122.8			
			$3p_{1/2,3/2}$	76.8			
$C_{20}H_{16}Br_2CuN_4\cdot 2H_2O$	$CuBr_2\cdot 2$ 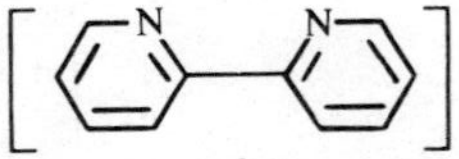 $\cdot 2H_2O$	s	$2p_{1/2}$	955.2	a 285.5	AlK_α	46
			$2p_{3/2}$	935.3			
			3s	124.8			

TABLE 3 (continued)

Compound		Phase	Orbital	E_B(eV)	Calibrant	Exciting Radiation	Reference
$C_{20}H_{16}Cl_2CuN_4 \cdot 3H_2O$	$CuCl_2 \cdot 2$ 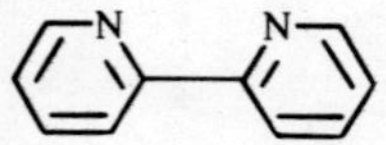 $\cdot 3H_2O$	s	$2p_{1/2}$	955.0	a 285.5	AlK_a	46
			$2p_{3/2}$	935.4			
			3s	125.4			
			$3p_{1/2,3/2}$	78.5			
$C_{30}H_{23}ClCuN_2P$	$CuCl \cdot$ [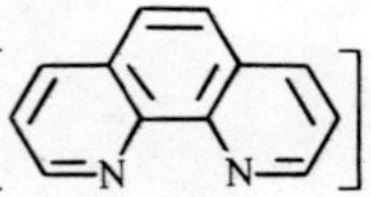] $[(C_6H_5)_3P]$	s	$2p_{1/2}$	953.0	a 285.5	AlK_a	46
			$2p_{3/2}$	933.0			
			3s	122.4			
			$3p_{1/2,3/2}$	76.0			
$C_{30}H_{24}CuN_6O_4S \cdot 7H_2O$	$CuSO_4 \cdot 3$ [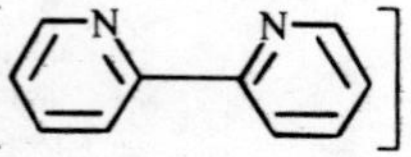] $\cdot 7H_2O$	s	$2p_{1/2}$	955.0	a 285.5	AlK_a	46
			$2p_{3/2}$	935.2			
			3s	125.4			
			$3p_{1/2,3/2}$	78.8			
$C_{36}H_{33}ClCuP_3$	$CuCl \cdot [(C_6H_5)_2PH]_3$	s	$2p_{1/2}$	953.9	a 285.5	AlK_a	46
			$2p_{3/2}$	934.0			
			3s	124.1			
			$3p_{1/2,3/2}$	78.0			
$C_{54}H_{45}ClCuP_3$	$CuCl \cdot [(C_6H_5)_3P]_3$	s	$2p_{1/2}$	953.7	a 285.5	AlK_a	46
			$2p_{3/2}$	934.1			
			3s	123.4			
			$3p_{1/2,3/2}$	77.2			
ClCu	CuCl	s	$2p_{3/2}$	932.5		AlK_a	54
ClCu	CuCl	s	$2p_{1/2}$	954.5	a 285.5	AlK_a	46
			$2p_{3/2}$	934.6			
			3s	124.2			
			$3p_{1/2,3/2}$	77.6			

TABLE 3 (continued)

Compound		Phase	Orbital	E_B(eV)	Calibrant	Exciting Radiation	Reference
Cl_2Cu	$CuCl_2$	s	$2p_{1/2}$	956.2	a 285.5	AlK_a	46
			$2p_{3/2}$	936.4			
			3s	126.3			
			$3p_{1/2,3/2}$	79.8			
$Cl_2Cu \cdot 2H_2O$	$CuCl_2 \cdot 2H_2O$	s	$2p_{1/2}$	956.6	a 285.5	AlK_a	46
			$2p_{3/2}$	936.6			
			3s	127.4			
			$3p_{1/2,3/2}$	80.2			
$Cl_2CuO_8 \cdot 2H_2O$	$Cu(ClO_4)_2 \cdot 2H_2O$	s	$2p_{1/2}$	957.3	a 285.5	AlK_a	46
			$2p_{3/2}$	937.1			
			3s	128.5			
			$3p_{1/2,3/2}$	81.2			
$Cl_2CuO_8 \cdot 4H_2O$	$Cu(ClO_4)_2 \cdot 4H_2O$	s	$2p_{1/2}$	958.2	a 285.5	AlK_a	46
			$2p_{3/2}$	938.3			
			3s	129.1			
			$3p_{1/2,3/2}$	81.6			
$Cl_2CuO_8 \cdot 6H_2O$	$Cu(ClO_4)_2 \cdot 6H_2O$	s	$2p_{1/2}$	958.5	a 285.5	AlK_a	46
			$2p_{3/2}$	938.5			
			3s	129.0			
			$3p_{1/2,3/2}$	82.0			
Cu	Cu(fcc)	s	3p	75 (0.5)		MgK_a	122
Cu	Cu	s	K	8,979.0	$CuK(MoK_{a1}, AgK_{a1})$	MoK_{a1}	123
			L_{III}	931.7			
Cu	Cu	s	L_I	1,096.0	MgO $MgK(CuK_{a1})$	CuK_{a1}	67
Cu	Cu	s	K	8,979.2	$CuK(MoK_{a1})$	MoK_{a1}	119
Cu	Cu	s	d band	–3.1 (2)	Pd Fermi level 0.0	MgK_a	51
Cu	Cu	s	$2p_{3/2}$	932.8 (1)	Pd $2p_{3/2}$	MgK_a	70
			$3p_{1/2,3/2}$	76.1 (1)			

TABLE 3 (continued)

Compound		Phase	Orbital	E_B(eV)	Calibrant	Exciting Radiation	Reference
CuF_2	CuF_2	s	$2p_{1/2}$	959.6	a 285.5	AlK_a	46
			$2p_{3/2}$	939.7			
			3s	129.9			
			$3p_{1/2,3/2}$	83.4			
$CuF_2 \cdot H_2O$	$CuF_2 \cdot 2H_2O$	s	$2p_{1/2}$	957.9	a 285.5	AlK_a	46
			$2p_{3/2}$	938.1			
			3s	128.0			
			$3p_{1/2,3/2}$	81.2			
CuH_2O_2	$Cu(OH)_2$	s	$2p_{1/2}$	957.3	a 285.5	AlK_a	46
			$2p_{3/2}$	937.4			
			3s	127.6			
			$3p_{1/2,3/2}$	80.4			
CuI	CuI	s	$2p_{1/2}$	955.0	a 285.5	AlK_a	46
			$2p_{3/2}$	935.2			
			$3p_{1/2,3/2}$	78.0			
$CuN_2O_6 \cdot 3H_2O$	$Cu(NO_3)_2 \cdot 3H_2O$	s	$2p_{1/2}$	956.0	a 285.5	AlK_a	46
			$2p_{3/2}$	935.9			
			3s	127.0			
			$3p_{1/2,3/2}$	79.6			
CuO	CuO	s	K	4.4 (5)	CuK 0.0		80
			L_I	4.4 (1.0)			
			L_{II}	3.3 (1.5)			
			L_{III}	2.5 (8)			
CuO	CuO	s	$2p_{1/2}$	956.3	a 285.5	AlK_a	46
			$2p_{3/2}$	936.2			
			3s	126.3			
			$3p_{1/2,3/2}$	81.8			
CuO	CuO	s	$2p_{3/2}$	954.6		AlK_a	102
CuO_4S	$CuSO_4$	s	$2p_{3/2}$	933.7		AlK_a	54

TABLE 3 (continued)

Compound		Phase	Orbital	E_B(eV)	Calibrant	Exciting Radiation	Reference
CuO_4S	$CuSO_4$	s	$2p_{1/2}$	957.3	a 285.5	AlK_a	46
			$2p_{3/2}$	937.2			
			3s	127.6			
			$3p_{1/2,3/2}$	81.1			
$CuO_4S \cdot H_2O$	$CuSO_4 \cdot H_2O$	s	$2p_{1/2}$	956.3	a 285.5	AlK_a	46
			$2p_{3/2}$	936.7			
			3s	127.4			
			$3p_{1/2,3/2}$	80.1			
$CuO_4S \cdot 3H_2O$	$CuSO_4 \cdot 3H_2O$	s	$2p_{1/2}$	957.7	a 285.5	AlK_a	46
			$2p_{3/2}$	937.9			
			3s	128.0			
			$3p_{1/2,3/2}$	81.4			
$CuO_4S \cdot 5H_2O$	$CuSO_4 \cdot 5H_2O$	s	$2p_{1/2}$	957.9	a 285.5	AlK_a	46
			$2p_{3/2}$	937.8			
			3s	128.2			
			$3p_{1/2,3/2}$	81.4			
$CuO_4S \cdot 5H_2O$	$CuSO_4 \cdot 5H_2O$	s	$2p_{1/2}$	961.7	a 290	AlK_a	30
				958.6			
			$2p_{3/2}$	941.4			
				938.7			
Cu_2O	Cu_2O	s	$2p_{3/2}$	954.4		AlK_a	102
Cu_2O	Cu_2O	s	$2p_{3/2}$	933.0		AlK_a	54
Cu_2O	Cu_2O	s	$2p_{1/2}$	954.7	a 285.5	AlK_a	46
			$2p_{3/2}$	934.7			
			3s	125.0			
			$3p_{1/2,3/2}$	78.8			
Cu_2S	Cu_2S	s	$2p_{1/2}$	954.3	a 285.5	AlK_a	46
			$2p_{3/2}$	934.6			
			3s	124.6			
			$3p_{1/2,3/2}$	78.0			

TABLE 3 (continued)

	Compound	Phase	Orbital	E_B(eV)	Calibrant	Exciting Radiation	Reference
Cu_3P	Cu_3P	s	$2p_{1/2}$	954.1	a 285.5	AlK_a	46
			$2p_{3/2}$	934.3			
			3s	124.0			
			$3p_{1/2,3/2}$	77.8			
$Cu_{0.60}Pd_{0.40}$	$Cu_{0.60}Pd_{0.40}$	s	$2p_{3/2}$	932.0 (1)	Au, Pt $4f_{7/2}$	MgK_a	70
			$3p_{1/2,3/2}$	75.4 (1)			
Dy							
Dy	Dy	s	4f	−3.8	Pd Fermi level	AlK_a	47
				−8.0			
Dy_2O_3	Dy_2O_3	s	L_I	9,046.7	e	MoK_{a1}	56
			L_{II}	8,580.7			
			L_{III}	7,789.9			
Er							
Er	Er	s	4f	−5.0	Pd Fermi level	AlK_a	47
				−8.5			
Er_2O_3	Er_2O_3	s	L_I	9,751.7	e	MoK_{a1}	56
			L_{II}	9,264.5			
			L_{III}	8,357.9			
Eu							
Al_2Eu	$EuAl_2$	s	$3d_{3/2}$	0	$EuAl_2$ $Eu3d_{3/2}$ 0	CrK_{a1}	1
			$3d_{5/2}$	0	$EuAl_2$ $Eu3d_{5/2}$ 0		
			$4p_{3/2}$	0	$EuAl_2$ $Eu4p_{3/2}$ 0		
Eu_2O_3	Eu_2O_3	s	$3d_{3/2}$	10.2	$EuAl_2$ $Eu3d_{3/2}$ 0	CrK_{a1}	1
			$3d_{5/2}$	9.6	$EuAl_2$ $Eu3d_{5/2}$ 0		
			$4p_{3/2}$	9.2	$EuAl_2$ $Eu4p_{3/2}$ 0		

TABLE 3 (continued)

Compound		Phase	Orbital	E_B(eV)	Calibrant	Exciting Radiation	Reference
Eu_2O_3	Eu_2O_3	s	L_I L_{II} L_{III}	8,052.0 7,617.9 6,977.1	e	$MoK_{\alpha 1}$	56
Eu_2O_3	Eu_2O_3	s	4s $4p_{1/2}$ $4p_{3/2}$ $4d_{3/2}$ $4d_{5/2}$ 4f	366.3 (8) 289.1 (7) 260.7 (6) 141.4 (6) 135.7 (6) 7.3 (7)	b	AlK_α	120
F							
AlF_6Na_3	Na_3AlF_6	s	ls	693.7	a 290.0	AlK_α	64
BF_4K	KBF_4	s	ls	694.0	a 290.0	AlK_α	64
BF_4K	KBF_4	s	ls	687.4	LiF Fls 685.4		114
BaF_2	BaF_2	s	2p	16.3	a 290	AlK_α	30
BaF_2	BaF_2	s	ls	693.2	a 290.0	AlK_α	64
BeF_2	BeF_2	s	ls	692.1	a 290.0	AlK_α	64
BeF_4K_2	K_2BeF_4	s	ls	692.8	a 290.0	AlK_α	64
CCl_3F	CCl_3F	s	ls	691.4	c 84	MgK_α	28
CF_2	CF_2 polymer	s	ls	695.7	a 290.0	AlK_α	64
CF_4	CF_4	g	ls	695.0	CHF_3, CH_4, or C_6H_6 from Ref. 6	MgK_α	121
CF_4	CF_4	g	ls	695.2	CHF_3 Fls 694.4	MgK_α	151
CHF_3	CHF_3	g	ls	694.1 (1)	Nels, 2s 869.7 (1), 48.5	MgK_α	6

TABLE 3 (continued)

Compound		Phase	Orbital	E_B(eV)	Calibrant	Exciting Radiation	Reference
CHF_3	CHF_3	g	ls	694.4	CHF_3 Fls 694.4	MgK_a	151
CHF_3	CHF_3	g	ls	694.1	CHF_3, CH_4, or C_6H_6 from Ref. 6	MgK_a	121
CH_3F	CH_3F	g	ls	692.4	CHF_3, CH_4, or C_6H_6 from Ref. 6	MgK_a	121
C_2ClF_3	$+CF_2-CFCl+_n$	s	ls	690.8 (3)	b 285.0	MgK_a	130
$C_2Cl_3F_3$	Cl_3CCF_3	s	ls	692.1	c 84	MgK_a	28
C_2F_4	$+CF_2-CF_2+_n$	s	ls	690.2 (3)	b 285.0	MgK_a	130
$C_2HCl_2F_3$	Cl_2HCCF_3	s	ls	691.7	c 84	MgK_a	28
C_2HF_3	$+CF_2-CFH+_n$	s	ls	690.1 (3)	b 285.0	MgK_a	130
$C_2H_2F_2$	$+CF_2-CH_2+_n$	s	ls	689.6 (3)	b 285.0	MgK_a	130
$C_2H_2F_2$	$+CFH-CFH+_n$	s	ls	689.3 (3)	b 285.0	MgK_a	130
C_2H_3F	$+CFH-CH_2+_n$	s	ls	689.3 (3)	b 285.0	MgK_a	130
C_3F_6	$+CF(CF_3)-CF_2+_n$	s	ls	690.2 (3)	b 285.0	MgK_a	130
$C_4F_4N_2$	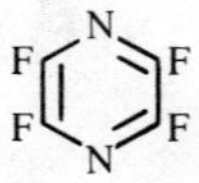	s	ls	691.0 (3)	c 84	MgK_a	96
$C_4F_4N_2$	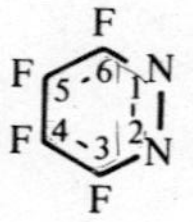	s	(3) ls (4) ls	691.2 691.2	c 84	MgK_a	96

TABLE 3 (continued)

Compound		Phase	Orbital	E_B(eV)	Calibrant	Exciting Radiation	Reference
$C_4F_4N_2$		s	(2) ls (4) ls (5) ls	691.2 691.2 691.2	c 84	MgK_α	96
C_5F_5N	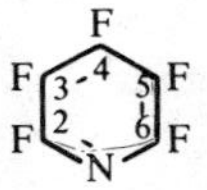	s	(2) ls (3) ls (4) ls	690.7 690.7 690.7	c 84	MgK_α	96
C_6F_6	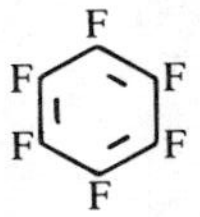	s	ls	690.9 (3)	c 84	MgK_α	27
C_6F_6		s	ls	690.9	c 84	MgK_α	96
C_6HF_5	C_6HF_5	g	ls	−0.31 (15)	C_6F_6 Fls 0.0	MgK_α	142
$C_6H_2F_4$	1,2,3,4-$C_6H_2F_4$	g	ls	−0.68 (10)	C_6F_6 Fls 0.0	MgK_α	142
$C_6H_2F_4$	1,2,4,5-$C_6H_2F_4$	g	ls	−0.48 (10)	C_6F_6 Fls 0.0	MgK_α	142
$C_6H_2F_4$	1,2,3,5-$C_6H_2F_4$	g	ls	−0.45 (6)	C_6F_6 Fls 0.0	MgK_α	142
$C_6H_3F_3$	1,3,5-$C_6H_3F_3$	g	ls	−0.87 (8)	C_6F_6 Fls 0.0	MgK_α	142
$C_6H_4F_2$	1,4-$C_6H_4F_2$	g	ls	−1.08 (5)	C_6F_6 Fls 0.0	MgK_α	142
$C_6H_4F_2$	1,2-$C_6H_4F_2$	g	ls	−1.01 (5)	C_6F_6 Fls 0.0	MgK_α	142
$C_6H_4F_2$	1,3-$C_6H_4F_2$	g	ls	−1.08 (5)	C_6F_6 Fls 0.0 (693.7)	MgK_α	142
C_6H_5F	C_6H_5F	g	ls	−1.38 (5)	C_6F_6 Fls 0.0	MgK_α	118

TABLE 3 (continued)

Compound		Phase	Orbital	E_B(eV)	Calibrant	Exciting Radiation	Reference
C_6H_5F	C_6H_5F	g	ls	689.6 (3)	c 84	MgK_α	118
$C_7H_5F_3$	$C_6H_5CF_3$	g	ls	690.8 (3)	c 84	MgK_α	118
$C_{10}F_8$	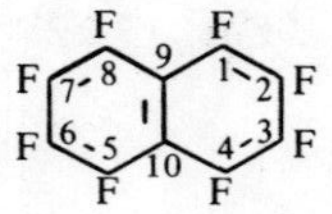	s	ls	690.9 (3)	c 84	MgK_α	27
$C_{10}H_2Cl_4F_{14}$	$-[CF_2-CFCl]_m-[CF_2-CH_2]_n-$ m:n, 4:1	s	ls	690.3 (3)	b 285.0	MgK_α	130
$C_{11}F_{12}$	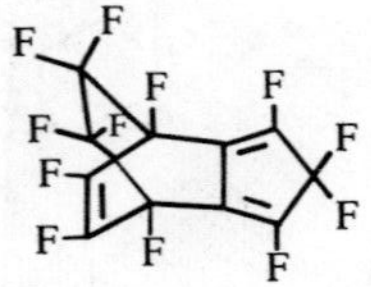	s	ls	690.9	c 84	MgK_α	52
$C_{12}F_8$	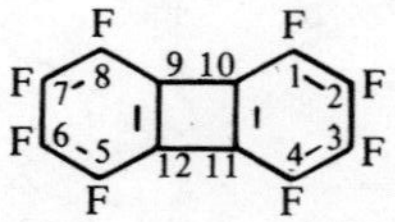	s	ls	690.6 (3)	c 84	MgK_α	27
$C_{12}F_8$	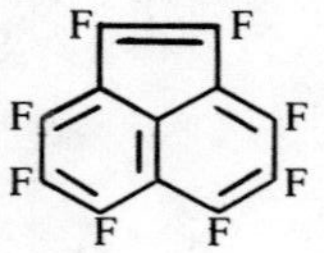	s	ls	690.6 (3)	c 84	MgK_α	27
$C_{12}F_{14}$	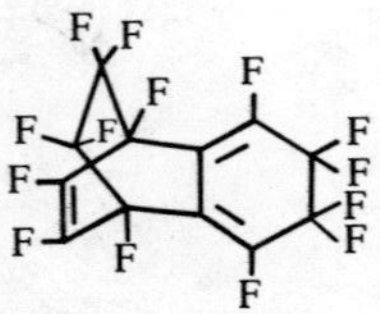	s	ls	691.0	c 84	MgK_α	52

TABLE 3 (continued)

Compound		Phase	Orbital	E_B(eV)	Calibrant	Exciting Radiation	Reference
$C_{12}H_6F_{18}$	$-[CF(CF_3)-CF_2]_m-[CF_2CH_2]_n-$ m:n, 2:3	s	1s	690.2 (3)	b 285.0	MgK_α	130
$C_{15}H_3CrF_{18}O_6$	$Cr(CF_3COCHCOCF_3)_3$	s	1s	690.9	c 84	MgK_α	26
$C_{18}H_{15}F_3N_3P_3$	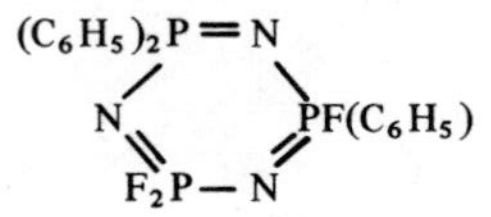	s	1s	688.1 (3)	d 285.0	AlK_α	105
$C_{20}H_{14}Cl_3F_{23}$	$-[CF_2-CFCl]_m-[CF_2-CH_2]_n-$ m:n, 3:7	s	1s	690.5 (3)	b 285.0	MgK_α	130
$C_{23}H_{14}F_{32}$	$-[CF(CF_3)-CF_2]_m-[CF_2-CH_2]_n-$ m:n, 3:7	s	1s	689.9 (3)	b 285.0	MgK_α	130
$C_{24}H_{20}F_2N_3P_3$	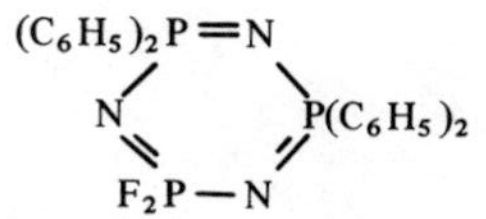	s	1s	688.1 (3)	d 285.0	AlK_α	105
$C_{37}H_{30}BClF_4IrNO_2P_2$	$[Ir(CO)(P(C_6H_5)_3)_2Cl(NO^+)]BF_4$	s	1s	684.0 (3)	d 285.0	AlK_α	82
$C_{37}H_{30}BF_4IIrNO_2P_2$	$[Ir(CO)(P(C_6H_5)_3)_2I(NO^+)BF_4$	s	1s	684.4 (3)	d 285.0	AlK_α	82
$C_{38}H_{30}ClF_4P_2Rh$	$((C_6H_5)_3P)_2Rh(C_2F_4)Cl$	s	1s	687.1 (3)	d 285.0	AlK_α	82
$C_{38}H_{30}F_4P_2Pt$	$((C_6H_5)_3P)_2PtC_2F_4$	s	1s	686.3 (3)	d 285.0	AlK_α	82
$C_{39}H_{30}ClF_4IrOP_2$	$Ir(CO)(P(C_6H_5)_3)_2(Cl)\ C_2F_4$	s	1s	686.2 (3)	d 285.0	AlK_α	82
CaF_2	CaF_2	s	2p	16.15	a 290	AlK_α	30
CaF_2	CaF_2	s	1s	692.7	a 290.0	AlK_α	64

TABLE 3 (continued)

Compound		Phase	Orbital	E_B(eV)	Calibrant	Exciting Radiation	Reference
CdF_2	CdF_2	s	2p	13.65	a 290	AlK_α	30
CdF_2	CdF_2	s	ls	692.05	a 290.0	AlK_α	64
CeF_3	CeF_3	s	ls	694.1	a 290.0	AlK_α	64
$CrF_6H_{12}N_3$	$(NH_4)_3CrF_6$	s	ls	689.5	a 290.0	AlK_α	64
CrF_6K_3	K_3CrF_6	s	ls	683.5	c		33
CsF	CsF	s	2p	14	a 290	AlK_α	30
CsF	CsF	s	ls	687.8	a 290.0	AlK_α	64
CsF_6Sb	$CsSbF_6$	s	ls	695.0	a 290.0	AlK_α	64
CuF_2	CuF_2	s	ls	687.9	a 285.5	AlK_α	46
$CuF_2 \cdot 2H_2O$	$CuF_2 \cdot 2H_2O$	s	ls	686.7	a 285.5	AlK_α	46
FK	KF	s	ls	690.35	a 290.0	AlK_α	64
FK	KF	s	2p	13.6	a 290	AlK_α	30
FLi	LiF	s	ls 2s	686.1 30.5	b 285.0	MgK_α	71
FLi	LiF	s	2p	15.6	a 290	AlK_α	30
FLi	LiF	s	ls	692.8	a 290.0	AlK_α	64
FNa	NaF	s	ls	693.8	a 290.0	AlK_α	64
FNa	NaF	s	K	685.4 (5)	e, i	CrK_α	76
FRb	RbF	s	ls	691.3	a 290.0	AlK_α	64
F_2Mg	MgF_2	s	ls	695.0	a 290.0	AlK_α	64

TABLE 3 (continued)

Compound		Phase	Orbital	E_B(eV)	Calibrant	Exciting Radiation	Reference
$F_2Ni \cdot 4H_2O$	$NiF_2 \cdot 4H_2O$	s	ls	691.5	a 290.0	AlK_{α}	64
F_2OS	SOF_2	g	ls	693.6	CHF_3 Fls 694.4	MgK_{α}	151
F_2Pb	PbF_2	s	ls	690.1	a 290.0	AlK_{α}	64
F_2Sr	SrF_2	s	ls	693.45	a 290.0	AlK_{α}	64
F_2Sr	SrF_2	s	2p	17.0	a 290	AlK_{α}	30
$F_3Ga \cdot 3H_2O$	$GaF_3 \cdot 3H_2O$	s	ls	692.9	a 290.0	AlK_{α}	64
F_3KNi	$KNiF_3$	s	ls	692.6	a 290.0	AlK_{α}	64
F_3La	LaF_3	s	ls	694.8	a 290.0	AlK_{α}	64
F_3Sm	SmF_3	s	ls	692.8	a 290.0	AlK_{α}	64
F_3Yb	YbF_3	s	ls	692.9	a 290.0	AlK_{α}	64
F_4Th	ThF_4	s	ls	693.6	a 290.0	AlK_{α}	64
F_4Zr	ZrF_4	s	ls	693.5	a 290.0	AlK_{α}	64
$F_5FeH_{10}N_2O$	$(NH_4)_2Fe(H_2O)F_5$	s	ls	689.45	a 290.0	AlK_{α}	64
$F_5H_{10}InN_2O$	$(NH_4)In(H_2O)F_5$	s	ls	691.0	a 290.0	AlK_{α}	64
$F_6GaH_{12}N_3$	$(NH_4)_3GaF_6$	s	ls	691.3	a 290.0	AlK_{α}	64
F_6GeK_2	K_2GeF_6	s	ls	694.1	a 290.0	AlK_{α}	64
$F_6H_{12}O_6SiZn$	$Zn(H_2O)_6SiF_6$	s	ls	692.15	a 290.0	AlK_{α}	64
F_6HfK_2	K_2HfF_6	s	ls	692.6	a 290.0	AlK_{α}	64
F_6KP	KPF_6	s	ls	694.0	a 290.0	AlK_{α}	64

TABLE 3 (continued)

Compound		Phase	Orbital	E_B(eV)	Calibrant	Exciting Radiation	Reference
F_6K_2Si	K_2SiF_6	s	ls	693.5	a 290.0	AlK_α	64
F_6K_2Ti	K_2TiF_6	s	ls	692.1	a 290.0	AlK_α	64
F_6K_2U	K_2UF_6	s	ls	691.9	a 290.0	AlK_α	64
F_6S	SF_6	g	ls	694.6	CHF_3 Fls 694.4	MgK_α	151
F_7K_2Nb	K_2NbF_7	s	ls	692.7	a 290.0	AlK_α	64
F_7K_2Ta	K_2TaF_7	s	ls	692.0	a 290.0	AlK_α	64
$SiF_6H_{12}N_3$	$(NH_4)_3SiF_6$	s	ls	690.9	a 290.0	AlK_α	64
Fe							
$Al_6Ca_4Fe_6H_2O_{22}Si_6$	Epidote 13575 86% Fe^{3+} $4Ca0.3(AlFe)_2O_3 \cdot 6SiO_2 \cdot H_2O$	s	$2p_{1/2}$ $2p_{3/2}$ 3p	723.1 (7) 709.4 (7) 56.5 (7)	c 84.0 (3)	Al, MgK_α	57
Br_2Fe	$FeBr_2$	s	$2p_{3/2}$ 3s	710.5 (3) 95.9 (3)	b 285.0	Al, MgK_α	112
Br_3Fe	$FeBr_3$	s	$2p_{3/2}$ 3s	710.3 (3) 96.7 (3)	b 285.0	Al, MgK_α	112
$C_5FeN_6Na_2O \cdot 2H_2O$	$Na_2[Fe(CN)_5NO] \cdot 2H_2O$	s	$2p_{3/2}$ 3p	709.1 (5) 55.9 (6)	c 84.0 (3)	AlK_α	89
C_5FeO_5	$Fe(CO)_5$	s	$2p_{1/2}$ $2p_{3/2}$	726.0 (3) 713.0 (3)		MgK_α	23
C_5FeO_5	$Fe(CO)_5$	s	3p	54.0 (2)			3
$C_6FeK_3N_6$	$K_3Fe(CN)_6$	s	3p	55.0 (2)			3

TABLE 3 (continued)

Compound		Phase	Orbital	E_B(eV)	Calibrant	Exciting Radiation	Reference
$C_6FeK_3N_6$	$K_3Fe(CN)_6$	s	$2p_{1/2}$ $2p_{3/2}$ 3s $3p_{3/2}$	724.8 711.3 95.6 57.1		MgK_α	34
$C_6FeK_3N_6$	$K_3Fe(CN)_6$	s s 1 *M* frozen H_2O soln s 0.5 *M* frozen H_2O soln s 0.1 *M* frozen H_2O soln s 0.05 *M* frozen H_2O soln	3p 3p 3p 3p 3p	55.0 (2) 55.2 (2) 55.3 (2) 55.3 (2) 55.2 (2)			5
$C_6FeK_4N_6$	$K_4Fe(CN)_6$	s	3p	54.0 (2)			3
$C_6FeK_4N_6$	$K_4Fe(CN)_6$	s	$2p_{1/2}$ $2p_{3/2}$ 3s $3p_{3/2}$	722.8 709.9 94.8 56.8		MgK_α	34
$C_6FeK_4N_6$	$K_4Fe(CN)_6$	s	$2p_{3/2}$ 3s	708.7 (3) 91.2 (3)	b 285.0	Al, MgK_α	112
$C_6FeK_4N_6$	$K_4Fe(CN)_6$	s	3p	54.0 (2)			5
$C_6FeK_4N_6$	$K_4Fe(CN)_6$	s 0.5 *M* frozen H_2O soln	3p	54.2 (2)			5
$C_6FeN_6Zn_2$	$Zn_2Fe(CN)_6$	s	$2p_{3/2}$	708.2 (3)	b 285.0	Al, MgK_α	112
$C_6Fe_2KN_6$	$KFe^{2+}Fe^{3+}(CN)_6$	s	$^{3+}2p_{1/2}$ $2p_{3/2}$ $3p_{3/2}$	727 714 ~60		MgK_α	34
$C_6Fe_2KN_6$	$KFe^{+2}Fe^{+3}(CN)_6$	s	$^{+2}2p_{1/2}$ $^{+2}2p_{3/2}$	722.6 709.6		MgK_α	34

TABLE 3 (continued)

Compound		Phase	Orbital	E_B(eV)	Calibrant	Exciting Radiation	Reference
$C_6H_9ClFe_3O_7$	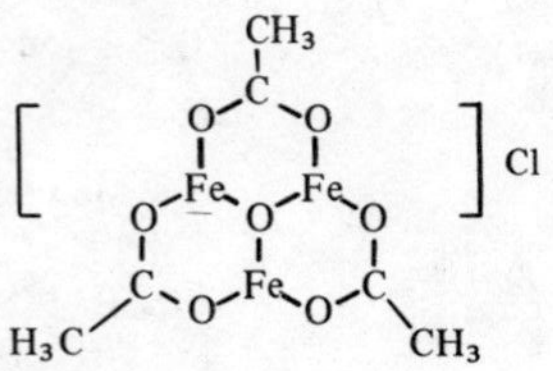	s	$(+3)2p_{3/2}$	711.8			126
$C_8H_{14}BrFeN_2S_4$	$FeBr(S_2CN(CH_2CH_3)C_2H_2)_2$	s	3p	54.1 (2)			3
$C_9Fe_2O_9$	$Fe_2(CO)_9$	s	3p	54.6 (2)			4
$C_{10}H_{10}Fe$	$Fe(\pi\text{-}C_5H_5)_2$	s	$2p_{1/2}$ $2p_{3/2}$	723.8 (3) 710.8 (3)		MgK_α	23
$C_{10}H_{10}Fe$	$Fe(C_5H_5)_2$	s	3p	53.7 (2)			3
$C_{15}H_{30}FeN_3S_6$	$Fe(S_2CN(C_2H_5)_2)_3$	s	3p	53.4 (2)			3
$C_{16}H_{12}FeN_3O_7$	$[Fe(C_5H_5)_2][(NO_2)_3C_6H_2O]$	s	3p	54.9 (2)			4
$C_{22}H_{48}FeNS_4$	$[Fe(S_2C_6H_3CH_3)_2][N(n\text{-}C_4H_9)_4]$	s	3p	53.2 (2)			4
$C_{26}H_{22}Fe_2N_3O_7$	$\begin{bmatrix}(\pi\text{-}C_5H_5)_2Fe^{II} \\ (\pi\text{-}C_5H_5)_2Fe^{III}\end{bmatrix}(2,4,6(NO_2)_3C_6H_2O^-)$	s	$Fe^{II}2p_{3/2}$ $Fe^{III}2p_{3/2}$	707.7 711.1		AlK_α	35
$C_{32}H_{16}ClFeN_8$	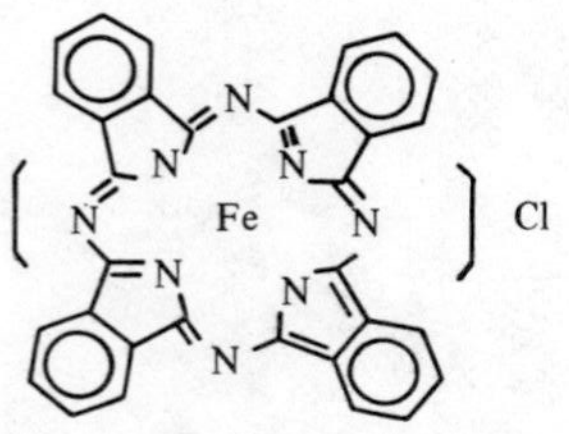	s	3p	54.4 (2)			3
$C_{32}H_{28}Cl_2FeN_4O_4$	*trans*-$FeCl_2(p\text{-}CNC_6H_4OCH_3)_4$	s	$2p_{3/2}$	707.3 (5)	c 84.0 (3)	AlK_α	89

TABLE 3 (continued)

	Compound	Phase	Orbital	E_B(eV)	Calibrant	Exciting Radiation	Reference
$C_{32}H_{28}Cl_6FeN_4O_4Sn_2$	*trans*-$Fe(SnCl_3)_2(p\text{-}CNC_6H_4OCH_3)_4$	s	$2p_{3/2}$ 3p	707.7 (3) 54.7 (5)	c 84.0 (3)	AlK_α	89
$C_{36}H_{24}Cl_2FeN_6O_8$	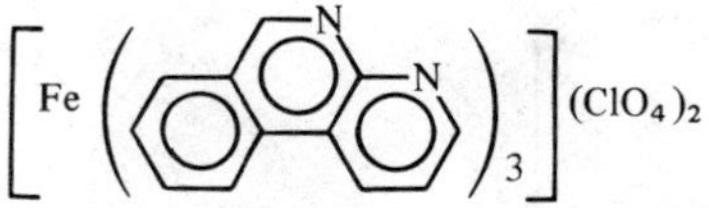	s	$2p_{3/2}$ 3s 3p	706.6 (3) 91.2 (8) 54.0 (5)	c 84.0 (3)	AlK_α	89
$C_{40}H_{35}Cl_4FeN_5O_9Sn$	$[Fe(SnCl_3)(p\text{-}CNC_6H_4OCH_3)_5]ClO_4$	s	$2p_{3/2}$ 3p	708.0 (4) 55.2 (6)	c 84.0 (3)	AlK_α	89
$C_{50}H_{44}FeP_4S_4$	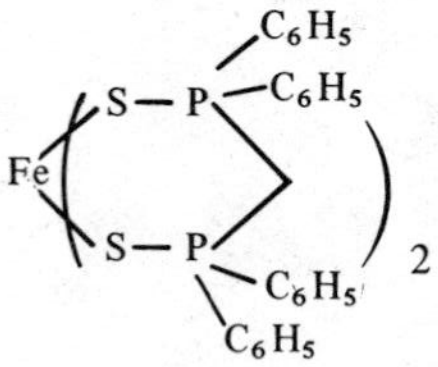	s	(+2) $2p_{3/2}$	708.5			126
$C_{56}H_{40}Fe_2S_8$	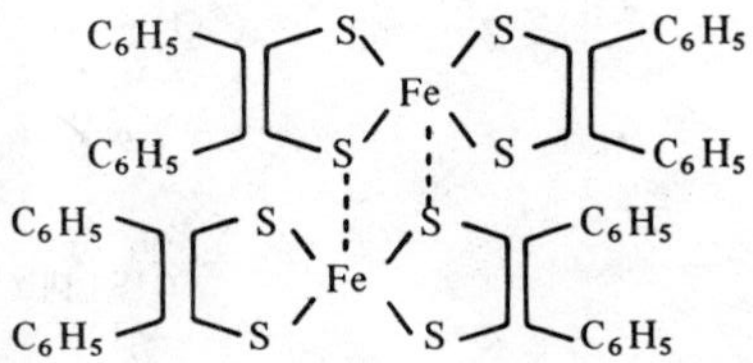	s	(+3) $2p_{3/2}$	710.3			126
$C_{56}H_{40}Fe_2S_8$	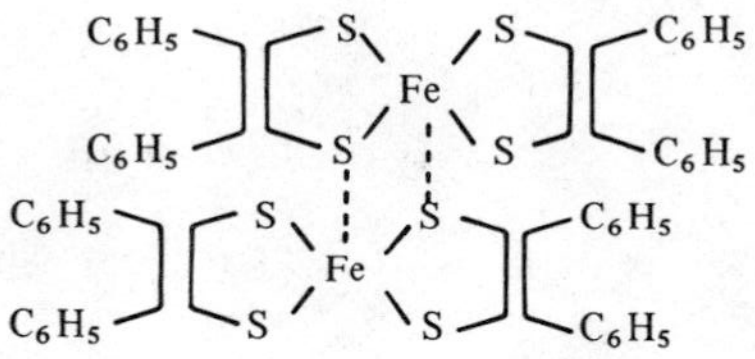	s	(+2) $2p_{3/2}$	707.9			126

TABLE 3 (continued)

Compound		Phase	Orbital	E_B(eV)	Calibrant	Exciting Radiation	Reference
$CaFeO_6Si_2$	Hedenbergite 103182 77% Fe^{2+} $CaFeSi_2O_6$	s	$2p_{1/2}$ $2p_{3/2}$ 3s 3p	723.3 (15) 710.2 (10) 92.3 (10) 56.1 (10)	Internal Ols 530.8 (7)	Al, MgK_α	57
$CaFeO_6Si_2$	Hedenbergite 2B 85% Fe^{2+} $CaFeSi_2O_6$	s	$2p_{1/2}$ $2p_{3/2}$ 3s 3p	722.7 (6) 709.4 (6) 92.5 (7) 55.6 (8)	Internal Ols 530.8 (7)	Al, MgK_α	57
$CaFeO_6Si_2$	Hedenbergite R6955 54% Fe^{2+} $CaFeSi_2O_6$	s	$2p_{1/2}$ $2p_{3/2}$ 3s 3p	723.1 (6) 710.0 (6) 92.0 (6) 55.6 (17)	c 84.0 (3)	Al, MgK_α	57
Cl_2Fe	$FeCl_2$	s	$2p_{3/2}$ 3s	710.8 (3) 95.6 (3)	b 285.0	Al, MgK_α	112
Cl_3Fe	$FeCl_3$	s	$2p_{3/2}$ 3s	711.5 (3) 96.4 (3)	b 285.0	Al, MgK_α	112
$Cl_4FeN_5S_5$	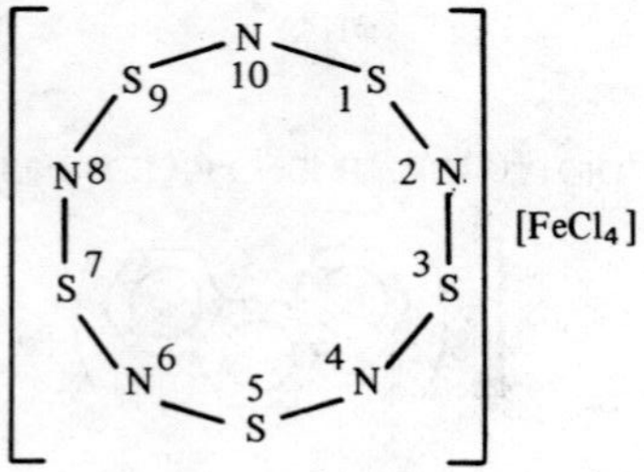		$2p_{3/2}$	713.8	a	MgK_α	106
$Cl_5FeN_2S_3$	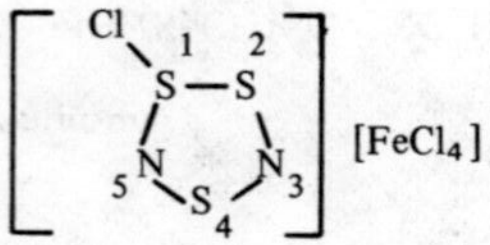		$2p_{3/2}$	713.8	a	MgK_α	106

TABLE 3 (continued)

Compound		Phase	Orbital	E_B(eV)	Calibrant	Exciting Radiation	Reference
F_2Fe	FeF_2	s	$2p_{3/2}$	711.5 (3)	b 285.0	Al, MgK_{α}	112
			3s	97.4 (3)			
F_2Fe	FeF_2	s	2p	729	a 284	MgK_{α}	31
				714			
			3p	60			
F_3Fe	FeF_3	s	$2p_{3/2}$	714.4 (3)	b 285.0	Al, MgK_{α}	112
			3s	100.4 (3)			
F_3Fe	FeF_3	s	2p	731	a 284	MgK_{α}	31
				718			
			3p	62			
F_3Fe	FeF_3	s	$2p_{1/2}$	731		MgK_{α}	34
			$2p_{3/2}$	717.2			
			3s	103			
			$3p_{3/2}$	61.5			
F_6FeK_3	K_3FeF_6	s	$2p_{3/2}$	714.6 (3)	b 285.0	Al, MgK_{α}	112
			3s	100.3 (3)			
F_6FeK_3	K_3FeF_6	s	3p	57.7 (2)			3
F_6FeNa_3	Na_3FeF_6	s	3s	101.0 (3)	b 285.0	Al, MgK_{α}	112
F_6Fe_2K	$K_{0.5}FeF_3$	s	2p	731	a 284	MgK_{α}	31
				729			
				718			
				714			
			3p	62			
				60			
Fe	Fe(bcc)	s	3p	52 (0.5)		MgK_{α}	122
Fe	Fe	s	K	7,113.6 (5)	e	Cu, MoK_{α}	75
Fe	Fe	s	3p	52.4 (2)			3

TABLE 3 (continued)

Compound		Phase	Orbital	E_B(eV)	Calibrant	Exciting Radiation	Reference
Fe	Fe	s	d band	−1.5 (2)	Pd Fermi level 0.0	MgK_a	51
Fe	Fe	s	K	7,116.9	$CuK(MoK_{al})$	MoK_{al}	119
Fe	Fe	s	L_I	846.1	MgO $MgK(CuK_{al})$	CuK_{al}	67
$FeH_8N_2O_8S_2 \cdot 6H_2O$	$FeSO_4(NH_4)_2SO_4 \cdot 6H_2O$	s	3p	54.2 (2)			3
FeK_2O_4	K_2FeO_4	s	3p	57.7 (2)			3
$FeN_3O_9 \cdot 9H_2O$	$Fe(NO_3)_3 \cdot 9H_2O$	s	3p	56.3 (2)			3
FeO_4S	$FeSO_4$	s	3p	55.2 (2)			3
$FeO_4S \cdot 7H_2O$	$FeSO_4 \cdot 7H_2O$	s	3p	54.7 (2)			3
FeS	FeS	s	3p	54.7 (2)			3
FeS	FeS	s	3p	52.4 (2)			3
FeS	FeS	s	$2p_{3/2}$ 3s	710.5 (3) 96.3 (3)	b 285.0	Al, MgK_a	112
FeS_2	FeS_2	s	3p	53.0 (2)			3
$Fe_2H_8N_2O_{16}S_4 \cdot 24H_2O$	$Fe_2(SO_4)_3(NH_4)_2SO_4 \cdot 24H_2O$	s	3p	56.6 (2)			3
Fe_2O_3	Fe_2O_3	s	3p	54.9 (2)			3
Fe_2O_3	Fe_2O_3	s	$2p_{3/2}$ 3s	711.5 (3) 97.9 (3)	b 285.0	Al, MgK_a	112
Fe_2O_3	α-Fe_2O_3	s	$2p_{1/2}$ $2p_{3/2}$ 3s $3p_{3/2}$	727 713 99 57.8		MgK_a	34

TABLE 3 (continued)

Compound		Phase	Orbital	E_B(eV)	Calibrant	Exciting Radiation	Reference
$Fe_2O_{12}S_3$	$Fe_2(SO_4)_3$	s	$2p_{1/2}$ $2p_{3/2}$ 3s $3p_{3/2}$	729 714.7 101.5 59.6		MgK_a	34
$Fe_2O_{12}S_3 \cdot XH_2O$	$Fe_2(SO_4)_3 \cdot XH_2O$	s	3p	57.0 (2)			3
$Fe_5H_2Na_2O_{24}Si_8$	Crocidolite 93720 55% Fe^{2+}, 40% Fe^{3+} $Na_2Fe_3{}^{(+2)}Fe_2{}^{(+3)}(Si_4O_{11})_2(OH)_2$	s	$2p_{1/2}$ $2p_{3/2}$ 3s	723.4 (8) 710.3 (6) 92.6 (6)	Internal O1s 530.8 (7)	Al, MgK_a	57
Ferredoxin from Clostridium pasteurianum		s	Fe(+3) $2p_{3/2}$	710.0			126
Ferredoxin from Clostridium acidi-urici		s	Fe(+3) $2p_{3/2}$	709.9			126
Ferredoxin from Chromatium		s	Fe(+2) $2p_{3/2}$	708.2			126
Iron phosvitin		s	Fe(+3) $2p_{3/2}$	711.0			126
Hemin chloride		s	Fe(+3) $2p_{3/2}$	710.2			126
Salen		s	Fe(+3) $2p_{3/2}$	710.1			126
Ga							
Ga	Ga	s	K	10,367.3	CuA6, CuK(MoK_{a1})	MoK_{a1}	123
Gd							
Gd_2O_3	Gd_2O_3	s	L_I L_{II} L_{III}	8,375.7 7,930.8 7,243.1	e	MoK_{a1}	56
Ge							
$BrGeH_3$	GeH_3Br	g	$3p_{3/2}$	123.38	Ar $2p_{3/2}$ 248.457		85

TABLE 3 (continued)

Compound		Phase	Orbital	E_B(eV)	Calibrant	Exciting Radiation	Reference
CH_6Ge	GeH_3CH_3	g	$3p_{3/2}$	122.64	Ar $2p_{3/2}$ 248.457		85
$C_4H_{12}Ge$	$Ge(CH_3)_4$	g	$3p_{3/2}$	120.55	Ar $2p_{3/2}$ 248.457		85
$ClGeH_3$	GeH_3Cl	g	$3p_{3/2}$	123.78	Ar $2p_{3/2}$ 248.457		85
Cl_4Ge	$GeCl_4$	g	$3p_{3/2}$	124.17	Ar $2p_{3/2}$ 248.457		85
F_4Ge	GeF_4	g	$3p_{3/2}$	128.91	Ar $2p_{3/2}$ 248.457		85
Ge	Ge	s	K	11,103.8	GeA6, CuK(MoK_{al})	MoK_{al}	123
			L_I	1,413.7	GeA6, CuA6		
Ge	Ge	s	X_4	2.4	Au E_{Fermi}	AlK_a	134
			W_2	3.6			
			V	4.9			
			L_1	7.2			
			W_1	8.6			
			L_2	10.3			
			T_1	13.0			
GeH_4	GeH_4	g	$3p_{3/2}$	123.69	Ar $2p_{3/2}$ 248.457		85
Hf							
Hf_2O_3	Hf_2O_3	s	L_I	11,271.7 (8)	e	MoK_{al}	68
			L_{II}	10,739.0 (8)			
			L_{III}	9,560.6 (9)			
Hg							
$C_4CoHgN_4S_4$	$Hg[Co(SCN)_4]$	s	$4f_{5/2}$	110.6	a 290.0	AlK_a	107
			$4f_{7/2}$	106.55			
$C_4HgK_2N_4S_4$	$K_2Hg(SCN)_4$	s	$4f_{5/2}$	110.85	a 290.0	AlK_a	107
			$4f_{7/2}$	106.75			

TABLE 3 (continued)

Compound		Phase	Orbital	E_B(eV)	Calibrant	Exciting Radiation	Reference
Hg	Hg	s	L_{III}	12,284.1 (4)	e	MoK_a	77
			M_{III}	2,847.0 (5)		CuK_a	
			M_{IV}	2,384.8 (4)			
			M_V	2,294.9 (4)		CrK_a	
Hg	Hg	s	L_{III}	11,284.6	CuK(MoK_{al})	MoK_{al}	119
HgI_4K_2	K_2HgI_4		$4f_{5/2}$	111.85	a 290.0	AlK_a	107
			$4f_{7/2}$	107.8			
HgO	HgO	s	4f	103 (0.5)		MgK_a	122
HgO	HgO		$4f_{5/2}$	112.6	a 290.0	AlK_a	107
			$4f_{7/2}$	108.55			
HgS	HgS	s	$5d_{5/2}$	8.48 (20)	k 283.8	AlK_a	109
			$5d_{3/2}$	10.27 (20)			
			$5p_{3/2}$	65.29 (20)			
			$5p_{1/2}$	84.50 (20)			
			$4f_{7/2}$	100.55 (20)			
			$4f_{5/2}$	104.61 (20)			
			$4d_{5/2}$	359.48 (20)			
			$4d_{3/2}$	378.80 (20)			
			$4p_{3/2}$	577.14 (20)			
			$4p_{1/2}$	680.17 (20)			
			4s	803.16 (20)			
HgSe	HgSe	s	$5d_{5/2}$	7.58 (20)	k 283.8	AlK_a	109
			$5d_{3/2}$	9.39 (20)			
			$5p_{3/2}$	65.15 (20)			
			$5p_{1/2}$	83.51 (20)			
			$4f_{7/2}$	99.50 (20)			
			$4f_{5/2}$	103.57 (20)			
			$4d_{5/2}$	358.62 (20)			
			$4d_{3/2}$	377.98 (20)			
			$4p_{3/2}$	575.89 (20)			
			$4p_{1/2}$	679.47 (20)			
			4s	802.22 (20)			

TABLE 3 (continued)

	Compound	Phase	Orbital	E_B(eV)	Calibrant	Exciting Radiation	Reference
HgTe	HgTe	s	$4f_{7/2}$	99.61	k 283.8	AlK_{α}	109
			$4f_{5/2}$	103.68			
			$4d_{5/2}$	358.75			
			$4d_{3/2}$	377.98			
			$4p_{3/2}$	577.00			
			$4p_{1/2}$	679.93			
			$5d_{5/2}$	7.53 (20)			
			$5d_{3/2}$	9.44 (20)			
			$5p_{3/2}$	64.33 (20)			
			$5p_{1/2}$	83.32 (20)			
Ho							
Ho_2O_3	Ho_2O_3	s	L_I	9,394.5	e	$MoK_{\alpha l}$	56
			L_{II}	8,918.4			
			L_{III}	8,070.9			
I							
$BiCsI_4$	$CsBiI_4$	s	$3d_{3/2}$	637.5	a 290.0	AlK_{α}	64
			$3d_{5/2}$	626.0			
			4d	57.6			
BiI_3	BiI_3	s	$3d_{3/2}$	637.25	a 290.0	AlK_{α}	64
			$3d_{5/2}$	625.8			
			4d	57.8			
CH_3I	CH_3I	g	$3d_{5/2}$	1.10 (3)	CF_3I I3$d_{5/2}$ 0.0	MgK_{α}	110
C_2H_5I	CH_3CH_2I	g	$3d_{5/2}$	1.36 (3)	CF_3I I3$d_{5/2}$ 0.0	MgK_{α}	110
C_3H_7I	$CH_3CH_2CH_2I$	g	$3d_{5/2}$	1.45 (4)	CF_5I I3$d_{5/2}$ 0.0	MgK_{α}	110
C_3H_7I	$(CH_3)_2CHI$	g	$3d_{5/2}$	1.57 (3)	CF_3I I3$d_{5/2}$ 0.0	MgK_{α}	110
C_4H_9I	$CH_3CH_2CH_2CH_2I$	g	$3d_{5/2}$	1.49 (4)	CF_3I I3$d_{5/2}$ 0.0	MgK_{α}	110
C_4H_9I	$(CH_3)_3CI$	g	$3d_{5/2}$	1.73 (5)	CF_3I I3$d_{5/2}$ 0.0	MgK_{α}	110

TABLE 3 (continued)

Compound		Phase	Orbital	E_B(eV)	Calibrant	Exciting Radiation	Reference
$C_4H_{12}IN$	$[N(CH_3)_4]I$	s	$3d_{3/2}$	635.6	a 290.0	AlK_α	64
			$3d_{5/2}$	624.15			
			4d	54.3			
$C_5H_{11}I$	$CH_3CH_2CH_2CH_2CH_2I$	g	$3d_{5/2}$	1.51 (3)	CF_3I I $3d_{5/2}$ 0.0	MgK_α	110
$C_6H_{18}I_2P_2Pt$	*cis*-$((CH_3)_3P)_2PtI_2$	s	$3d_{5/2}$	621.4	c 84	MgK_α	20
$C_6H_{18}I_2P_2Pt$	*trans*-$((CH_3)_3P)_2PtI_2$	s	$3d_{5/2}$	622.1	c 84	MgK_α	20
$C_8H_{20}IN$	$[N(C_2H_5)_4]I$	s	$3d_{3/2}$	636.9	a 290.0	AlK_α	64
			$3d_{5/2}$	625.6			
			4d	54.1			
$C_{12}H_{30}I_2P_2Pt_2$	$((C_2H_5)_3P)_2PtI_2$	s	$3d_{5/2}$	619.4 (1)	d 285.0	AlK_α	87
$C_{16}H_{36}IN$	$[N(C_4H_9)_4]I$	s	$3d_{3/2}$	635.1	a 290.0	AlK_α	64
			$3d_{5/2}$	623.6			
			4d	54.6			
$C_{37}H_{30}BF_4IIrNO_2P_2$	$[Ir(CO)(P(C_6H_5)_3)_2I(NO^+)]BF_4$	s	$3d_{5/2}$	618.8 (3)	d 285.0	AlK_α	82
$C_{37}H_{30}IIrO_3P_2$	$Ir(CO)(P(C_6H_5)_3)_2I(O_2)$	s	$3d_{5/2}$	618.6 (3)	d 285.0	AlK_α	82
$C_{38}H_{30}IIrO_2P_2$	$Ir(CO)_2(P(C_6H_5)_3)_2I$	s	$3d_{5/2}$	618.4 (3)	d 285.0	AlK_α	82
CdI_2	CdI_2	s	$3d_{3/2}$	638.4	a 290.0	AlK_α	64
			$3d_{5/2}$	626.8			
			4d	58.3			
CsI	CsI	s	$3d_{3/2}$	638.55	a 290.0	AlK_α	64
			$3d_{5/2}$	627.0			
			4d	57.95			
CsI	CsI	s	5p	11.85	a 290	AlK_α	30
Cs_2I_6Os	Cs_2OsI_6	s	$3d_{3/2}$	635.7	a 290.0	AlK_α	64
			$3d_{5/2}$	624.15			
			4d	56.0			

TABLE 3 (continued)

Compound		Phase	Orbital	E_B(eV)	Calibrant	Exciting Radiation	Reference
CuI	CuI	s	$3d_{5/2}$	622.2	a 285.5	AlK_{α}	46
HI	HI	g	$3d_{5/2}$	0.20 (4)	CF_3I $I3d_{5/2}$ 0.0	MgK_{α}	110
HgI_4K_2	K_2HgI_4	s	$3d_{3/2}$	637.6	a 290.0	AlK_{α}	64
			$3d_{5/2}$	626.1			
			4d	57.3			
IK	KI	s	$3d_{3/2}$	635.5	i	$CrK_{\alpha 1}$	1
			$3d_{5/2}$	623.5			
			$4s_{1/2}$	190.5			
			$4d_{3/2\text{-}5/2}$	54.4			
IK	KI	s	$2s_{1/2}$	5,191.6	i	$CuK_{\alpha 1}$	1
			$2p_{1/2}$	4,856.2			
			$2p_{3/2}$	4,561.0			
			$2p_{1/2}$	937.0			
			$3p_{3/2}$	880.7			
IK	KI	s	5p	11.0	a 290	AlK_{α}	30
IK	KI	s	$3d_{3/2}$	638.5	a 290.0	AlK_{α}	64
			$3d_{5/2}$	626.9			
			4d	57.4			
IKO_3	KIO_3	s	$3d_{3/2}$	642.5	a 290.0	AlK_{α}	64
			$3d_{5/2}$	631.0			
			4d	62.1			
IKO_3	KIO_3	s	$2s_{1/2}$	5,197.1	KI $I2s_{1/2}$ 5,191.6	$CuK_{\alpha 1}$	1
			$2p_{1/2}$	4,861.9	KI $I2p_{1/2}$ 4,856.2		
			$2p_{3/2}$	4,566.5	KI $I2p_{3/2}$ 4,561.0		
			$3d_{3/2}$	637.9	KI $I3d_{3/2}$ 6,355	$CrK_{\alpha 1}$	
			$3d_{5/2}$	628.1	KI $I3d_{5/2}$ 623.5		
			$4s_{1/2}$	195.8	KI $I4s_{1/2}$ 190.5		
			$4p_{3/2}$	128.1	KI $I4p_{1/2\text{-}3/2}$ 128		
			$4d_{3/2\text{-}5/2}$	59.5	KI $I4d_{3/2\text{-}5/2}$ 54.5		

TABLE 3 (continued)

Compound		Phase	Orbital	E_B(eV)	Calibrant	Exciting Radiation	Reference
IKO_4	KIO_4	s	$3d_{3/2}$	644.3	a 290.0	AlK_α	64
			$3d_{5/2}$	632.8			
			4d	63.7			
IKO_4	KIO_4	s	$2s_{1/2}$	5,197.4	KI $I2s_{1/2}$ 5,191.6	$CuK_{\alpha 1}$	1
			$2p_{1/2}$	4,861.7	KI $I2p_{1/2}$ 4,856.2		
			$2p_{3/2}$	4,567.4	KI $I2p_{3/2}$ 4,561.0		
			$3d_{3/2}$	641.6	KI $I3d_{3/2}$ 635.5	$CrK_{\alpha 1}$	
			$3d_{5/2}$	629.6	KI $I3d_{5/2}$ 623.5		
			$4s_{1/2}$	197.0	KI $I4s_{1/2}$ 190.5		
			$4p_{3/2}$	128.7	KI $I4p_{1/2\text{-}3/2}$ 128		
			$4d_{3/2\text{-}5/2}$	60.3	KI $I4d_{3/2\text{-}5/2}$ 54.4	$CrK_{\alpha 1}$	
INa	NaI	s	$3d_{3/2}$	638.9	a 290.0	AlK_α	64
			$3d_{5/2}$	627.3			
			4d	57.6			
$INaO_4$	$NaIO_4$	s	$3d_{3/2}$	643.75	a 290.0	AlK_α	64
			$3d_{5/2}$	632.25			
			4d	63.35			
INa_5O_6	Na_5IO_6	s	$3d_{3/2}$	643.25	a 290.0	AlK_α	64
			$3d_{5/2}$	631.65			
			4d	62.65			
IRb	RbI	s	L_I	5,188.0 (5)	e	CuK_α	78
			L_{II}	4,851.9 (5)			
			L_{III}	4,557.0 (7)			
ITl	TlI	s	$3d_{3/2}$	636.25	a 290.0	AlK_α	64
			$3d_{5/2}$	624.75			
			4d	56.25			
I_6K_2Pt	K_2PtI_6	s	$3d_{3/2}$	636.5	a 290.0	AlK_α	64
			$3d_{5/2}$	624.9			
			4d	56.3			

TABLE 3 (continued)

Compound		Phase	Orbital	E_B(eV)	Calibrant	Exciting Radiation	Reference
In							
In	In	s	L_I L_{II}	4,237.7 3,937.8	$InL_{III}(CuK_{\alpha1})$	$CuK_{\alpha1}$	45
In	In	s	L_{III}	3,730.0	CuA6	$CuK_{\alpha1}$	123
In	In	s	$4d_{3/2}$ $4d_{5/2}$ 5s 5p	17.64 (9) 16.74 (9) 4.1 (4) 0.75 (13)	Au E_{Fermi}	AlK_α	137
Ir							
$C_8H_{24}Cl_6IrN_2$	$[N(CH_3)_4]_2IrCl_6$		$4f_{5/2}$ $4f_{7/2}$	71.3 68.5	a 290.0	AlK_α	107
$C_{12}H_{30}Cl_4IrP_2$	*trans*-$IrCl_4(P(CH_2CH_3)_3)_2$	s	$4f_{5/2}$ $4f_{7/2}$	66.5 (3) 63.8 (3)	d 285	Mg, AlK_α	97
$C_{16}H_{22}Cl_4IrP_2$	*trans*-$IrCl_4(P(CH_3)_2C_6H_5)_2$	s	$4f_{5/2}$ $4f_{7/2}$	66.5 (3) 63.7 (3)	d 285	Mg, AlK_α	97
$C_{18}H_{42}IrO_6P_3S_6$	$Ir[S_2P(OC_3H_7)_2]_3$		$4f_{5/2}$ $4f_{7/2}$	69.8 66.85	a 290.0	AlK_α	107
$C_{24}H_{33}Cl_3IrP_3$	*fac*-$IrCl_3(P(CH_3)_2C_6H_5)_3$	s	$4f_{5/2}$ $4f_{7/2}$	65.5 62.7	d 285	Mg, AlK_α	97
$C_{24}H_{33}Cl_3IrP_3$	*mer*-$IrCl_3(P(CH_3)_2C_6H_5)_3$	s	$4f_{5/2}$ $4f_{7/2}$	65.3 62.4	d 285	Mg, AlK_α	97
$C_{37}H_{30}BClF_4IrNO_2P_2$	$[Ir(CO)(P(C_6H_5)_3)_2Cl(NO^+)]BF_4$	s	$4f_{7/2}$ $4f_{5/2}$	63.1 (3) 65.8 (3)	d 285.0	AlK_α	82
$C_{37}H_{30}BF_4IIrNO_2P_2$	$[Ir(CO)(P(C_6H_5)_3)_2I(NO^+)]BF_4$	s	$4f_{7/2}$ $4f_{5/2}$	63.7 (3) 66.0 (3)	d 285.0	AlK_α	82

TABLE 3 (continued)

Compound		Phase	Orbital	E_B(eV)	Calibrant	Exciting Radiation	Reference
$C_{37}H_{30}ClIrO_3P_2$	$Ir(CO)(P(C_6H_5)_3)_2(Cl)O_2$	s	$4f_{7/2}$ $4f_{5/2}$	61.9 (3) 64.6 (3)	d 285.0	AlK_a	82
$C_{37}H_{30}IIrO_3P_2$	$Ir(CO)(P(C_6H_5)_3)_2I(O_2)$	s	$4f_{7/2}$ $4f_{5/2}$	62.1 (3) 64.6 (3)	d 285.0	AlK_a	82
$C_{38}H_{30}ClIrO_2P_2$	$Ir(CO)_2(P(C_6H_5)_3)_2Cl$	s	$4f_{7/2}$ $4f_{5/2}$	62.1 (3) 64.7 (3)	d 285.0	AlK_a	82
$C_{38}H_{30}IIrO_2P_2$	$Ir(CO)_2(P(C_6H_5)_3)_2I$	s	$4f_{7/2}$ $4f_{5/2}$	62.4 (3) 65.0 (3)	d 285.0	AlK_a	82
$C_{39}H_{30}ClF_4IrOP_2$	$Ir(CO)(P(C_6H_5)_3)_2(Cl)C_2F_4$	s	$4f_{7/2}$ $4f_{5/2}$	62.4 (3) 64.9 (3)	d 285.0	AlK_a	82
$C_{42}H_{30}ClIrN_4P_2$	$Ir(P(C_6H_5)_3)_2Cl(C_2(CN)_4)$	s	$4f_{7/2}$ $4f_{5/2}$	62.9 (3) 65.8 (3)	d 285.0	AlK_a	82
$C_{43}H_{30}ClIrN_4OP_2$	$Ir(CO)(P(C_6H_5)_3)_2Cl(C_2(CN)_4)$	s	$4f_{7/2}$ $4f_{5/2}$	63.4 (3) 65.9 (3)	d 285.0	AlK_a	82
$C_{48}H_{108}Cl_6IrN_3$	$[N(C_4H_9)_4]_3IrCl_6$		$4f_{5/2}$ $4f_{7/2}$	69.8 67.1	a 290.0	AlK_a	107
$Cl_3H_{15}IrN_5$	$[Ir(NH_3)_5Cl]Cl_2$		$4f_{5/2}$ $4f_{7/2}$	71.5 68.65	a 290.0	AlK_a	107
Cl_6Cs_2Ir	Cs_2IrCl_6		$4f_{5/2}$ $4f_{7/2}$	73.4 70.7	a 290.0	AlK_a	107
Cl_6IrK_2	K_2IrCl_6	s	$4f_{5/2}$ $4f_{7/2}$	66.0 (3) 63.2 (3)	a 285	Mg, AlK_a	97
Cl_6IrK_2	K_2IrCl_6	s	$4f_{7/2}$	62.7 (2)	c 83.8	AlK_a	41
Ir	Ir	s	$4f_{7/2}$	61.0	c 83.8	AlK_a	41

TABLE 3 (continued)

Compound		Phase	Orbital	E_B(eV)	Calibrant	Exciting Radiation	Reference
Ir	Ir(fcc)	s	4f	60 (0.5)		MgK_{α}	122
Ir	Ir	s	d band	−1.7 (2)	Pd Fermi level 0.0	MgK_{α}	51
				−4.3 (2)			
Ir	Ir	s	L_{III}	11,215.3	CuK($MoK_{\alpha 1}$)	$MoK_{\alpha 1}$	119
			L_{II}	12,824.8			
Ir	Ir	s	L_{II}	12,824.2 (4)	e	MoK_{α}	77
			L_{III}	11,215.3 (4)			
			M_{II}	2,909.0 (5)		CuK_{α}	
			M_{III}	2,550.4 (5)			
			M_{IV}	2,116.1 (4)		CrK_{α}	
			M_V	2,040.5 (4)			
K							
BF_4K	KBF_4	s	$2p_{1/2}$	303.4	a 290.0	AlK_{α}	64
			$2p_{3/2}$	301.0			
			3s	39.6			
			3p	24.8			
BeF_4K_2	K_2BeF_4	s	$2p_{1/2}$	303.8	a 290.0	AlK_{α}	64
			$2p_{3/2}$	301.3			
$BrC_4ClK_2N_4Pt$	$K_2Pt(CN)_4ClBr$	s	2p	294.2	g	MgK_{α}	129
BrK	KBr	s	2p	295.3	g	MgK_{α}	129
BrK	KBr	s	3p	23.3	a 290	AlK_{α}	30
BrK	KBr	s	$2p_{1/2}$	302.4	a 290.0	AlK_{α}	64
			$2p_{3/2}$	299.8			
			3s	39.3			
			3p	23.3			
$Br_2C_4K_2N_4Pt$	$K_2Pt(CN)_4Br_2$	s	2p	294.3	g	MgK_{α}	129

TABLE 3 (continued)

Compound		Phase	Orbital	E_B(eV)	Calibrant	Exciting Radiation	Reference
Br_4K_2Pd	$K_2[PdBr_4]$	s	2s	377.6	b 285.0		86
Br_4K_2Pt	K_2PtBr_4	s	2p	294.7	g	MgK_α	129
Br_6K_2Pt	K_2PtBr_6	s	2p	294.5	g	MgK_α	129
Br_6K_2Pt	K_2PtBr_6	s	$2p_{1/2}$	301.45	a 290.0	AlK_α	64
			$2p_{3/2}$	298.8			
			3s	39.4			
			3p	23.1			
Br_6K_2Re	K_2ReBr_6	s	$2p_{1/2}$	302.1	a 290.0	AlK_α	64
			$2p_{3/2}$	299.3			
			3s	39.4			
			3p	22.9			
CKNSe	KSeCN	s	$2p_{1/2}$	301.0	a 290.0	AlK_α	64
			$2p_{3/2}$	298.1			
$C_2H_4Cl_3K_2Pt$	$K_2PtCl_3(C_2H_4)$	s	2p	294.8	g	MgK_α	129
$C_4Cl_2K_2N_4Pt$	$K_2Pt(CN)_4Cl_2$	s	2p	294.3	g	MgK_α	129
$C_4CuK_2O_8$	$K_2Cu(C_2O_4)_2$	s	$2p_{3/2}$	294.4	a 285.5	AlK_α	46
$C_4K_2N_4Pd$	$K_2[Pd(CN)_4]$	s	2s	377.7	b 285.0		86
$C_4K_2N_4Pt$	$K_2Pt(CN)_4$	s	2p	294.2	g	MgK_α	129
$C_6CrK_3N_6S_6$	$K_3Cr(NCS)_6$	s	$2p_{1/2}$	301.1	a 290.0	AlK_α	64
			$2p_{3/2}$	298.4			
			3s	38.7			
			3p	22.6			
$C_6CrK_3N_6$	$K_3Cr(CN)_6$	s	L_{III}	291.6	c 87.0		33
$C_6FeK_3N_6$	$K_3Fe(CN)_6$	s	$2p_{3/2}$	294.3		MgK_α	34

TABLE 3 (continued)

Compound		Phase	Orbital	E_B(eV)	Calibrant	Exciting Radiation	Reference
$C_6FeK_3N_6$	$K_3Fe(CN)_6$	s	$2p_{1/2}$	300.5	a 290.0	AlK_α	64
			$2p_{3/2}$	297.9			
			3s	38.1			
			3p	21.9			
$C_6FeK_4N_6$	$K_4Fe(CN)_6$	s	$2p_{1/2}$	301.3	a 290.0	AlK_α	64
			$2p_{3/2}$	298.6			
			3s	39.0			
			3p	22.8			
$C_6FeK_4N_6$	$K_4Fe(CN)_6$	s	$2p_{3/2}$	294.5		MgK_α	34
$C_6K_2N_6Pt$	$K_2Pt(CN)_6$	s	2p	294.2	g	MgK_α	129
$C_6K_2N_6PtS_6$	$K_2Pt(SCN)_6$	s	$2p_{1/2}$	301.0	a 290.0	AlK_α	64
			$2p_{3/2}$	298.3			
			3s	38.5			
			3p	22.5			
ClK	KCl	s	3p	23.9	a 290	AlK_α	30
ClK	KCl	s	2p	295.7	g	MgK_α	129
ClK	KCl	s	$2p_{1/2}$	303.0	a 290.0	AlK_α	64
			$2p_{3/2}$	300.3			
			3s	40.2			
			3p	23.9			
$ClKO_4$	$KClO_4$	s	$2p_{1/2}$	302.5	a 290.0	AlK_α	64
			$2p_{3/2}$	299.8			
			3s	39.9			
			3p	23.9			
$Cl_2K_2N_4O_8Pt$	$K_2Pt(NO_2)_4Cl_2$	s	2p	294.0	g	MgK_α	129
Cl_4K_2Pd	$K_2[PdCl_4]$	s	2s	377.8	b 285.0		86
Cl_4K_2Pd	K_2PdCl_4	s	$2p_{1/2}$	301.9	a 290.0	AlK_α	64
			$2p_{3/2}$	299.3			
			3s	39.2			
			3p	23.2			

TABLE 3 (continued)

Compound		Phase	Orbital	E_B(eV)	Calibrant	Exciting Radiation	Reference
Cl_4K_2Pt	K_2PtCl_4	s	$2p_{3/2}$	293.4 (1)	$((C_2H_5)_3P)_2PtCl_4$ Cl2p 199.4	AlK_α	87
Cl_4K_2Pt	K_2PtCl_4	s	2p	294.8	g	MgK_α	129
Cl_5K_2NORu	$K_2Ru(NO)Cl_5$	s	$2p_{1/2}$ $2p_{3/2}$ 3s 3p	302.1 299.4 39.4 23.2	a 290.0	AlK_α	64
Cl_6IrK_2	K_2IrCl_6	s	$2p_{3/2}$	293.0 (3)	a 285	Mg, AlK_α	97
Cl_6IrK_2	K_2IrCl_6	s	$2p_{3/2}$	292.7 (2)	c 83.8	AlK_α	41
Cl_6K_2Mo	K_2MoCl_6	s	$2p_{3/2}$	292.5 (2)	c 83.8	AlK_α	41
Cl_6K_2Os	K_2OsCl_6	s	$2p_{3/2}$	292.7 (2)	c 83.8	AlK_α	41
Cl_6K_2Os	K_2OsCl_6	s	$2p_{3/2}$	293.2 (3)	a 285	Mg, AlK_α	97
Cl_6K_2Os	K_2OsCl_6	s	$2p_{1/2}$ $2p_{3/2}$ 3s 3p	301.1 298.4 38.7 22.7	a 290.0	AlK_α	64
Cl_6K_2Pt	K_2PtCl_6	s	$2p_{3/2}$	293.2 (3)	a 285	Mg, AlK_α	97
Cl_6K_2Pt	K_2PtCl_6	s	$2p_{3/2}$	293.7 (1)	$((C_2H_5)_3P)_2PtCl_4$ Cl2p 199.4	AlK_α	87
Cl_6K_2Pt	K_2PtCl_6	s	2p	295.1	g	MgK_α	129
Cl_6K_2Pt	K_2PtCl_6	s	$2p_{3/2}$	292.5 (2)	c 83.8	AlK_α	41
Cl_6K_2Re	K_2ReCl_6	s	$2p_{3/2}$	292.6 (2)	c 83.8	AlK_α	41
Cl_6K_2Re	K_2ReCl_6	s	$2p_{3/2}$	293.9 (3)	a 285	Mg, AlK_α	97

TABLE 3 (continued)

Compound		Phase	Orbital	E_B(eV)	Calibrant	Exciting Radiation	Reference
Cl_6K_2Re	K_2ReCl_6	s	$2p_{1/2}$	301.3	a 290.0	AlK_α	64
			$2p_{3/2}$	298.7			
			3s	39.0			
			3p	22.4			
Cl_6K_2Sn	K_2SnCl_6	s	$2p_{3/2}$	292.6 (2)	c 83.8	AlK_α	41
Cl_6K_2W	K_2WCl_6	s	$2p_{3/2}$	293.5 (3)	a 285	Mg, AlK_α	97
CrF_6K_3	K_3CrF_6	s	L_{III}	292.3	c 87.0		33
FK	KF	s	$2p_{1/2}$	303.0	a 290.0	AlK_α	64
			$2p_{3/2}$	300.35			
			3s	40.3			
			3p	24.15			
FK	KF	s	3p	24.15	a 290	AlK_α	30
F_3KNi	$KNiF_3$	s	$2p_{1/2}$	303.7	a 290.0	AlK_α	64
			$2p_{3/2}$	300.9			
			3s	(38)			
			3p	25.2			
F_6HfK_2	K_2HfF_6	s	$2p_{1/2}$	303.5	a 290.0	AlK_α	64
			$2p_{3/2}$	300.8			
			3s	(41)			
F_6KP	KPF_6	s	$2p_{1/2}$	303.8	a 290.0	AlK_α	64
			$2p_{3/2}$	301.05			
			3s	39.0			
			3p	24.75			
F_6K_2Si	K_2SiF_6	s	$2p_{1/2}$	303.7	a 290.0	AlK_α	64
			$2p_{3/2}$	301.2			
			3s	41.0			
			3p	25.0			
F_6K_2Ti	K_2TiF_6	s	$2p_{1/2}$	303.1	a 290.0	AlK_α	64
			$2p_{3/2}$	300.45			
			3s	(36.9)			
			3p	24.3			

TABLE 3 (continued)

Compound		Phase	Orbital	E_B(eV)	Calibrant	Exciting Radiation	Reference
F_7K_2Nb	K_2NbF_7	s	$2p_{1/2}$	303.2	a 290.0	AlK_α	64
			$2p_{3/2}$	300.5			
			3s	40			
F_7K_2Ta	K_2TaF_7	s	$2p_{1/2}$	302.3	a 290.0	AlK_α	64
			$2p_{3/2}$	299.6			
			3s	(36)			
			3p	23.8			
IK	KI	s	$2p_{1/2}$	303.75	a 290.0	AlK_α	64
			$2p_{3/2}$	301.0			
			3s	40.7			
			3p	24.8			
IK	KI	s	3p	24.8	a 290	AlK_α	30
IK	KI	s	$1s_{1/2}$	0	KI $K1s_{1/2}$ 0	$CrK_{\alpha 1}$	1
IKO_3	KIO_3	s	$1s_{1/2}$	−1.3 (2)	KI $K1s_{1/2}$ 0	$CrK_{\alpha 1}$	1
IKO_3	KIO_3	s	$2p_{1/2}$	303.1	a 290.0	AlK_α	64
			$2p_{3/2}$	300.2			
			3s	40.5			
			3p	23.8			
IKO_4	KIO_4	s	$2p_{1/2}$	303.4	a 290.0	AlK_α	64
			$2p_{3/2}$	300.5			
			3s	40.1			
			3p	24.3			
IKO_4	KIO_4	s	$1s_{1/2}$	−1.3 (2)	KI $K1s_{1/2}$ 0	$CrK_{\alpha 1}$	1
KNO_3	KNO_3	s	$2p_{1/2}$	301.4	a 290.0	AlK_α	64
			$2p_{3/2}$	298.8			
			3s	38.9			
			3p	22.7			

TABLE 3 (continued)

Compound		Phase	Orbital	E_B(eV)	Calibrant	Exciting Radiation	Reference
KN_3	KN_3	s	2s	377.39	b 285.0	Mg, AlK_α	66
			2p	292.74			
			3s	32.38			
			3p	16.21			
KO_4Re	$KReO_4$	s	$2p_{1/2}$	302.1	a 290.0	AlK_α	64
			$2p_{3/2}$	299.4			
			3p	23.6			
$K_2N_4O_8Pd$	$K_2Pd(NO_2)_4$	s	2s	377.8	b 285.0		86
$K_2N_4O_8Pt$	$K_2Pt(NO_2)_4$	s	2p	294.3	g	MgK_α	129
$K_2N_6O_{12}Pt$	$K_2Pt(NO_2)_6$	s	2p	294.0	g	MgK_α	129
K_2O	K_2O	s	K	3,607.3 (5)	e, i	CuK_α	76
K_2O	K_2O	s	L_I	377.1	MgO MgK($CuK_{\alpha 1}$)	$CuK_{\alpha 1}$	67
Kr							
Kr	Kr	g	2s	1,924.6 (8)	Kr 4p 14.08	MgK_α	151
			$2p_{1/2}$	1,730.9 (5)			
			$2p_{3/2}$	1,678.4 (5)			
			3s	292.8 (3)			
			$3p_{1/2}$	222.2 (2)			
			$3p_{3/2}$	214.4 (2)			
			$3d_{3/2}$	94.9 (2)			
			$3d_{5/2}$	93.7 (2)			
			4s	27.4 (2)			
			4p	14.08			
La							
La	La	s	$3dM_4$	856.3		AlK_α	58
				852.3			
			M_5	839.4			
				835.4			

TABLE 3 (continued)

Compound		Phase	Orbital	E_B(eV)	Calibrant	Exciting Radiation	Reference
La (cont.)			$4pN_2$	215.6			
				211.3			
			N_3	200.7			
				196.4			
			$4dN_{4,5}$	105.5			
				102.8			
			$5sO_1$	35.7			
			$5pO_{2,3}$	18.1			
La_2O_3	La_2O_3	s	L_I	6,266.7	e	$MoK_{\alpha 1}$	56
			L_{II}	5,891.1			
			L_{III}	5,483.1			
Li							
FLi	LiF	s	ls	56.9	b 285.0	MgK_α	71
FLi	LiF	s	ls	63.5	a 290	AlK_α	30
LiN_3	LiN_3	s	ls	55.44	b 285.0	Mg, AlK_α	66
Lu							
Lu_2O_3	Lu_2O_3	s	L_I	10,870.2	e	$MoK_{\alpha 1}$	56
			L_{II}	10,349.1			
			L_{III}	9,244.0			
Mg							
Al_2MgO_3	Spinel $MgO \cdot Al_2O_3$	s	2p	49.8	Au4f(N_7 82.8)	AlK_α	133
			2s	89.8	(N_6 86.4)		
$CaFeMgO_6Si_2$	Hedenbergite R6955 46% Mg $CaFeSi_2O_6$	s	2s	88.5 (5)	b 284.6 (5)	Al, MgK_α	57
F_2Mg	MgF_2	s	2p	55.1	Au 4f(N_7 82.8)	AlK_α	133
			2s	93.7	(N_6 86.4)		

TABLE 3 (continued)

Compound		Phase	Orbital	E_B(eV)	Calibrant	Exciting Radiation	Reference
$FeMgO_3Si$	Anthophyllite 77% Mg (Mg, Fe)SiO_3	s	2s	88.4 (5)	b 284.6	Al, MgK_α	57
MgO	MgO	s	2p	56.4	a 290	AlK_α	30
MgO	MgO	s	K	1,305.0 (5)	e, i	CrK_α	76
MgO	MgO	s	L_I	89.2		$CrK_{\alpha 1}$	65
MgO	MgO	s	L_I	89.4	MgO MgK($CrK_{\alpha 1}$)	$CrK_{\alpha 1}$	67
MgO	MgO	s	2p 2s	52.2 91.0	Au4f(N_7 82.8) (N_6 86.4)	AlK_α	133
MgO_3Si	Enstatite 86% Mg MgO·SiO_2	s	2s	88.3 (5)	b 284.6 (5)	Al, MgK_α	57
Mn							
$C_6K_3MnN_6$	$K_3Mn(CN)_6$	s	$2p_{3/2}$	641.3 (3)	b 285.0	Al, MgK_α	112
$C_6K_4MnN_6$	$K_4Mn(CN)_6$	s	$2p_{3/2}$	641.4 (3)	b 285.0	Al, MgK_α	112
$C_8H_5MnO_3$	$Mn(CO)_3(\pi\text{-}C_5H_5)$	s	$2p_{1/2}$ $2p_{3/2}$	654.4 (3) 643.4 (3)		MgK_α	23
$C_{12}H_8MnN_2O_5$	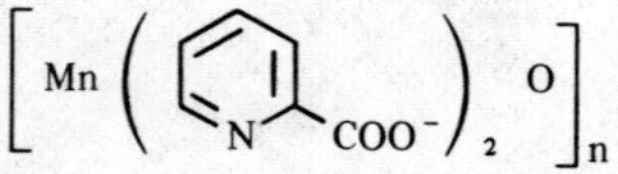	s	$2p_{1/2}$ $2p_{3/2}$	653.9 (2) 642.7 (2)	f 284.0	Mono-AlK_α	148
Mn	Mn	s	L_I	769.0	MgO MgK($CuK_{\alpha 1}$)	$CuK_{\alpha 1}$	67
Mn	Mn	s	K	6,539.6	CuK($MoK_{\alpha 1}$)	$MoK_{\alpha 1}$	119
MnS	MnS	s	$2p_{3/2}$ 3s	640.5 (3) 86.1	b 285.0	Al, MgK_α	112

TABLE 3 (continued)

Compound		Phase	Orbital	E_B(eV)	Calibrant	Exciting Radiation	Reference
Mo							
$AlH_{18}N_3Mo_6O_{24}$	$(NH_4)_3(AlMo_6O_{24}H_6)$	s	$3d_{3/2}$ $3d_{5/2}$	234.7 (1) 231.5 (1)	h 133.3	AlK_α	102
C_6MoO_6	$Mo(CO)_6$	s	$3d_{3/2}$ $3d_{5/2}$	229.7 (2) 226.6 (2)	h 133.3	AlK_α	102
$C_{10}H_{10}Cl_4MoN_2$	$MoCl_4(C_5H_5N)_2$	s	$3d_{3/2}$ $3d_{5/2}$	233.8 (1) 230.8 (1)	h 133.3	AlK_α	102
$C_{10}H_{14}MoO_6$	$MoO_2(CH_3COCHCOCH_3)_2$	s	$3d_{3/2}$ $3d_{5/2}$	233.8 (3) 230.8 (1)	h 133.3	AlK_α	102
$C_{24}H_{33}Cl_3MoP_3$	*mer*-$MoCl_3(P(CH_3)_2C_6H_5)_3$	s	$3d_{3/2}$ $3d_{5/2}$	232.6 (3) 229.6 (3)	d 285	Mg, AlK_α	97
Cl_5Mo	$MoCl_5$	s	$3d_{3/2}$ $3d_{5/2}$	234.5 (2) 231.0 (1)	h 133.3	AlK_α	102
$CoH_{22}N_4Mo_6O_{24}$	$(NH_4)_4(CoMo_6O_{24}H_6)$	s	$3d_{3/2}$ $3d_{5/2}$	234.2 (1) 231.1 (2)	h 133.3	AlK_α	102
$CoH_{24}N_6Mo_{10}O_{36}$	$(NH_4)_6(CoMo_{10}O_{36})$	s	$3d_{3/2}$ $3d_{5/2}$	234.3 (1) 231.1 (1)	h 133.3	AlK_α	102
$CrH_{18}N_3Mo_6O_{24}$	$(NH_4)_3(CrMo_6O_{24}H_6)$	s	$3d_{3/2}$ $3d_{5/2}$	234.3 (1) 231.2 (1)	h 133.3	AlK_α	102
Cs_2MoS_4	Cs_2MoS_4	s	$3d_{3/2}$ $3d_{5/2}$	239.0 (3) 235.8 (3)	a 290.0	AlK_α	62
$FeH_{18}N_3Mo_6O_{24}$	$(NH_4)_3(FeMo_6O_{24}H_6)$	s	$3d_{3/2}$ $3d_{5/2}$	234.7 (2) 231.5 (2)	h 133.3	AlK_α	102
$Fe_2Mo_3O_{12}$	$Fe_2(MoO_4)_3$	s	$3d_{3/2}$ $3d_{5/2}$	235.3 (1) 232.2 (1)	h 133.3	AlK_α	102

TABLE 3 (continued)

Compound		Phase	Orbital	E_B(eV)	Calibrant	Exciting Radiation	Reference
$H_3Mo_{12}O_{40}P$	$H_3(PMo_{12}O_{40})$	s	$3d_{3/2}$ $3d_{5/2}$	234.2 (1) 231.1 (1)	h 133.3	AlK_a	102
$H_3Mo_{12}O_{40}P$	$H_3(PMo_{12}O_{40})$	s	$3p_{1/2}$ $3p_{3/2}$ $3d_{3/2}$ $3d_{5/2}$ 4p	421.9 (3) 404.4 (3) 241.7 (3) 238.6 (3) 46.4 (3)	a 290.0	AlK_a	62
$H_4Mo_{12}O_{40}Si$	$H_4(SiMo_{12}O_{40})$	s	$3d_{3/2}$ $3d_{5/2}$	234.7 (1) 231.6 (1)	h 133.3	AlK_a	102
$H_8MoN_2O_4$	$(NH_4)_2MoO_4$	s	$3d_{3/2}$ $3d_{5/2}$	235.2 (2) 232.1 (1)	h 133.3	AlK_a	102
$H_{22}N_4NiMo_6O_{24}$	$(NH_4)_4(NiMo_6O_{24}H_6)$	s	$3d_{3/2}$ $3d_{5/2}$	234.6 (1) 231.6 (1)	h 133.3	AlK_a	102
$H_{24}N_6NiMo_9O_{32}$	$(NH_4)_6(NiMo_9O_{32})$	s	$3d_{3/2}$ $3d_{5/2}$	234.3 (1) 231.2 (1)	h 133.3	AlK_a	102
Mo	Mo (powder)	s	$3d_{3/2}$ $3d_{5/2}$	233.7 (1) 230.6 (1)	h 133.3	AlK_a	102
Mo	Mo (foil) Exp. 1 month to air	s	$3d_{3/2}$ $3d_{5/2}$	233.8 (1) 230.4 (1)		AlK_a	102
Mo	Mo (foil) cleaned	s	$3d_{3/2}$ $3d_{5/2}$	229.6 (1) 226.1 (2)		AlK_a	102
Mo	Mo	s	L_I L_{II} L_{III}	2,866.0 (5) 2,624.6 (5) 2,520.3 (5)		CuK_a	79
$MoNa_2O_4$	Na_2MoO_4	s	$3d_{3/2}$ $3d_{5/2}$	235.2 (2) 232.1 (2)	h 133.3	AlK_a	102

TABLE 3 (continued)

Compound		Phase	Orbital	E_B(eV)	Calibrant	Exciting Radiation	Reference
$MoNa_2O_4 \cdot 2H_2O$	$Na_2MoO_4 \cdot 2H_2O$	s	$3p_{1/2}$	421.8 (3)	a 290.0	AlK_α	62
			$3p_{3/2}$	404.3 (3)			
			$3d_{3/2}$	241.9 (3)			
			$3d_{5/2}$	238.85			
			4p	47.4 (3)			
MoO_2	MoO_2	s	$3d_{3/2}$	233.9 (1)	h 133.3	AlK_α	102
			$3d_{5/2}$	230.9 (1)			
$MoOS_3Tl_2$	Tl_2MoOS_3	s	$3p_{1/2}$	421	a 290.0	AlK_α	62
			$3p_{3/2}$	403.1 (3)			
			$3d_{3/2}$	240.1 (3)			
			$3d_{5/2}$	237.2 (3)			
			4p	45.5 (3)			
$MoO_2S_2Tl_2$	$Tl_2MoO_2S_2$	s	$3p_{1/2}$	421	a 290.0	AlK_α	62
			$3p_{3/2}$	403.7 (3)			
			$3d_{3/2}$	240.6 (3)			
			$3d_{5/2}$	237.6 (3)			
MoO_3	MoO_3	s	$3p_{1/2}$	421.5 (3)	a 290.0	AlK_α	62
			$3p_{3/2}$	404.1 (3)			
			$3d_{3/2}$	241.6 (3)			
			$3d_{5/2}$	238.6 (3)			
MoO_3	MoO_3	s	$3d_{3/2}$	235.6 (1)	h 133.3	AlK_α	102
			$3d_{5/2}$	232.5 (1)			
MoO_4Tl_2	Tl_2MoO_4	s	$3d_{3/2}$	242.0 (3)	a 290.0	AlK_α	62
			$3d_{5/2}$	239.0 (3)			
MoS_4Tl_2	Tl_2MoS_4	s	$3p_{1/2}$	419	a 290.0	AlK_α	62
			$3p_{3/2}$	402			
			$3d_{3/2}$	239.6 (3)			
			$3d_{5/2}$	236.7 (3)			
$Mo_{12}Na_4O_{40}Si$	$Na_4(SiMo_{12}O_{40})$	s	$3d_{3/2}$	234.7 (1)	h 133.3	AlK_α	102
			$3d_{5/2}$	231.1 (1)			
N							
BN	BN	s	ls	396.2	LiF Fls 685.4		114

TABLE 3 (continued)

Compound		Phase	Orbital	E_B(eV)	Calibrant	Exciting Radiation	Reference
BN	BN	s	ls 2s	398.3 19.4	b 285.0	MgK_α	71
BN	BN	s	ls	398.2 (2)	b	MgK_α	117
$Br_2H_{15}N_6O_2Rh$	$[Rh(\overset{a}{N}H_3)_5\overset{b}{N}O_2]Br_2$	s	[a]ls [b]ls	400.3 (2) 404.4 (2)	b	MgK_α	117
CCuN	CuCN	s	ls	401.0	a 285.5	AlK_α	46
CCuNS	CuSCN	s	ls	401.0	a 285.5	AlK_α	46
CHN	HCN	g	ls	406.8 (1)	N_2 Nls 409.9	MgK_α	11
CH_5N	CH_3NH_2	g	ls	405.1 (1)	N_2 Nls 409.9	MgK_α	11
CKN	KCN	s	ls	399.2 (4)	b	Al, MgK_α	32
CKN	KCN	s	ls	399.0		MgK_α	2
CKN	KCN	s	ls	399.0 (2)	b	MgK_α	117
CKNO	KOCN	s	ls	398.3 (2)	b	MgK_α	117
CKNO	KOCN	s	ls	398.3		MgK_α	2
CKNS	KSCN	s	ls	398.5 (2)	b	MgK_α	117
$C_2H_4NNaO_2$	$[H_2NCH_2COO]Na$	s	ls	397.3 (4)	b	Al, MgK_α	32
$C_2H_4N_2O_2$	$(CONH_2)_2$	s	ls	400.0 (2)	b	MgK_α	117
$C_2H_4N_2O_2$	$(CONH_2)_2$	s	ls	400.0		MgK_α	2
$C_2H_4N_4$	$(NH_2)_2CNCN$	s	ls	399.2 (2)(br)	b	MgK_α	117
$C_2H_4N_4$	$(NH_2)_2CNCN$	s	ls	399.2 (br)		MgK_α	2

TABLE 3 (continued)

Compound		Phase	Orbital	E_B(eV)	Calibrant	Exciting Radiation	Reference
C_2H_7N	$(CH_3)_2NH$	g	ls	404.9 (1)	N_2 Nls 409.9	MgK_α	11
$C_2H_8Br_2CuN_2 \cdot H_2O$	$CuBr_2 \cdot H_2NCH_2CH_2NH_2 \cdot H_2O$	s	ls	401.9	a 285.5	AlK_α	46
$C_2H_8Cl_2CuN_2 \cdot H_2O$	$CuCl_2 \cdot H_2NCH_2CH_2NH_2 \cdot H_2O$	s	ls	401.8	a 285.5	AlK_α	46
$C_2H_8CuN_2O_3S \cdot H_2O$	$CuSO_3 \cdot H_2NCH_2CH_2NH_2 \cdot H_2O$	s	ls	401.3	a 285.5	AlK_α	46
C_3H_3NO	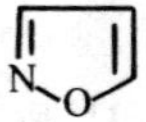	s	ls	402.1 (3)	c 84	MgK_α	25
C_3H_3NS		s	ls	400.5 (3)	c 84	MgK_α	25
$C_3H_4N_2$	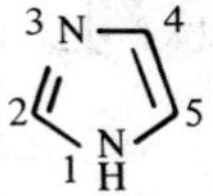	s	(1) ls (3) ls	402.3 (3) 400.7 (3)	c 84	MgK_α	25
$C_3H_4N_2$	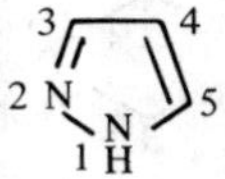	s	(1) ls (2) ls	402.4 (3) 401.1 (3)	c 84	MgK_α	25
$C_3H_6NNaS_2$	$(CH_3)_2NCS_2Na$	s	ls	400.5	b 285.0	AlK_α	49
$C_3H_8NO_2S$	$HSCH_2CHNH_2COOH$	s	ls	401.5	b 285.0	AlK_α	49
$C_3H_9ClNO_2S$	$[HSCH_2CHNH_3COOH]Cl$	s	ls	401.6	b 285.0	AlK_α	49
C_3H_9N	$(CH_3)_3N$	g	ls	404.7 (1)	N_2 Nls 409.9	MgK_α	11
C_3H_9NO	$ON(CH_3)_3$	s	ls	402.2 (4)	b	Al, MgK_α	32
$C_4Cl_4N_2$	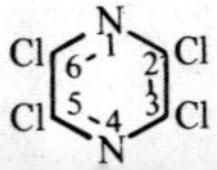	s	(1) ls	401.7	c 84	MgK_α	96

TABLE 3 (continued)

Compound		Phase	Orbital	E_B(eV)	Calibrant	Exciting Radiation	Reference
$C_4Cl_4N_2$	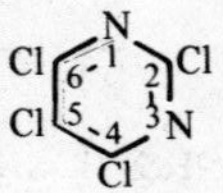	s	(3) ls	401.4	c 84	MgK_α	96
$C_4Cl_4N_2$	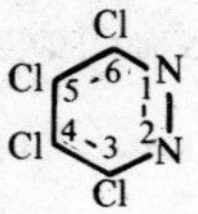	s	(2) ls	401.8	c 84	MgK_α	96
$C_4F_4N_2$		s	(2) ls	402.7	c 84	MgK_α	96
$C_4F_4N_2$	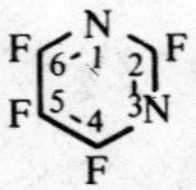	s	(3) ls	402.3	c 84	MgK_α	96
$C_4F_4N_2$	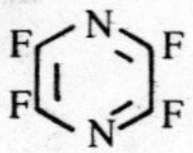	s	(1) ls	402.9 (3)	c 84	MgK_α	96
$C_4H_4N_2$		s	(2) ls	401.3	c 84	MgK_α	96
$C_4H_4N_2$		s	(3) ls	400.5	c 84	MgK_α	96
$C_4H_4N_2$	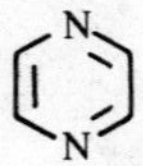	s	(1) ls	401.4	c 84	MgK_α	96

TABLE 3 (continued)

Compound		Phase	Orbital	E_B(eV)	Calibrant	Exciting Radiation	Reference
$C_4H_5BF_4N_2$	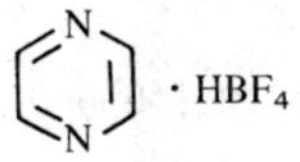	s	(+) ls	401.5 (2)	f 284.3		150
$C_4H_5BrN_2$	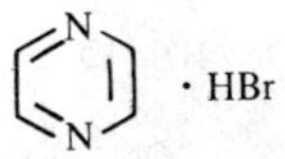	s	(+) ls	400.8 (2)	f 284.3		150
$C_4H_5IN_2$	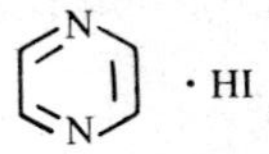	s	(+) ls	401.6 (2)	f 284.3		150
C_4H_5N	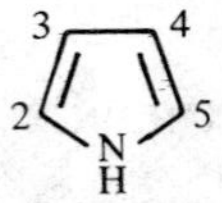	g	ls	406.1	d, N_2 Nls 409.9	MgK_α	69
C_4H_5N	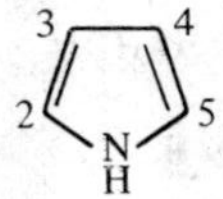	s	ls	401.2 (3)	c 84	MgK_α	25
$C_4H_5N_3O$	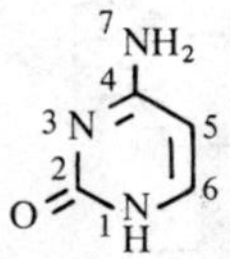	s	(3) ls (7) ls (1) ls	399.6 (3) 400.5 (3) 401.4 (3)		AlK_α	18
$C_4H_7O_2S$	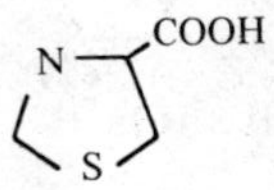	s	ls	401.4	b 285.0	AlK_α	49
C_4H_9N	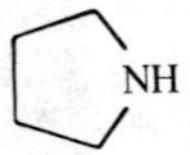	s	ls	848.4 (E_{kin})		MgK_α	132

TABLE 3 (continued)

Compound		Phase	Orbital	E_B(eV)	Calibrant	Exciting Radiation	Reference
$C_4H_9NO_2S$	$CH_3SCH_2CH(NH_2)COOH$	s	ls	401.5	b 285.0	AlK_α	49
$C_4H_{10}N_2$		s	ls	398.5 (4)	b	Al, MgK_α	32
$C_4H_{11}ClN_2$	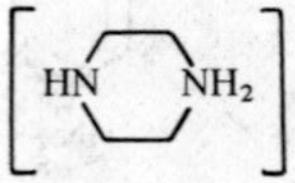 Cl	s	ls	400.0 (4) 401.7 (4)	b	Al, MgK_α	32
$C_4H_{11}N$	$CH_3CH_2CH_2CH_2NH_2$	s	ls	398.1 (4)	b	Al, MgK_α	32
$C_4H_{12}BrN$	$[(CH_3)_4N]Br$	s	ls	400.7 (0.24)	j 406.9	AlK_α	14
$C_4H_{12}Br_3N$	$[(CH_3)_4N]Br_3$	s	ls	399.8 (0.11)	j 406.9	AlK_α	14
$C_4H_{12}ClN$	$[N(CH_3)_4]Cl$	s	ls	401.5 (4)	b	Al, MgK_α	32
$C_4H_{12}FN$	$[(CH_3)_4N]F$	s	ls	401.2 (0.33)	j 406.9	AlK_α	14
$C_4H_{16}Br_2CuN_4 \cdot H_2O$	$CuBr_2 \cdot 2(H_2NCH_2CH_2NH_2) \cdot H_2O$		ls	401.0	a 285.5	AlK_α	46
$C_4H_{16}Cl_2CoN_5O_3$	[*trans*-$Co(\overset{a}{N}H_2CH_2CH_2\overset{a}{N}H_2)_2$ $Cl_2]\overset{b}{N}O_3$	s	^{a}ls ^{b}ls	403.2 409.7	a 290	AlK_α	30
$C_4H_{16}Cl_2CuN_4 \cdot H_2O$	$CuCl_2 \cdot (H_2NCH_2CH_2NH_2) \cdot H_2O$	s	ls	400.7	a 285.5	AlK_α	46
$C_4H_{16}CoN_7O_7$	*trans*-$[Co(H_2\overset{a}{N}CH_2CH_2\overset{a}{N}H_2)_2$ $(\overset{b}{N}O_2)_2]\overset{c}{N}O_3$	s	^{a}ls ^{b}ls ^{c}ls	400.4 (2) 403.8 (2) 406.8 (2)	b	MgK_α	117
$C_4H_{16}CuN_4O_4S \cdot H_2O$	$CuSO_4 \cdot 2(H_2NCH_2CH_2NH_2) \cdot H_2O$	s	ls	401.0	a 285.5	AlK_α	46
$C_4H_{20}B_3N$	$[(CH_3)_4N]B_3H_8$	s	ls	402.2 (2)	b	MgK_α	117
$C_4H_{20}B_3N$	$[(CH_3)_4N]B_3H_8$	s	ls	402.2		MgK_α	2

TABLE 3 (continued)

Compound		Phase	Orbital	E_B(eV)	Calibrant	Exciting Radiation	Reference
$C_4N_4K_2Pt$	$K_2Pt(CN)_4$	s	ls	399.3 (1)	K_2PtCl_4 K $2p_{3/2}$ 293.4	AlK_α	87
$C_4N_6O_4Ph_2$	$[Rh(\overset{b}{N}\overset{a}{N}\overset{b}{N})(CO)_2]_2$	s	^{a}ls ^{b}ls	403.2 399.3	b	MgK_α	99
C_5Cl_5N	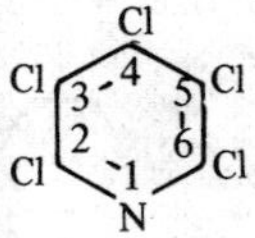	s	ls	401.3	c 84	MgK_α	96
$C_5CrK_3N_6O$	$K_3[Cr(NO)(CN)_5]$	s	ls	400.7 (2)	b	MgK_α	83
$C_5CrK_3N_6O$	$K_3[Cr(C\overset{a}{N})_5\overset{b}{N}O]$	s	^{b}ls ^{a}ls	400.7 (2) 398.4 (2)	b	MgK_α	117
C_5F_5N	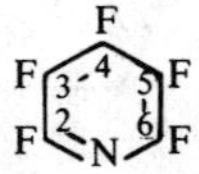	s	ls	402.3	c 84	MgK_α	96
$C_5FeN_6Na_2O \cdot 2H_2O$	$Na_2[Fe(C\overset{a}{N})_5\overset{b}{N}O] \cdot 2H_2O$	s	^{b}ls ^{a}ls	403.3 (2) 398.2 (2)	b	MgK_α	117
$C_5FeN_6Na_2O \cdot 2H_2O$	$Na_2[Fe(NO)(CN)_5] \cdot 2H_2O$	s	ls	403.3 (2)	b	MgK_α	83
C_5H_5N		s	ls	398.0 (4)	b	Al, MgK_α	32
C_5H_5N		s	ls	400.2	c 84	MgK_α	96
$C_5H_5N_5$	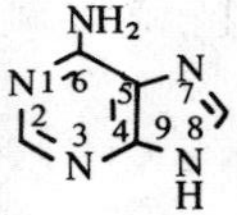	s	(1) ls (3) ls (7) ls (10) ls (9) ls	398.6 (3) 399.1 (3) 399.5 (3) 399.6 (3) 400.9 (3)		AlK_α	17

TABLE 3 (continued)

Compound		Phase	Orbital	E_B(eV)	Calibrant	Exciting Radiation	Reference
C_5H_6BrN	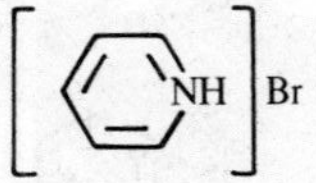	s	ls	399.3 (0.24)	j 406.9	AlK_a	14
C_5H_6ClN	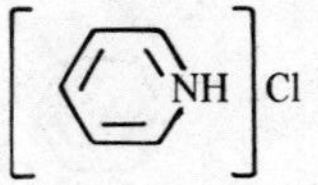	s	ls	400.2 (2)	b	MgK_a	117
$C_5H_6N_2O_2$	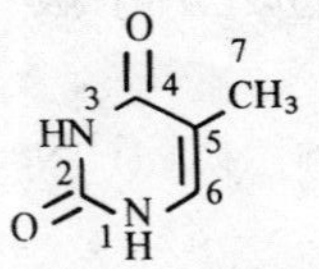	s	(3) ls (1) ls	401.1 (3) 402.1 (3)		AlK_a	18
$C_5H_6N_2O_3S$	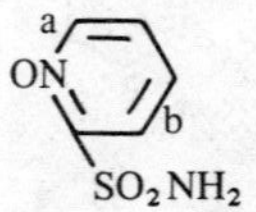	s	[a]ls [b]ls	402.2 (4) 398.7 (4)	b	Al, MgK_a	32
$C_5H_{10}NNaS_2$	$(CH_3CH_2)_2NCS_2Na$	s	Nls	400.4	b 285.0	AlK_a	49
$C_5H_{11}N$		s	ls	397.8 (4)	b	Al, MgK_a	32
$C_5H_{11}NO_2$	$(CH_3)_3NCH_2COO$	s	ls	400.6 (0.24)	j 406.9	AlK_a	14
$C_5H_{11}NO_2$	$CH_3(CH_2)_4ONO$	s	ls	403.7 (4)	b	Al, MgK_a	32
$C_5H_{12}ClN$	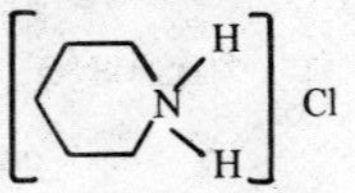	s	ls	400.4 (4)	b	Al, MgK_a	32
$C_6CrK_3N_6$	$K_3[Cr(CN)_6]$	s	ls	398.6 (2)	b	MgK_a	117
$C_6CrK_3N_6$	$K_3Cr(CN)_6$	s	ls	397.0	c		33

TABLE 3 (continued)

Compound		Phase	Orbital	E_B(eV)	Calibrant	Exciting Radiation	Reference
$C_6FeK_4N_6 \cdot 3H_2O$	$K_4[Fe(CN)_6] \cdot 3H_2O$	s	ls	397.6 (2)	b	MgK_α	117
$C_6H_4ClNO_2S$	*o*-$NO_2C_6H_4SCl$	s	ls	406.0	b 285.0	AlK_α	49
$C_6H_4ClNO_4S$	*m*-$NO_2C_6H_4SO_2Cl$	s	ls	405.6	b 285.0	AlK_α	49
$C_6H_4ClNO_4S$	*p*-$NO_2C_6H_4SO_2Cl$	s	ls	406.3	b 285.0	AlK_α	49
$C_6H_4ClNO_4S$	*o*-$NO_2C_6H_4SO_2Cl$	s	ls	406.2	b 285.0	AlK_α	49
$C_6H_4FNO_4S$	*o*-$NO_2C_6H_4SO_2F$	s	ls	405.9	b 285.0	AlK_α	49
$C_6H_4NNaO_2S$	[*p*-$NO_2C_6H_4S$]Na	s	ls	405.8	b 285.0	AlK_α	49
$C_6H_4NNaO_4$	*p*-$NO_2C_6H_4SO_2Na$	s	ls	406.1	b 285.0	AlK_α	49
$C_6H_4NNaO_5S$	*p*-$NO_2C_6H_4SO_3Na$	s	ls	406.2	b 285.0	AlK_α	49
$C_6H_4NNaO_5S$	*m*-$NO_2C_6H_4SO_3Na$	s	ls	405.8	b 285.0	AlK_α	49
$C_6H_4NNaO_5S$	*o*-$NO_2C_6H_4SO_3Na$	s	ls	406.0	b 285.0	AlK_α	49
$C_6H_5BF_4N_2$	$[C_6H_5(N_2)]BF_4$	s	ls	405.1 403.8	b	MgK_α	99
$C_6H_5NO_2$	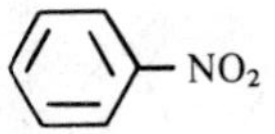	s	ls	405.1 (4)	b	Al, MgK_α	32
$C_6H_5NO_2$	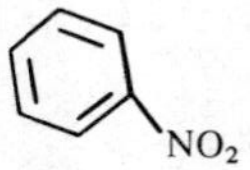	g	ls	411.6	N_2 N1s 409.9	MgK_α	151
$C_6H_5NO_2S$	*o*-$NO_2C_6H_4SH$	s	ls	405.9	b 285.0	AlK_α	49
$C_6H_5NO_2S$	*p*-$NO_2C_6H_4SH$	s	ls	405.7	b 285.0	AlK_α	49

TABLE 3 (continued)

Compound		Phase	Orbital	E_B(eV)	Calibrant	Exciting Radiation	Reference
$C_6H_6NNaO_3S$		s	ls	398.1 (4)	b	Al, MgK_α	32
$C_6H_6NNaO_3S$	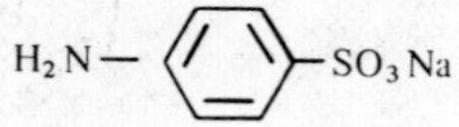	s	ls	399.1	b 285.0	AlK_α	49
$C_6H_6NO_3$	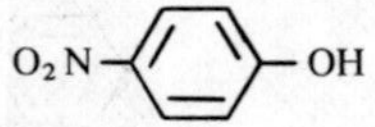	s	ls	405.3 (4)	b	Al, MgK_α	32
$C_6H_6N_2O_2$	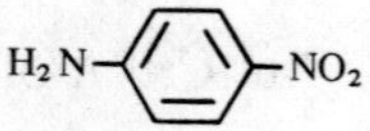	s	ls	398.7 (4) 404.4 (4) 406.0 (4)	b	Al, MgK_α	32
$C_6H_6N_2O_2S$	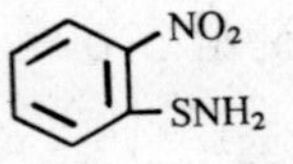	s	ls	405.5 (4) 399.1 (4)	b	Al, MgK_α	32
$C_6H_6N_2O_2S$	*o*-$NO_2C_6H_4SNH_2$	s	ls	406.2	b 285.0	AlK_α	49
$C_6H_6N_2O_4S$	*m*-$NO_2C_6H_4SO_2NH_2$	s	ls	405.9	b 285.0	AlK_α	49
C_6H_7N	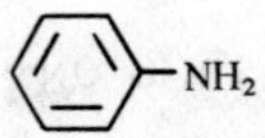	g	ls	405.5	N_2 Nls 409.9	MgK_α	151
C_6H_7N	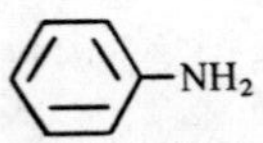	s	ls	398.6 (4)	b	Al, MgK_α	32
$C_6H_7NO_3S$		s	ls	401.0 (4)	b	Al, MgK_α	32
C_6H_8BrN	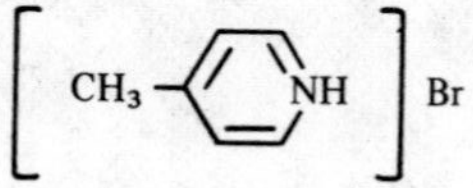	s	ls	399.1 (0.16)	j 406.9	AlK_α	14

TABLE 3 (continued)

Compound		Phase	Orbital	E_B(eV)	Calibrant	Exciting Radiation	Reference
C_6H_8ClNO	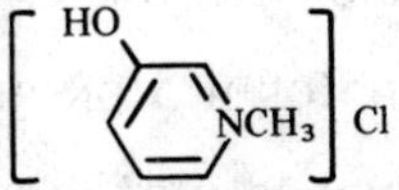	s	ls	400.3 (0.39)	j 406.9	AlK_a	14
$C_6H_8N_2O_2S$	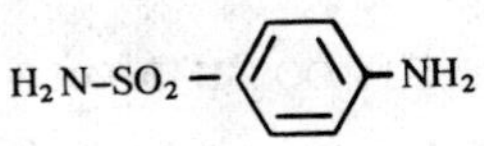	s	ls	399.0 (4)	b	Al, MgK_a	32
$C_6H_8N_2O_2S$	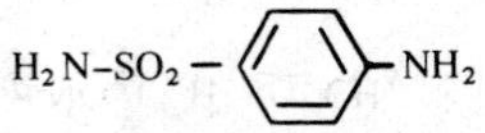	s	ls	400.0	b 285.0	AlK_a	49
$C_6H_9N_2 \cdot HCl$	$C_6H_5NH_2NH_2 \cdot HCl$	s	ls	401.4 (2)	b	MgK_a	117
$C_6H_{12}N_2S_4$	$(CH_3)_2NC(S)SSC(S)N(CH_3)_2$	s	ls	409.5	b 285.0	AlK_a	49
$C_6H_{12}N_4$	$(CH_2)_6N_4$	s	ls	398.6 (4)	b	Al, MgK_a	32
$C_6H_{16}BrN$	$[(C_2H_5)_3NH]Br$	s	ls	399.7 (0.25)	j 406.9	AlK_a	14
$C_6H_{16}ClN$	$[HN(C_2H_5)_3]Cl$	s	ls	400.4 (4)	b	Al, MgK_a	32
$C_6H_{24}Br_2CuN_6 \cdot 5H_2O$	$CuBr_2 \cdot 3(H_2NCH_2CH_2NH_2) \cdot 5H_2O$	s	ls	401.5	a 285.5	AlK_a	46
C_6N_4	$(NC)_2C{=}C(CN)_2$	g	ls	−3.2 (2)	Nls N_2 (409.9) 0.0	MgK_a	149
C_6N_4O	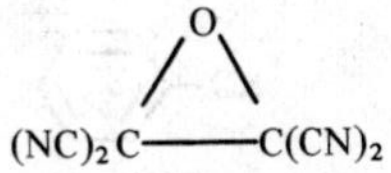	g	ls	−2.8 (2)	Nls N_2 (409.9) 0.0	MgK_a	149
$C_6N_6O_6$	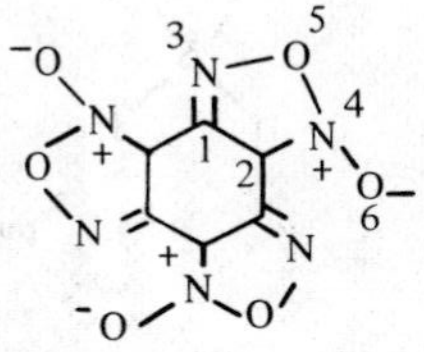	s	(4) ls (3) ls	405.0 401.3	f 284.2	MgK_a	115

TABLE 3 (continued)

	Compound	Phase	Orbital	E_B(eV)	Calibrant	Exciting Radiation	Reference
$C_7H_2N_4$	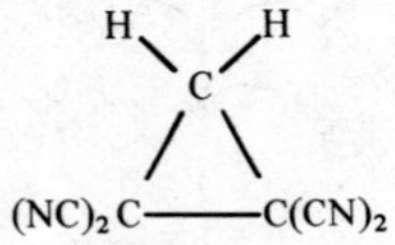	s	ls	398.4 (4)	Nls N_2 (409.9) 0.0	MgK_α	149
C_7H_5N	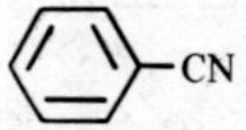	s	ls	−3.2 (2)	b	Al, MgK_α	32
$C_7H_6N_2O_3$	p-$\overset{a}{N}O_2C_6H_4CO\overset{b}{N}H_2$	s	[a]ls [b]ls	405.9 (2) 399.6 (2)	b	MgK_α	117
C_7H_7NO	$C_6H_5CONH_2$	s	ls	399.4 (2)	b	MgK_α	117
$C_7H_7NO_2S$	p-$NO_2C_6H_4SCH_3$	s	ls	405.7	b 285.0	AlK_α	49
$C_7H_7NO_3S$	o-$NO_2C_6H_4SOCH_3$	s	ls	405.9	b 285.0	AlK_α	49
$C_7H_7NO_3S$	p-$NO_2C_6H_4S(O)CH_3$	s	ls	406.1	b 285.0	AlK_α	49
$C_7H_7NO_3S$	o-$NO_2C_6H_4S(O)CH_3$	s	ls	406.3	b 285.0	AlK_α	49
$C_7H_7NO_4S$	p-$NO_2C_6H_4SO_2CH_3$	s	ls	406.3	b 285.0	AlK_α	49
$C_7H_7NO_4S$	m-$NO_2C_6H_4SOOCH_3$	s	ls	405.7	b 285.0	AlK_α	49
$C_7H_7NO_4S$	o-$NO_2C_6H_4SOOCH_3$	s	ls	405.9	b 285.0	AlK_α	49
$C_7H_7NO_4S$	p-$NO_2C_6H_4SOOCH_3$	s	ls	405.8	b 285.0	AlK_α	49
$C_7H_7NO_4S$	m-$NO_2C_6H_4SO_2CH_3$	s	ls	405.8	b 285.0	AlK_α	49
$C_7H_7NO_5S$	o-$NO_2C_6H_4SO_2OCH_3$	s	ls	405.9	b 285.0	AlK_α	49
$C_7H_7NO_5S$	m-$NO_2C_6H_4SO_2OCH_3$	s	ls	405.8	b 285.0	AlK_α	49
$C_7H_7NO_5S$	p-$NO_2C_6H_4SO_2OCH_3$	s	ls	405.9	b 285.0	AlK_α	49

TABLE 3 (continued)

Compound		Phase	Orbital	E_B(eV)	Calibrant	Exciting Radiation	Reference
$C_7H_8ClNO_2$	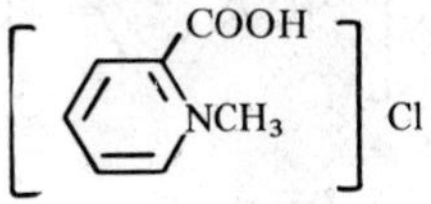	s	ls	399.6 (0.24)	j 406.9	AlK_α	14
$C_7H_8NO_4S$	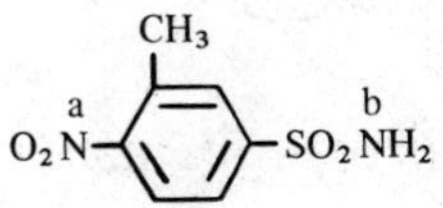	s	[a]ls [b]ls	404.9 (4) 398.7 (4)	b	Al, MgK_α	32
$C_7H_{10}BrN$	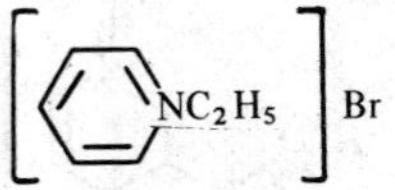	s	ls	400.4 (0.27)	j 406.9	AlK_α	14
$C_7H_{10}IN$	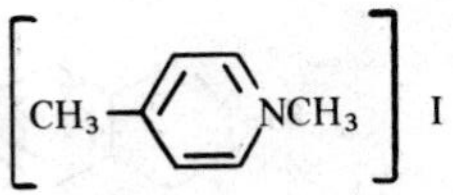	s	ls	400.4 (0.14)	j 406.9	AlK_α	14
$C_7H_{11}NO_3S_2$	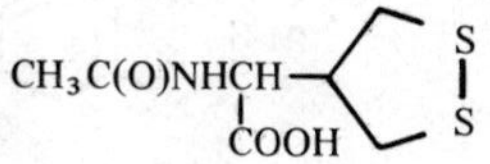	s	ls	399.7 (4)	b	Al, MgK_α	32
$C_7H_{12}INS$	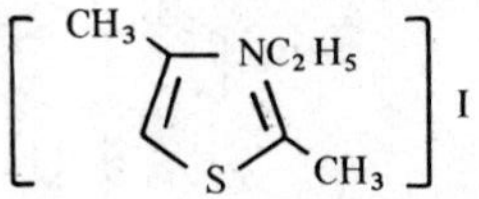	s	ls	400.1 (0.15)	j 406.9	AlK_α	14
$C_7H_{13}Cl_2N$	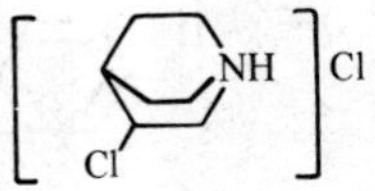	s	ls	400.1 (0.36)	j 406.9	AlK_α	14
$C_7H_{16}BrNO_2$	$[(CH_3)_3NCH_2CH_2C(O)OCH_3]Br$	s	ls	400.8 (0.11)	j 406.9	AlK_α	14

TABLE 3 (continued)

Compound		Phase	Orbital	E_B(eV)	Calibrant	Exciting Radiation	Reference
$C_8H_6N_2O_2$	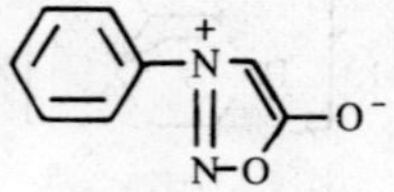	s	ls	399.4 401.4	a 284.0	AlK_α	98
$C_8H_7IN_2$	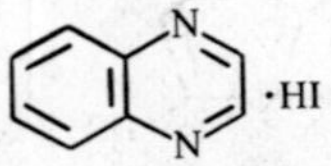	s	(+) ls	400.7 (2)	f 284.3		150
$C_8H_7IN_2$	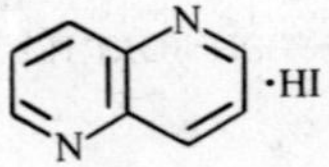	s	(+) ls	400.6 (2)	f 284.3		150
$C_8H_7IN_2$	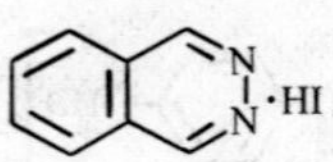	s	(+) ls	400.8 (2)	f 284.3		150
$C_8H_{10}INO_2$	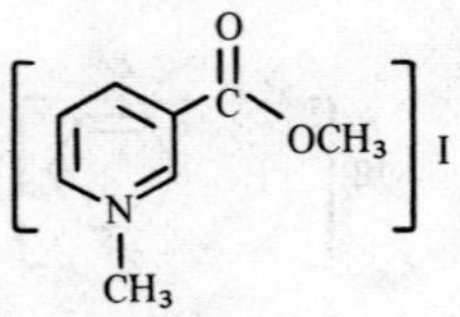	s	ls	400.4 (0.11)	j 406.9	AlK_α	14
$C_8H_{10}NNaO_3S$	*p*-$N(CH_3)_2C_6H_4SO_3Na$	s	ls	399.3	b 285.0	AlK_α	49
$C_8H_{10}N_2O_2$	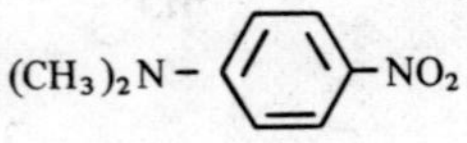	s	ls	398.3 (4) 403.8 (4) 405.2 (4)	b	Al, MgK_α	32
$C_8H_{12}BrN$	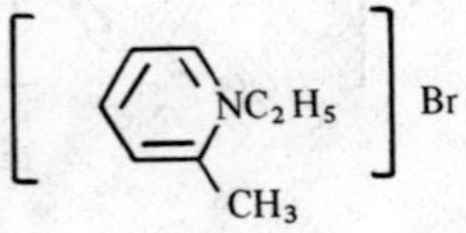	s	ls	400.4 (0.15)	j 406.9	AlK_α	14

TABLE 3 (continued)

Compound		Phase	Orbital	E_B(eV)	Calibrant	Exciting Radiation	Reference
$C_8H_{12}BrN$	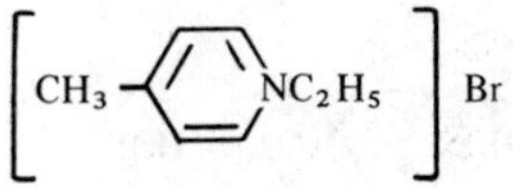	s	ls	400.5 (0.13)	j 406.9	AlK_α	14
$C_8H_{16}N_2O_2S$	$S(N(CH_2CH_2)_2O)_2$	s	ls	399.8	b 285.0	AlK_α	49
$C_8H_{20}BrN$	$[(C_2H_5)_4N]Br$	s	ls	400.7 (0.15)	j 406.9	AlK_α	14
$C_8H_{20}ClN$	$[(C_2H_5)_4N]Cl$	s	ls	401.1 (0.21)	j 406.9	AlK_α	14
$C_8H_{20}ClNO_4$	$[(C_2H_5)_4N]ClO_4$	s	ls	400.5 (0.24)	j 406.9	AlK_α	14
$C_8H_{20}IN$	$[(C_2H_5)_4N]I$	s	ls	401.1 (0.06)	j 406.9	AlK_α	14
$C_8H_{20}IN$	$[(C_2H_5)_4N]I$	s	ls	397.1 (4) 402.3 (4)	b	Al, MgK_α	32
$C_8H_{22}CuN_4O_4 \cdot H_2O$	$Cu(CH_3COO)_2 \cdot 2(H_2NCH_2CH_2NH_2) \cdot H_2O$	s	ls	401.6	a 285.5	AlK_α	46
$C_8H_{24}BN$	$[(C_2H_5)_4N]BH_4$	s	ls	400.6 (0.21)	j 406.9	AlK_α	14
$C_9H_7ClN_2S_2$	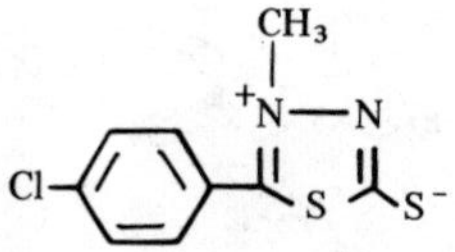	s	ls	398.3 400.5	a 284.0	AlK_α	98
C_9H_7NO	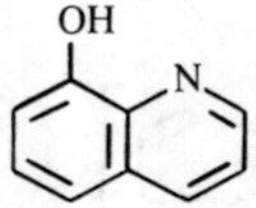	s	ls	400.3	c 84	MgK_α	36
C_9H_8BrN	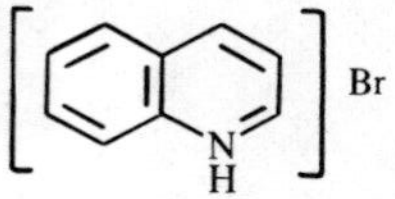	s	ls	398.5 (0.32)	j 406.9	AlK_α	14

TABLE 3 (continued)

Compound		Phase	Orbital	E_B(eV)	Calibrant	Exciting Radiation	Reference
C_9H_8ClNO	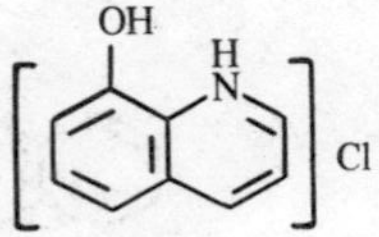	s	ls	402.1	c 84	MgK_α	36
$C_9H_8N_2S_2$	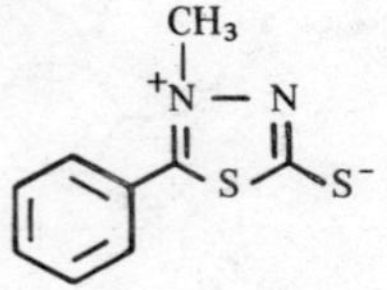	s	ls	398.2 400.6	a 284.0	AlK_α	98
$C_9H_8N_2S_2$	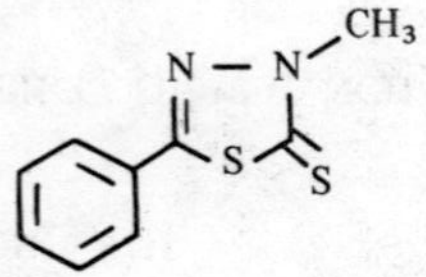	s	ls	399.7 400.6	a 284.0	AlK_α	98
$C_9H_9IN_2$	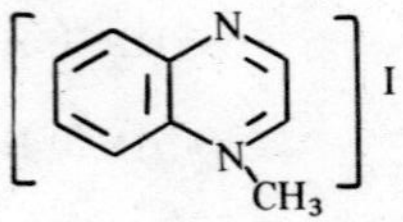	s	(+) ls	401.0 (2)	f 284.3		150
$C_9H_9IN_2$	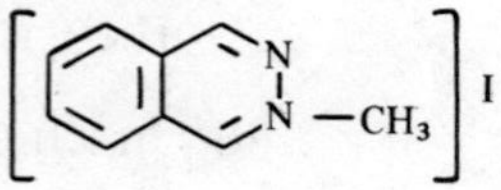	s	(+) ls	401.8 (2)	f 284.3		150
$C_9H_{12}INO_2$		s	ls	400.1 (0.25)	j 406.9	AlK_α	14
$C_9H_{13}ClN_2O$	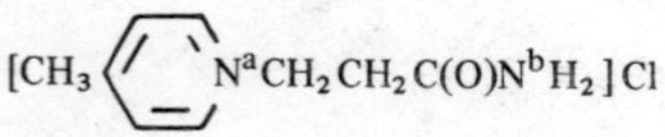	s	^{a}ls ^{b}ls	399.2 (0.16) 397.1 (0.18)	j 406.9	AlK_α	14

TABLE 3 (continued)

Compound		Phase	Orbital	E_B(eV)	Calibrant	Exciting Radiation	Reference
$C_9H_{14}BrN$	$[(CH_3)_3C_6H_5N]Br$	s	ls	400.7 (0.15)	j 406.9	AlK_α	14
$C_9H_{14}BrN$	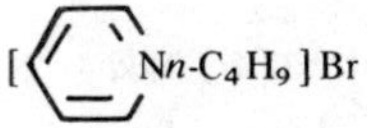	s	ls	400.6 (0.24)	j 406.9	AlK_α	14
$C_9H_{14}IN$	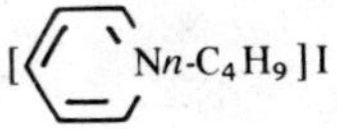	s	ls	400.9 (0.11)	j 406.9	AlK_α	14
$C_9H_{22}AsF_6N$	$[(n\text{-}C_3H_7)_3NH]AsF_6$	s	ls	401.1 (0.11)	j 406.9	AlK_α	14
$C_{10}H_8Br_2CuN_2$	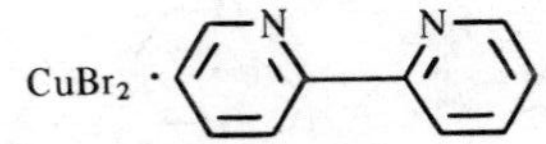	s	ls	401.3	a 285.5	AlK_α	46
$C_{10}H_8Cl_2CuN_2$	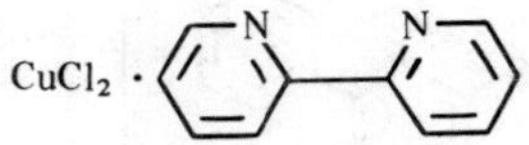	s	ls	401.0	a 285.5	AlK_α	46
$C_{10}H_8CuN_2O_4S \cdot 2H_2O$	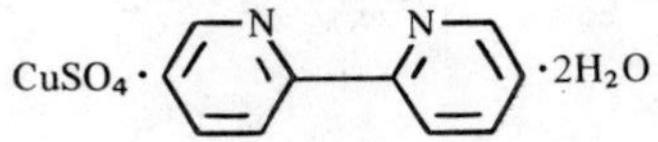	s	ls	400.6	a 285.5	AlK_α	46
$C_{10}H_9IN_2$	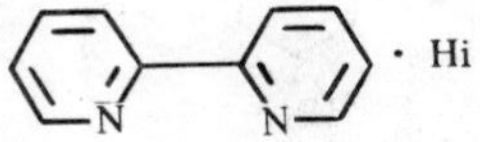	s	(+) ls	400.3 (2)	f 284.3		150
$C_{10}H_{10}ClIN_2S_2$	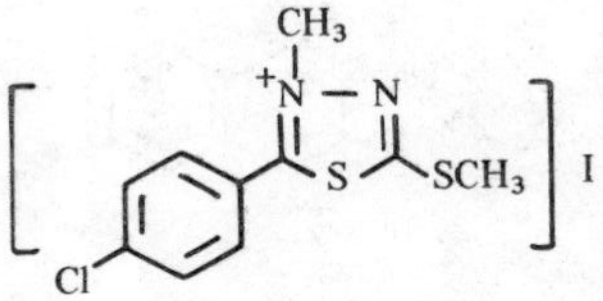	s	ls	399.1 400.1	a 284.0	AlK_α	98
$C_{10}H_{10}Cr_2N_4O_4$	$[\pi\text{-}C_5H_5Cr(NO)_2]_2$	s	ls	400.7 (2)	b	MgK_α	83

TABLE 3 (continued)

Compound		Phase	Orbital	E_B(eV)	Calibrant	Exciting Radiation	Reference
$C_{10}H_{11}IN_2$	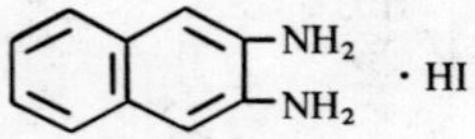	s	(+) ls	399.8 (2)	f 284.3		150
$C_{10}H_{11}IN_2$	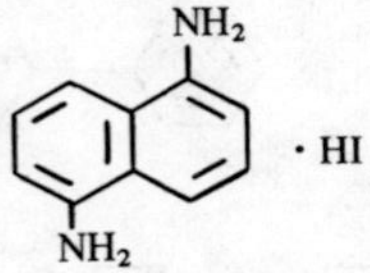	s	(+) ls	400.4 (2)	f 284.3		150
$C_{10}H_{11}IN_2S_2$	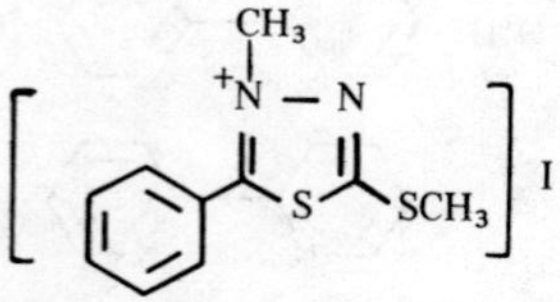	s	ls	399.4 400.7	a 284.0	AlK_α	98
$C_{10}H_{14}NO_3P$	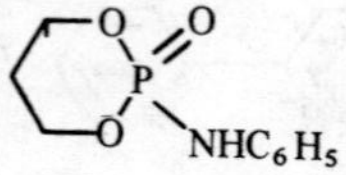	s	ls	399.8 (3)	d 285.0	AlK_α	105
$C_{10}H_{14}NO_3P$	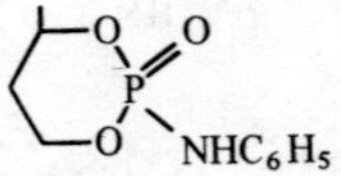	s	ls	399.8 (3)	d 285.0	AlK_α	105
$C_{10}H_{16}As_2Cl_2MoN_2O_2$	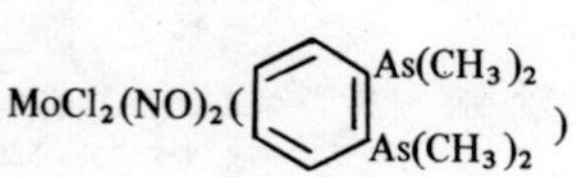	s	ls	399.6 (2)	b	MgK_α	83
$C_{10}H_{16}BrN$	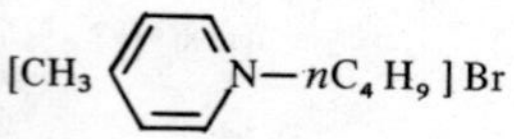	s	ls	400.4 (0.11)	j 406.9	AlK_α	14
$C_{10}H_{16}IN$	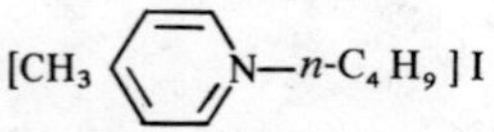	s	ls	400.7 (0.24)	j 406.9	AlK_α	14

TABLE 3 (continued)

Compound		Phase	Orbital	E_B(eV)	Calibrant	Exciting Radiation	Reference
$C_{10}H_{22}BrNO$	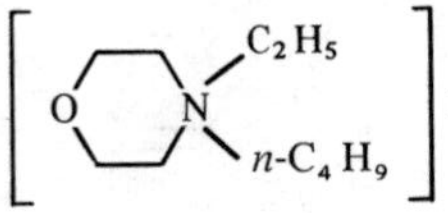	s	ls	400.4 (0.09)	j 406.9	AlK_a	14
$C_{10}N_2O_{12}Ru_3$	$Ru_3(NO)_2(CO)_{10}$	s	ls	400.4 (2)[d]	b	MgK_a	83
$C_{11}H_8ClN_3O_4$	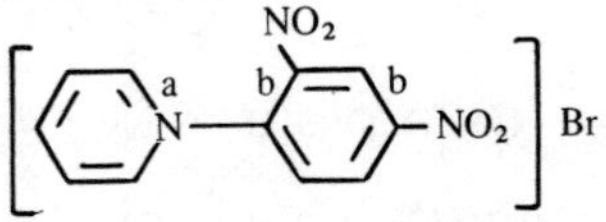	s	^{a}ls ^{b}ls	403.8 399.8 (0.24)	j 406.9	AlK_a	14
$C_{11}H_8N_2O_2$	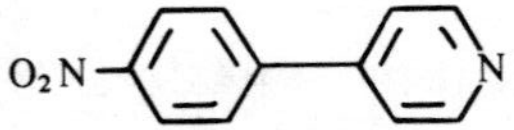	s	ls	401.8 (2)	f 284.3		150
$C_{11}H_9IN_2O_2$	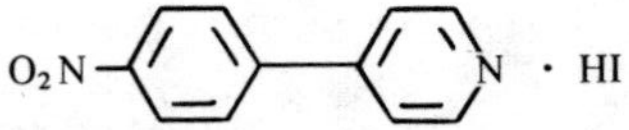	s	(+) ls	403.2 (2)	f 284.3		150
$C_{11}H_9N_3O_4S$	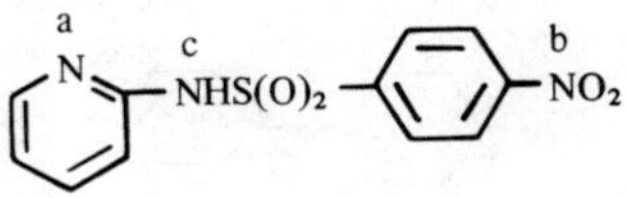	s	^{a}ls ^{b}ls ^{c}ls	398.0 (4) 405.5 (4) 400.1 (4)	b	Al, MgK_a	32
$C_{11}H_{12}BrN$	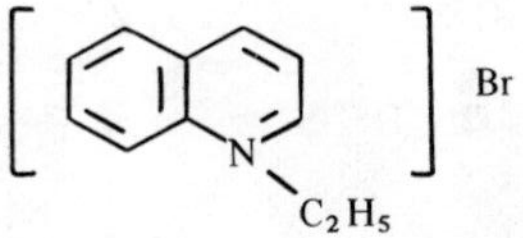	s	ls	399.2 (0.17)	j 406.9	AlK_a	14
$C_{11}H_{12}N_2O_6S$	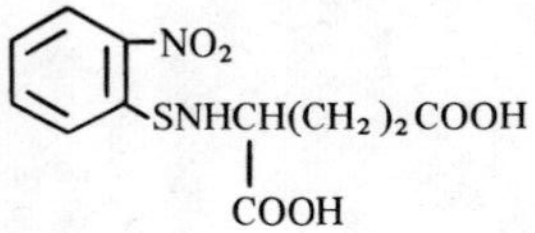	s	ls	405.1 (4) 398.8 (4)	b	Al, MgK_a	32

TABLE 3 (continued)

Compound		Phase	Orbital	E_B(eV)	Calibrant	Exciting Radiation	Reference
$C_{11}H_{25}BrN$	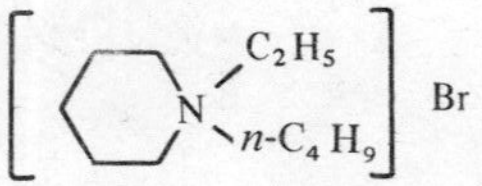	s	ls	400.5 (0.27)	j 406.9	AlK_α	14
$C_{12}H_8N_2O_4S$	*o,o'*-$NO_2C_6H_4SC_6H_4NO_2$	s	ls	406.0	b 285.0	AlK_α	49
$C_{12}H_8N_2O_4S$	*p- p'*-$NO_2C_6H_4SC_6H_4NO_2$	s	ls	405.8	b 285.0	AlK_α	49
$C_{12}H_8N_2O_4S$	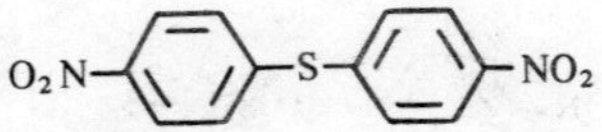	s	ls	405.1 (4)	b	Al, MgK_α	32
$C_{12}H_8N_2O_4S_2$	*m-,m'*-$NO_2C_6H_4SSC_6H_4NO_2$	s	ls	405.7	b 285.0	AlK_α	49
$C_{12}H_8N_2O_4S_2$	*o-,o'*-$NO_2C_6H_4SSC_6H_4NO_2$	s	ls	405.7	b 285.0	AlK_α	49
$C_{12}H_8N_2O_4S_2$	*p,p'*-$NO_2C_6H_4SSC_6H_4NO_2$	s	ls	405.6	b 285.0	AlK_α	49
$C_{12}H_8N_2O_5S$	*o,o'*-$NO_2C_6H_4S(O)C_6H_4NO_2$	s	ls	405.8	b 285.0	AlK_α	49
$C_{12}H_8N_2O_5S$	*p,p'*-$NO_2C_6H_4S(O)C_6H_4NO_2$	s	ls	405.9	b 285.0	AlK_α	49
$C_{12}H_8N_2O_6S$	*p,p'*-$NO_2C_6H_4SO_2C_6H_4NO_2$	s	ls	405.8	b 285.0	AlK_α	49
$C_{12}H_8N_2O_6S_2$	*p,p'*-$NO_2C_6H_4SSO_2C_6H_4NO_2$	s	ls	405.8	b 285.0	AlK_α	49
$C_{12}H_9BF_4N_2$	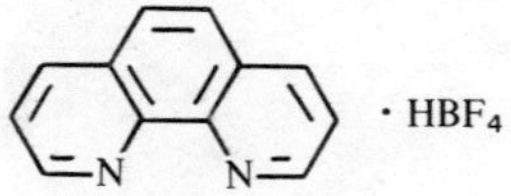	s	(+) ls	399.9 (2)	f 284.3		150
$C_{12}H_9BrN_2$	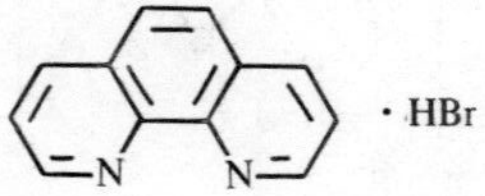	s	(+) ls	399.7 (2)	f 284.3		150
$C_{12}H_9IN_2$	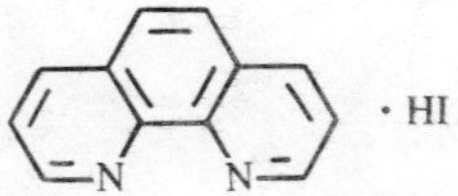	s	(+) ls	400.0 (2)	f 284.3		150

TABLE 3 (continued)

Compound		Phase	Orbital	E_B(eV)	Calibrant	Exciting Radiation	Reference
$C_{12}H_9NO_4S$	p-$NO_2C_6H_4SO_2C_6H_5$	s	ls	406.0	b 285.0	AlK_a	49
$C_{12}H_{10}N_2$	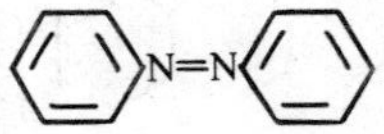	s	ls	399.3 (4)	b	Al, MgK_a	32
$C_{12}H_{10}N_4O_2$	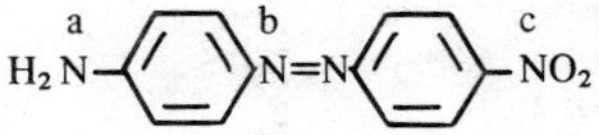	s	^{a}ls ^{b}ls ^{c}ls	399.6 (4) 398.8 (4) 405.0 (4)	b	Al, MgK_a	32
$C_{12}H_{12}N_2O_2S$	$SO_2(p$-$C_6H_4NH_2)_2$	s	ls	399.4	b 285.0	AlK_a	49
$C_{12}H_{14}BrNO_3$	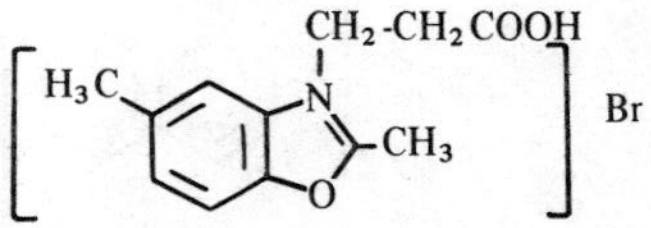	s	ls	399.1 (0.28)	j 406.9	AlK_a	14
$C_{12}H_{16}IN$	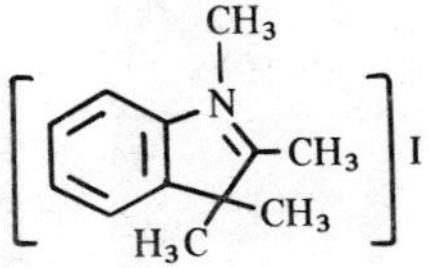	s	ls	400.4 (0.27)	j 406.9	AlK_a	14
$C_{12}H_{27}N$	$(n$-$C_4H_9)_3N$	s	ls	398.1 (4)	b	Al, MgK_a	32
$C_{12}H_{28}BF_4N$	$[(n$-$C_3H_7)_4N]BF_4$	s	ls	400.4 (0.09)	j 406.9	AlK_a	14
$C_{12}H_{28}F_6BP$	$[(n$-$C_3H_7)_4N]PF_6$	s	ls	401.1 (0.18)	j 406.9	AlK_a	14
$C_{13}H_9N$	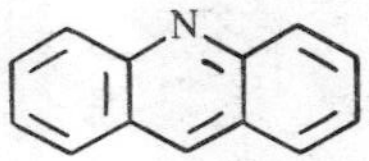	s	ls	395.1	j 406.9	AlK_a	14
$C_{13}H_{10}BrN$	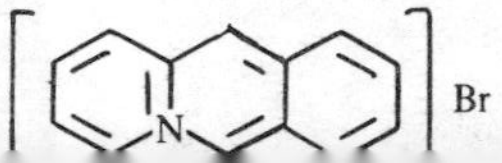	s	ls	399.1 (0.37)	j 406.9	AlK_a	14

TABLE 3 (continued)

	Compound	Phase	Orbital	E_B(eV)	Calibrant	Exciting Radiation	Reference
$C_{13}H_{10}ClN$	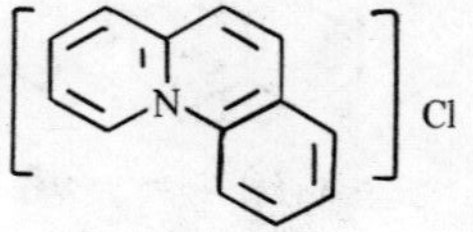	s	ls	398.8 (0.82)	j 406.9	AlK_α	14
$C_{13}H_{11}IN_2$	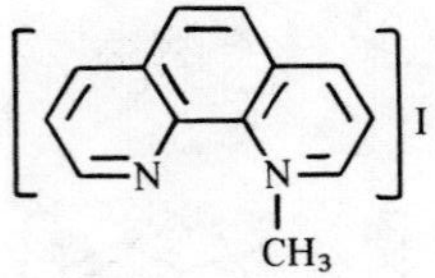	s	(+) ls	400.2 (2)	f 284.3		150
$C_{13}H_{11}NO_2S$	*o*-,*p*′-$NO_2C_6H_4SC_6H_4CH_3$	s	ls	405.9	b 285.0	AlK_α	49
$C_{13}H_{11}NO_2S$	*p*-,*p*′-$NO_2C_6H_4SC_6H_4CH_3$	s	ls	405.8	b 285.0	AlK_α	49
$C_{13}H_{16}BrN$	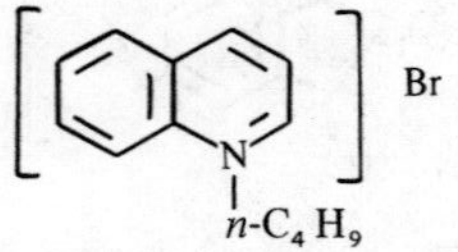	s	ls	399.3 (0.24)	j 406.9	AlK_α	14
$C_{13}H_{16}BrN$	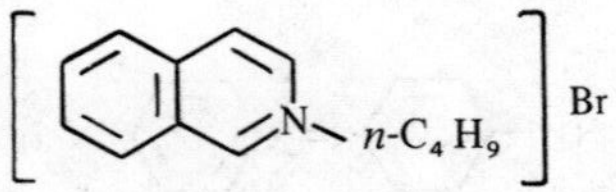	s	ls	399.9 (0.25)	j 406.9	AlK_α	14
$C_{13}H_{16}IN$	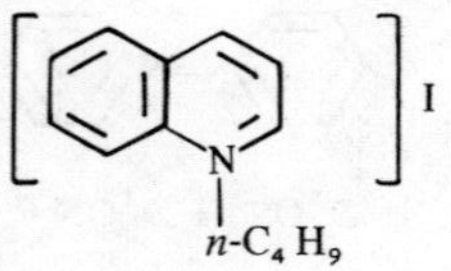	s	ls	399.6 (0.21)	j 406.9	AlK_α	14
$C_{14}H_{12}BN_9O_3W$	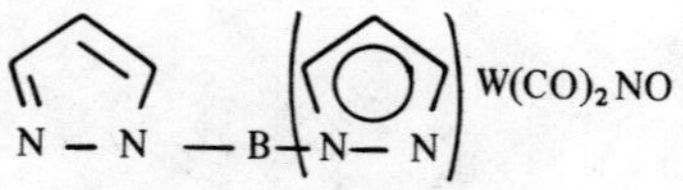	s	ls	400.6 (2)	b	MgK_α	117

TABLE 3 (continued)

Compound		Phase	Orbital	E_B(eV)	Calibrant	Exciting Radiation	Reference
$C_{14}H_{12}BrN$	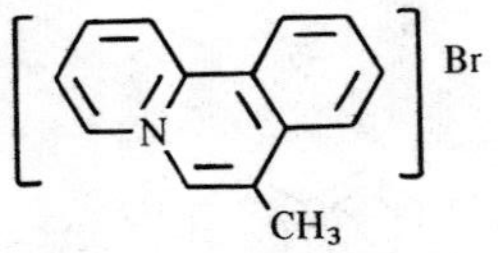	s	ls	399.1 (0.36)	j 406.9	AlK_α	14
$C_{14}H_{12}ClN$	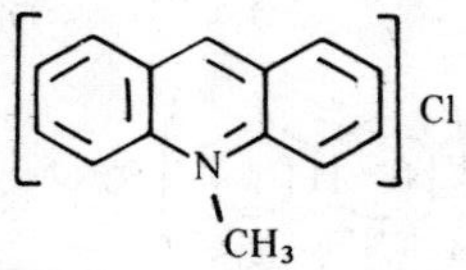	s	ls	399.2 (0.37)	j 406.9	AlK_α	14
$C_{14}H_{13}BF_4N_2$	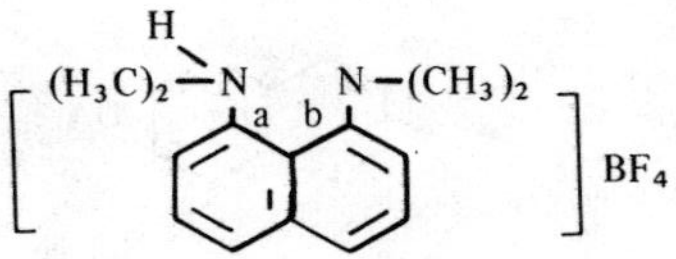	s	^{a}ls ^{b}ls	400.1 401.5	b 285.0		59
$C_{14}H_{14}ClN_3$	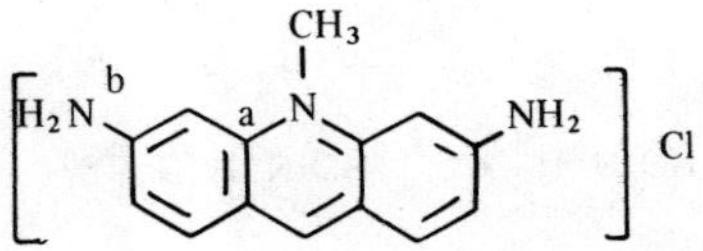	s	^{a}ls ^{b}ls	397.2 (0.24) 395.6 (0.32)	j 406.9	AlK_α	14
$C_{14}H_{14}IN$	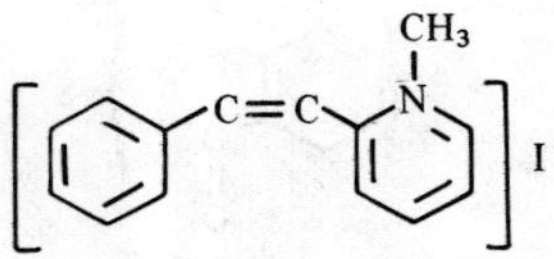	s	ls	400.0 (0.15)	j 406.9	AlK_α	14
$C_{14}H_{30}N_2P_2Pt$	*cis*-$((C_2H_5)_3P)_2Pt(CN)_2$	s	ls	398.5 (1)	d 285.0	AlK_α	87
$C_{15}H_{16}INO$	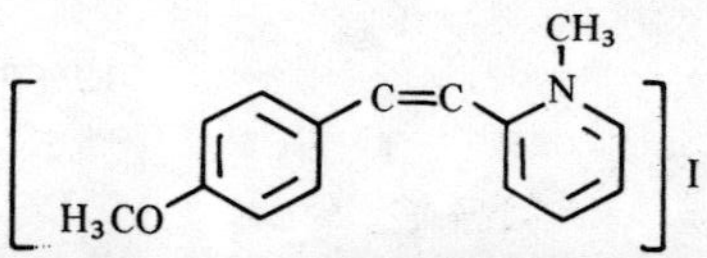	s	ls	399.8 (0.20)	j 406.9	AlK_α	14

TABLE 3 (continued)

Compound		Phase	Orbital	E_B(eV)	Calibrant	Exciting Radiation	Reference
$C_{15}H_{24}NO_3S$	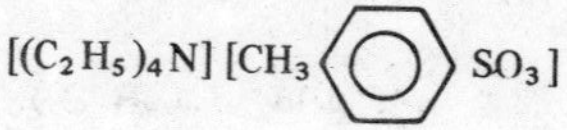	s	ls	400.4 (0.11)	j 406.9	AlK_α	14
$C_{16}H_8N_2O_4S$	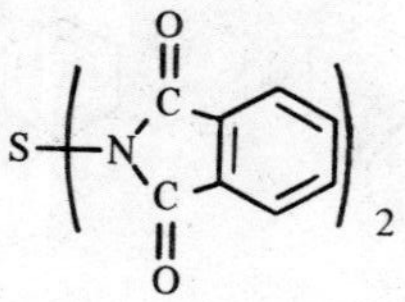	s	ls	400.3	b 285.0	AlK_α	49
$C_{16}H_{20}N_2S_2$	*p*-,*p*'-$C_6H_4N(CH_3)_2SSC_6H_4N(CH_3)_2$	s	ls	399.7	b 285.0	AlK_α	49
$C_{16}H_{36}BrN$	$[(n\text{-}C_4H_9)_4N]Br$	s	ls	400.7 (0.24)	j 406.9	AlK_α	14
$C_{16}H_{64}B_{20}N_2Pt$	$[(C_2H_5)_4N]_2Pt(B_{10}H_{12})_2$	s	ls	402.0 (1)	d 285.0	AlK_α	87
$C_{18}H_{12}N_2O_3V$	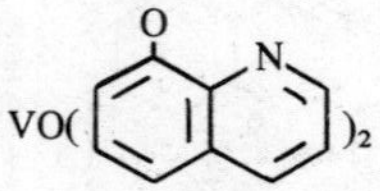	s	ls	398.6	Pt $4f_{7/2}$ 71.0	AlK_α	146
$C_{18}H_{12}N_2O_4U$	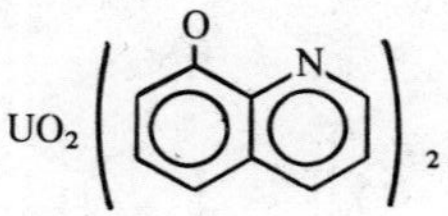	s	ls	400.6	c 84	MgK_α	36
$C_{18}H_{12}N_2O_4U \cdot C_9H_7NO$	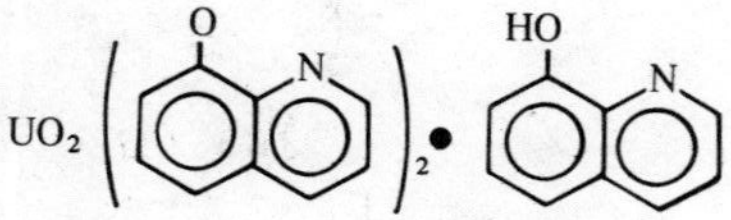	s	[a]ls [b]ls	400.5 402.1	c 84	MgK_α	36
$C_{18}H_{13}N_2O_4V$	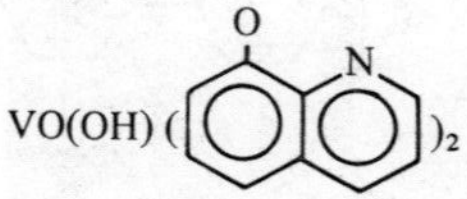	s	ls	398.8	Pt $4f_{7/2}$ 71.0	AlK_α	146

TABLE 3 (continued)

Compound		Phase	Orbital	E_B(eV)	Calibrant	Exciting Radiation	Reference
$C_{18}H_{15}F_3N_3P_3$	$(C_6H_5)_2P=N$, $PF(C_6H_5)$, $N-N$, F_2P-N	s	1s	398.6 (3)	d 285.0	AlK$_\alpha$	105
$C_{18}H_{30}N_4P_2Pt$	$((C_2H_5)_3P)_2Pt((CN)_2CC(CN)_2)$	s	1s	399.3 (1)	d 285.0	AlK$_\alpha$	87
$C_{20}H_{16}Br_2CuN_4 \cdot 2H_2O$	$CuBr_2 \cdot 2[\text{bipyridine}] \cdot 2H_2O$	s	1s	400.9	a 285.5	AlK$_\alpha$	46
$C_{20}H_{16}Cl_2CuN_4 \cdot 3H_2O$	$CuCl_2 \cdot 2[\text{bipyridine}] \cdot 3H_2O$	s	1s	400.7	a 285.5	AlK$_\alpha$	46
$C_{20}H_{32}As_4ClCoN_6O_4$	$trans\text{-}[Co(N_3)_2(\text{As(CH}_3)_2\text{-}C_6H_4\text{-As(CH}_3)_2)_2]ClO_4$	s	1s	403.2[1] 399.1[2]	b	MgK$_\alpha$	99
$C_{20}H_{32}As_4ClN_2Ru$	$trans\text{-}[Ru(N_2)Cl(\text{As(CH}_3)_2\text{-}C_6H_4\text{-As(CH}_3)_2)_2]$	s	1s	402.3 Ru 400.7[1]	b	MgK$_\alpha$	99
$C_{20}H_{32}As_4ClN_3Ru$	$trans\text{-}[Ru(N_3)Cl(\text{As(CH}_3)_2\text{-}C_6H_4\text{-As(CH}_3)_2)_2]$	s	1s	403.9[1] 399.2[2]	b	MgK$_\alpha$	99
$C_{20}H_{32}As_4Cl_2CoNO$	$[trans\text{-}CoCl(NO)(\text{As(CH}_3)_2\text{-}C_6H_4\text{-As(CH}_3)_2)_2]Cl$	s	1s	400.5 (2)	b	MgK$_\alpha$	83
$C_{20}H_{32}As_4Cl_2CoNO_9$	$[Co(NO)(\text{As(CH}_3)_2\text{-}C_6H_4\text{-As(CH}_3)_2)_2](ClO_4)_2$	s	1s	402.3 (2)	b	MgK$_\alpha$	83
$C_{20}H_{32}As_4Cl_2CrNO_5$	$[trans\text{-}CrCl(NO)(\text{As(CH}_3)_2\text{-}C_6H_4\text{-As(CH}_3)_2)_2]ClO_4$	s	1s	400.7 (2)	b	MgK$_\alpha$	83

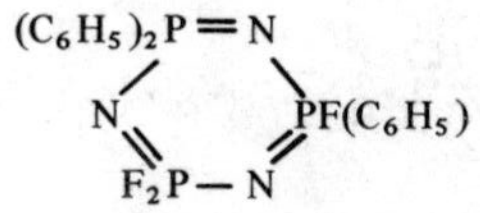

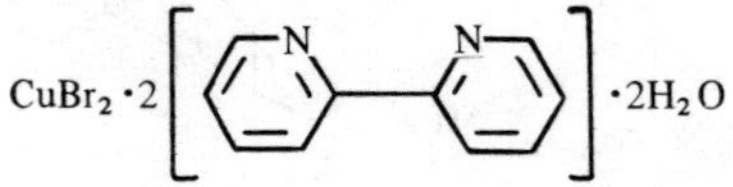

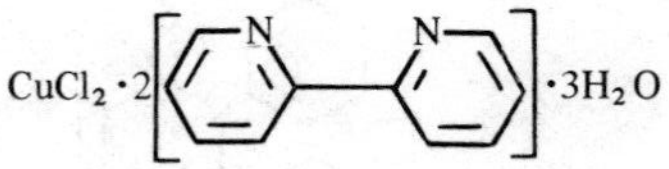

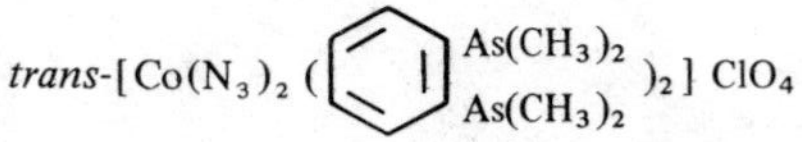

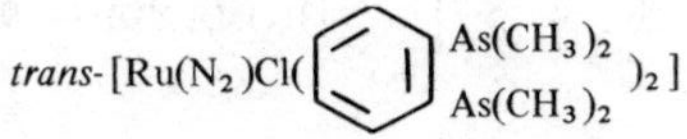

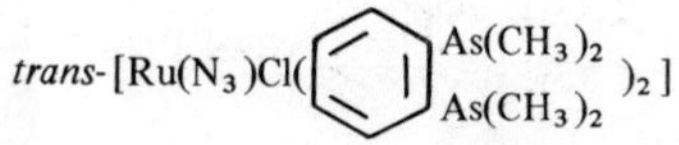

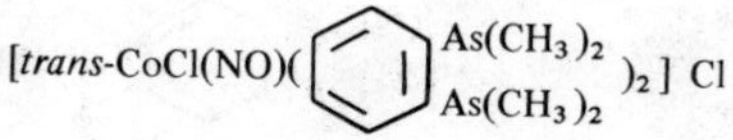

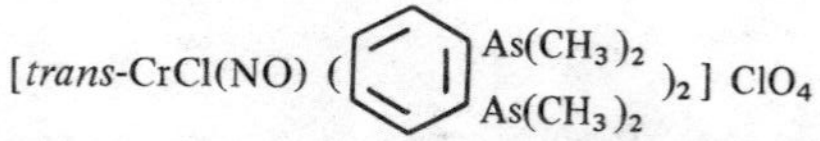

TABLE 3 (continued)

Compound	Phase	Orbital	E_B(eV)	Calibrant	Exciting Radiation	Reference
$C_{20}H_{32}As_4Cl_2FeNO_5$ [trans-FeCl(NO)($\bigcirc$[As(CH$_3$)$_2$ / As(CH$_3$)$_2$]$_2$) ClO$_4$	s	1s	400.0 (2)	b	MgK$_\alpha$	83
$C_{20}H_{32}As_4Cl_2FeNO_9$ [Fe(NO)($\bigcirc$[As(CH$_3$)$_2$ / As(CH$_3$)$_2$]$_2$)] (ClO$_4$)$_2$	s	1s	401.2 (2) 399.6 (2)	b	MgK$_\alpha$	83
$C_{20}H_{32}As_4Cl_3FeNO_9$ [trans-FeCl(NO)($\bigcirc$[As(CH$_3$)$_2$ / As(CH$_3$)$_2$]$_2$] (ClO$_4$)$_2$	s	1s	402.9 (2)[d]	b	MgK$_\alpha$	83
$C_{20}H_{32}As_4Cl_3NORu$ [trans-RuCl(NO)($\bigcirc$[As(CH$_3$)$_2$ / As(CH$_3$)$_2$]$_2$] Cl$_2$	s	1s	400.0 (2)	b	MgK$_\alpha$	83
$C_{22}H_{17}NO$	s	1s	399.8	b 284	Al	147
$C_{22}H_{17}NS$	s	1s	400.1	b 284	Al	147
$C_{22}H_{24}CoN_3O_3$ Co^{III}((C$_6$H$_5$C(O)CH$_2$C=NCH$_2$)$_2$)(NO)[a] CH$_3$	s	1s[a]	400.1	d 285.0	AlK$_\alpha$	127
$C_{24}H_{20}F_2N_3P_3$	s	1s	398.2 (3)	d 285.0	AlK$_\alpha$	105

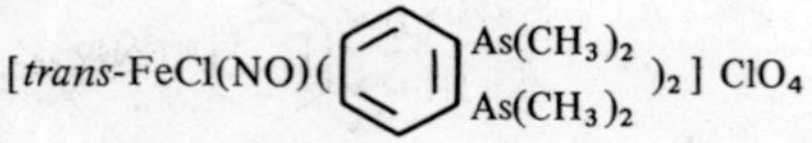

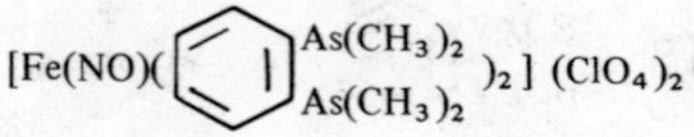

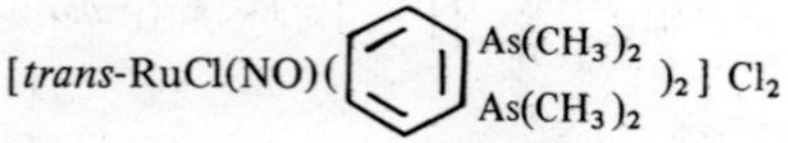

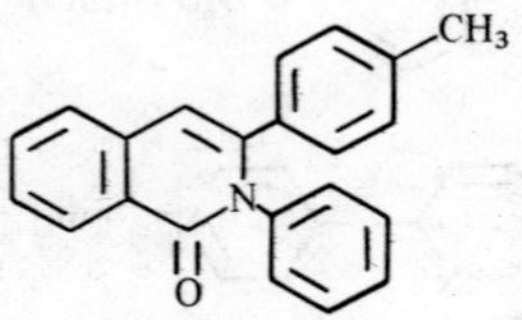

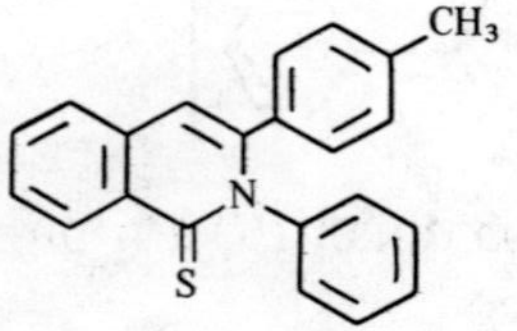

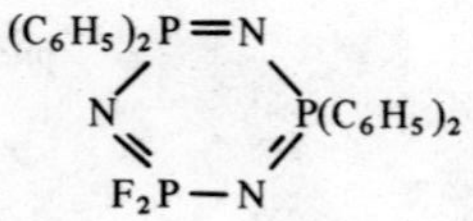

TABLE 3 (continued)

Compound		Phase	Orbital	E_B(eV)	Calibrant	Exciting Radiation	Reference
$C_{24}H_{54}Cl_2CoNOP_2$	$CoCl_2NO(P(n\text{-}C_4H_9)_3)_2$	s	ls	401.5 (2) 399.7 (2)	b	MgK_α	83
$C_{24}H_{60}Cl_{15}N_3PtSn_5$	$[(CH_3CH_2)_4N]_3Pt(SnCl_3)_5$	s	ls	402.2 (1)	d 285.0	AlK_α	87
$C_{25}H_{20}AsNO$	$[(C_6H_5)_4As]NCO$	s	ls	397.0	c 84	MgK_α	145
$C_{25}H_{20}AsNS$	$[(C_6H_5)_4As]NCS$	s	ls	396.6	c 84	MgK_α	145
$C_{25}H_{20}AsNSe$	$[(C_6H_5)_4As]NCSe$	s	ls	397.0	c 84	MgK_α	145
$C_{25}H_{20}AsNTe$	$[(C_6H_5)_4As]NCTe$	s	ls	396.8	c 84	MgK_α	145
$C_{26}H_{22}N_2O_5S_2$	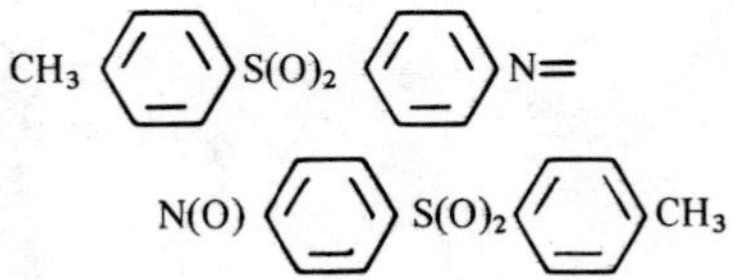	s	[a]ls [b]ls	399.3 (4) 403.6 (4)	b	Al, MgK_α	32
$C_{26}H_{24}Cl_2CoNOP_2$	$CoCl_2(NO)((C_6H_5)_2PCH_2CH_2P(C_6H_5)_2)$	s	ls	400.7 (2)	b	MgK_α	83
$C_{26}H_{26}Cl_2CoNOP$	$CoCl_2(NO)(P(CH_3)(C_6H_5)_2)_2$	s	ls	401.7 399.6	b	MgK_α	83
$C_{26}H_{26}I_2NOP_2Rh$	$RhI_2(NO)(P(CH_3)(C_6H_5)_2)_2$	s	ls	400.3 (2)	b	MgK_α	83
$C_{28}H_{20}N_4O_5$	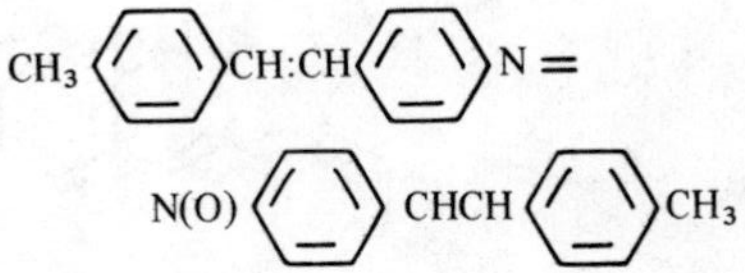	s	[a]ls [b]ls	399.4 (4) 403.4 (4)	b	Al, MgK_α	32

TABLE 3 (continued)

Compound		Phase	Orbital	E_B(eV)	Calibrant	Exciting Radiation	Reference
$C_{28}H_{22}NO$	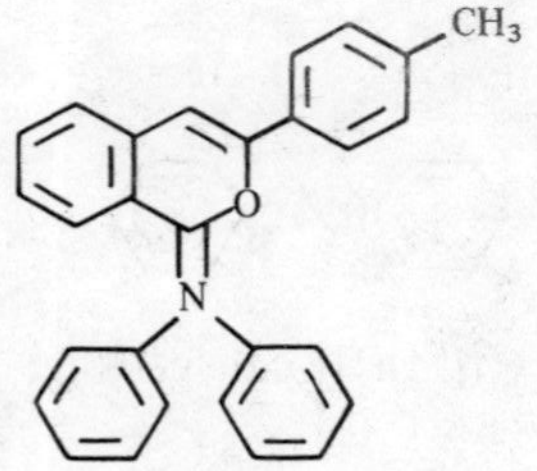	s	ls	397.7	b 284	Al	147
$C_{28}H_{22}NS$	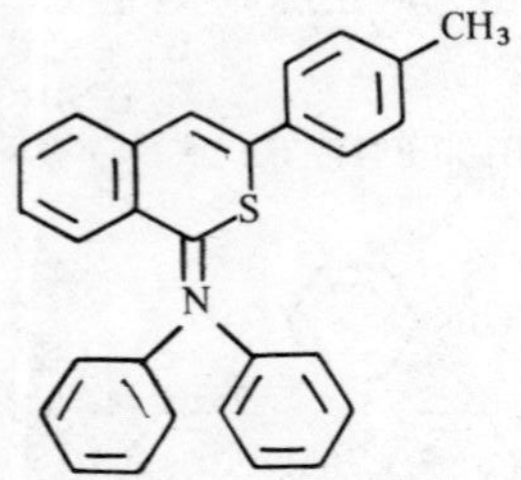	s	ls	398.0	b 284	Al	147
$C_{28}H_{22}N_4O_6$	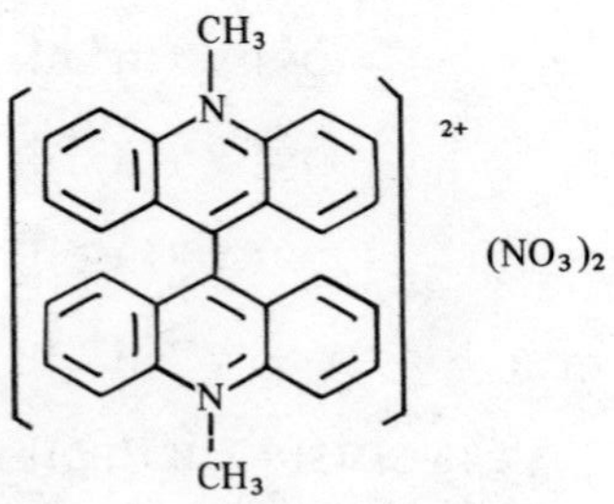	s	ls ls	398.1 (0.23) 402.8 (0.15)	KNO_3 Nls 406.9	AlK_α	14
$C_{30}H_{23}ClCuN_2P$	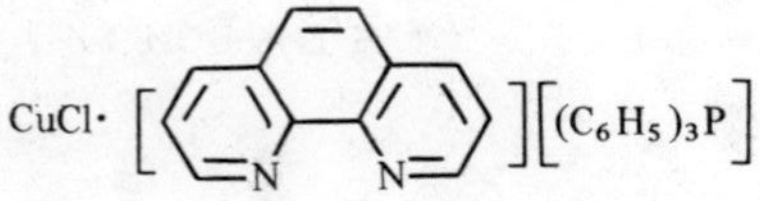	s	ls	400.2	a 285.5	AlK_α	46

TABLE 3 (continued)

Compound		Phase	Orbital	E_B(eV)	Calibrant	Exciting Radiation	Reference
$C_{30}H_{24}CuN_6O_4S \cdot 7H_2O$	$CuSO_4 \cdot 3$ 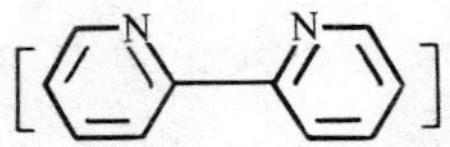 $\cdot 7H_2O$	s	ls	400.4	a 285.5	AlK_a	46
$C_{32}H_{16}N_8OV$	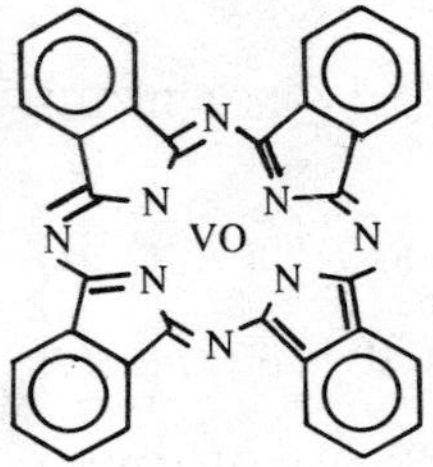	s	ls	399.1	Pt $4f_{7/2}$ 71.0	AlK_a	146
$C_{32}H_{80}Cl_{20}N_4Pt_3Sn_8$	$[(C_2H_5)_4N]_4Pt_3Sn_8Cl_{20}$	s	ls	402.3	d 285.0	AlK_a	87
$C_{34}H_{27}N_2$	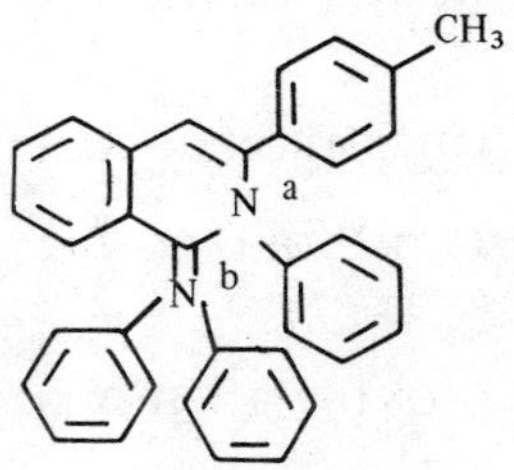	s	[a]ls [b]ls	399.8 397.4	b 284	Al	147
$C_{36}H_{30}BrNP_2$	$\{[(C_6H_5)_3P]_2N\}Br$	s	ls	397.4 (3)	d 285.0	AlK_a	128
$C_{36}H_{30}ClF_6N_2O_2P_3Ru$	$[RuCl(NO)_2(P(C_6H_5)_3)_2]PF_6$	s	ls	402.6 (2) 400.2 (2)	b	MgK_a	83
$C_{36}H_{30}ClNNiOP_2$	$NiCl(NO)(P(C_6H_5)_3)_2$	s	ls	399.8 (2)	b	MgK_a	83
$C_{36}H_{30}ClNP_2$	$\{[(C_6H_5)_3P]_2N\}Cl$	s	ls	397.6 (3)	d 285.0	AlK_a	128
$C_{36}H_{30}Cl_2NOPRh$	$RhCl_2(NO)(P(C_6H_5)_3)_2$	s	ls	401.5	b	MgK_a	83
$C_{36}H_{30}Cl_2NP_2Re$	$ReN(Cl)_2[P(C_6H_5)_3]_2$	s	ls	398.8	b	MgK_a	99

TABLE 3 (continued)

Compound		Phase	Orbital	E_B(eV)	Calibrant	Exciting Radiation	Reference
$C_{36}H_{30}FNP_2$	$\{[(C_6H_5)_3P]_2N\}F$	s	ls	397.6 (2)	d 285.0	AlK_α	128
$C_{36}H_{30}F_6IrN_2O_2P_3$	$[Ir(NO)_2(P(C_6H_5)_3)_2]PF_6$	s	ls	400.2 (2)	b	MgK_α	83
$C_{36}H_{30}F_6N_2O_2P_3Rh$	$[Rh(NO)_2(P(C_6H_5)_3)_2]PF_6$	s	ls	401.1 (2)	b	MgK_α	83
$C_{36}H_{30}INP_2$	$\{[(C_6H_5)_3P]_2N\}I$	s	ls	397.5 (2)	d 285.0	AlK_α	128
$C_{36}H_{30}IrNOP_2$	$Ir(NO)(P(C_6H_5)_3)_2$	s	ls	400.3 (2)	b	MgK_α	83
$C_{36}H_{30}N_2O_3P_2$	$\{[(C_6H_5)_3P]_2\overset{a}{N}\}\overset{b}{N}O_3$	s	^{a}ls ^{b}ls	397.2 (2) 404.8 (2)	d 285.0	AlK_α	128
$C_{36}H_{30}N_4NiOP_2$	$Ni(N_3)(NO)(P(C_6H_5)_3)_2$	s	ls	399.6 (2)	b	MgK_α	83
$C_{36}H_{30}N_4NiOP_2$	$Ni(\overset{b}{N}\overset{a}{N}\overset{b}{N})(NO)[P(C_6H_5)_3]_2$	s	^{a}ls ^{b}ls	403.8 399.6	b	MgK_α	99
$C_{36}H_{30}N_4P_2$	$\{[(C_6H_5)_3P]_2\overset{a}{N}\}N\overset{b}{N}N$	s	^{a}ls ^{b}ls	397.2 405.3	d 285.0	AlK_α	128
$C_{37}H_{30}CoNO_2P_2$	$Co(NO)(CO)(P(C_6H_5)_3)_2$	s	ls	400.8 (2)	b	MgK_α	83
$C_{37}H_{30}IrNO_2P_2$	$Ir(NO)(CO)(P(C_6H_5)_3)_2$	s	ls	399.6 (2)	b	MgK_α	83
$C_{37}H_{30}N_2OP_2$	$\{[(C_6H_5)_3P]_2\overset{a}{N}\}OC\overset{b}{N}$	s	^{a}ls ^{b}ls	397.2 (1) 400.5 (2)	d 285.0	AlK_α	128
$C_{37}H_{30}N_2P_2S$	$\{[(C_6H_5)_3P]_2\overset{a}{N}\}SC\overset{b}{N}$	s	^{a}ls ^{b}ls	397.3 (3) 400.2 (3)	d 285.0	AlK_α	128
$C_{38}H_{44}B_9NP_2Pt$	$((C_6H_5)_3P)_2PtB_9H_{11}(CH_3CN)$	s	ls	401.4 (1)	d 285.0	AlK_α	87
$C_{42}H_{30}ClIrN_4P_2$	$Ir(P(C_6H_5)_3)_2Cl(C_2(CN)_4)$	s	ls	398.9 (3)	d 285.0	AlK_α	82
$C_{42}H_{30}NO_6P_2V$	$\{[(C_6H_5)_3P]_2N\}V(CO)_6$	s	ls	397.5 (2)	d 285.0	AlK_α	128
$C_{42}H_{30}N_4P_2Pt$	$((C_6H_5)_3P)_2Pt(C_2(CN)_4)$	s	ls	399.4 (3)	d 285.0	AlK_α	82

TABLE 3 (continued)

Compound		Phase	Orbital	E_B(eV)	Calibrant	Exciting Radiation	Reference
$C_{43}H_{30}ClIrN_4OP_2$	$Ir(CO)(P(C_6H_5)_3)_2Cl(C_2(CN)_4)$	s	ls	399.1 (3)	d 285.0	AlK_α	82
$C_{43}H_{30}ClN_4OP_2Rh$	$((C_6H_5)_3P)_2RhCl(CO)(C_2(CN)_4)$	s	ls	399.2 (3)	d 285.0	AlK_α	82
$C_{48}H_{40}As_2FeN_{15}$	$[As(C_6H_5)_4]_2[Fe(\overset{bab}{NNN})_5]$	s	^{a}ls ^{b}ls	402.8 398.7	b	MgK_α	99
$C_{52}H_{48}ClN_2P_4Re$	$Re(N_2)Cl((C_6H_5)_2PCH_2CH_2P(C_6H_5)_2)_2$	s	ls	399.9^{Re} 397.9	b	MgK_α	99
$C_{52}H_{48}ClN_2P_4Re$	$[ReCl(N_2)\{\langle(C_6H_5)_2PCH_2\rangle_2\}_2]$	s	ls ^{Re}ls	397.9 399.9	d 284		81
$C_{52}H_{48}Cl_5FeN_2P_4Re$	$[ReCl(N_2)\{\langle(C_6H_5)_2PCH_2\rangle_2\}_2][FeCl_4]$	s	N_{ls}	399.6 (br)	d 284		81
$C_{54}H_{45}CoNOP_3$	$Co(NO)(P(C_6H_5)_3)_3$	s	ls	400.0 (2)	b	MgK_α	83
$C_{54}H_{45}NOP_3Rh$	$Rh(NO)(P(C_6H_5)_3)_3$	s	ls	400.8 (2)	b	MgK_α	83
$C_{72}H_{60}Cu_2N_6P_4$	$\{(Cu(\overset{bab}{NNN})[P(C_6H_5)_3]_2\}_2$	s	^{a}ls	403.7	b	MgK_α	99
			^{b}ls	399.2			
$C_{77}H_{60}MnN_6OP_3 \cdot 3H_2O$	$[(C_6H_5)_4P]_3[Mn(NO)(CN)_5] \cdot 3H_2O$	s	ls	399.7 (2)	b	MgK_α	83
ClH_4N	NH_4Cl	s	K	401.6 (5)	e, i	CrK_α	76
ClH_4NO	$[NH_3OH]Cl$	s	ls	402.1 (2)	b	MgK_α	117
ClH_4NO	$[NH_3OH]Cl$	s	ls	402.1		MgK_α	2
ClNO	ONCl	g	ls	411.4 (1)	N_2 Nls 409.9	MgK_α	11
ClN_3S_4	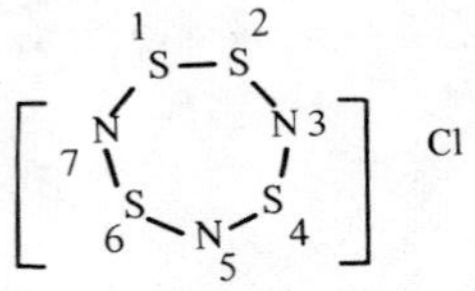		ls (3,7) (5)	401.0 401.0	a	MgK_α	106

TABLE 3 (continued)

Compound		Phase	Orbital	E_B(eV)	Calibrant	Exciting Radiation	Reference
ClN_3S_4	S_4N_3Cl	s	ls	399.6 (2)	b	MgK_α	117
$Cl_2CoH_{15}N_6O$	$[Co(NO)(NH_3)_5]Cl_2$	s	ls	400.7	b	MgK_α	83
$Cl_2CoH_{15}N_6O$	$[Co(\overset{a}{N}H_3)_5\overset{b}{N}O]Cl_2$	s	[a]ls [b]ls	400.2 (2) 402.0 (2)	b	MgK_α	117
$Cl_2CoH_{15}N_6O_2$	$[Co(\overset{b}{N}H_3)_5\overset{a}{N}O_2]Cl_2$	s	[a]ls [b]ls	404.0 (2) 400.0 (2)	b	MgK_α	117
$Cl_3CoH_{15}N_5$	$[Co(NH_3)_5Cl]Cl_2$	s	ls	400.0 (2)	b	MgK_α	117
$Cl_3CrH_{18}N_6$	$Cr(NH_3)_6Cl_3$	s	ls	399.9 (2)	b	MgK_α	117
$Cl_3H_{15}IrN_5$	$[Ir(NH_3)_5Cl]Cl_2$	s	ls	400.6 (2)	b	MgK_α	117
$Cl_4FeN_5S_5$	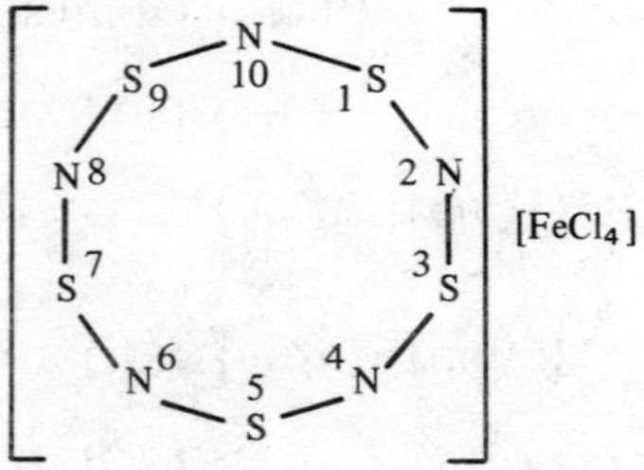		ls (10) (2) (4) (6) (8)	400.4 400.4 400.4 400.4 400.4	a	MgK_α	106
$Cl_5FeN_2S_3$	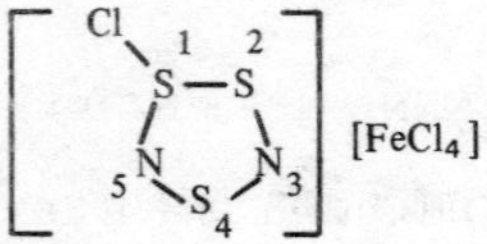		ls (3) (5)	401.6 400.5	a	MgK_α	106
$Cl_6N_3P_3$	$(NPCl_2)_3$	s	ls	399.5 (2)	b	MgK_α	117
$Cl_8H_4K_3NO_2Ru_2$	$K_3[Ru_2N(Cl)_8(H_2O)_2]$	s	ls	399.8	b	MgK_α	99
$Cl_8N_4P_4$	$(NPCl_2)_4$	s	ls	399.2 (2)	b	MgK_α	117

TABLE 3 (continued)

Compound		Phase	Orbital	E_B(eV)	Calibrant	Exciting Radiation	Reference
$CoH_6KN_6O_8$	$K[Co(\overset{a}{N}H_3)_2(\overset{b}{N}O_2)_4]$	s	^{a}1s ^{b}1s	400.0 (2) 404.0 (2)	b	MgK_α	117
$CoH_9N_6O_6$	$Co(\overset{b}{N}H_3)_3(\overset{a}{N}O_2)_3$	s	^{a}1s ^{b}1s	404.1 (2) 400.2 (2)	b	MgK_α	117
$CoH_{12}N_6O_8S$	*trans*-$[Co(\overset{a}{N}H_3)_4(\overset{b}{N}O_2)_2]SO_4$	s	^{a}1s ^{b}1s	399.2 (2) 403.9 (2)	b	MgK_α	117
$CoK_3N_6O_{12}$	$K_3Co(NO_2)_6$	s	1s	404.0 (2)	b	MgK_α	117
$Co_2H_{36}N_{12}O_{12}S_3$	$[Co(NH_3)_6]_2[SO_4]_3$	s	1s	400.0 (2)	b	MgK_α	117
CrN	CrN	s	1s	396.6 (2)	b	MgK_α	117
CsN_3	CsN_3	s	1s	398.12 402.40	b 285.0	Mg, AlK_α	66
$CuN_2O_6 \cdot 3H_2O$	$Cu(NO_3)_2 \cdot 3H_2O$	s	1s	408.3	a 285.5	AlK_α	46
F_3N	NF_3	g	1s	414.2 (1)	N_2 N1s 409.9	MgK_α	11
F_3NO	ONF_3	g	1s	417.0 (1)	N_2 N1s 409.9	MgK_α	11
F_4N_2	N_2F_4	g	1s	412.3 (1)	N_2 N1s 409.9	MgK_α	11
HNS_7	S_7NH	s	1s	400.2 (2)	b	MgK_α	117
HN_3	HN_3	s	1s	401.5 402.5 405.6	c	Al, MgK_α	63
H_3N	NH_3	g	1s	405.6	N_2 N1s 409.9	MgK_α	151
H_3N	NH_3	s	1s	398.8 (2)	b	MgK_α	117
H_3N	NH_3	g	1s	405.6 (1)	N_2 N1s 409.9	MgK_α	11

TABLE 3 (continued)

Compound		Phase	Orbital	E_B(eV)	Calibrant	Exciting Radiation	Reference
H_3NO_3S	NH_3SO_3	s	ls	401.8 (2)	b	MgK_α	117
$H_3N_3Na_3O_6P_3$	$Na_3(PO_2NH)_3$	s	ls	398.5 (2)	b	MgK_α	117
H_4N_2	N_2H_4	g	ls	406.1 (1)	N_2 Nls 409.9	MgK_α	11
$H_4N_2O_3$	$\overset{b}{N}H_4\overset{a}{N}O_3$	s	^{a}ls ^{b}ls	407.2 (2) 402.3 (2)	b	MgK_α	117
$H_4N_2O_3$	NH_4NO_3	s	ls	402.3		MgK_α	2
$H_4N_2O_3$	$\overset{a}{N}H_4\overset{b}{N}O_3$	s	(a) $ls_{1/2}$ (b) $ls_{1/2}$	407.24 (1) 402.19 (1)		MgK_α	136
$H_4N_4S_4$	$S_4N_4H_4$	s	ls	399.5 (2)	b	MgK_α	117
$H_6N_2O_4S$	$N_2H_6SO_4$	s	ls	402.5		MgK_α	2
$H_6N_2O_4S$	$N_2H_6SO_4$	s	ls	402.5 (2)	b	MgK_α	117
$H_{18}N_9O_9Rh$	$[Rh(\overset{b}{N}H_3)_6](\overset{a}{N}O_3)_3$	s	^{a}ls ^{b}ls	407.3 (2) 400.7 (2)	b	MgK_α	117
KNO_2	KNO_2	s	ls	403.3	c	Al, MgK_α	63
KNO_3	KNO_3	s	ls	406.9 (0.05)	$NaNO_3$ Nls 407.2	AlK_α	14
KNO_3	KNO_3	s	ls	407.4	c	Al, MgK_α	63
KN_3	KN_3	s	ls	402.6 398.2	c	Al, MgK_α	63
KN_3	KN_3	s	ls	398.66 403.05	b 285.0	Mg, AlK_α	66
LiN_3	LiN_3	s	ls	398.9 403.28	b 285.0	Mg, AlK_α	66
$NNaO_2$	$NaNO_2$	s	ls	404.1		MgK_α	2

TABLE 3 (continued)

Compound		Phase	Orbital	E_B(eV)	Calibrant	Exciting Radiation	Reference
$NNaO_2$	$NaNO_2$	s	ls	404.1 (2)	b	MgK_α	117
$NNaO_2$	$NaNO_2$	s	ls	404.3 (4)	b	Al, MgK_α	32
$NNaO_3$	$NaNO_3$	s	ls	407.2 (4)	b	Al, MgK_α	32
$NNaO_3$	$NaNO_3$	s	ls	407.4 (2)	b	MgK_α	117
$NNaO_3$	$NaNO_3$	s	ls	407.4		MgK_α	2
NO	NO	g	ls	410.7 (1)	N_2 Nls 409.9	MgK_α	11
NO	NO	g	ls	410.3	N_2 Nls 409.9	MgK_α	151
NO_2	NO_2	g	ls	412.4	N_2 Nls 409.9	MgK_α	151
NO_2	NO_2	g	ls	412.9 (1)	N_2 Nls 409.9	MgK_α	11
NV	VN	s	ls	397.2 (2)	b	MgK_α	117
N_2	N_2	g	ls	409.9 (1)	N_2 Nls 409.9	MgK_α	11
N_2	N_2	g	ls	4.35 (20)	NH_3 Nls 0.0	MgK_α	61
N_2	N_2	g	ls	409.9	N_2 Nls 409.9	MgK_α	151
$N_2Na_2O_2$	$Na_2N_2O_2$	s	ls	401.3		MgK_α	2
$N_2Na_2O_2$	$Na_2N_2O_2$	s	ls	401.3 (2)	b	MgK_α	117
$N_2Na_2O_3$	$Na_2(ON^bN^aO_2)$	s	^{a}ls ^{b}ls	403.9 (2) 400.9 (2)	b	MgK_α	117
$N_2Na_2O_3$	$Na_2[ONNO_2]$	s	ls	403.9 400.9		MgK_α	2
N_2O	N_2O	g	ls	3.17 (10) 7.04 (5)	NH_3 Nls 0.0	MgK_α	61

Compound		Phase	Orbital	E_B(eV)	Calibrant	Exciting Radiation	Reference
N_2O	$\overset{ab}{NNO}$	g	$^{b}1s$ $^{a}1s$	412.5 (1) 408.6 (1)	N_2 N1s 409.9	MgK_α	11
N_2O	$\overset{ab}{NNO}$	g	$^{a}1s$ $^{b}1s$	408.5 412.5	N_2 N1s 409.9	MgK_α	151
N_3Na	Na $\overset{aba}{NNN}$	s	$^{a}1s$ $^{b}1s$	399.2 (4) 403.7 (4)	b	Al, MgK_α	32
N_3Na	Na(NNN)	s	1s	403.7 399.3		MgK_α	2
N_3Na	NaN_3	s	1s	398.7 403.12	b 285.0	Mg, AlK_α	66
N_3Na	Na($\overset{bab}{NNN}$)	s	$^{a}1s$ $^{b}1s$	403.7 (2) 399.3 (2)	b	MgK_α	117
N_3Rb	RbN_3	s	1s	398.30 402.61	b 285.0	Mg, AlK_α	66
N_4S_4	S_4N_4	s	1s	402.1 (2)	b	MgK_α	117
$N_4S_4 \cdot SbCl_5$	$S_4N_4 \cdot SbCl_5$	s	1s	400.2 (2)	b	MgK_α	117
N_5P_3	P_3N_5	s	1s	397.8 (2)	b	MgK_α	117
Na							
$B_4Na_2O_7$	$Na_2B_4O_7$	s	1s	1,069.8	Lif F1s 685.4		114
ClNa	NaCl	s 1 *M* frozen H_2O+CH_3OH (1:1) soln (−50°C)	1s	1,070.4 (2)			5
ClNa	NaCl	s 1*M* frozen H_2O+CH_3OH (1:1) soln (−196°C)	1s	1,070.6 (2)			5

TABLE 3 (continued)

Compound		Phase	Orbital	E_B(eV)	Calibrant	Exciting Radiation	Reference
ClNa	NaCl	s 1 *M* frozen H_2O soln	ls	1,070.4 (2)			5
ClNa	NaCl	s	ls	1,070.4 (2)			5
ClNa	NaCl	s	ls 2s 2p ls	1,072.7 (3) 63.7 (3) 30.5 (3) 1,072.7 (3)		$MgK_{\alpha 1}$ $AlK_{\alpha 1}$	53
N_3Na	NaN_3	s	ls 2s 2p	1,071.00 62.95 30.17	b 285.0	Mg, AlK_α	66
Na_2O	Na_2O	s	K	1,072.1 (5)	e, i	CrK_α	76
Na_2O	Na_2O	s	L_I	63.3	e	$CrK_{\alpha 1}$	67
Nb							
CNb	$NbC_{0.940}$ $NbC_{0.904}$ $NbC_{0.774}$	s	$3d_{5/2}$	203.01 (10) 203.05 (10) 203.17 (10)	Metal Nb $3d_{5/2}$	201.77 AlK_α	73
$C_3N_7Nb_{10}$	$NbC_{0.3}N_{0.7}$	s	$3d_{5/2}$	203.75 (30)	a 284.0	AlK_α	108
$C_{98}Nb_{100}$	$NbC_{0.98}$	s	$3d_{5/2}$	202.65 (30)	a 284.0	AlK_α	108
F_7K_2Nb	K_2NbF_7	s	$3p_{1/2}$ $3p_{3/2}$ $3d_{3/2}$ $3d_{5/2}$ 4p	389.6 (3) 374.4 (3) 219 216.0 (3) 44.8 (3)	a 290.0	AlK_α	62
Nb	Nb	s	L_I L_{II} L_{III}	2,697.8 (5) 2,464.6 (5) 2,370.7 (5)		CuK_α	79

TABLE 3 (continued)

Compound		Phase	Orbital	E_B(eV)	Calibrant	Exciting Radiation	Reference
Nb	Nb	s	$3d_{5/2}$	201.05 (30)	a 284.0	AlK_a	108
NbN	$NbN_{0.91}$	s	$3d_{5/2}$	203.35 (30)	a 284.0	AlK_a	108
NbS_4Tl_3	Tl_3NbS_4	s	$3p_{1/2}$	387.0 (3)	a 290.0	AlK_a	62
			$3p_{3/2}$	371.2 (3)			
			$3d_{3/2}$	216.1 (3)			
			$3d_{5/2}$	213.4 (3)			
			4p	41.8 (3)			
$NbSe_4Tl_3$	Tl_3NbSe_4	s	$3p_{1/2}$	387	a 290.0	AlK_a	62
			$3p_{3/2}$	371.3 (3)			
			$3d_{3/2}$	216.2 (3)			
			$3d_{5/2}$	213.5 (3)			
			4p	41			
Nb_2O_5	Nb_2O_5	s	$3p_{1/2}$	386.0 (3)	a 290.0	AlK_a	62
			$3p_{3/2}$	307.6 (3)			
			$3d_{3/2}$	215.4 (3)			
			$3d_{5/2}$	212.7 (3)			
			4p	40.8 (3)			
Nd							
Nd	Nd	s	4f	−0.4	Pd Fermi level	AlK_a	47
				−4.2			
Nd_2O_3	Nd_2O_3	s	L_I	7,126.2	e	MoK_{a1}	56
			L_{II}	6,722.2			
			L_{III}	6,208.4			
Ne							
Ne	Ne	g	ls	870.2 (1)	Ne 2p 21.59	MgK_a	151
			2s	48.42 (5)			
			2p	21.59			
Ne	Ne	g	ls	869.7 (1)	Ne 2s, 2p 48.5, 21.6	MgK_a	6

TABLE 3 (continued)

	Compound	Phase	Orbital	E_B(eV)	Calibrant	Exciting Radiation	Reference
Ni							
C_2N_2Ni	$Ni(CN)_2$	s	$2p_{3/2}$	856.3 (1)	c 83.0		125
$C_2NiO_4 \cdot 2H_2O$	$NiC_2O_4 \cdot 2H_2O$	s	$2p_{1/2}$	885.7 879.9	a 290.0	AlK_α	30
			$2p_{3/2}$	867.9 862.1			
$C_3K_2N_3Ni$	$K_2Ni(CN)_3$	s	$2p_{3/2}$	854.7 (1)	c 83.0		125
$C_4H_{12}N_2NiO_6$	$Ni(NH_2CH_2CO_2)_2(H_2O)_2$	s	$2p_{1/2}$	883 887.8	a 290.0	AlK_α	30
			$2p_{3/2}$	865.6 860.4			
$C_4H_{16}Cl_2N_4NiO_8$	$[Ni(NH_2CH_2CH_2NH_2)_2](ClO_4)_2$	s	$2p_{1/2}$ $2p_{3/2}$	877.6 860.5	a 290.0	AlK_α	30
$C_4K_2N_4Ni$	$K_2Ni(CN)_4$	s	$2p_{3/2}$	855.6 (2)	c 83.0		125
C_4NiO_4	$Ni(CO)_4$	s	$2p_{1/2}$ $2p_{3/2}$	876.4 (3) 859.2 (3)		MgK_α	23
$C_6H_{24}N_6NiO_4S$	$[Ni(NH_2CH_2CH_2NH_2)_3]SO_4$	s	$2p_{1/2}$	883.2 877.5	a 290.0	AlK_α	30
			$2p_{3/2}$	866.0 859.9			
$C_8H_{14}N_4NiO_4$	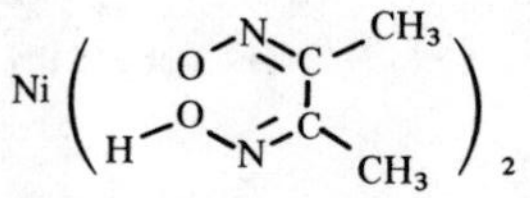	s	$2p_{1/2}$ $2p_{3/2}$	876.6 859.6	a 290.0	AlK_α	30
$C_8H_{18}N_6NiS_2$	$Ni(N(CH_2CH_2NH_2)_3)(NCS)_2$	s	$2p_{1/2}$	833 878.2	a 290.0	AlK_α	30
			$2p_{3/2}$	867 860.3			

TABLE 3 (continued)

Compound		Phase	Orbital	E_B(eV)	Calibrant	Exciting Radiation	Reference
$C_{10}H_{10}Ni$	$Ni(\pi\text{-}C_5H_5)_2$	s	$2p_{1/2}$ $2p_{3/2}$	874.9 (3) 857.7 (3)		MgK_α	23
$C_{10}H_{20}N_2NiS_4$	$Ni[S_2CN(C_2H_5)_2]_2$	s	$2p_{1/2}$ $2p_{3/2}$	875.8 858.7	a 290.0	AlK_α	30
$C_{12}H_{28}NiO_4P_2S_4$	$Ni((C_3H_7O)_2PS_2)_2$	s	$2p_{1/2}$ $2p_{3/2}$	876.7 859.2	a 290.0	AlK_α	30
$C_{14}H_{32}Br_2N_4Ni$	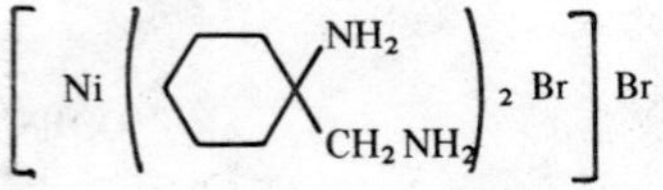	s	$2p_{1/2}$ $2p_{3/2}$	876.9 859.8	a 290.0	AlK_α	30
$C_{14}H_{32}N_6NiO_6$	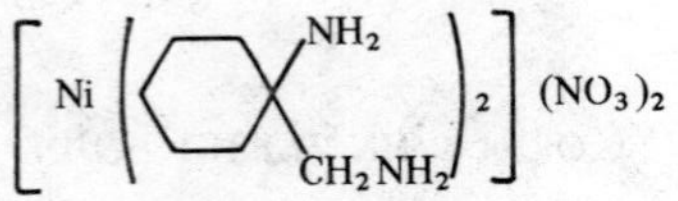	s	$2p_{1/2}$ $2p_{3/2}$	877.2 860.1	a 290.0	AlK_α	30
$C_{16}H_{20}N_5NiS_4$	$[(C_2H_5)_4N][Ni(S_2C_2(CN)_2)_2]$	s	$2p_{3/2}$	853.1 (1)	c 83.0		125
$C_{16}H_{32}Cl_2N_4NiO_8$	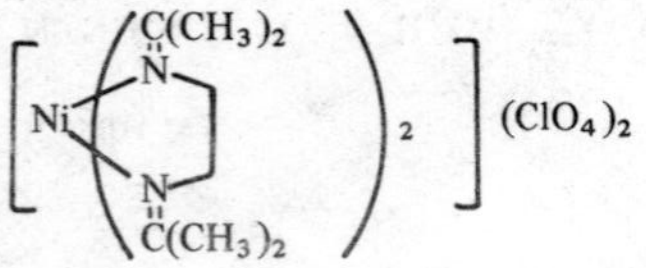	s	$2p_{1/2}$ $2p_{3/2}$	877.5 860.1	a 290.0	AlK_α	30
$C_{18}H_{26}Cl_2N_6NiO_8$	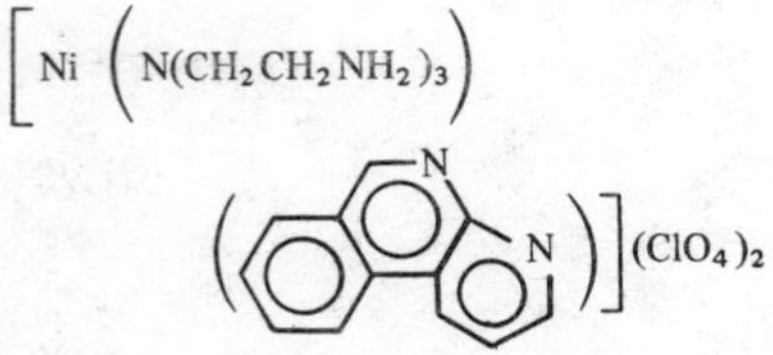	s	$2p_{1/2}$ $2p_{3/2}$	882 877.8 866 860.2	a 290.0	AlK_α	30
$C_{24}H_{24}NiO_2P_2$	$Ni[(C_6H_5)_2PCH_2CH_2P(C_6H_5)(C_2H_5)](CO)_2$	s	$2p_{3/2}$	852.9 (1)	c 83.0		125

TABLE 3 (continued)

Compound		Phase	Orbital	E_B(eV)	Calibrant	Exciting Radiation	Reference
$C_{24}H_{36}N_2NiO_4P_2S_4$	$Ni((C_3H_7O)_2PS_2)_2$ 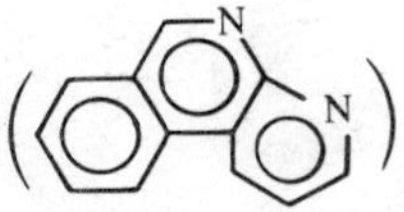	s	$2p_{1/2}$ $2p_{3/2}$	877 865 859.6	a 290.0	AlK_{α}	30
$C_{24}H_{40}N_6NiS_4$	$[(C_2H_5)_4N]_2[Ni(S_2C_2(CN)_2)_2]$	s	$2p_{3/2}$	853.1 (1)	c 83.0		125
$C_{24}H_{54}Cl_2NiP_2$	Square planar $((n\text{-}C_4H_9)_3P)_2NiCl_2$	s	$2p_{3/2}$ $2p_{1/2}$	853.7 (2) 870.9 (2)	c 83.0	MgK_{α}	124
$C_{28}H_{20}NiS_4$	$Ni(S_2C_2(C_6H_5)_2)_2$	s	$2p_{3/2}$	852.9 (1)	c 83.0		125
$C_{28}H_{30}N_4NiS_4$	$(N_2H_5)_2\{Ni[S_2C_2(C_6H_5)_2]_2\}$	s	$2p_{3/2}$	852.8 (1)	c 83.0		125
$C_{30}H_{34}Br_2NiP_2$	Tetrahedral $(n\text{-}C_3H_7P(C_6H_5)_2)_2NiBr_2$	s	$2p_{3/2}$ 3d-4s Shake-up $2p_{1/2}$ 3d-4s Shake-up d-d Shake-up	853.7 (2) 860.0 (2) 871.5 (2) 880.0 (2) 873.5 (2)	c 83.0	MgK_{α}	124
$C_{30}H_{34}Br_2NiP_2$	Square planar $(n\text{-}C_3H_7P(C_6H_5)_2)_2NiBr_2$	s	$2p_{3/2}$ $2p_{1/2}$	853.3 (2) 870.5 (2)	c 83.0	MgK_{α}	124
$C_{36}H_{24}Cl_2N_6NiO_8$	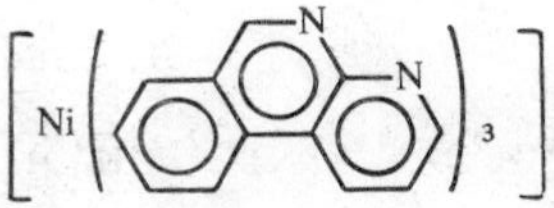 $(ClO_4)_2$	s	$2p_{1/2}$ $2p_{3/2}$	884 877.6 867 860.0	a 290.0	AlK_{α}	30
$C_{36}H_{30}Cl_2NiP_2$	$Ni(P(C_6H_5)_3)_2Cl_2$	s	$2p_{3/2}$	855.2 (8)	d 285.0	Mg, AlK_{α}	116
$C_{36}H_{30}Cl_2NiP_2$	Tetrahedral $[(C_6H_5)_3P]_2NiCl_2$	s	$2p_{3/2}$ 3d-4s Shake-up $2p_{1/2}$ 3d-4s Shake-up	853.6 (2) 860.1 (2) 871.6 (2) 879.1 (2)	c 83.0	MgK_{α}	124

TABLE 3 (continued)

Compound		Phase	Orbital	E_B(eV)	Calibrant	Exciting Radiation	Reference
$C_{36}H_{30}Cl_2NiP_2$ (cont.)			d-d Shake-up	873.6 (2)			
$C_{36}H_{40}NNiS_4$	$[(C_2H_5)_4N][Ni(S_2C_2(C_6H_5)_2)_2]$	s	$2p_{3/2}$	852.5 (1)	c 83.0		125
$F_2Ni \cdot 4H_2O$	$NiF_2 \cdot 4H_2O$	s	$2p_{1/2}$ $Ni2p_{3/2}$	887.8 882.5 870.5 864.4	a 290.0	AlK_α	30
F_3KNi	$KNiF_3$	s	$2p_{1/2}$ $2p_{3/2}$	882.25 869.9 864.0	a 290.0	AlK_α	30
$H_{12}NiO_{10}S$	$[Ni(H_2O)_6]SO_4$	s	$2p_{1/2}$ $2p_{3/2}$	885.2 879.2 867 861.9	a 290.0	AlK_α	30
Ni	Ni	s	K	8,333.3	CuK($MoK_{\alpha 1}$)	$MoK_{\alpha 1}$	119
Ni	Ni	s	L_I	1,008.1	MgO MgK($CuK_{\alpha 1}$)	$CuK_{\alpha 1}$	67
Ni	Ni(fcc)	s	3p	66 (0.5)		MgK_α	122
Ni	Ni	s	d band	−1.0 (2)	Pd Fermi level 0.0	MgK_α	51
Ni	Ni	s	$2p_{3/2}$	852.8 (1)	c 83.0		125
Ni	Ni	s	$2p_{1/2}$ $2p_{3/2}$	878.2 876 860.5 857.8	a 290.0	AlK_α	30
NiO	NiO	s	$2p_{3/2}$	856.2 (1)	c 83.0		125

TABLE 3 (continued)

Compound		Phase	Orbital	E_B(eV)	Calibrant	Exciting Radiation	Reference
NiO	NiO	s	$2p_{1/2}$	886.8 879.9	a 290.0	AlK_α	30
			$2p_{3/2}$	868.6 862.4			
Ni_2O_3	Ni_2O_3	s	$2p_{1/2}$	884.8 878.0	a 290.0	AlK_α	30
			$2p_{3/2}$	866.3 860.3			
O							
$AlNaO_8Si_3$	Albite $NaAlSi_3O_8$	s	ls	531.0 (5)	Internal Si 2p 102.0	Al, MgK_α	57
$Al_2Fe_3Mg_3O_{12}Si_3$	Garnet $(MgFe)_3Al_2(SiO_4)_3$	s	ls	531.1 (5)	Internal Si 2p 102.0	Al, MgK_α	57
BH_3O_3	H_3BO_3	s	ls	531.3	LiF Fls 685.4		114
B_2O_3	B_2O_3	s	ls	531.3	LiF Fls 685.4		114
$B_4Na_2O_7$	$Na_2B_4O_7$	s	ls	530.1	LiF Fls 685.4		114
BeO	BeO	s	ls	532.1	b 285.0	MgK_α	71
			2s	24.4			
BrCu	CuBr	s	excess O, ls	532.9		AlK_α	54
$CCuO_3$	$CuCO_3$	s	ls	533.9	a 285.5	AlK_α	46
CH_2O_2	HCO_2H	g	ls	0.67 (5) −0.95 (5)	H_2O Ols 0.0	MgK_α	61
CH_3ClO_2S	CH_3SO_2Cl	s	ls	532.7	b 285.0	AlK_α	49
CH_4O	CH_3OH	g	ls	−0.80 (10)	H_2O Ols 0.0	MgK_α	61

TABLE 3 (continued)

Compound		Phase	Orbital	E_B(eV)	Calibrant	Exciting Radiation	Reference
CH_4O	CH_3OH	g	ls	538.9	O_2 Ols 543.1	MgK_α	151
CO	CO	g	ls	542.1	O_2 Ols 543.1	MgK_α	151
CO	CO	s	ls	536.7		MgK_α	23
CO	CO	g	ls	542.3	Ne2s, 2p	Mg_α	60
CO	CO	g	ls Shake-up	542.6 555–561		Al, MgK_α	88
COS	COS	g	ls Shake-up	540.3 (1) −8.8 (2) −13.8 (3) −15.5 (3)	 COS Ols 0.0	MgK_α	38
CO_2	CO_2	g	ls Shake-up	541.1 (1) −11.5 (2) −12.7 (2) −13.8 (2) −16.1 (2) −17.9 (2) −19.9 (2) −22.3 (4)	 CO_2 Ols 0.0	MgK_α	38
CO_2	CO_2	g	ls	1.44 (5)	H_2O Ols 0.0	MgK_α	61
CO_2	CO_2	g	ls	540.8	O_2 Ols 543.1	MgK_α	151
$C_2H_3F_3O_2S_2$	$CF_3SSO_2CH_3$	s	ls	532.5	b 285.0	AlK_α	49
C_2H_4O	C_2H_4O	g	ls	−1.05 (5)	H_2O Ols 0.0	MgK_α	61
C_2H_4O	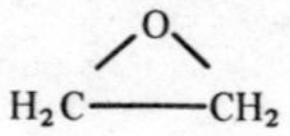	g	ls	−4.5 (2)	Ols O_2 (543.1) 0.0	MgK_α	149
C_2H_4O	CH_3CHO	g	ls	537.6	O_2 Ols 543.1	MgK_α	151

TABLE 3 (continued)

Compound		Phase	Orbital	E_B(eV)	Calibrant	Exciting Radiation	Reference
$C_2H_4O_2$	$CH_3C(\overset{a}{O})\overset{b}{O}H$	g	^{a}ls ^{b}ls	540.0 538.2	O_2 Ols 543.1	MgK_a	151
C_2H_6O	CH_3CH_2OH	g	ls	538.6	O_2 Ols 543.1	MgK_a	151
C_2H_6OS	$OS(CH_3)_2$	s	ls	531.7	b 285.0	AlK_a	49
$C_2H_6O_2S$	$S(O)_2(CH_3)_2$	s	ls	532.6	b 285.0	AlK_a	49
$C_2H_6O_2S_2$	$H_3COSSOCH_3$	s	ls	534.0	b 285.0	AlK_a	49
$C_2H_6O_3S$	$CH_3OS(O)OCH_3$	s	ls	532.3 533.6	b 285.0	AlK_a	49
$C_2H_8Cl_2CuN_2 \cdot H_2O$	$CuCl_2 \cdot H_2NCH_2CH_2NH_2 \cdot H_2O$	s	ls	533.5	a 285.5	AlK_a	46
$C_2H_8CuN_2O_3S \cdot H_2O$	$CuSO_3 \cdot H_2NCH_2CH_2NH_2 \cdot H_2O$	s	ls	533.3	a 285.5	AlK_a	46
C_3H_3NO	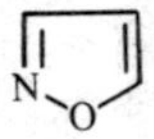	s	ls	536.6 (3)	c 84	MgK_a	25
C_3H_6O	$(CH_3)_2CO$	g	ls	539.0	O_2 Ols 543.1	MgK_a	151
$C_3H_6O_4S$	$O_2S(OCH_2)_2CH_2$	s	ls	532.5 534.1	b 285.0	AlK_a	49
$C_3H_8NO_2S$	$HSCH_2CHNH_2C\overset{ab}{OO}H$	s	^{a}ls ^{b}ls	532.0 532.5	b 285.0	AlK_a	49
$C_3H_9ClNO_2S$	$[HSCH_2CHNH_3C\overset{ab}{OO}H]Cl$	s	^{a}ls ^{b}ls	531.6 532.5	b 285.0	AlK_a	49
C_3H_9IOS	$[(CH_3)_3S(O)]I$	s	ls	533.3	b 285.0	AlK_a	49
C_3O_2	OCCCO	g	ls	539.7 (1)	O_2, CO_2 Ols	MgK_a	19
$C_4CuK_2O_8$	$K_2Cu(C_2O_4)_2$	s	ls	533.2	a 285.5	AlK_a	46

TABLE 3 (continued)

Compound		Phase	Orbital	E_B(eV)	Calibrant	Exciting Radiation	Reference
C_4H_4O		s	ls	535.8 (3)	c 84	MgK_α	25
C_4H_4O		g	ls	539.4 (1)	CO_2, Co Ols 540.8 542.1	MgK_α	69
$C_4H_5NaO_3S$	$[OS(CH_2)_2CHCOO]Na$	s	ls	532.0 532.8	b 285.0	AlK_α	49
$C_4H_6CuO_4 \cdot H_2O$	$Cu(CH_3COO)_2 \cdot H_2O$	s	ls	534.0	a 285.5	AlK_α	46
$C_4H_6O_2S_2$	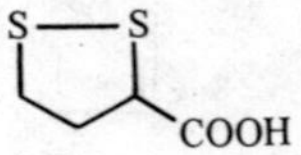	s	ls	533.0 534.0	b 285.0	AlK_α	49
$C_4H_6O_4S$	$S(CH_2COOH)_2$	s	ls	532.7	b 285.0	AlK_α	49
C_4H_8O	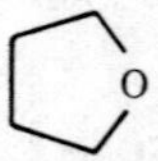	s	ls	713.5 (E_{kin})		MgK_α	132
$C_4H_9NO_2S$	$CH_3SCH_2CH(NH_2)COOH$	s	ls	531.8	b 285.0	AlK_α	49
$C_4H_{16}Br_2CuN_4 \cdot H_2O$	$CuBr_2 \cdot 2(H_2NCH_2CH_2NH_2) \cdot H_2O$	s	ls	533.3	a 285.5	AlK_α	46
$C_4H_{16}Cl_2CuN_4 \cdot H_2O$	$CuCl_2 \cdot 2(H_2NCH_2CH_2NH_2) \cdot H_2O$	s	ls	533.3	a 285.5	AlK_α	46
$C_4H_{16}CuN_4O_4S \cdot H_2O$	$CuSO_4 \cdot 2(H_2NCH_2CH_2NH_2) \cdot H_2O$	s	ls	532.4	a 285.5	AlK_α	46
C_4NiO_4	$Ni(CO)_4$	s	ls	536.4 (3)		MgK_α	23
C_4NiO_4	$Ni(CO)_4$	s	ls	1.0	H_2O Ols 0.0	Al, MgK_α	22
$C_5H_3CrNO_5$	$Cr(CO)_5NH_3$	s	ls	533.4	Hexane Cls 285.0		40

TABLE 3 (continued)

Compound		Phase	Orbital	E_B(eV)	Calibrant	Exciting Radiation	Reference
C_5H_8OS	$S(CH_2CH_2)_2CO$	s	ls	532.5	b 285.0	AlK_a	49
$C_5H_8O_2S$	$OS(CH_2CH_2)_2CO$	s	ls	532.4 532.6	b 285.0	AlK_a	49
$C_5H_8O_6S_2$	$C((CH_2O)_2SO)_2$	s	ls	533.2 533.6	b 285.0	AlK_a	49
$C_5H_{10}O_2$	$C_2H_5C(\overset{a}{O})\overset{b}{O}C_2H_5$	g	[a]ls	538.8	O_2 Ols 543.1	MgK_a	151
$C_5H_{10}O_2S_2$	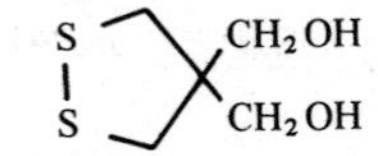	s	ls	533.1	b 285.0	AlK_a	49
$C_5H_{10}O_3S_2$	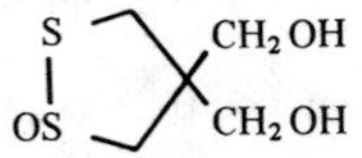	s	ls	531.6 532.9	b 285.0	AlK_a	49
$C_5H_{10}O_4S_2$		s	ls	531.6 533.0	b 285.0	AlK_a	49
$C_5H_{12}NaO_4S_2$	$NaOS(O)O(CH_2)_3OS^+(CH_3)_2$	s	ls	532.1 533.6	b 285.0	AlK_a	49
$C_5H_{12}NaO_4S_2$	$NaOS(O)O(CH_2)_3S^+(O)(CH_3)_2$	s	ls	531.9 533.4	b 285.0	AlK_a	49
C_5FeO_5	$Fe(CO)_5$	s	ls	536.7 (3)	-	MgK_a	23
C_5FeO_5	$Fe(CO)_5$	s	ls	0.8	H_2O Ols 0.0	Al, MgK_a	22
C_6CrO_6	$Cr(CO)_6$	s	ls	0.7	H_2O Ols 0.0	Al, MgK_a	22
C_6CrO_6	$Cr(CO)_6$	s	ls	536.2	c 84	MgK_a	26
C_6CrO_6	$Cr(CO)_6$	s	ls	534.2	Hexane Cls 285.0		40

TABLE 3 (continued)

Compound		Phase	Orbital	E_B(eV)	Calibrant	Exciting Radiation	Reference
C_6CrO_6	$Cr(CO)_6$	s	ls	536.2 (3)		MgK_a	23
$C_6H_4ClNO_2S$	*o*-$NO_2C_6H_4SCl$	s	ls	533.0	b 285.0	AlK_a	49
$C_6H_4ClNO_4S$	*o*-$NO_2C_6H_4SO_2Cl$	s	ls	532.7 533.6	b 285.0	AlK_a	49
$C_6H_4ClNO_4S$	*m*-$NO_2C_6H_4SO_2Cl$	s	ls	532.2 533.0	b 285.0	AlK_a	49
$C_6H_4ClNO_4S$	*p*-$NO_2C_6H_4SO_2Cl$	s	ls	532.8 533.6	b 285.0	AlK_a	49
$C_6H_4ClNaO_2S$	*p*-$ClC_6H_4SO_2Na$	s	ls	531.8	b 285.0	AlK_a	49
$C_6H_4ClNaO_3S_2$	*p*-$ClC_6H_4SSO_3Na$	s	ls	532.7	b 285.0	AlK_a	49
$C_6H_4FNO_4S$	*p*-$NO_2C_6H_4SO_2F$	s	ls	531.5	b 285.0	AlK_a	49
$C_6H_4FNO_4S$	*o*-$NO_2C_6H_4SO_2F$	s	ls	532.6 533.6	b 285.0	AlK_a	49
$C_6H_4KNO_2S$	[*m*-$NO_2C_6H_4S$] K	s	ls	533.1	b 285.0	AlK_a	49
$C_6H_4NNaO_2S$	[*p*-$NO_2C_6H_4S$] Na	s	ls	533.2	b 285.0	AlK_a	49
$C_6H_4NNaO_4$	*o*-$NO_2C_6H_4SO_2Na$	s	ls	531.7 533.3	b 285.0	AlK_a	49
$C_6H_4NNaO_4$	*m*-$NO_2C_6H_4SO_2Na$	s	ls	531.5 533.3	b 285.0	AlK_a	49
$C_6H_4NNaO_4$	*p*-$NO_2C_6H_4SO_2Na$	s	ls	531.6 533.4	b 285.0	AlK_a	49
$C_6H_4NNaO_5S$	*m*-$NO_2C_6H_4SO_3Na$	s	ls	531.9 532.5	b 285.0	AlK_a	49

TABLE 3 (continued)

Compound		Phase	Orbital	E_B(eV)	Calibrant	Exciting Radiation	Reference
$C_6H_4NNaO_5S$	*p*-$NO_2C_6H_4SO_3Na$	s	ls	532.2 533.1	b 285.0	AlK_a	49
$C_6H_4NNaO_5S$	*o*-$NO_2C_6H_4SO_3Na$	s	ls	532.1 532.7	b 285.0	AlK_a	49
$C_6H_5NO_2S$	*o*-$NO_2C_6H_4SH$	s	ls	533.0	b 285.0	AlK_a	49
$C_6H_5NO_2S$	*p*-$NO_2C_6H_4SH$	s	ls	532.8	b 285.0	AlK_a	49
$C_6H_5NaO_2S$	$C_6H_5SO_2Na$	s	ls	531.7	b 285.0	AlK_a	49
$C_6H_6Cl_3NO_4S_2$	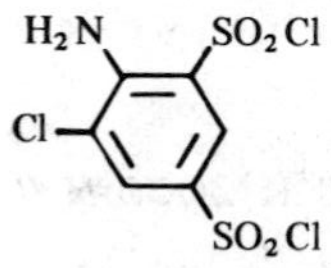	s	ls	532.1	b 285.0	AlK_a	49
$C_6H_6NNaO_3S$	*p*-$NH_2C_6H_4SO_3Na$	s	ls	532.4	b 285.0	AlK_a	49
$C_6H_6N_2O_2S$	*o*-$NO_2C_6H_4SNH_2$	s	ls	533.2	b 285.0	AlK_a	49
$C_6H_6N_2O_4S$	*m*-$NO_2C_6H_4SO_2NH_2$	s	ls	532.7 533.1	b 285.0	AlK_a	49
$C_6H_8N_2O_2S$	*p*-$NH_2C_6H_4SO_2NH_2$	s	ls	532.6	b 285.0	AlK_a	49
$C_6H_{12}N_2O_4S_2$	$(HO_2CCH(NH_2)CH_2S)_2$	s	ls	531.5	b 285.0	AlK_a	49
$C_6H_{12}N_2O_5S_2$	$HO_2CCHCH_2SS(O)CH_2CHCO_2H$ NH_2 NH_2	s	ls	531.7	b 285.0	AlK_a	49
$C_6H_{12}N_2O_6S_2$	$HO_2CCHCH_2SS(O)_2CH_2CHCO_2H$ NH_2 NH_2	s	ls	531.5	b 285.0	AlK_a	49
$C_6H_{24}Br_2CuN_6 \cdot 5H_2O$	$CuBr_2 \cdot 3(H_2NCH_2CH_2NH_2) \cdot 5H_2O$	s	ls	533.4	a 285.5	AlK_a	46

TABLE 3 (continued)

Compound		Phase	Orbital	E_B(eV)	Calibrant	Exciting Radiation	Reference
C_6N_4O	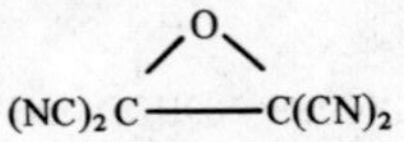	g	ls	−3.2 (2)	OlsO_2 (543.1) 0.0	MgK_α	149
$C_6N_6O_6$	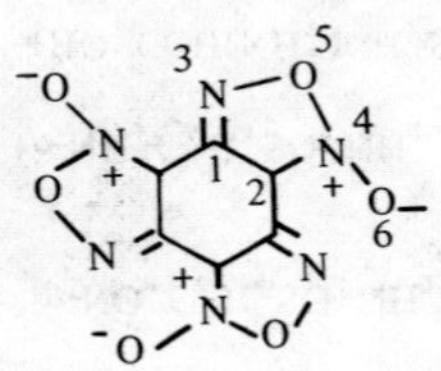	s	(5) ls (6) ls	535.0 533.4	f 284.2	MgK_α	115
C_6O_6W	$W(CO)_6$	s	ls	1.0	H_2O Ols 0.0	Al, MgK_α	22
$C_7H_3Cl_5O_2S$	$C_6Cl_5SCH_2COOH$	s	ls	532.0 533.2	b 285.0	AlK_α	49
$C_7H_4Na_2O_4S$	*m*-$NaCOOC_6H_4SO_2Na$	s	ls	531.6 531.9	b 285.0	AlK_α	49
$C_7H_4Na_2O_4S$	*p*-$NaCOOC_6H_4SO_2Na$	s	ls	531.6 531.8	b 285.0	AlK_α	49
$C_7H_4Na_2O_5S$	*p*-$NaCOOC_6H_4SO_3Na$	s	ls	531.8 532.6	b 285.0	AlK_α	49
$C_7H_4Na_2O_5S$	*m*-$NaCOOC_6H_4SO_3Na$	s	ls	531.6 532.5	b 285.0	AlK_α	49
$C_7H_5CrNO_5$	$Cr(CO)_5$(HN 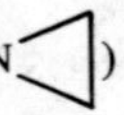)	s	ls	533.1	Hexane Cls 285.0		40
$C_7H_6Cl_2O_2S$	$ClC_6H_4CH_2SO_2Cl$	s	ls	532.3	b 285.0	AlK_α	49
C_7H_7ClOS	*p*-$ClC_6H_4SOCH_3$	s	ls	532.8	b 285.0	AlK_α	49
$C_7H_7NO_2S$	*p*-$NO_2C_6H_4SCH_3$	s	ls	532.9	b 285.0	AlK_α	49
$C_7H_7NO_3S$	*o*-$NO_2C_6H_4S(O)CH_3$	s	ls	532.2 533.4	b 285.0	AlK_α	49

TABLE 3 (continued)

Compound		Phase	Orbital	E_B(eV)	Calibrant	Exciting Radiation	Reference
$C_7H_7NO_3S$	*p*-$NO_2C_6H_4S(O)CH_3$	s	ls	531.8 533.1	b 285.0	AlK_α	49
$C_7H_7NO_3S$	*o*-$NO_2C_6H_4SOCH_3$	s	ls	533.2 533.9	b 285.0	AlK_α	49
$C_7H_7NO_3S$	*m*-$NO_2C_6H_4S(O)CH_3$	s	ls	531.9 533.1	b 285.0	AlK_α	49
$C_7H_7NO_4S$	*o*-$NO_2C_6H_4SOOCH_3$	s	ls	531.9 532.9 533.8	b 285.0	AlK_α	49
$C_7H_7NO_4S$	*m*-$NO_2C_6H_4SO_2CH_3$	s	ls	532.2 533.1	b 285.0	AlK_α	49
$C_7H_7NO_4S$	*p*-$NO_2C_6H_4SOOCH_3$	s	ls	532.1 533.1 533.7	b 285.0	AlK_α	49
$C_7H_7NO_4S$	*m*-$NO_2C_6H_4SOOCH_3$	s	ls	532.2 532.9 533.6	b 285.0	AlK_α	49
$C_7H_7NO_5S$	*p*-$NO_2C_6H_4SO_2OCH_3$	s	ls	532.6 533.2 533.7	b 285.0	AlK_α	49
$C_7H_7NO_5S$	*m*-$NO_2C_6H_4SO_2OCH_3$	s	ls	532.5 533.1 533.7	b 285.0	AlK_α	49
$C_7H_7NO_5S$	*o*-$NO_2C_6H_4SO_2OCH_3$	s	ls	532.2 533.3 533.7	b 285.0	AlK_α	49
C_7H_8OS	$C_6H_5SOCH_3$	s	ls	532.8	b 285.0	AlK_α	49

TABLE 3 (continued)

Compound		Phase	Orbital	E_B(eV)	Calibrant	Exciting Radiation	Reference
$C_7H_8O_3S$	$C_6H_5SO_3CH_3$	s	ls	532.3 532.6	b 285.0	AlK_α	49
$C_7H_{11}NO_3S_2$	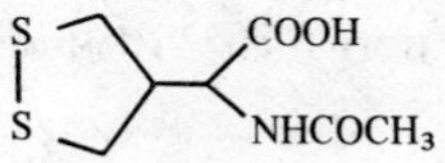	s	ls	532.8	b 285.0	AlK_α	49
$C_8H_5MnO_3$	$Mn(CO)_3(\pi\text{-}C_5H_5)$	s	ls	535.6 (3)		MgK_α	23
$C_8H_6N_2O_2$	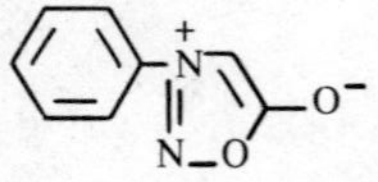	s	ls	530.3 532.7	a 284.0	AlK_α	98
$C_8H_9CrO_5P$	$Cr(CO)_5P(CH_3)_3$	s	ls	533.1	Hexane Cls 285.0		40
$C_8H_{16}N_2O_2S$	$S(N(CH_2CH_2)_2O)_2$	s	ls	532.9	b 285.0	AlK_α	49
$C_8H_{22}CuN_4O_4\cdot H_2O$	$Cu(CH_3COO)_2\cdot 2(H_2NCH_2CH_2NH_2)\cdot H_2O$	s	ls	533.1	a 285.5	AlK_α	46
C_9H_7NO	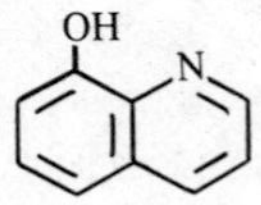	s	ls	534.6	c 84	MgK_α	36
C_9H_8ClNO	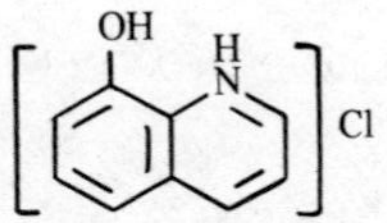	s	ls	534.7	c 84	MgK_α	36
$C_9H_{11}NaO_3S_2$	$NaOS(O)O(CH_2)_3SC_6H_5$	s	ls	532.2	b 285.0	AlK_α	49
$C_9H_{12}NNaO_3S_2$	$o\text{-}NaOS(O)O(CH_2)_3SC_6H_4NH_2$	s	ls	532.5	b 285.0	AlK_α	49
$C_{10}H_8CuN_2O_4S\cdot 2H_2O$	$CuSO_4\cdot$ 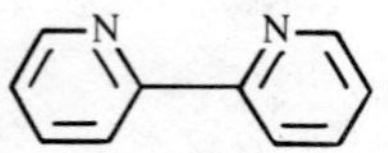 $\cdot 2H_2O$	s	ls	532.1	a 285.5	AlK_α	46

TABLE 3 (continued)

Compound		Phase	Orbital	E_B(eV)	Calibrant	Exciting Radiation	Reference
$C_{10}H_{14}CuO_4$	$Cu(H_3CC(O)CHC(O)CH_3)_2$	s	ls	532.6	a 285.5	AlK_α	46
$C_{10}H_{14}NO_3P$	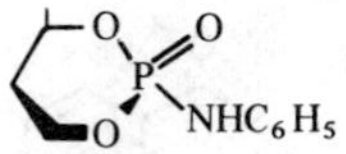	s s	$ls^{(2)}$ $ls^{(1)}$	533.5 (3) 531.7 (3)	a 285.0	AlK_α	105
$C_{10}H_{14}NO_3P$	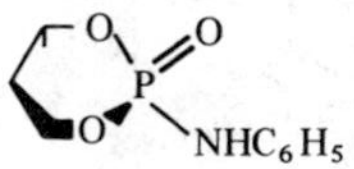	s	$ls^{(2)}$ $ls^{(1)}$	533.5 (3) 531.7 (3)	d 285.0	AlK_α	105
$C_{10}H_{14}O_5V$	$VO(CH_3C(O)CHC(O)CH_3)_2$	s	ls	529.4	$Pt4f_{7/2}$ 71.0	AlK_α	146
$C_{12}H_8N_2O_4S$	p,p'-$NO_2C_6H_4SC_6H_4NO_2$	s	ls	533.2	b 285.0	AlK_α	49
$C_{12}H_8N_2O_4S$	o,o'-$NO_2C_6H_4SC_6H_4NO_2$	s	ls	533.0	b 285.0	AlK_α	49
$C_{12}H_8N_2O_4S_2$	p,p'-$NO_2C_6H_4SSC_6H_4NO_2$	s	ls	532.7	b 285.0	AlK_α	49
$C_{12}H_8N_2O_4S_2$	o,o'-$NO_2C_6H_4SSC_6H_4NO_2$	s	ls	533.1	b 285.0	AlK_α	49
$C_{12}H_8N_2O_4S_2$	m,m'-$NO_2C_6H_4SSC_6H_4NO_2$	s	ls	532.9	b 285.0	AlK_α	49
$C_{12}H_8N_2O_6S$	p,p'-$NO_2C_6H_4SO_2C_6H_4NO_2$	s	ls	532.3 533.2	b 285.0	AlK_α	49
$C_{12}H_8N_2O_6S_2$	p,p'-$NO_2C_6H_4SSO_2C_6H_4NO_2$	s	ls	532.5 533.2	b 285.0	AlK_α	49
$C_{12}H_9NO_4S$	p-$NO_2C_6H_4SO_2C_6H_5$	s	ls	532.3 533.2	b 285.0	AlK_α	49
$C_{12}H_{10}OS$	$OS(C_6H_5)_2$	s	ls	531.6	b 285.0	AlK_α	49
$C_{12}H_{11}O_2P$	$(C_6H_5)_2P(O)OH$	s	ls	532.5 (5)	d 285.0	AlK_α	104
$C_{12}H_{12}N_2O_2S$	$SO_2(p$-$C_6H_4NH_2)_2$	s	ls	532.1	b 285.0	AlK_α	49
$C_{12}H_{16}ClNO_2S$	p-$ClC_6H_4CH_2SO_2N$ 	s	ls	532.5	b 285.0	AlK_α	49

TABLE 3 (continued)

Compound		Phase	Orbital	E_B(eV)	Calibrant	Exciting Radiation	Reference
$C_{13}H_{11}NO_2S$	*o,p'*-$NO_2C_6H_4SC_6H_4CH_3$	s	ls	532.9	b 285.0	AlK_a	·49
$C_{13}H_{11}NO_2S$	*p,p'*-$NO_2C_6H_4SC_6H_4CH_3$	s	ls	532.9	b 285.0	AlK_a	49
$C_{14}H_{10}CuO_4$	$Cu(C_6H_5COO)_2$	s	ls	532.1	a 285.5	AlK_a	46
$C_{14}H_{14}OS$	$OS(CH_2C_6H_5)_2$	s	ls	531.5	b 285.0	AlK_a	49
$C_{14}H_{14}OS_2$	$C_6H_5CH_2SS(O)CH_2C_6H_5$	s	ls	532.6	b 285.0	MgK_a	151
$C_{14}H_{14}O_2S_2$	$C_6H_5CH_2SS(O)_2CH_2C_6H_5$	s	ls	533.0	b 285.0	MgK_a	151
$C_{14}H_{16}NOP$	$(C_6H_5)_2P(O)N(CH_3)_2$	s	ls	531.9 (7)	d 285.0	AlK_a	104
$C_{15}H_3CrF_{18}O_6$	$Cr(CF_3COCHCOCF_3)_3$	s	ls	531.1	c 84	MgK_a	26
$C_{15}H_{21}O_6V$	$V(CH_3C(O)CHC(O)CH_3)_3$	s	ls	529.6	$Pt4f_{7/2}$ 71.0	AlK_a	146
$C_{16}H_8N_2O_4S$	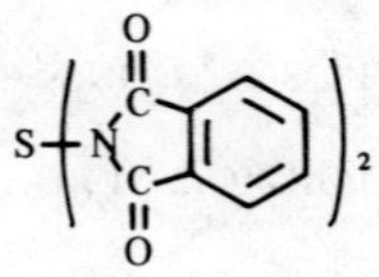	s	ls	532.4	b 285.0	AlK_a	49
$C_{16}H_{12}OS$	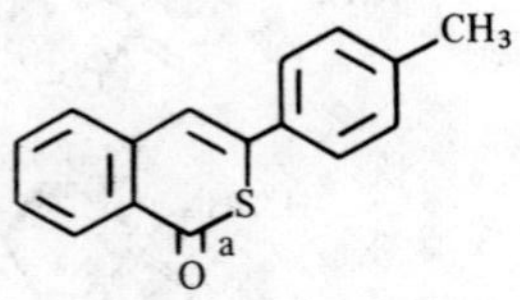	s	ls (adsorb) (a) ls	533.3 530.8	b 284	Al	147
$C_{16}H_{12}OS$	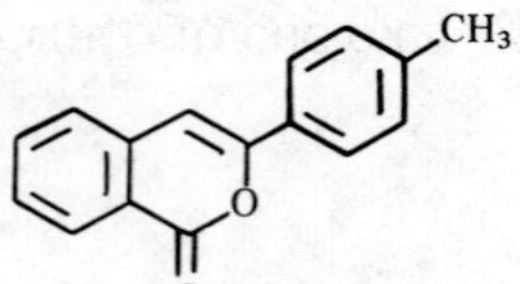	s	ls	532.9	b 284	Al	147

TABLE 3 (continued)

Compound		Phase	Orbital	E_B(eV)	Calibrant	Exciting Radiation	Reference
$C_{16}H_{12}S_2$	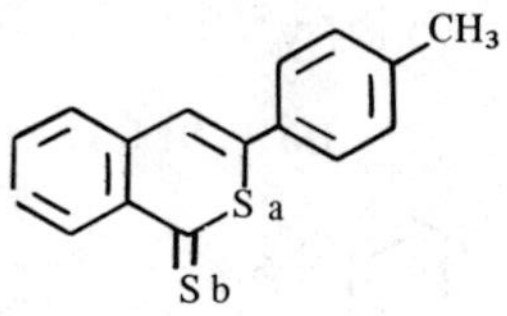	s	1s (adsorb)	532.9	b 284	Al	147
$C_{16}H_{32}NO_3PS$	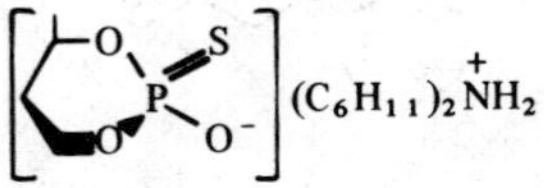	s	$1s^{(2)}$ $1s^{(1)}$	532.8 (3) 531.0 (3)	d 285.0	AlK_α	104
$C_{16}H_{32}NO_3PS$	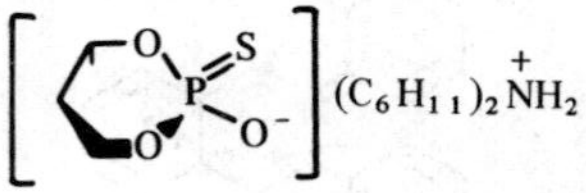	s	$1s^{(2)}$ $1s^{(1)}$	532.6 (3) 530.8 (3)	d 285.0	AlK_α	104
$C_{18}H_{12}N_2O_3V$	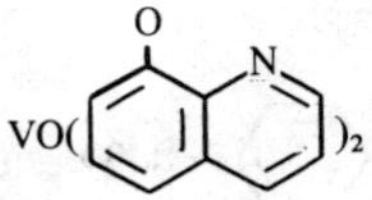	s	1s	529.8	Pt $4f_{7/2}$ 71.0	AlK_α	146
$C_{18}H_{12}N_2O_4U$	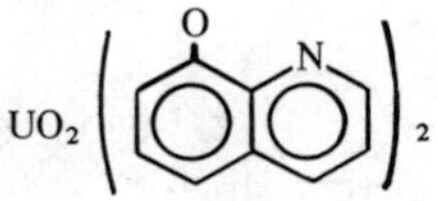	s	1s	533.2	c 84	MgK_α	36
$C_{18}H_{12}N_2O_4U \cdot C_9H_7NO$	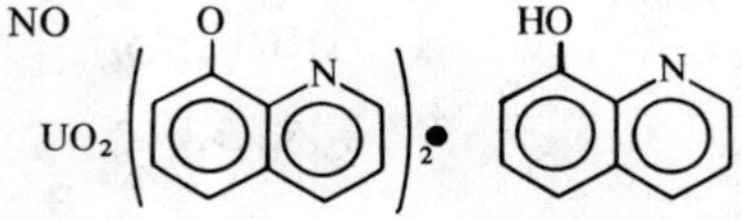	s	1s	533.1	c 84	MgK_α	36
$C_{18}H_{13}N_2O_4V$	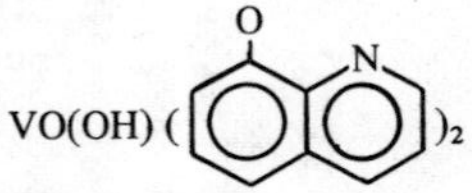	s	1s	530.7	Pt $4f_{7/2}$ 71.0	AlK_α	146

TABLE 3 (continued)

Compound		Phase	Orbital	E_B(eV)	Calibrant	Exciting Radiation	Reference
$C_{18}H_{15}O_3PS$	$(C_6H_5O)_3PS$	s	ls	533.5 (3)	d 285.0	AlK_{α}	104
$C_{18}H_{15}O_3PSe$	$(C_6H_5O)_3PSe$	s	ls	533.0 (6)	d 285.0	AlK_{α}	104
$C_{18}H_{15}O_4P$	$(C_6H_5O)_3PO$	s	ls	533.7 (1)	d 285.0	AlK_{α}	104
$C_{20}H_{16}Br_2CuN_4 \cdot 2H_2O$	$CuBr_2 \cdot 2$ [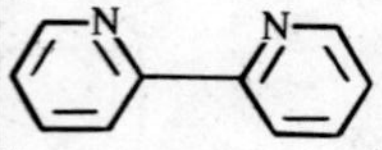] $\cdot 2H_2O$	s	ls	533.3	a 285.5	AlK_{α}	46
$C_{20}H_{16}Cl_2CuN_4 \cdot 3H_2O$	$CuCl_2 \cdot 2$ 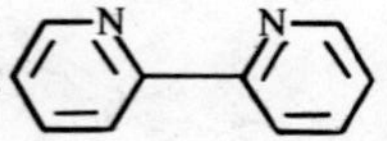 $\cdot 3H_2O$	s	ls	533.6	a 285.5	AlK_{α}	46
$C_{22}H_{17}NO$	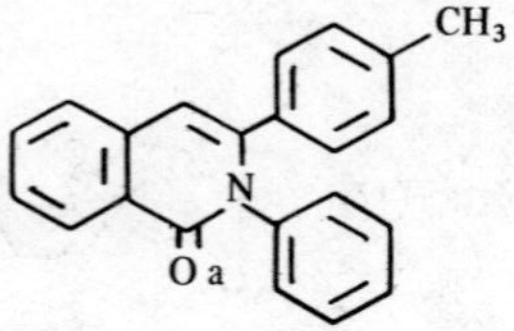	s	ls (adsorb) (a) ls	533.0 530.3	b 284	Al	147
$C_{22}H_{17}NS$	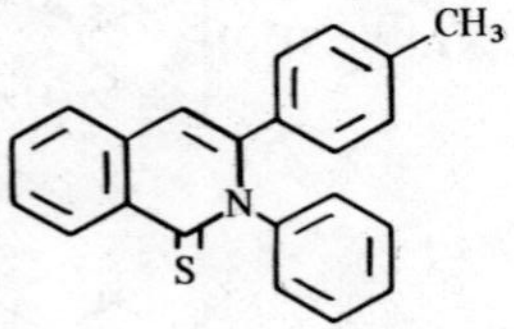	s	ls (adsorb)	532.9	b 284	Al	147
$C_{24}H_{51}OP$	$(C_8H_{17})_3PO$	s	ls	531.1 (7)	d 285.0	AlK_{α}	104
$C_{25}H_{20}AsNO$	$[(C_6H_5)_4As]NCO$	s	ls	532.0	c 84	MgK_{α}	145

TABLE 3 (continued)

Compound		Phase	Orbital	E_B(eV)	Calibrant	Exciting Radiation	Reference
$C_{26}H_{22}N_2O_5S_2$	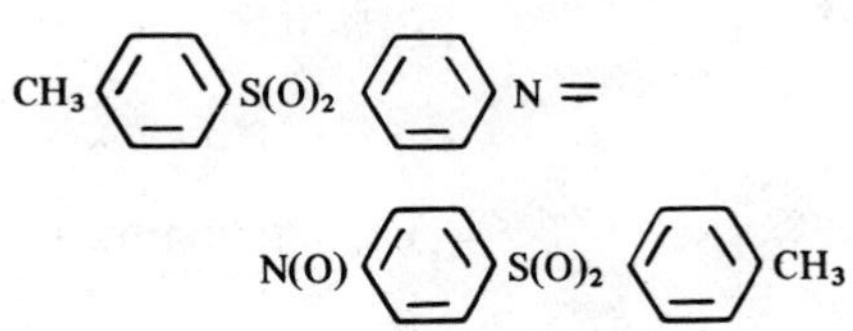	s	ls	532.4	b 285.0	AlK_α	49
$C_{26}H_{44}O_6P_2PtS_2$	*cis*-$((C_2H_5)_3P)_2Pt(CH_3C_6H_4SO_3)_2$	s	ls	531.9 (1)	d 285.0	AlK_α	87
$C_{28}H_{22}NO$	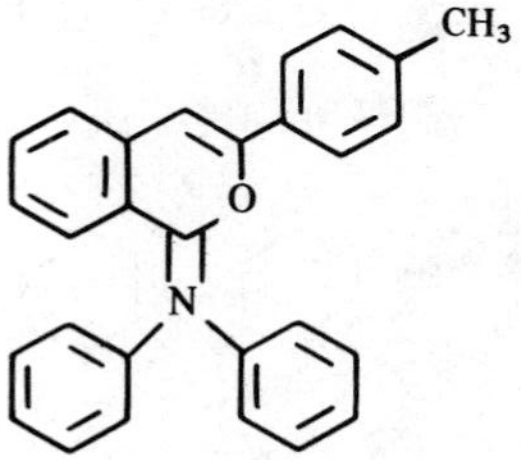	s	ls	533.0	b 284	Al	147
$C_{28}H_{22}NS$	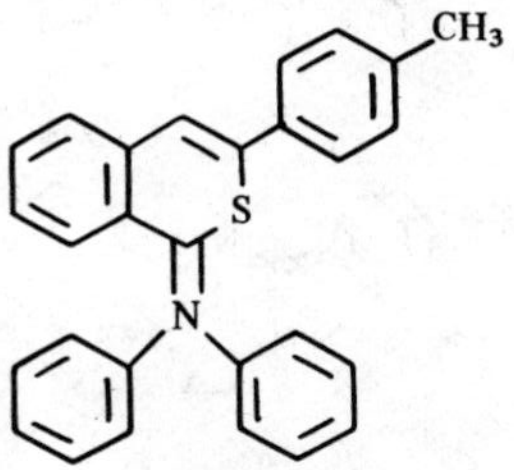	s	ls (adsorb)	533.2	b 284	Al	147
$C_{30}H_{24}CuN_6O_4S \cdot 7H_2O$	$CuSO_4 \cdot 3$[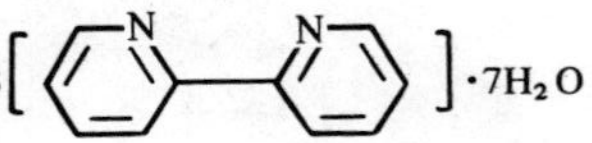]$\cdot 7H_2O$	s	ls	532.2	a 285.5	AlK_α	46

TABLE 5 (continued)

Compound		Phase	Orbital	E_B(eV)	Calibrant	Exciting Radiation	Reference
$C_{32}H_{16}N_8OV$	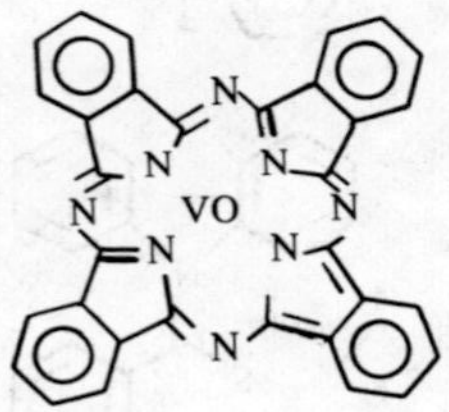	s	ls	531.7	Pt $4f_{7/2}$ 71.0	Al, MgK_α	57
$C_{34}H_{27}N_2$	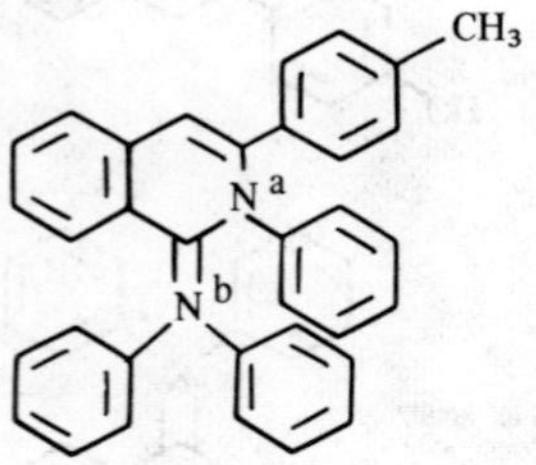	s	ls (adsorb)	532.3	b 284	Al	147
$C_{36}H_{30}HgI_2O_2P_2$	$[(C_6H_5)_3PO]_2HgI_2$	s	ls	532.2	d 285.0	AlK_α	104
$C_{36}H_{30}O_2P_2Pt$	$((C_6H_5)_3P)_2PtO_2$	s	ls	531.3 (1)	d 285.0	AlK_α	87
$C_{37}H_{30}BClF_4IrNO_2P_2$	$[Ir(CO)(P(C_6H_5)_3)_2Cl(NO^+)]BF_4$	s	ls	532.5 (3)	d 285.0	AlK_α	82
$C_{37}H_{30}BF_4IIrNO_2P_2$	$[Ir(CO)(P(C_6H_5)_3)_2I(NO^+)]BF_4$	s	ls	531.7 (3)	d 285.0	AlK_α	82
$C_{37}H_{30}ClIrO_3P_2$	$Ir(CO)(P(C_6H_5)_3)_2(Cl)O_2$	s	ls	531.9 (3)	d 285.0	AlK_α	82
$C_{37}H_{30}IIrO_3P_2$	$Ir(CO)(P(C_6H_5)_3)_2I(O_2)$	s	ls	532.0 (3)	d 285.0	AlK_α	82
$C_{38}H_{30}ClIrO_2P_2$	$Ir(CO)_2(P(C_6H_5)_3)_2Cl$	s	ls	532.1 (3)	d 285.0	AlK_α	82
$C_{38}H_{30}IIrO_2P_2$	$Ir(CO)_2(P(C_6H_5)_3)_2I$	s	ls	531.8 (3)	d 285.0	AlK_α	82
$C_{39}H_{30}ClF_4IrOP_2$	$Ir(CO)(P(C_6H_5)_3)_2(Cl)C_2F_4$	s	ls	532.6 (3)	d 285.0	AlK_α	82
$C_{43}H_{30}ClIrN_4OP_2$	$Ir(CO)(P(C_6H_5)_3)_2Cl(C_2(CN)_4)$	s	ls	532.3 (3)	d 285.0	AlK_α	82

TABLE 3 (continued)

Compound		Phase	Orbital	E_B(eV)	Calibrant	Exciting Radiation	Reference
$C_{43}H_{30}ClN_4OP_2Rh$	$((C_6H_5)_3P)_2RhCl(CO)(C_2(CN)_4)$	s	ls	532.4 (3)	d 285.0	AlK_α	82
$CaFeMgO_6Si_2$	Hedenbergite R6955 46% Mg $CaFeSi_2O_6$	s	ls	531.0 (5)	b 284.6 (5)	Al, MgK_α	57
CdO	CdO	s	ls	531.28 (27)	k 283.8	AlK_α	109
ClCu	CuCl	s, excess O, Ols	ls	532.5		AlK_α	54
$Cl_2Cu \cdot 2H_2O$	$CuCl_2 \cdot 2H_2O$	s	ls	533.7	a 285.5	AlK_α	46
$Cl_2CuO_8 \cdot 2H_2O$	$Cu(ClO_4)_2 \cdot 2H_2O$	s	ls	534.6	a 285.5	AlK_α	46
$Cl_2CuO_8 \cdot 4H_2O$	$Cu(ClO_4)_2 \cdot 4H_2O$	s	ls	534.2	a 285.5	AlK_α	46
$Cl_2CuO_8 \cdot 6H_2O$	$Cu(ClO_4)_2 \cdot 6H_2O$	s	ls	534.6	a 285.5	AlK_α	46
Cl_2OS	$SOCl_2$	s	ls	533.6	b 285.0	AlK_α	49
Cl_2OV	$VOCl_2$	s	ls	531.1 532.3 (sh)	$Pt4f_{7/2}$ 71.0	AlK_α	146
$CuF_2 \cdot 2H_2O$	$CuF_2 \cdot 2H_2O$	s	ls	534.9	a 285.5	AlK_α	46
$CuN_2O_6 \cdot 3H_2O$	$Cu(NO_3)_2 \cdot 3H_2O$	s	ls	533.5	a 285.5	AlK_α	46
CuO	CuO	s	ls	532.9	a 285.5	AlK_α	46
CuO	CuO	s Excess O	ls ls	530.7 532.7		AlK_α	54
CuO_4S	$CuSO_4$	s	ls	532.8		AlK_α	54
CuO_4S	$CuSO_4$	s	ls	534.0	a 285.5	AlK_α	46
$CuO_4S \cdot H_2O$	$CuSO_4 \cdot H_2O$	s	ls	533.8	a 285.5	AlK_α	46

TABLE 3 (continued)

Compound		Phase	Orbital	E_B(eV)	Calibrant	Exciting Radiation	Reference
$CuO_4S \cdot 3H_2O$	$CuSO_4 \cdot 3H_2O$	s	ls	533.5	a 285.5	AlK_a	46
$CuO_4S \cdot 5H_2O$	$CuSO_4 \cdot 5H_2O$	s	ls	533.9	a 285.5	AlK_a	46
Cu_2O	Cu_2O	s	ls	533.6	a 285.5	AlK_a	46
Cu_2O	Cu_2O	s Excess O	ls ls	531.0 532.9		AlK_a	54
F_2OS	SOF_2	s	ls	533.0	b 285.0	AlK_a	49
F_2OS	SOF_2	g	ls	539.4	O_2 Ols 543.1	MgK_a	151
$FeMgO_3Si$	Anthophyllite 77% Mg (Mg, Fe) SiO_3	s	ls	531.1 (5)	b 284.6	Al, MgK_a	57
FeO_4S	$FeSO_4$	s	ls	532.5	b 285.0	AlK_a	49
$Fe_2O_{12}S_3$	$Fe(SO_4)_3$	s	ls	531.8	b 285.0	AlK_a	49
H_2O	H_2O	g	ls	539.7	O_2 Ols 543.1	MgK_a	151
MgO	MgO	s	K	532.0 (5)	e, i	CrK_a	76
MgO	MgO	s	L_I	23.7		CrK_{a1}	65
MgO_3Si	Enstatite 86% Mg $MgO \cdot SiO_2$	s	ls	531.4 (5)	b 284.6 (5)	Al, MgK_a	57
NO	NO	g	ls	543.3	O_2 Ols 543.1	MgK_a	151
NO_2	NO_2	g	ls	541.3	O_2 Ols 543.1	MgK_a	151
N_2O	N_2O	g	ls	541.2	O_2 Ols 543.1	MgK_a	151
N_2O	N_2O	g	ls	1.54 (10)	H_2O Ols 0.0	MgK_a	61

TABLE 3 (continued)

Compound		Phase	Orbital	E_B(eV)	Calibrant	Exciting Radiation	Reference
Na_2O_3S	Na_2SO_3	s	ls	531.9	b 285.0	AlK_a	49
$Na_2O_3S_2$	$Na_2S_2O_3$	s	ls	531.8	b 285.0	AlK_a	49
Na_2O_4S	Na_2SO_4	s	ls	532.3	b 285.0	AlK_a	49
$Na_2O_5S_2$	$Na_2S_2O_5$	s	ls	531.8	b 285.0	AlK_a	49
OZn	ZnO	s	ls	530.60	k 283.8	AlK_a	109
O_2	$O_2\ ^2\Sigma$	g	ls	4.59 (5)	H_2O Ols 0.0	MgK_a	61
O_2	$O_2\ ^4\Sigma$	g	ls	3.47 (5)	H_2O Ols 0.0	MgK_a	61
O_2	Wtd. av.	g	ls	3.84 (6)	H_2O Ols 0.0	MgK_a	61
O_2	O_2	g	ls	543.1	O_2 Ols 543.1	MgK_a	151
O_2S	SO_2	g	ls	539.6	O_2 Ols 543.1	MgK_a	151
O_5SV	$VOSO_4$	s	ls	530.9	$Pt4f_{7/2}$ 71.0	AlK_a	146
O_5V_2	V_2O_5	s	ls	529.6 530.9 (sh)	$Pt4f_{7/2}$ 71.0	AlK_a	146
V	V	s	ls	531.7 530.3 (sh)	Pt $4f_{7/2}$ 71.0	AlK_a	146
Os							
Br_6Cs_2Os	Cs_2OsBr_6		$4f_{5/2}$ $4f_{7/2}$	61.8 59.1	a 290.0	AlK_a	107
Br_6OsTl_2	Tl_2OsBr_6		$4f_{5/2}$ $4f_{7/2}$	60.7 57.9	a 290.0	AlK_a	107
$C_6N_6Ni_2Os$	$Ni_2[Os(CN)_6]$		$4f_{5/2}$	60.6	a 290.0	AlK_a	107

TABLE 3 (continued)

Compound		Phase	Orbital	E_B(eV)	Calibrant	Exciting Radiation	Reference
$C_{12}H_{30}Cl_4OsP_2$	*trans*-$OsCl_4(P(CH_2CH_3)_3)_2$		$4f_{5/2}$ $4f_{7/2}$	55.3 (3) 52.8 (3)	d 285	Mg, AlK_α	97
$C_{16}H_{22}Cl_4OsP_2$	*trans*-$OsCl_4(P(CH_3)_2C_6H_5)_2$	s	$4f_{5/2}$ $4f_{7/2}$	55.5 (3) 53.2 (3)	d 285	Mg, AlK_α	97
$C_{24}H_{33}Cl_3OsP_3$	*mer*-$OsCl_3(P(CH_3)_2C_6H_5)_3$	s	$4f_{5/2}$ $4f_{7/2}$	54.4 51.8	d 285	Mg, AlK_α	97
$C_{32}H_{44}Cl_2OsP_4$	*trans*-$OsCl_2(P(CH_3)_2C_6H_5)_4$		$4f_{5/2}$ $4f_{7/2}$	53.4 50.7	d 285	Mg, AlK_α	97
Cl_6Cs_2Os	Cs_2OsCl_6		$4f_{5/2}$ $4f_{7/2}$	62.4 59.8	a 290.0	AlK_α	107
Cl_6K_2Os	K_2OsCl_6	s	$4f_{5/2}$ $4f_{7/2}$	56.4 (3) 53.7 (3)	a 285	Mg, AlK_α	97
Cl_6K_2Os	K_2OsCl_6	s	$4f_{7/2}$	53.0 (2)	c 83.8	AlK_α	41
Cl_6K_2Os	K_2OsCl_6		$4f_{5/2}$ $4f_{7/2}$	61.6 58.9	a 290.0	AlK_α	107
$H_4K_2O_6Os$	$K_2OsO_2(OH)_4$		$4f_{5/2}$ $4f_{7/2}$	63.2 60.7	a 290.0	AlK_α	107
Os	Os(hcp)	s	4f	50 (0.5)		MgK_α	122
Os	Os	s	L_{III} M_{II} M_{III} M_{IV} M_V	10,870.9 (4) 2,791.8 (5) 2,457.3 (5) 2,031.0 (4) 1,960.2 (4)		MoK_α CuK_α CrK_α	77
Os	Os	s	d band	3	Pd Fermi level 0.0	MgK_α	51
Os	Os	s	$4f_{7/2}$	50.8	c 83.8	AlK_α	41

TABLE 3 (continued)

Compound		Phase	Orbital	E_B(eV)	Calibrant	Exciting Radiation	Reference
P							
BP	BP	s	2p	129.4	LiF F1s 685.4		114
BP	BP	s	2p	129.5	b	MgK_{α}	7
$BaHO_3P$	$BaHPO_3$	s	2p	132.9	b	MgK_{α}	7
Br_3OP	$OPBr_3$	s	2p	134.4	b	MgK_{α}	7
Br_5P	PBr_5	s	2p	138.4	b	MgK_{α}	7
$CH_{11}N_2O_3P$	$(NH_4)_2CH_3PO_3$	s	2p	133.8	b	MgK_{α}	7
$C_2H_6P_2S_4$	$(CH_3PS_2)_2$	s	2p	133.4	b	MgK_{α}	7
$C_4H_{10}NaO_3S$	$(C_2H_5O)_2PO^-,Na^+$ (with S on P)	s	2p	134.3 (1)	b 285.0	Mg, AlK_{α}	100
$C_6H_7O_3P$	$C_6H_5PO(OH)_2$	s	2p	134.1	b 285.0	AlK_{α}	9
$C_6H_{18}I_2P_2Pt$	*cis*-$((CH_3)_3P)_2PtI_2$	s	$2p_{3/2}$	132.6	c 84	MgK_{α}	20
$C_6H_{18}I_2P_2Pt$	*trans*-$((CH_3)_3P)_2PtI_2$	s	$2p_{3/2}$	132.1	c 84	MgK_{α}	20
$C_7H_9O_3P$	$C_6H_5CH_2PO_3H_2$	s	2p	133.8	b	MgK_{α}	7
$C_{10}H_{14}NO_3P$	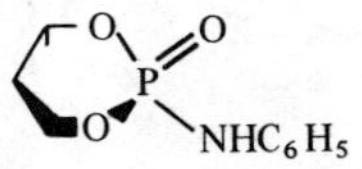	s	2p	134.4 (3)	d 285.0	AlK_{α}	105
$C_{10}H_{14}NO_3P$	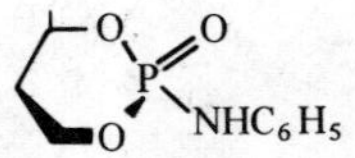	s	2p	134.4 (3)	d 285.0	AlK_{α}	105
$C_{10}H_{20}O_5P_2S$	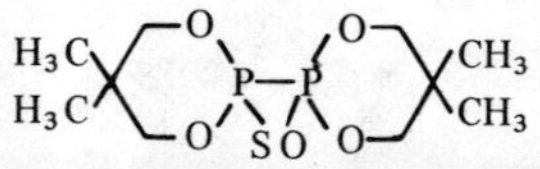	s	2p	133.5 (1)	b 285.0	Mg, AlK_{α}	100

TABLE 3 (continued)

Compound		Phase	Orbital	E_B(eV)	Calibrant	Exciting Radiation	Reference
$C_{10}H_{20}O_5P_2S_2$	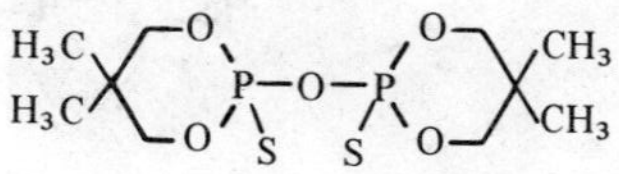	s	2p	134.3 (2)	b 285.0	Mg, AlK_a	100
$C_{10}H_{20}O_5P_2S_2$	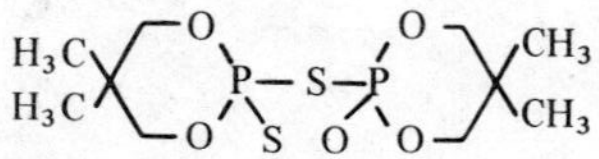		2p	133.9 (2)	b 285.0	Mg, AlK_a	100
$C_{10}H_{20}O_6P_2$	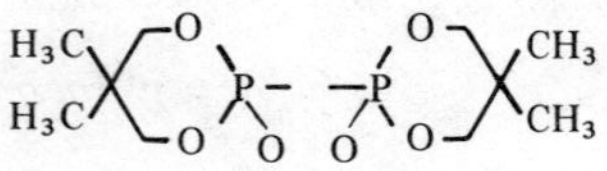	s	2p	133.4	b 285.0	Mg, AlK_a	100
$C_{10}H_{20}O_6P_2S$	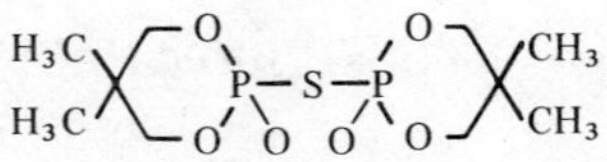	s	2p	133.9 (2)	b 285.0	Mg, AlK_a	100
$C_{10}H_{20}O_6P_2S$	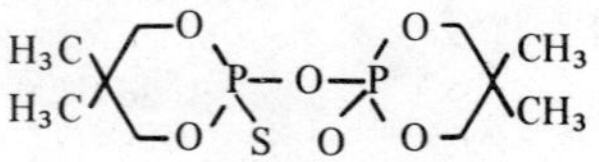	s	2p	134.2 (2)	b 285.0	Mg, AlK_a	100
$C_{10}H_{20}O_7P_2$	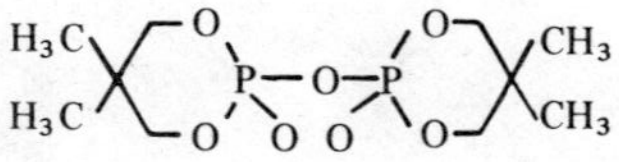	s	2p	134.3	b 285.0	Mg, AlK_a	100
$C_{11}H_{24}NO_3PS$	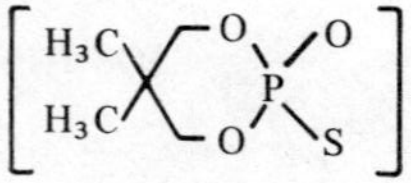 $[C_6H_{11}NH_3]$	s	2p	133.4 (2)	b 285.0	Mg, AlK_a	100
$C_{12}H_{11}O_2P$	$(C_6H_5)_2P(O)OH$	s	2p	133.5 (5)	d 285.0	AlK_a	104
$C_{12}H_{30}Cl_2P_2Pt$	$((C_2H_5)_3P)_2PtCl_2$	s	2p	131.6 (1)	d 285.0	AlK_a	87
$C_{12}H_{30}Cl_4IrP_2$	*trans*-$IrCl_4(P(CH_2CH_3)_3)_2$	s	$2p_{3/2}$	131.7 (3)	d 285	Mg, AlK_a	97
$C_{12}H_{30}Cl_4OsP_2$	*trans*-$OsCl_4(P(CH_2CH_3)_3)_2$	s	$2p_{3/2}$	131.2 (3)	d 285	Mg, AlK_a	97

TABLE 3 (continued)

Compound		Phase	Orbital	E_B(eV)	Calibrant	Exciting Radiation	Reference
$C_{12}H_{30}Cl_4P_2Pt$	*trans*-$PtCl_4(P(CH_2CH_3)_3)_2$	s	$2p_{3/2}$	131.8 (3)	d 285	Mg, AlK_a	97
$C_{12}H_{30}Cl_4P_2Pt$	$((C_2H_5)_3P)_2PtCl_4$	s	2p	131.7 (1)	d 285.0	AlK_a	87
$C_{12}H_{30}Cl_4P_2Re$	*trans*-$ReCl_4(P(C_2H_5)_3)_2$	s	$2p_{3/2}$	131.6 (3)	d 285	Mg, AlK_a	97
$C_{12}H_{30}Cl_4P_2W$	*trans*-$WCl_4(P(C_2H_5)_3)_2$	s	$2p_{3/2}$	131.5 (3)	d 285	Mg, AlK_a	97
$C_{12}H_{30}I_2P_2Pt_2$	$((C_2H_5)_3P)_2PtI_2$	s	2p	131.1 (1)	d 285.0	AlK_a	87
$C_{12}H_{31}ClP_2Pt$	$((C_2H_5)_3P)_2PtHCl$	s	2p	131.3 (1)	d 285.0	AlK_a	87
$C_{12}H_{37}B_3P_2Pt$	$((C_2H_5)_3P)_2PtB_3H_7$	s	2p	131.6	d 285.0	AlK_a	87
$C_{12}H_{42}B_8P_2Pt$	$((C_2H_5)_3P)_2PtB_8H_{12}$	s	2p	131.3 (1)	d 285.0	AlK_a	87
$C_{12}H_{42}B_{10}P_2Pt$	$((C_2H_5)_3P)_2PtB_{10}H_{12}$	s	2p	131.6 (1)	d 285.0	AlK_a	87
$C_{13}H_{33}ClP_2Pt$	$((C_2H_5)_3P)_2Pt(CH_3)Cl$	s	2p	131.5 (1)	d 285.0	AlK_a	87
$C_{14}H_{16}NOP$	$(C_6H_5)_2P(O)N(CH_3)_2$	s	2p	133.1 (6)	d 285.0	AlK_a	104
$C_{14}H_{30}N_2P_2Pt$	*cis*-$((C_2H_5)_3P)_2Pt(CN)_2$	s	2p	131.8 (1)	d 285.0	AlK_a	87
$C_{14}H_{36}P_2Pt$	*cis*-$((C_2H_5)_3P)_2Pt(CH_3)_2$	s	2p	131.4 (1)	d 285.0	AlK_a	87
$C_{16}H_{22}Cl_4IrP_2$	*trans*-$IrCl_4(P(CH_3)_2C_6H_5)_2$	s	$2p_{3/2}$	131.8 (3)	d 285	Mg, AlK_a	97
$C_{16}H_{22}Cl_4OsP_2$	*trans*-$OsCl_4(P(CH_3)_2C_6H_5)_2$	s	$2p_{3/2}$	131.7 (3)	d 285	Mg, AlK_a	97
$C_{16}H_{22}Cl_4P_2Pt$	*trans*-$PtCl_4(P(CH_3)_2C_6H_5)_2$	s	$2p_{3/2}$	132.1 (3)	d 285	Mg, AlK_a	97
$C_{16}H_{22}Cl_4P_2Re$	*trans*-$ReCl_4(P(CH_3)_2C_6H_5)_2$	s	$2p_{3/2}$	132.1 (3)	d 285	Mg, AlK_a	97
$C_{16}H_{22}Cl_4P_2W$	*trans*-$WCl_4(P(CH_3)_2C_6H_5)_2$	s	$2p_{3/2}$	131.8 (3)	d 285	Mg, AlK_a	97

TABLE 3 (continued)

Compound		Phase	Orbital	E_B(eV)	Calibrant	Exciting Radiation	Reference
$C_{16}H_{32}NO_3PS$	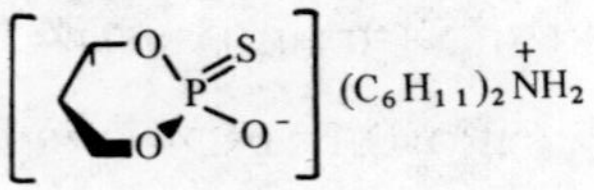	s	2p	133.2 (3)	d 285.0	AlK_α	104
$C_{16}H_{32}NO_3PS$	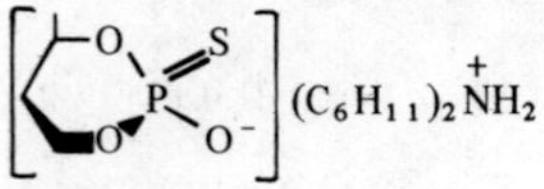	s	2p	133.1 (3)	d 285.0	AlK_α	104
$C_{16}H_{36}BrP$	$[(n\text{-}C_4H_9)_4P]Br$	s	2p	131.6 (0.30)	h 133.3	AlK_α	15
$C_{16}H_{36}ClP$	$[n\text{-}(C_4H_9)_4P]Cl$	s	2p	132.3	b	MgK_α	7
$C_{16}H_{36}ClP$	$[(n\text{-}C_4H_9)_4P]Cl$	s	2p	132.3 (0.30)	h 133.3	AlK_α	15
$C_{18}H_{15}ClCuP$	$CuCl \cdot (C_6H_5)_3P$	s	2p	132.2	a 285.5	AlK_α	46
$C_{18}H_{15}F_3N_3P_3$	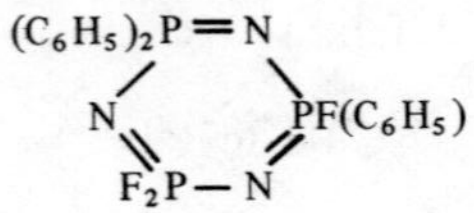	s	2p(F_2) (FC) (C_2)	135.3 (3) 134.3 (3) 133.3 (3)	d 285.0	AlK_α	105
$C_{18}H_{15}HgI_2PS$	$\{[(C_6H_5)_3PS]HgI_2\}_X$, X = 2?	s	2p	131.8 (4)	d 285.0	AlK_α	104
$C_{18}H_{15}HgI_2PSe$	$[(C_6H_5)_3PSe]HgI_2$	s	2p	132.4 (3)	d 285.0	AlK_α	104
$C_{18}H_{15}OP$	$(C_6H_5)_3PO$	s	2p	132.7	b	MgK_α	7
$C_{18}H_{15}OP$	$(C_6H_5)_3PO$	s	2p	132.8 (2)	d 285.0	AlK_α	104
$C_{18}H_{15}OP$	$(C_6H_5)_3PO$	s	2p	132.9 (1)	d 285.0	Mg, AlK_α	116
$C_{18}H_{15}O_3PS$	$(C_6H_5O)_3PS$	s	2p	134.9 (3)	d 285.0	AlK_α	104
$C_{18}H_{15}O_3PSe$	$(C_6H_5O)_3PSe$	s	2p	134.5 (5)	d 285.0	AlK_α	104
$C_{18}H_{15}O_4P$	$(C_6H_5O)_3PO$	s	2p	134.9 (6)	d 285.0	AlK_α	104

TABLE 3 (continued)

Compound		Phase	Orbital	E_B(eV)	Calibrant	Exciting Radiation	Reference
$C_{18}H_{15}O_4P$	$(C_6H_5O)_3PO$	s	2p	134.2	b	MgK_α	7
$C_{18}H_{15}P$	$(C_6H_5)_3P$	s	2p	131.0	b 285.0	AlK_α	9
$C_{18}H_{15}P$	$(C_6H_5)_3P$	s	2p	130.6	b	MgK_α	7
$C_{18}H_{15}P$	$P(C_6H_5)_3$	s	2p	131.3 (3)	d 285.0	AlK_α	104
$C_{18}H_{15}P$	$(C_6H_5)_3P$	s	2p	131.9 (4)	d 285.0	Mg, AlK_α	116
$C_{18}H_{15}PS$	$(C_6H_5)_3PS$	s	2p	132.3	b	MgK_α	7
$C_{18}H_{15}PS$	$(C_6H_5)_3PS$	s	2p	132.9 (1)	d 285.0	AlK_α	104
$C_{18}H_{15}PS_3$	$(C_6H_5S)_3P$	s	2p	134.4	b	MgK_α	7
$C_{18}H_{15}PS_3$	$(C_6H_5S)_3P$	s	2p	134.4 (4)	d 285.0	AlK_α	104
$C_{18}H_{15}PS_4$	$(C_6H_5S)_3PS$	s	2p	133.3 (7)	d 285.0	AlK_α	104
$C_{18}H_{15}PSe$	$(C_6H_5)_3PSe$	s	2p	133.0 (2)	d 285.0	AlK_α	104
$C_{18}H_{16}BrP$	$[(C_6H_5)_3PH]Br$	s	2p	131.1 (0.10)	h 133.3	AlK_α	15
$C_{18}H_{17}Cl_2P$	$[(C_6H_5)_3PCH_2Cl]Cl$	s	2p	130.7 (0.15)	h 133.3	AlK_α	15
$C_{18}H_{30}N_4P_2Pt$	$((C_2H_5)_3P)_2Pt((CN)_2CC(CN)_2)$	s	2p	131.3 (1)	d 285.0	AlK_α	87
$C_{18}H_{42}Cl_4P_2Pt_2$	$(n\text{-}C_3H_7)_3PClPtCl_2PtClP(n\text{-}C_3H_7)_3$	s	$2p_{3/2}$	130.8	c 84	MgK_α	20
$C_{18}H_{54}Cl_2P_2Pd$	*cis*-$((C_6H_5CH_2CH_2)_3P)_2PdCl_2$	s	$2p_{3/2}$	130.9	c 84	MgK_α	20
$C_{18}H_{54}Cl_2P_2Pd$	*trans*-$((C_6H_5CH_2CH_2)_3P)_2PdCl_2$	s	$2p_{3/2}$	130.6	c 84	MgK_α	20
$C_{19}H_{18}ClP$	$[(C_6H_5)_3PCH_3]Cl$	s	2p	130.2 (0.10)	h 133.3	AlK_α	15
$C_{20}H_{20}BrOP$	$[(C_6H_5)_3PCH_2OCH_3]Br$	s	2p	129.7 (0.16)	h 133.3	AlK_α	15
$C_{21}H_{19}P$	*o*-$(C_6H_5)_2PC_6H_4CHCHCH_3$	s	2p	131.3	b	MgK_α	7

TABLE 3 (continued)

Compound		Phase	Orbital	E_B(eV)	Calibrant	Exciting Radiation	Reference
$C_{21}H_{20}BrP$	$[(C_6H_5)_3PCH_2CH{=}CH_2]Br$	s	2p	130.5 (0.14)	h 133.3	AlK_α	15
$C_{22}H_{15}ClMnO_4P$	$Mn(CO)_4P(C_6H_5)_3Cl$	s	2p	131.2	b	MgK_α	7
$C_{23}H_{22}BrO_2P$	$[(C_6H_5)_3PCH_2C(O)COC_2H_5]Br$	s	2p	130.1 (0.14)	h 133.3	AlK_α	15
$C_{24}H_{19}BrNO_2P$	$[p\text{-}NO_2C_6H_4P(C_6H_5)_3]Br$	s	2p	130.4 (0.14)	h 133.3	AlK_α	15
$C_{24}H_{19}IMnO_3P$	$(o\text{-}(C_6H_5)_2PC_6H_4CH_2CHCH_2)Mn(CO)_3I$	s	2p	133.0	b	MgK_α	7
$C_{24}H_{19}IMnO_3P$	$(o\text{-}(C_6H_5)_2PC_6H_4CHCHCH_3)Mn(CO)_3I$	s	2p	133.2	b	MgK_α	7
$C_{24}H_{20}BrP$	$[(C_6H_5)_4P]Br$	s	2p	130.7 (0.20)	h 133.3	AlK_α	15
$C_{24}H_{20}F_2N_3P_3$	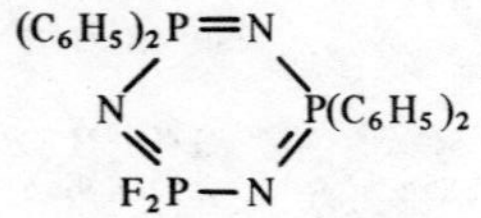	s	2p(1) 2p(2)	134.8 (3) 133.0 (3)	d 285.0	AlK_α	105
$C_{24}H_{33}Cl_3IrP_3$	*mer*-$IrCl_3(P(CH_3)_2C_6H_5)_3$	s	$2p_{3/2}$	131.6	d 285	Mg, AlK_α	97
$C_{24}H_{33}Cl_3IrP_3$	*fac*-$IrCl_3(P(CH_3)_2C_6H_5)_3$	s	$2p_{3/2}$	132.0	d 285	Mg, AlK_α	97
$C_{24}H_{33}Cl_3MoP_3$	*mer*-$MoCl_3(P(CH_3)_2C_6H_5)_3$	s	$2p_{3/2}$	131.1 (3)	d 285	Mg, AlK_α	97
$C_{24}H_{33}Cl_3OsP_3$	*mer*-$OsCl_3(P(CH_3)_2C_6H_5)_3$	s	$2p_{3/2}$	131.3	d 285	Mg, AlK_α	97
$C_{24}H_{33}Cl_3P_3Re$	*mer*-$ReCl_3(P(CH_3)_2C_6H_5)_3$	s	$2p_{3/2}$	131.4	d 285	Mg, AlK_α	97
$C_{24}H_{33}Cl_3P_3Rh$	*fac*-$RhCl_3(P(CH_3)_2C_6H_5)_3$	s	$2p_{3/2}$	131.8	d 285	Mg, AlK_α	97
$C_{24}H_{33}Cl_3P_3Ru$	*mer*-$RuCl_3(P(CH_3)_2C_6H_5)_3$	s	$2p_{3/2}$	131.3	d 285	Mg, AlK_α	97
$C_{24}H_{40}P_2Pt$	$((C_2H_5)_3P)_2Pt(C_6H_5)_2$	s	2p	131.4 (1)	d 285.0	AlK_α	87
$C_{24}H_{51}OP$	$(C_8H_{17})_3PO$	s	2p	132.6 (2)	d 285.0	AlK_α	104

TABLE 3 (continued)

Compound		Phase	Orbital	E_B(eV)	Calibrant	Exciting Radiation	Reference
$C_{24}H_{54}Cl_2P_2Pt$	*trans*-$((n\text{-}C_4H_9)_3P)_2PtCl_2$	s	$2p_{3/2}$	130.7	c 84	MgK_α	20
$C_{24}H_{54}Cl_2P_2Pt$	*cis*-$((n\text{-}C_4H_9)_3P)_2PtCl_2$	s	$2p_{3/2}$	131.1	c 84	MgK_α	20
$C_{25}H_{22}ClP$	$[(C_6H_5CH_2)(C_6H_5)_3P]Cl$	s	2p	132.5	b	MgK_α	7
$C_{25}H_{22}ClP$	$[(C_6H_5)_3PCH_2C_6H_5]Cl$	s	2p	130.5 (0.17)	h 133.3	AlK_α	15
$C_{26}H_{24}Cl_2P_2Pt$	$(C_6H_5)_2PCH_2CH_2P(C_6H_5)_2Cl_2$	s	$2p_{3/2}$	130.9	c 84	MgK_α	20
$C_{26}H_{44}O_6P_2PtS_2$	*cis*-$((C_2H_5)_3P)_2Pt(CH_3C_6H_4SO_3)_2$	s	2p	132.0 (1)	d 285.0	AlK_α	87
$C_{28}H_{30}P_2Pt$	$(C_6H_5)_2PCH_2CH_2P(C_6H_5)_2Pt(CH_3)_2$	s	$2p_{3/2}$	130.5	c 84	MgK_α	20
$C_{30}H_{21}P$	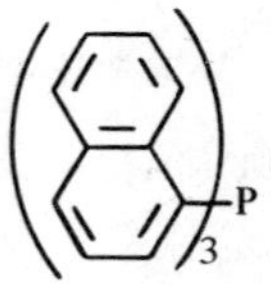	s	2p	130.9	b	MgK_α	7
$C_{30}H_{23}ClCuN_2P$	CuCl· 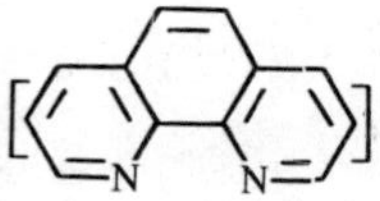 $[(C_6H_5)_3P]$	s	2p	132.0	a 285.5	AlK_α	46
$C_{30}H_{25}NOP_2$	$(C_6H_5)_2(O)PNP(C_6H_5)_3$	s	2p	132.5	d 285.0	AlK_α	105
$C_{32}H_{44}ClN_2P_4Re$	*trans*-$[ReCl(N_2)(P(CH_3)_2C_6H_5)_4]$	s	$2p_{3/2}$	131.8 (0.3)	d 285	Mg, AlK_α	97
$C_{32}H_{44}Cl_2OsP_4$	*trans*-$OsCl_2(P(CH_3)_2C_6H_5)_4$	s	$2p_{3/2}$	131.5	d 285	Mg, AlK_α	97
$C_{32}H_{44}Cl_2P_4Re$	*trans*-$ReCl_2(P(CH_3)_2C_6H_5)_4$	s	$2p_{3/2}$	131.3	d 285	Mg, AlK_α	97
$C_{36}H_{27}P$	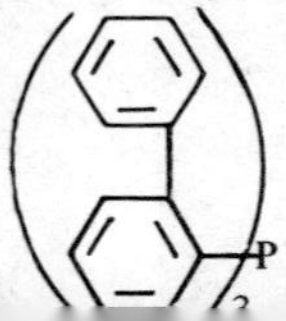	s	2p	134.3	b	MgK_α	7

TABLE 3 (continued)

Compound		Phase	Orbital	E_B(eV)	Calibrant	Exciting Radiation	Reference
$C_{36}H_{30}BrNP_2$	$\{[(C_6H_5)_3P]_2N\}Br$	s	2p	133.2 (2)	d 285.0	AlK_α	128
$C_{36}H_{30}Br_2P_2Pd$	$Pd(P(C_6H_5)_3)_2Br_2$	s	2p	131.8 (1)	b 285.0		86
$C_{36}H_{30}CdCl_2P_2$	$Cd(P(C_6H_5)_3)_2Cl_2$	s	2p	131.6 (2)	d 285.0	Mg, AlK_α	116
$C_{36}H_{30}ClNP_2$	$\{[(C_6H_5)_3P]_2N\}Cl$	s	2p	133.0 (2)	d 285.0	AlK_α	128
$C_{36}H_{30}Cl_2HgO_2P_2$	$((C_6H_5)_3PO)_2HgCl_2$	s	2p	133.4	b 285.0	AlK_α	9
$C_{36}H_{30}Cl_2NiP_2$	$Ni(P(C_6H_5)_3)_2Cl_2$	s	2p	131.6 (3)	d 285.0	Mg, AlK_α	116
$C_{36}H_{30}Cl_2P_2Pd$	$Pd(P(C_6H_5)_3)_2Cl_2$	s	2p	131.7 (1)	d 285.0	Mg, AlK_α	116
$C_{36}H_{30}Cl_2P_2Pd$	$Pd(P(C_6H_5)_3)_2Cl_2$	s	2p	131.8 (3)	b 285.0		86
$C_{36}H_{30}Cl_2P_2Pt$	*cis*-$((C_6H_5)_3P)_2PtCl_2$	s	$2p_{3/2}$	131.0	c 84	MgK_α	20
$C_{36}H_{30}Cl_2P_2Pt$	*cis*-$((C_6H_5)_3P)_2PtCl_2$	s	2p	131.9 (1)	d 285.0	AlK_α	87
$C_{36}H_{30}FNP_2$	$\{[(C_6H_5)_3P]_2N\}F$	s	2p	132.8 (3)	d 285.0	AlK_α	128
$C_{36}H_{30}HgI_2O_2P_2$	$[(C_6H_5)_3PO]_2HgI_2$	s	2p	132.9 (2)	d 285.0	AlK_α	104
$C_{36}H_{30}HgI_2P_2$	$((C_6H_5)_3P)_2HgI_2$	s	2p	131.9	b 285.0	AlK_α	9
$C_{36}H_{30}HgI_2P_2$	$[(C_6H_5)_3P]_2HgI_2$	s	2p	131.1 (3)	d 285.0	AlK_α	104
$C_{36}H_{30}Hg_2I_4P_2$	$\{[(C_6H_5)_3P]HgI_2\}_2$	s	2p	131.5 (3)	d 285.0	AlK_α	104
$C_{36}H_{30}INP_2$	$\{[(C_6H_5)_3P]_2N\}I$	s	2p	132.9 (3)	d 285.0	AlK_α	128
$C_{36}H_{30}I_2P_2Pd$	$Pd(P(C_6H_5)_3)_2I_2$	s	2p	131.6 (2)	b 285.0		86
$C_{36}H_{30}N_2O_3P_2$	$\{[(C_6H_5)_3P]_2N\}NO_3$	s	2p	132.5 (2)	d 285.0	AlK_α	128
$C_{36}H_{30}N_4P_2$	$\{[(C_6H_5)_3P]_2N\}NNN$	s	2p	133.2	d 285.0	AlK_α	128

TABLE 3 (continued)

Compound		Phase	Orbital	E_B(eV)	Calibrant	Exciting Radiation	Reference
$C_{36}H_{30}O_2P_2Pt$	$((C_6H_5)_3P)_2PtO_2$	s	2p	132.1 (1)	d 285.0	AlK_α	87
$C_{36}H_{33}ClCuP_3$	$CuCl.[(C_6H_5)_2PH]_3$	s	2p	133.8	a 285.5	AlK_α	46
$C_{36}H_{42}B_{10}P_2Pt$	$((C_6H_5)_3P)_2PtB_{10}H_{12}$	s	2p	131.8 (1)	d 285.0	AlK_α	87
$C_{36}H_{54}Cl_4P_2Pd_2$	$(n\text{-}C_4H_9)_3PClPdCl_2PdClP(n\text{-}C_4H_9)_3$	s	$2p_{3/2}$	130.7	c 84	MgK_α	20
$C_{37}H_{30}BClF_4IrNO_2P_2$	$[Ir(CO)(P(C_6H_5)_3)_2Cl(NO^+)]BF_4$	s	2p	132.0 (3)	d 285.0	AlK_α	82
$C_{37}H_{30}BF_4IIrNO_2P_2$	$[Ir(CO)(P(C_6H_5)_3)_2I(NO^+)]BF_4$	s	2p	132.1 (3)	d 285.0	AlK_α	82
$C_{37}H_{30}ClIrO_3P_2$	$Ir(CO)(P(C_6H_5)_3)_2(Cl)O_2$	s	2p	131.9 (3)	d 285.0	AlK_α	82
$C_{37}H_{30}ClOP_2Rh$	*trans*-$Rh(CO)Cl(P(C_6H_5)_3)_2$	s	2p	131.6	b	MgK_α	7
$C_{37}H_{30}IIrO_3P_2$	$Ir(CO)(P(C_6H_5)_3)_2I(O_2)$	s	2p	131.9 (3)	d 285.0	AlK_α	82
$C_{37}H_{30}N_2OP_2$	$\{[(C_6H_5)_3P]_2N\}OCN$	s	2p	133.0 (2)	d 285.0	AlK_α	128
$C_{37}H_{30}N_2P_2S$	$\{[(C_6H_5)_3P]_2N\}SCN$	s	2p	133.3 (3)	d 285.0	AlK_α	128
$C_{38}H_{30}ClF_4P_2Rh$	$((C_6H_5)_3P)_2Rh(C_2F_4)Cl$	s	2p	131.7 (3)	d 285.0	AlK_α	82
$C_{38}H_{30}ClIrO_2P_2$	$Ir(CO)_2(P(C_6H_5)_3)_2Cl$	s	2p	132.0 (3)	d 285.0	AlK_α	82
$C_{38}H_{30}Cl_4P_2Pt$	$((C_6H_5)_3P)_2Pt(Cl_2C{=}CCl_2)$	s	$2p_{3/2}$	130.7 (2)		MgK_α	93
$C_{38}H_{30}Cl_4P_2Pt$	$((C_6H_5)_3P)_2PtC_2Cl_4$	s	2p	131.7 (3)	d 285.0	AlK_α	82
$C_{38}H_{30}Cl_4P_2Pt$	$((C_6H_5)_3P)_2PtCl(CCl{=}CCl_2)$	s	$2p_{3/2}$	130.6 (2)		MgK_α	93
$C_{38}H_{30}F_4P_2Pt$	$((C_6H_5)_3P)_2PtC_2F_4$	s	2p	131.6 (3)	d 285.0	AlK_α	82
$C_{38}H_{30}IIrO_2P_2$	$Ir(CO)_2(P(C_6H_5)_3)_2I$	s	2p	131.7 (3)	d 285.0	AlK_α	82
$C_{38}H_{30}N_2P_2Pd$	$Pd(P(C_6H_5)_3)_2(CN)_2$	s	2p	131.9 (2)	b 285.0		86

TABLE 3 (continued)

Compound		Phase	Orbital	E_B(eV)	Calibrant	Exciting Radiation	Reference
$C_{38}H_{32}P_2Pt$	*cis*-$((C_6H_5)_3P)_2PtC_2H_2$	s	$2p_{3/2}$	131.0	c 84	MgK_α	30
$C_{38}H_{34}P_2Pt$	*cis*-$((C_6H_5)_3P)_2PtC_2H_4$	s	$2p_{3/2}$	131.1	c 84	MgK_α	30
$C_{38}H_{34}P_2Pt$	$((C_6H_5)_3P)_2PtC_2H_4$	s	2p	131.7 (3)	d 285.0	AlK_α	82
$C_{38}H_{34}ClP_2Rh$	$((C_6H_5)_3P)_2Rh(C_2H_4)Cl$	s	2p	131.7 (3)	d 285.0	AlK_α	82
$C_{38}H_{36}P_2Pt$	*trans*-$((C_6H_5)_3P)_2Pt(CH_3)_2$	s	$2p_{3/2}$	130.7	c 84	MgK_α	20
$C_{38}H_{44}B_9NP_2Pt$	$((C_6H_5)_3P)_2PtB_9H_{11}(CH_3CN)$	s	2p	131.5 (1)	d 285.0	AlK_α	87
$C_{39}H_{30}ClF_4IrOP_2$	$Ir(CO)(P(C_6H_5)_3)_2(Cl)C_2F_4$	s	2p	131.2 (3)	d 285.0	AlK_α	82
$C_{39}H_{34}P_2Pt$	*cis*-$((C_6H_5)_3P)_2Pt(CH_3CCH)$	s	$2p_{3/2}$	130.9	c 84	MgK_α	30
$C_{42}H_{30}ClIrN_4P_2$	$Ir(P(C_6H_5)_3)_2Cl(C_2(CN)_4)$	s	2p	131.6 (3)	d 285.0	AlK_α	82
$C_{42}H_{30}NO_6P_2V$	$\{[(C_6H_5)_3P]_2N\}V(CO)_6$	s	2p	133.3 (2)	d 285.0	AlK_α	128
$C_{42}H_{30}N_4P_2Pt$	$((C_6H_5)_3P)_2Pt(C_2(CN)_4)$	s	2p	131.8 (3)	d 285.0	AlK_α	82
$C_{43}H_{30}ClIrN_4OP_2$	$Ir(CO)(P(C_6H_5)_3)_2Cl(C_2(CN)_4)$	s	2p	131.4 (3)	d 285.0	AlK_α	82
$C_{43}H_{30}ClN_4OP_2Rh$	$((C_6H_5)_3P)_2RhCl(CO)(C_2(CN)_4)$	s	2p	131.7 (3)	d 285.0	AlK_α	82
$C_{43}H_{36}P_2Pt$	*cis*-$((C_6H_5)_3P)_2Pt(C_6H_5CCH)$	s	$2p_{3/2}$	130.9	c 84	MgK_α	30
$C_{54}H_{45}ClCuP_3$	$CuCl\cdot[(C_6H_5)_3P]_3$	s	2p	132.0	a 285.5	AlK_α	46
$C_{54}H_{45}ClP_3Rh$	$((C_6H_5)_3P)_3RhCl$	s	2p	131.8 (3)	d 285.0	AlK_α	82
$C_{54}H_{45}P_3Pt$	$((C_6H_5)_3P)_3Pt$	s	2p	131.4 (1)	d 285.0	AlK_α	87
$C_{72}H_{60}P_4Pt$	$((C_6H_5)_3P)_4Pt$	s	2p	131.4 (1)	d 285.0	AlK_α	87
Cl_3OP	$POCl_3$	s	2p	2.5	PCl_3 P2p 0.0		24

TABLE 3 (continued)

Compound		Phase	Orbital	E_B(eV)	Calibrant	Exciting Radiation	Reference
Cl_3P	PCl_3	s	2p	0	PCl_3 P2p 0.0		24
$Cl_6N_3P_3$	$(NPCl_2)_3$	s	2p	134.5	b	MgK_α	7
CrP	CrP	s	2p	128.8	b	MgK_α	7
Cu_3P	Cu_3P	s	2p	136.2	a 285.5	AlK_α	46
$FH_8N_2O_3P$	$(NH_4)_2PFO_3$	s	2p	134.1	b	MgK_α	7
F_2KO_2P	KPF_2O_2	s	2p	134.8	b	MgK_α	7
F_6H_4NP	NH_4PF_6	s	2p	137.3	b	MgK_α	7
F_6KP	KPF_6	s	2p	137.8	b 285.0	AlK_α	9
HK_2O_4P	K_2HPO_4	s	2p	132.7	b	MgK_α	7
HNa_2O_4P	Na_2HPO_4	s	2p	133.6	b 285.0	AlK_α	9
HOP_4	P_4OH	s	2p	129.9	b	MgK_α	7
$H_2KO_2P \cdot H_2O$	$KH_2PO_2 \cdot H_2O$	s	2p	132.4	b	MgK_α	7
H_2KO_4P	KH_2PO_4	s	2p	133.9	b	MgK_α	7
$H_2Na_2O_7P_2$	$Na_2H_2P_2O_7$	s	2p	133.9	b	MgK_α	7
$H_3N_3Na_3O_6P_3$	$Na_3(PO_2NH)_3$	s	2p	133.0	b	MgK_α	7
$H_3O_{40}PW_{12}$	$H_3PW_{12}O_{40}$	s	2p	133.0	b	MgK_α	7
$H_5N_2O_2P$	$HOPO(NH_2)_2$	s	2p	133.6	b	MgK_α	7
K_3O_4P	K_3PO_4	s	2p	133.6	b 285.0	AlK_α	9
MnP	MnP	s	2p	129.3	b	MgK_α	7

TABLE 3 (continued)

Compound		Phase	Orbital	E_B(eV)	Calibrant	Exciting Radiation	Reference
N_5P_3	P_3N_5	s	2p	132.2	b	MgK_α	7
NaO_3P	$NaPO_3$ glass	s	2p	134.5	b	MgK_α	7
Na_3O_3PS	Na_3PSO_3	s	2p	133.0	b	MgK_α	7
Na_3O_4P	Na_3PO_4	s	2p	132.1	b	MgK_α	7
Na_3O_4P	Na_3PO_4	s	2p	132.7	b 285.0	AlK_α	9
$Na_3O_9P_3$	$(NaPO_3)_3$	s	2p	134.0	b	MgK_α	7
$Na_4O_7P_2$	$Na_4P_2O_7$	s	2p	133.3	b	MgK_α	7
$Na_4O_7P_2$	$Na_4P_2O_7$	s	2p	134.7	b 285.0	AlK_α	9
$Na_4O_{12}P_4 \cdot 4H_2O$	$(NaPO_3)_4 \cdot 4H_2O$	s	2p	134.1	b	MgK_α	7
$Na_5O_{10}P_3$	$Na_5P_3O_{10}$ form I	s	2p	133.6	b	MgK_α	7
O_5P_2	P_2O_5	s	K	2,149.0 (4)	e, i	CrK_α	76
P	P(red)	s	L_I	189.3	MgO MgK($CrK_{\alpha 1}$)	$CrK_{\alpha 1}$	67
P	P_{red}	s	2p	130.1	b	MgK_α	7
P_4S_3	P_4S_3	s	2p	134.9 (1)	b 285.0	Mg, AlK_α	100
P_4S_3	P_4S_3	s	2p	130.5	b	MgK_α	7
P_4S_5	P_4S_5	s	2p	132.0	b	MgK_α	7
P_4S_7	P_4S_7	s	2p	134.3 132.7	b	MgK_α	7
P_4S_{10}	P_4S_{10}	s	2p	134.0	b	MgK_α	7
P_4S_{10}	P_4S_{10}	s	2p	134.5 (3)	b 285.0	Mg, AlK_α	100

TABLE 3 (continued)

Compound		Phase	Orbital	E_B(eV)	Calibrant	Exciting Radiation	Reference
Pb							
Br_2Pb	$PbBr_2$	s	$4f_{5/2}$ $4f_{7/2}$	150.85 145.95	a 290.0	AlK_a	107
CO_3Pb	$PbCO_3$	s	$4f_{5/2}$ $4f_{7/2}$	149.8 145.0	a 290.0	AlK_a	107
CO_3Pb	$PbCO_3$	s	$4f_{5/2}$ $4f_{7/2}$	148.8 144.0	a 290	AlK_a	30
$C_8H_{20}O_4P_2PbS_4$	$Pb[S_2P(OC_2H_5)_2]_2$	s	$4f_{5/2}$ $4f_{7/2}$	148.2 143.3	a 290.0	AlK_a	107
Cl_2Pb	$PbCl_2$	s	$4f_{5/2}$ $4f_{7/2}$	151.0 146.1	a 290.0	AlK_a	107
CrO_4Pb	$PbCrO_4$	s	$4f_{5/2}$ $4f_{7/2}$	148.6 143.75	a 290.0	AlK_a	107
CrO_4Pb	$PbCrO_4$	s	$4f_{5/2}$ $4f_{7/2}$	148.6 143.75	a 290	AlK_a	30
F_2Pb	PbF_2	s	$4f_{5/2}$ $4f_{7/2}$	150.75 145.9	a 290	AlK_a	30
F_2Pb	PbF_2	s	$4f_{5/2}$ $4f_{7/2}$	150.75 145.9	a 290.0	AlK_a	107
I_2Pb	PbI_2	s	$4f_{5/2}$ $4f_{7/2}$	149.6 144.7	a 290	AlK_a	30
I_2Pb	PbI_2	s	$4f_{5/2}$ $4f_{7/2}$	151.7 146.75	a 290.0	AlK_a	107
N_2O_6Pb	$Pb(NO_3)_2$	s	$4f_{5/2}$ $4f_{7/2}$	152.1 147.2	a 290.0	AlK_a	107

TABLE 3 (continued)

Compound		Phase	Orbital	E_B(eV)	Calibrant	Exciting Radiation	Reference
N_2O_6Pb	$Pb(NO_3)_2$	s	$4f_{5/2}$ $4f_{7/2}$	150.2 145.35	a 290	AlK_a	30
OPb	PbO	s	$4f_{5/2}$ $4f_{7/2}$	149.0 144.15	a 290	AlK_a	30
OPb	PbO	s	$4f_{7/2}$	139.8		AlK_a	102
OPb	PbO	s	$4f_{5/2}$ $4f_{7/2}$	149.0 144.15	a 290.0	AlK_a	107
O_2Pb	PbO_2	s	$4f_{5/2}$ $4f_{7/2}$	147.2 142.4	a 290.0	AlK_a	107
O_2Pb	PbO_2	s	$4f_{7/2}$	141.0		AlK_a	102
O_2Pb	PbO_2	s	$4f_{5/2}$ $4f_{7/2}$	147.2 142.4	a 290	AlK_a	30
O_4PbS	$PbSO_4$	s	$4f_{5/2}$ $4f_{7/2}$	150.95 146.1	a 290.0	AlK_a	107
O_4PbS	$PbSO_4$	s	$4f_{5/2}$ $4f_{7/2}$	149.75 144.9	a 290.0	AlK_a	107
O_4Pb_3	Pb_3O_4	s	$4f_{5/2}$ $4f_{7/2}$	148.8 143.9	a 290	AlK_a	30
Pb	Pb	s	L_{III} M_{II} M_{III} M_{IV} M_V	13,035.1 (4) 3,554.1 (4) 3,066.2 (5) 2,585.5 (4) 2,484.2 (4)	e	MoK_a CuK_a CrK_a	77
Pb	Pb	s	L_{III}	13,035.7	CuK(MoK_{a1})	MoK_{a1}	119
PbS	PbS	s	$4f_{5/2}$ $4f_{7/2}$	149.9 145.05	a 290	AlK_a	30

TABLE 3 (continued)

Compound		Phase	Orbital	E_B(eV)	Calibrant	Exciting Radiation	Reference
PbS	PbS	s	$4f_{5/2}$ $4f_{7/2}$	149.85 145.0	a 290.0	AlK_a	107
Pd							
$Ag_{0.71}Pd_{0.29}$	$Ag_{0.71}Pd_{0.29}$	s	$2p_{3/2}$ $3d_{5/2}$	3,173.8 (5) 335.1 (1)	Au, Pt $4f_{7/2}$	CrK_a MgK_a	70
$Au_{0.45}Pd_{0.55}$	$Au_{0.45}Pd_{0.55}$	s	$2p_{3/2}$ $3d_{5/2}$	3,173.8 (5) 335.0 (1)	Au, Pt $4f_{7/2}$	CrK_a MgK_a	70
Br_2Pd	$PdBr_2$	s	$3d_{3/2}$ $3d_{5/2}$	342.5 (2) 337.3 (2)	b 285.0		86
Br_4K_2Pd	$K_2[PdBr_4]$	s	$3d_{3/2}$ $3d_{5/2}$	342.8 (1) 337.5 (1)	b 285.0		86
C_2N_2Pd	$Pd(CN)_2$	s	$3d_{3/2}$ $3d_{5/2}$	344.9 (2) 339.6 (2)	b 285.0		86
$C_4K_2N_4Pd$	$K_2[Pd(CN)_4]$	s	$3d_{3/2}$ $3d_{5/2}$	344.4 (3) 339.2 (2)	b 285.0		86
$C_6H_6Cl_4Pd_2$	$(CH_3CH{=}CH_2)ClPdCl_2PdCl$ $(CH_3CH{=}CH_2)$	s	$3d_{5/2}$	337.9	c 84	MgK_a	20
$C_{18}H_{54}Cl_2P_2Pd$	*cis*-$((C_6H_5CH_2CH_2)_3P)_2PdCl_2$	s	$3d_{5/2}$	338.0	c 84	MgK_a	20
$C_{18}H_{54}Cl_2P_2Pd$	*trans*-$((C_6H_5CH_2CH_2)_3P)_2PdCl_2$	s	$3d_{5/2}$	338.0	c 84	MgK_a	20
$C_{36}H_{30}Cl_2P_2Pd$	$Pd(P(C_6H_5)_3)_2Cl_2$	s	$3d_{3/2}$ $3d_{5/2}$	343.1 (3) 338.1 (3)	b 285.0	Mg, AlK_a	116
$C_{36}H_{30}I_2P_2Pd$	$Pd(P(C_6H_5)_3)_2I_2$	s	$3d_{3/2}$ $3d_{5/2}$	343.0 (4) 337.7 (4)	b 285.0		86
$C_{36}H_{54}Cl_4P_2Pd_2$	$(n\text{-}C_4H_9)_3PClPdCl_2PdClP(n\text{-}C_4H_9)_3$	s	$3d_{5/2}$	337.7	c 84	MgK_a	20

TABLE 3 (continued)

Compound		Phase	Orbital	E_B(eV)	Calibrant	Exciting Radiation	Reference
$C_{38}H_{30}N_2P_2Pd$	$Pd(P(C_6H_5)_3)_2(CN)_2$	s	$3d_{3/2}$ $3d_{5/2}$	343.7 (4) 338.4 (4)	b 285.0		86
Cl_2Pd	$PdCl_2$	s	$3d_{3/2}$ $3d_{5/2}$	343.2 (4) 337.9 (3)	b 285.0		86
Cl_4K_2Pd	$K_2[PdCl_4]$	s	$3d_{3/2}$ $3d_{5/2}$	343.7 (3) 338.4 (2)	b 285.0		86
Cl_6K_2Pd	$K_2[PdCl_6]$	s	$3d_{3/2}$ $3d_{5/2}$	345.6 (5) 340.3 (3)	b 285.0		86
$Cu_{0.60}Pd_{0.40}$	$Cu_{0.60}Pd_{0.40}$	s	$2p_{3/2}$ $3d_{5/2}$	3,174.0 (5) 335.3 (1)	Au, Pt $4f_{7/2}$	CrK_α MgK_α	70
I_2Pd	PdI_2	s	$3d_{3/2}$ $3d_{5/2}$	341.9 (1) 336.6 (1)	b 285.0		86
$K_2N_4O_8Pd$	$K_2[Pd(NO_2)_4]$	s	$3d_{3/2}$ $3d_{5/2}$	344.4 (4) 339.2 (2)	b 285.0		86
Pd	Pd(fcc)	s	3d	335 (0.5)		MgK_α	122
Pd	Pd	s	$3d_{3/2}$ $3d_{5/2}$	340.9 (3) 335.7 (3)	b 285.0		86
Pd	Pd	s	$3d_{5/2}$	336.3	c 84	MgK_α	20
Pd	Pd	s	L_I L_{II} L_{III}	3,604.6 (4) 3,330.3 (4) 3,173.1 (4)		CuK_α	79
Pd	Pd	s	L_{III}	3,172.9	CuA6	$CuK_{\alpha 1}$	123
Pd	Pd	s	$2p_{3/2}$ $3d_{5/2}$	3,174.0 (5) 335.2 (1)	Pd Fermi level	CrK_α MgK_α	70
$Pd_{0.40}Rh_{0.60}$	$Rh_{0.60}Pd_{0.40}$	s	$2p_{3/2}$ $3d_{5/2}$	3,174.5 (5) 335.5 (1)	Au, Pt $4f_{7/2}$	CrK_α MgK_α	70

TABLE 3 (continued)

Compound		Phase	Orbital	E_B(eV)	Calibrant	Exciting Radiation	Reference
Pm							
Pm	$^{147}_{61}Pm$	s	2s	7,430.2 (1.6)	e	$MoK_{\alpha 1}$	50
			$2p_{1/2}$	7,014.6 (1.4)			
			$2p_{3/2}$	6,464.6 (1.4)		Cu, $MoK_{\alpha 1}$	
			3s	1,655.6 (1.8)		$CuK_{\alpha 1}$	
			$3p_{1/2}$	1,477.5 (1.6)			
			$3p_{3/2}$	1,363.8 (1.1)			
			$3d_{3/2}$	1,060.0 (1.0)		$MoK_{\alpha 1}$	
			$3d_{5/2}$	1,033.7 (1.0)			
			4s	337.2 (1.4)			
			$4p_{1/2}$	264 (3)			
			$4p_{3/2}$	242.3 (8)	b	$AlK_{\alpha 1}$	
			$4d_{3/2}$	132.6 (8)			
			$4d_{5/2}$	128.5 (7)			
Pr							
$O_{11}Pr_6$	Pr_6O_{11}	s	L_I	6,835.3	e	$MoK_{\alpha 1}$	56
			L_{II}	6,440.6			
			L_{III}	5,964.7			
Pt							
$BrC_4ClK_2N_4Pt$	$K_2Pt(CN)_4BrCl$	s	$4f_{7/2}$	4.6	Pt $4f_{7/2}$ 0.0	MgK_α	129
$Br_2C_4K_2N_4Pt$	$K_2Pt(CN)_4Br_2$	s	$4f_{7/2}$	4.5	Pt $4f_{7/2}$ 0.0	MgK_α	129
$Br_2K_2N_4O_8Pt$	$K_2Pt(NO_2)_4Br_2$	s	$4f_{7/2}$	4.4	Pt $4f_{7/2}$ 0.0	MgK_α	129
Br_4K_2Pt	K_2PtBr_4	s	$4f_{7/2}$	1.7	Pt $4f_{7/2}$ 0.0	MgK_α	129
Br_6K_2Pt	K_2PtBr_6	s	$4f_{7/2}$	3.8	Pt $4f_{7/2}$ 0.0	MgK_α	129
Br_6K_2Pt	K_2PtBr_6	s	$4f_{5/2}$	84.6	a 290.0	AlK_α	107
			$4f_{7/2}$	81.3			
$C_2H_4Cl_3KPt$	$KPt(C_2H_4)Cl_3$	s	$4f_{7/2}$	2.6	Pt $4f_{7/2}$ 0.0	MgK_α	129

TABLE 3 (continued)

Compound		Phase	Orbital	E_B(eV)	Calibrant	Exciting Radiation	Reference
$C_4Cl_2K_2N_4Pt$	$K_2Pt(CN)_4Cl_2$	s	$4f_{7/2}$	4.8	Pt $4f_{7/2}$ 0.0	MgK_α	129
$C_4K_2N_4Pt$	$K_2Pt(CN)_4$	s	$4f_{7/2}$	2.0	Pt $4f_{7/2}$ 0.0	MgK_α	129
$C_4K_2N_4Pt$	$K_2Pt(CN)_4$	s	$4f_{7/2}$	74.0 (1)	$K2p_{3/2}$ 293.5	AlK_α	87
$C_6H_{12}Cl_4Pt_2$	$(CH_3CH{=}CH_2)ClPtCl_2PtCl$ $(CH_3CH{=}CH_2)$	s	$4f_{7/2}$	72.7	c 84	MgK_α	20
$C_6H_{18}I_2P_2Pt$	*cis*-$((CH_3)_3P)_2PtI_2$	s	$4f_{7/2}$	72.9	c 84	MgK_α	20
$C_6H_{18}I_2P_2Pt$	*trans*-$((CH_3)_3P)_2PtI_2$	s	$4f_{7/2}$	72.9	c 84	MgK_α	20
$C_6K_2N_6Pt$	$K_2Pt(CN)_6$	s	$4f_{7/2}$	4.2	Pt $4f_{7/2}$ 0.0	MgK_α	129
$C_6K_2N_6PtS_6$	$K_2Pt(SCN)_6$	s	$4f_{5/2}$ $4f_{7/2}$	83.1 80.0	a 290.0	AlK_α	107
$C_6K_2N_6PtSe_6$	$K_2Pt(SeCN)_6$	s	$4f_{5/2}$ $4f_{7/2}$	83.9 80.6	a 290.0	AlK_α	107
$C_8H_{12}Cl_2Pt$	$C_8H_{12}PtCl_2$	s	$4f_{7/2}$	74.0 (1)	d 285.0	AlK_α	87
$C_8H_{16}N_8NiPt$	$[Ni(NH_2CH_2CH_2NH_2)_2][Pt(CN)_4]$	s	$4f_{5/2}$ $4f_{7/2}$	82.3 79.2	a 290.0	AlK_α	107
$C_{12}H_{30}Cl_2P_2Pt$	$((C_2H_5)_3P)_2PtCl_2$	s	$4f_{7/2}$	73.3 (1)	d 285.0	AlK_α	87
$C_{12}H_{30}Cl_4P_2Pt$	$[(C_2H_5)_3P]_2PtCl_4$	s	$4f_{7/2}$	76.1 (1)	d 285.0	AlK_α	87
$C_{12}H_{30}Cl_4P_2Pt$	*trans*-$PtCl_4(P(CH_2CH_3)_3)_2$	s	$4f_{5/2}$ $4f_{7/2}$	78.8 (3) 75.5 (3)	d 285	MgK_α	97
$C_{12}H_{30}I_2P_2Pt_2$	$((C_2H_5)_3P)_2PtI_2$	s	$4f_{7/2}$	72.7 (1)	d 285.0	AlK_α	87
$C_{12}H_{31}ClP_2Pt$	$((C_2H_5)_3P)_2PtHCl$	s	$4f_{7/2}$	72.8 (1)	d 285.0	AlK_α	87
$C_{12}H_{37}B_3P_2Pt$	$((C_2H_5)_3P)_2PtB_3H_7$	s	$4f_{7/2}$	72.9	d 285.0	AlK_α	87

TABLE 3 (continued)

Compound		Phase	Orbital	E_B(eV)	Calibrant	Exciting Radiation	Reference
$C_{12}H_{42}B_8P_2Pt$	$((C_2H_5)_3P)_2PtB_8H_{12}$	s	$4f_{7/2}$	72.9 (1)	d 285.0	AlK_α	87
$C_{12}H_{42}B_{10}P_2Pt$	$((C_2H_5)_3P)_2PtB_{10}H_{12}$	s	$4f_{7/2}$	73.6 (1)	d 285.0	AlK_α	87
$C_{13}H_{33}ClP_2Pt$	$((C_2H_5)_3P)_2Pt(CH_3)Cl$	s	$4f_{7/2}$	72.8 (1)	d 285.0	AlK_α	87
$C_{14}H_{30}N_2P_2Pt$	*cis*-$((C_2H_5)_3P)_2Pt(CN)_2$	s	$4f_{7/2}$	73.9 (1)	d 285.0	AlK_α	87
$C_{14}H_{36}P_2Pt$	*cis*-$((C_2H_5)_3P)_2Pt(CH_3)_2$	s	$4f_{7/2}$	72.4 (1)	d 285.0	AlK_α	87
$C_{16}H_{22}Cl_4P_2Pt$	*trans*-$PtCl_4(P(CH_3)_2C_6H_5)_2$	s	$4f_{5/2}$ $4f_{7/2}$	78.4 (3) 75.8 (3)	d 285	Mg, AlK_α	97
$C_{16}H_{64}B_{20}N_2Pt$	$[(C_2H_5)_4N]_2Pt(B_{10}H_{12})_2$	s	$4f_{7/2}$	72.3 (1)	d 285.0	AlK_α	87
$C_{18}H_{30}N_4P_2Pt$	$((C_2H_5)_3P)_2Pt((CN)_2CC(CN)_2)$	s	$4f_{7/2}$	73.0 (1)	d 285.0	AlK_α	87
$C_{18}H_{42}Cl_4P_2Pt_2$	$(n\text{-}C_3H_7)_3PClPtCl_2PtClP(n\text{-}C_3H_7)_3$	s	$4f_{7/2}$	71.9	c 84	MgK_α	20
$C_{24}H_{36}Cl_6Pt_3Sn_2$	$(C_8H_{12})_3Pt_3Sn_2Cl_6$	s	$4f_{7/2}$	73.2 (1)	d 285.0	AlK_α	87
$C_{24}H_{40}P_2Pt$	$((C_2H_5)_3P)_2Pt(C_6H_5)_2$	s	$4f_{7/2}$	72.7 (1)	d 285.0	AlK_α	87
$C_{24}H_{54}Cl_2P_2Pt$	*cis*-$((n\text{-}C_4H_9)_3P)_2PtCl_2$	s	$4f_{7/2}$	72.0	c 84	MgK_α	20
$C_{24}H_{54}Cl_2P_2Pt$	*trans*-$((n\text{-}C_4H_9)_3P)_2PtCl_2$	s	$4f_{7/2}$	72.0	c 84	MgK_α	20
$C_{24}H_{60}Cl_{15}N_3PtSn_5$	$[(CH_3CH_2)_4N]_3Pt(SnCl_3)_5$	s	$4f_{7/2}$	73.2 (1)	d 285.0	AlK_α	87
$C_{26}H_{24}Cl_2P_2Pt$	$(C_6H_5)_2PCH_2CH_2P(C_6H_5)_2PtCl_2$	s	$4f_{7/2}$	72.1	c 84	MgK_α	20
$C_{26}H_{44}O_6P_2PtS_2$	*cis*-$((C_2H_5)_3P)_2Pt(CH_3C_6H_4SO_3)_2$	s	$4f_{7/2}$	73.5 (1)	d 285.0	AlK_α	87
$C_{28}H_{30}P_2Pt$	$(C_6H_5)_2PCH_2CH_2P(C_6H_5)_2Pt(CH_3)_2$	s	$4f_{7/2}$	71.2	c 84	MgK_α	20
$C_{32}H_{80}Cl_{20}N_4Pt_3Sn_8$	$[(C_2H_5)_4N]_4Pt_3Sn_8Cl_{20}$	s	$4f_{7/2}$	72.9	d 285.0	AlK_α	87
$C_{36}H_{30}Cl_2P_2Pt$	*cis*-$((C_6H_5)_3P)_2PtCl_2$	s	$4f_{7/2}$	72.2	c 84	MgK_α	20

TABLE 3 (continued)

Compound		Phase	Orbital	E_B(eV)	Calibrant	Exciting Radiation	Reference
$C_{36}H_{30}Cl_2P_2Pt$	*cis*-$((C_6H_5)_3P)_2PtCl_2$	s	$4f_{7/2}$	73.2 (1)	d 285.0	AlK_α	87
$C_{36}H_{30}O_2P_2Pt$	$((C_6H_5)_3P)_2PtO_2$	s	$4f_{7/2}$	73.2 (1)	d 285.0	AlK_α	87
$C_{36}H_{42}B_{10}P_2Pt$	$((C_6H_5)_3P)_2PtB_{10}H_{12}$	s	$4f_{7/2}$	73.2 (1)	d 285.0	AlK_α	87
$C_{38}H_{30}Cl_4P_2Pt$	$((C_6H_5)_3P)_2Pt(Cl_2C{=}CCl_2)$	s	$4f_{7/2}$	70.8 (2)		MgK_α	93
$C_{38}H_{30}Cl_4P_2Pt$	$((C_6H_5)_3P)_2PtCl(CCl{=}CCl_2)$	s	$4f_{7/2}$	71.9 (2)		MgK_α	93
$C_{38}H_{30}Cl_4P_2Pt$	$((C_6H_5)_3P)_2PtC_2Cl_4$	s	$4f_{7/2}$ $4f_{5/2}$	73.2 (3) 76.5 (3)	d 285.0	AlK_α	82
$C_{38}H_{30}F_4P_2Pt$	$((C_6H_5)_3P)_2PtC_2F_4$	s	$4f_{7/2}$ $4f_{5/2}$	73.0 (3) 76.2 (3)	d 285.0	AlK_α	82
$C_{38}H_{32}P_2Pt$	*cis*-$((C_6H_5)_3P)_2PtC_2H_2$	s	$4f_{7/2}$	72.3	c 84	MgK_α	20
$C_{38}H_{34}P_2Pt$	*cis*-$((C_6H_5)_3P)_2PtC_2H_4$	s	$4f_{7/2}$	72.4	c 84	MgK_α	30
$C_{38}H_{34}P_2Pt$	$((C_6H_5)_3P)_2PtC_2H_4$	s	$4f_{7/2}$ $4f_{5/2}$	73.0 (3) 76.1 (3)	d 285.0	AlK_α	82
$C_{38}H_{36}P_2Pt$	*trans*-$((C_6H_5)_3P)_2Pt(CH_3)_2$	s	$4f_{7/2}$	71.2	c 84	MgK_α	20
$C_{38}H_{44}B_9NP_2Pt$	$((C_6H_5)_3P)_2PtB_9H_{11}(CH_3CN)$	s	$4f_{7/2}$	72.5 (1)	d 285.0	AlK_α	87
$C_{39}H_{34}P_2Pt$	*cis*-$((C_6H_5)_3P)_2Pt(CH_3CCH)$	s	$4f_{7/2}$	72.4	c 84	MgK_α	20
$C_{42}H_{30}N_4P_2Pt$	$((C_6H_5)_3P)_2Pt(C_2(CN)_4)$	s	$4f_{7/2}$ $4f_{5/2}$	73.2 (3) 76.5 (3)	d 285.0	AlK_α	82
$C_{43}H_{36}P_2Pt$	*cis*-$((C_6H_5)_3P)_2Pt(C_6H_5CCH)$	s	$4f_{7/2}$	72.4	c 84	MgK_α	30
$C_{54}H_{45}P_3Pt$	$((C_6H_5)_3P)_3Pt$	s	$4f_{7/2}$	71.6 (1)	d 285.0	AlK_α	87
$C_{72}H_{60}P_4Pt$	$((C_6H_5)_3P)_4Pt$	s	$4f_{7/2}$	71.6 (1)	d 285.0	AlK_α	87

TABLE 3 (continued)

Compound		Phase	Orbital	E_B(eV)	Calibrant	Exciting Radiation	Reference
$Cl_2K_2N_4O_8Pt$	$K_2Pt(NO_2)_4Cl_2$	s	$4f_{7/2}$	4.7	Pt $4f_{7/2}$ 0.0	MgK_α	129
Cl_2Pt	$PtCl_2$	s	$4f_{7/2}$	2.3	Pt $4f_{7/2}$ 0.0	MgK_α	129
Cl_4K_2Pt	K_2PtCl_4	s	$4f_{7/2}$	2.4	Pt $4f_{7/2}$ 0.0	MgK_α	129
Cl_4K_2Pt	K_2PtCl_4	s	$4f_{7/2}$	73.4 (1)	$((C_2H_5)_3P)_2PtCl_4$ Cl2p 199.4	AlK_α	87
Cl_4K_2Pt	K_2PtCl_4		$4f_{5/2}$ $4f_{7/2}$	82.2 79.0	a 290.0	AlK_α	107
$Cl_6H_8N_2Pt$	$(NH_4)_2PtCl_6$	s	$4f_{5/2}$ $4f_{7/2}$	84.15 80.9	a 290.0	AlK_α	107
Cl_6K_2Pt	K_2PtCl_6	s	$4f_{7/2}$	75.0 (2)	c 83.8	AlK_α	41
Cl_6K_2Pt	K_2PtCl_6	s	$4f_{7/2}$	4.8	Pt $4f_{7/2}$ 0.0	MgK_α	129
Cl_6K_2Pt	K_2PtCl_6	s	$4f_{7/2}$	75.9 (1)	Cl2p 199.4	AlK_α	87
Cl_6K_2Pt	K_2PtCl_6	s	$4f_{5/2}$ $4f_{7/2}$	78.8 (3) 75.6 (3)	d 285	Mg, AlK_α	97
$K_2N_4O_8Pt$	$K_2Pt(NO_2)_4$	s	$4f_{7/2}$	2.8	Pt $4f_{7/2}$ 0.0	MgK_α	129
$K_2N_6O_{12}Pt$	$K_2Pt(NO_2)_6$	s	$4f_{7/2}$	4.5	Pt $4f_{7/2}$ 0.0	MgK_α	129
$O_2Pt \cdot H_2O$	$PtO_2 \cdot H_2O$	s	$4f_{7/2}$ $4f_{5/2}$	74.5 77.8	f 284.0	AlK_α	103
Pt	Pt	s	$4f_{7/2}$	70.8	c 83.8	AlK_α	41
Pt	Pt	s	$4f_{7/2}$	72.0 (2)	g	MgK_α	129
Pt	Pt	s	$4f_{7/2}$	71.1	c 84	MgK_α	20

TABLE 3 (continued)

	Compound	Phase	Orbital	E_B(eV)	Calibrant	Exciting Radiation	Reference
Pt	Pt, surface refluxed in conc. HNO_3	s	$4f_{7/2,5/2}$		f 284.0	AlK_α	103
	Pt			70.7, 74.0			
	$PtO_{adsorbed}$			71.8, 75.1			
	PtO			73.4, 76.6			
	PtO_2			74.2, 77.5			
	$O_{adsorbed}$		Ols	531.8			
Pt	Pt, electrode oxidized vs. SCE in 1*M* $HClO_4$ at +0.7, 1.2, and 2.2V, 3 min	s	$4f_{7/2,5/2}$		f 284.0	AlK_α	103
	Pt			70.7, 74.0			
	$PtO_{adsorbed}$			71.6, 74.9			
	PtO			73.3, 76.6			
	PtO_2			74.1, 77.4			
Pt	Pt	s	$4f_{5/2}$	80.1	a 290.0	AlK_α	107
			$4f_{7/2}$	76.8			
Pt	Pt(fcc)	s	4f	71 (0.5)		MgK_α	122
Pt	Pt	s	L_I	13,880.5 (6)		MoK_α	74
			L_{II}	13,272.6 (7)			
			L_{III}	11,563.8 (6)			
			M_I	3,297.6 (6)		CuK_α	
			M_{II}	3,027.0 (6)			
			M_{III}	2,645.3 (6)			
			M_{IV}	2,201.5 (4)		Cu, CrK_α	
			M_V	2,121.1 (4)			
			N_I	724.0 (1.0)		CuK_α	
			N_{II}	608.0 (6)		Cu, AlK_α	
			N_{III}	519.8 (6)		AlK_α	
			N_{IV}	331.5 (6)			
			N_V	314.6 (6)			
			N_{VI}	74.6 (6)			
			N_{VII}	71.3 (6)			
			O_{III}	52.0 (7)			
			$O_{IV,V}$	3.2 (7)			

TABLE 3 (continued)

Compound		Phase	Orbital	E_B(eV)	Calibrant	Exciting Radiation	Reference
Pt	Pt	s	L_{III}	11,563.8	CuK($MoK_{\alpha 1}$)	$MoK_{\alpha 1}$	119
			L_{II}	13,273.8			
Pt	Pt	s	L_{II}	13,272.7 (4)	e	MoK_α	77
			L_{III}	11,564.0 (4)			
			M_{II}	3,026.4 (5)		CuK_α	
			M_{III}	2,645.4 (5)			
			M_{IV}	2,201.9 (4)		CrK_α	
			M_V	2,121.6 (4)			
Pt	Pt	s	d band	−1.1 (2)	Pd Fermi level 0.0	MgK_α	51
				−4.0 (2)			
Pu							
O_2 Pu	PuO_2	s	M_{IV}	3,972.7	MgK($CuK_{\alpha 1}$)	$CuK_{\alpha 1}$	139
			M_V	3,778.0			
			N_{IV}	848.9	MgK($CrK_{\alpha 1}$)	$CrK_{\alpha 1}$	
			N_V	801.4			
Rb							
IRb	RbI	s	L_{II}	1,863.4 (7)	e	CrK_α	78
			L_{III}	1,804.6 (7)			
NO_3 Rb	$RbNO_3$	s	L_I	2,065.3 (7)	MgK	CuK_α	78
N_3 Rb	RbN_3	s	$3p_{1/2}$	246.60	b 285.0	Mg, AlK_α	66
			$3p_{3/2}$	237.66			
			3d	110.11			
			4s	28.9			
			4p	13.96			
Re							
AgO_4 Re	$AgReO_4$	s	$4d_{5/2}$	272.6 (3)	a 290.0	AlK_α	62
			$4f_{5/2}$	55.4 (3)			
			$4f_{7/2}$	53.4 (3)			

TABLE 3 (continued)

Compound		Phase	Orbital	E_B(eV)	Calibrant	Exciting Radiation	Reference
AgO_4Re	$AgReO_4$	s	$4f_{5/2}$ $4f_{7/2}$	(55.5) 53.4	a 290.0	AlK_α	107
$C_4H_{12}NReS_4$	$[N(CH_3)_4][ReS_4]$	s	$4d_{5/2}$ $4f_{5/2}$ $4f_{7/2}$	267.6 (3) 51 48.2 (3)	a 290.0	AlK_α	62
$C_4H_{12}NReS_4$	$[N(CH_3)_4].[ReS_4]$	s	$4f_{5/2}$ $4f_{7/2}$	(50.8) 48.2	a 290.0	AlK_α	107
$C_{12}H_{30}Cl_4P_2Re$	*trans*-$ReCl_4(P(C_2H_5)_3)_2$	s	$4f_{5/2}$ $4f_{7/2}$	45.9 (3) 43.5 (3)	d 285	Mg, AlK_α	97
$C_{16}H_{22}Cl_4P_2Re$	*trans*-$ReCl_4(P(CH_3)_2C_6H_5)_2$	s	$4f_{5/2}$ $4f_{7/2}$	46.5 (3) 43.8 (3)	d 285	Mg, AlK_α	97
$C_{24}H_{20}AsO_4Re$	$[As(C_6H_5)_4][ReO_4]$	s	$4f_{5/2}$ $4f_{7/2}$	53.0 50.6	a 290.0	AlK_α	107
$C_{24}H_{33}Cl_3P_3Re$	*mer*-$ReCl_3(P(CH_3)_2C_6H_5)_3$	s	$4f_{5/2}$ $4f_{7/2}$	44.4 (3) 42.0 (3)	d 285	Mg, AlK_α	97
$C_{32}H_{44}ClN_2P_4Re$	*trans*-$[ReCl(N_2)(P(CH_3)_2C_6H_5)_4]$	s	$4f_{5/2}$ $4f_{7/2}$	42.9 (0.3) 40.5 (0.3)	d 285	Mg, AlK_α	97
$C_{32}H_{44}Cl_2P_4Re$	*trans*-$ReCl_2(P(CH_3)_2C_6H_5)_4$	s	$4f_{5/2}$ $4f_{7/2}$	43.0 40.7	d 285	Mg, AlK_α	97
Cl_6K_2Re	K_2ReCl_6	s	$4f_{7/2}$	43.9 (2)	c 83.8	AlK_α	41
Cl_6K_2Re	K_2ReCl_6	s	$4f_{5/2}$ $4f_{7/2}$	46.9 (3) 44.5 (3)	d 285	Mg, AlK_α	97
Cl_6K_2Re	K_2ReCl_6	s	$4f_{5/2}$ $4f_{7/2}$	51.5 49.15	a 290.0	AlK_α	107

TABLE 3 (continued)

Compound		Phase	Orbital	E_B(eV)	Calibrant	Exciting Radiation	Reference
CsO_4Re	$CsReO_4$	s	$4d_{5/2}$ $4f_{5/2}$ $4f_{7/2}$	273.7 (3) 56.7 (3) 54.3 (3)	a 290.0	AlK_a	62
CsO_4Re	$CsReO_4$	s	$4f_{5/2}$ $4f_{7/2}$	56.5 54.3	a 290.0	AlK_a	107
KO_4Re	$KReO_4$	s	$4f_{5/2}$ $4f_{7/2}$	55.1 52.9	a 290.0	AlK_a	107
KO_4Re	$KReO_4$	s	$4d_{5/2}$ $4f_{5/2}$ $4f_{7/2}$	272.5 (3) 55.1 (3) 52.9 (3)	a 290.0	AlK_a	62
O_4ReTl	$TlReO_4$	s	$4d_{5/2}$ $4f_{5/2}$ $4f_{7/2}$	273.2 (3) 56.1 (3) 53.9 (3)	a 290.0	AlK_a	62
O_4ReTl	$TlReO_4$	s	$4f_{5/2}$ $4f_{7/2}$	56.1 53.9	a 290.0	AlK_a	107
Re	Re	s	L_{II} L_{III} M_{III} M_{IV} M_V	11,957.1 (4) 10,534.4 (4) 2,367.3 (4) 1,948.9 (4) 1,882.9 (4)	e	MoK_a CrK_a	77
Re	Re	s	$4f_{7/2}$	40.3	c 83.8	AlK_a	41
Rh							
$C_{24}H_{33}Cl_3P_3Rh$	*fac*-$RhCl_3(P(CH_3)_2C_6H_5)_3$	s	$3d_{3/2}$ $3d_{5/2}$	314.2 309.5	d 285	Mg, AlK_a	97
$C_{38}H_{30}ClF_4P_2Rh$	$((C_6H_5)_3P)_2Rh(C_2H_4)Cl$	s	$3d_{3/2}$ $3d_{5/2}$	313.9 (3) 309.3 (3)	d 285.0	AlK_a	82

TABLE 3 (continued)

Compound		Phase	Orbital	E_B(eV)	Calibrant	Exciting Radiation	Reference
$C_{38}H_{34}ClP_2Rh$	$((C_6H_5)_3P)_2Rh(C_2H_4)Cl$	s	$3d_{3/2}$ $3d_{5/2}$	313.5 (3) 308.9 (3)	d 285.0	AlK_α	82
$C_{43}H_{30}ClN_4OP_2Rh$	$((C_6H_5)_3P)_2RhCl(CO)(C_2(CN)_4)$	s	$3d_{3/2}$ $3d_{5/2}$	314.3 (3) 309.7 (3)	d 285.0	AlK_α	82
$C_{54}H_{45}ClP_3Rh$	$((C_6H_5)_3P)_3RhCl$	s	$3d_{3/2}$ $3d_{5/2}$	314.0 (3) 309.4 (3)	d 285.0	AlK_α	82
$Pd_{0.40}Rh_{0.60}$	$Rh_{0.60}Pd_{0.40}$	s	$2p_{3/2}$ $3d_{5/2}$	3,004.2 (5) 307.2 (1)	Au, Pt $4f_{7/2}$	CrK_α MgK_α	70
Rh	Rh	s	$2p_{3/2}$ $3d_{5/2}$	3,004.6 (5) 307.4 (1)	Pd $2p_{3/2}$	CrK_α MgK_α	70
Rh	Rh(fcc)	s	3d	307 (0.5)		MgK_α	122
Rh	Rh	s	L_I L_{II} L_{III}	3,412.0 (4) 3,146.3 (4) 3,003.8 (4)		CuK_α	79
Rh	Rh	s	d band	–2	Pd Fermi level 0.0	MgK_α	51
Rh	Rh	s	L_{III}	3,003.2	CuA6	$CuK_{\alpha1}$	123
Ru							
$B_3F_{12}H_{18}N_6Ru$	$[Ru(NH_3)_6][BF_4]_3$	s	$3d_{5/2}$	282.2 (5)	f 284.0		37
BaO_4Ru	$Ba[RuO_4]$	s	$3d_{5/2}$	284.4 (5)	$Ba[RuO_4]$ $Ru3d_{3/2}$		37
$C_6H_{20}I_2N_6Ru$	$[Ru(H_2NCH_2CH_2NH_2)_2(HNCHCHNH)]I_2$	s	$3d_{5/2}$	281.3 (5)	d 285.7		37
$C_6H_{24}Cl_4N_6RuZn$	$[Ru(H_2NCH_2CH_2NH_2)_3][ZnCl_4]$	s	$3d_{5/2}$	280.4 (5)	d 285.7		37
$C_{24}H_{33}Cl_3P_3Ru$	*mer*-$RuCl_3(P(CH_3)_2C_6H_5)_3$	s	$3d_{3/2}$ $3d_{5/2}$	281.1 276.8	d 285	Mg, AlK_α	97

TABLE 3 (continued)

Compound		Phase	Orbital	E_B(eV)	Calibrant	Exciting Radiation	Reference
$H_{18}I_2N_6Ru$	$[Ru(NH_3)_6]I_2$	s	$3d_{5/2}$	279.8 (5)	f 284.0		37
Ru	Ru	s	d band	−1.8 (2)	Pd Fermi level 0.0	MgK_a	51
Ru	Ru metal	s	$3d_{5/2}$	279 (0.5)			37
Ru	Ru(hcp)	s	3d	280 (0.5)		MgK_a	122
Ru	Ru	s	L_I	3,224.3 (4)		CuK_a	79
			L_{II}	2,966.8 (4)			
			L_{III}	2,837.8 (5)			
S							
$Al_2O_{12}S_3$	$Al_2(SO_4)_3$	s	2p	169.0	b 285.0	AlK_a	49
Ag_2S	Ag_2S	s	2p	166.9 (3)	a 290.0	AlK_a	62
BeH_8O_8S	$Be(H_2O)_4SO_4$	s	2p	175.2 (3)	a 290.0	AlK_a	62
CCuNS	CuSCN	s	2p	165.9	a 285.5	AlK_a	46
CH_3ClO_2S	CH_3SO_2Cl	s	2p	169.5	b 285.0	AlK_a	49
CH_4S	CH_3SH	s	2p	162.7			4
COS	COS	g	2s	235.0 (2)		MgK_a	38
			Shake-up	−9.4 (2)	COS S2s 0.0		
				−14.8 (5)			
			$2p_{3/2}$	170.6 (1)			
			$2p_{1/2}$	171.8 (1)			
			Shake-up	−9.6 (2)	COS S2p 0.0		
				−15.3 (2)			
CS_2	CS_2	g	2s	234.2 (2)		MgK_a	38
			Shake-up	−7.3 (2)	CS_2 S2s 0.0		
				−13.1 (3)			
				−15.0 (3)			

TABLE 3 (continued)

Compound		Phase	Orbital	E_B(eV)	Calibrant	Exciting Radiation	Reference
CS_2 (cont.)			$2p_{3/2}$ $2p_{1/2}$ Shake-up	169.8 (1) 171.0 (1) −7.3 (2) −13.6 (3) −16.4 (3)	CS_2 S2p 0.0		
CS_2	CS_2	s	2p	163.9	b 285.0	AlK_α	49
CS_2	CS_2	g	$2p_{3/2}$	169.8	CS_2 S $2p_{3/2}$ 169.8	MgK_α	151
C_2H_3AgOS	$CH_3C(O)SAg$	s	2p	161.8 (3)	b 285.0	Mg, AlK_α	100
$C_2H_3F_3O_2S_2$	$CF_3\overset{ab}{S}S(O)_2CH_3$	s	${}^a2p$ ${}^b2p$	165.1 169.2	b 285.0	AlK_α	49
C_2H_3NaOS	$CH_3C(S)O^- Na^+$	s	2p	162.5 (4)	b 285.0	Mg, AlK_α	100
C_2H_6OS	$OS(CH_3)_2$	s	2p	166.7	b 285.0	AlK_α	49
C_2H_6OS	CH_3SOCH_3	s	2p	165.5 (2)			4
$C_2H_6O_2S$	$SO_2(CH_3)_2$	s	2p	169.2	b 285.0	AlK_α	49
$C_2H_6O_2S_2$	$H_3COSSOCH_3$	s	2p	164.7	b 285.0	AlK_α	49
$C_2H_6O_3S$	$CH_3OS(O)OCH_3$	s	2p	168.6	b 285.0	AlK_α	49
$C_2H_6S_2$	CH_3SSCH_3	s	2p	162.7			4
$C_2H_8CuN_2O_3S{\cdot}H_2O$	$CuSO_3{\cdot}H_2NCH_2CH_2NH_2{\cdot}H_2O$	s	2p	170.3	a 285.5	AlK_α	46
C_3H_3NS		s	2s $2p_{1/2}$ $2p_{3/2}$	229.7 (3) 166.3 (3) 165.3 (3)	c 84	MgK_α	25
$C_3H_4S_3$	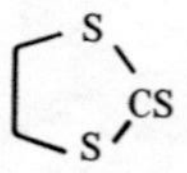	s	2p	163.4	b 285.0	AlK_α	49

TABLE 3 (continued)

Compound		Phase	Orbital	E_B(eV)	Calibrant	Exciting Radiation	Reference
$C_3H_5KOS_2$	$CH_3CH_2OCS_2K$	s	2p	162.2	b 285.0	AlK_α	49
$C_3H_6NNaS_2$	$(CH_3)_2NCS_2Na$	s	2p	161.8	b 285.0	AlK_α	49
$C_3H_6OS_3$	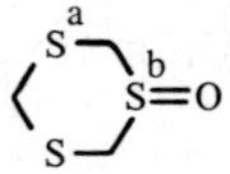	s	[a]2s [b]2s [a]2p [b]2p	228.0 (1) 230.0 (1) 163.8 (1) 165.8 (1)		MgK_α	84
$C_3H_6O_2O_3$	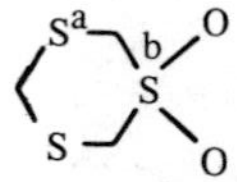	s	[a]2s [b]2s [a]2p [b]2p	228.2 (1) 232.3 (1) 164.2 (1) 168.4 (1)		MgK_α	84
$C_3H_6O_3S_3$	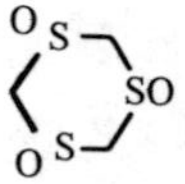	s	2s 2p	230.9 (1) 166.5 (1)		MgK_α	84
$C_3H_6O_4S$	$O_2S(OCH_2)_2CH_2$	s	2p	169.7	b 285.0	AlK_α	49
$C_3H_6O_6S_3$	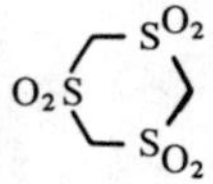	s	2s 2p	233.5 169.5		MgK_α	84
$C_3H_6S_3$	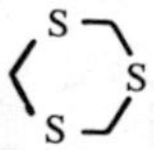	s	2s 2p	227.5 (1) 163.5 (1)		MgK_α	84
$C_3H_8NO_2S$	$HSCH_2CHNH_2COOH$	s	2p	163.6	b 285.0	AlK_α	49
$C_3H_9ClNO_2S$	$[HSCH_2CHNH_3COOH]Cl$	s	2p	163.8	b 285.0	AlK_α	49
C_3H_9IOS	$[(CH_3)_3S(O)]I$	s	2p	168.4	b 285.0	AlK_α	49
C_3H_9IS	$[(CH_3)_3S]I$	s	2p	166.0	b 285.0	AlK_α	49

TABLE 3 (continued)

Compound		Phase	Orbital	E_B(eV)	Calibrant	Exciting Radiation	Reference
C_4H_4S		s	2p	164.5	b 285.0	AlK_a	49
C_4H_4S		s	2s $2p_{1/2}$ $2p_{3/2}$	228.6 (3) 165.3 (3) 164.3 (3)	c 84	MgK_a	25
C_4H_4S			$2p_{3/2}$ $2p_{1/2}$	169.9 (2) 171.2 (2)	d	MgK_a	69
$C_4H_5NaO_3S$	$[OS(CH_2)_2CHCOO]Na$	s	2p	166.4	b 285.0	AlK_a	49
$C_4H_6O_2S_2$	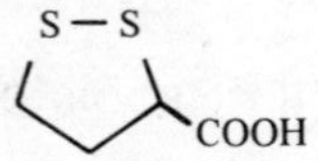	s	2p	164.0	b 285.0	AlK_a	49
$C_4H_6O_4S$	$S(CH_2COOH)_2$	s	2p	163.9	b 285.0	AlK_a	49
$C_4H_7NO_2S$	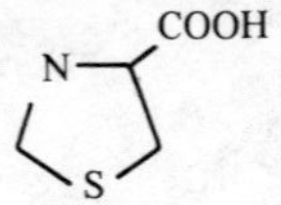	s	2p	164.1	b 285.0	AlK_a	49
C_4H_8S		s	2s 2p	1,019 (E_{kin}) 1,082.5		MgK_a	132
$C_4H_8S_2$	$S(CH_2CH_2)_2S$	s	2p	163.4	b 285.0	AlK_a	49
$C_4H_9NO_2S$	$CH_3SCH_2CH(NH_2)COOH$	s	2p	163.7	b 285.0	AlK_a	49
$C_4H_{10}NaO_3PS$	$(C_2H_5O)_2PSO^-\ Na^+$	s	2p	163.2 (1)	b 285.0	Mg, AlK_a	100
$C_4H_{12}N_4ReS_4$	$[N(CH_3)_4][ReS_4]$	s	2p	167.5 (3)	a 290.0	AlK_a	62
$C_4H_{16}CuN_4O_4S \cdot H_2O$	$CuSO_4 \cdot 2(H_2NCH_2CH_2NH_2) \cdot H_2O$	s	2p	169.4	a 285.5	AlK_a	46
$C_4N_2Na_2S_2$	$Na_2S_2C_2(CN)_2$	s	$2p_{1/2,3/2}$	161.4 (1)	c 83.0		125

TABLE 3 (continued)

Compound		Phase	Orbital	E_B(eV)	Calibrant	Exciting Radiation	Reference
$C_5H_4S_3$	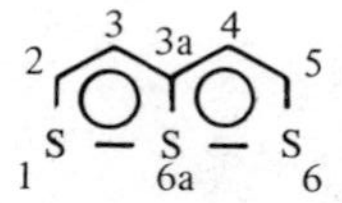	s	(6a) $2p_{3/2}$ (6a) 2s (1,6) 2s (1,6) $2p_{3/2}$	164.1 228.5 227.0 162.6		MgK_a	21
C_5H_8OS	$S(CH_2CH_2)_2CO$	s	2p	164.0	b 285.0	AlK_a	49
$C_5H_8O_2S$	$OS(CH_2CH_2)_2CO$	s	2p	166.5	b 285.0	AlK_a	49
$C_5H_8O_6S_2$	$C[(CH_2O)_2SO]_2$	s	2p	168.2	b 285.0	AlK_a	49
$C_5H_{10}NNaS_2$	$(CH_3CH_2)_2NCS_2Na$	s	2p	161.7	b 285.0	AlK_a	49
$C_5H_{10}O_2S_2$	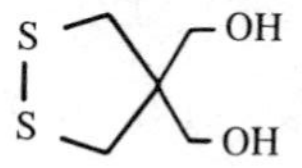	s	2p	163.9	b 285.0	AlK_a	49
$C_5H_{10}O_3S_2$	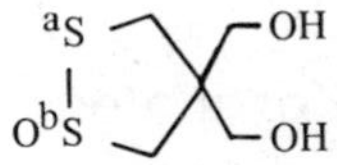	s	a2p b2p	163.9 166.3	b 285.0	AlK_a	49
$C_5H_{10}O_4S_2$	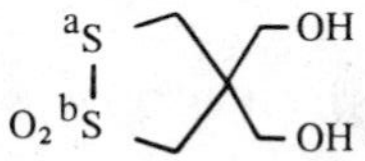	s	a2p b2p	164.1 168.6	b 285.0	AlK_a	49
$C_5H_{12}NaO_4S_2$	$NaO\overset{a}{S}(O)O(CH_2)_3OS^+(CH_3)_2$	s	a2p	168.8	b 285.0	AlK_a	49
$C_5H_{12}NaO_4S_2$	$NaO\overset{a}{S}(O)O(CH_2)_3S^+(O)(CH_3)_2$	s	a2p	168.4	b 285.0	AlK_a	49
$C_6H_4ClNO_2S$	*o*-$NO_2C_6H_4SCl$	s	2p	164.1	b 285.0	AlK_a	49
$C_6H_4ClNO_4S$	*o*-$NO_2C_6H_4SO_2Cl$	s	2p	168.7	b 285.0	AlK_a	49
$C_6H_4ClNO_4S$	*m*-$NO_2C_6H_4SO_2Cl$	s	2p	168.5	b 285.0	AlK_a	49
$C_6H_4ClNO_4S$	*p*-$NO_2C_6H_4SO_2Cl$	s	2p	168.5	b 285.0	AlK_a	49
$C_6H_4ClNaO_2S$	*p*-$ClC_6H_4SO_2Na$	s	2p	166.5	b 285.0	AlK_a	49

TABLE 3 (continued)

Compound		Phase	Orbital	E_B(eV)	Calibrant	Exciting Radiation	Reference
$C_6H_4ClNaO_3S_2$	p-$ClC_6H_4\overset{a}{S}\overset{b}{S}O_3Na$	s	^{a}2p ^{b}2p	164.0 169.0	b 285.0	AlK_a	49
$C_6H_4FNO_4S$	p-$NO_2C_6H_4SO_2F$	s	2p	164.2	b 285.0	AlK_a	49
$C_6H_4FNO_4S$	o-$NO_2C_6H_4SO_2F$	s	2p	169.8	b 285.0	AlK_a	49
$C_6H_4FNO_4S$	p-$NO_2C_6H_4SO_2F$	s	2p	170.2	b 285.0	AlK_a	49
$C_6H_4KNO_2S$	[m-$NO_2C_6H_4S$]K	s	2p	161.3	b 285.0	AlK_a	49
$C_6H_4NNaO_2S$	[p-$NO_2C_6H_4S$]Na	s	2p	161.2	b 285.0	AlK_a	49
$C_6H_4NNaO_4$	o-$NO_2C_6H_4SO_2Na$	s	2p	166.0	b 285.0	AlK_a	49
$C_6H_4NNaO_4$	m-$NO_2C_6H_4SO_2Na$	s	2p	165.9	b 285.0	AlK_a	49
$C_6H_4NNaO_4$	p-$NO_2C_6H_4SO_2Na$	s	2p	166.0	b 285.0	AlK_a	49
$C_6H_4NNaO_5S$	p-$NO_2C_6H_4SO_3Na$	s	2p	168.2	b 285.0	AlK_a	49
$C_6H_4NNaO_5S$	m-$NO_2C_6H_4SO_3Na$	s	2p	168.3	b 285.0	AlK_a	49
$C_6H_4NNaO_5S$	o-$NO_2C_6H_4SO_3Na$	s	2p	168.3	b 285.0	AlK_a	49
$C_6H_5NO_2S$	o-$NO_2C_6H_4SH$	s	2p	164.1	b 285.0	AlK_a	49
$C_6H_5NO_2S$	p-$NO_2C_6H_4SH$	s	2p	163.7	b 285.0	AlK_a	49
$C_6H_5NaO_2S$	$C_6H_5SO_2Na$	s	2p	166.5	b 285.0	AlK_a	49
$C_6H_6Cl_3NO_4S_2$	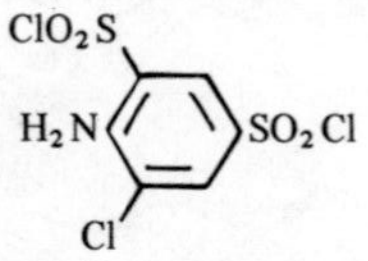	s	2p	168.4	b 285.0	AlK_a	49
$C_6H_6NNaO_3S$	p-$NH_2C_6H_4SO_3Na$	s	2p	168.3	b 285.0	AlK_a	49

TABLE 3 (continued)

Compound		Phase	Orbital	E_B(eV)	Calibrant	Exciting Radiation	Reference
$C_6H_6N_2O_2S$	*o*-$NO_2C_6H_4SNH_2$	s	2p	164.3	b 285.0	AlK_a	49
$C_6H_6N_2O_4S$	*m*-$NO_2C_6H_4SO_2NH_2$	s	2p	168.4	b 285.0	AlK_a	49
C_6H_6S	C_6H_5SH	s	2p	163.3	b 285.0	AlK_a	49
$C_6H_6S_3$	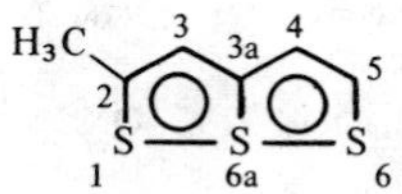	s	(6a) 2s (6a) $2p_{3/2}$ (1) 2s (1) $2p_{3/2}$ (6) 2s (6) $2p_{3/2}$	228.5 163.7 227.6 163.0 226.4 161.7		MgK_a	21
$C_6H_8N_2O_2S$	*p*-$NH_2C_6H_4SO_2NH_2$	s	2p	168.6	b 285.0	AlK_a	49
$C_6H_8O_6S$	$(HOOCCH_2)_2SCH_2COO$	s	2p	166.4	b 285.0	AlK_a	49
$C_6H_{12}N_2O_4S_2$	$(HO_2CCH(NH_2)CH_2S)_2$	s	2p	164.2	b 285.0	AlK_a	49
$C_6H_{12}N_2O_5S_2$	$HO_2C(NH_2)CHCH_2\overset{ab}{SS}(O)CH_2CH(NH_2)CO_2H$	s	^{a}2p ^{b}2p	164.1 166.5	b 285.0	AlK_a	49
$C_6H_{12}N_2O_6S_2$	$HO_2C(NH_2)CHCH_2\overset{ab}{SS}(O)_2CH_2CH(NH_2)CO_2H$	s	^{a}2p ^{b}2p	164.2 168.8	b 285.0	AlK_a	49
$C_6H_{12}N_2S_4$	$(CH_3)_2NC(S)SSC(S)N(CH_3)_2$	s	2p	163.8 161.8	b 285.0	AlK_a	49
$C_6K_3N_6RhS_6$	$K_3[Rh(SCN)_6]$	s	2p	168.3 (3)	a 290.0	AlK_a	62
$C_7H_3Cl_5O_2S$	$C_6Cl_5SCH_2COOH$	s	2p	163.5	b 285.0	AlK_a	49
$C_7H_4Na_2O_4S$	*p*-$NaCOOC_6H_4SO_2Na$	s	2p	166.3	b 285.0	AlK_a	49
$C_7H_4Na_2O_4S$	*m*-$NaCOOC_6H_4SO_2Na$	s	2p	166.2	b 285.0	AlK_a	49
$C_7H_4Na_2O_5S$	*m*-$NaOOCC_6H_4SO_3Na$	s	2p	168.4	b 285.0	AlK_a	49

TABLE 3 (continued)

Compound		Phase	Orbital	E_B(eV)	Calibrant	Exciting Radiation	Reference
$C_7H_4Na_2O_5S$	*p*-$NaOOCC_6H_4SO_3Na$	s	2p	168.4	b 285.0	AlK_a	49
$C_7H_6Cl_2O_2S$	$ClC_6H_4CH_2SO_2Cl$	s	2p	168.7	b 285.0	AlK_a	49
C_7H_7ClOS	*p*-$ClC_6H_4SOCH_3$	s	2p	164.6	b 285.0	AlK_a	49
$C_7H_7ClO_2S$	*p*-$CH_3C_6H_4SO_2Cl$	s	2p	168.6	b 285.0	AlK_a	49
$C_7H_7NO_2S$	*o*-$NO_2C_6H_4SCH_3$	s	2p	163.9	b 285.0	AlK_a	49
$C_7H_7NO_2S$	*p*-$NO_2C_6H_4SCH_3$	s	2p	163.7	b 285.0	AlK_a	49
$C_7H_7NO_3S$	*m*-$NO_2C_6H_4S(O)CH_3$	s	2p	166.0	b 285.0	AlK_a	49
$C_7H_7NO_3S$	*p*-$NO_2C_6H_4S(O)CH_3$	s	2p	165.9	b 285.0	AlK_a	49
$C_7H_7NO_3S$	*o*-$NO_2C_6H_4S(O)CH_3$	s	2p	166.0	b 285.0	AlK_a	49
$C_7H_7NO_3S$	*o*-$NO_2C_6H_4SOCH_3$	s	2p	165.2	b 285.0	AlK_a	49
$C_7H_7NO_4S$	*m*-$NO_2C_6H_4SO_2CH_3$	s	2p	168.0	b 285.0	AlK_a	49
$C_7H_7NO_4S$	*o*-$NO_2C_6H_4SO_2CH_3$	s	2p	168.1	b 285.0	AlK_a	49
$C_7H_7NO_4S$	*m*-$NO_2C_6H_4SOOCH_3$	s	2p	167.2	b 285.0	AlK_a	49
$C_7H_7NO_4S$	*p*-$NO_2C_6H_4SO_2CH_3$	s	2p	168.2	b 285.0	AlK_a	49
$C_7H_7NO_4S$	*p*-$NO_2C_6H_4SOOCH_3$	s	2p	167.5	b 285.0	AlK_a	49
$C_7H_7NO_4S$	*o*-$NO_2C_6H_4SOOCH_3$	s	2p	167.4	b 285.0	AlK_a	49
$C_7H_7NO_5S$	*m*-$NO_2C_6H_4SO_2OCH_3$	s	2p	168.4	b 285.0	AlK_a	49
$C_7H_7NO_5S$	*o*-$NO_2C_6H_4SO_2OCH_3$	s	2p	168.5	b 285.0	AlK_a	49
$C_7H_7NO_5S$	*p*-$NO_2C_6H_4SO_2OCH_3$	s	2p	168.4	b 285.0	AlK_a	49

TABLE 3 (continued)

Compound		Phase	Orbital	E_B(eV)	Calibrant	Exciting Radiation	Reference
C_7H_8OS	$C_6H_5SOCH_3$	s	2p	164.6	b 285.0	AlK_a	49
$C_7H_8O_3S$	$C_6H_5SO_3CH_3$	s	2p	168.7	b 285.0	AlK_a	49
$C_7H_8S_3$	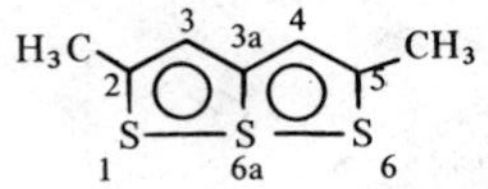	s	(6a) 2s (6a) $2p_{3/2}$ (1,6) 2s (1,6) $2p_{3/2}$	228.7 164.2 227.1 162.7		MgK_a	21
$C_7H_8S_3$	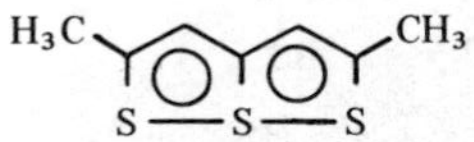	s	2p	162.3 163.2 164.1			143
$C_7H_{11}NO_3S_2$	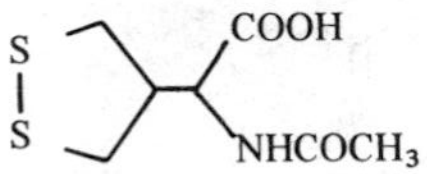	s	2p	164.1	b 285.0	AlK_a	49
$C_8H_{10}NNaO_3S$	p-$N(CH_3)_2C_6H_4SO_3Na$	s	2p	168.3	b 285.0	AlK_a	49
$C_8H_{16}N_2O_2S$	$S(N(CH_2CH_2)_2O)_2$	s	2p	164.1	b 285.0	AlK_a	49
$C_9H_7ClN_2S_2$	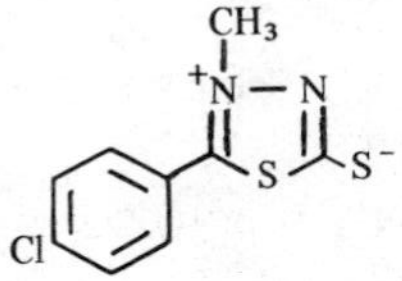	s	2p	160.7 163.2	a 284.0	AlK_a	98
$C_9H_8N_2S_2$	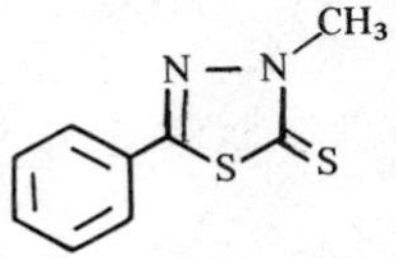	s	2p	161.6 163.7	a 284.0	AlK_a	98
$C_9H_8N_2S_2$	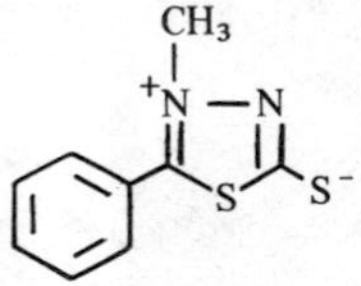	s	2p	161.1 163.7	a 284.0	AlK_a	98

TABLE 3 (continued)

Compound		Phase	Orbital	E_B(eV)	Calibrant	Exciting Radiation	Reference
$C_9H_{10}ClNaO_3S_2$	p-$NaO\overset{a}{S}(O)O(CH_2)_3\overset{b}{S}C_6H_4Cl$	s	^a2p ^b2p	168.1 163.4	b 285.0	AlK_α	49
$C_9H_{10}NNaO_5S_2$	o-$NaO\overset{a}{S}(O)O(CH_2)_3\overset{b}{S}C_6H_4NO_2$	s	^a2p ^b2p	168.2 163.8	b 285.0	AlK_α	49
$C_9H_{10}NNaO_5S_2$	p-$NaOS(O)O(CH_2)_3\overset{a}{S}C_6H_4NO_2$	s	^a2p	163.6	b 285.0	AlK_α	49
$C_9H_{11}NaO_3S_2$	$Na\overset{a}{O}S(O)O(CH_2)_3\overset{b}{S}C_6H_5$	s	^a2p ^b2p	168.2 163.8	b 285.0	AlK_α	49
$C_9H_{12}NNaO_3S_2$	o-$NaO\overset{a}{S}(O)O(CH_2)_3\overset{b}{S}C_6H_4NH_2$	s	^a2p ^b2p	168.3 163.4	b 285.0	AlK_α	49
$C_{10}H_8CuN_2O_4S\cdot 2H_2O$	$CuSO_4\cdot$ 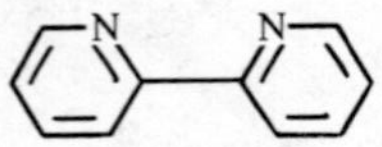 $\cdot 2H_2O$	s	2p	169.1	a 285.5	AlK_α	46
$C_{10}H_{10}ClIN_2S_2$	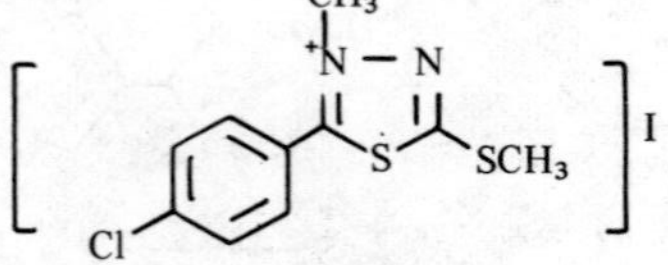	s	2p	163.5	a 284.0	AlK_α	98
$C_{10}H_{11}IN_2S_2$	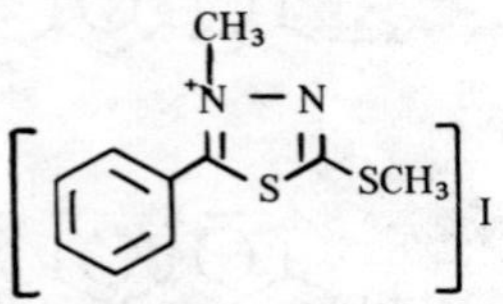	s	2p	164.5	a 284.0	AlK_α	98
$C_{10}H_{12}S_3$	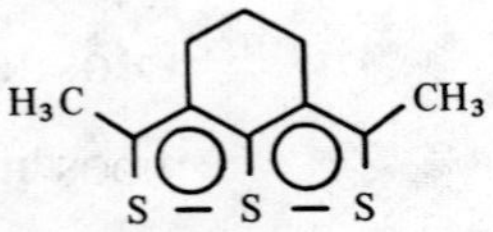	s	2p	162.3 163.2 164.3			143
$C_{10}H_{14}BrFeN_2S_4$	$FeBr(S_2CN(CH_2CH_3)C_2H_2)_2$	s	2p	161.4 (2)			3
$C_{10}H_{20}N_2NiS_4$	$Ni(S_2CN(C_2H_5)_2)_2$	s	2p	166.8 (3)	a 290.0	AlK_α	62

TABLE 3 (continued)

Compound		Phase	Orbital	E_B(eV)	Calibrant	Exciting Radiation	Reference
$C_{10}H_{20}O_5P_2S$	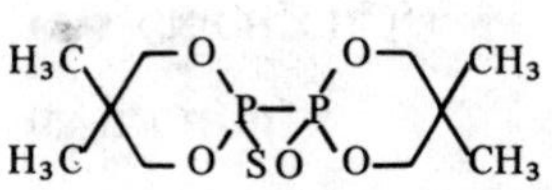	s	2p	162.7 (1)	b 285.0	Mg, AlK_α	100
$C_{10}H_{20}O_5P_2S_2$	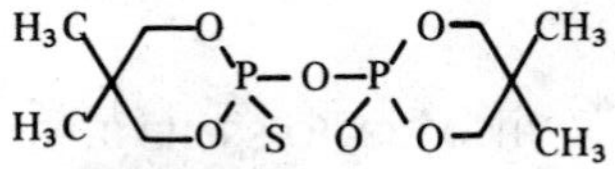	s	2s 2p	227.1 162.6 (2)	b 285.0	Mg, AlK_α	100
$C_{10}H_{20}O_5P_2S_2$	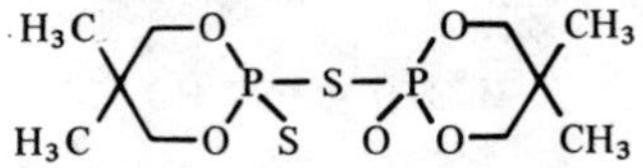	s	2s 2p	227.3 163.6 162.3 (3)	b 285.0	Mg, AlK_α	100
$C_{10}H_{20}O_6P_2S$	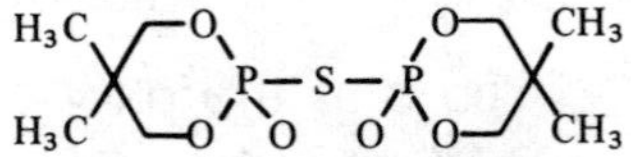	s	2s 2p	228.0 163.8 (2)	b 285.0	Mg, AlK_α	100
$C_{10}H_{20}O_6P_2S$	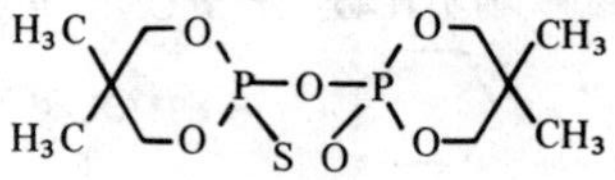	s	2s 2p	227.2 162.7 (2)	b 285.0	Mg, AlK_α	100
$C_{11}H_{24}NO_3PS$	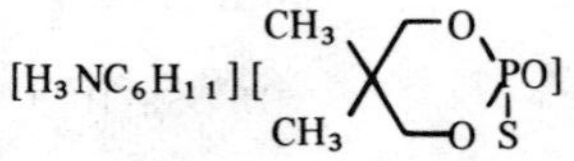	s	2p	162.0 (2)	b 285.0	Mg, AlK_α	100
$C_{12}H_8N_2O_4S$	*o,o'*-$NO_2C_6H_4SC_6H_4NO_2$	s	2p	164.2	b 285.0	AlK_α	49
$C_{12}H_8N_2O_4S$	*p,p'*-$NO_2C_6H_4SC_6H_4NO_2$	s	2p	163.7	b 285.0	AlK_α	49
$C_{12}H_8N_2O_4S_2$	*m,m'*-$NO_2C_6H_4SSC_6H_4NO_2$	s	2p	163.8	b 285.0	AlK_α	49
$C_{12}H_8N_2O_4S_2$	*o,o'*-$NO_2C_6H_4SSC_6H_4NO_2$	s	2p	164.1	b 285.0	AlK_α	49
$C_{12}H_8N_2O_4S_2$	*p,p'*-$NO_2C_6H_4SSC_6H_4NO_2$	s	2p	163.7	b 285.0	AlK_α	49
$C_{12}H_8N_2O_5S$	*p,p'*-$NO_2C_6H_4S(O)C_6H_4NO_2$	s	2p	166.1	b 285.0	AlK_α	49
$C_{12}H_8N_2O_5S$	*o,o'*-$NO_2C_6H_4S(O)C_6H_4NO_2$	s	2p	166.2	b 285.0	AlK_α	49
$C_{12}H_8N_2O_6S$	*p,p'*-$NO_2C_6H_4SO_2C_6H_4NO_2$	s	2p	167.9	b 285.0	AlK_α	49

TABLE 3 (continued)

Compound		Phase	Orbital	E_B(eV)	Calibrant	Exciting Radiation	Reference
$C_{12}H_8N_2O_6S_2$	p,p'-$NO_2C_6H_4\overset{ab}{S}SO_2C_6H_4NO_2$	s	^a2p ^b2p	164.0 168.0	b 285.0	AlK_α	49
$C_{12}H_9NO_4S$	p-$NO_2C_6H_4SO_2C_6H_5$	s	2p	167.8	b 285.0	AlK_α	49
$C_{12}H_{10}OS$	$OS(C_6H_5)_2$	s	2p	166.2	b 285.0	AlK_α	49
$C_{12}H_{10}O_5S_2$	$O(S(O)_2C_6H_5)_2$	s	2p	169.1	b 285.0	AlK_α	49
$C_{12}H_{10}S$	$S(C_6H_5)_2$	s	2p	163.4	b 285.0	AlK_α	49
$C_{12}H_{10}S_2$	$C_6H_5SSC_6H_5$	s	2p	164.2	b 285.0	AlK_α	49
$C_{12}H_{12}N_2O_2S$	$SO_2(p$-$C_6H_4NH_2)_2$	s	2p	168.1	b 285.0	AlK_α	49
$C_{12}H_{16}ClNO_2S$	p-$ClC_6H_4CH_2SO_4N$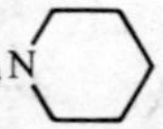	s	2p	168.3	b 285.0	AlK_α	49
$C_{13}H_{11}NO_2S$	p,p'-$NO_2C_6H_4SC_6H_4CH_3$	s	2p	163.6	b 285.0	AlK_α	49
$C_{13}H_{11}NO_2S$	o,p'-$NO_2C_6H_4SC_6H_4CH_3$	s	2p	164.0	b 285.0	AlK_α	49
$C_{14}H_{14}OS$	$OS(CH_2C_6H_5)_2$	s	2p	166.1	b 285.0	AlK_α	49
$C_{14}H_{14}OS_2$	$C_6H_5CH_2\overset{ab}{S}S(O)CH_2C_6H_5$	s	^a2p ^b2p	163.9 166.1	b 285.0	AlK_α	49
$C_{14}H_{14}O_2S_2$	$C_6H_5CH_2\overset{ab}{S}S(O)_2CH_2C_6H_5$	s	^a2p ^b2p	164.1 168.2	b 285.0	AlK_α	49
$C_{14}H_{14}S$	$S(CH_2C_6H_5)_2$	s	2p	163.5	b 285.0	AlK_α	49
$C_{14}H_{14}S_2$	$(C_6H_5CH_2S)_2$	s	2p	163.8	b 285.0	AlK_α	49
$C_{15}H_{30}FeN_3S_6$	$Fe(S_2CN(CH_2CH_3)_2)_3$	s	2p	161.5 (2)			3
$C_{15}H_{30}InN_3S_6$	$In(S_2CN(C_2H_5)_2)_3$	s	2p	168.1 (3)	a 290.0	AlK_α	62

TABLE 3 (continued)

Compound		Phase	Orbital	E_B(eV)	Calibrant	Exciting Radiation	Reference
$C_{16}H_8N_2O_4S$	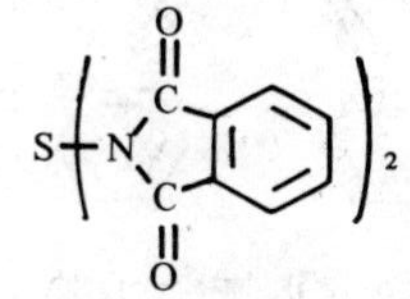	s	2p	165.3	b 285.0	AlK_a	49
$C_{16}H_{12}OS$	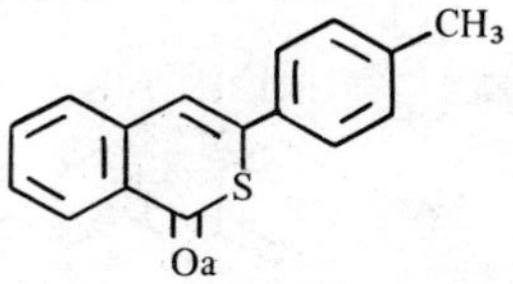	s	2p	163.5	b 284	Al	147
$C_{16}H_{12}OS$	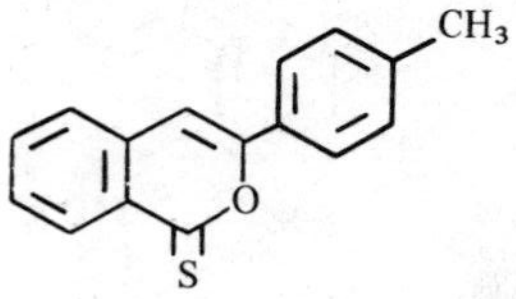	s	2p	161.8	b 284	Al	147
$C_{16}H_{12}S_2$	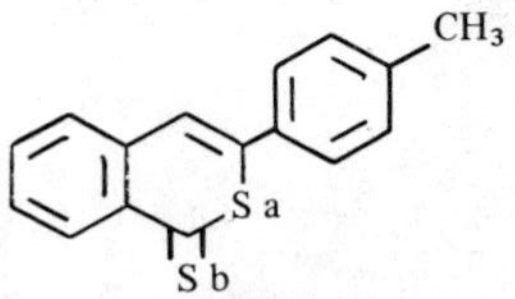	s	^a2p ^b2p	163.2 161.3	b 284	Al	147
$C_{16}H_{20}N_2S_2$	*p,p'*-$C_6H_4N(CH_3)_2SSC_6H_4N(CH_3)_2$	s	2p	163.5	b 285.0	AlK_a	49
$C_{16}H_{20}N_5NiS_4$	$[(C_2H_5)_4N][Ni(S_2C_2(CN)_2)_2]$	s	$2p_{1/2,3/2}$	161.3 (2)	c 83.0		125
$C_{16}H_{32}NO_3PS$	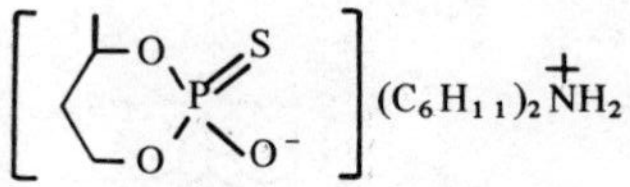	s	2p	161.7 (3)	d 285.0	AlK_a	104
$C_{16}H_{32}NO_3PS$	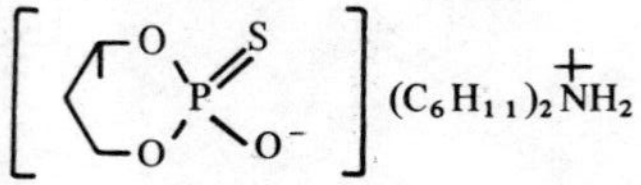	s	2p	161.6 (3)	d 285.0	AlK_a	104

TABLE 3 (continued)

Compound		Phase	Orbital	E_B(eV)	Calibrant	Exciting Radiation	Reference
$C_{17}H_{12}S_3$	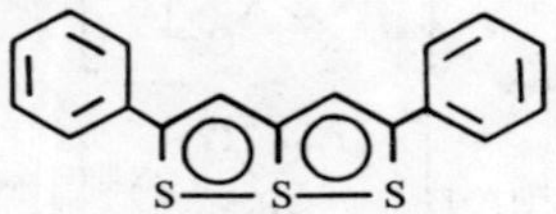	s	2p	162.4 163.6 164.8			143
$C_{17}H_{12}S_3$	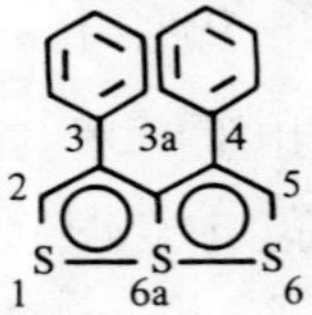	s	(6a) 2s (6a) $2p_{3/2}$ (1) 2s (1) $2p_{3/2}$ (6) 2s (6) $2p_{3/2}$	228.3 163.8 227.8 163.3 226.5 161.9		MgK_α	21
$C_{18}H_{15}O_3PS$	$(C_6H_5O)_3PS$	s	2p	163.0 (1)	d 285.0	AlK_α	104
$C_{18}H_{15}PS$	$(C_6H_5)_3PS$	s	2p	162.7 (5)	d 285.0	AlK_α	104
$C_{18}H_{15}PS_3$	$(C_6H_5S)_3P$	s	2p	163.8 (3)	d 285.0	AlK_α	104
$C_{18}H_{15}PS_4$	$(C_6H_5\overset{a}{S})_3PS$	s	[a]2p	163.7 (2)	d 285.0	AlK_α	104
$C_{22}H_{17}NS$	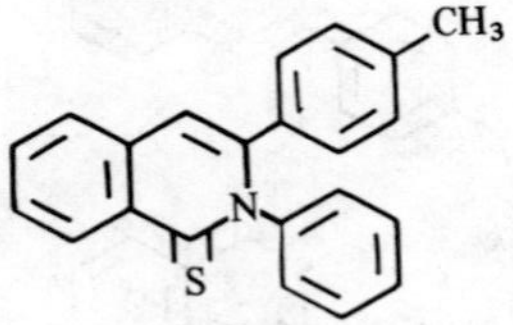	s	2p	161.2	b 284	Al	147
$C_{24}H_{40}N_6NiS_4$	$[(C_2H_5)_4N]_2[Ni(S_2C_2(CN)_2)_2]$	s	$2p_{1/2,3/2}$	161.4 (1)	c 83.0		125
$C_{25}H_{20}AsNS$	$[(C_6H_5)_4As]NCS$	s	2p	161.8	c 84	MgK_α	145
$C_{26}H_{22}N_2O_5S_2$	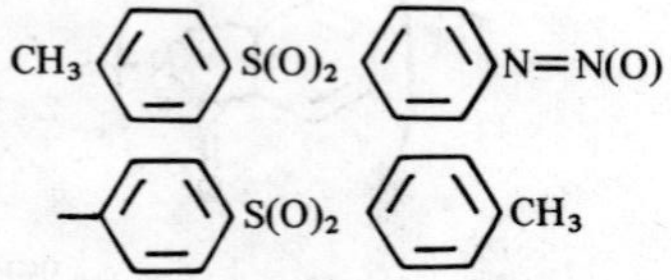	s	2p	168.3	b 285.0	AlK_α	49
$C_{26}H_{44}O_6P_2PtS_2$	*cis*-$((C_2H_5)_3P)_2Pt(CH_3C_6H_4SO_3)_2$	s	2p	168.3 (1)	d 285.0	AlK_α	87

TABLE 3 (continued)

Compound		Phase	Orbital	E_B(eV)	Calibrant	Exciting Radiation	Reference
$C_{28}H_{22}NS$	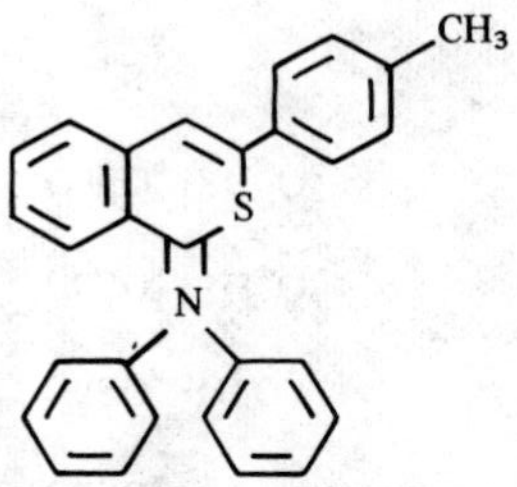	s	2p	163.9	b 284	Al	147
$C_{28}H_{20}NiS_4$	$Ni(S_2C_2(C_6H_5)_2)_2$	s	$2p_{1/2,3/2}$	161.1 (1)	c 83.0		125
$C_{28}H_{30}N_4NiS_4$	$[N_2H_5]_2[Ni(S_2C_2(C_6H_5)_2)_2]$	s	$2p_{1/2,3/2}$	160.5 (1)	c 83.0		125
$C_{30}H_{24}CuN_6O_4S\cdot 7H_2O$	$CuSO_4\cdot 3$ 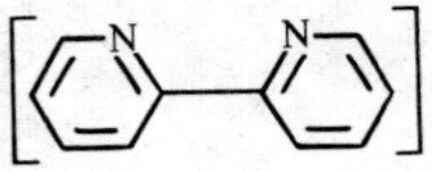 $\cdot H_2O$	s	2p	169.9	a 285.5	AlK_α	46
$C_{36}H_{40}NNiS_4$	$[(C_2H_5)_4N][Ni(S_2C_2(C_6H_5)_2)_2]$	s	$2p_{1/2,3/2}$	160.8 (1)	c 83.0		125
CdS	CdS	s	$2p_{3/2}$ $2p_{1/2}$ 2s	161.60 162.74 225.84	k 283.8	AlK_α	109
ClN_3S_4	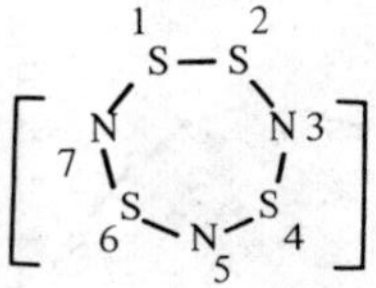 Cl	s	$2p_{3/2}$ (1,2) (4,6)	165.5 166.5	a	MgK_α	106
Cl_2OS	$SOCl_2$	s	2p	168.3	b 285.0	AlK_α	49
Cl_2S_2	ClSSCl	s	2p	163.7	b 285.0	AlK_α	49

TABLE 3 (continued)

Compound		Phase	Orbital	E_B(eV)	Calibrant	Exciting Radiation	Reference
$Cl_4FeN_5S_5$	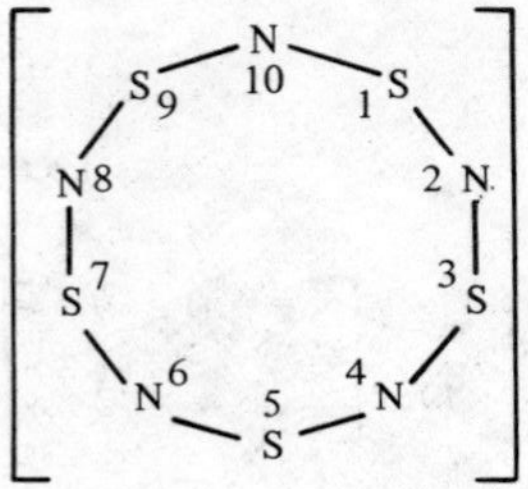 [$FeCl_4$]	s	$2p_{3/2}$ (1) (5) (9) (3) (7)	166.2 166.2 166.2 165.3 165.3	a	MgK_α	106
$Cl_5FeN_2S_3$	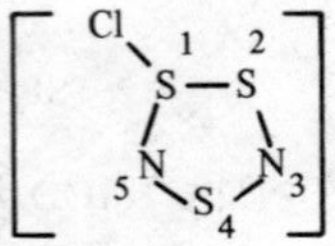 [$FeCl_4$]	s	$2p_{3/2}$ (2) (4) (1)	166.3 167.2 165.5	a	MgK_α	106
Cs_2MoS_4	Cs_2MoS_4	s	2p (el. S?)	167.2 (3) 164.5 (3)	a 290.0	AlK_α	62
Cs_2S_4W	Cs_2WS_4	s	2p (el. S?)	168.6 (3) 165.8 (8)	a 290.0	AlK_α	62
CuO_4S	$CuSO_4$	s	2p	171.2	a 285.5	AlK_α	46
$CuO_4S\cdot H_2O$	$CuSO_4\cdot H_2O$	s	2p	170.8	a 285.5	AlK_α	46
$CuO_4S\cdot 3H_2O$	$CuSO_4\cdot 3H_2O$	s	2p	170.3	a 285.5	AlK_α	46
$CuO_4S\cdot 5H_2O$	$CuSO_4\cdot 5H_2O$	s	2p	170.4	a 285.5	AlK_α	46
Cu_2S	Cu_2S	s	2p	164.5	a 285.5	AlK_α	46
F_2OS	SOF_2	g	$2p_{3/2}$	176.2	CS_2 S $2p_{3/2}$ 169.8	MgK_α	151
F_3OS	SOF_2	s	2p	170.2	b 285.0	AlK_α	49
F_6S	SF_6	s	2p	177.4	b 285.0	AlK_α	49

TABLE 3 (continued)

Compound		Phase	Orbital	E_B(eV)	Calibrant	Exciting Radiation	Reference
F_6S	SF_6	g	$2p_{3/2}$	180.4	CS_2 S $2p_{3/2}$ 169.8	MgK_α	151
$F_{10}S_2$	F_5SSF_5	s	2p	174.6	b 285.0	AlK_α	49
$FeKS_2$	$KFeS_2$	s	2p	161.1			4
FeO_4S	$FeSO_4$	s	2p	168.9	b 285.0	AlK_α	49
FeS	FeS	s	2p	160.7 (2)			3
FeS_2	FeS_2	s	2p	161.5 (3)			3
$Fe_2O_{12}S_3$	$Fe_2(SO_4)_3$	s	2p	169.3	b 285.0	AlK_α	49
GaS	GaS	s	$2p_{3/2,1/2}$ 2s	162.2 (6) 226.4 (6)	c 84	Al, MgK_α	94
H_2S	H_2S	g	$2p_{3/2}$	170.2	CS_2 S $2p_{3/2}$ 169.8	MgK_α	151
$H_8FeN_2O_8S_2 \cdot 6H_2O$	$FeSO_4(NH_4)_2SO_4 \cdot 6H_2O$	s	2p	167.7 (2)			3
$H_8Fe_2N_2O_{16}S_4 \cdot 24H_2O$	$Fe_2(SO_4)_3(NH_4)_2SO_4 \cdot 24H_2O$	s	2p	167.9 (2)			3
$H_8N_2O_4S$	$(NH_4)_2SO_4$	s	2p	167.8 (2)			3
$H_{12}N_3S_4V$	$(NH_4)_3VS_4$	s	2p	167.4 (3)	a 290.0	AlK_α	62
HgS	HgS	s	$2p_{3/2}$ $2p_{1/2}$ 2s	161.44 162.63 225.76	k 283.8	AlK_α	109
In_2S_3	In_2S_3	s	2p	168.1 (3)	a 290.0	AlK_α	62
Li_2O_4S	Li_2SO_4	s	2p	174.7 (3)	a 290.0	AlK_α	62
Na_2O_3S	Na_2SO_3	s	2p	166.7	b 285.0	AlK_α	49

TABLE 3 (continued)

Compound		Phase	Orbital	E_B(eV)	Calibrant	Exciting Radiation	Reference
$Na_2O_3S_2$	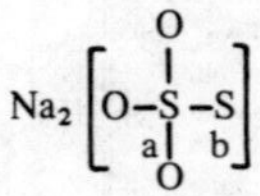	s	^a2p ^b2p	173.8 (3) 167.8 (3)	a 290.0	AlK_α	62
$Na_2O_3S_2$	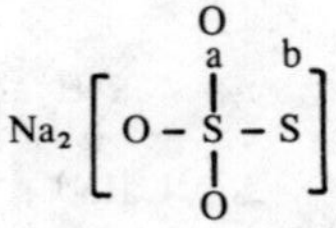	s	^a2p ^b2p	161.9 167.9	b 285.0	AlK_α	49
$Na_2O_3S_2$	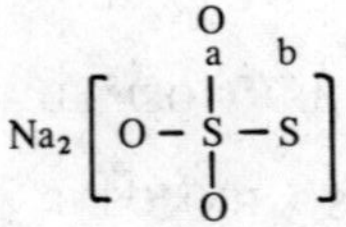	s	$^a2p_{1/2}$ $^a2p_{3/2}$ ^a2s $^b2p_{1/2}$ $^b2p_{3/2}$ ^b2s	171.61 (2) 170.32 (1) 234.41 (1) 165.44 (4) 164.28 (1) 228.62 (2)		MgK_α	136
Na_2O_4S	Na_2SO_4	s	2p	168.9	b 285.0	AlK_α	49
$Na_2O_5S_2$	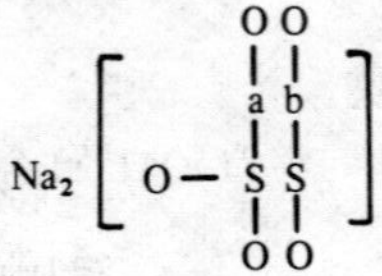	s	^b2p ^a2p	167.2 169.0	b 285.0	AlK_α	49
Na_2S	Na_2S	s	2p	162.0	b 285.0	AlK_α	49
O_2S	SO_2	g	$2p_{3/2}$	174.8	CS_2 S $2p_{3/2}$ 169.8	MgK_α	151
O_2S	SO_2	s	2p	168.3	b 285.0	AlK_α	49
O_3S	$[SO_3]^=$ ION	s	2p	166.4 (2)			3
O_4SSr	$SrSO_4$	s	2p	176.2 (3)	a 290.0	AlK_α	62
P_4S_3	P_4S_3	s	2p	163.1 (4)	b 285.0	Mg, AlK_α	100
P_4S_{10}	P_4S_{10}	s	2p	163.4 (1)	b 285.0	Mg, AlK_α	100

TABLE 3 (continued)

Compound		Phase	Orbital	E_B(eV)	Calibrant	Exciting Radiation	Reference
PbS	PbS	s	2p($PbSO_4$) 2p	174.6 (3) 167.7 (3)	a 290.0	AlK_a	62
S	S	s	L_I	229.2	MgO MgK(CuK_{a1})	CuK_{a1}	67
S	S	s	K	2,471.9 (5)	MgO MgK(CrK_a)	Cr, CuK_a	76
S	S	s	2p	164.8	b 285.0	AlK_a	49
S	S	s	2p	162.8 (2)			3
S	S	s	2s 2p	227.9 (1) 163.9 (1)	b 285.0	Mg, AlK_a	100
SZn	ZnS	s	$2p_{3/2}$ $2p_{1/2}$ 2s	161.71 162.75 225.97	k 283.8	AlK_a	109
Sb							
$Cl_6CoH_{18}N_6Sb$	$[Co(NH_3)_6]SbCl_6$	s	$3d_{3/2}$ $3d_{5/2}$	545.4 536.1	a 290	AlK_a	30
Cl_6CsSb	$CsSbCl_6$	s	$3d_{5/2}$ $3d_{3/2}$	531.1 (3) 540.6 (3)	b 285	AlK_a	111
Cl_6CsSb	$CsSbCl_6$	s	$3d_{3/2}$ $3d_{5/2}$	548.7 539.1	a 290	AlK_a	30
Cl_6Cs_2Sb	Cs_2SbCl_6	s	$3d_{3/2}$ $3d_{5/2}$	548.9 547.1 537.9	a 290	AlK_a	30
$Cl_9Cs_3Sb_2$	$Cs_3Sb_2Cl_9$	s	$3d_{5/2}$ $3d_{3/2}$	530.6 (3) 540.1 (3)	b 285	AlK_a	111
H_6KO_6Sb	$KSb(OH)_6$	s	$3d_{3/2}$	545.4	a 290	AlK_a	30

TABLE 3 (continued)

Compound		Phase	Orbital	E_B(eV)	Calibrant	Exciting Radiation	Reference
Sb	Sb	s	$4d_{3/2}$	33.44 (9)	Au E_{Fermi}	AlK_a	137
			$4d_{5/2}$	32.14 (9)			
			5s	9.1 (2)			
			5p	2.35 (25)			
Sb	Sb	s	L_{III}	4,132.2	CuA6	CuK_{a1}	123
Sb	Sb	s	L_I	4,698.3	$SbL_{III}(CuK_{a1})$	CuK_{a1}	45
			L_{II}	4,380.6			
Sb_2Se_3	Sb_2Se_3	amorph		~24			138
			$4d_{3/2,5/2}$	~33			
			$3d_{3/2}$	537			
			$3d_{5/2}$	528			
Sc							
O_3Sc_2	Sc_2O_3	s	L_I	500.4	MgO $MgK(CuK_{a1})$	CuK_{a1}	67
O_3Sc_2	Sc_2O_3	s	K	4,492.7 (4)	e, i	CuK_a	76
Se							
BaO_4Se	$BaSeO_4$	s	$3p_{1/2}$	180	a 290.0	AlK_a	62
			$3p_{3/2}$	174.1 (3)			
CKNSe	KSeCN	s	$3p_{1/2}$	174.2 (3)	a 290.0	AlK_a	62
			$3p_{3/2}$	168.5 (3)			
CKNSe	KSeCN	s	$3p_{1/2}$	165.1 (3)	b 285	AlK_a	101
			$3p_{3/2}$	159.3 (3)			
$C_6H_5BrO_3Se$	$HOSe(O)_2$ (p-C_6H_4Br)	s	3d	60.0 (3)	b 285.0	Mg, AlK_a	144
			$3p_{3/2}$	165.9 (3)			
$C_6H_5ClO_2Se$	$HOSe(O)$(p-C_6H_4Cl)	s	3d	59.1 (3)	b 285.0	Mg, AlK_a	144

TABLE 3 (continued)

Compound		Phase	Orbital	E_B(eV)	Calibrant	Exciting Radiation	Reference
$C_6H_5ClO_3Se$	$HOSe(O)_2(p\text{-}C_6H_4Cl)$	s	3d $3p_{3/2}$	60.0 (3) 165.7 (3)	b 285.0	Mg, AlK_α	144
$C_6H_5FO_2Se$	$HOSe(O)(m\text{-}C_6H_4F)$	s	3d	59.1 (3)	b 285.0	Mg, AlK_α	144
$C_6H_5FO_2Se$	$HOSe(O)(p\text{-}C_6H_4F)$	s	3d $3p_{3/2}$	59.1 (3) 165.0 (3)	b 285.0	Mg, AlK_α	144
$C_6H_6O_2Se$	$HOSe(O)(C_6H_5)$	s	3d	58.6 (3)	b 285.0	Mg, AlK_α	144
$C_6H_8O_4Se$	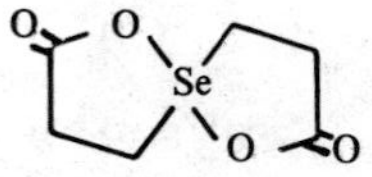	s	3d	58.1 (3)	b 285.0	Mg, AlK_α	144
$C_6H_8O_4Se$	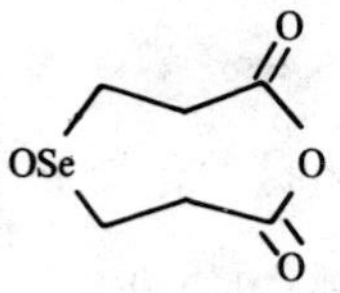	s	3d $3p_{3/2}$	58.6 (3) 164.2 (3)	b 285.0	Mg, AlK_α	144
$C_6K_2N_6PtSe$	$K_2[Pt(SeCN)_6]$	s	$3p_{1/2}$ $3p_{3/2}$	174.0 (3) 168.3 (3)	a 290.0	AlK_α	62
$C_7H_8O_2Se$	$HOSe(O)(m\text{-}C_6H_4CH_3)$	s	3d $3p_{3/2}$	58.9 (3) 164.9 (3)	b 285.0	Mg, AlK_α	144
$C_9H_{12}O_3Se$	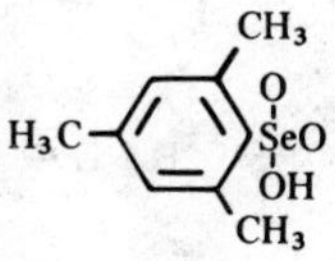	s	3d	60.0 (3)	b 285.0	Mg, AlK_α	144
$C_{10}H_{18}O_4Se$	$Se(n\text{-}C_4H_8COOH)_2$	s	3d	58.3 (3)	b 285.0	Mg, AlK_α	144
$C_{12}H_8Br_2OSe$	$OSe(p\text{-}C_6H_4Br)_2$	s	3d	58.2 (3)	b 285.0	Mg, AlK_α	144
$C_{12}H_8Br_2Se$	$Se(p\text{-}C_6H_4Br)_2$	s	3d	56.2 (3)	b 285.0	Mg, AlK_α	144

TABLE 3 (continued)

Compound		Phase	Orbital	E_B(eV)	Calibrant	Exciting Radiation	Reference
$C_{12}H_{10}Cl_2Se$	$SeCl_2(C_6H_5)_2$	s	3d $3p_{3/2}$	58.6 (3) 164.6 (3)	b 285.0	Mg, AlK_a	144
$C_{12}H_{26}O_2Se$	$(n\text{-}C_{12}H_{25})Se(O)OH$	s	3d	58.3 (3)	b 285.0	Mg, AlK_a	144
$C_{14}H_8O_4Se$	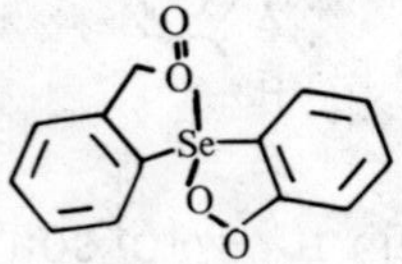	s	3d	58.8 (3)	b 285.0	Mg, AlK_a	144
$C_{14}H_{14}OSe$	$SeO(CH_2C_6H_5)_2$	s	3d $3p_{3/2}$	58.0 (3) 164.0 (3)	b 285.0	Mg, AlK_a	144
$C_{14}H_{14}O_4Se$	$O_2Se(p\text{-}C_6H_4OCH_3)_2$	s	3d	59.8 (3)	b 285.0	Mg, AlK_a	144
$C_{16}H_{34}O_2Se$	$(n\text{-}C_{16}H_{33})Se(O)OH$	s	3d	58.6 (3)	b 285.0	Mg, AlK_a	144
$C_{17}H_{33}NSe$	$n\text{-}C_{16}H_{33}SeCN$	s	3d $3p_{3/2}$	57.5 (3) 163.2 (3)	b 285.0	Al, MgK_a	144
$C_{18}H_{15}O_3PSe$	$(C_6H_5O)_3PSe$	s	3p	160.9	d 285.0	AlK_a	104
$C_{18}H_{15}PSe$	$(C_6H_5)_3PSe$	s	3p	160.8 (6)	d 285.0	AlK_a	104
$C_{19}H_{37}NSe$	$n\text{-}C_{18}H_{37}SeCN$	s	3d	57.4 (3)	b 285.0	Mg, AlK_a	144
$C_{28}H_{58}Se_2$	$(n\text{-}C_{14}H_{29}Se)_2$	s	3d	55.9 (3)	b 285.0	Mg, AlK_a	144
$C_{32}H_{66}Se_2$	$(n\text{-}C_{16}H_{33}Se)_2$	s	3d $3p_{3/2}$	56.0 (3) 161.8 (3)	b 285.0	Mg, AlK_a	144
CdSe	CdSe	s	$3d_{5/2}$ $3d_{3/2}$ $3p_{3/2}$ $3p_{1/2}$ 3s	54.18 55.07 160.32 166.04 228.96	k 283.8	AlK_a	109

TABLE 3 (continued)

Compound		Phase	Orbital	E_B(eV)	Calibrant	Exciting Radiation	Reference
GaSe	GaSe	s	$3d_{5/2,3/2}$	54.5 (6)	c 84	Al, MgK_α	94
			$3p_{3/2}$	160.3 (6)			
			$3p_{1/2}$	166.8 (6)			
$HNaO_3Se$	$NaHSeO_3$	s	$3p_{1/2}$	178.3 (3)	a 290.0	AlK_α	62
			$3p_{3/2}$	173.5 (3)			
H_2O_3Se	H_2SeO_3	s	3d	59.7 (3)	b 285.0	Mg, AlK_α	144
HgSe	HgSe	s	$3d_{5/2}$	53.26	k 283.8	AlK_α	109
			$3d_{3/2}$	54.00			
			$3p_{3/2}$	159.59			
			$3p_{1/2}$	165.40			
			3s	228.46			
Na_2O_3Se	Na_2SeO_3	s	$3p_{1/2}$	169.6 (1)	b 285	AlK_α	101
			$3p_{3/2}$	164.1 (1)			
Na_2O_4Se	Na_2SeO_4	s	$3p_{1/2}$	170.1 (1)	b 285	AlK_α	101
			$3p_{3/2}$	164.6 (1)			
$Na_2O_4Se \cdot 10H_2O$	$Na_2SeO_4 \cdot 10H_2O$	s	$3p_{1/2}$	179.3 (3)	a 290.0	AlK_α	62
			$3p_{3/2}$	173.5 (3)			
$NbSe_4Tl_3$	Tl_3NbSe_4	s	$3p_{1/2}$	173	a 290.0	AlK_α	62
			$3p_{3/2}$	166.7 (3)			
O_2Se	$(SeO_2)n$	s	3d	59.6 (3)	b 285.0	Mg, AlK_α	144
			$3p_{3/2}$	165.4 (3)			
O_2Se	SeO_2	s	$3p_{1/2}$	176.9 (3)	a 290.0	AlK_α	62
			$3p_{3/2}$	171.2 (3)			
O_2Se	SeO_2	s	$3p_{1/2}$	169.8 (1)	b 285		101
			$3p_{3/2}$	163.8 (1)			
Sb_2Se_3	Sb_2Se_3	amorph	$3d_{3/2,5/2}$	53			138

TABLE 3 (continued)

Compound		Phase	Orbital	E_B(eV)	Calibrant	Exciting Radiation	Reference
Se	Se	s	3s $3p_{1/2}$ $3p_{3/2}$ 3d	230.5 (6) 167.4 (6) 161.7 (6) 55.5 (6)	b 285.0	Mg, AlK_a	144
Se	Se	s	$3p_{1/2}$ $3p_{3/2}$	165.9 (2) 159.9 (2)	b 285	AlK_a	101
Se	Se	s	K	12,657.7	CuA6, CuK(MoK_{a1}), TlL_{III} (MoK_{a1})	MoK_{a1}	123
Se_4TaTl_3	Tl_3TaSe_4	s	$3p_{1/2}$ $3p_{3/2}$	173 166.5	a 290.0	AlK_a	62
Se_4Tl_3V	Tl_3VSe_4	s	$3p_{1/2}$ $3p_{3/2}$	173 168.0 (3)	a 290.0	AlK_a	62
SeZn	ZnSe	s	$3d_{5/2}$ $3d_{3/2}$ $3p_{3/2}$ $3p_{1/2}$ 3s	54.02 54.97 160.23 166.07 229.09	k 283.8	AlK_a	109
SeZn	ZnSe	s	$3p_{1/2}$ $3p_{3/2}$	165.8 (2) 159.7 (4)	b 285	AlK_a	101
Si							
$Al_6Ca_4Fe_6H_2O_{22}Si_6$	Epidote 13575 86% Fe^{3+} $4CaO{\cdot}3(AlFe)_2O_3{\cdot}6SiO_2{\cdot}H_2O$	s	2p	101.8 (5)	c 84.0 (3)	Al, MgK_a	57
B_4Si	SiB_4	s	2p	100.9	LiF Fls 685.4		114
B_4Si	SiB_4	s	2p	102.4 (1)	f 283.0	MgK_a	12
BrH_3Si	SiH_3Br	g	$2p_{3/2}$	107.96	Ar $2p_{3/2}$ 248.457		85

TABLE 3 (continued)

Compound		Phase	Orbital	E_B(eV)	Calibrant	Exciting Radiation	Reference
CSi	$(SiC)_\infty$	s	2p	102.2 (9)	f 283.0	MgK_α	12
C_2H_6OSi	$((CH_3)_2SiO)_\infty$	s	2p	102.8 (3)	f 283.0	MgK_α	12
$C_4H_{12}Si$	$Si(CH_3)_4$	g	$2p_{3/2}$	105.83	Ar $2p_{3/2}$ 248.457		85
$C_{12}H_{12}O_2Si$	$(C_6H_5)_2Si(OH)_2$	s	2p	101.9 (2)	f 283.0	MgK_α	12
$C_{18}H_{16}OSi$	$(C_6H_5)_3SiOH$	s	2p	102.4 (7)	f 283.0	MgK_α	12
$C_{24}H_{20}Si$	$Si(C_6H_5)_4$	s	2p	102.4 (3)	f 283.0	MgK_α	12
$C_{36}H_{30}Si_2$	$(C_6H_5)_3SiSi(C_6H_5)_3$	s	2p	101.3 (1)	f 283.0	MgK_α	12
$CaFeMgO_6Si_2$	Hedenbergite R6955 46% Mg $CaFeSi_2O_6$	s	2p	102.3 (5)	b 284.6 (5)	Al, MgK_α	57
$CaFeO_6Si_2$	Hedenbergite 2B 85% Fe^{2+} $CaFeSi_2O_6$	s	2p	102.0 (5)	Internal Ols 530.8 (7)	Al, MgK_α	57
$CaFeO_6Si_2$	Hedenbergite 103182 77% Fe^{2+} $CaFeSi_2O_6$	s	2p	102.1 (3)	Internal Ols 530.8 (7)	Al, MgK_α	57
$CaFeO_6Si_2$	Hedenbergite R6955 54% Fe^{2+} $CaFeSi_2O_6$	s	2p	102.1 (6)	c 84.0 (3)	Al, MgK_α	57
ClH_3Si	SiH_3Cl	g	$2p_{3/2}$	107.98	Ar $2p_{3/2}$ 248.457		85
Cl_4Si	$SiCl_4$	g	$2p_{3/2}$	110.25	Ar $2p_{3/2}$ 248.457		85
F_4Si	SiF_4	g	$2p_{3/2}$	111.54	Ar $2p_{3/2}$ 248.457		85
F_6Na_2Si	Na_2SiF_6	s	2p	107.4 (1)	f 283.0	MgK_α	12

TABLE 3 (continued)

Compound		Phase	Orbital	E_B(eV)	Calibrant	Exciting Radiation	Reference
$FeMgO_3Si$	Anthophyllite 77% Mg (Mg, Fe) SiO_3	s	2p	101.9 (5)	b 284.6 (5)	Al, MgK_α	57
$Fe_5H_2Na_2O_{24}Si_8$	Crocidolite 93720 55% Fe^{2+}, 40% Fe^{3+} $Na_2Fe_3(^{+2})Fe_2(^{+3})(Si_4O_{11})_2(OH)_2$	s	2p	102.4 (5)	Internal Ols 530.8 (7)	Al, MgK_α	57
$H_2O_3Si_2$	$(HSiO_{3/2})_\infty$	s	2p	104.2 (6)	f 283.0	MgK_α	12
H_4Si	SiH_4	g	$2p_{3/2}$	107.09	Ar $2p_{3/2}$ 248.457		85
H_6OSi_2	$(SiH_3)_2O$	g	$2p_{3/2}$	107.68	Ar $2p_{3/2}$ 248.457		85
I_4Si	SiI_4	s	2p	103.8 (6)	f 283.0	MgK_α	12
MgO_3Si	Enstatite 86% Mg $MgO{\cdot}SiO_2$	s	2p	102.0 (5)	b 284.6 (5)	Al, MgK_α	57
N_4Si	$(SiN_4)_\infty$	s	2p	101.8 (6)	f 283.0	MgK_α	12
Na_2O_3Si	$(Na_2SiO_3)_n$	s	2p	102.0 (3)	f 283.0	MgK_α	12
OSi	$(SiO)_\infty$	s	2p	103.5 (9)	f 283.0	MgK_α	12
O_2Si	SiO_2	s	K	1,838.9 (4)	e, i	CrK_α	76
O_2Si	$(SiO_2)_\infty$quartz	s	2p	103.0 (2)	f 283.0	MgK_α	12
O_4SiZn_2	Zn_2SiO_4	s	2p	102.2 (3)	f 283.0	MgK_α	12
S_2Si	$(SiS_2)_\infty$	s	2p	103.1 (7)	f 283.0	MgK_α	12
Si	Si_∞	s	2p	~99	f 283.0	MgK_α	12
Si	Si	s	L_I	148.7	MgO MgK($CuK_{\alpha 1}$)	$CuK_{\alpha 1}$	67

TABLE 3 (continued)

Compound		Phase	Orbital	E_B(eV)	Calibrant	Exciting Radiation	Reference
Si	Si	cryst	X_4 W_2 V L_1 N_1 L_2 Γ_1	2.2 3.6 4.4 6.6 7.8 9.2 14.7	Au E_{Fermi}	AlK_α	134
Sm							
O_3Sm_2	Sm_2O_3	s	L_I L_{II} L_{III}	7,736.5 7,312.3 6,717.2	e	$MoK_{\alpha 1}$	56
Sm	Sm	s	4f	−1.2 −5.8 −7.5	Pd Fermi level	AlK_α	47
Sn							
Br_6K_2Sn	K_2SnBr_6	s	$3d_{5/2}$	487.6 (1)	MoO_3 Mo $3d_{5/2}$ 232.5	MgK_α	10
Br_6K_2Sn	K_2SnBr_6	s	$3d_{5/2}$	487.6 (1)	MoO_3 Mo $3d_{5/2}$ 233.0	MgK_α	140
Br_6K_2Sn	K_2SnBr_6	s	$3d_{5/2}$	488.2 (2)	c 83.00	MgK_α	140
$C_{16}H_{40}Br_2Cl_4N_2Sn$	$[(CH_3CH_2)_4N]_2SnCl_4Br_2$	s	$3d_{5/2}$	487.7 (2)	MoO_3 Mo $3d_{5/2}$ 233.0	MgK_α	140
$C_{16}H_{40}Br_2Cl_4N_2Sn$	$((CH_3CH_2)_4N)_2SnCl_4Br_2$	s	$3d_{5/2}$	487.2 (2)	MoO_3 Mo $3d_{5/2}$ 232.5	MgK_α	10
$C_{16}H_{40}Br_2Cl_4N_2Sn$	$[(CH_3CH_2)_4N]_2SnCl_4Br_2$	s	$3d_{5/2}$	487.3 (1)	c 83.00	MgK_α	140
$C_{16}H_{40}Br_2I_4N_2Sn$	$[(CH_3CH_2)_4N]_2SnI_4Br_2$	s	$3d_{5/2}$	487.3 (2)	MoO_3 Mo $3d_{5/2}$ 233.0	MgK_α	140
$C_{16}H_{40}Br_2I_4N_2Sn$	$[(CH_3CH_2)_4N]_2SnI_4Br_2$	s	$3d_{5/2}$	487.4 (1)	c 83.00	MgK_α	140
$C_{16}H_{40}Br_2I_4N_2Sn$	$((CH_3CH_2)_4N)_2SnI_4Br_2$	s	$3d_{5/2}$	486.8 (2)	MoO_3 Mo $3d_{5/2}$ 232.5	MgK_α	10

TABLE 3 (continued)

Compound		Phase	Orbital	E_B(eV)	Calibrant	Exciting Radiation	Reference
$C_{16}H_{40}Br_4Cl_2N_2Sn$	$((CH_3CH_2)_4N)_2SnBr_4Cl_2$	s	$3d_{5/2}$	487.1 (1)	MoO_3 Mo $3d_{5/2}$ 232.5	MgK_α	10
$C_{16}H_{40}Br_4Cl_2N_2Sn$	$[(CH_3CH_2)_4N]_2SnBr_4Cl_2$	s	$3d_{5/2}$	487.6 (1)	MoO_3 $Mo3d_{5/2}$ 233.0	MgK_α	140
$C_{16}H_{40}Br_4Cl_2N_2Sn$	$[(CH_3CH_2)_4N]_2SnBr_4Cl_2$	s	$3d_{5/2}$	487.2 (1)	c 83.00	MgK_α	140
$C_{16}H_{40}Br_4F_2N_2Sn$	$[(CH_3CH_2)_4N]_2SnBr_4F_2$	s	$3d_{5/2}$	487.7 (1)	MoO_3 Mo $3d_{5/2}$ 233.0	MgK_α	140
$C_{16}H_{40}Br_4F_2N_2Sn$	$[(CH_3CH_2)_4N]_2SnBr_4F_2$	s	$3d_{5/2}$	487.1 (1)	c 83.00	MgK_α	140
$C_{16}H_{40}Br_4F_2N_2Sn$	$((CH_3CH_2)_4N)_2SnBr_4F_2$	s	$3d_{5/2}$	487.2 (1)	MoO_3 Mo $3d_{5/2}$ 232.5	MgK_α	10
$C_{16}H_{40}Br_4I_2N_2Sn$	$((CH_3CH_2)_4N)_2SnBr_4I_2$	s	$3d_{5/2}$	487.0 (1)	MoO_3 Mo $3d_{5/2}$ 232.5	MgK_α	10
$C_{16}H_{40}Br_4I_2N_2Sn$	$[(CH_3CH_2)_4N]_2SnBr_4I_2$	s	$3d_{5/2}$	487.5 (1)	MoO_3 Mo $3d_{5/2}$ 233.0	MgK_α	140
$C_{16}H_{40}Br_4I_2N_2Sn$	$[(CH_3CH_2)_4N]_2SnBr_4I_2$	s	$3d_{5/2}$	487.1 (1)	c 83.00	MgK_α	140
$C_{16}H_{40}Br_6N_2Sn$	$[(CH_3CH_2)_4N]_2SnBr_6$	s	$3d_{5/2}$	487.7 (1)	MoO_3 Mo $3d_{5/2}$ 233.0	MgK_α	140
$C_{16}H_{40}Br_6N_2Sn$	$[(CH_3CH_2)_4N]_2SnBr_6$	s	$3d_{5/2}$	487.7 (1)	c 83.00	MgK_α	140
$C_{16}H_{40}Br_6N_2Sn$	$((CH_3CH_2)_4N)_2SnBr_6$	s	$3d_{5/2}$	487.2 (1)	MoO_3 Mo $3d_{5/2}$ 232.5	MgK_α	10
$C_{16}H_{40}Cl_2I_4N_2Sn$	$((CH_3CH_2)_4N)_2SnI_4Cl_2$	s	$3d_{5/2}$	486.9 (1)	MoO_3 Mo $3d_{5/2}$ 232.5	MgK_α	10
$C_{16}H_{40}Cl_2I_4N_2Sn$	$[(CH_3CH_2)_4N]_2SnI_4Cl_2$	s	$3d_{5/2}$	487.4 (1)	MoO_3 Mo $3d_{5/2}$ 233.0	MgK_α	140
$C_{16}H_{40}Cl_2I_4N_2Sn$	$[(CH_3CH_2)_4N]_2SnI_4Cl_2$	s	$3d_{5/2}$	487.3 (2)	c 83.00	MgK_α	140
$C_{16}H_{40}Cl_4F_2N_2Sn$	$[(CH_3CH_2)_4N]_2SnCl_4F_2$	s	$3d_{5/2}$	487.8 (1)	MoO_3 Mo $3d_{5/2}$ 233.0	MgK_α	140
$C_{16}H_{40}Cl_4F_2N_2Sn$	$[(CH_3CH_2)_4N]_2SnCl_4F_2$	s	$3d_{5/2}$	487.1 (2)	c 83.00	MgK_α	140
$C_{16}H_{40}Cl_4F_2N_2Sn$	$((CH_3CH_2)_4N)_2SnCl_4F_2$	s	$3d_{5/2}$	487.3 (1)	MoO_3 Mo $3d_{5/2}$ 232.5	MgK_α	10
$C_{16}H_{40}Cl_4I_2N_2Sn$	$((CH_3CH_2)_4N)_2SnCl_4I_2$	s	$3d_{5/2}$	487.4 (1)	MoO_3 Mo $3d_{5/2}$ 232.5	MgK_α	10

TABLE 3 (continued)

Compound		Phase	Orbital	E_B(eV)	Calibrant	Exciting Radiation	Reference
$C_{16}H_{40}Cl_4I_2N_2Sn$	$[(CH_3CH_2)_4N]_2SnCl_4I_2$	s	$3d_{5/2}$	487.9 (1)	MoO_3 Mo $3d_{5/2}$ 233.0	MgK_α	140
$C_{16}H_{40}Cl_4I_2N_2Sn$	$[(CH_3CH_2)_4N]_2SnCl_4I_2$	s	$3d_{5/2}$	487.5 (1)	c 83.00	MgK_α	140
$C_{16}H_{40}Cl_6N_2Sn$	$[(CH_3CH_2)_4N]_2SnCl_6$	s	$3d_{5/2}$	487.6 (2)	MoO_3 Mo $3d_{5/2}$ 233.0	MgK_α	140
$C_{16}H_{40}Cl_6N_2Sn$	$[(CH_3CH_2)_4N]_2SnCl_6$	s	$3d_{5/2}$	487.6 (1)	c 83.00	MgK_α	140
$C_{16}H_{40}Cl_6N_2Sn$	$((CH_3CH_2)_4N)_2SnCl_6$	s	$3d_{5/2}$	487.1 (2)	MoO_3 Mo $3d_{5/2}$ 232.5	MgK_α	10
$C_{16}H_{40}I_6N_2Sn$	$((CH_3CH_2)_4N)_2SnI_6$	s	$3d_{5/2}$	486.7 (2)	MoO_3 Mo $3d_{5/2}$ 232.5	MgK_α	10
$C_{16}H_{40}I_6N_2Sn$	$[(CH_3CH_2)_4N]_2SnI_6$	s	$3d_{5/2}$	487.2 (2)	MoO_3 Mo $3d_{5/2}$ 233.0	MgK_α	140
$C_{16}H_{40}I_6N_2Sn$	$[(CH_3CH_2)_4N]_2SnI_6$	s	$3d_{5/2}$	486.9 (2)	c 83.00	MgK_α	140
$C_{24}H_{36}Cl_6Pt_3Sn_2$	$(C_8H_{12})_3Pt_3Sn_2Cl_6$	s	$3d_{5/2}$	487.3 (1)	d 285.0	AlK_α	87
$C_{24}H_{60}Cl_{15}N_3PtSn_5$	$[(C_2H_5)_4N]_3Pt(SnCl_3)_5$	s	$3d_{5/2}$	487.1 (1)	d 285.0	AlK_α	87
$C_{32}H_{80}Cl_{20}N_4Pt_3Sn_8$	$[(C_2H_5)_4N]_4Pt_3Sn_8Cl_{20}$	s	$3d_{5/2}$	487.3	d 285.0	AlK_α	87
F_6K_2Sn	K_2SnF_6	s	$3d_{5/2}$	488.8 (1)	MoO_3 Mo $3d_{5/2}$ 233.0	MgK_α	140
F_6K_2Sn	K_2SnF_6	s	$3d_{5/2}$	489.6 (1)	c 83.00	MgK_α	140
F_6K_2Sn	K_2SnF_6	s	$3d_{5/2}$	488.3 (1)	MoO_3 Mo $3d_{5/2}$ 232.5	MgK_α	10
Sn	Sn (β)	s	$3d_{5/2}$	486.4 (2)	MoO_3 Mo $3d_{5/2}$ 233.0	MgK_α	140
Sn	Sn (β)	s	$3d_{5/2}$	486.5 (2)	c 83.00	MgK_α	140
Sn	Sn (β)	s	$3d_{5/2}$	486.9 (2)	MoO_3 Mo $3d_{5/2}$ 232.5	MgK_α	10
Sn	Sn	s	L_{III} L_{II} L_I	3,928.8 4,156.2 4,464.5	CuA6 SnL_{III} ($CuK_{\alpha 1}$)	$CuK_{\alpha 1}$	123

TABLE 3 (continued)

Compound		Phase	Orbital	E_B(eV)	Calibrant	Exciting Radiation	Reference
Sn	Sn	s	L_I	4,464.5	SnL_{III} ($CuK_{\alpha 1}$)	$CuK_{\alpha 1}$	45
			L_{II}	4,156.2			
Sn	Sn	s	$4d_{3/2}$	24.76 (9)	Au E_{Fermi}	AlK_α	137
			$4d_{5/2}$	23.68 (9)			
			5s	7.0 (5)			
			5p	1.25 (27)			
Sr							
F_2Sr	SrF_2	s	4p	28.6	a 290	AlK_α	30
Sr	Sr	s	L_I	2,216.3 (5)		CuK_α	79
			L_{II}	2,006.7 (5)			
			L_{III}	1,940.0 (5)			
Ta							
CTa	$TaC_{0.990}$	s	$4f_{7/2}$	23.1 (2)	Metal $Ta4f_{7/2}$ 21.5	AlK_α	73
	$TaC_{0.963}$			23.2 (2)			
	$TaC_{0.887}$			23.1 (2)			
	$TaC_{0.743}$			23.3 (2)			
CTa	TaC (oxidized)	s	$4d_{3/2}$	249.2 (3)	a 290.0	AlK_α	62
			$4d_{5/2}$	237.6 (3)			
			$4f_{5/2}$	35.6 (3)			
			$4f_{7/2}$	33.6 (3)			
FK_2Ta	K_2TaF_Y	s	$4f_{5/2}$	37.5	a 290.0	AlK_α	107
			$4f_{7/2}$	35.7			
F_7K_2Ta	K_2TaF_7	s	$4d_{3/2}$	250.7 (3)	a 290.0	AlK_α	62
			$4d_{5/2}$	239.2 (3)			
			$4f_{5/2}$	37.5 (3)			
			$4f_{7/2}$	35.7 (3)			

TABLE 3 (continued)

Compound		Phase	Orbital	E_B(eV)	Calibrant	Exciting Radiation	Reference
O_5Ta_2	Ta_2O_5	s	$4f_{5/2}$	35.1	a 290.0	AlK_α	107
			$4f_{7/2}$	33.3			
O_5Ta_2	Ta_2O_5	s	$4d_{3/2}$	248.8 (3)	a 290.0	AlK_α	62
			$4d_{5/2}$	237.4 (3)			
			$4f_{5/2}$	35.1 (3)			
			$4f_{7/2}$	33.3 (3)			
S_4TaTl_3	Tl_3TaS_4	s	$4d_{3/2}$	248.6 (3)	a 290.0	AlK_α	62
			$4d_{5/2}$	237.1 (3)			
			$4f_{5/2}$	35			
			$4f_{7/2}$	33.2 (3)			
Ta	Ta (oxidized)	s	$4d_{3/2}$	248.7 (3)	a 290.0	AlK_α	62
			$4d_{5/2}$	237.3 (3)			
			$4f_{5/2}$	35.3 (3)			
			$4f_{7/2}$	33.4 (3)			
Ta	Ta	s	L_I	11,680.4 (5)	e	MoK_α	77
			L_{II}	11,136.3 (4)			
			L_{III}	9,880.5 (4)			
			M_{II}	2,468.6 (4)		CrK_α	
			M_{III}	2,194.1 (4)			
			M_{IV}	1,793.1 (4)			
			M_V	1,735.2 (4)			
Tb							
O_3Tb_2	Tb_2O_3	s	L_I	8,707.8	e	$MoK_{\alpha 1}$	56
			L_{II}	8,252.1			
			L_{III}	7,514.5			
Tc							
Tc	Tc	s	L_I	3,042.5 (4)		CuK_α	79
			L_{II}	2,793.3 (5)			
			L_{III}	2,677.0 (5)			

TABLE 3 (continued)

Compound		Phase	Orbital	E_B(eV)	Calibrant	Exciting Radiation	Reference
Te							
$C_{25}H_{20}AsNTe$	$[(C_6H_5)_4As]NCTe$	s	$3d_{5/2}$	573.3	c 84	MgK_α	145
			$3d_{3/2}$	583.6			
CdTe	CdTe	s	$4d_{5/2}$	39.92 (31)	k 283.8	AlK_α	109
			$4d_{3/2}$	41.42 (25)			
			4s	168.77			
			$3d_{5/2}$	572.11 (23)			
			$3d_{3/2}$	582.54			
			$3p_{3/2}$	818.74			
			$3p_{1/2}$	869.52			
			3s	1,005.39			
D_2O_4Te	D_2TeO_4	s	$3d_{3/2}$	586.8 (2)	b 285	AlK_α	101
			$3d_{5/2}$	576.4 (2)			
GaTe	GaTe	s	$4d_{5/2}$	40.3 (6)	c 84	Al, MgK_α	94
			$4d_{3/2}$	41.7 (6)			
			4s	169.1 (6)			
			$3d_{5/2}$	572.4 (7)			
			$3d_{3/2}$	582.8 (7)			
			$3p_{3/2}$	818.6 (7)			
			$3p_{1/2}$	869.5 (7)			
$H_8N_2O_4Te$	$(NH_4)_2TeO_4$	s	$3d_{3/2}$	587.4 (2)	b 285	AlK_α	101
			$3d_{5/2}$	576.7 (2)			
HgTe	HgTe	s	$4d_{5/2}$	39.61	k 283.8	AlK_α	109
			$4d_{3/2}$	41.12			
			4s	168.11			
			$3d_{5/2}$	571.88			
			$3d_{3/2}$	582.39			
			$3p_{3/2}$	818.58			
			$3p_{1/2}$	869.47			
			3s	1,004.60			
K_2O_3Te	K_2TeO_3	s	$3d_{3/2}$	586.1 (2)	b 285	AlK_α	101
			$3d_{5/2}$	575.7 (2)			

TABLE 3 (continued)

Compound		Phase	Orbital	E_B(eV)	Calibrant	Exciting Radiation	Reference
Na_2Te	Na_2Te	s	$3d_{3/2}$	582.6 (3)	b 285	AlK_α	101
			$3d_{5/2}$	572.4 (2)			
O_3Te	TeO_3	s	$3d_{3/2}$	587.3 (1)	b 285	AlK_α	101
			$3d_{5/2}$	576.8 (2)			
Te	Te	s	$3d_{3/2}$	583.2 (2)	b 285	AlK_α	101
			$3d_{5/2}$	572.9 (3)			
Te	Te	s	$4d_{3/2}$	41.80 (9)	Au E_{Fermi}	AlK_α	137
			$4d_{5/2}$	40.31 (9)			
			5s	11.5 (2)			
			5p (bonding)	4.0 (2)			
			5p (lone-pair)	1.13 (5)			
Te	Te	s	L_{III}	4,341.2	CuA6	$CuK_{\alpha 1}$	123
Te	Te	s	L_I	4,939.3	TeL_{III} ($CuK_{\alpha 1}$)	$CuK_{\alpha 1}$	45
			L_{II}	4,612.0			
TeZn	ZnTe	s	$3d_{5/2}$	572.16	k 283.8	AlK_α	109
			$3d_{3/2}$	582.56			
			$3p_{3/2}$	818.75			
			$3p_{1/2}$	869.63			
			3s	1,005.48			
			$4d_{5/2}$	39.97 (29)			
			$4d_{3/2}$	41.47 (24)			
			4s	168.80			
TeZn	ZnTe	s	$3d_{3/2}$	583.6 (4)	b 285	AlK_α	101
			$3d_{5/2}$	573.1 (4)			
Th							
$CeO_{10}Th_3U$	$Th_{.6}Ce_{.2}U_{.2}O_2$	s	$4f_{5/2}$	351.4	a 290.0	AlK_α	107
			$4f_{7/2}$	342.1			
$Eu_2O_7Th_2$	$Th_{.5}Eu_{.5}O_{1.75}$	s	$4f_{5/2}$	351.1	a 290.0	AlK_α	107

TABLE 3 (continued)

Compound		Phase	Orbital	E_B(eV)	Calibrant	Exciting Radiation	Reference
F_4 Th	ThF_4	s	$4f_{5/2}$	354.75	a 290.0	AlK_a	107
			$4f_{7/2}$	345.4			
O_2 Th	ThO_2	s	$4f_{5/2}$	352.0	a 290.0	AlK_a	107
			$4f_{7/2}$	342.65			
$O_{2\,0}$ $PrTh_9$	$Th_{0.9}Pr_{0.1}O_2$	s	$4f_{5/2}$	351.1	a 290.0	AlK_a	107
			$4f_{7/2}$	341.8			
$O_{4\,0}$ $Th_{1\,9}$ U	$Th_{0.95}U_{0.05}O_2$	s	$4f_{5/2}$	352.35	a 290.0	AlK_a	107
			$4f_{7/2}$	343.0			
Th	Th	s	L_{III}	16,299.8 (9)	$MgK(CuK_{a1})$, CuA6	AgK_{a1}	91
			M_I	5,182.2 (5)	$MgK(CuK_{a1})$	CuK_{a1}	
			M_{II}	4,830.5 (6)			
			M_{III}	4,046.0 (7)			
			M_{IV}	3,490.6 (7)			
			M_V	3,332.0 (8)			
			N_I	1,329.7 (1)			
			N_{II}	1,168.2 (1)			
			N_{III}	967.5 (1)	$MgK(CuK_{a1}, CrK_{a1})$	Cu, CrK_{a1}	
			N_{IV}	714.3 (8)			
			N_V	676.3 (8)			
			N_{VI}	344.1 (8)			
			N_{VII}	334.9 (8)			
			O_{III}	181.8 (8)	$MgK(CrK_{a1})$	CrK_{a1}	
			O_{IV}	94.4 (9)			
			O_V	88.1 (9)			
Ti							
B_2 Ti	TiB_2	s	$2p_{3/2}$	0.3 (2)	Metal Ti $2p_{3/2}$ 0.0	AlK_a	72
CTi	TiC	s	$2p_{3/2}$	1.3 (1)	Metal Ti $2p_{3/2}$ 0.0	AlK_a	72
			ls	1.0 (4)	Metal Ti ls 0.0		
NTi	TiN	s	$2p_{3/2}$	1.5 (2)	Metal Ti $2p_{3/2}$ 0.0	AlK_a	72
			ls	1.2 (4)	Metal Ti ls 0.0		

TABLE 3 (continued)

Compound		Phase	Orbital	E_B(eV)	Calibrant	Exciting Radiation	Reference
OTi	TiO	s	$2p_{3/2}$	1.0 (2)	Metal Ti $2p_{3/2}$ 0.0	AlK_{α}	72
				4.8 (2)			
			ls	1.0 (4)	Metal Ti ls 0.0		
O_2 Ti	TiO_2	s	$2p_{3/2}$	4.9 (2)	Metal Ti $2p_{3/2}$ 0.0	AlK_{α}	72
			ls	4.3 (4)	Metal Ti ls 0.0		
O_2 Ti	TiO_2	s	K	4,965.2 (4)	e, i	CrK_{α}	76
Ti	Ti	s	L_I	563.7	MgO MgK($CuK_{\alpha 1}$)	$CuK_{\alpha 1}$	67
Tl							
BrTl	TlBr	s	$4f_{5/2}$	129.9 (3)	a 290.0	AlK_{α}	62
			$4f_{7/2}$	125.45			
			$5d_{3/2}$	22.2 (3)			
			$5d_{5/2}$	20.1 (3)			
BrTl	TlBr	s	$4f_{5/2}$	128.75	a 290	AlK_{α}	30
			$4f_{7/2}$	124.3			
BrTl	TlBr	s	$4f_{5/2}$	129.9	a 290.0	AlK_{α}	107
			$4f_{7/2}$	125.45			
BrTl	TlBr	s	$4f_{5/2}$	128.75	a 290.0	AlK_{α}	107
			$4f_{7/2}$	124.3			
Br_6 $OsTl_2$	Tl_2 $OsBr_6$	s	$4f_{5/2}$	128.75	a 290.0	AlK_{α}	107
			$4f_{7/2}$	124.4			
Br_6 $OsTl_2$	Tl_2 $OsBr_6$	s	$4f_{5/2}$	128.75	a 290.0	AlK_{α}	62
			$4f_{7/2}$	124.4 (3)			
			$5d_{3/2}$	21.1 (3)			
			$5d_{5/2}$	19.1 (3)			
CO_3 Tl_2	Tl_2 CO_3	s	$4f_{5/2}$	130.35	a 290.0	AlK_{α}	107
			$4f_{7/2}$	125.9			

TABLE 3 (continued)

Compound		Phase	Orbital	E_B(eV)	Calibrant	Exciting Radiation	Reference
CO_3Tl_2	Tl_2CO_3	s	$4f_{5/2}$	129.1	a 290	AlK_α	30
			$4f_{7/2}$	124.65			
$C_{24}H_{20}BTl$	$Tl[B(C_6H_5)_4]$	s	$4f_{5/2}$	129.55	a 290.0	AlK_α	107
			$4f_{7/2}$	125.1			
$Cl_6CoH_{18}N_6Tl$	$[Co(NH_3)_6]TlCl_6$	s	$4f_{5/2}$	129.0	a 290.0	AlK_α	107
			$4f_{7/2}$	124.6			
CrO_4Tl_2	Tl_2CrO_4	s	$4f_{5/2}$	129.95	a 290.0	AlK_α	62
			$4f_{7/2}$	125.55			
			$3d_{3/2}$	22.8 (3)			
			$3d_{5/2}$	20.4 (3)			
CrO_4Tl_2	Tl_2CrO_4	s	$4f_{5/2}$	129.95	a 290.0	AlK_α	107
			$4f_{7/2}$	125.55			
FTl	TlF	s	$4f_{5/2}$	131.6	a 290.0	AlK_α	107
			$4f_{7/2}$	127.2			
IO_3Tl	$TlIO_3$	s	$4f_{5/2}$	131.4	a 290.0	AlK_α	107
			$4f_{7/2}$	126.95			
ITl	TlI	s	$4f_{5/2}$	129.4 (3)	a 290.0	AlK_α	62
			$4f_{7/2}$	125.05			
			$5d_{3/2}$	23.4 (3)			
			$5d_{5/2}$	20.35			
ITl	TlI	s	$4f_{5/2}$	129.4	a 290.0	AlK_α	107
			$4f_{7/2}$	125.05			
$MoOS_3Tl_2$	Tl_2MoOS_3	s	$4f_{5/2}$	129.95	a 290.0	AlK_α	62
			$4f_{7/2}$	125.5 (3)			
			$5d_{3/2}$	22.7 (3)			
			$5d_{5/2}$	20.2 (3)			

TABLE 3 (continued)

Compound		Phase	Orbital	E_B(eV)	Calibrant	Exciting Radiation	Reference
$MoO_2S_2Tl_2$	$Tl_2MoO_2S_2$	s	$4f_{5/2}$	130.1 (3)	a 290.0	AlK_α	62
			$4f_{7/2}$	125.65			
			$5d_{3/2}$	23.2 (3)			
			$5d_{5/2}$	20.4 (3)			
MoO_4Tl_2	Tl_2MoO_4	s	$4f_{5/2}$	130.4 (3)	a 290.0	AlK_α	62
			$4f_{7/2}$	125.95			
			$5d_{3/2}$	23.1 (3)			
			$5d_{5/2}$	20.8 (3)			
MoO_4Tl_2	Tl_2MoO_4	s	$4f_{5/2}$	130.4	a 290.0	AlK_α	107
			$4f_{7/2}$	125.95			
MoS_4Tl_2	Tl_2MoS_4	s	$4f_{5/2}$	129.75	a 290.0	AlK_α	62
			$4f_{7/2}$	125.3 (3)			
			$5d_{3/2}$	22.5 (3)			
			$5d_{5/2}$	20.2 (3)			
NbS_4Tl_3	Tl_3NbS_4	s	$4f_{5/2}$	129.7 (3)	a 290.0	AlK_α	62
			$4f_{7/2}$	125.25			
			$5d_{3/2}$	22.3 (3)			
			$5d_{5/2}$	20.4 (3)			
$NbSe_4Tl_3$	Tl_3NbSe_4	s	$4f_{5/2}$	129.7 (3)	a 290.0	AlK_α	62
			$4f_{7/2}$	125.25 (3)			
			$5d_{3/2}$	22			
			$5d_{5/2}$	20.3 (3)			
$O_2S_2Tl_2W$	$Tl_2WO_2S_2$	s	$4f_{5/2}$	130.3 (3)	a 290.0	AlK_α	62
			$4f_{7/2}$	125.6 (3)			
			$5d_{3/2}$	23.2 (3)			
			$5d_{5/2}$	20.5 (3)			
O_3Tl_2	Tl_2O_3	s	$4f_{5/2}$	127.35	a 290	AlK_α	30
			$4f_{7/2}$	123.0			

TABLE 3 (continued)

Compound		Phase	Orbital	E_B(eV)	Calibrant	Exciting Radiation	Reference
O_3Tl_2	Tl_2O_3	s	$4f_{5/2}$	127.35	a 290.0	AlK_α	107
			$4f_{7/2}$	123.0			
O_4ReTl	$TlReO_4$	s	$4f_{5/2}$	131.45 (3)	a 290.0	AlK_α	62
			$4f_{7/2}$	127.0 (3)			
			$5d_{3/2}$	23.9 (3)			
			$5d_{5/2}$	21.8 (3)			
O_4ReTl	$TlReO_4$	s	$4f_{5/2}$	131.45	a 290.0	AlK_α	107
			$4f_{7/2}$	127.0			
O_4STl_2	Tl_2SO_4	s	$4f_{5/2}$	131.25	a 290.0	AlK_α	107
			$4f_{7/2}$	126.8			
O_4STl_2	Tl_2SO_4	s	$4f_{5/2}$	129.3	a 290	AlK_α	30
			$4f_{7/2}$	124.85			
O_4STl_2	Tl_2SO_4	s	$4f_{5/2}$	131.25	a 290.0	AlK_α	62
			$4f_{7/2}$	126.8 (3)			
			$5d_{3/2}$	23.7 (3)			
			$5d_{5/2}$	21.5 (3)			
O_4Tl_2W	Tl_2WO_4	s	$4f_{5/2}$	130.8 (3)	a 290.0	AlK_α	62
			$4f_{7/2}$	126.35			
			$5d_{3/2}$	23.4 (3)			
			$5d_{5/2}$	21.1 (3)			
O_4Tl_2W	Tl_2WO_4	s	$4f_{5/2}$	130.9	a 290.0	AlK_α	107
			$4f_{7/2}$	126.45			
S_4TaTl_3	Tl_3TaS_4	s	$4f_{5/2}$	130.05	a 290.0	AlK_α	62
			$4f_{7/2}$	125.6 (3)			
			$5d_{3/2}$	22.8 (3)			
			$5d_{5/2}$	20.8 (3)			
S_4Tl_3V	Tl_3VS_4	s	$4f_{5/2}$	129.4 (3)	a 290.0	AlK_α	62
			$4f_{7/2}$	124.95			
			$5d_{3/2}$	22.3 (3)			
			$5d_{5/2}$	20.0 (3)			

TABLE 3 (continued)

Compound		Phase	Orbital	E_B(eV)	Calibrant	Exciting Radiation	Reference
S_4Tl_2W	Tl_2WS_4	s	$4f_{5/2}$ $4f_{7/2}$ $5d_{3/2}$ $5d_{5/2}$	129.6 (3) 125.15 21.8 (3) 19.5 (3)	a 290.0	AlK_a	62
S_4Tl_2W	Tl_2WS_4	s	$4f_{5/2}$ $4f_{7/2}$	129.3 124.85	a 290.0	AlK_a	107
Se_4TaTl_3	Tl_3TaSe_4	s	$4f_{5/2}$ $4f_{7/2}$ $5d_{3/2}$ $5d_{5/2}$	129.1 (3) 124.65 22.2 (3) 19.9 (3)	a 290.0	AlK_a	62
Se_4Tl_3V	Tl_3VSe_4	s	$4f_{5/2}$ $4f_{7/2}$ $5d_{3/2}$ $5d_{5/2}$	129.7 (3) 125.25 (3) 22.8 (3) 20.4 (4)	a 290.0	AlK_a	62
Tl	Tl	s	L_{II} L_{III} M_{II} M_{III} M_{IV} M_V	14,697.6 (5) 12,656.7 (4) 3,415.6 (4) 2,956.4 (5) 2,485.2 (4) 2,389.4 (4)	e	AgK_a MoK_a CuK_a CrK_a	77
Tl	Tl	s	L_{III}	12,656.0	CuK(MoK_{a1})	MoK_{a1}	119
Tm							
O_3Tm_2	Tm_2O_3	s	L_I L_{II} L_{III}	10,115.8 9,617.3 8,648.1	e	MoK_{a1}	56
U							
$C_{18}H_{12}N_2O_4U$	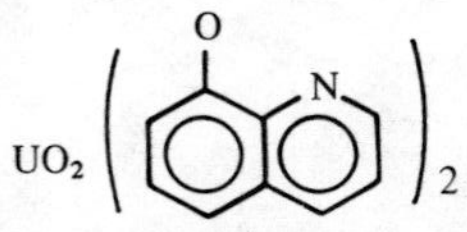	s	$4f_{7/2}$	383.2	c 84	MgK_a	36

TABLE 3 (continued)

Compound		Phase	Orbital	E_B(eV)	Calibrant	Exciting Radiation	Reference
$C_{18}H_{12}N_2O_4U \cdot C_9H_7NO$	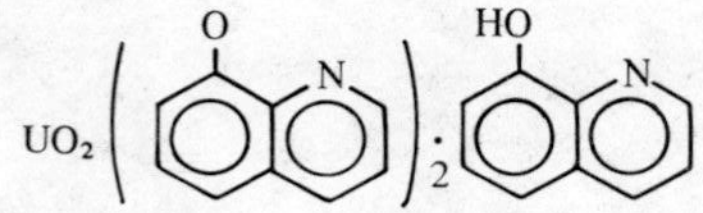	s	$4f_{7/2}$	383.1	c 84	MgK_α	36
$C_{36}H_{32}Cl_6P_2U$	$[P(C_6H_5)_3H]_2UCl_6$	s	$4f_{5/2}$ $4f_{7/2}$	396.6 386.0	a 290.0	AlK_α	107
CeO_4U	$Ce_{0.5}U_{0.5}O_2$	s	$4f_{5/2}$ $4f_{7/2}$	399.5 388.8	a 290.0	AlK_α	107
$CeO_{10}Th_3U$	$Th_{0.2}Ce_{0.6}U_{0.2}O_2$	s s	$4f_{5/2}$ $4f_{7/2}$	400.05 382.15	a 290.0	AlK_α	107
$CuO_{12}P_2U_2$	$Cu(UO_2)_2(PO_4)_2$	s	$4f_{5/2}$ $4f_{7/2}$	400.9 390.0	a 290.0	AlK_α	107
F_6K_2U	K_2UF_6	s	$4f_{5/2}$ $4f_{7/2}$	400.4 389.5	a 290.0	AlK_α	107
$H_8N_2O_7U_2$	$(NH_4)_2U_2O_7$	s	$4f_{5/2}$ $4f_{7/2}$	399.9 389.05	a 290.0	AlK_α	107
$N_3O_{11}RbU$	$RbUO_2(NO_3)_3$	s	$4f_{5/2}$ $4f_{7/2}$	400.6 389.7	a 290.0	AlK_α	107
O_2U	UO_2	s	$4f_{5/2}$ $4f_{7/2}$	398.1 387.3	a 290.0	AlK_α	107
O_2U	$UO_{2.00}$	s	$4f_{7/2}$ $4f_{5/2}$	380.7 (1) 391.5 (1)	c 84.0	AlK_α	92
$O_{2.103}U$	$UO_{2.103}$	s	$4f_{7/2}$ $4f_{5/2}$	380.7 (1) 391.5 (1)	c 84.0	AlK_α	92
O_3U	UO_3	s	$4f_{7/2}$ $4f_{5/2}$	381.9 (1) 392.7 (1)	c 84.0	AlK_α	92

TABLE 3 (continued)

Compound		Phase	Orbital	E_B(eV)	Calibrant	Exciting Radiation	Reference
$O_{3.12}U \cdot H_2O$	$UO_{3.12} \cdot H_2O$	s	$4f_{7/2}$ $4f_{5/2}$	381.8 (1) 392.5 (1)	c 84.0	AlK_α	92
O_8U_3	U_3O_8	s	$4f_{7/2}$ $4f_{5/2}$	381.1 (1) 391.9 (1)	c 84.0	AlK_α	92
O_8U_3	U_3O_8	s	$4f_{5/2}$ $4f_{7/2}$	398.0 387.2	a 290.0	AlK_α	107
$O_{40}Th_{19}U$	$Th_{0.95}U_{0.05}O_2$	s	$4f_{5/2}$ $4f_{7/2}$	400.1 389.2	a 290.0	AlK_α	107
U	U	s	L_{III} M_{II} M_{III} M_{IV} M_V N_I N_{II} N_{III} N_{IV} N_V	17,168.3 5,180.9 4,303.6 3,728.1 3,551.7 1,441.4 1,272.7 1,045.1 779.9 737.8	CuA6	Ag, $PdK_{\alpha 1}$ $GeK_{\alpha 1}$ Ge, $CuK_{\alpha 1}$ $CuK_{\alpha 1}$	44
U	U (oxide layer)	s	$4f_{7/2}$ $4f_{5/2}$	380.7 (1) 391.5 (1)	c 84.0	AlK_α	92
U	U (abrasively cleaned)	s	$4f_{7/2}$ $4f_{5/2}$	380.2 (1) 391.0 (1)	c 84.0	AlK_α	92
V							
CV	$VC_{0.876}$ $VC_{0.716}$	s	$2p_{3/2}$	513.6 (1) 513.3 (1)	Metal V $2p_{3/2}$ 511.8	AlK_α	73
CV	VC	s	ls $2p_{3/2}$	1.5 (4) 1.8 (3)	Metal V ls 0.0 Metal V $2p_{3/2}$ 0.0		72
$C_{10}H_{14}O_5V$	$VO(CH_3C(O)CHC(O)CH_3)_2$	s	$2p_{3/2}$	515.0	Pt $4f_{7/2}$ 71.0	AlK_α	146

TABLE 3 (continued)

Compound		Phase	Orbital	E_B(eV)	Calibrant	Exciting Radiation	Reference
$C_{15}H_{21}O_6V$	$V(CH_3C(O)CHC(O)CH_3)_3$	s	$2p_{3/2}$	514.0	Pt $4f_{7/2}$ 71.0	AlK_α	146
$C_{18}H_{12}N_2O_3V$	VO(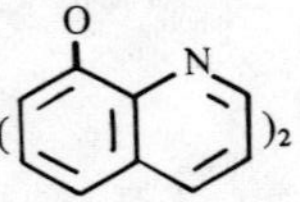)$_2$	s	$2p_{3/2}$	515.5	Pt $4f_{7/2}$ 71.0	AlK_α	146
$C_{18}H_{13}N_2O_4V$	VO(OH) (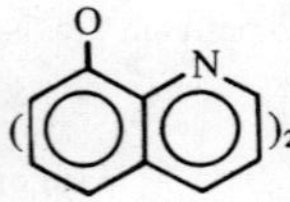)$_2$	s	$2p_{3/2}$	516.6	Pt $4f_{7/2}$ 71.0	AlK_α	146
$C_{32}H_{16}N_8OV$	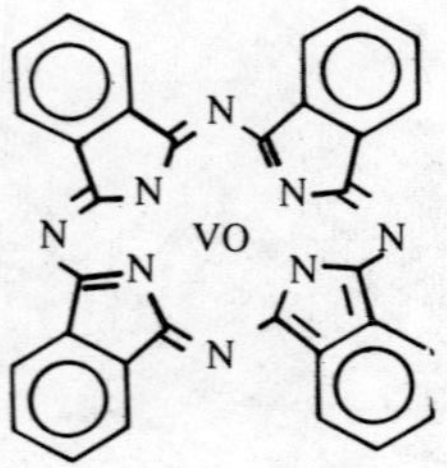	s	$2p_{3/2}$	516.1	Pt $4f_{7/2}$ 71.0	AlK_α	146
Cl_2OV	$VOCl_2$	s	$2p_{3/2}$	516.3	Pt $4f_{7/2}$ 71.0	AlK_α	146
$H_{12}N_3O_9V_3$	$(NH_4)_3V_3O_9$	s	$2p_{1/2}$ $2p_{3/2}$ 3p	529.5 (3) 521.6 (3) 47.6 (3)	a 290.0	AlK_α	62
$H_{12}N_3S_4V$	$(NH_4)_3VS_4$	s	$2p_{1/2}$ $2p_{3/2}$ 3p	526.6 (3) 519.1 (3) 43.7 (3)	a 290.0	AlK_α	62
$Na_3O_4V \cdot 14H_2O$	$Na_3VO_4 \cdot 14H_2O$	s	$2p_{1/2}$ $2p_{3/2}$ 3p	528.0 (3) 522.0 (3) 47.0 (3)	a 290.0	AlK_α	62
O_3V_2	V_2O_3	s	K	5,465.0 (4)	e, i	CuK_α	76

TABLE 3 (continued)

Compound		Phase	Orbital	E_B(eV)	Calibrant	Exciting Radiation	Reference
O_4PrV	$PrVO_4$	s	$2p_{1/2}$	530.5 (3)	a 290.0	AlK_α	62
			$2p_{3/2}$	522.9 (3)			
			3p	49.3 (3)			
O_4V_2	V_2O_4	s	$2p_{3/2}$	516.6		AlK_α	102
O_5SV	$VOSO_4$	s	$2p_{3/2}$	515.9	Pt $4f_{7/2}$ 71.0	AlK_α	146
O_5V_2	V_2O_5	s	$2p_{3/2}$	516.6	Pt $4f_{7/2}$ 71.0	AlK_α	146
O_5V_2	V_2O_5	s	$2p_{1/2}$	529.6 (3)	a 290.0	AlK_α	62
			$2p_{3/2}$	522.2 (3)			
			3p	47.4 (3)			
O_5V_2	V_2O_5	s	$2p_{3/2}$	516.6		AlK_α	102
Se_4Tl_3V	Tl_3VSe_4	s	$2p_{1/2}$	528.5 (3)	a 290.0	AlK_α	62
			$2p_{3/2}$	522:7 (3)			
V	V	s	L_I	628.2	MgO MgK($CuK_{\alpha 1}$)	$CuK_{\alpha 1}$	67
V	V	s	$2p_{3/2}$	512.4	Pt $4f_{7/2}$ 71.0	AlK_α	146
W							
$C_{12}H_{30}Cl_4P_2W$	*trans*-$WCl_4(P(C_2H_5)_3)_2$	s	$4f_{5/2}$	36.8 (3)	d 285	Mg, AlK_α	97
			$4f_{7/2}$	34.8 (3)			
$C_{16}H_{22}Cl_4P_2W$	*trans*-$WCl_4(P(CH_3)_2C_6H_5)_2$	s	$4f_{5/2}$	36.5 (3)	d 285	Mg, AlK_α	97
			$4f_{7/2}$	34.3 (3)			
Cl_6K_2W	K_2WCl_6	s	$4f_{5/2}$	36.8 (3)	d 285	Mg, AlK_α	97
			$4f_{7/2}$	35.1 (3)			

TABLE 3 (continued)

Compound		Phase	Orbital	E_B(eV)	Calibrant	Exciting Radiation	Reference
Cs_2S_4W	Cs_2WS_4	s	$4d_{3/2}$	264.8 (3)	a 290.0	AlK_α	62
			$4d_{5/2}$	252.6 (3)			
			$4f_{5/2}$	42.7 (3)			
			$4f_{7/2}$	40.9 (3)			
Cs_2S_4W	Cs_2WS_4	s	$4f_{5/2}$	42.7	a 290.0	AlK_α	107
			$4f_{7/2}$	40.9			
$H_3O_{40}PW_{12}$	$H_3PW_{12}O_{40}$	s	$4f_{5/2}$	42.95	a 290.0	AlK_α	107
			$4f_{7/2}$	41.1			
Na_2O_4W	Na_2WO_4	s	$4f_{5/2}$	44.7	a 290.0	AlK_α	107
			$4f_{7/2}$	42.9			
Na_2O_4W	Na_2WO_4	s	$4d_{3/2}$	267.3 (3)	a 290.0	AlK_α	62
			$4d_{5/2}$	254.6 (3)			
			$4f_{5/2}$	44.7 (3)			
			$4f_{7/2}$	42.9 (3)			
$O_2S_2Tl_2W$	$Tl_2WO_2S_2$	s	$4d_{3/2}$	265.9 (3)	a 290.0	AlK_α	62
			$4d_{5/2}$	253.2 (3)			
			$4f_{5/2}$	43.3 (3)			
			$4f_{7/2}$	41.7 (3)			
O_2W	WO_2	s	$4f_{7/2}$	36.1		AlK_α	102
O_3W	WO_3	s	$4f_{7/2}$	36.3		AlK_α	102
O_4Tl_2W	Tl_2WO_4	s	$4d_{3/2}$	266.7 (3)	a 290.0	AlK_α	62
			$4d_{5/2}$	254.1 (3)			
			$4f_{5/2}$	44.2 (3)			
			$4f_{7/2}$	42.7 (3)			
$O_{12}W_3Yb_2$	$Yb_2(WO_4)_3$	s	$4d_{3/2}$	267.1 (3)	a 290.0	AlK_α	62
			$4d_{5/2}$	254.6 (3)			
			$4f_{5/2}$	45.1 (3)			
			$4f_{7/2}$	43.2 (3)			

TABLE 3 (continued)

Compound		Phase	Orbital	E_B(eV)	Calibrant	Exciting Radiation	Reference
W	W (oxidized)	s	$4d_{3/2}$	265.5 (3)	a 290.0	AlK_a	62
			$4d_{5/2}$	253.0 (3)			
			$4f_{5/2}$	43.0 (3)			
			$4f_{7/2}$	41.2 (3)			
W	W	s	L_I	12,098.4 (5)	e	MoK_a	77
			L_{II}	11,541.6 (4)			
			L_{III}	10,204.4 (4)			
			M_{II}	2,575.0 (4)		CrK_a	
			M_{III}	2,281.0 (4)			
			M_{IV}	1,871.4 (4)			
			M_V	1,809.3 (4)			
Xe							
F_2Xe	XeF_2	g	$3d_{5/2}$	679.35	Xe Xe $3d_{5/2}$ 676.4	MgK_a	151
F_4OXe	$XeOF_4$	g	$3d_{5/2}$	683.42	Xe Xe $3d_{5/2}$ 676.4	MgK_a	151
F_4Xe	XeF_4	g	$3d_{5/2}$	681.87	Xe Xe $3d_{5/2}$ 676.4	MgK_a	151
F_6Xe	XeF_6	g	$3d_{5/2}$	684.28	Xe Xe $3d_{5/2}$ 676.4	MgK_a	151
Xe	Xe	g	2s	5,453.2 (4)	Xe $5p_{3/2}$ 12.13	CuK_{a1}	151
			$2p_{1/2}$	5,107.2 (4)			
			$2p_{3/2}$	4,787.3 (4)			
			3s	1,148.7 (5)		Cr, AlK_a	
			$3p_{1/2}$	1,002.1 (3)		Al, MgK_a	
			$3p_{3/2}$	940.6 (2)			
			$3d_{3/2}$	689.0 (2)			
			$3d_{5/2}$	676.4 (1)			
			4s	213.2 (2)			
			$4p_{3/2}$	145.5 (2)			
			$4d_{3/2}$	69.5 (1)			
			$4d_{5/2}$	67.5 (1)			
			5s	23.3 (1)			
			$5p_{1/2}$	13.4 (1)			
			$5p_{3/2}$	12.13			

TABLE 3 (continued)

Compound		Phase	Orbital	E_B(eV)	Calibrant	Exciting Radiation	Reference
Y							
Y	Y	s	L_I	2,372.8 (5)		CuK_α	79
			L_{II}	2,155.1 (5)			
			L_{III}	2,080.3 (5)			
Y	Y	s	$3pM_2$	312.8		AlK_α	58
			M_3	301.0			
			$3dM_{4,5}$	158.5			
			$4sN_1$	45.7			
			$4pN_{2,3}$	25.8			
Yb							
O_3Yb_2	Yb_2O_3	s	L_I	10,487.4	e	$MoK_{\alpha 1}$	56
			L_{II}	9,978.1			
			L_{III}	8,942.8			
Yb	Yb	s	$4f_{7/2}$	−1.4 (4)	Pd Fermi level	AlK_α	55
			$4f_{5/2}$	−2.7 (0)			
			$4d_{3/2}$	181.2 (8)			
			$4d_{5/2}$	190.0 (8)			
Zn							
OZn	ZnO	s	$3d_{5/2}$	10.04 (20)	k 283.8	AlK_α	109
			$3d_{3/2}$	10.79 (27)			
			$3p_{3/2}$	88.82 (20)			
			$3p_{1/2}$	91.92 (23)			
			3s	139.60 (20)			
			$2p_{3/2}$	1,021.38 (21)			
			$2p_{1/2}$	1,044.46 (21)			
			2s	1,195.11 (20)			
OZn	ZnO	s	3d	15.65	a 290	AlK_α	30
OZn	ZnO	s	$2p_{3/2}$	1,026.7	a 290	AlK_α	30
			$2p_{1/2}$	1,049.8			

TABLE 3 (continued)

Compound		Phase	Orbital	E_B(eV)	Calibrant	Exciting Radiation	Reference
SZn	ZnS	s	3d	15.7	a 290	AlK_a	30
SZn	ZnS	s	$3d_{5/2}$	10.05 (20)	k 283.8	AlK_a	109
			$3d_{3/2}$	10.61 (20)			
			$3p_{3/2}$	89.00 (20)			
			$3p_{1/2}$	92.15 (20)			
			3s	139.96 (20)			
			$2p_{3/2}$	1,021.65 (20)			
			$2p_{1/2}$	1,044.73 (20)			
			2s	1,195.69 (20)			
SZn	ZnS	s	3p	90 (0.5)		MgK_a	122
SeZn	ZnSe	s	$3d_{5/2}$	10.09 (20)	k 283.8	AlK_a	109
			$3d_{3/2}$	10.85 (26)			
			$3p_{3/2}$	88.99 (20)			
			$3p_{1/2}$	92.22 (20)			
			3s	139.84 (20)			
			$2p_{3/2}$	1,021.54 (21)			
			$2p_{1/2}$	1,044.64 (20)			
			2s	1,195.39 (20)			
TeZn	ZnTe	s	$3d_{5/2}$	9.66 (37)	k 283.8	AlK_a	109
			$3d_{3/2}$	10.35 (40)			
			$3p_{3/2}$	88.69 (20)			
			$3p_{1/2}$	91.86 (20)			
			3s	139.80 (20)			
			$2p_{3/2}$	1,021.29 (24)			
			$2p_{1/2}$	1,044.36 (27)			
			2s	1,195.06 (20)			
Zn	Zn	s	K	9,658.8	CuA6, CuK(MoK_{a1})	MoK_{a1}	123
Zr							
Zr	Zr	s	L_I	2,531.7 (5)		CuK_a	79
			L_{II}	2,306.6 (5)			
			L_{III}	2,222.6 (5)			

REFERENCES

1. Fadley, C. S., Hagström, S. B. M., Klein, M. P., and Shirley, D. A., *J. Chem. Phys.*, 48, 3799, 1968.
2. Hollander, J. M., Hendrickson, D. N., and Jolly, W. L., *J. Chem. Phys.*, 49, 3315, 1968.
3. Kramer, L. N. and Klein, M. P., *J. Chem. Phys.*, 51, 3618, 1969.
4. Kramer, L. N. and Klein, M. P.,*Chem. Phys. Lett.*, 8, 183, 1971.
5. Kramer, L. N. and Klein, M. P., *J. Chem. Phys.*, 51, 3620, 1969.
6. Thomas, T. D., *J. Chem. Phys.*, 52, 1373, 1970.
7. Pelavin, M., Hendrickson, D. N., Hollander, J. M., and Jolly, W. L., *J. Phys. Chem.*, 74, 1116, 1970.
8. Hendrickson, D. N., Hollander, J. M., and Jolly, W. L., *Inorg. Chem.*, 9, 612, 1970.
9. Stec, W. J., Morgan, W. E., Albridge, R. G., and Van Wazer, J. R., *Inorg. Chem.*, 11, 219, 1972.
10. Swartz, W. E., Jr., Watts, P. H., Jr., Lippincott, E. R., Watts, J. C., and Huheey, J. E., *Inorg. Chem.*, 11, 2632, 1972.
11. Finn, P., Pearson, R. K., Hollander, J. M., and Jolly, W. L., *Inorg. Chem.*, 10, 378, 1971.
12. Nordberg, R., Brecht, H., Albridge, R. G., Fahlman, A., and Van Wazer, J. R., *Inorg. Chem.*, 9, 2469, 1970.
13. Hulett, L. D. and Carlson, T. A., *Appl. Spectrosc.*, 25, 33, 1971.
14. Jack, J. J. and Hercules, D. M., *Anal. Chem.*, 43, 729, 1971.
15. Swartz, W. E. and Hercules, D. M., *Anal. Chem.*, 43, 1066, 1971.
16. Olah, G. A., Mateescu, G. D., Wilson, L. A., and Gross, M. H., *J. Am. Chem. Soc.*, 92, 7231, 1970.
17. Barber, M. and Clark, D. T., *Chem. Commun. (J. Chem. Soc. Sect. D)*, 23, 1970.
18. Barber, M. and Clark, D. T., *Chem. Commun. (J. Chem. Soc. Sect. D)*, 24, 1970.
19. Gelius, U., Allan, C. J., Allison, D. A., Siegbahn, H., and Siegbahn, K., *Chem. Phys. Lett.*, 11, 224, 1971.
20. Clark, D. T., Adams, D. B., and Briggs, D., *Chem. Commun. (J. Chem. Soc. Sect. D)*, p. 602, 1971.
21. Clark, D. T., Kilcast, D., and Reid, D. H., *Chem. Commun. (J. Chem. Soc. Sect. D)*, p. 638, 1971.
22. Barber, M., Connor, J. A., Hillier, I. H., and Saunders, V. R., *Chem. Commun. (J. Chem. Soc. Sect. D)*, p. 682, 1971.
23. Clark, D. T. and Adams, D. B., *Chem. Commun. (J. Chem. Soc. Sect. D)*, p. 740, 1971.
24. Barber, M., Connor, J. A., Guest, M. F., Hillier, I. H., and Saunders, V. R., *Chem. Commun.(J. Chem. Soc. Sect. D)*, p. 943, 1971.
25. Clark, D. T. and Lilley, D. M. J., *Chem. Phys. Lett.*, 9, 234, 1971.
26. Clark, D. T. and Adams, D. B., *Chem. Phys. Lett.*, 10, 121, 1971.
27. Clark, D. T. and Kilcast, D.,*J. Chem. Soc. B*, p. 2243, 1971.
28. Clark, D. T. and Kilcast, D., *J. Chem. Soc. A*, p. 3286, 1971.
29. Frost, D. C., McDowell, C. A., and Woolsey, I. S., *Chem. Phys. Lett.*, 17, 320, 1972.
30. Jφrgensen, C. K., *Chimia*, 25, 213, 1971.
31. Buchanan, D. N. E., Robbins, M., Guggenheim, H. J., Wertheim, G. K., and Lambrecht, V. G., *Solid State Commun.*, 9, 583, 1971.
32. Nordberg, R., Albridge, R. G., Bergmark, T., Ericson, U., Hedman, J., Nordling, C., Siegbahn, K., and Lindberg, B. J., *Ark. Kemi*, 257, 1968.
33. Zeller, M. V. and Hayes, R. G., *Chem. Phys. Lett.*, 10, 610, 1971.
34. Wertheim, G. K. and Rosencwaig, A., *J. Chem. Phys.*, 54, 3235, 1971.
35. Cowan, D. O., Park, J., Barber, M., and Swift, P., *Chem. Commun. (J. Chem. Soc. Sect. D)*, p. 1444, 1971.
36. Adams, D. B., Clark, D. T., Baker, A. D., and Thompson, M., *Chem. Commun. (J. Chem. Soc. Sect. D)*, p. 1600, 1971.
37. Lane, B. C., Lester, J. E., and Basolo, F., *Chem. Commun. (J. Chem. Soc. Sect. D)*,p. 1618, 1971.
38. Allan, C. J., Gelius, U., Allison, D. A., Johansson, G., Siegbahn, H., and Siegbahn, K., *J. Electron Spectrosc.*, 1, 131, 1972.
39. Hamrin, K., Johansson, G., Gelius, U., Fahlman, A., Nordling, C., and Siegbahn, K., *Chem. Phys. Lett.*, 1, 613, 1968.
40. Barber, M., Connor, J. A., Hillier, I. H., and Meredith, W. N. E., *J. Electron Spectrosc.*, 1, 110, 1972.
41. Cox, L. E. and Hercules, D. M., *J. Electron Spectrosc.*, 1, 193, 1973.
42. Adams, I., Thomas, J. M., Barber, M., and Williams, R. H., *Chem. Phys. Lett.*, 10, 297, 1971.
43. Prins, R. and Novakov, T., *Chem. Phys. Lett.*, 9, 593, 1971.
44. Nordling, C. and Hagström, S., *Ark. Fysik*, 15, 431, 1959.
45. Bergvall, P., Hörnfeldt, O., and Nordling, C., *Ark. Fysik*, 17, 113, 1960.
46. Frost, D. C., Ishitani, A., and McDowell, C. A., *Mol. Phys.*, 24, 861, 1972.
47. Hedén, P. F., Löfgren, H., and Hagström, S. B. M., *Phys. Rev. Lett.*, 26, 432, 1971.
48. Gelius, U., Hedén, P. F., Hedman, J., Lindberg, B. J., Manne, R., Nordberg, R., Nordling, C., and Siegbahn, K., *Physica Scripta*, 2, 70, 1970.
49. Lindberg, B. J., Hamrin, K., Johansson, G., Gelius, U., Fahlman, A., Nordling, C., and Siegbahn, K., *Physica Scripta*, 1, 286, 1970.
50. Malmsten, G., Nilsson, Ö., Thorén, I., and Bergmark, J.-E., *Physica Scripta*, 1, 37, 1970.

51. Baer, Y., Hedén, P. F., Hedman, J., Klasson, M., Nordling, C., and Siegbahn, K., *Physica Scripta,* 1, 55, 1970.
52. Clark, D. T., Feast, W. J., Kilcast, D., Adams, D. B., and Preston, W. E., *J. Fluorine Chem.,* 2, 199, 1972.
53. Siegbahn, K., Gelius, U., Siegbahn, H., and Olson, E., *Physica Scripta,* 1, 272, 1970.
54. Novakov, T. and Prins, R., *Solid State Commun.,* 9, 1975, 1971.
55. Hagström, S. B. M., Hedén, P. O., and Löfgren, H., *Solid State Commun.,* 8, 1245, 1970.
56. Bergvall, P. and Hagström, S., *Ark. Fysik,* 17, 61, 1960.
57. Adams, I., Thomas, J. M., and Bancroft, G. M., *Earth Planetary Sci. Lett..* 16, 429, 1972.
58. Nagakura, I., Ishii, T., and Sagawa, T., *J. Phys. Soc. Jap.,* 33, 754, 1972.
59. Haselbach, E., Henriksson, A., Jachimorvicz, F., and Wirz, J., *Helv. Chim. Acta,* 55, 1757, 1972.
60. Thomas, T. D., *J. Chem. Phys.,* 53, 1744, 1970.
61. Davis, D. W., Hollander, J. M., Shirley, D. A., and Thomas, T. D., *J. Chem. Phys.,* 52, 3295, 1970.
62. Müller, V. A., Jϕrgensen, C. K., and Diemen, E., *Z. Anorg. Allg. Chem.,* 391, 38, 1972.
63. Wyatt, J. F., Hillier, I. H., Saunders, V. R., Connor, J. A., and Barber, M., *J. Chem. Phys.,* 54, 5311, 1971.
64. Jϕrgensen, C. K., Berthou, H., and Balsenc, L., *J. Fluorine Chem.,* 1, 327, 1971/72.
65. Fahlman, A., Hamrin, K., Nordberg, R., Nordling, C., and Siegbahn, K., *Phys. Rev. Lett.,* 14, 127, 1965.
66. Sharma, J., Gora, T., Rimstidt, J. D., and Staley, R., *Chem. Phys. Lett.,* 15, 232, 1972.
67. Nordberg, R., Hamrin, K., Fahlman, A., Nordling, C., and Siegbahn, K., *Z. Phys.,* 192, 462, 1966.
68. Hagström, S., *Z. Phys.,* 178, 82, 1964.
69. Gelius, U., Allan, C. J., Johansson, G., Siegbahn, H., Allison, D. A., and Siegbahn, K., *Physica Scripta,* 3, 237, 1971.
70. Hedman, J., Klasson, M., Nilsson, R., Nordling, C., Sorokina, M. F., Kljushnikov, O. I., Nemnonov, S. A., Trapeznikov, V. A., and Zyryanov, V. G., *Physica Scripta,* 4, 195, 1971.
71. Hamrin, K., Johansson, G., Gelius, U., Nordling, C., and Siegbahn, K., *Physica Scripta,* 1, 277, 1970.
72. Ramqvist, L., Hamrin, K., Johansson, G., Fahlman, A., and Nordling, C., *J. Phys. Chem. Solids,* 30, 1835, 1969.
73. Ramqvist, L., Hamrin, K., Johansson, G., Gelius, U., and Nordling, C., *J. Phys. Chem. Solids,* 31, 2669, 1970.
74. Karlsson, S.-E., Norberg, C.-H., Nilsson, Ö., Högberg, S., El-Farrash, A. H., Nordling, C., and Siegbahn, K., *Ark. Fysik,* 38, 341, 1968.
75. Fahlman, A., Hagström, S., Hamrin, K., Nordberg, R., Nordling, C., and Siegbahn, K., *Ark. Fysik,* 31, 479, 1966.
76. Hagström, S. and Karlsson, S.-E., *Ark. Fysik,* 26, 451, 1964.
77. Fahlman, A. and Hagström, S., *Ark. Fysik,* 27, 69, 1965.
78. Andersson, I. and Hagström, S., *Ark. Fysik,* 27, 161, 1965.
79. Fahlman, A., Hörnfeldt, O., and Nordling, C., *Ark. Fysik,* 23, 75, 1962.
80. Sokolowski, E., Nordling, C., and Siegbahn, K., *Phys. Rev.,* 110, 776, 1958.
81. Leigh, G. J., Murrell, J. N., Bremser, W., and Proctor, W. G., *Chem. Commun. (J. Chem. Soc. Sect. D),* p. 1661, 1970.
82. Mason, R., Mingos, D. M. P., Rucci, G., and Connor, J. A., *J. Chem. Soc. Dalton Trans.,* p. 1729, 1972.
83. Finn, P. and Jolly, W. L., *Inorg. Chem.,* 11, 893, 1972.
84. Iwamura, H., Fukunaga, M., and Kushida, K., *J. Chem. Soc. D,* p. 450, 1972.
85. Perry, W. B. and Jolly, W. L., *Chem. Phys. Lett.,* 17, 611, 1972.
86. Kusnar, G., Blackburn, J. R., Albridge, R. G., Moddeman, W. E., and Jones, M. M., *Inorg. Chem.,* 11, 296, 1972.
87. Riggs, W. M., *Anal. Chem.,* 44, 830, 1972.
88. Shaw, R. W., Jr. and Thomas, T. D., *Chem. Phys. Lett.,* 14, 121, 1972.
89. Adams, I., Thomas, J. M., Bancroft, G. M., Butler, K. D., and Barber, M., *J. Chem. Soc. D,* p. 751, 1972.
90. Gora, T., Staley, R., Rimstidt, J. D., and Sharma, J., *Phys. Rev. B,* 5, 2309, 1972.
91. Nordling, C. and Hagström, S., *Z. Phys.,* 178, 418, 1964.
92. Chadwick, D. and Graham, J., *Nat. Phys. Sci.,* 237, 127, 1972.
93. Clark, D. T. and Briggs, D., *Nat. Phys. Sci.,* 237, 15, 1972.
94. Thomas, J. M., Adams, I., Williams, R. H., and Barber, M., *J. Chem. Soc. Faraday Trans. II,* 68, 755, 1972.
95. Ginnard, C. R. and Riggs, W. M., *Anal. Chem.,* 44, 1310, 1972.
96. Clark, D. T., Chambers, R. D., Kilcast, D., and Musgrave, W. K. R., *J. Chem. Soc. Faraday Trans. II,* 68, 309, 1972.
97. Leigh, G. J. and Bremser, W., *J. Chem. Soc. Dalton Trans.,* p. 1216, 1972.
98. Patsch, M. and Theime, P., *Angew. Chem.,* 83, 588, 1971.
99. Finn, P. and Jolly, W. L., *Inorg. Chem.,* 11, 1434, 1972.
100. Stec, W. J., Moddeman, W. E., Albridge, R. G., and Van Wazer, J. R., *J. Phys. Chem.,* 75, 3975, 1971.
101. Swartz, W. E., Jr., Wynne, K. J., and Hercules, D. M., *Anal. Chem.,* 43, 1884, 1971.
102. Swartz, W. E., Jr. and Hercules, D. M., *Anal Chem.,* 43, 1774, 1971.
103. Kim, K. S., Winograd, N., and Davis, R. E., *J. Am. Chem. Soc.,* 93, 6296, 1971.
104. Morgan, W. E., Stec, W. J., Albridge, R. G., and Van Wazer, J. R., *Inorg. Chem.,* 10, 926, 1971.
105. Stec, W. J., Morgan, W. E., Van Wazer, J. R., and Proctor, W. G., *J. Inorg. Nucl. Chem.,* 34, 1100, 1972.
106. Adams, D. B., Banister, A. J., Clark, D. T., and Kilcast, D., *Int. J. Sulfur Chem. A,* 1, 143, 1971.
107. Jϕrgensen, C. K., *Theor. Chim. Acta,* 24, 241, 1972.
108. Novakov, T. and Geballe, T. H., *Solid State Commun.,* 10, 225, 1972.
109. Vesely, C. J. and Langer, D. W., *Phys. Rev. B,* 4, 451, 1971.

110. Hashmall, J. A., Mills, B. E., Shirley, D. A., and Streitweiser, A., Jr., *J. Am. Chem. Soc.*, 94, 4445, 1972.
111. Tricker, M. J., Adams, I., and Thomas, J. M., *Inorg. Nucl. Chem. Lett.*, 8, 633, 1972.
112. Carver, J. C., Schweitzer, G. K., and Carlson, T. A., *J. Chem. Phys.*, 57, 973, 1972.
113. Finn, P. and Jolly, W. L., *J. Am. Chem. Soc.*, 94, 1540, 1972.
114. Bremser, W. and Linnemann, F., *Chem. Ztg.*, 96, 36, 1972.
115. Bus, J., *Recl. Trav. Chim. Pays-Bas Belg.*, 91, 552, 1972.
116. Blackburn, J. R., Nordberg, R., Stevie, F., Albridge, R. G., and Jones, M. M., *Inorg. Chem.*, 9, 2374, 1970.
117. Hendrickson, D. N., Hollander, J. M., and Jolly, W. L., *Inorg. Chem.*, 8, 2642, 1969.
118. Clark, D. T., Kilcast, D., and Musgrave, W. K. R., *Chem. Commun. (J. Chem. Soc. Sect. D)*, p. 516, 1971.
119. Sokolowski, E., *Ark. Fysik*, 15, 1, 1959.
120. Nilsson, Ö., Norberg, C.-H., Bergmark, J.-E., Fahlman, A., Nordling, C., and Siegbahn, K., *Helv. Phys. Acta*, 41, 1064, 1968.
121. Thomas, T. D., *J. Am. Chem. Soc.*, 92, 4184, 1970.
122. Fadley, C. S. and Shirley, D. A., *J. Res. Nat. Bur. Stands.*, 74A, 543, 1970.
123. Nordling, C., *Ark. Fysik*, 15, 397, 1959.
124. Matienzo, L. J., Swartz, W. E., Jr., and Grim, S. O., *Inorg. Nucl. Chem. Lett.*, 8, 1085, 1972.
125. Grim, S. O., Matienzo, L. J., and Swartz, W. E., Jr., *J. Am. Chem. Soc.*, 94, 5116, 1972.
126. Leibfritz, D., *Angew. Chem.*, 84, 156, 1972.
127. Lauher, J. W. and Lester, J. E., *Inorg. Chem.*, 12, 244, 1973.
128. Swartz, W. E., Jr., Ruff, J. K., and Hercules, D. M., *J. Am. Chem. Soc.*, 94, 5227, 1927.
129. Moddeman, W. E., Blackburn, J. R., Kumar, G., Morgan, K. A., Albridge, R. G., and Jones, M. M., *Inorg. Chem.*, 11, 1715, 1972.
130. Clark, D. T., Feast, W. J., Kilcast, D., and Musgrave, W. K. R., *J. Polym. Sci. Polym. Chem.*, 11, 389, 1973.
131. Morrison, W. K., Jr. and Hendrickson, D. N., *Inorg. Chem.*, 11, 2600, 1972.
132. Maccagnani, G., Mangini, A., and Pignataro, S., *Tetrahedron Lett.*, p. 3853, 1972.
133. Nicholls, C. J., Urch, D. S., and Kay, A. N. L., *J. Chem. Soc. D*, p. 1198, 1972.
134. Ley, L., Kowalczyk, S., Pollak, R., and Shirley, D. A., *Phys. Rev. Lett.*, 29, 1088, 1972.
135. Pollak, R. A., Ley, L., Kowalczyk, S., Shirley, D. A., Joannopoulos, J. D., Chadi, D. J., and Cohen, M. L., *Phys. Rev. Lett.*, 29, 1103, 1972.
136. Friedman, R. M., Hudis, J., and Perlman, M. L., *Phys. Rev. Lett.*, 29, 692, 1972.
137. Pollak, R. A., Kowalczyk, S., Ley, L., and Shirley, D. A., *Phys. Rev. Lett.*, 29, 274, 1972.
138. Wood, C., Shaffer, J. C., and Proctor, W. G., *Phys. Rev. Lett.*, 29, 485, 1972.
139. Fahlman, A., Hamrin, K., Nordberg, R., Nordling, C., Siegbahn, K., and Holm, L. W., *Phys. Lett.*, 19, 643, 1966.
140. Swartz, W. E., Jr., Watts, P. H., Jr., Watts, J. C., Brasch, J. W., and Lippincott, E. R., *Anal. Chem.*, 44, 2001, 1972.
141. Mateescu, G. D., Riemenschneider, J. L., Svoboda, J. J., and Olah, G. A., *J. Am. Chem. Soc.*, 94, 7191, 1972.
142. Davis, D. W., Shirley, D. A., and Thomas, T. D., *J. Am. Chem. Soc.*, 94, 6565, 1972.
143. Gleiter, R., Hornung, V., Lindberg, B., Högberg, S., and Lozac'h, N., *Chem. Phys. Lett.*, 11, 401, 1971.
144. Malmsten, G., Thorén, I., Högberg, S., Bergmark, J.-E., and Karlsson, S.-E., *Physica Scripta*, 3, 96, 1971.
145. Norbury, A. H., Thompson, M., and Songstad, J., *Inorg. Nucl. Chem. Lett.*, 9, 347, 1973.
146. Larsson, R., Folkesson, B., and Schön, G., *Chemica Scripta*, 3, 88, 1973.
147. Escard, J., Mavel, G., Lozac'h, N., and Legrand, L., *Tetrahedron Lett.*, p. 249, 1973.
148. Hoof, D. L., Tisley, D. G., and Walton, R. A., *Inorg. Nucl. Chem. Lett.*, 9, 571, 1973.
149. Stucky, G. D., Mathews, D. A., Hedman, J., Klasson, M., and Nordling, C., *J. Am. Chem. Soc.*, 94, 8009, 1972.
150. Cox, L. E., Jack, J. J., and Hercules, D. M., *J. Am. Chem. Soc.*, 94, 6575, 1972.
151. Siegbahn, K., Nordling, C., Johansson, G., Hedman, J., Hedén, P. F., Hamrin, K., Gelius, U., Bergmark, T., Werme, L. O., Manne, R., and Baer, Y., *ESCA Applied to Free Molecules*, North-Holland Publishing Co., Amsterdam, 1969.

Section C

Flame Spectroscopy

Molecular Spectra of Flames

MOLECULAR SPECTRA OF FLAMES

A. G. Gaydon, Imperial College, and R. E. Smith, Imperial College

The following data should enable the various spectra that are encountered in flames to be identified. The ultraviolet, visible, and infrared regions of the spectrum are covered. For convenience, the three main types of flames are dealt with separately as follows:

I. Molecular spectra of organic flames (fuel containing carbon and one or more of the elements hydrogen, oxygen, nitrogen).
II. Molecular spectra of flames containing nonmetals (B, halogens, N, P, S).
III. Molecular spectra of flames containing added metals (Al, Ba, Ca, Cu, Fe, Mg, Mn, Pb, Sr).

Because of the relative importance of organic flames over those described in Sections II and III, Section I contains more information on the various molecular species in organic flames than do Sections II and III on the species in flames containing nonmetals or metals.

In Section I, wavelengths, dissociation energies, radiative lifetimes, oscillator strengths, the more important spectroscopic constants, and references for Franck-Condon factors and details of the rotational structure are given for the various molecules. Unless otherwise stated, the wavelengths, dissociation energies, and spectroscopic constants are taken from references given in the following publications, which should be consulted for a complete bibliography:

Gaydon, A. G., *Dissociation Energies,* 3rd ed., Chapman & Hall, London, 1968.

Gaydon, A. G., *Spectroscopy of Flames,* Chapman & Hall, London, 1957. 2nd ed. in press, 1974.

Mavrodineanu, R. and Boiteux, H., *Flame Spectroscopy,* J. Wiley & Sons, New York, 1965.

Pearse, R. W. B. and Gaydon, A. G., *Identification of Molecular Spectra,* 3rd ed., Chapman & Hall, London, 1965.

Rosen, B., Ed., *International Tables of Selected Constants: Spectroscopic Data Relative to Diatomic Molecules,* Pergamon Press, Oxford, 1970.

Sections II and III describe the various spectra that are characteristic of flames containing nonmetals and metals, giving wavelengths but not molecular constants. The latter can be found in the above publications.

Intensities are denoted by the following symbols:

vS	Very strong
S	Strong
M	Moderate
W	Weak
vW	Very weak

In the tables of wavelengths given under each molecule separately, they are a guide to the relative strength of each band within a system and are not to be used for comparing the intensities of one band system with another.

Abbreviations and symbols used are as follows:

Deg.	Degraded (V = Violet, R = Red, Max = Maximum of intensity)
Int.	Intensity
λ_H	Band head wavelength (Å)
ν_H	Band head frequency (cm^{-1})
λ_o	Origin wavelength (Å)
ν_o	Origin frequency (cm^{-1})
D_o	Dissociation energy (ground state)
$f_{(0,0)}$	Band absorption oscillator strength
$f_{(A-X)}$	System absorption oscillator strength
τ_{rad}	Radiative lifetime
v', v''	Upper and lower state vibrational quantum numbers, respectively
r_e	Equilibrium internuclear distance (Å)
T_e	Electronic energy
T_o	Electronic energy (of v=0 level)
B_e, α_e	Rotational constants, such that $B_v = B_e - \alpha_e(v+½)$
ω_e	Equilibrium vibrational frequency and
$\omega_e x_e$	Anharmonicity constant, such that the vibrational energy $G(v) = \omega_e(v+½) - \omega_e x_e(v+½)^2$

Unless otherwise stated, all molecular constants are given in cm^{-1}.

I. MOLECULAR SPECTRA OF ORGANIC FLAMES (FUEL CONTAINING CARBON AND ONE OR MORE OF THE ELEMENTS HYDROGEN, OXYGEN, NITROGEN)

Wavelengths, wavenumbers, molecular constants, and characteristic features of the emission spectra of the following molecules are presented in the order:

C_2, C_3, CH, CHO, CH_2O, CN, CO, CO_2, H_2O, NCN, NH, NO, O_2, OH

The types of flames in which the various spectra can be seen are given, and if the spectrum can also be observed in absorption, this is indicated. A table, in order of wavelength, of the characteristic bands occurring in organic flames is also given.

C_2

There are eleven known band systems of C_2, and five of these have been reported in hydrocarbon flames.

A. The Swan System ($A^3\Pi_g - X^3\Pi_u$)

This is the strongest system of C_2 and can be seen in most organic flames and in all hydrocarbon flames, giving rise to the characteristic blue-green color. It can also be obtained in absorption.

The bands are single headed and degraded to the violet. They form well-marked sequences. Weaker red-degraded "tail bands" with higher vibrational quantum numbers are found in oxyacetylene flames.

TABLE 1

λ_H(Å)	ν_H(cm^{-1})	Int.	v'v''	λ_H(Å)	ν_H(cm^{-1})	Int.	v'v''
4,364.9	22,903	M	4,2	5,470.3	18,276	vW	4,5
4,371.4	22,869	W	3,1	5,501.9	18,170	W	3,4
4,382.2	22,813	vW	2,0	5,540.7	18,043	M	2,3
4,678.6	21,368	vW	5,4	5,585.5	17,899	S	1,2
4,680.2	21,361	vW	6,5	5,635.5	17,740	S	0,1
4,684.9	21,339	W	4,3	5,901.0	16,942	vW	6,8
4,697.6	21,282	S	3,2	5,923.9	16,876	vW	5,7
4,715.3	21,202	S	2,1	5,959.0	16,777	vW	4,6
4,737.1	21,104	vS	1,0	6,004.9	16,648	W	3,5
*4,770.2	20,958	vW	10,9	6,059.7	16,498	W	2,4
*4,836.1	20,672	vW	11,10	6,122.2	16,330	W	1,3
*4,911.0	20,357	vW	12,11	6,191.3	16,147	W	0,2
*4,996.7	20,008	vW	13,12	6,444.7	15,512	vW	6,9
5,070.9	19,715	vW	3,3	6,481.8	15,424	vW	5,8
5,097.7	19,611	vW	2,2	6,533.6	15,301	vW	4,7
5,129.4	19,490	M	1,1	6,599.1	15,149	vW	3,6
5,165.2	19,355	vS	0,0	6,675.9	14,975	vW	2,5
5,447.7	18,351	vW	5,6	6,762.4	14,784	vW	1,4

* Tail bands

Oscillator strength (Smith [1969a]): $f_{(0,0)} = 0.0178 \pm 0.0018$

$f_{(1,0)} = 0.0061 \pm 0.0007$

See Phillips and Davis (1968) for wavelengths, wavenumbers, identifications, and relative intensities of the rotational lines of the Swan bands. Franck-Condon factors are given by Tyte et al. (1967).

B. The Fox-Herzberg System ($B^3\Pi_g - X^3\Pi_u$)

This is a weak system observed under high dispersion in hot flames such as oxyacetylene.

The heads are not pronounced, and it is not easy to ascertain their existence. The bands are strongly degraded to the red. Usually there is some masking by OH bands.

TABLE 2

λ_H(Å)	ν_H(cm^{-1})	v′v″	λ_H(Å)	ν_H(cm^{-1})	v′v″
2,378.2	42,036	4,1	2,731.6	36,598	0,2
2,429.9	41,141	3,1	2,772.1	36,063	1,3
2,486.3	40,208	2,1	**2,855	35,015	0,3
2,527.9	39,547	3,2	2,896.4	34,516	1,4
2,589.0	38,613	2,2	**2,987	33,468	0,4
2,656.3	37,635	1,2	*3,129	31,949	0,5
2,698.8	37,043	2,3	*3,283	30,451	0,6

** Strong band
*Probably fairly strong

Wavenumbers and identifications of individual rotational lines are given by Phillips (1949). For Franck-Condon factors, see Hallmann and Laulicht (1966).

C. Mulliken's System ($d^1\Sigma_u^+ - x^1\Sigma_g^+$)

This is a weak system present in oxyhydrocarbon flames.

There is no obvious head and the intensity distribution presents a minimum between two maxima. The latter are the P and R branches of the superposed (0,0), (1,1), (2,2), and (3,3) bands. A very weak (0,1) band may also be observed.

TABLE 3

λ_o(Å)	ν_o(cm^{-1})	v′v″
2,312.7	43,227	0,0
2,314.0	43,201	1,1
2,315.4	43,176	2,2
2,316.8	43,151	3,3
2,414.8	41,399	0,1

Oscillator strength (Smith [1969a]): $f_{(0,0)} = 0.055 \pm 0.006$

Wavenumbers and identifications of the individual rotational lines of the (0,0) sequence are given by Landsverk (1939). For Franck-Condon factors, see Hallmann and Laulicht (1966).

D. The Deslandres d'Azambuja System ($c^1\Pi_g$ - $b^1\Pi_u$)

This is a weak system present in hot, rich hydrocarbon flames. They are strongly overlapped by CN bands if air is used instead of oxygen.

The bands are single headed and degraded to shorter wavelengths, except for weak "tail bands," which are degraded to longer wavelengths.

TABLE 4

λ_H(Å)	ν_H(cm^{-1})	Int.	Deg.	v'v''	λ_H(Å)	ν_H(cm^{-1})	Int.	Deg.	v'v''
3,398.1	29,419	W	V	3,1	3,617.9	27,632	vW	R	5,4
3,399.8	29,406	W	V	2,0	3,689.0	27,100	vW	R	6,5
3,405.1[a]	29,359[a]	vW	—	4,2	3,825.6	26,132	M	V	1,1
3,431.9	29,129	vW	R	5,3	3,852.2	25,952	vS	V	0,0
3,587.6	27,866	M	V	3,2	4,026.9	24,826	vW	V	3,4
3,592.9	27,825	S	V	2,1	4,041.9	24,735	W	V	2,3
3,599.3	27,775	W	V	4,3	4,068.1	24,574	M	V	1,2
3,607.3	27,714	S	V	1,0	4,102.3	24,370	vS	V	0,1

[a] Origin of headless band

For the rotational structure, see Herzberg and Sutton (1940).

E. The Phillips System ($b^1\Pi_u$ - $x^1\Sigma_g^+$)

These bands are the most prominant feature of hydrocarbon flames in the photographic infrared region.

The bands are degraded to longer wavelengths with a strong Q branch and weaker R and P branches. The R heads are given below.

TABLE 5

λ_H(Å)	ν_H(cm^{-1})	v'v''	λ_H(Å)	ν_H(cm^{-1})	v'v''
7,714.6	12,959	3,0	8,980.5	11,132	3,1
7,907.7	12,642	4,1	10,147[a]	9,852[a]	1,0
8,108.2	12,330	5,2	12,070.2	8,283	0,0
8,750.8	11,424	2,0	15,484.1	6,456	0,1

[a] Origin

See Phillips (1948) and Ballik and Ramsay (1963b) for wavenumbers and identifications of rotational lines. Franck-Condon factors are given by Hallmann and Laulicht (1966).

F. The Ballik-Ramsay System ($A'^3\Sigma_g^-$ - $X^3\Pi_u$)

Although not yet identified in flame spectra, these bands are included since they probably do occur, involving an excitation energy of about 1 eV, much smaller than that corresponding to the Swan and Fox-Herzberg Systems.

The bands appear in the far infrared region and are degraded to longer wavelengths.

TABLE 6

λ_H(Å)	ν_H(cm^{-1})	v′v″
11,724	8,527	2,0
14,075	7,103	1,0
17,675	5,656	0,0
24,745	4,040	0,1

See Ballik and Ramsay (1963a) for wavenumbers and identifications of rotational lines. Franck-Condon factors are given by Hallmann and Laulicht (1966).

TABLE 7

Molecular Constants for the Electronic States of C_2 that Are Involved in Flame Spectra

State	T_e	ω_e	$\omega_e x_e$	B_e	a_e	r_e(Å)	Ref.
$d^1\Sigma_u^+$	43,240.23	1,829.57	13.97	1.8334	0.0204	1.2378	
$B^3\Pi_g$	40,796.65	1,106.56	39.260	1.1922	0.0242	1.5350	
$c^1\Pi_g$	34,261.9	1,809.1	15.81	1.7834	0.0180	1.2552	
$A^3\Pi_g$	20,022.50	1,788.22	16.440	1.7527	0.01608	1.2660	
$b^1\Pi_u$	8,391.267	1,608.220	12.055	1.616110	0.01678	1.31852	Marenin and Johnson (1970)
$A'^3\Sigma_g^-$	6,434.27	$1,470.4_5$	11.1_9	1.4985_2	0.01634	1.3692_8	
$X^3\Pi_u$	$716._{24}$	1,641.35	11.67	1.6324_6	0.01661	1.3119_0	
$x^1\Sigma_g^+$	0	1,854.783	13.389	1.819839	0.017697	1.24253	Marenin and Johnson (1970)

Radiative lifetimes (Smith [1969a]): Swan System ($A^3\Pi_g$–$X^3\Pi_u$), Δv=0,1 sequences, τ_{rad} = 170 ± 20 nsec. Mulliken's System ($d^1\Sigma^+$–$x^1\Sigma_g^+$), τ_{rad} = 14.6 ± 1.5 nsec.

Dissociation energy: D_o = 6.25 ± 0.2 eV

C_3

A. The 4,050 Å Comet-head Group

This group of narrow bands lying between the two main CH systems occurs in very rich hydrocarbon flames, superimposed on a strong continuum. Under small dispersion they appear rather diffuse, but with big dispersion they show rotational structure. The strongest head is at 4,049.8 Å and is degraded to the red. The bands have also been observed in absorption in oxyacetylene flames.

The following heads were obtained in an oxyacetylene flame. The "weight" column is an estimate of the relative probability that the band is actually present, ascending number indicating a greater probability. This was necessary because of the difficulty in measuring the weak band heads superimposed on the strong continuum (Kiess and Broida [1956]).

TABLE 8

λ_H(Å)	ν_H(cm^{-1})	Int.	Weight	λ_H(Å)	ν_H(cm^{-1})	Int.	Weight
3,634	27,510	vW	1	3,966.9	25,201	W	2
3,651.5	27,378	vW	3	3,971.9	25,170	vW	1
3,668.9	27,248	vW	2	3,975.4	25,147	vW	1
3,677.7	27,183	vW	1	3,981.8	25,107	vW	1
3,687.3	27,112	vW	3	3,988.3	25,066	vW	2
3,705.8	26,977	vW	3	3,994.6	25,027	W	3
3,714.8	26,912	vW	3	4,007.6	24,946	M	3
3,729.0	26,809	vW	2	4,008.7	24,939	M	2
3,738.0	26,745	vW	3	4,018.4	24,880	M	3
3,760.4	26,585	vW	3	4,022.7	24,852	M	4
3,783.7	26,421	vW	3	4,029.1	24,812	M	2
3,802.5	26,291	vW	3	4,038.0	24,758	M	4
3,814.2	26,210	vW	1	4,041.7	24,735	W	2
3,824.1	26,143	vW	3	4,049.8	24,686	vS	5
3,833.3	26,080	vW	1	4,065.0	24,594	W	3
3,844.8	26,002	vW	2	4,072.4	24,550	S	5
3,893.8	25,675	vW	1	4,093.8	24,421	W	4
3,925.0	25,471	vW	3	4,115.2	24,293	vW	3
3,939.9	25,374	vW	1	4,138.3	24,158	vW	3
3,944.9	25,342	vW	1	4,160.2	24,031	vW	-3

A rotational analysis of the 4050 Å Comet-Head Group is given by Gausset et al. (1965). The electronic transition is $^1\Pi_u - ^1\Sigma_g^+$.

CH

Bands of CH are a main feature of organic flames and are readily excited during the combustion of hydrocarbons. Three systems are known, in the regions of 4,300 Å, 3,900 Å, and 3,143 Å, the intensities decreasing in the order given. They can also be observed in absorption.

A. The 4,300 Å System ($A^2\Delta - X^2\Pi$)

This system is degraded to the violet. The (0,0) band shows sharp Q branch maxima, and the P branch piles up to form what looks like a head under small dispersion near 4,385 Å. The (1,1) and (2,2) bands are overlaid by the (0,0); a line-like feature at 4,324 Å is the piled up Q branch of the (2,2) band. The Δv=1 sequence is usually rather weak.

TABLE 9

λ_H(Å)	ν_H(cm^{-1})	Int.	Branch	v'v''
4,314.2	23,173	vS	Q	0,0
4,323	23,126	M	Q	2,2
(4,385)	(22,799)	M	(P)	0,0
4,858.8	20,576	vW	Q	1,2
4,890.3	20,443	W	Q	0,1
4,913.5	20,346	vW	P	1,2
4,941.2	20,232	vW	P	0,1

Oscillator strength (Bennett and Dalby [1960] and Fink and Welge [1967]): $f_{(A-X)} = 0.005 \pm 0.0005$

Wavelengths, wavenumbers, identifications, and relative intensities of rotational lines are tabulated by Moore and Broida (1959). For identification only, see Bass and Broida (1961). Franck-Condon factors are given by Hallmann and Laulicht (1966).

B. The 3,900 Å System ($B^2\Sigma^- - X^2\Pi$)

This system is degraded to the red, with a more open rotational structure than the 4,300 Å System. The rotational structure of bands with v′=1 is curtailed by predissociation.

TABLE 10

λ_H(Å)	ν_H(cm^{-1})	Int.	Branch	v′v″
3,627.2	27,562	vW	R	1,0
3,633.3	27,515	vW	Q	1,0
3,871.4	25,823	vS	R	0,0
3,886.4	25,723	S	Q	0,0
4,025.3	24,836	W	R	1,1
4,033.8	24,783	vW	Q	1,1
4,495.5?	22,238?	vW	R	1,2

Oscillator strength (Fink and Welge [1967]): $f_{(0,0)}$ = 0.0023 ± 0.0005

Wavelengths, wavenumbers, identifications, and relative intensities of rotational lines are tabulated by Moore and Broida (1959). For identification only, see Bass and Broida (1961). Franck-Condon factors are given by Hallmann and Laulicht (1966).

C. The 3,143 Å System ($C^2\Sigma^+ - X^2\Pi$)

The (0,0) and (1,1) bands of this system are known. The (0,0) band has a piled up Q head at 3,144 Å, and the (1,1) forms a similar, less intense head at 3,157 Å. The branches are usually heavily overlapped by OH.

TABLE 11

λ_H(Å)	ν_H(cm^{-1})	Int.	v′v″
3,144	31,797	vS	0,0
3,157	31,667	M	1,1

Oscillator strength (Linevsky [1967]): $f_{(0,0)}$ = 0.006 ± 0.001

Wavelengths, wavenumbers, identifications, and relative intensities of rotational lines are tabulated by Moore and Broida (1959). For identification only, see Bass and Broida (1961). Franck-Condon factors are given by Hallmann and Laulicht (1966).

TABLE 12

Molecular Constants for CH

State	T_e	ω_e	$\omega_e x_e$	B_e	α_e	r_e(Å)	τ_{rad}(nsec)
$C^2\Sigma^+$	31,792.3	2,824.1	105.8	14.629	0.744	1.1132	
$B^2\Sigma^-$	26,045.2	2,246.4	225.7	12.887	0.485	1.1861	345 ± 50
$A^2\Delta$	23,189.9	2,931.1	97.0	14.930	0.696	1.1019	470 ± 75
$X^2\Pi$	0	2,859.1	63.3	14.448	0.530	1.1202	

Radiative lifetimes from Hesser and Lutz (1970).
Dissociation energy: D_o = 3.47 eV

CHO

A. The Hydrocarbon Flame Bands (Vaidya's Ethylene Flame Bands)

These bands occur in the inner cone of hydrocarbon and other flames, especially in low-temperature flames. They are degraded to the red and form fairly definite heads but have complex rotational structure. Most of the strong bands fall into three progressions, denoted A_o, A_1, and B. The A_o and A_1 progressions have both their upper and lower electronic states in common, the transition being denoted ($\tilde{B} - \tilde{X}$). The B progression has a different upper electronic state ($\tilde{C} - \tilde{X}$). The ($\tilde{A} - \tilde{X}$) transition has not been observed in flames but has been obtained in flash photolysis.

TABLE 13

λ_H(Å)	ν_H(cm^{-1})	$v_1'v_2'v_3'$	–	$v_1''v_2''v_3''$	Progression	Int.
2,796.1	35,754	000	–	011	A_o ($\tilde{B} - \tilde{X}$)	M
2,947.4	33,918	000	–	021	A_o ($\tilde{B} - \tilde{X}$)	S
3,114.8	32,095	000	–	031	A_o ($\tilde{B} - \tilde{X}$)	vS
3,298.2	30,311	000	–	041	A_o ($\tilde{B} - \tilde{X}$)	vS
3,501.0	28,551	000	–	051	A_o ($\tilde{B} - \tilde{X}$)	S
3,729.3	26,807	000	–	061	A_o ($\tilde{B} - \tilde{X}$)	M
2,584.1	38,687	000	–	000	A_1 ($\tilde{B} - \tilde{X}$)	W
2,714.7	36,825	000	–	010	A_1 ($\tilde{B} - \tilde{X}$)	M
2,857.8	34,982	000	–	020	A_1 ($\tilde{B} - \tilde{X}$)	M
3,013.7	33,172	000	–	030	A_1 ($\tilde{B} - \tilde{X}$)	S
3,186.0	31,378	000	–	040	A_1 ($\tilde{B} - \tilde{X}$)	vS
3,376.3	29,610	000	–	050	A_1 ($\tilde{B} - \tilde{X}$)	vS
3,587.5	27,867	000	–	060	A_1 ($\tilde{B} - \tilde{X}$)	S
3,823.3	26,148	000	–	070	A_1 ($\tilde{B} - \tilde{X}$)	W
4,088.2	24,454	000	–	080	A_1 ($\tilde{B} - \tilde{X}$)	W
2,422.2	41,272				B ($\tilde{C} - \tilde{X}$)	
2,487.4	40,190				B ($\tilde{C} - \tilde{X}$)	
2,537.0	39,405				B ($\tilde{C} - \tilde{X}$)	
2,661.3	37,565				B ($\tilde{C} - \tilde{X}$)	
2,796.8	35,745				B ($\tilde{C} - \tilde{X}$)	

The above wavelengths were taken from Dixon (1969), in which can be found a partial rotational analysis of some of these bands. Intensities refer to a low-temperature source. The vibrational analysis is uncertain.

CH_2O

Bands due to CH_2O occur in the cool flame of ether, acetaldehyde, hexane, and other organic substances. They have also been observed in the normal flame of methyl alcohol. They are sometimes known as Eméleus's Cool Flame Bands and consist of a number of narrow, approximately equally spaced bands, probably degraded to the red.

TABLE 14

λ(Å)	ν(cm⁻¹)	Int.	λ(Å)	ν(cm⁻¹)	Int.
3,405	29,359	vW	4,347	22,997	S
3,544	28,207	W	4,434	22,547	S
3,679–98	27,173–036	S	4,551–69	21,971–881	S
3,763–77	26,569–469	M	4,673–95	21,393–294	M
3,846.5	25,991	S	4,821	20,735	W
3,952	25,297	vS	4,947	20,207	vW
4,044	24,721	M	5,097	19,613	vW
4,121	24,258	S	5,227	19,125	vW
4,220–40	23,687–579	vS			

CN

Two CN systems, the Red and Violet Systems, occur in organic flames. In flames of acetylene burning in air, they occur weakly, but with fuels containing combined nitrogen, such as aniline, these systems are strong. They are the main feature of cyanogen flames. The Violet System can be obtained readily in absorption in cyanogen flames.

A. The Violet System ($B^2\Sigma^+$ - $X^2\Sigma^+$)

These bands have single heads and form marked sequences. They are degraded to the violet. The (0,0) and (1,1) bands and the (0,1) sequence are sometimes masked by CH. In certain flames, e.g., cyanogen, very weak red-degraded "tail bands" are found. In some of the "tail bands," the heads are weak or even absent. In this case the origins are given in the table below.

TABLE 15

λ_H(Å)	ν_H(cm^{-1})	Int.	v′v″	λ_H(Å)	ν_H(cm^{-1})	Int.	v′v″
*3,127.6	31,964	vW	6,3	3,854.7	25,935	S	3,3
*3,142.6	31,812	vW	7,4	3,861.9	25,887	S	2,2
*3,159.9	31,637	vW	8,5	3,871.4	25,823	vS	1,1
*3,180.2	31,436	vW	9,6	3,883.4	25,743	vS	0,0
*3,203.5	31,207	vW	10,7	*3,894.1[a]	25,673[a]	?	10,10
*3,234.3[a]	30,909[a]	vW	11,8	*3,909.5	25,571	W	11,11
*3,296.3	30,328	?	5,3	*3,944.5	25,345	W	12,12
*3,322.3	30,091	vW	6,4	*3,984.6	25,089	vW	13,13
*3,340.6	29,926	vW	7,5	*4,029.3	24,811	vW	14,14
*3,359.1	29,762	?	8,6	*4,078.7	24,510	vW	15,15
*3,380.3	29,575	vW	9,7	4,152.4	24,076	W	5,6
*3,404.8	29,362	vW	10,8	4,158.1	24,043	W	4,5
*3,433.0	29,121	vW	11,9	4,167.8	23,987	W	3,4
*3,465.3	28,849	vW	12,10	4,181.0	23,911	M	2,3
*3,501.4	28,551	?	13,11	4,197.2	23,819	M	1,2
3,583.9	27,894	M	3,2	4,216.0	23,712	W	0,1
3,585.9	27,879	M	2,1	4,502.2	22,205	W	5,7
3,590.4	27,844	M	1,0	4,514.8	22,143	W	4,6
*3,603.0	27,746	vW	9,8	4,531.9	22,060	W	3,5
*3,628.9	27,548	vW	10,9	4,553.1	21,957	W	2,4
*3,658.1	27,328	vW	11,10	4,578.0	21,838	W	1,3
*3,697.1[a]	27,040[a]	vW	12,11	4,606.2	21,704	W	0,2
3,851.0	25,960	M	4,4				

*"Tail bands"
[a] Origin

Oscillator strength (Bennett and Dalby [1962]): $f_{(0,0\text{-}4,4)} = 0.027 \pm 0.003$

For a rotational analysis of the above bands, see Jevons (1926), Jenkins (1928), and Douglas and Routly (1955). Hallmann and Laulicht (1966) and Chakraborty and Pan (1972) list Franck-Condon factors.

B. The Red System ($A^2\Pi_i - X^2\Sigma^+$)

This system consists of many bands from the green region of the spectrum to the near infrared. With organic flames burning in air, only a few of the strong bands in the infrared have been observed, but with cyanogen flames and other fuels containing combined nitrogen, the system has been observed well into the visible region.

The bands are triple headed and degraded to longer wavelengths. The first (R_2) heads are shown on the following page.

TABLE 16

λ_H(Å)	ν_H(cm^{-1})	Int.	v'v''	λ_H(Å)	ν_H(cm^{-1})	Int.	v'v''
5,239.3	19,081	vW	7,1	6,925.8	14,435	vW	3,0
5,354.1	18,672	vW	8,2	7,088.7	14,103	vW	4,1
5,473.3	18,265	vW	9,3	7,259.0	13,772	vW	5,2
5,597.9	17,859	vW	10,4	7,437.3	13,442	vW	6,3
5,729.9	17,447	vW	6,1	7,872.7	12,699	M	2,0
5,858.2	17,065	vW	7,2	8,067.1	12,393	W	3,1
5,992.6	16,682	vW	8,3	8,270.8	12,087	W	4,2
6,132.4	16,302	vW	9,4	9,140.6	10,937	vS	1,0
6,192.1	16,145	vW	4,0	9,381.1	10,657	S	2,1
6,332.2	15,788	W	5,1	10,925.5	9,150.4	vS	0,0
6,478.5	15,432	W	6,2				
6,631.3	15,076	W	7,3				
6,791.9	14,719	vW	8,4				

Oscillator strength (Jeunehomme [1965]): $f_{(0,0)} = 0.0034 \pm 0.0003$

Wavelengths, wavenumbers, identifications, and relative intensities of rotational lines are given by Davis and Phillips (1963). For Franck-Condon factors, see Brocklehurst et al. (1971).

TABLE 17

Molecular Constants for the $B^2\Sigma^+$, $A^2\Pi_i$, and $X^2\Sigma^+$ States of CN

State	T_o	ω_e	$\omega_e x_e$	B_e	$\alpha_e x10^2$	r_e(Å)	τ_{rad}(nsec)
$B^2\Sigma^+$	25,797.84	2,164.13	20.25	1.9701	2.215	1.1493	82 ± 9
$A^2\Pi_i$	9,118.02	1,814.43	12.883	1.7165	1.746	1.2296	≈ 6,500
$X^2\Sigma^+$	0	2,068.70	13.144	1.8991	1.735	1.17198	

Radiative lifetimes from Moore and Robinson (1968), Liszt and Hesser (1970), and Brocklehurst et al. (1971).
Dissociation energy: D_o = 8.0 eV (see Ramakrishna Rao and Lakshman [1972]).

CO

Many electronic states and transitions of CO are known, but only four transitions, the Fourth Positive System, the Cameron System, the Triplet System, and the Herman System are found in organic flames. Infrared vibration-rotation bands also occur.

A. The Fourth Positive System ($A^1\Pi - X^1\Sigma^+$)

This system has been found in low-pressure hydrocarbon/oxygen flames and in the inner cone of fuel-lean oxyacetylene welding flames.

The bands are degraded to the red and possess P, Q, and R branches. They usually appear single headed. The most intense bands lie in the vacuum ultraviolet region. The following heads have been observed in low-pressure oxyacetylene flames. Wavelengths less than 2,000 Å are in vacuum.

TABLE 18

λ_H(Å)	ν_H(cm^{-1})	Int.	v'v''	λ_H(Å)	ν_H(cm^{-1})	Int.	v'v''	λ_H(Å)	ν_H(cm^{-1})	Int.	v'v''
1,408.9	70,980	vW	6,1	1,829.8	54,651	M	3,7	2,173.0	46,005	vW	5,13
1,452.2	68,863	vW	6,2	1,841.5	54,305	M	0,5	2,191.5	45,617	vW	2,11
1,463.4	68,333	W	4,1	1,859.4	53,780	M	1,6	2,196.8	45,506	vW	6,14
1,493.6	66,952	W	3,1	1,878.3	53,239	M	2,7	2,215.8	45,116	vW	3,12
1,510.4	66,206	W	4,2	1,897.8	52,692	W	3,8	2,221.5	45,001	vW	7,15
1,525.8	65,542	W	2,1	1,918.1	52,135	vW	4,9	2,238.3	44,664	vW	4,13
1,544.2	64,758	M	0,0	1,930.7	51,795	W	1,7	2,261.7	44,200	vW	5,14
1,560.1	64,097	M	1,1	1,950.1	51,280	W	2,8	2,286.1	43,729	vW	6,15
1,576.7	63,425	M	2,2	1,970.1	50,759	W	3,9	2,311.5	43,249	vW	7,16
1,597.1	62,612	S	0,1	1,990.9	50,229	vW	4,10	2,338.0	42,759	vW	8,17
1,630.4	61,335	S	2,3	2,011.8	49,691	vW	5,11	2,356.5	42,422	vW	5,15
1,653.0	60,495	vS	0,2	2,025.8	49,348	vW	2,9	2,365.5	42,262	vW	9,18
1,669.7	59,892	vS	1,3	2,046.3	48,853	vW	3,10	2,381.6	41,975	vW	6,16
1,712.2	58,405	vS	0,3	2,067.7	48,347	vW	4,11	2,394.2	41,754	vW	10,19
1,729.3	57,829	vS	1,4	2,089.9	47,834	vW	5,12	2,407.6	41,552	vW	7,17
1,747.2	57,234	S	2,5	2,107.2	47,440	vW	2,10	2,424.2	41,238	vW	11,20
1,774.9	56,341	S	0,4	2,113.1	47,310	vW	6,13	2,433.9	41,058	vW	8,18
1,792.4	55,792	vS	1,5	2,137.0	46,780	vW	7,14	2,463.2	40,585	vW	9,19
1,810.8	55,224	S	2,6	2,150.2	46,493	vW	4,12				

Oscillator strength: (see Pilling, Bass, and Braun [1971]).

B. The Cameron System ($a^3\Pi_r - X^1\Sigma^+$)

The (0,2), (0,3), and (0,4) bands of this system have been observed in fuel-rich oxyacetylene diffusion flames.

The bands are degraded to the red, and each band has five close heads.

TABLE 19

λ_H(Å)	ν_H(cm^{-1})	Branch	v'v''	λ_H(Å)	ν_H(cm^{-1})	Branch	v'v''
2,257.7	44,279	R_3	0,2	2,451.8	40.774	R_3	4,7
2,259.5	44,244	Q_3		2,453.9	40,739	Q_3	
2,260.1	44,229	R_2		2,455.0	40,721	R_2	
2,261.2	44,211	Q_2		2,456.0	40,704	Q_2	
–	–	R_1		2,457.8	40,674	R_1	
2,277.0	43,904	R_3	1,3	2,491	40,132	R_3	0,4
2,278.5	43,875	Q_3		2,492.9	40,102	Q_3	
2,279.7	43,853	R_2		2,494.4	40,078	R_2	
2,280.5	43,837	Q_2		2,495.7	40,057	Q_2	
–	–	R_1		2,497.5	40,028	R_1	
2,369.0	42,199	R_3	0,3	2,510.9	39,814	R_3	1,5
2,371.2	42,160	Q_3		2,513.7	39,770	Q_3	
2,372.4	42,139	R_2		2,514.9	39,751	R_2	
2,373.3	42,123	Q_2		2,516.2	39,731	Q_2	
2,375.0	42,093	R_1		2,517.8	39,705	R_1	
2,388.8	41,849	R_3	1,4	2,531.9	39,484	R_3	2,6
2,391.1	41,809	Q_3		2,534.5	39,444	Q_3	
2,392.1	41,790	R_2		2,535.6	39,427	R_2	
2,393.1	41,774	Q_2		2,536.7	39,409	Q_2	
2,394.8	41,744	R_1		2,538.6	39,380	R_1	

TABLE 19 (continued)

λ_H(Å)	ν_H(cm^{-1})	Branch	v'v''	λ_H(Å)	ν_H(cm^{-1})	Branch	v'v''
2,409.2	41,495	R_3	2,5	2,553.3	39,153	R_3	3,7
2,411.4	41,457	Q_3		2,555.9	39,113	Q_3	
2,412.6	41,437	R_2		2,557.1	39,095	R_2	
2,413.5	41,421	Q_2		2,558.2	39.078	Q_2	
2,415.3	41,390	R_1		2,560.2	39,048	R_1	
2,430.3	41,135	R_3	3,6	2,575.3	38,819	R_3	4,8
2,432.4	41,099	Q_3		2,577.7	38,783	Q_3	
2,433.4	41,082	R_2		2,579.1	38,762	R_2	
2,434.5	41,064	Q_2		2,580.2	38,745	Q_2	
2,436.2	41,035	R_1		2,582.2	38,715	R_1	

Oscillator strength (James [1971]): $F_{(0,0)} = (1.50 \pm 0.1) \times 10^{-7}$

C. The Triplet System ($d^3\Delta_r - a^3\Pi_r$)

This system has been observed in acetylene/atomic oxygen and carbon suboxide/atomic oxygen flames.

The bands are triple headed and are degraded to the red. The intensity increases towards the red.

TABLE 20

λ_H(Å)	ν_H(cm^{-1})	v'v''	λ_H(Å)	ν_H(cm^{-1})	v'v''	d_H(Å)	λ_H(cm^{-1})	v'v''
4,374.0	22,856	10,0	4,959.0	20,160	9,1	5,624	17,776	5,0
4,390.9	23,768		4,979.0	20,079		5,647.6	17,702	
4,405.0	22,695		4,996.9	20,007		5,670.5	17,630	
4,524.0	22,098	11,1	5,033	19,864	7,0	5,982	16,712	4,0
4,541.0	22,015		5,052.7	19,786		6,010.5	16,633	
4,556.5	21,941		5,070.9	19,715		6,037.0	16,560	
4,571	21,871	9,0	5,216	19,166	8,1	6,401.0	15,618	3,0
4,586.4	21,797		5,238.4	19,085		6,433.1	15,540	
4,602.6	21,721		5,258.3	19,012		6,464.6	15,465	
4,729.1	21,148	10,1	5,308	18,834	6,0			
4,747.5	21,058		5,330.5	18,755				
4,764.8	20,981		5,351.2	18,682				
4,787	20,804	8,0	5,508	18,150	7,1			
4,806.7	20,793		5,532.5	18,070				
4,823.5	20,726		5,554.1	18,000				

D. The Herman System ($e^3\Sigma^- - a^3\Pi_r$)

This system is found in carbon suboxide/atomic oxygen flames and probably in acetylene/atomic oxygen flames, but strong C_2 Swan bands in the latter are present in the wavelength region where they occur.

The bands are triple headed and degraded to the red, but the triplet structure is less prominent than in the Triplet System.

TABLE 21

λ_H(Å)	ν_H(cm^{-1})	v'v''	λ_H(Å)	ν_H(cm^{-1})	v'v''
–	–	8,0	–	–	5,0
–	–		–	–	
4,270.8	23,408		4,885.0	20,465	
4,437	22,531	7,0	5,116.2	19,540	4,0
4,445.5	22,488		5,128.1	19,495	
4,454.5	22,443		5,140.3	19,448	
–	–	6,0	5,402.5	18,505	3,0
–	–		5,414.5	18,464	
4,657.2	21,466		5,428.3	18,417	

E. Vibration-rotation Bands (Ground State $X^1\Sigma^+$)

These infrared bands are very strong in hydrocarbon/oxygen and carbon monoxide/oxygen flames.

The bands consist of P and R branches, the latter forming fairly good red-degraded heads, although in some bands these are strongly absorbed by atmospheric CO_2.

TABLE 22

λ_H(Å)	ν_H(cm^{-1})	λ_o(Å)	ν_o(cm^{-1})	Band
22,929	4,360.0	23,467	4,260.1	2 → 0
23,221	4,305.2	23,762	4,207.2	3 → 1
23,519	4,250.8	24,064	4,154.4	4 → 2
23,823	4,196.5	24,373	4,101.7	5 → 3
R Head and most of		46,644	2,143.3	1 → 0
the R branch absorbed		47,228	2,116.8	2 → 1
by atmospheric CO_2.		47,825	2,090.4	3 → 2

TABLE 23

Molecular Constants for the Electronic States of CO That Are Involved in Flame Spectra

State	T_e	ω_e	$\omega_e x_e$	B_e	α_e	r_e(Å)
$A^1\Pi$	65,076.8	1,515.4	17.25	1.6104	0.0205	1.2356
$e^3\Sigma^-$	64,236.32	1,113.67	9.596	1.2848	0.0181	1.3834
$d^3\Delta_i$	61,154.06	1,152.58	7.2812	1.3099	0.01677	1.3700
$a^3\Pi_r$	47,687.40	1,743.55	14.47	1.6911	0.0195	1.2058
$X^1\Sigma^+$	0	2,169.8233	13.2939	1.931271	0.017513	1.128322

Radiative lifetimes: Fourth Positive System ($A^1\Pi-X^1\Sigma^+$) (Imhof and Read [1971] and Pilling, Bass, and Braun [1971]), τ_{rad} = 7.1 – 10.7 nsec; Cameron System ($a^3\Pi_r-X^1\Sigma^+$) (Lawrence [1971]), τ_{rad} = 7.5 ± 1 msec.

Dissociation energy: D_o = 11.09 ± 0.02 eV

For details of the rotational structure, Franck-Condon factors, etc., of the above transitions of CO, see Krupenie (1966).

CO_2

Two systems of CO_2 occur in flames. The so-called "carbon monoxide flame bands" are the characteristic feature of carbon monoxide flames, and vibration-rotation bands are a predominant feature of organic flames in the infrared region.

A. The Carbon Monoxide Flame Bands

The carbon monoxide flame shows a strong continuous spectrum stretching from below 3,000 Å to beyond 5,000 Å, with a large number of narrow, headless bands superimposed on this continuum. The following are the approximate positions of the strongest bands, observed under low dispersion. Under higher dispersion many of the longer wavelength bands are found to be double.

TABLE 24

λ(Å)	ν(cm^{-1})	λ(Å)	ν(cm^{-1})	λ(Å)	ν(cm^{-1})
3,912	25,555	4,411	22,665	4,893	20,430
4,035	24,775	4,527	22,085	4,933	20,265
4,045	24,715	4,553	21,955	4,980	20,075
4,093	24,425	4,567	21,890	5,129	19,490
4,104	24,360	4,646	21,520	5,169	19,340
4,156	24.055	4,674	21,390	5,276	18,950
4,260	23,465	4,768	20,965	5,318	18,800
4,335	23,060	4,798	20,835	5,430	18,410
4,344	23,015				

The bands have been studied under high resolution, and an analysis is given by Dixon (1963). The electronic transition is ($^1B_2$–$X^1\Sigma_g^+$).

B. Vibration-rotation Bands

These bands are very complex. Some of the bands form heads that are degraded to longer wavelengths. Many bands are known, but only the strongest are shown below. Part of the bands around 4.26μ are usually absorbed by atmospheric CO_2.

TABLE 25

λ_o(Å)	ν_o(cm^{-1})	λ_H(Å)	ν_H(cm^{-1})	$v_1'v_2^{1'}v_3'$	–	$v_1''v_2^{1''}v_3''$
26,912	3,714.7			10^01	–	00^00
27,672	3,612.8			02^01	–	00^00
42,557	2,349.2	41,713	2,396.7	00^01	–	00^00
42,790	2,336.7	41,912	2,385.3	01^11	–	01^10
42,955	2,327.4	42,110	2,374.1	02^01	–	02^00
42,970	2,326.6	42,057	2,377.1	10^01	–	10 0
43,014	2,324.2	42,140	2,372.4	00^02	–	00 1
138,699	720.79			10^00	–	01^10
149,794	667.40			01^10	–	00^00

H_2O

A. Vibration-rotation Bands

These bands, together with CO_2 vibration-rotation bands, account for almost all the emitted energy from flames in the infrared region.

The bands are very complex, with some of the bands in the visible and photographic infrared regions forming red-degraded heads. The fundamental bands in the regions of 1.87 μ, 2.66 μ, and 6.26 μ show maxima on either side of the origins. These are much stronger than the bands in the visible and photographic infrared regions.

TABLE 26

λ_o(Å)	ν_o(cm^{-1})	λ_H(Å)	ν_H(cm^{-1})	$v_1'v_2'v_3'$	–	$v_1''v_2''v_3''$
5,714.2	17,495			203	–	000
5,915.9	16,899			401	–	000
5,943.1	16,822			321	–	000
6,314.4	15,832	6,165	16,216	113	–	000
6,513.8	15,348	6,457	15,482	311	–	000
6,981.9	14,319	6,919	14,449	103	–	000
7,228.2	13,831	7,165	13,954	301	–	000
7,956.4	12,565			013	–	000
8,227.4	12,151	8,097	12,347	211	–	000
9,061.8	11,032	8,916	11,213	003	–	000
9,419.6	10,613	9,277	10,776	201	–	000
11,351	8,807.0			111	–	000
13,782	7,253.6			101	–	000
18,752	5,331.2			011	–	000
26,618	3,755.8			001	–	000
27,337	3,657.1			100	–	000
31,722	3,151.5			020	–	000
62,698	1,594.5			010	–	000

NCN

A very complex group of bands attributed to NCN has been observed in cyanogen/oxygen flames. The system is very weak, and the strongest bands are listed below.

TABLE 27

λ_H(Å)	ν_H(cm^{-1})	$v_1'v_2'v_3'$	–	$v_1''v_2''v_3''$
3,271.3	30,561	020	–	020
3,280.4	30,475	010	–	010
3,283.8	30,443	001	–	001
3,290.1	30,385	000	–	000

For details of the rotational structure, see Herzberg and Travis (1964). The electronic transition is $A^3\Pi_u - X^3\Sigma_g^-$

NH

Four electronic transitions of NH are known, but only the 3,360 Å system, $(A^3\Pi_i - X^3\Sigma^-)$, occurs in organic flames. When nitrogen is present, as in the acetylene/air flame, and especially in fuels containing combined nitrogen, e.g., aniline, a broad "line" appears at 3,360 Å and a much weaker broad "line" at 3,370 Å. Under high resolution these features are seen as the strong maxima of the Q branches of the (0,0) and (1,1) bands. The P and R branches appear on either side of the Q branches as series of narrow triplets. Under favorable conditions the (1,0) and (0,1) sequences may be observed, but they are usually masked by OH, etc.

TABLE 28

λ_H(Å)	ν_H(cm^{-1})	Int.	Deg.	Branch	v'v''	λ_H(Å)	ν_H(cm^{-1})	Int.	Deg.	Branch	v'v''
3,023	33,070	vW	R	R	1,0	3,336.0	29,967	vW	R	R	2,2
3,047.3	32,806	vW	R	Q_2	1,0	3,360	29,753	vS	Max	Q	0,0
3,050.3	32,775	vW	R	Q_1	1,0	3,370	29,665	M	Max	Q	1,1
3,119.5	32,047	vW	R		2,1?	3,383	29,551	W	Max	Q	2,2
3,137.0	31,868	vW	R		2,1?	3,635.0	27,502	vW	V	Q	1,2?
3,281.0	30,470	W	R	R	0,0	3,637.7	27,482	W	V	Q	0,1?
3,317.0	30,139	W	R	R	1,1?	3,676.3	27,194	vW	V	P	0,1?

Oscillator strength (Smith and Liszt [1971]): $f_{(0,0)} = 0.00745 \pm 0.0015$

For a rotational analysis of the (0,0), (1,1), and (1,0) bands, see Dixon (1959), Guenebaut and Pannetier (1960), and Murai and Shimauchi (1966). Franck-Condon factors are given by Smith and Liszt (1971).

TABLE 29

Molecular Constants for the $A^3\Pi_i$ and $X^3\Sigma^-$ States of NH

State	T_o	$\Delta G_{1/2}$	B_o	α_e	r_e(Å)	τ_{rad}(nsec)
$A^3\Pi_i$	29,776.8		16.3181	0.7440	1.046	455 ± 90
$X^3\Sigma^-$	0	3,125.6	16.3447	0.646	1.045	

Radiative lifetime from Smith (1969b)
Dissociation energy: $D_o = 3.21 \pm 0.16$ eV

NO

NO bands (the γ and β Systems) are emitted from flames of organic fuels containing combined nitrogen. The β System is usually weak.

A. The γ System ($A^2\Sigma^+$ – $X^2\Pi$)

This system consists of double double-headed bands degraded to shorter wavelengths. The heads of the strongest bands are shown below.

TABLE 30

λ_H(Å)	ν_H(cm^{-1})	Branch	v'v''	Int.	λ_H(Å)	ν_H(cm^{-1})	Branch	v'v''	Int
2,261.8	44,198	Q_1	0,0	M	2,586.3	38,654	Q_1	0,3	S
2,262.9	44,177	P_1			2,587.5	38,636	P_1		
2,268.0	44,078	P_2			2,594.3	38,534	P_2		
2,269.3	44,052	$^OP_{12}$			2,595.7	38,514	$^OP_{12}$		
2,362.2	42,321	Q_1	0,1	vS	2,712.0	36,862	Q_1	0,4	M
2,363.2	42,302	P_1			2,713.2	36,845	P_1		
2,368.9	42,201	P_2			2,720.8	36,743	P_2		
2,370.2	42,178	$^OP_{12}$			2,722.2	36,724	$^OP_{12}$		
2,470.1	40,473	Q_1	0,2	vS	2,848.2	35,099	Q_1	0,5	M
2,471.2	40,454	P_1			2,849.6	35,083	P_1		
2,477.4	40,353	P_2			2,858.0	34,980	P_2		
2,478.7	40,331	$^OP_{12}$			2,859.5	34,961	$^OP_{12}$		

Oscillator strength (Farmer, Hasson, and Nicholls [1972]): $f_{(0,0)} = 0.0004 \pm 0.00002$

The rotational structure of the above bands is given by Deézsi (1958).

B. The β System ($B^2\Pi$ - $X^2\Pi$)

The bands of this system have double heads and are degraded to the red. The strongest bands are shown below.

TABLE 31

λ_H(Å)	ν_H(cm^{-1})	v'v''	λ_H(Å)	ν_H(cm^{-1})	v'v''
2,885.2	34,649	0,6	3,376.4	29,609	0,9
2,892.6	34,561		3,386.4	29,522	
3,034.9	32,941	0,7	3,572.4	27,984	0,10
3,043.0	32,853		3,583.5	27,898	
3,198.0	31,261	0,8	3,788.5	26,388	0,11
3,206.9	31,173		3,800.9	26,302	

Oscillator strength (Hasson and Nicholls [1971]): $f_{(0,0)} = 2.46 \times 10^{-8}$

A rotational analysis of these bands is given by Jenkins, Barton, and Mulliken (1927).

TABLE 32

Molecular Constants for the $B^2\Pi$, $A^2\Sigma^+$, and $X^2\Pi$ States of NO

State	T_e	ω_e	$\omega_e x_e$	B_e	α_e	r_e(Å)	τ_{rad}(nsec)
$B^2\Pi_{3/2}$	45,947.3	1,038.3	7.455	1.178	0.0189	1.383	
$B^2\Pi_{1/2}$	45,919.5	1,036.9	7.460	1.076	0.0116	1.449	
$A^2\Sigma^+$	43,965.7	2,371.3	14.48	1.9977	0.0198	1.0630	108 ± 6 (v=o)
$X^2\Pi_{3/2}$	121	1,903.68	13.97	1.7046	0.0178	1.1508	
$X^2\Pi_{1/2}$	0	1,903.03					

Radiative lifetime from Copeland (1972). See also Weinstock et al. (1972).

Dissociation energy: $D_o = 6.50 \pm 0.01$ eV

O_2

Two of the many known O_2 systems are emitted in flames. These are the Schumann-Runge System and the Atmospheric Bands.

A. The Schumann-Runge System ($B^3\Sigma_u^-$ - $X^3\Sigma_g^-$)

This system, in the 3,000 to 4,000 Å region, occurs in hydrogen/oxygen and carbon monoxide/oxygen flames and weakly in various oxyhydrocarbon flames. It can also be obtained in absorption fairly readily.

The bands show open rotational structure, and the heads are not pronounced. They are degraded to the red. In hot flames the (0,12), (0,13), (0,14), and (0,15) bands are the most prominent.

TABLE 33

λ_H(Å)	ν_H(cm^{-1})	v′v″	λ_H(Å)	ν_H(cm^{-1})	v′v″	λ_H(Å)	ν_H(cm^{-1})	v′v″
2,440	40,971	3,7	2,923	34,201	1,11	3,671	27,232	0,16
2,480	40,310	2,7	2,984	33,502	0,11	3,743	26,708	1,17
2,528	39,545	3,8	3,039	32,896	1,12	3,841	26,027	0,17
2,570	38,898	2,8	(3,104)	32,207	0,12	3,914	25,542	1,18
2,613	38,258	1,8	3,232	30,931	0,13	4,021	24,862	0,18
2,663	37,540	2,9	3,370	29,665	0,14	4,096	24,407	1,19
2,710	36,889	1,9	3,434	29,112	1,15	4,179	23,922	2,20
2,762	36,194	0,9	3,517	28,425	0,15	4,294	23,281	1,20
*2,813	35,538	1,10	3,582	27,909	1,16	4,375	22,850	2,21
2,870	34,833	0,10						

* Overlapped with OH

Oscillator strengths, Franck-Condon factors, and details of rotational structure are given by Hébert, Innanen, and Nicholls (1967).

B. The Atmospheric Bands ($b^1\Sigma_g^+ - X^3\Sigma_g^-$)

The (0,0) and (1,1) bands of this system have been observed in carbon monoxide/oxygen flames and weakly in the outer cones of oxyhydrocarbon flames. They are degraded to longer wavelengths. Some of the other bands have weak heads.

TABLE 34

λ_H(Å)	ν_H(cm^{-1})	v′v″	λ_H(Å)	ν_H(cm^{-1})	v′v″
6,867.2	14,558	1,0	7,879.2	12,688	3,3
7,593.7	13,165	0,0	(8,597.8)	(11,628)	0,1
7,683.8	13,011	1,1	8,697.8	11,494	1,2
7,779.0	12,851	2,2	8,803	11,357	2,3

For the rotational structure, see Babcock and Herzberg (1948).

TABLE 35

Molecular Constants for the $B^3\Sigma_u^-$, $b^1\Sigma_g^+$, and $X^3\Sigma_g^-$ States of O_2

State	T_o	ω_e	$\omega_e x_e$	B_e	a_ex10^2	r_e(Å)
$B^3\Sigma_u^-$	49,358.15	709.31	10.65	0.81902	12.06	1.6042
$b^1\Sigma_g^+$	13,120.9080	1,432.6874	13.95008	1.4004_{16}	1.8170	1.22685
$X^3\Sigma_g^-$	0	1,580.211	11.99	1.445572	1.581	1.207536

Radiative Lifetime (Calculated from $1/\sum_{v''} A_{v'v''}$ where $A_{v'v''}$ is the Einstein A Coefficient given by Hebert, Innanen, & Nicholls (1967)): Schumann-Runge System ($B^3\Sigma_u^- - X^3\Sigma_g^-$), v′=o, τ_{rad} = 41.9 nsec.

Dissociation Energy D_o = 5.115 ± 0.002 eV

OH

Four electronic transitions of OH are known, but only one, the 3,064 Å System, appears in flames. This is one of the commonest and best known band systems and can be observed in emission and absorption readily in most organic flames. Rotation-vibration bands in the red and infrared regions and the pure rotational spectrum in the far infrared region have been observed in oxyacetylene flames. The latter is usually masked by the rotational spectrum of H_2O.

A. The 3,064 Å System ($A^2\Sigma^+ - X^2\Pi_i$)

This system consists of red-degraded bands with a very open but rather complicated rotational structure. There are four main heads, R_1, R_2, Q_1, and Q_2, the former two being the most definite. There is also a weak $^SR_{21}$ head in the (0,0) band.

TABLE 36

λ_H(Å)	ν_H(cm^{-1})	Branch	v′v″	Int.	λ_H(Å)	ν_H(cm^{-1})	Branch	v′v″	Int.
2,444	40,904	R_1	3,0	vW	3,121.6	32,025	R_1	1,1	W
2,608.5	38,325	R_1	2,0	vW	3,126.3	31,977	R_2		
2,613.4	38,253	R_2			3,134.6	31,893	Q_1		
2,613.4	38,253	Q_1			3,146.6	31,772	Q_2		
2,622.1	38,127	Q_2			3,184.7	31,391	R_1	2,2	vW
2,677.3	37,340	R_1	3,1	vW	3,190.1	31,338	R_2		
2,681.8	37,277	Q_1			3,195.9	31,282	Q_1		
2,683.1	37,259	R_2			3,208.5	31,159	Q_2		
2,691.1	37,148	Q_2			3,253.9	30,724	R_1	3,3	vW
2,811.3	35,560	R_1	1,0	M	3,260.2	30,664	R_2		
2,816.0	35,501	R_2			3,263.4	30,634	Q_1		
2,819.1	35,461	Q_1			3,276.7	30,510	Q_2		
2,829.0	35,338	Q_2			3,428.0	29,163	R_1	0,1	vW
2,875.3	34,769	R_1	2,1	W	3,432.0	29,129	R_2		
2,880.6	34,705	R_2			3,458.5	28,906	Q_1		
2,882.3	34,684	Q_1			3,472.2	28,792	Q_2		
2,892.7	34,560	Q_2			3,483.7	28,697	R_1	1,2	vW
2,945.0	33,946	R_1	3,2	vW	3,488.4	28,658	R_2		
2,951.2	33,875	R_2			3,509.0	28,490	Q_1		
2,951.3	33,873	Q_1			3,523.4	28,374	Q_2		
2,962.4	33,747	Q_2							
3,021.3	33,089	$^SR_{21}$	0,0	vS					
3,063.6	32,632	R_1							
3,067.7	32,589	R_2							
3,078.4	32,475	Q_1							
3,090.4	32,349	Q_2							

Oscillator strength (Bennett and Dalby [1964] and Anketell and Pery-Thorne [1967]): $f_{(0,0)}$ = 0.0008. $f_{(1,0)}/f_{(0,0)}$ = 0.60 ± 0.1

Wavelengths, wavenumbers, identifications, and relative intensities of rotational lines, Franck–Condon factors, etc., are given by Dieke and Crosswhite (1962) and Learner (1962). For identification only, see Bass and Broida (1953).

B. Vibration-rotation Bands (Ground State $X^2\Pi$)

These infrared bands occur in hydrocarbon/oxygen flames, being particularly strong in the outer cone of oxyacetylene flames.

P, Q, and R branches are present, the P branch being the strongest. The R branch is sufficiently well developed in some bands to form a head degraded to longer wavelengths. The Q branch is rather weak. Some bands are obscured by H_2O vibration-rotation emission bands.

TABLE 37

λ_H(Å)	ν_H(cm^{-1})	λ_o(Å)	ν_o(cm^{-1})	Band
7,461.4	13,399	7,521.5	13,291.5	4 → 0
7,849.3	12,736	7,911.0	12,637.1	5 → 1
8,278.3	12,076	8,341.7	11,984.6	6 → 2
9,653	10,356	9,788.0	10,213.8	3 → 0
10,143	9,856	10,273	9,721.9	4 → 1
13,909	7,187.7	14,336	6,973.6	2 → 0
14,606	6,844.5	15,047	6,644.2	3 → 1
15,369	6,504.7	15,824	6,317.9	4 → 2
R branches obscured		28,007	3,569.6	1 → 0
by H_2O emission.		29,369	3,404.0	2 → 1

C. Pure Rotational Spectrum (Ground State $X^2\Pi$, v=o)

Pure rotational lines of OH (with N″ = 11 to 29) have been observed in the far infrared region (430 cm^{-1} to 1,000 cm^{-1}, 23 μ to 10 μ) in oxyacetylene flames. This region of the spectrum is masked by strong H_2O pure rotational emission lines.

TABLE 38

Molecular Constants for the $A^2\Sigma^+$ and $X^2\Pi$ States of OH

State	T_e	ω_e	$\omega_e x_e$	B_e	α_e	r_e(Å)	τ_{rad}(nsec)
$A^2\Sigma^+$	32,682.5	3,184.28	97.84	17.355	0.807	1.0121	1010 ± 50
$X^2\Pi_i$	0	3,735.21	82.81	18.871	0.714	0.9706	

Radiative Lifetime from Bennett & Dalby (1964).

Dissociation Energy D_o = 4.40 ± 0.01 eV

TABLE 39

Characteristic Band Heads Occurring in Organic Flames

Band Head Wavelengths (Å)	Degraded	Emitter	System	Transition		Int. in C_2H_2/air Flames	Int. in Other Organic Flames
1,597.1	R	CO	Fourth Positive	$A^1\Pi - X^1\Sigma^+$	(0,1)	–	S in C_2H_2/O_2
1,630.4	R	CO	Fourth Positive	$A^1\Pi - X^1\Sigma^+$	(2,3)	–	S in C_2H_2/O_2
1,653.0	R	CO	Fourth Positive	$A^1\Pi - X^1\Sigma^+$	(0,2)	–	S in C_2H_2/O_2
1,669.7	R	CO	Fourth Positive	$A^1\Pi - X^1\Sigma^+$	(1,3)	–	S in C_2H_2/O_2
1,712.2	R	CO	Fourth Positive	$A^1\Pi - X^1\Sigma^+$	(0,3)	–	S in C_2H_2/O_2
1,729.3	R	CO	Fourth Positive	$A^1\Pi - X^1\Sigma^+$	(1,4)	–	S in C_2H_2/O_2
1,747.2	R	CO	Fourth Positive	$A^1\Pi - X^1\Sigma^+$	(2,5)	–	S in C_2H_2/O_2
1,774.9	R	CO	Fourth Positive	$A^1\Pi - X^1\Sigma^+$	(0,4)	–	S in C_2H_2/O_2
1,792.4	R	CO	Fourth Positive	$A^1\Pi - X^1\Sigma^+$	(1,5)	–	S in C_2H_2/O_2
1,810.8	R	CO	Fourth Positive	$A^1\Pi - X^1\Sigma^+$	(2,6)	–	S in C_2H_2/O_2
2,322	Max	C_2	Mulliken	$d^1\Sigma^+ - x^1\Sigma_g^+$	(0,0)	–	W in C_2H_2/O_2
2,370.2	V	NO		$A^2\Sigma^+ - X^2\Pi$	(0,1)	–	M in C_2N_2/O_2;C_2H_2/N_2O
2,478.7	V	NO		$A^2\Sigma^+ - X^2\Pi$	(0,2)	–	M in C_2N_2/O_2;C_2H_2/N_2O
2,595.7	V	NO		$A^2\Sigma^+ - X^2\Pi$	(0,3)	–	M in C_2N_2/O_2;C_2H_2/N_2O
2,608.5	R	OH		$A^2\Sigma^+ - X^2\Pi_i$	(2,0)	W	Present in most flames
2,811.3	R	OH		$A^2\Sigma^+ - X^2\Pi_i$	(1,0)	M	Present in most flames
2,947.4	R	CHO	Hydrocarbon flame	$\tilde{B} - \tilde{X}$	(000,021)	W	S in low-temp. flames
3,013.7	R	CHO	Hydrocarbon flame	$\tilde{B} - \tilde{X}$	(000,030)	W	S in low-temp. flames
3,063.6	R	OH		$A^2\Sigma^+ - X^2\Pi_i$	(0,0)	S	Present in most flames
3,104	R	O_2	Schumann-Runge	$B^3\Sigma_u^- - X^3\Sigma_g^-$	(0,12)	vW	W in fuel-lean flames
3,114.8	R	CHO	Hydrocarbon flame	$\tilde{B} - \tilde{X}$	(000,031)	W	vS in low-temp. flames
3,144	Max	CH		$C^2\Sigma^+ - X^2\Pi$	(0,0)	vS	
3,157	Max	CH		$C^2\Sigma^+ - X^2\Pi$	(1,1)	M	
3,186.0	R	CHO	Hydrocarbon flame	$\tilde{B} - \tilde{X}$	(000,040)	W	vS in low-temp. flames
3,232	R	O_2	Schumann-Runge	$B^3\Sigma_u^- - X^3\Sigma_g^-$	(0,13)	vW	W in fuel-lean flames
3,298.2	R	CHO	Hydrocarbon flame	$\tilde{B} - \tilde{X}$	(000,041)	W	vS in low-temp. flames
3,360	Max	NH		$A^3\Pi_i - X^3\Sigma^-$	(0,0)	M	vS in C_2H_2/N_2O
3,370	Max	NH		$A^3\Pi_i - X^3\Sigma^-$	(1,1)	vW	M in C_2H_2/N_2O
3,370	R	O_2	Schumann-Runge	$B^3\Sigma_u^- - X^3\Sigma_g^-$	(0,14)	vW	W in fuel-lean flames
3,376.3	R	CHO	Hydrocarbon flame	$\tilde{B} - \tilde{X}$	(000,050)	W	vS in low-temp. flames

TABLE 39 (continued)

Characteristic Band Heads Occurring in Organic Flames

Band Head Wavelengths (Å)	Degraded	Emitter	System	Transition		Int. in C_2H_2/Air Flames	Int. in Other Organic Flames
3,428	R	OH		$A^2\Sigma^+-X^2\Pi_i$	(0,1)	vW	Present in most flames
3,501.0	R	CHO	Hydrocarbon flame	$\tilde{B}-\tilde{X}$	(000,051)	W	S in low-temp. flames
3,517	R	O_2	Schumann-Runge	$B^3\Sigma_u^--X^3\Sigma_g^-$	(0,15)	vW	W in fuel-lean flames
3,587.5	R	CHO	Hydrocarbon flame	B–X	(000,060)	W	S in low-temp. flames
3,590.4	V	CN	Violet	$B^2\Sigma^+-X^2\Sigma^+$	(1,0)	W	M in C_2N_2/O_2;C_2H_2/N_2O
3,679 to 3,698	Max	CH_2O	Emeleus cool flame			–	S in cool flames
3,846.5	Max	CH_2O	Emeleus cool flame			–	S in cool flames
3,871.4	R	CH		$B^2\Sigma^--X^2\Pi$	(0,0)	S	
3,871.4	V	CN	Violet	$B^2\Sigma^+-X^2\Sigma^+$	(1,1)	M	vS in C_2N_2/O_2;C_2H_2/N_2O
3,883.4	V	CN	Violet	$B^2\Sigma^+-X^2\Sigma^+$	(0,0)	M	vS in C_2N_2/O_2;C_2H_2/N_2O
3,952	Max	CH_2O	Emeleus cool flame			–	vS in cool flames
4,049.8	R	C_3	Comet-Head group			–	S in v.rich flames
4,121	Max	CH_2O	Emeleus cool flame			–	S in cool flames
4,216.0	V	CN	Violet	$B^2\Sigma^+-X^2\Sigma^+$	(0,1)	vW	W in C_2N_2/O_2;C_2H_2/N_2O
4,220 to 4,240	Max	CH_2O	Emeleus cool flame			–	vS in cool flames
4,314.2	V	CH		$A^2\Delta-X^2\Pi$	(0,0)		vS
4,347	Max	CH_2O	Emeleus cool flame			–	S in cool flames
4,382.2	V	C_2	Swan	$A^3\Pi_g-X^3\Pi_u$	(2,0)		vW
4,434	Max	CH_2O	Emeleus cool flame			–	S in cool flames
4,551 to 4,669	Max	CH_2O	Emeleus cool flame			–	S in cool flames
4,715.3	V	C_2	Swan	$A^3\Pi_g-X^3\Pi_u$	(2,1)	S	
4,737.1	V	C_2	Swan	$A^3\Pi_g-X^3\Pi_u$	(1,0)	vS	
5,129.4	V	C_2	Swan	$A^3\Pi_g-X^3\Pi_u$	(1,1)	M	
5,165.2	V	C_2	Swan	$A^3\Pi_g-X^3\Pi_u$	(0,0)	vS	
5,585.5	V	C_2	Swan	$A^3\Pi_g-X^3\Pi_u$	(1,2)	S	

TABLE 39 (continued)

Characteristic Band Heads Occurring in Organic Flames

Band Head Wavelengths (Å)	Degraded	Emitter	System	Transition		Int. in C_2H_2/ Air Flames	Int. in Other Organic Flames
5,635.5	V	C_2	Swan	$A^3\Pi_g-X^3\Pi_u$	(0,1)	S	
6,191.3	V	C_2	Swan	$A^3\Pi_g-X^3\Pi_u$	(0,2)	W	
7,165	IR	H_2O	Vibration-Rotation		(301→000)	M	
7,461.4	IR	OH	Vibration-Rotation	$X^2\Pi$	(4→0)	M	
7,593.7	IR	O_2	Atmospheric	$b^1\Sigma_g^+-x^3\Sigma_g^-$	(0,0)	–	M in CO/O_2
7,683.8	IR	O_2	Atmospheric	$b^1\Sigma_g-x^3\Sigma_g$	(1,1)	–	W in CO/O_2
7,714.6	IR	C_2	Phillips	$b^1\Pi_u-x^1\Sigma_g^+$	(3,0)	M	
8,097	IR	H_2O	Vibration-Rotation		(211→000)	M	
8,750.8	IR	C_2	Phillips	$b^1\Pi_u-x^1\Sigma_g^+$	(2,0)	M	
8,916	IR	H_2O	Vibration-Rotation		(003→000)	M	
9,140.6	IR	CN	Red	$A^2\Pi_i-X^2\Sigma^+$	(1,0)	vW	vS in C_2N_2/O_2;C_2H_2/N_2O
9,277	IR	H_2O	Vibration-Rotation		(201→000)	M	
9,653	IR	OH	Vibration-Rotation	$X^2\Pi$	(3→0)	M	
10,147	origin	C_2	Phillips	$b^1\Pi_u-x^1\Sigma_g^+$	(1,0)	M	
10,925.5	IR	CN	Red	$A^2\Pi_i-X^2\Sigma^+$	(0,0)	vW	vS in C_2N_2/O_2;C_2H_2/N_2O
11,351	origin	H_2O	Vibration-Rotation		(111→000)	M	
12,070.2	IR	C_2	Phillips	$b^1\Pi_u-x^1\Sigma_g^+$	(0,0)	M	
13,782	origin	H_2O	Vibration-Rotation		(101→000)	M	
13,909	IR	OH	Vibration-Rotation	$X^2\Pi$	(2→0)	M	
15,484.1	IR	C_2	Phillips	$b^1\Pi_u-X^1\Sigma_g^+$	(0,1)	M	
18,752	origin	H_2O	Vibration-Rotation		(011→000)	S	
22,929	IR	CO	Vibration-Rotation	$X^1\Sigma^+$	(2→0)	S	
26,618	origin	H_2O	Vibration-Rotation		(001→000)	S	
26,912	origin	CO_2	Vibration-Rotation		(10°1→00°0)	S	
27,337	origin	H_2O	Vibration-Rotation		(100→000)	S	
27,672	origin	CO_2	Vibration-Rotation		(02°1→00°0)	S	
28,007	origin	OH	Vibration-Rotation	$X^2\Pi$	(1→0)	S	
31,722	origin	H_2O	Vibration-Rotation		(020→000)	S	
41,713	IR	CO_2	Vibration-Rotation		(00°1→00°0)	S	
46,644	origin	CO	Vibration-Rotation		(1→0)	S	
62,698	origin	H_2O	Vibration-Rotation		(010→000)	S	
149,794	origin	CO_2	Vibration-Rotation		(01^10→00°0)	S	

II. MOLECULAR SPECTRA OF FLAMES CONTAINING NONMETALS

The spectra of flames containing boron, halogens, nitrogen, phosphorus, and sulphur are described. Wavelengths and wavenumbers of the band heads of characteristic features are given, but detailed spectroscopic constants of the molecules involved are omitted. Unless otherwise stated, all spectra are observed in emission.

A. Boron-containing Flames

Flames containing boron compounds such as pentaborane, B_5H_9, or trimethyl borate, $B(OCH_3)_3$, show bands due to BO and BO_2.

BO

Of the four known electronic transitions of BO, only the main *a* system ($A^2\Pi - X^2\Sigma^+$) has been observed in flames.

The bands are double double-headed and degraded to the red. The following are the strongest heads of ^{11}BO. The natural abundance of the isotope ^{10}B is 19.6%, and bands of ^{10}BO also appear.

TABLE 40

λ_H(Å)	ν_H(cm^{-1})	Branch	v'v''	Int.	λ_H(Å)	ν_H(cm^{-1})	Branch	v'v''	Int.
3,374.7	29,624	R_2	5,0	W	4,227.5	23,648	R_2	0.0	M
3,387.6	29,510	R_1			4,247.9	23,534	R_1		
3,389.1	29,498	Q_1			4,250.4	23,521	Q_1		
3,510.0	28,482	R_{21}	4,0	M	4,339.4	23,038	R_{21}	1,1	vS
3,511.2	28,472	R_2			4,341.9	23,025	R_2		
3,525.5	28,356	R_1			4,363.4	22,911	R_1		
3,526.8	28,346	Q_1			4,365.9	22,898	Q_1		
3,660.6	27,310	R_{21}	3,0	S	4,585.7	21,801	R_{21}	0,1	vS
3,662.2	27,298	R_2			4,588.8	21,786	R_2		
3,677.8	27,182	R_1			4,612.7	21,673	R_1		
3,679.1	27,173	Q_1			4,615.4	21,661	Q_1		
3,828.0	26,116	R_{21}	2,0	S	4,715.5	21,201	R_{21}	1,2	S
3,829.9	26,103	R_2			4,718.7	21,187	R_2		
3,847.0	25,987	R_1			4,744.0	21,074	R_1		
3,848.7	25,976	Q_1			4,746.9	21,060	Q_1		
3,950.5	25,306	Q_1	3,1	W	5,011.7	19,948	R_2	0,2	S
					5,040.1	19,835	R_1		
4,015.0	24,900	R_{21}	1,0	S	5,043.5	19,822	Q_1		
4,017.1	24,887	R_2							
4,035.5	24,773	R_1			5,513.0	18,134	R_2	0,3	S
4,037.4	24,761	Q_1			5,547.5	18,021	R_1		
					5,551.5	18,008	Q_1		
4,124.1	24,241	R_2	2,1	M					
4,134.4	24,128	R_1			6,159.7	16,230	R_1	0,4	M
4,145.5	24,116	Q_1			6,165.4	16,215	Q_1		

For the rotational structure of the *a* bands of BO, see Jenkins and McKellar (1932).

BO_2

Bands due to BO_2 are known as the "Boric Acid Fluctuation Bands." They arise from two electronic transitions ($A^2\Pi_u - X^2\Pi_g$) and ($B^2\Sigma_u^+ - X^2\Pi_g$) and consist of waves of red-degraded, narrow, diffuse bands. At lower temperatures and under high dispersion, they show fairly well-resolved rotational structure. The following are the strongest heads of $^{11}BO_2$. Weaker heads due to $^{10}BO_2$ are also present.

TABLE 41

λ_H(Å)	ν_H(cm^{-1})	Branch	Upper Level	Lower Level
4,065.5	24,590	R_1	0 0°0 $^2\Sigma^+$	– 0 0°0 $^2\Pi$
4,090.7	24,439	Q_2	0 0°0 $^2\Sigma^+$	– 0 0°0 $^2\Pi$
4,929.3	20,281	R_1	2 0°0 $^2\Pi$	– 0 0°0 $^2\Pi$
4,941.3	20,232	R_2	2 0°0 $^2\Pi$	– 0 0°0 $^2\Pi$
4,965.4	20,134	R_1	0 4°0 $^2\Pi$	– 0 0°0 $^2\Pi$
4,973.6	20,101	R_2	0 4°0 $^2\Pi$	– 0 0°0 $^2\Pi$
5,168.8	19,341	R_1	1 0°0 $^2\Pi$	– 0 0°0 $^2\Pi$
5,180.7	19,297	R_2	1 0°0 $^2\Pi$	– 0 0°0 $^2\Pi$
5,196.1	19,240	R_1	0 2°0 $^2\Pi$	– 0 0°0 $^2\Pi$
5,207.2	19,199	R_2	0 2°0 $^2\Pi$	– 0 0°0 $^2\Pi$
5,456.8	18,321	R_1	0 0°0 $^2\Pi$	– 0 0°0 $^2\Pi$
5,470.9	18,274	R_2	0 0°0 $^2\Pi$	– 0 0°0 $^2\Pi$
5,790.7	17,264	R_1	0 0°0 $^2\Pi$	– 1 0°0 $^2\Pi$
5,813.2	17,198	R_2	0 0°0 $^2\Pi$	– 1 0°0 $^2\Pi$
6,171.6	16,199	R_1	0 0°0 $^2\Pi$	– 2 0°0 $^2\Pi$
6,202.2	16,119	R_2	0 0°0 $^2\Pi$	– 2 0°0 $^2\Pi$
6,376.6	15,678	R_1	0 0°0 $^2\Pi$	– 0 0°2 $^2\Pi$
6,396.0	15,630	R_2	0 0°0 $^2\Pi$	– 0 0°2 $^2\Pi$

A rotational analysis of these bands is given by Johns (1961). Under low dispersion the waves show maxima in the regions of 4,520, 4,710, 4,930, 5,180, 5,450, 5,800, 6,030, 6,200, and 6,390 Å.

B. Halogen-containing Flames

The spectra of ClO, BrO, IO, CF, CCl, HF, HCl, and HBr are described. Other less important spectra that have been observed in halogen-containing flames include Cl_2, Br_2, I_2, BrF, IF, and NBr.

ClO, BrO, and IO

Bands due to these molecules are found in hydrogen/oxygen flames containing Cl_2, Br_2, or I_2 and when organic halides such as CH_3Cl, CH_3Br, or CH_3I are introduced into a flame.

The spectra of ClO, BrO, and IO are very similar, being due to a $A^2\Pi - X^2\Pi$ transition and consisting of long progressions of bands degraded to the red. Many of the ClO bands and IO bands with v′ = 1, 4, and 5 are diffuse due to predissociation.

TABLE 42

ClO				BrO				IO			
λ_H(Å)	ν_H(cm^{-1})	Int.	v′v″	λ_H(Å)	ν_H(cm^{-1})	Int.	v′v″	λ_H(Å)	ν_H(cm^{-1})	Int.	v′v″
3,652.5	27,371	M	1,5	3,958	25,258	W	1,4	4,189.0	23,865	S	5,0
3,729.5	26,805	S	0,5	3,999	24,999	W	2,5	4,268.2	23,423	S	4,0
3,761	26,581	vS	1,6	4,029	24,813	W	0,4	4,355.6	22,953	vS	3,0
3,841	26,027	vS	0,6	4,069	24,569	M	1,5	4,396.7	22,738	M	4,1
3,874	25,806	vS	1,7	4,109	24,330	W	2,6	4,448.9	22,471	S	2,0
3,957	25,265	S	0,7	4,147	24,107	M	0,5	4,487.2	22,279	vS	3,1
3,991	25,049	S	1,8	4,186	23,882	W	1,6	4,586.2	21,798	vS	2,1
4,078	24,515	M	0,8	4,225	23,662	vW	2,7	4,693.5	21,300	vS	1,1
4,114	24,300	vS	1,9	4,270	23,413	vS	0,6	4,730.3	21,134	S	2,2
4,154	24,066	W	2,10	4,349	22,987	W	2,8	4,844.5	20.636	vS	1,2
4,241	23,573	M	1,10	4,398	22,731	vS	0,7	4,964.2	20,139	M	0,2
4,283	23,341	S	2,11	4,533	22,055	vS	0,8	5,002.3	19,985	M	1,3
4,373	22,861	W	1,11	4,673	21,394	S	0,9	5,131.2	19,483	vS	0,3
4,417	22,633	W	2,12	4,817	20,754	W	0,10	5,208.5	19,194	M	2,5
4,459	22,420	W	3,13	4,856	20,587	vW	1,11	5,307.3	18,837	vS	0,4
								5,493.2	18,199	vS	0,5
								5,533	18,069	S	1,6
								5,689.7	17,571	S	0,6
								5,730	17,447	S	1,7
								5,900	16,945	M	0,7
								5,939	16,832	M	1,8
								5,973.4	16,736	S	2,9
								6,192.2	16,145	W	2,10
								6,231.5	16,043	W	3,11

The rotational structure of some of the IO bands listed above has been analyzed by Durie, Legoy, and Ramsay (1960).

CF

CF bands ($A^2\Sigma^+ - X^2\Pi_r$) have been observed in flames containing fluorine compounds, e.g., CF_4 in an oxyacetylene flame, and flames of CH_4, etc., supported by ClF_3 or F_2.

The bands are double double-headed and degraded to shorter wavelengths. They resemble the NO γ System.

TABLE 43

λ_H(Å)	ν_H(cm^{-1})	Branch	v′v″	Int.	λ_H(Å)	ν_H(cm^{-1})	Branch	v′v″	Int.
2,237.5	44,680	Q_1	1,0	W	2,398.8	41,674	Q_1	0,1	vS
2,238.2	44,664	P_1			2,399.6	41,661	P_1		
2,241.2	44,605	P_2			2,403.1	41.600	P_2		
2,242.2	44,586	$^OP_{12}$			2,404.1	41,584	$^OP_{12}$		
2,303.8	43,394	Q_1	1,1	W	2,473.9	40.409	Q_1	0,2	vS
2,304.6	43,379	P_1			2,474.7	40.397	P_1		
2,307.7	43,319	P_2			2,478.4	40,336	P_2		
2,308.7	43,302	$^OP_{12}$			2,479.4	40,321	$^OP_{12}$		
2,327.0	42,961	Q_1	0,0	M	2,552.5	39,165	Q_1	0,3	S
2,327.8	42,946	P_1			2,553.3	39,153	P_1		
2,331.1	42,886	P_2			2,557.3	39,092	P_2		
2,332.0	42,868	$^OP_{12}$			2,558.2	39,078	$^OP_{12}$		

A rotational analysis is given by Porter, Mann, and Acquista (1965).

CCl

CCl bands ($A^2\Delta$ - $X^2\Pi$) occur in flames of CH_3Cl, $CHCl_3$, and CCl_4. They are complex and are degraded to shorter wavelengths. Each band has about four heads, the most prominent being shown below.

TABLE 44

λ_H(Å)	ν_H(cm^{-1})	Int.	Branch	v'v''	λ_H(Å)	ν_H(cm^{-1})	Int.	Branch	v'v''
2,713.9	36,836	vW	Q_1	1,0	2,845.9	35,134	W	Q_1	0,1
2,723.9	36,700	vW	P_2	1,0	2,846.2	35,131	vW	Q_1	1,2
2,777.6	35,992	S	Q_1	0,0	2,856.7	35,002	W	P_2	0,1
2,778.8	35.976	M	Q_1	1,1	2,856.8	35,000	vW	P_2	1,2
2,788.3	35,854	S	P_2	0,0	2,916.1	34,284	vW	Q_1	0,2
2,789.5	35,838	S	P_2	1,1	2,927.7	34,147	vW	P_2	0,2

For a rotational analysis of the (0,0) and (0,1) bands, see Gordon and King (1961) and Verma and Mulliken (1961).

HF, HCl, and HBr

Infrared vibration-rotation bands of HF, HCl, and HBr occur in H_2/F_2, H_2/Cl_2, and H_2/Br_2 flames, respectively. Pure rotational lines of HCl in the far infrared have also been noted in H_2/Cl_2 flames.

1. HF Vibration-rotation Bands ($X^1\Sigma^+$ Ground State)

P and R branches are present, the latter being sufficiently well developed to form a head that is degraded to longer wavelengths.

TABLE 45

λ_H(Å)	ν_H(cm^{-1})	Band	λ_H(Å)	ν_H(cm^{-1})	Band
5,485.3	18,225	5→0	8,666.4	11,536	3→0
5,742.1	17,402	6→1	9,068.0	11,025	4→1
6,024.2	16,595	7→2	9,497.5	10,526	5→2
6,326.1	15,803	8→3	9,959.1	10,038	6→3
6,655.1	15,022	9→4	12,505	7,994.6	2→0
6,686.3	14,952	4→0	13,080	7,643.2	3→1
6,999.2	14,284	5→1	13,695	7,299.7	4→2
7,334.5	13,630	6→2	14,355	6,964.4	5→3
7,696.0	12,990	7→3	15,065	6,636.1	6→4
8,008.2	12,360	8→4	22,696	4,404.9	1→0
8,517.3	11,738	9→5	23,742	4,210.8	2→1
			24,867	4,020.3	3→2

2. HCl Vibration-rotation Bands ($X^1\Sigma^+$ Ground State)

The (1,0), (2,0), and (3,1) bands have been observed. The R branch heads are given here:

TABLE 46

λ_H(Å)	ν_H(cm^{-1})	Band
17,138	5,833	2→0
17,787	5,620	3→1
31,428	3,181.0	1→0

3. HCl Pure Rotational Spectrum ($X^1\Sigma^+$, v=0 Ground State)

Pure rotational lines of HCl (with J″ = 17 to 33) have been observed in the region 345 cm^{-1} to 623 cm^{-1} (28.93 μ to 16.04 μ).

4. HBr Vibration-rotation Bands ($X^1\Sigma^+$ Ground State)

The (1,0), (2,1), and (2,0) bands have been observed. The R branch heads are shown below.

TABLE 47

λ_H(Å)	ν_H(cm^{-1})	Band
19,365	5,162.6	2 → 0
35,572	2,810.4	1 → 0
36,940	2,706	2 → 1

C. Nitrogen-containing Flames

Flames of organic compounds with combined nitrogen were included in Section I, and organic compounds supported by nitrous oxide show the same band spectra. Other nitrogenous flames such as ammonia/oxygen or hydrazine/oxygen show bands due to NH, NO, O_2, and OH, which were described in Section I; in addition, the NH_2 ammonia *a* band and a yellow-green continuum due to the NO + O reaction occur. The latter is particularly strong when NO is added to lean flames. NH, O_2, and OH can also be observed in absorption in ammonia/oxygen flames.

NH_2

This is a many-line system extending throughout the visible and near infrared; it is strongest in the yellow and green. The following are the maxima obtained under small dispersion.

TABLE 48

λ(Å)	ν(cm^{-1})	λ(Å)	ν(cm^{-1})
5,265	18,990	5,870	17,030
5,384	18,570	*6,042	16,545
*5,436	18,390	*6,302	15,860
5,575	17,930	6,470	15,450
*5,713	17,500	*6,652	15,030

*Strongest bands

In addition, there is a group of lines from 7,099 Å, leading to a head at 7,350 Å (13,600 cm^{-1}).

These bands have been analysed by Dressler and Ramsay (1959). The electronic transition is $^2A_1 - {}^2B_1$

D. Phosphorus-containing Flames

The β and γ systems of PO occur in the flame of phosphorus burning in air. They are also present when $POCl_3$ is added to premixed organic flames.

PO

1. The β System ($A^2\Sigma^+ - X^2\Pi_r$)

The (0,0) sequence commences at around 3,240 Å and gets weaker to longer wavelengths; this sequence has no marked head, and the bands of which it is formed show heads degraded in both directions. There are two similar weaker sequences further to the red. The following are the strongest heads.

TABLE 49

λ_H(Å)	ν_H(cm^{-1})	Int.	Deg.	Branch	v'v''	λ_H(Å)	ν_H(cm^{-1})	Int.	Deg.	Branch	v'v''
3,218.1	31,065	W	R	R_1	7,6	3,365.9	29,701	S	R	$^QR_{12}$	7,7
3,246.2	30,796	vS	V	$^QP_{21}$	0,0	3,379.8	29,579	M	V	$^QP_{21}$	0,1
3,255.3	30,710	S	V	$^QP_{21}$	1,1	3,385.5	29,529	vW	R	R_1	9,9
3,270.5	30,568	vS	V	P_2	0,0	3,387.6	29,511	W	R	$^QR_{12}$	8,8
3,302.9	30,268	M	R	R_1	5,5	3,387.9	29,508	M	V	$^QR_{12}$	1,2
3,311.8	30,186	M	R	$^QR_{12}$	4,4	3,397.8	29,422	W	V	$^QP_{21}$	2,3
3,321.0	30,103	S	R	R_1	6,6	3,405.7	29,354	M	V	P_2	0,1
3,328.2	30,037	S	R	$^QR_{12}$	5,5	3,409.8	29,319	vW	V	$^QP_{21}$	3,4
3,340.6	29,926	S	R	R_1	7,7	3,414.1	29,282	M	V	P_2	1,2
3,346.2	29,876	S	R	$^QR_{12}$	6,6	3,424.6	29,192	vW	V	P_2	2,3
3,362.1	29,735	W	R	R_1	8,8	3,460.1	28,893	vW	R	$^QR_{12}$	5,6

For the rotational structure, see Singh (1959) and Meinel and Krauss (1966).

2. The γ System ($B^2\Sigma^+ - X^2\Pi_r$)

This system consists of double double-headed bands, degraded to shorter wavelengths. The sequences are fairly well marked. The strongest bands are given below.

TABLE 50

λ_H(Å)	ν_H(cm^{-1})	Int.	Branch	v'v''	λ_H(Å)	ν_H(cm^{-1})	Int.	Branch	v'v''
2,305.3	43,364	W	P_2,Q_2	4,2	2,477.9	40,345	vS	$^OP_{12}$	0,0
2,306.9	43,334	W	$^OP_{12}$	4,2	2,528.2	39,541	S	Q_1	1,2
2,312.1	43,238	W	P_2,Q_2	3,1	2,529.4	39,523	S	P_1	1,2
2,313.7	43,208	W	$^OP_{12}$	3,1	2,531.4	39,492	W	P_2,Q_2	2,3
2,318.8	43,112	vW	P_2,Q_2	2,0	2,533.0	39,467	W	$^OP_{12}$	2,3
2,320.6	43,079	vW	$^OP_{12}$	2,0	2,539.1	39,373	vS	Q_1	0,1
2,374.0	42,110	S	Q_1	2,1	2,540.4	39,352	vS	P_1	0,1
2,375.2	42,088	S	P_1	2,1	2,542.4	39,321	S	P_2,Q_2	1,2
2,382.2	41.965	S	Q_1	1,0	2,543.9	39,297	S	$^OP_{12}$	1,2
2,383.5	41,942	S	P_1	1,0	2,553.6	39,149	vS	P_2,Q_2	0,1
2,386.5	41,890	S	P_2,Q_2	2,1	2,555.1	39,126	vS	$^OP_{12}$	0,1
2,387.9	41,864	S	$^OP_{12}$	2,1	2,606.8	38,350	S	Q_1	1,3
2,394.7	41,747	S	P_2,Q_2	1,0	2,608.0	38,332	S	P_1	1,3
2,396.3	41,718	S	$^OP_{12}$	1,0	2,609.1	38,316	vW	P_2,Q_2	2,4
2,453.3	40,749	M	Q_1	1,1	2,610.7	38,293	vW	$^OP_{12}$	2,4
2,454.6	40,728	M	P_1	1,1	2,619.2	38,169	S	Q_1	0,2
2,457.4	40,681	vW	P_2,Q_2	2,2	2,620.5	38,149	S	P_1	0,2
2,462.9	40,590	vS	Q_1	0,0	2,621.9	38,129	S	P_2,Q_2	1,3
2,464.2	40,568	vS	P_1	0,0	2,623.4	38,107	S	$^OP_{12}$	1,3
2,466.8	40,527	M	P_2,Q_2	1,1	2,634.8	37,942	S	P_2,Q_2	0,2
2,468.3	40,501	M	$^OP_{12}$	1,1	2,636.3	37,921	S	$^OP_{12}$	0,2
2,476.4	40,369	vS	P_2,Q_2	0,0					

For the rotational structure of some of these bands, see Rao (1958) and Coquart et al. (1967).

E. Sulphur-containing Flames

The characteristic spectra of sulphur-containing flames are those of CS, S_2, SH, SO, and SO_2.

CS

CS bands ($A^1\Pi - X^1\Sigma^+$) are present in bunsen or hydrocarbon flames containing SO_2 or H_2S. They also occur in a low-temperature phosphorescent flame of CS_2.

They are close double-headed bands, degraded to the red and with fairly well-marked sequences. The (0,0) band head is often very outstanding. The following are the strongest Q heads.

TABLE 51

λ_H(Å)	ν_H(cm^{-1})	Int.	v′v″	λ_H(Å)	ν_H(cm^{-1})	Int.	v′v″
2,509.5	39,837	W	1,0	2,606.8	38,350	M	2,2
2,524.0	39,608	M	2,1	2,622.5	38,120	vW	3,3
2,539.4	39,367	M	3,2	2,664.1	37,525	vS	0,1
2,556.3	39,107	W	4,3	2,680.1	37,301	S	1,2
2,576.8	38,797	vS	0,0	2,694.4	37,103	M	2,3
2,592.6	38,561	vS	1,1	2,710.1	36,888	W	3,4

For a rotational analysis, see Lagerqvist et al. (1958).

S_2

S_2 bands ($B^3\Sigma_u^- - X^3\Sigma_g^-$) occur in most flames containing sulphur. They are a persistent impurity in hydrogen flames.

The system extends from the ultraviolet to the near infrared and consists of a large number of red-degraded bands. In flame sources the bands with low values of v′ occur most strongly, and the appearance is less complex. The strongest heads only are listed below.

TABLE 52

λ_H(Å)	ν_H(cm^{-1})	Int.	v′v″	λ_H(Å)	ν_H(cm^{-1})	Int.	v′v″
3,091.7	32,335	S	5,2	4,610.0	21,686	S	2,16
3,500.5	28,559	S	1,5	4,747.6	21,057	S	2,17
3,587.4	27,867	S	1,6	4,790.8	20,868	vS	3,18
*3,645.2	27,426	S	0.6	4,842.2	20,646	vS	4,19
*3,740.0	26,730	vS	0.7	4,893.8	20,428	S	2,18
*3,837.3	26,053	vS	0,8	4,937.2	20,249	S	3,19
*3,939.1	25,379	vS	0,9	4,990.1	20,034	vS	4,20
*4,045.8	24,710	vS	0,10	5,036.8	19,848	vS	5,21
*4,157.2	24,048	S	0,11	5,090.9	19,637	S	{3.20, 6,22
4,193.8	23,838	vS	1,12				
4,311.0	23,190	vS	1,13	5,193.7	19,249	S	5,22
4,433.6	22,549	vS	1,14	5,249.8	19,043	S	6,23

* Fainter head to violet

For a rotational analysis of some of the S_2 bands, see Naudé (1948) and Ikenoue (1953) and (1960).

SH

The ($A^2\Sigma^+$ - $X^2\Pi_i$) system of SH is found in certain organic flames containing SO_2 or H_2S.

The (0,0) band is very similar in appearance to the analogous OH band. It is degraded to the red, the R_1 and Q_2 heads having about equal intensity, with the Q_1 being masked by structure from R_1. The band is predissociated.

TABLE 53

λ_H(Å)	ν_H(cm^{-1})	Branch	v'v"
3,236.6	30,888	R_1	0,0
3,240.7	30,849	Q_1	0,0
3,279.3	30,486	Q_2	0,0

For a rotational analysis, see Ramsay (1952).

SO

SO bands ($B^3\Sigma^-$ - $X^3\Sigma^-$) are found in flames containing sulphur and oxygen.

They are red-degraded single-headed bands with rather extended rotational structure. The following are the strongest bands.

TABLE 54

λ_H(Å)	ν_H(cm^{-1})	Int.	v'v"	λ_H(Å)	ν_H(cm^{-1})	Int.	v'v"
2,664.8	37,515	W	1,4	3,271.0	30,563	vS	0,10
2,744.0	36,432	M	1,5	3,383.2	29,549	vS	0,11
2,791.3	35,815	W	0,5	3,502.1	28,546	S	0,12
2,827.4	35,358	M	1,6	3,628.2	27,554	M	0,13
2,877.7	34,740	S	0,6	3,675.6	27,199	M	1,14
2,968.4	33,678	vS	0,7	3,761.6	26,577	W	0,14
*3,064.1	32,627	vS	0,8	3,810.8	26,234	M	1,15
3,164.7	31,589	vS	0,9				

*Partially masked by OH band.

A rotational analysis of some of the above bands is given by Martin (1932). (Martin's value of v" should be increased by 2.)

SO_2

SO_2 bands usually appear in absorption against the continuous background from most sulphur-containing flames. They have also been noted in emission.

The bands are degraded to the red and are fairly closely spaced in the region 3,200 to 2,750 Å. Below 2,750 Å they become diffuse, and the long wavelength end of the system consists of narrow headless bands.

The heads are about 1 Å to the violet of the measurements for the maxima of the strongest absorption bands on the next page.

TABLE 55

λ(Å)	ν(cm⁻¹)	Int.	λ(Å)	ν(cm⁻¹)	Int.	λ(Å)	ν(cm⁻¹)	Int.
2,646.6	37,773	W	2,832.3	35,297	S	3,022.1	33,080	vS
2,685.0	37,233	W	2,852.0	35,053	vS	3,043.3	32,850	S
2,727.5	36,653	W	2,868.9	34,846	S	3,065.9	32,607	M
2,734.6	36,558	M	2,887.7	34,620	vS	3,087.7	32,377	W
2,738.1	36,511	W	2,900.9	34,462	M	3,108.4	32,162	W
2,751.2	36,337	W	2,906.5	34,396	S	3,129.5	31,945	?
2,754.6	36,292	W	2,923.1	34,200	S	3,131.3	31,926	W
2,765.2	36,153	W	2,924.8	34,180	S	3,151.8	31,719	vW
2,772.0	36,064	W	2,937.7	34,030	S	3,159.0	31,646	vW
2,780.0	35,961	M	2,943.8	33,960	vS	3,167.0	31,567	vW
2,789.4	35,839	S	2,961.2	33,760	vS	3,173.0	31,507	vW
2,797.0	35,742	S	2,980.0	33,547	vS	3,181.1	31,428	vW
2,815.5	35,507	S	3,001.0	33,313	vS	3,190.9	31,330	vW
2,818.1	35,474	S						

III. MOLECULAR SPECTRA OF FLAMES CONTAINING ADDED METALS

This section contains details of the emission spectra that are produced when certain metals are added to flames and of spectra that are frequently found as an impurity in other flames. Many metal oxide spectra can be excited in flames, but only the most important are listed below. Only spectra produced by the following elements are described:

Al, Ba, Ca, Cu, Fe, Mg, Mn, Pb, Sr

Wavelengths and wavenumbers of the band heads or characteristic features are given. Molecular constants are not listed.

AlO

The Green System ($A^2\Sigma^+ - X^2\Sigma^+$) of AlO is emitted from flames containing aluminum salts and in the flame of burning aluminum powder.

The bands are single headed, degraded to the red, and form marked sequences. The following are the strongest heads.

TABLE 56

λ_H(Å)	ν_H(cm⁻¹)	Int.	v′v″	λ_H(Å)	ν_H(cm⁻¹)	Int.	v′v″
4,352.6	22,968	W	5,2	4,842.3	20,646	vS	0,0
4,373.7	22,858	W	6,3	4,866.4	20,543	M	1,1
4,393.8	22,753	W	7,4	5,079.4	19,682	S	0,1
4,412.6	22,656	W	8,5	5,102.1	19,594	S	1,2
4,430.3	22,565	W	9,6	5,123.3	19,513	M	2,3
4,470.5	22,362	M	2,0	5,142.9	19,439	M	3,4
4,494.0	22,245	M	3,1	5,161.0	19,371	W	4,5
4,516.4	22,135	M	4,2	5,177.3	19,310	W	5,6
4,537.6	22,032	M	5,3	5,337.1	18,732	W	0,2
4,557.6	21,935	W	6,4	5,357.7	18,659	M	1,3
4,576.3	21,845	W	7,5	5,376.8	18,593	M	2,4
4,648.2	21,508	S	1,0	5,394.1	18,533	M	3,5
4,672.0	21,398	M	2,1	5,409.5	18,481	M	4,6
4,694.6	21,295	M	3,2	5,422.8	18,436	W	5,7
4,715.5	21,201	W	4,3				
4,735.8	21,110	W	5,4				

BaO

When barium salts are added to flames, weak BaO bands ($A^1\Sigma - X^1\Sigma$) occur.

The system consists of single-headed bands degraded to the red. The strongest bands are listed below.

TABLE 57

λ_H(Å)	ν_H(cm^{-1})	Int.	v'v"	λ_H(Å)	ν_H(cm^{-1})	Int.	v'v"
4,680.3	21,360	M	11,1	5,864.5	17,047	vS	2,1
4,850.6	20,610	M	8,0	5,976.3	16,728	W	0,0
4,965.4	20,134	W	7,0	6,039.6	16,553	vS	1,1
5,086.7	19,654	M	6,0	6,102.3	16,383	M	2,2
5,214.7	19,171	S	5,0	6,165.1	16,216	M	3,3
5,349.7	18,688	S	4,0	6,224.7	16,061	M	0,1
5,492.7	18,201	vS	3,0	6,291.0	15,891	S	1,2
5,644.1	17,713	vS	2,0	6,493.1	15,397	vS	0,2
5,701.0	17,536	S	3,1	6,782.8	14,739	S	0,3
5,805.1	17,221	M	1,0	7,097.4	14,086	M	0,4

BaOH

The strong green coloration of flames containing barium salts is due to BaOH. Between 4,700 and 5,200 Å a continuous emission appears showing two diffuse maxima at 4,870 and 5,120 Å.

Stronger BaOH emission occurs in the infrared, consisting of two diffuse bands with maxima near 8,280 and 8,670 Å and a weaker band with a maximum near 7,400 Å.

CaO

Three systems of CaO are found in flames containing calcium compounds: the Ultraviolet System, the Blue System, and the Infrared System. The latter is the most intense. The Ultraviolet and Blue Systems are very weak.

A. The Ultraviolet System ($C^1\Sigma - X^1\Sigma$)

The bands are single headed and degraded to the red. The strongest bands are given below.

TABLE 58

λ_H(Å)	ν_H(cm^{-1})	v'v"
3,793.7	26,352	2,5
3,854.1	25,939	0,4
3,858.3	25,911	5,8
3,894.7	25,669	2,6
3,915.7	25,531	3,7

B. The Blue System ($B^1\Pi - X^1\Sigma$)

Under high dispersion the bands appear double headed. They are degraded to the red. The following are the strongest heads.

TABLE 59

λ_H(Å)	ν_H(cm^{-1})	v'v''	λ_H(Å)	ν_H(cm^{-1})	v'v''
4,205.1	23,774	0,3	4,309.5	23,198	5,8
4,221.9	23,679	1,4	4,403.9	22,701	4,8
4,240.8	23,574	2,5	4,425.8	22,588	5,9
4,261.8	23,458	3,6	4,449.9	22,466	6,10
4,284.6	23,333	4,7			

C. The Infrared System ($A^1\Sigma - X^1\Sigma$)

These bands are single headed and degraded to the red.

TABLE 60

λ_H(Å)	ν_H(cm^{-1})	Int.	v'v''	λ_H(Å)	ν_H(cm^{-1})	Int.	v'v''
6,956.2	14,372	vW	4,0	7,715.5	12,957	S	3,1
6,968.4	14,347	vW	5,1	7,721.1	12,947	M	4,2
6,982.9	14,317	vW	6,2	8,153.1	12,261	vS	1,0
7,308.3	13,679	vW	3,0	8,164.7	12,244	vW	3,2
7,318.5	13,660	S	4,1	8,167.3	12,240	S	2,1
7,327.6	13,643	S	5,2	8,652.2	11,554	vS	0,0
7,712.2	12,962	S	2,0	9,229	10,832	S	0,1

Further infrared bands of CaO are known around 10,000 Å. It is not certain whether these bands are an extension of the above system or are a new system.

CaOH

Bands due to CaOH are a persistent impurity in the spectra of flames and are much stronger than the CaO bands.

A system around 5,550 Å consists of a very strong and broad band, with an ill-defined maximum, accompanied on both sides by weaker maxima, also badly defined.

TABLE 61

λ_{Max}(Å)	ν_{Max}(cm^{-1})	Int.
5,305	18,564	vW
5,425	18,428	W
5,550	18,013	vS
5,780	17,296	W
5,825	17,162	W

A further, similar system exists around 6,230 Å, but the assignment of CaOH as the emitter is not conclusive.

TABLE 62

λ_{Max}(Å)	ν_{Max}(cm^{-1})	Int.
6,038	16,557	M
6,230	16,046	vS
6,453	15,492	M
6,653	15,026	W
6,830	14,637	vW
6,980	14,322	vW

CuCl

CuCl bands frequently appear as an impurity in flames of burning CO, in cool flames, and in furnaces and coal fires.

Five systems occur, denoted as A, B, C, D, and E, the transitions being ($A^1\Pi$ - $X^1\Sigma^+$), ($B^1\Pi$ - $X^1\Sigma^+$), ($C^1\Sigma^+$ - $X^1\Sigma^+$), ($D^1\Pi$ - $X^1\Sigma^+$), and ($E^1\Sigma^+$ - $X^1\Sigma^+$), respectively. All five systems are degraded to the red and form marked sequences. The groups of pairs of bands formed by systems D and E are characteristic.

TABLE 63

λ_H(Å)	ν_H(cm^{-1})	Int.	System	v'v''	λ_H(Å)	ν_H(cm^{-1})	Int.	System	v'v''
4,187.9	23,871	W	E	2,0	4,515.9	22,137	M	D	0,2
4,210.9	23,741	W	D	2,0	4,755.7	21,021	vW	C	1,0
4,259.0	23,473	S	E	1,0	4,788.5	20,877	vW	B	1,0
4,280.9	23,353	vS	D	1,0	4,846.9	20,625	W	C	0,0
4,333.2	23,071	vS	E	0,0	4,881.5	20,479	W	B	0,0
4,353.9	22,961	vS	D	0,0	4,946.1	20,212	vW	C	0,1
4,412.4	22,657	S	E	0,1	4,982.2	20,065	vW	B	0,1
4,433.8	22,547	vS	D	0,1	5,152.4	19,403	M	A	1,0
4,493.8	22,246	M	E	0,2	5,262.4	18,997	W	A	0,0

CuH

The ($A^1\Sigma^+$ - $X^1\Sigma^+$) transition of CuH is found in flames containing copper salts.

The bands are single headed and degraded to the red. Usually the (0,0) and the (1,1) bands are the only ones to appear.

TABLE 64

λ_H(Å)	ν_H(cm^{-1})	v'v''
4,279.6	23,360	0,0
4,327.7	23,100	1,1

CuO

Bands due to CuO ($B^2\Sigma$ - $A^2\Sigma_i$) around 6,100 Å are found in flames containing copper salts.

They consist of widely spaced double-headed bands degraded to the red. They are usually weak.

TABLE 65

λ_H(Å)	ν_H(cm^{-1})	v'v''
6,045.1	16,537	1,0
6,059.3	16,498	1,0
6,146.8	16,264	0,0
6,161.5	16,225	0,0

CuOH

Weak bands due to CuOH are responsible for the green coloration of flames containing copper salts.

In the green region, the spectrum consists of four broad and diffuse maxima near 5,220, 5,400, 5,660, and 5,760 Å. In the yellow region, the spectrum shows a broad and diffuse maximum near 6,200 Å.

FeO

Strong, complex bands in the orange and infrared regions are emitted by flames containing iron compounds, e.g., iron carbonyl. They are also frequently found as an impurity.

A. The Orange Bands

Most of these bands have been classified into three systems, involving the same lower level which may or may not be the ground state. Most of the bands are degraded to the red, but some features appear to be maxima of headless structures. Only the strongest bands are listed below.

TABLE 66

λ_H(Å)	ν_H(cm^{-1})	Int.	System	v'v''	λ_H(Å)	ν_H(cm^{-1})	Int.	System	v'v''
5,531.4	18,073	W			5,903.0	16,935	M	C – (X)	0,1
5,543.2	18,035	vW	B – (X)	2,1	*5,911	16,912	W		
5,582.8	17,907	M	D – (X)	0,0	*5,919	16,890	W		
5,614.0	17,807	M	C – (X)	0,0	5,974.6	16,732	M	C – (X)	1,2
5,621.3	17,784	W			*6,097.3	16,396	vS		
5,624.1	17,775	W			6,109.9	16,362	vS	B – (X)	1,2
5,646.6	17,704	M	D – (X)	1,1	6,180.5	16,175	vS	D – (X)	0,2
5,789.8	17,266	vS	B – (X)	0,0	6,218.9	16,075	vS	C – (X)	0,2
5,807.4	17,214	vW	B – (X)	1,1	6,524.1	15,323	vW	D – (X)	0,3
5,819.2	17,179	M	B – (X)	2,2	6,566.7	15,224	vW	C – (X)	0,3
5,868.1	17,036	vS	D – (X)	0,1					

*Maximum of intensity of narrow headless structures

B. The Infrared System

All the bands of this system are degraded to the red. The upper level involved in the transition may be the D level of the Orange Bands. No satisfactory vibrational analysis has been proposed. The following are the strongest heads.

TABLE 67

λ_H(Å)	ν_H(cm^{-1})	Int.	λ_H(Å)	ν_H(cm^{-1})	Int.	λ_H(Å)	ν_H(cm^{-1})	Int.
7,265	13,760	W	7,775	12,858	M	8,230	12,147	S
7,428	13,458	W	8,112	12,324	S	8,302	12,041	S
7,527	13,281	W	8,137	12,286	S	8,578	11,654	vS
7,690	13,000	M						

Another infrared system has been observed in a carbon monoxide flame containing iron carbonyl. The strongest bands are shown below.

TABLE 68

λ_H(Å)	ν_H(cm^{-1})	Int.	v'v''	λ_H(Å)	ν_H(cm^{-1})	Int.	v'v''	λ_H(Å)	ν_H(cm^{-1})	Int.	v'v''
8,620	11,598	W	2,0	9,893	10,105	vS	1,1	11,634	8,593	S	0,2
8,742	11,436	W	3,1	10,102	9,896	vS	2,2	11,916	8,390	vS	1,3
9,120	10,962	S	1,0	10,553	9,473	vS	0,1	12,911	7,743	W	0,3
9,286	10,766	S	2,1	10,803	9,254	vS	1,2	13,238	7,552	M	1,4
9,676	10,332	S	0,0								

FeOH

Two diffuse groups of bands have been observed in the ultraviolet when iron carbonyl is introduced into a hydrogen flame. The emitter is probably FeOH. The first group lies in the region 3,530 to 3,580 Å and the second in 3,630 to 3,675 Å, with a diffuse head, degraded to shorter wavelengths, at 3,675 Å (27,203 cm^{-1}).

MgO

The Green System ($B^1\Sigma^+ - X^1\Sigma^+$) of MgO has been observed in oxyhydrogen flames containing magnesium salts and in the flame of burning magnesium ribbon. The bands are degraded to the violet. The (0,0) sequence is very marked. Only the strongest bands are shown below.

TABLE 69

λ_H(Å)	ν_H(cm^{-1})	Int.	v'v''	λ_H(Å)	ν_H(cm^{-1})	Int.	v'v''
4,935.3	20,257	W	6,6	4,996.7	20,008	vS	1,1
4,949.5	20,198	M	5,5	5,007.3	19,965	vS	0,0
4,962.1	20,147	M	4,4	5,192.0	19,255	W	1,2
4,974.5	20,097	S	3,3	5,206.0	19,203	W	0,1
4,985.9	20,051	S	2,2				

The complex system of bands in the ultraviolet region (3,640 to 3,960 Å) that are ascribed to MgO may be present in flames, but strong emission from MgOH occurs in the same region, making identification difficult.

MgOH

Two groups of strong, diffuse bands around 3,600 and 3,830 Å are emitted in flames containing magnesium salts. Most of the bands are degraded to shorter wavelengths, but some appear as maxima. The following are the strongest bands.

TABLE 70

λ_H(Å)	ν_H(cm^{-1})	Int.	Deg.	λ_H(Å)	ν_H(cm^{-1})	Int.	Deg.	λ_H(Å)	ν_H(cm^{-1})	Int.	Deg.
3,627	27,560	vW	V	3,751	26,650	W	Max	3,848	25,980	W	V
3,645	27,430	vW	Max	3,801	26,300	M	V	3,855	25,930	W	V
3,696	27,050	S	V	3,807	26,260	vS	Max	3,859	25,910	W	V
3,703	27,000	vS	V	3,810	26,240	vS	V	3,882	25,750	W	V
3,707	26,970	S	Max	3,815	26,200	S	Max	3,914	25,540	vW	Max
3,719	26,880	S	V	3,822	26,160	S	Max	3,942	25,360	vW	V
3,731	26,790	M	V	3,834	26,070	vS	Max	3,969	25,190	vW	V

MnO

MnO bands are emitted from flames containing manganese salts. They have also been observed in furnace flames. The bands are degraded to the red and form well-marked sequences. The strongest heads are given below.

TABLE 71

λ_H(Å)	ν_H(cm^{-1})	Int.	v'v''	λ_H(Å)	ν_H(cm^{-1})	Int.	v'v''
5,158.9	19,379	M	2,0	5,853.1	17,080	vS	0,1
5,192.0	19,255	M	3,1	5,879.5	17,004	vS	1,2
5,227.7	19,124	M	4,2	5,910.1	16,916	M	2,3
5,266.0	18,984	vW	5,3	6,148.3	16,260	W	0,2
5,359.6	18,653	S	1,0	6,174.8	16,191	W	1,3
5,390.0	18,548	S	2,1	6,203.6	16,115	W	2,4
5,423.2	18,434	S	3,2	6,236.5	16,030	vW	3,5
5,582.2	17,909	vS	0,0	6,497.6	15,386	vW	1,4
5,608.4	17,825	W	1,1	6,524.0	15,324	vW	2,5
5,639.7	17,727	?	2,2	6,556.6	15,248	vW	3,6
5,672.1	17,625	vW	3,3				

MnOH

Diffuse bands in the ultraviolet and infrared regions are emitted from flames containing manganese salts. They are ascribed to MnOH. The following are the maxima.

TABLE 72

λ_{Max}(Å)	ν_{Max}(cm^{-1})	System	λ_{Max}(Å)	ν_{Max}(cm^{-1})	System
3,650	27,390	UV	4,140	24,150	UV
3,750	26,660	UV	8,010	12,480	IR
3,820	26,170	UV	8,110	12,327	IR
3,880	25,765	UV	8,365	11,951	IR
3,960	25,245	UV	8,580	11,651	IR
4,050	24,680	UV	8,710	11,478	IR

PbO

Three band systems of PbO have been observed in flames containing lead salts or lead tetraethyl. These are the A system ($AO^+ - X^1\Sigma^+$), the B system ($B1 - X^1\Sigma^+$), and the D system ($D1 - X^1\Sigma^+$). The strongest heads of these systems, all degraded to the red, are given below.

TABLE 73

λ_H(Å)	ν_H(cm^{-1})	Int.	System	v'v''	λ_H(Å)	ν_H(cm^{-1})	Int.	System	v'v''
3,209.2	31,151	M	D	2,0	4,983.8	20,051	M	B	0,3
3,264.4	30,625	M	D	1,0	5,138.2	19,457	M	A	1,1
3,341.8	29,915	M	D	1,1	5,162.3	19,366	M	B	0,4
3,401.9	29,387	vS	D	0,1	5,331.1	18,753	M	A	1,2
3,485.7	28,681	vS	D	0,2	5,459.4	18,312	S	A	0,2
4,229.0	23,640	vS	B	3,0	5,677.8	17,608	vS	A	0,3
4,317.1	23,157	vS	B	2,0	5,910.7	16,914	S	A	0,4
4,410.4	22,667	S	B	1,0	6,160.5	16,228	S	A	0,5
4,553.7	21,954	vS	B	1,1	6,250.8	15,993	vS	A	1,6
4,658.0	21,463	vS	B	0,1	6,427.7	15,553	S	A	0,6
4,816.9	20,755	S	B	0,2					

SrO

SrO bands appear in flames containing strontium salts. Three systems are present: the Ultraviolet System, the Blue System, and the Infrared System. They are very similar to the CaO bands, the latter system again being the most intense.

A. The Ultraviolet System ($C^1\Sigma - X^1\Sigma^+$)

The strongest heads of this system, all degraded to the red, are shown below.

TABLE 74

λ_H(Å)	ν_H(cm^{-1})	v'v"
3,503.8	28,532	0,0
3,525.4	28,357	1,1
3,546.6	28,188	2,2
3,567.1	28,026	3,3
3,586.9	27,871	0,1
3,607.1	27,715	1,2
3,671.5	27,229	0,2

B. The Blue System ($B^1\Pi - X^1\Sigma^+$)

The strongest heads, all degraded to the red, are shown below.

TABLE 75

λ_H(Å)	ν_H(cm^{-1})	v'v"
3,752.4	26,642	4,0
3,775.3	26,480	5,1
3,897.1	25,653	2,0
3,919.6	25,506	3,1

C. The Infrared System ($A^1\Sigma - X^1\Sigma^+$)

This system consists of red-degraded single-headed bands. The strongest heads are shown below.

TABLE 76

λ_H(Å)	ν_H(cm^{-1})	v'v"	λ_H(Å)	ν_H(cm^{-1})	v'v"
7,500.6	13,329	4,0	8,700.0	11,491	1,0
7,522.8	13,289	5,1	8,722.5	11,462	2,1
7,852.8	12,731	3,0	9,195.8	10,872	0,0
7,882.3	12,683	4,1	9,776.2	10,226	0,1
8,257.8	12,106	2,0	10,426.2	9,588.6	0,2
8,272.2	12,085	3,1	10,437.1	9,578.6	0.3

SrOH

The strong red color of flames containing strontium is due to SrOH. Two systems are present, both exhibiting broad and diffuse maxima, centered around 6,060 and 6,710 Å, respectively. The band around 6,060 Å shows some structure on the long wavelength side, with close double heads degraded to the violet. The positions of the maxima are on the next page.

TABLE 77

λ_H(Å)	ν_H(cm^{-1})	Int.
6,060	16,497	vS
6,200	16,124	vW
6,260	15,970	vW
6,460	15,475	M
6,590	15,170	W
6,710	14,899	vS
6,820	14,658	vS
7,070	14,140	M
7,220	13,846	W

REFERENCES

1. **Anketell, J. and Pery-Thorne, A.,** *Proc. Roy. Soc.,* A301, 343, 1967.
2. **Babcock, H. D. and Herzberg, L.,** *Astrophys. J.,* 108, 167, 1948.
3. **Ballik, E. A. and Ramsay, D. A.,** *Astrophys. J.,* 137, 61, 1963a.
4. **Ballik, E. A. and Ramsay, D. A.,** *Astrophys. J.,* 137, 84, 1963b.
5. **Bass, A. M. and Broida, H. P.,** NBS Circular, No. 541, 1953.
6. **Bass, A. M. and Broida, H. P.,** NBS Monograph, No. 24, 1961.
7. **Bennett, R. G. and Dalby, F. W.,** *J. Chem. Phys.,* 32, 1716, 1960.
8. **Bennett, R. G. and Dalby, F. W.,** *J. Chem. Phys.,* 36, 399, 1962.
9. **Bennett, R. G. and Dalby, F. W.,** *J. Chem. Phys.,* 40, 1414, 1964.
10. **Brocklehurst, B., Hébert, G. R., Innanen, S. H., Seel, R. M., and Nicholls, R. W.,** *Identification Atlas of Molecular Spectra,* 8, York University, Toronto, 1971.
11. **Chakraborty, B. and Pan, Y. K.,** *J. Chem. Phys.,* 56, 3722, 1972.
12. **Copeland, G. E.,** *J. Chem. Phys.,* 56, 689, 1972.
13. **Coquart, B., Couet, C., Tuan, N., and Guenebaut, H.,** *J. Chim. Phys.,* 64, 1197, 1967.
14. **Davis, S. P. and Phillips, J. G.,** *Berkeley Analyses of Molecular Spectra,* 1, University of California Press, Berkeley, 1963.
15. **Deézsi, I.,** *Acta. Phys. Hungar.,* 9, 125, 1958.
16. **Dieke, G. M. and Crosswhite, H. M.,** *J. Quant. Spectrosc. Radiat. Transfer,* 2, 97, 1962.
17. **Dixon, R. N.,** *Can. J. Phys.,* 37, 1171, 1959.
18. **Dixon, R. N.,** *Proc. Roy. Soc.,* A275, 431, 1963.
19. **Dixon, R. N.,** *Trans. Faraday Soc.,* 65, 3141, 1969.
20. **Douglas, A. E. and Routly, P. M.,** *Astrophys. J. Suppl. Ser.,* 1, 295, 1955.
21. **Dressler, K. and Ramsay, D. A.,** *Phil. Trans. Roy. Soc.,* A251, 553, 1959.
22. **Durie, R. A., Legoy, F., and Ramsay, D. A.,** *Can. J. Phys.,* 38, 444, 1960.
23. **Farmer, A. J. D., Hasson, V., and Nicholls, R. W.,** *J. Quant. Spectrosc. Radiat. Transfer,* 12, 627, 1972.
24. **Fink, E. H. and Welge, K. H.,** *J. Chem. Phys.,* 46, 4315, 1967.
25. **Gausset, L., Herzberg, G., Lagerqvist, A., and Rosen, B.,** *Astrophys. J.,* 142, 45, 1965.
26. **Gordon, R. D. and King, G. W.,** *Can. J. Phys.,* 39, 252, 1961.
27. **Guenebaut, H. and Pannetier, G.,** *C.R. Acad. Sci.,* 250, 3613, 1960.
28. **Hallmann, M. and Laulicht, I.,** *Astrophys. J. Suppl. Ser.,* 12, 307, 1966.
29. **Hasson, V. E. and Nicholls, R. W.,** *J. Phys. B. (Atom. Molec. Phys.),* 4, 1769, 1971.
30. **Hébert, G. R., Innanen, S. H., and Nicholls, R. W.,** *Identification Atlas of Molecular Spectra,* 4, York University, Toronto, 1967.
31. **Herzberg, G. and Sutton, R. B.,** *Can. J. Res.,* 40, 74, 1940.
32. **Herzberg, G. and Travis, N.,** *Can. J. Phys.,* 42, 1658, 1964.
33. **Hesser, J. E. and Lutz, B. L.,** *Astrophys. J.,* 159, 703, 1970.
34. **Ikenoue, K.,** *J. Phys. Soc. Jap.,* 8, 646, 1953.
35. **Ikenoue, K.,** *Sci. Light,* 9, 79, 1960.
36. **Imhof, R. E. and Read, F. H.,** *Chem Phys. Lett.,* 11, 326, 1971.
37. **James, T. C.,** *J. Mol. Spectrosc.,* 40, 545, 1971.
38. **Jenkins, F. A.,** *Phys. Rev.,* 31, 539, 1928.

39. Jenkins, F. A., Barton, H. A., and Mulliken, R. S., *Phys. Rev.*, 30, 150, 1927.
40. Jenkins, F. A. and McKellar, A., *Phys. Rev.*, 42, 464, 1932.
41. Jeunehomme, M., *J. Chem. Phys.*, 42, 4086, 1965.
42. Jevons, W., *Proc. Roy. Soc.*, A112, 407, 1926.
43. Johns, J. W. C., *Can. J. Phys.*, 39, 1738, 1961.
44. Kiess, N. H. and Broida, H. P., *Can. J. Phys.*, 34, 1471, 1956.
45. Krupenie, P. H., NBS Reference Data Series, NSRDS-NBS 5, 1966.
46. Lagerqvist, A., Westerlund, H., Wright, C. V., and Barrow, R. F., *Ark. Fys.*, 14, 387, 1958.
47. Landsverk, O. G., *Phys. Rev.*, 56, 769, 1939.
48. Lawrence, G. M., *Chem Phys. Lett.*, 9, 575, 1971.
49. Learner, R. C. M., *Proc. Roy. Soc.*, A269, 311, 1962.
50. Linevsky, M. J., *J. Chem. Phys.*, 47, 3485, 1967.
51. Liszt, H. S. and Hesser, J. E., *Astrophys. J.*, 159, 1101, 1970.
52. Marenin, I. R. and Johnson, H. R., *J. Quant. Spectrosc. Radiat. Transfer*, 10, 305, 1970.
53. Martin, E. V., *Phys. Rev.*, 41, 167, 1932.
54. Meinel, H. and Krauss, L., *Z. Naturforsch.*, 21A, 1878, 1966.
55. Moore, C. E. and Broida, H. P., *J. Res. Natl. Bur. Stand.*, 63A, 19, 1959.
56. Moore, J. H. and Robinson, D. W., *J. Chem. Phys.*, 48, 4870, 1968.
57. Murai, T. and Shimauchi, M., *Sci. Light*, 15, 48, 1966.
58. Naudé, S. M., *Ann. Phys.*, 3, 201, 1948.
59. Phillips, J. G., *Astrophys. J.*, 107, 389, 1948.
60. Phillips, J. G., *Astrophys. J.*, 110, 73, 1949.
61. Phillips, J. G. and Davis, S. P., *Berkeley Analyses of Molecular Spectra*, 2, University of California Press, Berkeley, 1968.
62. Pilling, M. J., Bass, A. M., and Braun, W., *J. Quant. Spectrosc. Radiat. Transfer*, 11, 1593, 1971.
63. Porter, T. L., Mann, D. E., and Acquista, N., *J. Molec. Spectr.*, 16, 228, 1965.
64. Ramakrishna Rao, T. V. and Lakshman, S. V. J., *J. Quant. Spectrosc. Radiat. Transfer*, 12, 1063, 1972.
65. Ramsay, D. A., *J. Chem. Phys.*, 20, 1920, 1952.
66. Rao, K. S., *Can. J. Phys.*, 36, 1526, 1958.
67. Singh, N. L., *Can. J. Phys.*, 37, 136, 1959.
68. Smith, W. H., *Astrophys. J.*, 156, 791, 1969a.
69. Smith, W. H., *J. Chem. Phys.*, 51, 520, 1969b.
70. Smith, W. H. and Liszt, H. S., *J. Quant. Spectrosc. Radiat. Transfer*, 11, 45, 1971.
71. Tyte, D. C., Innanen, S. H., and Nicholls, R. W., *Identification Atlas of Molecular Spectra*, 5, York University, Toronto, 1967.
72. Verma, R. D. and Mulliken, R. S., *J. Mol. Spectrosc.*, 6, 419, 1961.
73. Weinstock, E. M., Zare, R. N., and Melton, L. A., *J. Chem. Phys.*, 56, 3456, 1972.

Section D

Atomic Spectroscopy

ATOMIC ABSORPTION, ATOMIC FLUORESCENCE, AND FLAME EMISSION SPECTROSCOPY

J. B. Willis, Commonwealth Scientific and Industrial Research Organization, Australia

I. CHARACTERISTIC CONCENTRATIONS AND LIMITS OF DETECTION FOR METALS IN FLAME ATOMIC ABSORPTION

Table 1 lists the characteristic concentration of each metal at the most sensitive line normally accessible in flame spectroscopy. This quantity is the concentration of metal in aqueous solution required to produce 1% absorption when sprayed into the flame. It is of course influenced by the efficiency of the nebulizer and spray chamber and the length of the light path in the flame and is frequently dependent on the stoichiometry of the gas mixture and the region in the flame measured. In spite of this, however, characteristic concentration values do not vary by more than a factor of about three between most well-designed instruments.

In the past this quantity has frequently been referred to as the sensitivity, but the later term is more correctly used to mean the slope, dx/dc, of the calibration curve, where x is the measure of the signal and c the concentration (IUPAC Information Bulletin: Appendices on Tentative Nomenclature, Symbols, Units and Standards, No. 27, November 1972).

Limit of detection in atomic absorption spectroscopy is usually defined as the concentration of metal producing absorption equal to twice the magnitude of the background fluctuation. Since this fluctuation depends on the signal-to-noise ratio of the light source and on the stability of the electronic system of the spectrometer, limits of detection are more difficult to reproduce than are characteristic concentrations. The values given in the table were obtained on a commercial double-beam instrument and are intended to illustrate differences between one metal and another rather than to indicate the ultimate attainable limits, which in any case can be expected to change with improvements in instrumentation.

Usually, but not invariably, the most sensitive line is also the line with the best limit of detection. Exceptions include Gd, Ir, Lu, Pb, U, W, and Y, and for these metals the table shows both the most sensitive line and also the line with the best limit of detection.

TABLE 1

Characteristic Concentrations and Limits of Detection for Metals in Flame Atomic Absorption

Metal	Wavelength nm	Flame[a]	Characteristic Concentration μg ml^{-1}	Limit of Detection μg ml^{-1}
Ag	328.07	A,C	0.05	0.005
Al	309.27	N	1.0	0.1
As	193.70	H,A	1.0	0.2
Au	242.80	A,C	0.3	0.02
B	249.77	N	50	6
Ba	553.55	N	0.4[b]	0.05[b]
Be	234.86	N	0.02	0.002
Bi	223.06	A,C	0.4	0.05
Ca	422.67	A,N	0.08[b]	0.002[b]
Cd	228.80	A,C	0.02	0.005
Ce	520.0	N	80	
Co	240.73	A	0.1	0.005
Cr	357.87	A	0.15	0.005

TABLE 1 (continued)

Characteristic Concentrations and Limits of Detection for Metals in Flame Atomic Absorption

Metal	Wavelength nm	Flame[a]	Characteristic Concentration μg ml⁻¹	Limit of Detection μg ml⁻¹
Cs	852.11	A,C	0.15	0.05[b]
Cu	324.75	A,C	0.07	0.005
Dy	421.17	N	0.7[b]	0.4[b]
Er	400.80	N	0.9[b]	0.1[b]
Eu	459.40	N	0.8[b]	0.2[b]
Fe	248.33	A	0.1	0.005
Ga	287.42	A,C	2	0.1
Gd	407.87	N	15[b]	
	368.41	N		4[b]
Ge	265.16	N	1.5	1
Hf	307.29	N	15	15
Hg	253.65	A,C	5	0.5
Ho	410.38	N	1.5[b]	0.3[b]
In	303.94	A,C	0.4	0.05
Ir	208.88	A	3	
	263.97	N		2
K	766.49	A,C	0.03	0.005
La	550.13	N	40	2
Li	670.78	A,C	0.02	0.0006
Lu	335.96	N	10	
	331.21	N		3
Mg	285.21	A	0.008	0.0005
Mn	279.48	A,C	0.06	0.003
Mo	313.26	A,N	0.4	0.1
Na	589.00	A,C	0.02	0.005
Nb	334.91	N	25	
	334.37	N		5
Nd	463.42	N	10[b]	2[b]
Ni	232.00	A,C	0.1	0.005
Os	290.91	N	1.0	0.6
Pb	217.00	A,C	0.4	
	283.31	A		0.01
Pd	247.64	A,C	0.2	0.02
Pr	495.14	N	15[b]	10[b]
Pt	265.95	A	5	0.1
Rb	780.02	A,C	0.04	0.005[b]
Re	346.05	N	10	1.5
Rh	343.49	A	0.3	0.03
Ru	349.89	A	0.9	0.3
Sb	217.58	A,C	1	0.2
Sc	391.18	N	0.6[b]	0.2
Se	196.03	H,A	0.5	0.5
Si	251.61	N	2.5	0.1
Sm	429.67	N	9[b]	5[b]
Sn	224.61	H	0.5	0.06
Sr	460.73	A	0.15	0.01
Ta	271.47	N	10	6.0
Tb	432.65	N	8[b]	2[b]
Tc	261.42 / 261.59	A	3	
Te	214.28	A,C	0.3	0.3
Th	324.58	N	850	

TABLE 1 (continued)

Characteristic Concentrations and Limits of Detection for Metals in Flame Atomic Absorption

Metal	Wavelength nm	Flame[a]	Characteristic Concentration $\mu g\ ml^{-1}$	Limit of Detection $\mu g\ ml^{-1}$
Ti	364.27	N	3.5	0.2
Tl	276.79	A,C	0.5	0.2
Tm	371.79	N	0.5[b]	0.15
U	358.49	N	120	
	351.46	N		30
V	318.40	N	1.5	0.04
W	255.14	N	5	
	400.88	N		0.5
Y	410.24	N	1.5[b]	
	407.74	N		0.3[b]
Yb	398.80	N	0.2[b]	0.04[b]
Zn	213.86	A,C	0.02	0.002
Zr	360.12	N	15	5[b]

[a] A = air-acetylene, 10 cm flame.
C = air-coal gas, air-natural gas or air-propane, 10 cm flame.
H = air-hydrogen, 10 cm flame.
N = nitrous oxide-acetylene, 5 cm flame.
[b] Ionization suppressed by addition of high concentration of another easily ionizable metal.

Based on Slavin, W. and Slavin, S., *Appl. Spectrosc.*, 23, 421, 1969, and Willis, J. B., in *Analytical Flame Spectroscopy*, Mavrodineanu, R., Ed., Macmillan, London, 1970. With permission.

II. SOME LESS SENSITIVE LINES FOR USE IN ATOMIC ABSORPTION SPECTROSCOPY

Table 2 shows the ratio of the concentration of metal required to give 1% absorption at the line quoted and at the most sensitive line (see Table 1).

TABLE 2

Some Less Sensitive Lines for Use in Atomic Absorption Spectroscopy

Metal	Wavelength nm	Relative Concentration	Metal	Wavelength nm	Relative Concentration
Ag	338.29	2	Bi	306.77	4
Al	237.31 } 237.34 }	4	Ca	227.66	14
				239.86	120 (?45)
	256.80	13	Cd	326.11	440
As	197.20	2	Co	243.58	3
Au	267.60	2		304.40	12
	312.28	900		346.58	30
Ba	350.11	16 (?110)	Cr	425.44	3

TABLE 2 (continued)

Some Less Sensitive Lines for Use in Atomic Absorption Spectroscopy

Metal	Wavelength nm	Relative Concentration
Cs	455.54	85
Cu	327.40	2
	222.57	15
	244.16	290
Dy	416.80	7
Er	408.77	7
Eu	311.14	15
Fe	371.99	6
	305.91	25
	346.59	110
Ga	245.01	10
Gd	394.55	7
Ge	269.13	4
Hf	294.08	6
Ho	410.86	10
	395.57	45
In	410.48	3
	275.39	30
Ir	263.97	2
	351.36	15
K	769.90	2
	404.41	300
La	392.76	4
Li	323.26	240
Lu	356.78	2
	451.86	11
Mg	202.58	25
Mn	280.11	2
	403.08	10
Mo	320.88	9
	311.21	20
Na	589.59	2
	330.23 330.30	150
Nb	357.58	2.5
	415.26	5
Nd	471.90	2
Ni	341.48	3.5
	323.30	30
Os	305.87	1.5
	264.41	5
Pb	283.31	2.5
	261.42	25
Pd	340.46	3
Pr	491.40	3.5
Pt	292.98	3.5
	271.90	8
Rb	794.76	2
	420.18	120
Re	345.19	2.5
Rh	365.80	6
	350.73	45
Ru	379.94	2
	392.59	11
Sb	231.15	2
Sc	326.99	3
	327.36	12
Se	203.98	3
	206.28	11
Si	250.69	3
	221.09	8
Sm	458.16	2.5
Sn	286.33	2
	254.66	5
	266.12	30
Sr	242.81	?
Ta	275.83	3
Tb	410.54	3.5
Tc	318.24	10
Te	225.90	15
Ti	399.86	1.5
Tl	377.57	2.5
	258.01	24
Tm	341.00	14
U	356.66	1.5
	351.46	3
V	306.64	2.5
	390.22	6.5
W	400.88	2
	287.94	3.5
Y	407.74	1.1
	362.09	2
Yb	346.44	3.5
	267.20	40
Zn	307.59	4,700
Zr	302.95	1.5
	362.39	1.9

From *Analytical Methods for Atomic Absorption Spectrophotometry,* Perkin-Elmer Corporation, Norwalk, Conn., March 1971, and Slavin, W., *Atomic Absorption Spectroscopy,* Interscience, New York, 1968. With permission.

III. SPECTRAL INTERFERENCES IN FLAME ATOMIC ABSORPTION

Table 3 gives the approximate concentration of interfering metal required to produce absorption equal to that given by 1 μg/ml of the metal being determined. Use of a hollow-cathode lamp of the pure metal, operating under normal temperature conditions, is assumed. Wavelengths are those given in the *M.I.T. Wavelength Tables,* Harrison, G. R., Ed., M.I.T. Press, Cambridge, 1969.

TABLE 3

Spectral Interferences in Flame Atomic Absorption

Metal Determined	Wavelength nm	Interfering Metal	Wavelength nm	Flame	Concentration of Interferent μg ml^{-1}
Cu	324.7540	Eu	324.7530	N_2O-C_2H_2	2,500
Si	250.6899	V	250.6905	N_2O-C_2H_2	8
Fe	271.9025	Pt	271.9038	N_2O-C_2H_2	50
Al	308.2155	V	308.2111	N_2O-C_2H_2	190
Mn	403.3073	Ga	403.2982	N_2O-C_2H_2	20
				Air-C_2H_2	160
				Air-C_3H_8	260
				Air-H_2	35
Ga	403.2982	Mn	403.3073	N_2O-C_2H_2	30
				Air-C_2H_2	3
				Air-C_3H_8	1.3
				Air-H_2	5
Hg	253.6519	Co	253.6493	Air-C_2H_2	7

Based on Fassel, V. A., Rasmuson, J. O., and Cowley, T. G., *Spectrochim. Acta,* 23B, 579, 1968; Allan, J. E., *Spectrochim. Acta,* 24B, 13, 1969; Manning, D. C. and Fernandez, F., *At. Absorp. Newslett.,* 7, 24, 1968. With permission.

IV. PERFORMANCE OF NON-FLAME METHODS OF ATOMIZATION IN ATOMIC ABSORPTION SPECTROSCOPY

These data, in Table 4, which should be taken only as indicative of orders of magnitude in the present state of the art, show the mass of element required to give a peak absorption of 1%.

TABLE 4

Performance of Non-flame Methods of Atomization in Atomic Absorption Spectroscopy

Element	Wavelength nm	Mass of element giving 1% absorption picogram		
		L'vov Furnace[a]	Massmann Furnace[b]	Carbon Rod Atomizer[c]
Ag	328.07	0.1	8	1
Al	309.27	1	170[d]	60
As	193.70	8	160 (?2,000)	90
Au	242.80	1	60	20
B	249.77	200		
Ba	553.55	6		
Be	234.86	0.03	3	1
Bi	223.06		120	10
	306.77	4		
Ca	422.67	0.4	3	0.7
Cd	228.80	0.08	2	0.6
Co	240.73	2	140	10
Cr	357.87	2	30	9
Cs	852.11	0.4	70	30
Cu	324.75	0.6	70	20
Eu	459.40	5.		60
Fe	248.33	10	50	4
Ga	287.42	1	1,200	
	294.36			30
Ge	265.16	3		
Hg	253.65	20	15,000	350
I	183.0	30		
	206.2	1,000		
In	303.94	0.4		
K	766.49		20	2
	404.41	40		
Li	670.78	3	50	6
Mg	285.21	0.04	3	0.4
Mn	279.48	0.2	8	0.7
Mo	313.26	3	400	50
Na	589.00		20	0.15
Ni	232.00	9	200	30
P	177.50	3		
	213.62	200		
Pb	217.00		80	7
	283.31	2		
Pd	247.64	4	250	150
Pt	265.95	10	750	200
Rb	780.02	1	40	4
Rh	343.49	8		
S	180.73	100		
Sb	217.58		500	
	231.15	5		50
Sc	391.18	60		
Se	196.03	9	3,000	70
Si	251.61	0.05	2	
Sn	224.61			100
	286.33	2	5,500	
Sr	460.73	1	30	6
Te	214.28	1		
Ti	364.27		300	

TABLE 4 (continued)

Performance of Non-flame Methods of Atomization in Atomic Absorption Spectroscopy

Element	Wavelength nm	Mass of element giving 1% absorption picogram		
		L'vov Furnace[a]	Massmann Furnace[b]	Carbon Rod Atomizer[c]
	365.35	40		
Ti	276.79	1	120	10
V	318.40	3	300	90
Yb	398.80	0.7		
Zn	213.86	0.03	0.7	0.4

[a]Graphite cuvette 40 mm long and 2.5 mm diameter, heated to the minimum temperature required to atomize the material, and maintained in argon at 2 atm pressure.
[b]Commercial Massmann furnace, with a carbon tube 50 mm long and 9 mm diameter, heated to optimum temperature for atomization, and purged with nitrogen. Data based mostly on 50 μl or 100 μl samples.
[c]Commercial "Mini-Massmann" furnace, with graphite cavity 4.7 mm long and 1.5 mm diameter, and with nitrogen flowing around it. Sample volume 0.5 to 1 μl.
[d]Purged with argon.

Based on L'vov, B. V., *Atomic Absorption Spectrochemical Analysis,* Hilger, London, 1970; Matousek, J. P., *American Laboratory,* 3, 45, 1971; Manning, D. C. and Slavin, S., unpublished data. With permission.

V. LIMITS OF DETECTION FOR METALS IN FLAME ATOMIC EMISSION.

Limit of detection is usually defined as the concentration of metal giving a signal-to-noise ratio of two. The figures in Table 5 were all obtained with fairly similar equipment, employing pre-mixed flames fed (unless otherwise indicated) with aqueous solutions. Many of the values obtained with the acetylene-fueled flames could be improved considerably by flame separation.

It is important to note that detection limits, though carefully measured, are still rather nebulous quantities. Even under controlled experimental conditions there is at least a factor of two uncertainty in the values measured, and furthermore the numbers depend sensitively on the exact experimental conditions employed.

TABLE 5

Limits of Detection for Metals in Flame Atomic Emission

Metal	Wavelength nm	Limit of Detection μg ml^{-1}			
		$O_2 - H_2$[a]	Air – C_2H_2[b]	$O_2 - C_2H_2$[c]	$N_2O - C_2H_2$[d]
Ag	328.07	0.05	0.5[e]	0.3[e]	0.02
Al	396.15	4	60[e]	0.2[e]	0.005[f]
As	234.98			50[e]	
Au	267.60			4[e]	0.5
B	249.77, 249.68			30[e]	
Ba	553.55	0.08[f]	0.05[e]	0.05[e]	0.001[f]

TABLE 5 (continued)

Limits of Detection for Metals in Flame Atomic Emission

Metal	Wavelength nm	Limit of Detection, $\mu g\ ml^{-1}$ $O_2 - H_2$[a]	$Air - C_2H_2$[b]	$O_2 - C_2H_2$[c]	$N_2O - C_2H_2$[d]
Be	234.86			1[e]	
Bi	223.06			40[e]	
Ca	422.67	0.002[f]	0.005[f]	0.005[e]	0.0001[f]
Cd	326.11			30[e]	2
	228.80	5.0			
Ce	569.92			10[e]	30
Co	352.98 } 352.90 }		1[e]		
	345.35			1[e]	0.05
Cr	425.44		0.1[e]		0.005[f]
	357.87			0.1[e]	
Cs	852.11			0.008[e]	
	455.54			8[e]	
Cu	327.40		1[e]	0.2[e]	0.01
	324.75	0.04		0.1[e]	
Dy	421.17			0.1[e]	
	404.60				0.07[g]
Er	400.80			0.3[e]	0.04[g]
Eu	459.40			0.003[e]	0.0006[g]
Fe	371.99	0.2	1[e]	0.7[e]	0.05
Ga	417.21			0.07[e]	0.02[f]
	403.30				0.01[f]
Gd	451.97			2[e]	
	440.19				2[g]
Ge	265.12			0.6[e]	0.5
Hf	368.22			75[e]	
Hg	253.65			40[e]	
Ho	410.38			0.1[e]	
	405.39				0.02[g]
In	451.13			0.03[e]	0.002[f]
Ir	380.01			100[e]	30
K	766.49		0.0005	0.003[e]	
	769.90			0.02[e]	
La	579.13			1[e]	
	550.13				8[g]
Li	670.78		0.005[e]	0.000003[e]	0.00003[f]
	610.36			0.001[e]	
Lu	451.86				1.0[g]
	331.21			0.2[e]	
Mg	285.21	0.7	0.5[e]	0.2[e]	0.005
Mn	403.08		0.1[e]	0.1[e]	0.005
Mo	390.30				
	379.83		1,000[e]	0.03[e]	
Na	589.00	0.00007	0.0005	0.0001[e]	0.0005
	589.59			0.0002[e]	
Nb	405.89			1[e]	1
Nd	492.45			1[e]	0.2[g]
Ni	352.45		4[e]	0.6[e]	
	341.48			1[e]	0.03
Os	442.05			10[e]	
Pb	405.78		20[e]		0.2

TABLE 5 (continued)

Limits of Detection for Metals in Flame Atomic Emission

Metal	Wavelength nm	Limit of Detection, $\mu g\ ml^{-1}$ $O_2 - H_2$ [a]	Air $- C_2H_2$ [b]	$O_2 - C_2H_2$ [c]	$N_2O - C_2H_2$ [d]
	368.35			3[e]	
Pb	363.47			1[e]	0.05
Pr	495.14				1
	493.97			2[e]	
Pt	265.95			40[e]	2
Rb	780.02		0.001	0.002[e]	
Re	346.05			1[e]	0.2
Rh	369.24			0.3[e]	0.02
Ru	372.80			0.3[e]	0.02
Sb	259.81			20[e]	
Sc	402.04			0.1[e]	0.03
	391.18			0.07[e]	
Si	251.61			5[e]	
Sm	488.39			0.6[e]	
	476.03				0.2
Sn	303.41			4[e]	
	284.00				0.5
Sr	460.73	0.02[f]	0.004[e]	0.004[e]	0.001[f]
Ta	481.28			18[e]	5
Tb	432.65			1[e]	0.5[g]
	431.89				0.4[g]
Te	238.33			200[e]	
Th	576.06			150[e]	
Ti	399.86			0.5[e]	0.2
Tl	535.05				0.02
	377.57			0.09[e]	0.05
Tm	410.58			0.2[e]	
	371.79				0.02[g]
U	591.54			10[e]	
V	437.92		140[e]	0.3[e]	0.01
W	400.88			4[e]	0.5
Y	407.74			0.3[e]	
	362.09				0.4[g]
Yb	398.80			0.05[e]	0.002[g]
Zn	213.86			50[e]	
Zr	360.12			75[e]	3
	351.96			50[e]	

[a]Mossholder, N. V., Fassel, V. A., and Kniseley R. N., *Anal. Chem.*, 45, 1614, 1973.
[b]Pickett, E. E. and Koirtyohann, S. R., *Anal. Chem.*, 41, 28A, 1969; Chapman, J. F. and Dale, L. S., *Analyst*, 94, 563, 1969.
[c]Fassel, V. A. and Golightly, D. W., *Anal. Chem.*, 39, 466, 1967.
[d]Pickett, E. E. and Koirtyohann, S. R., *Anal. Chem.*, 41, 28A, 1969; Kniseley, R. N., Butler, C.C., and Fassel, V. A., *Anal. Chem.*, 41, 1494, 1969.
[e]Ethanol – water solution.
[f]Ionization suppressed.
[g]Suppression of ionization would improve limit of detection.

VI. LIMITS OF DETECTION FOR METALS IN FLAME ATOMIC FLUORESCENCE

Limit of detection is usually defined as the concentration of metal giving a signal-to-noise ratio of two. The limits of detection found in flame atomic fluorescence spectroscopy depend on the intensity of the light source, the background emission of the flame, the signal-to-noise ratio of the detector, and sometimes the band-pass of the monochromator. The limits shown in Table 6 were obtained with various types of light source and flame and should be taken only as indicative of orders of magnitude in the present state of the art. They refer to aqueous solutions in the absence of other material.

TABLE 6

Limits of Detection for Metals in Flame Atomic Fluorescence

Metal	Wavelength nm	Limit of detection $\mu g\ ml^{-1}$
Ag	328.07	0.0001
Al	396.15	0.1
As	193.70	0.1
Au	267.60	0.005
Be	234.86	0.01
Bi	223.06	0.005
Ca	422.67	0.02
Cd	228.80	0.000001
Co	240.73	0.005
Cr	357.87	0.05
Cu	324.70	0.001
Fe	248.33	0.008
Ga	417.21	0.01
Ge	265.12	0.1
Hg	253.65	0.08 (0.0002)
In	410.48	0.1
Ir	254.40	100
Mg	285.21	0.001
Mn	279.48	0.006
Mo	313.26	0.5
Ni	232.00	0.003
Pb	405.78	0.01
Pd	340.46	0.04
Pt	265.95	50
Rh	369.24	3
Ru	372.80	100
Sb	231.15	0.05
Se	196.03	0.04
Si	251.61	0.6
Sn	303.41	0.1
Sr	460.73	0.03
Te	214.28	0.04 (0.005)
Ti	319.99	4
Tl	377.57	0.008
V	318.40	0.07
Zn	213.86	0.00002

Based on Winefordner, J. D. and Elser, R. C., *Anal. Chem.*, 43, 24A, 1971, and Syty, A., in *Flame Emission and Atomic Absorption Spectrometry*, Vol. 2, Dean, J. A. and Rains, T. C., Eds., Marcel Dekker, New York, 1971. With permission.

VII. OSCILLATOR STRENGTHS (*f*-VALUES) OF INTEREST IN ATOMIC ABSORPTION SPECTROSCOPY

The *f*-values for elements up to and including atomic number 20 (calcium) are the recommended "best" values from the National Standards Reference Data, Series 4 and 22, issued by the National Bureau of Standards, Washington, 1966 and 1969. These compilations also indicate the accuracy of each value.

For other elements the *f*-values have been compiled from various sources, and where sufficient data are available, an attempt has been made to estimate the accuracy of the values given.

TABLE 7

Oscillator Strengths (*f*-values) of Interest in Atomic Absorption Spectroscopy

Metal	Wavelength nm	*f*-value	Accuracy[a]	Metal	Wavelength nm	*f*-value	Accuracy[a]
Ag	328.07	0.46	B	K	766.49	0.682	B+
	338.29	0.22	B		769.90	0.339	B+
Al	309.27	0.16	C+		404.41	0.0061	C
	309.28	0.18	D		404.72	0.00305	C
	396.15	0.12	C+	Li	670.78[b]	0.753	A
	237.31	0.11	C		323.26	0.00552	B
	237.34	0.012	D	Mg	285.21	1.81	B
	256.80	0.044	C		202.58	0.22	D
Au	242.80	0.29	C	Mg^+	279.55	0.920	B
	267.60	0.13	C		280.27	0.313	B^+
B	249.77	0.11	D	Mn	279.48	0.57	B
	249.68	0.11	D		403.08	0.056	B
Ba	553.55	1.5	B	Mo	313.26	0.2	
Be	234.86	1.36	C+	Na	589.00	0.655	A
Be^+	313.06[b]	0.505	A		589.59	0.327	A
Bi	306.77	0.12	C		330.24	0.0094	C+
C	165.72[b]	0.17	D		330.30	0.0048	C+
Ca	422.67	1.75	B+	Ni	341.48	0.14 (?0.3)	D
	239.86	0.0433	C+	P	177.50	0.15	C
Ca^+	393.37	0.69	C+	Pb	283.31	0.20	A
	396.85	0.344	C+	Rb	780.02	0.675	A
Cd	228.80	1.3	B		794.76	0.335	A
	326.11	0.001	D		420.18	0.015	B
Co	304.40	0.023	C	S	181.37[b]	0.12	C
	346.58	0.018	C	Sb	231.15	0.04	
Cr	357.87	0.3	C	Si	251.61	0.12	C+
	425.44	0.08	B	Sn	286.33	0.19	B
Cs	852.11	0.73	A	Sr	460.73	1.55	B+
	893.45	0.36	A	Te	225.90	0.0018	
	455.54	0.017	B	Ti	364.27	0.14	D
Cu	324.75	0.32 (?0.43)	C		399.86	0.09	D
	327.40	0.16	C+	Tl	276.79	0.30	B
Fe	371.99	0.035	B		377.57	0.13	B
Ga	287.42	0.32	C	V	318.40	0.7	
Hg	253.65	0.025	B		437.92	0.25	C
In	303.94	0.28	B–		390.22	0.04	C
	410.48	0.12	B–	Zn	213.86	1.5	B+
					307.59	0.00013	C

TABLE 7 (continued)

Oscillator Strengths (*f*-values) of Interest in Atomic Absorption Spectroscopy

[a]A uncertainties within 3%
B uncertainties within 10%
C uncertainties within 25%
D uncertainties within 50%
[b]Two or more closely spaced lines

From National Standards Reference Data, Series 4 and 22, National Bureau of Standards, Washington, 1966 and 1969. With permission.

VIII. DOPPLER HALF-WIDTHS OF ATOMIC SPECTRAL LINES

The Doppler half-intensity width of an atomic spectral line of wavelength λ or frequency ν is given at thermal equilibrium by

$$\frac{\Delta\lambda_L}{\lambda} = \frac{\Delta\nu_L}{\nu} = \frac{2\sqrt{2R\ln 2}}{c}\sqrt{\frac{T}{M}} = 7.16 \times 10^{-7}\sqrt{\frac{T}{M}},$$

where R is the gas constant, c the velocity of light, T the absolute temperature, and M the atomic weight (C = 12).

The accompanying graph shows the variation of the quantity $\Delta\lambda_L/\lambda$ with atomic weight at temperatures between 300°K and 5,000°K.

Where hyperfine structure is present, the Doppler width will of course apply to each component of the line.

TABLE 8

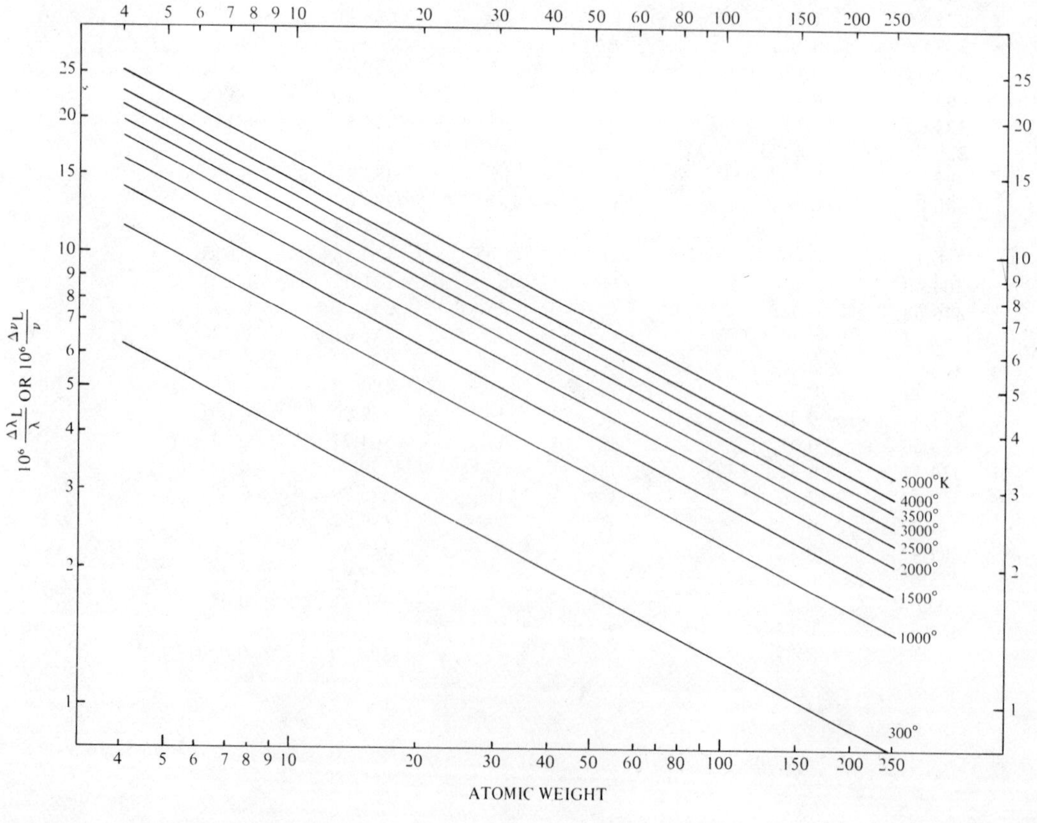

IX. IONIZATION POTENTIALS OF THE ELEMENTS; i.e., THE ENERGY REQUIRED FOR THE PROCESS $M \rightarrow M^{+} + e^{-}$

TABLE 9

Ionization Potentials of the Elements

Element	Ionization Potential eV	Element	Ionization Potential eV	Element	Ionization Potential eV	Element	Ionizati Potent eV
Ar	15.755	Eu	5.67	Na	5.138	Sc	6.54
Ac	6.9	F	17.418	Nb	6.88	Se	9.75
Ag	7.574	Fe	7.87	Nd	5.51	Si	8.149
Al	5.984	Fr	4.0	Ne	21.559	Sm	5.6
As	9.81	Ga	6.0	Ni	7.633	Sn	7.342
At	9.5	Gd	6.16	O	13.614	Sr	5.692
Au	9.22	Ge	7.88	Os	8.5	Ta	7.88
B	8.296	H	13.595	P	10.484	Tb	5.98
Ba	5.21	He	24.481	Pb	7.415	Tc	7.28
Be	9.32	Hf	7	Pd	8.33	Te	9.01
Bi	7.287	Hg	10.43	Po	8.43	Th	6.95
Br	11.84	I	10.454	Pr	5.46	Ti	6.82
C	11.256	In	5.785	Pt	9.0	Tl	6.106
Ca	6.111	Ir	9	Pu	5.1	Tm	5.81
Cd	8.991	K	4.339	Ra	5.277	U	6.08
Ce	5.6	Kr	13.996	Rb	4.176	V	6.74
Cl	13.01	La	5.61	Re	7.87	W	7.98
Co	7.86	Li	5.39	Rh	7.46	Xe	12.127
Cr	6.764	Mg	7.644	Rn	10.746	Y	6.38
Cs	3.893	Mn	7.432	Ru	7.364	Yb	6.2
Cu	7.724	Mo	7.10	S	10.357	Zn	9.391
Dy	6.8	N	14.53	Sb	8.639	Zr	6.84
Er	6.08						

From *Handbook of Chemistry and Physics,* 52nd ed., The Chemical Rubber Co., Cleveland, 1971.

X. DISSOCIATION ENERGIES OF DIATOMIC OXIDE MOLECULES

TABLE 10

Dissociation Energies of Diatomic Oxide Molecules

Molecule	Dissociation Energy eV	Molecule	Dissociation Energy eV
AgO	2.0 ± 0.5	MoO	5.0 ± 0.65
AlO	4.6 ± 0.1	NO	6.50 ± 0.01
AsO	4.9 ± 0.1	NbO	7.0 ± 2.0
BO	8.0 ± 0.3	NdO	7.1 ± 0.2
BaO	5.75 ± 0.15	NiO	⩽ 4.2
BeO	4.6 ± 0.2	OH	4.40 ± 0.01
BiO	3.1 ± 0.5	PO	6.4 ± 0.3
BrO	2.40 ± 0.02	PbO	3.87 ± 0.05
CO	11.09 ± 0.02	PrO	7.4 ± 0.3
CaO	4.3 ± 0.7	RuO	1.8 ± 0.4
CdO	<3.8	SO	5.357 ± 0.003
CeO	8.03 ± 0.2	SbO	4.0 ± 1.0
ClO	2.746 ± 0.001	ScO	6.97 ± 0.15
CrO	4.38 ± 0.3	SeO	4.3 ± 0.1
CuO	?4.1 ± 0.3	SiO	?8.1 ± 0.3
FO	?2.4 ± 0.4	SnO	5.40 ± 0.07
FeO	4.3 ± 0.5	SrO	4.2 ± 0.6
GaO	3.0 ± 0.5	TaO	8.45 ± 0.5
GdO	7.0 ± 0.5	TeO	?3.9 ± 0.1
GeO	6.78 ± 0.08	ThO	8.5 ± ?0.2
HfO	7.6 ± 1.5	TiO	7.2 ± 0.1
HoO	7.6 ± 1.5	TlO	Probably unstable
IO	2.0 ± 0.2	UO	7.8 ± 0.3
InO	3.3 ± 0.5	VO	6.4 ± 0.22
LaO	8.2 ± 0.1	WO	6.8 ± 0.4
LiO	3.5 ± 0.2	YO	7.31 ± 0.1
LuO	?5.3	YbO	5.3 ± 1.5
MgO	4.1 ± 0.6	ZnO	2.8 ± 0.4
MnO	4.16 ± 0.13	ZrO	7.8 ± 0.4

From Gaydon, A. G., *Dissociation Energies and Spectra of Diatomic Molecules,* 3rd ed., Chapman and Hall, London, 1968. With permission.

XI. PROPERTIES OF PREMIXED FLAMES USED IN ATOMIC SPECTROSCOPY

TABLE 11

Properties of Premixed Flames Used in Atomic Spectroscopy

Gas Mixture	Maximum Flame speed cm sec^{-1}	Maximum Temperature °C Calculated	Measured
Air–hydrogen	320	2,100	2,045
Air–propane	43	1,925	1,925
Air–coal gas	ca 55	ca 1,840	ca 1,840
Air–acetylene	170	2,290	2,275
50% oxygen–50% nitrogen–acetylene	640	2,815	–
Oxygen–hydrogen	1,190	2,815	2,660
Oxygen–propane	390	2,835	2,850
Oxygen–coal gas	–	–	2,720
Oxygen–acetylene	1,130	3,060	3,140
Oxygen–cyanogen (1:1 molar ratio)	270	4,540	4,370
Nitrous oxide–hydrogen	390	ca 2,660	2,650
Nitrous oxide–60% propane–40% butane	300	–	2,550
Nitrous oxide–acetylene	285	2,950	2,800
Nitrous oxide–MAPP[a] gas	140	–	2,750
Nitric oxide–acetylene	87	3,090	3,095

[a]Proprietary mixture of methylacetylene and propadiene (60-70%) with propylene and other stabilizing hydrocarbons.

Based on Willis, J. B., *Applied Optics,* 7, 1295, 1968, and *Analytical Flame Spectroscopy,* Mavrodineanu, R., Ed., Macmillan, London, 1970.

XII. EFFICIENCIES OF ATOMIZATION OF METALS IN FLAMES

The efficiency of atomization (β_a) of an element is defined as that fraction of the total element in the gaseous state that is present as free neutral or ionized atoms at the observation height in the flame.

For metals such as the alkali earths, which form stable oxides in many flames, β_a depends critically on the stoichiometry of the flame and on the region of the flame measured. At the time of writing, most β_a values are regarded as reliable to within a factor of about two.

The values quoted here were measured either by the "curve of growth" method in emission (References 1 and 2) or by absorption measurements using a continuum source (References 3–8).

TABLE 12

Efficiencies of Atomization of Metals in Flames

Metal	Flame: Air – H_2[a]	O_2 – H_2 – Ar[b]	Air – C_2H_2[c]	N_2O – H_2[a]	N_2O – C_2H_2[a,d]
Ag	0.85	1.0	1.0[e]	0.7	0.6
Al	< 0.00008	–	< 0.00005	< 0.0001	0.2
Au	0.5	–	1.0[e]	0.4	0.5
B	< 0.001	–	< 0.0006	< 0.001	0.004
Ba	0.005	–	0.001[e]	0.005	0.2
Be	0.00002	–	0.00005	0.0004	0.1
Bi	0.6	–	0.2	0.3	0.35
Ca	0.15	–	0.07[e]	0.04	0.5
Cd	0.4	–	0.5	0.6	0.6
Co	0.2	–	0.3	0.3	0.25
Cr	0.3	–	0.065	0.04	0.6
Cs	–	–	0.7[e,f]	–	–
Cu	1.0	0.7	1.0[e]	0.9	0.7
Fe	0.8	–	0.4[e]	0.9	0.8
Ga	0.45	–	0.2	0.2	0.7
In	1.0	–	0.6	0.6	0.9
K	0.4	–	0.4[e,f]	0.2	0.1
Li	0.1	–	0.2[e,f]	0.09	0.4
Mg	0.9	0.02	0.6[e]	1.0	1.0
Mn	0.75	0.01	0.6[e]	0.5	0.8
Na	1.0	–	1.0[e,f]	0.9	1.0
Pb	1.0	–	0.7	0.9	0.8
Rb	–	–	1.0[e,f]	–	–
Si	0.002	–	–	< 0.001	0.06
Sn	0.4	–	0.04	0.06	0.8
Sr	0.2	{0.0002 {0.0004[f]	0.075[e]	0.04	0.3
Ti	0.002	–	–	< 0.003	0.2
Tl	0.7	–	0.5	0.6	0.55
V	0.02	–	0.01	0.008	0.3 (?0.8)
Zn	–	–	0.7	–	0.9

[a]From Reference 5. Unshielded flame, burning at 5 cm slot burner. Ionization suppressed where necessary with cesium.

[b]From Reference 8. Shielded flame, burning at Meker-type burner. These figures refer to an H_2/O_2 molar ratio of 2:1, with measurements made 3.5 cm above the burner top.

[c]From References 1–7. Mostly measured with unshielded flames burning at slot burners.

[d]From References 5 and 6. Unshielded flame, burning at 5 cm slot burner. Ionization suppressed where necessary.

[e]From References 1, 2, 4, and 7. Shielded flames, burning at Meker-type burners.

[f]Ionization suppressed as far as possible.

REFERENCES:

1. Hinnov, E. and Kohn, H., *J. Opt. Soc. Am.*, 47, 156, 1957.
2. Hofmann, F. W. and Kohn, H., *J. Opt. Soc. Am.*, 51, 512, 1961.
3. de Galan, L. and Winefordner, J. D., *J. Quant. Spectrosc. Radiative Transfer*, 7, 251, 1967.
4. Zeegers, P. J. Th., Townsend, W. P., and Winefordner, J. D., *Spectrochim. Acta*, 24B, 243, 1969.
5. de Galan, L. and Samaey, G. F., *Spectrochim. Acta*, 25B, 245, 1970.
6. Willis, J. B., *Spectrochim. Acta*, 25B, 487, 1970.
7. Willis, J. B., *Spectrochim. Acta*, 26B, 177, 1971.
8. Smyly, D. S., Townsend, W. P., Zeegers, P. J. Th., and Winefordner, J. D., *Spectrochim. Acta*, 26B, 531, 1971.

XIII. MEASURED DEGREES OF IONIZATION OF METALS IN FLAMES

Data in Table 13 were obtained by measuring the ratio of the absorbances of the metal solution with and without the addition of a large excess of a salt of an easily ionized metal such as potassium or cesium. This method involves the assumption that the presence of a large amount of such a salt does not affect the efficiency of vaporization of the metal studied. The results will depend to some extent on the stoichiometry of the flame and the region measured.

TABLE 13

Measured Degrees of Ionization of Metals in Flames

			Measured Degree of Ionization	
Metal	**Ionization Potential eV**	**Concentration $\mu g\ ml^{-1}$**	**Air-acetylene Flame**	**Nitrous Oxide-Acetylene Flame**
Na	5.14	2	0.12	
K	4.34	4	0.38	
		8	0.33	
Rb	4.18	17	0.52	
Cs	3.89	27	> 0.73	
Be	9.32	2		0.0
Mg	7.64	2		0.06
Ca	6.11	2–5		0.4
Sr	5.69	5	0.13	0.84
Ba	5.21	50	0.0[a]	0.92
Al	5.98	100		ca 0.14
La	5.61	1,000		0.40
Eu	5.67	50–100		0.6
Gd	6.16	1,000		0.20
Dy	6.8	50		0.58
Ho		100		0.47
Er	6.08	100		0.43
Tm	5.81	200		0.57
Yb	6.2	15		0.20
Lu	?	1,000		0.50
Nb	6.88	100–200		ca 0.26
		1,000		ca 0.13

[a] Atomization very inefficient.

Based on Manning, D. C. and Capacho-Delgado, L., *Anal. Chim. Acta,* 36, 312, 1966, and unpublished data; Sanui, H. and Pace, N., *Appl. Spectrosc.,* 20, 135, 1966, and *Anal. Biochem.,* 25, 330, 1968; Willis, J. B., in *Analytical Flame Spectroscopy,* Mavrodineanu, R., Ed., Macmillan, London, 1970. With permission.

XIV. ELECTRICAL FLAMES

L. R. P. Butler, H. G. C. Human, and R. H. Scott, Council for Scientific and Industrial Research, South Africa

A. Introduction

Electrical flames (also called plasma flames, plasma torches, plasma jets) are flamelike discharges from electrical power sources. Although sometimes having similar physical properties to chemical flames which obtain their energy from the exothermic chemical reactions between gaseous species, electrical flames obtain their energies from collisional processes induced by electrical currents (while normal arc and spark discharges may fall within this definition, only those devices giving rise to discharges with "flamelike" structures at atmospheric pressures will be discussed in this section).

The term "plasma" has been used for these flames because they often rise to relatively high temperatures which result in ionization of the particles present. When more than 1% of the atoms or molecules of a gas are ionized, it may be called a plasma. A plasma is thus a gas containing neutral atoms and molecules, free electrons, and ions, which although electrically conductive, is itself electrically neutral because the negatively charged particles are balanced by the positively charged particles. The relative proportions of the various species (i.e., neutral atoms and ions) will depend on the mode of excitation, the pressure (i.e., number of collisions), and the temperature. The question of "temperature" must be approached with considerable care when discussing plasmas. Being able to operate under a wide range of pressures and frequencies, conditions for thermal equilibrium are not always satisfactory, and significant differences between electron, ion, and gas "temperatures" may be found. Plasmas with high electron temperatures are more easily generated at lower than atmospheric pressures where the collisional mean free paths are longer.

For analytical spectroscopy there are many practical advantages in having sources operating at atmospheric pressures; e.g., they are closer to thermal equilibrium, samples are more easily introduced, and little, if any, vacuum pumping and measuring equipment is required. Consequently, most electrical flame plasmas used for analytical purposes operate at atmospheric pressure.

B. Classification of Electrical Flames

Electrical flames may be classified broadly as:

1. Flames from Discharges Between Two Electrodes (Plasma Jets)

a. Current-Carrying Flames (Figure 1a). The discharge is usually a DC arc which causes ionization between electrodes in a flow of gas.

The electrical conductive and thermal properties of the plasma depend on the constituents of the gas. If a low ionization potential element is present (as when a sample is introduced), the increased ion and electron concentrations may change the resistance of the arc, which has a marked influence on temperature.

b. Noncurrent-Carrying Flames (Figure 1b). In these cases the discharge is "transferred" either by blowing the arc away from the electrodes or by the introduction of further electrodes. When a sample is introduced in a region where the conductive properties of the arc are not affected by ionization of the elements in the gas, the gas temperature of the plasma is largely independent of the sample.

2. Radio Frequency Plasmas

If a radio frequency discharge is used, it is possible to transfer considerable energy from an electrical source to a gas, often without the use of electrodes and giving rise to high temperatures. The classification of these discharges depends on the coupling, the frequency of the discharge, and the energy. A clear distinction between the various types of physical properties of the plasma is not possible, but for the purpose of simplicity, the following separation has been selected:

a. Inductance coupled
b. Capacitance coupled
c. Microwave

C. Flames from Discharges Between Electrodes (The D.C. Plasma Jet)

The first experiments to achieve a plasma with

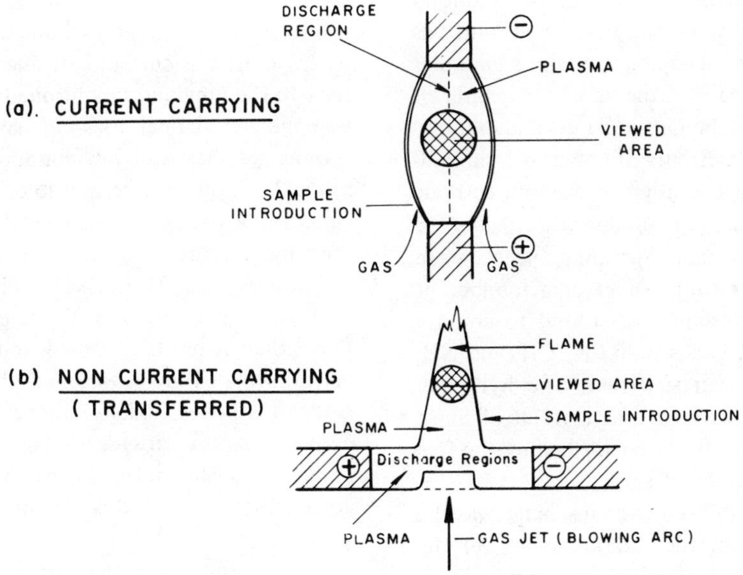

FIGURE 1. Schematic diagram of the principle of (a) current-carrying and (b) noncurrent-carrying flames.

higher temperature than that of the DC arc were conducted by Gerdien and Lotz[1] in 1923. Interest in this device arose again only after 1950, when the potentialities of this source as a high temperature tool for cutting metals, alloying elements, machining refractories, etc., were realized by Weiss[2] and others.[3,4] Excellent reviews of these types of flames are in the literature.[5-7]

The operation of such a plasma jet can be described with the aid of Figure 2. The arc burns between the cathode and anode electrodes, both of which are usually water-cooled. Into the arc chamber is fed a tangential gas supply. When this gas emerges through the central opening in the cathode, it cools the outer layers of the arc column, and as a result the thermal and electrical conductivity is decreased in these outer layers. The arc therefore tends to decrease in diameter, resulting in an increased current density and higher temperature. The increased current density is accompanied by self-induced magnetic fields which further tend to decrease the arc diameter. There is still some question whether this magnetic "pinch" effect is indeed operative in laboratory sources.[8] The increased current density in the arc channel results in increased frequency of collision between particles whereby the temperature is raised. The plasma flame emerges from the cathode orifice at a large velocity (it may reach supersonic values). The temperature of the plasmas

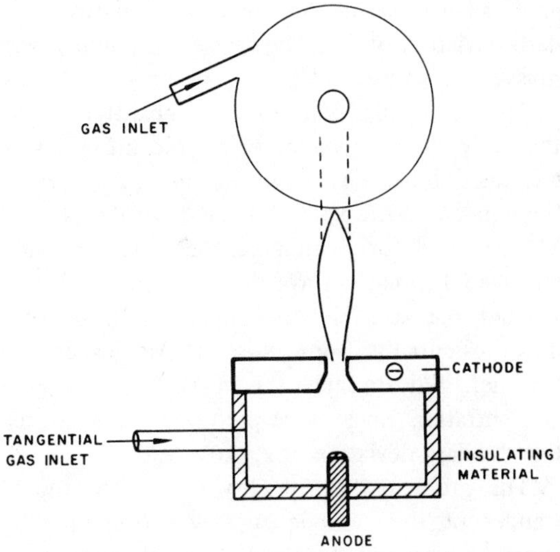

FIGURE 2. Schematic representation of the first plasma jets.

may be as high as 10,000 K just above the orifice, for arc currents of 20 A.

1. Types of Plasma Jets and Main Features

Among the first to apply the plasma jet as a source for spectrochemical purposes were Margoshes and Scribner[8] in the United States and Korolev and Vainshtein in the USSR.[9,10] The former used basically the same source as shown in Figure 2 for the analysis of solutions. A pneumatic nebulizer, placed in the position of the anode in Figure 2 but electrically neutral, sprayed solutions directly into the arc. The anode was of an annular shape and positioned over the tip of the nebulizer. Helium was used as the tangential gas and argon as the nebulizing gas. Currents of between 15 and 20 A gave satisfactory operation. A 5.5-mm cathode orifice and 3-mm arc gap produced a "flame" of conical shape 1-cm high. Sparklike spectra were produced with many ionic lines of a number of elements. The background was found to contain the noble gas lines, bands from CN, OH, and NH, and also the hydrogen spectrum. The hydrogen Balmer lines were broadened as a result of Stark effect due to electric fields established by the free ions and electrons in the plasma.

A source of instability of the discharge was the random movement of the cathode spot over the surface of the cathode, which to some extent influenced the flame. Nevertheless, very accurate results were obtained in the analysis of NBS steel samples for the major elements. Iron, chromium, and nickel were determined with a relative standard deviation of 2%. The device was audibly very noisy.

The Korolev and Vainshtein design differed from this only in the manner of sample introduction and gas stabilization. A spray chamber from which the condensed droplets could be drained was used. The gas used for nebulizing the sample solution streamed laminarly through the orifice and constricted the arc. The analytical results did not differ essentially from those of Margoshes and Scribner. Silicate analyses in the 0.1 to 80% concentration range were performed with a relative standard deviation of 2.5 to 3.5%.

The problem of instability of the arc due to wander of the cathode spot was overcome by Owen,[11] who added a third, external electrode to the configuration. The same principle for stabilizing a high power plasma jet was previously applied by Osborn.[12] The external electrode, made of graphite or tungsten, was mounted horizontally with its tip right above the cathode ring and was electrically connected to the cathode. The arc first burns to the cathode, but as soon as the flame reaches the external electrode, it burns to the external electrode. The arc voltage drops, and there is a reduction of the noise. The cathode electrode now merely serves as a stabilizing disk, and the discharge resembles other types of disk- and gas-stabilized DC arcs. The essential difference is that the region of the plasma viewed by the spectrometer (between cathode and external electrode) is now a current-carrying portion, in contrast to the previously mentioned devices. The fact that the arc channel does not have to traverse the cooling gas sheath of low conductivity in order to reach the cathode is responsible for the preferential burning to the external electrode which is at the same potential.

Scribner and Margoshes[13] obtained good results with an electrically floating "cathode ring." Since then it has been called, more correctly, the control ring. They positioned the external electrode (cathode) axially above the anode and control ring. A cross-sectional view of this construction is shown in Figure 3. A commercial apparatus based on this design was produced in 1963.[14]

The plasma jet design of Yamamoto[15] produces, like the original designs, a current-free plasma. Wandering of the arc column is eliminated by means of a transverse magnetic field (see Figure 4) which confines the anode spot to a fixed position (the upper electrode was the anode in this case). Field strengths of 300 to 400 G are required. This design also differs from the previous in the manner of sample introduction (see Figure 4). This jet is operated at a current of approxi-

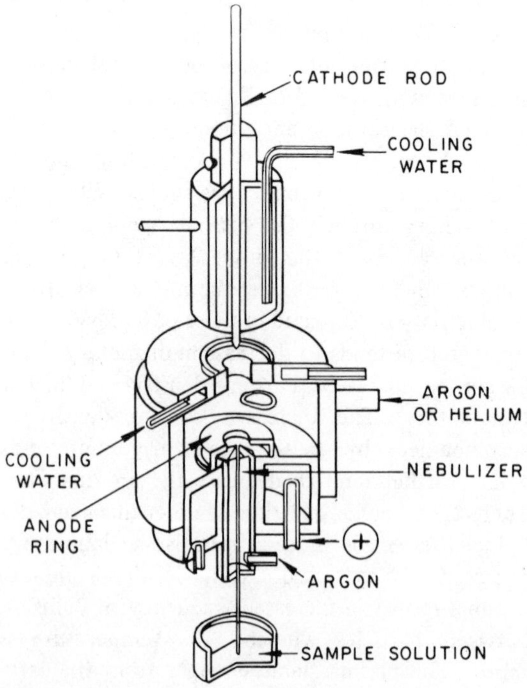

FIGURE 3. Cross section of the Scribner and Margoshes plasma jet.

mately 300 A, a rather formidable power requirement. The arc temperature calculated from the measured broadening of the hydrogen Balmer lines was 11,500 K. Using a similar plasma jet, Goto and Atsuya[16] deduced a temperature of only 7,200 K from the relative intensities of two spectral lines. In spite of the high power requirements of this source, the temperature obtained is not much higher than that of other jets operated at 20 A.

A different kind of plasma jet with a noncurrent-carrying analytical zone was developed by Kranz.[17,18] Figure 5 shows a simplified diagram of this apparatus. The hot plasma produced by a disk- and gas-stabilized arc is blown out of the arc chamber perpendicular to the arc axis. The tangential gas supply (argon or nitrogen) is fed in through holes in the stabilizing disks. A certain portion of the gas flows back through the holes in the stabilizing disks into the electrode compartments and blows electrode vapors out through three or more small holes (~ 1-mm diameter) drilled radially into the electrode compartment. The result is that the plasma of the analytical zone is free from electrode elemental spectra. The amount of stabilizing gas supply is not critical (3 to 6 l/min) and should be optimized for elements with different excitation potentials. Kranz realized the problems encountered in injecting a nebulized liquid sample into a hot plasma. He found it advisable to create a turbulent zone where the aerosol is introduced into the plasma and finally recommended the introduction to take place right in the orifice where the plasma emerges. A depressurized zone is created by a sudden widening of the channel, and a turbulent plasma results. Temperatures reported for a nitrogen plasma in the turbulent zone range from 5,000 K above the orifice to 2,000 K some 8 cm away from it.

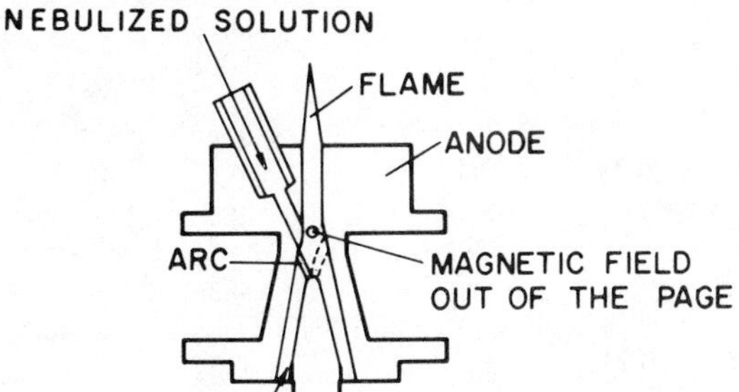

FIGURE 4. Plasma jet design of Yamamoto.

Valente and Schrenk[19] constructed a quite different plasma jet with identical anode and cathode chambers, each with control orifice and tangential stabilizing gas supply (Figure 6). The two chambers are set up axially in line with each other, but as soon as the arc is initiated they are rotated about the center of the discharge with respect to each other so that the angle between the axes is approximately 30°. The background continuum intensity contours (Figure 7) form a more or less symmetrical pattern, but owing to the fact that sample is only introduced at the cathodic electrode, the analytical line emission extends from the cathode vertically upwards with a distribution as shown in Figure 8. Spatial resolution of the current-carrying and noncurrent-carrying portions of the plasma is easily obtained by proper focusing on the spectrometer slit or diaphragm. Maximum temperature occurs at the foot of the dark area in Figure 8 and was measured by the authors to be 5,800 K. This source is claimed to be very economical to use since it consumes only 2.5 l/min of argon gas. The optimum operational current is between 8 and 14 A. Reproducibility of measurement is approximately 4%, but the source stability is better than 1%. Excellent detection limits were obtained for 12 elements (see Table 14).

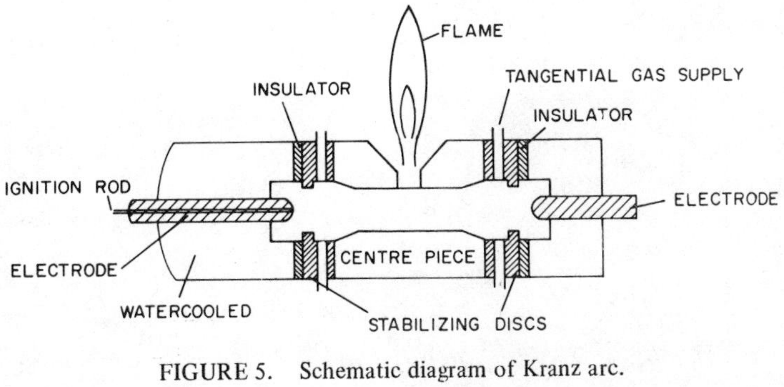

FIGURE 5. Schematic diagram of Kranz arc.

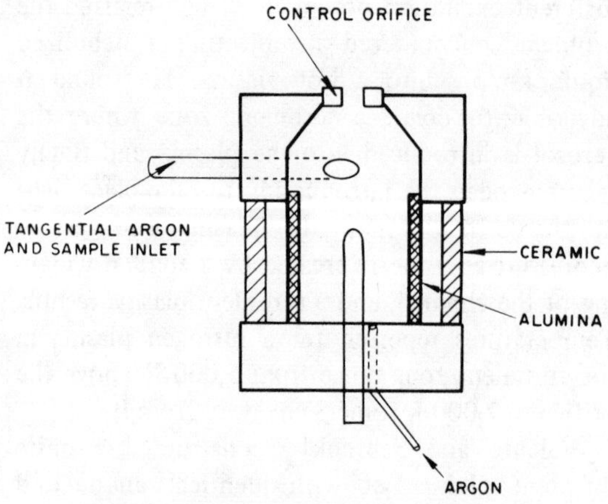

FIGURE 6. Valente and Schrenk anode chamber.

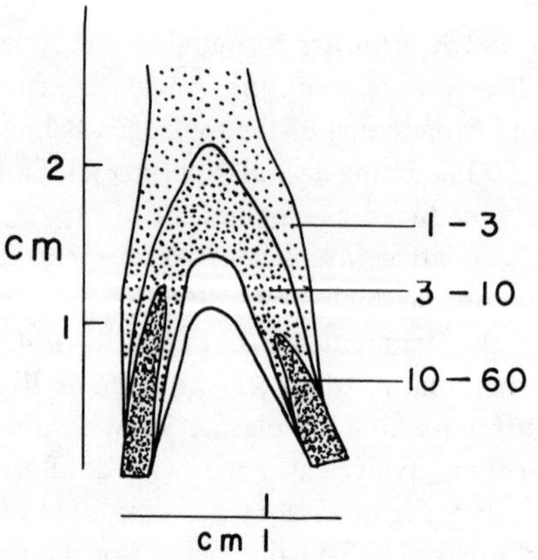

FIGURE 7. The distribution of the background continuum of the Valente and Schrenk jet.

TABLE 14
Some Detection Limits for DC Plasma Flames (ppm)

	Literature Reference Number							
Element	**14**	**16**	**17**	**19**	**23**	**56**	**65**	**62**
Ag		1.3						0.3
Al		2	0.2			0.005		
As								0.5
B		0.2		0.4			10	0.05
Ba		0.6	0.3					0.2
Be							1	0.003
Ca		0.05	0.1	0.002	0.5	0.0001		0.008
Cd		0.7		0.03				
Co		5						0.8
Cr		3		0.003	0.25	0.004		0.4
Cu	0.05	1.5	1.0			0.4		0.2
Cl							100	
Dy								0.3
F							100	
Fe	0.2	6	2.0	0.005	0.25			0.2
La				0.07				0.5
Li				0.001		0.00003		0.08
Mg		0.1	0.2		0.05			0.02
Mn		7	0.2		0.12	0.004		0.04
Mo		5			0.04		0.1	
Na		0.05						0.02
Nb						0.3		0.4
Ni	0.3	10		0.003				
P							100	0.6
Pb	0.3	7		0.03				0.2
S							1,000	
Sb								0.2
Si								0.2
Sn					10			
Sr			1.0			0.0004		0.02
Ta								1.5
Ti						0.2		
V	0.05				0.2	0.07		
W						1.1		2
Zn			20	0.01			50	0.1

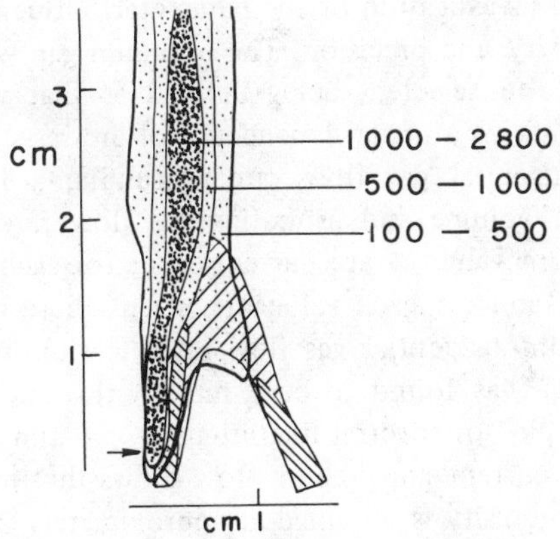

FIGURE 8. Spatial distribution of analytical line intensity in the Valente and Schrenk jet (Ca II 3933).

The idea of bending the arc so that a hot plasma of low background emission may be spatially separated from the bright continuum of the arc channel was followed up in a commercial plasma jet.[20] The cathode chamber is the same as that of Valente and Schrenk, but only the anode is water-cooled and not contained in a chamber. The construction therefore closely resembles that of Scribner and Margoshes.[13] It is operated with an angle of 90° between the anode and cathode axes. The resultant plasma (Figure 9) produces temperatures as high as 10,000 K in the arc column and from 7,700 K downwards with increasing vertical separation from the arc channel. The sample is nebulized into a heated spray chamber and enters the tangential gas supply line. Gas consumption is approximately 5 l/min.

Another variation of the gas- and disk-stabilized plasma arc is the low-temperature arc developed by Marinkovic et al.[56,57] Figure 10 shows the construction of the arc, the sample being tangentially introduced into the central section. The main feature characterizing this arc is its operation in a low temperature mode, which is obtained by introducing high concentrations of alkali element salts with the sample. Figure 11 shows the appearance of the analytical gap when different concentrations of potassium solutions are sprayed. At sufficiently high concentrations, the analytical zone is very wide and has a temperature of 3,100 K. The central discharge column disappears, as do the spectral lines of argon, oxygen, and hydrogen. Continuum emission is considerably reduced, and only spectral lines of potassium and OH bands remain. This source, which is very flamelike, was

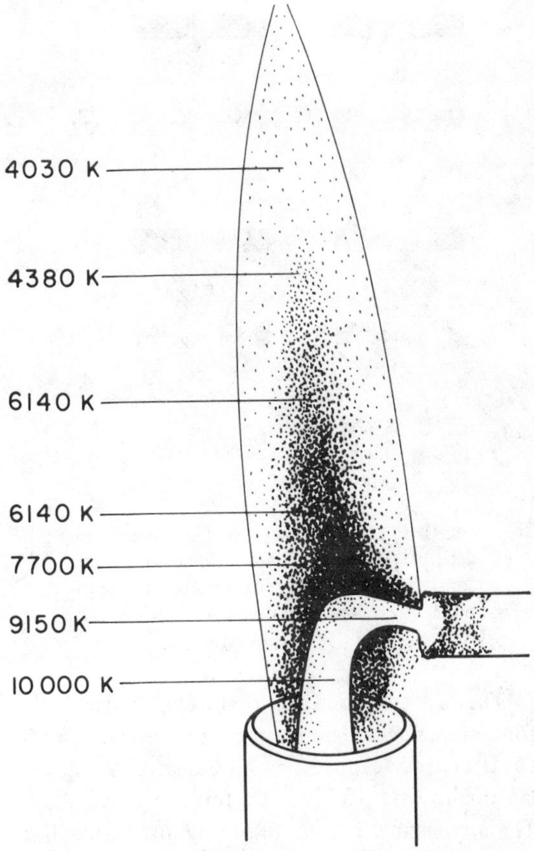

FIGURE 9. Temperature distribution in the commercial "Spectrajet."

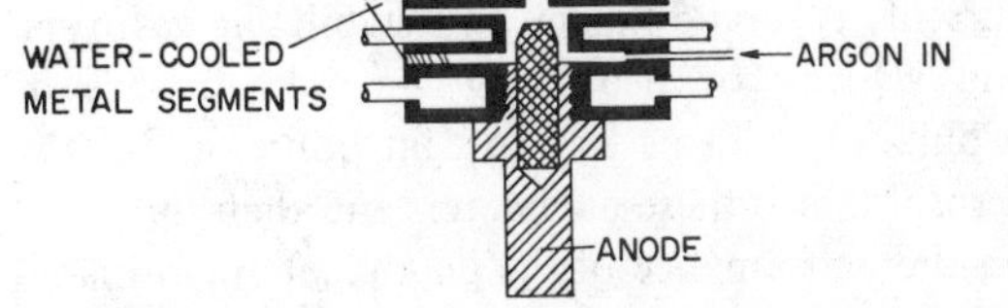

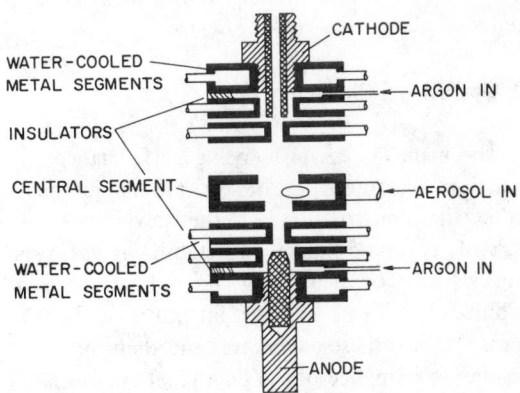

FIGURE 10. Low temperature arc construction of Marinkovic.

found suitable for the analysis of refractory oxide-forming elements such as tungsten, vanadium, and titanium. Low detection limits were claimed for a dozen elements (see Table 14). Chemical interferences are of the same nature as found in chemical flames, but the effects are less serious.

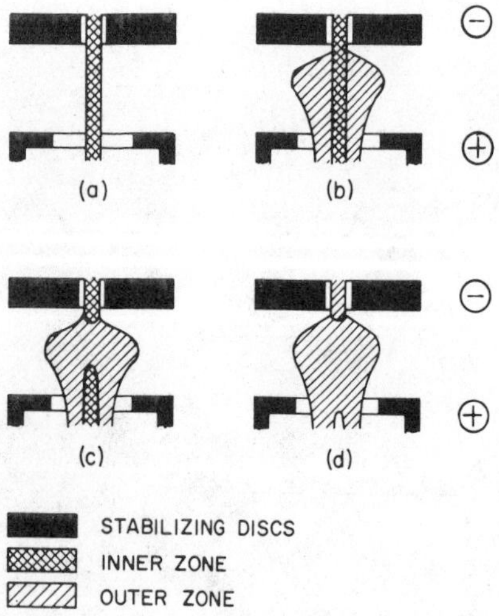

FIGURE 11. Appearance of the analytical gap of Marinković arc: (a) only water sprayed into the arc; (b), (c), and (d) with increasing concentrations of potassium sprayed.

The disk-stabilized arc, first used by Maecker[60] for obtaining high-temperature plasmas, was further developed by Riemann[60,61] and Hoffmann and Holdt[27,63] for analytical usage. The arc channel is compressed by stabilizing disks only (no tangential gas whirl). A maximum temperature of 7,300 K was reported.[64] This arc was used for the determination of the main constituents of alloys and rocks.

D. Operational Characteristics

The main factors influencing performance and emission characteristics of the plasma jet apart from the construction of the device are arc current, type and velocity of stabilizing gas, type and velocity of nebulizing gas, performance of nebulizer, and method of introduction of the aerosol. Since these parameters and their influence on the performance of the plasma jet are intimately connected with the construction of the arc chamber, it is a difficult task to lay down specific rules to be adhered to, keeping the diversity of constructions in mind. However, the experiences of a few selected authors who undertook detailed investigations of the mentioned parameters will now be shortly described, and their results should be considered as general guidelines.

Sirois,[21,22] using a commercial Spex Industries plasma jet with helium as tangential gas, made a careful investigation of the parameters influencing sensitivity and precision. The optimum gap width should be selected, being defined as that value which yields a linear dependence of arc resistance on tangential gas flow rate. Assuming a fixed sample volume and aspirating gas flow rate, an optimum value of arc current exists for each gap width, and for each value of current there is an optimum tangential gas flow rate. The optimum arc gap was found to be 8 mm. A three-dimensional plot of spectral line intensity as a function of arc current and helium flow shows that maximum intensity is obtained at approximately 24 A and 40 l/min helium. The optimum helium flow rate increases with decreasing current up to 70 l/min for a current of 12 A. Under these conditions, spectral line intensity is a factor of six lower.

It might be expected[14] that lines of ionized atoms are more sensitive to the helium flow than atomic lines. This is generally confirmed by Serin and Ashton,[23] but a few exceptions are pointed out, viz., the sensitivity of lead and tin atomic lines to the helium flow (the same Spex plasma jet was used). Optimum flow for these elements was as high as 65 l/min, which makes it an expensive method to use.

It is generally accepted that the emission of the plasma jet is very constant (stability better than 1%) but that the limiting factor in obtaining good analytical precision is the reproducibility of the supply of the sample to the source.[19,20,24] This can be checked by monitoring the emission of a spectral line of the tangential gas supply. The introduction of a wet aerosol poses a practical limit of approximately 2 to 4% on the precision of measurement. The constant performance of the nebulizer in the environment of a heat generating plasma of a few kilowatts, as well as the reproducible mixing of a wet aerosol at room temperature or less with a plasma at a typical temperature of 5,000 K, are formidable requirements. The former can be readily achieved by thermostating and shielding the analytical solutions from the heat, while the latter is determined by the geometry of the sample feeding system. Lerner[25] found that during a 1-min run a sample solution temperature may rise by 7°C, causing a drift of 3% in the emission of the Mn II 2576 Å line, mainly as a result of the change of viscosity of the sample with temperature. By thermostating the sample beaker holder and shielding it with aluminum foil, temperature variations were reduced to 0.4°C, and this source of error was eliminated.

The Poiseuille equation for capillary flow shows that the flow rate Q is directly proportional to the fourth power of the capillary radius R and the driving force P and inversely proportional to the coefficient of viscosity of the liquid and the capillary length L:

$$Q = \pi \frac{R^4 P}{8 \eta L}$$

From this it is clear how important it is to keep the capillary temperature constant, a requirement which is very difficult to fulfill with plasma jets utilizing a direct injection system with the nebulizer tip situated approximately a millimeter from the arc anode. Because of this, an indirect injection system with a spray chamber shielded from the heat of the arc is to be preferred. This has the additional advantage that coarse droplets which are a major factor in causing arc fluctuations separate from the aerosol on the walls of the spray chamber before reaching the analytical zone.

Since the capillary flow is also directly related to the driving force P, it is evident that the nebulizing gas pressure should be kept very constant by good quality pressure and flow regulators. Furthermore, it is found[25] that the control or tangential gas flow has a certain influence on the nebulizing gas flow as a result of a back pressure developed in the chamber. Therefore, the control gas flow must be accurately controlled to keep the nebulizing rate constant.

This then brings us to a most important aspect of the design of a plasma jet, viz., the manner of introduction of the aerosol into the plasma. The physics involved in mixing the slowly moving, cold, wet aerosol with the fast-flowing hot plasma has been given little attention in the literature presenting analytically useful plasma jets. Kranz[17,18] was the first to make some calculations about the diffusion of aerosol particles into the plasma. He found that the analytically useful particles of approximately 10^{-4} cm have practically no possibility of diffusing into a laminarly flowing plasma jet. Large particles, on the other hand, fly through the plasma before they are vaporized. He came to the conclusion that it is essential that the plasma flows turbulently at the position where the aerosol is introduced. Therefore, he constructed the "ausströmöffnung" of his current-free plasma jet with a channel widened at the position of aerosol introduction (see Figure 5). The low pressure zone thus created ensures a turbulent plasma and thorough mixing of aerosol and plasma gas. Kranz found optimum emission from the plasma when the nebulizing gas flow is approximately equal to the control gas flow.

In most of the other types of plasma jets, the aerosol is introduced axially into the current-carrying portion of the plasma jet. A certain degree of turbulence is created in these regions by arc wander, but the efficiency of mixing has not been studied. The presence of highly ionized species in the arc, however, does imply that some mixing occurs.

For the last mentioned type of plasma arc, Boyd[26] made an extensive investigation into sample introduction systems. He found that direct axial injection into the arc (employed in the commercial apparatus) was very unsatisfactory with regard to precision, especially when used with concentrated solutions. Tangential, radial, and conical tangential introduction methods were tried. The conical tangential system also used by Hoffmann and Holdt[27] proved to be superior. A special chamber containing the conical channels as well as a mixing funnel was added right on top of the vortex chamber of the arc (Figure 12). A constriction in the funnel probably caused turbulence and thorough mixing of the aerosol with the plasma. For economical reasons argon was used as nebulizing and control gas at flows of 3 to 4 l/min for both.

Chapman et al.[62] simply replaced the direct injection nebulizer of the Spex plasma jet by a capillary feeding the arc with aerosol nebulized in a remote spray chamber. The increased stability of operation resulted in an order of magnitude improvement in detection limits for a very wide range of elements (Table 14).

Using the same gas supply for both control and nebulizing purposes seems to be very economical. This approach was used by Valente and Schrenk[19] and by Elliot.[20] The tangential gas supply to the cathode is also used for nebulizing the sample and feeds the arc with sample. Desolvation of the aerosol was found essential. Improper mixing of sample and plasma may be inferred from the emission profiles presented in Figure 8 and the fact that resonance lines of atomic species yielded the best detection limits for most elements.

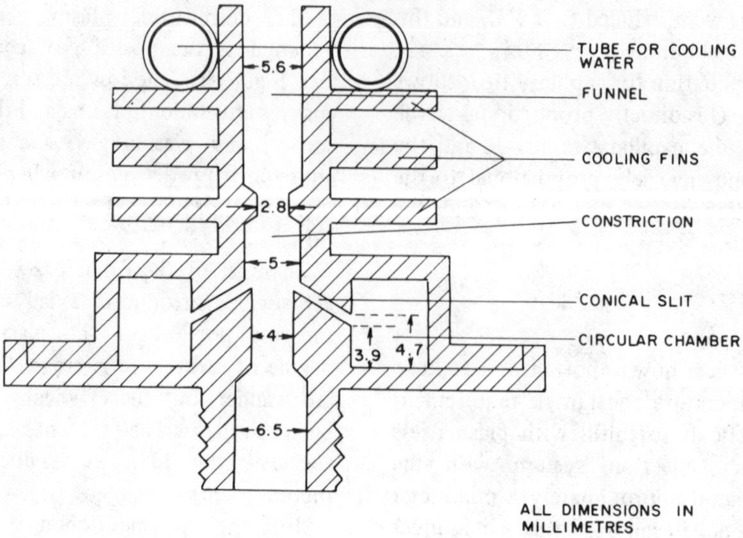

FIGURE 12. Boyd system for introduction of aerosol.

Nevertheless, these detection limits are generally superior to other types of plasma arc for the 12 elements studied.

Desolvation of the aerosol before introduction into the plasma has a very beneficial effect on sensitivity. When used with tangential sample supply to the plasma, it seems to be essential.[19,20] Figure 13 shows the desolvation apparatus used by Veillon and Margoshes.[28] In the heated chamber the aerosol is converted to water vapor and dry particles. When conducted through a condenser kept at 10°C, the water vapor condenses and is drained off, but most of the dry particles emerge and are carried into the plasma. An efficiency (metal out to metal in ratio) of 35% is claimed for this nebulizer system, and the analytical sensitivity is increased 10-fold in a r.f. plasma torch. A similar system employed by Uny et al.[29] yielded an increase of 10- to 30-fold in sensitivity in a flame atomic absorption measurement. Kleinmann and Svoboda[30] reported on the use of a desolvation system in conjunction with the use of the "plasmatron." These authors stabilized the pressure in the desolvation apparatus by constricting the outlet of the system through a capillary, whereas Valente and Schrenk employed a ballast volume and constriction at the outlet for this purpose.

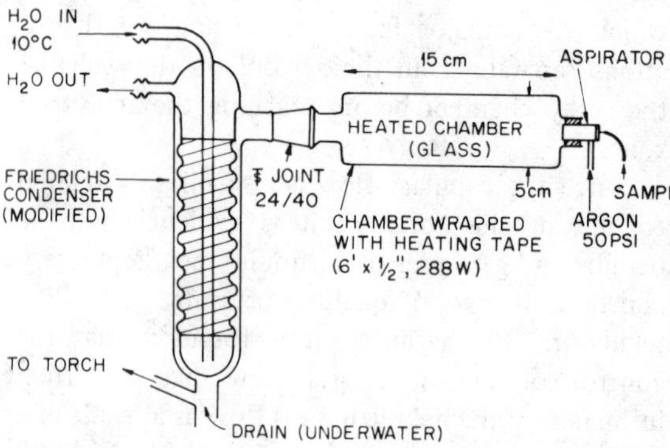

FIGURE 13. Desolvation apparatus of Veillon and Margoshes.

1. Temperature

The most important characteristic of a plasma used for thermal excitation of atoms is, of course, its temperature. If the temperature and plasma composition are known, quantities relevant to excitation can be calculated, e.g., emission coefficients of atoms and ions, degree of ionization, and electron concentration. The majority of measurements of plasma temperature have been based on the measurement of relative line intensities, the theory of which is given in standard texts.[31]

Korolev and Kvaratskheli[32] were the first to establish that thermal equilibrium does prevail in the plasma jet of the original Margoshes and Scribner type. For currents not exceeding 30 A, a maximum temperature of 10,000 K was measured in the core of the jet. Using a jet of the same type, Frisch and Startsev[33] found that the temperature of the plasma directly above the cathode corresponds to that of a conventional DC arc (~ 5,000 K) and is independent of gas flow. In the higher regions of the plasma, however, a maximum temperature of 11,000 to 14,000 K was measured, depending on the arc current used. The value of 14,000 K corresponds to an electron concentration of 1.6×10^{17} cm^{-3} and a 40% degree of ionization of argon. Complete ionization of elements like iron and titanium is therefore accomplished when introduced into the arc. (Such increase in temperature downstream can, in our opinion, only be achieved if a considerable deviation from thermal equilibrium exists in the cathode region and the higher electron energy is equipartitioned higher up in the plasma).

This characteristic of the plasma jet is in another way confirmed by measurements of Yudelevich and Cherevko,[34] who found that only regions near the base and the axis show a dependence of plasma temperature on the ionization potential of the element introduced.

Measurements performed on the current-carrying version of the Margoshes and Scribner plasma jet indicated temperatures of 8,000 K[15] and 10,000 K[20] in the current-carrying core. However, Elliot[20] states that it is likely that the plasma is not in local thermal equilibrium in the cathode region. The value of 8,000 K measured by Scribner and Margoshes[13] is an average value, i.e., a value obtained without using the Abel inversion technique[35] to obtain the radial distribution of emission intensities. Such a measurement necessarily yields values of temperature lower than the maximum because it represents an average value of the viewed portion of the arc. The results of Boyd,[26] who obtained a temperature of 8,650 K in similar manner, agree reasonably well with those of Scribner and Margoshes.

The high-current plasmatron (100 A) was studied by Golubovskaya et al.[36] and Bykhovskii et al.[37] Radial distributions of electron concentration, temperature, and atom concentration were determined in argon and argon/hydrogen plasmas. Thermal equilibrium was found to exist, and maximum electron concentration of ~ 10^{17} cm^{-3} and temperature of 13,000 K were found. Both increase somewhat when hydrogen is added to the stabilizing gas. For another high current (150 A) plasma jet, Bögershausen and Consée[40] measured a maximum temperature of 16,000 K, while Yamamoto obtained a value of only 11,500 K for his high current jet.[15] The last value was obtained indirectly by determining the ionic density from the line broadening of the Balmer lines and use of the Saha equation.

Kranz[17] thoroughly investigated the temperature distribution in his noncurrent-carrying plasma jet and obtained a maximum temperature of 5,000 K directly above the orifice of the turbulently flowing plasma. Schirrmeister[38] obtained a maximum of only 4,700 K for the same type of the plasma jet. These lower temperatures in comparison with the previous can be expected in view of the remoteness of the analytical region from the arc channel.

Thus, depending on the type of plasma and the current used, maximum temperatures measured range from 4,700 K to 16,000 K. For any plasma temperature regions with temperatures lower than the maximum can, of course, be utilized by proper spatial resolution of the different zones of temperature (see, for instance, Figure 9).

2. Analytical Properties and Interferences in Plasma Jet Flames

Ionization interference plays an important role in these high temperature excitation sources. When an element of low ionization potential is introduced into a medium of such high temperature, it is ionized to a high degree. The large concentration of ions and electrons then suppresses ionization of species with low ionization potentials and increases the population of atoms, with the result that atomic emission is enhanced and normally ionic emission is decreased. However, it was found in both current-carrying[26] and noncurrent-carrying[38] plasma jets that both atomic and ionic emission is enhanced.

Schirrmeister[38,39] made a thorough study of this effect in the Kranz plasma jet. He found that the temperature is not changed by additional potassium salts in a current-free plasma. Although the presence of such an element decreases ionic concentration of the analytical element, the effect of electrical fields in the plasma should be considered. The movement of ions is largely influenced by electrical fields generated by the process of ambipolar diffusion,[42] the effect of which is to expel ions out of the core of the plasma. The presence of an easily ionized element diminishes the magnitude of these fields, resulting in more ions being present in the hot core of the plasma.

Kaiser et al.[41] noted a fundamental difference between current-carrying and noncurrent-carrying plasmas. The temperature of the former is very sensitive to introduction of easily ionized elements, dropping as much as 600 K with introduction of 8 mg/ml potassium. The temperature of the current-free plasma, on the other hand, is insensitive to the potassium content of the sample but sensitive to the amount of water vapor supplied to the arc, dropping 300 K for a 50% increase in water vapor above the normal dose.

The drop in temperature in the current-carrying arc when introducing a low ionization potential element is the result of the fact that the conductivity of the plasma is increased by the larger concentration of ions and electrons, and less heat is generated by the constant current.

Interelement effects have been investigated by a number of authors in the plasma jet of the current-carrying type (with external cathode). Serin and Ashton[23] found enhancement of intensities by lithium and depression by sodium silicate and state that "the matrix effect is obviously one that cannot be neglected when using the plasma jet, but is probably less serious than in many types of excitation." Muntz[43] found interference by the elements aluminum, sodium, iron, cobalt, and titanium at concentration levels of 1 mg/ml. For alloy analyses, he advises standards to be prepared in a matrix of the base metal of the alloy to be analyzed. Buffering was not considered feasible, owing to problems with nebulizers at high concentrations. Boyd[26] also found the use of accurately analyzed rock standards unavoidable for elimination of matrix effects when analyzing rocks for major elements silicon, aluminum, iron, magnesium, and calcium. Using a buffer element (lithium) does not eliminate all interference effects, particularly not the depression of aluminum emission by silicon.

Sirois[22] explained the importance of using dilute solutions so that the concentration of the matrix element (in the solid sample) is negligible in the plasma. Each interfering element has a threshold value above which it starts interfering on other elements. It was found that in the determination of aluminum the zinc concentration of a zinc base alloy should not exceed 6.8 mg/ml, the magnesium concentration of a magnesium base alloy should not exceed 2.4 mg/ml, etc. The concentration of the base should not alter the effective mass of the plasma or the equilibrium of the arc. Matrix effects can be eliminated by considering these requirements, as was experimentally demonstrated in obtaining unshifted calibration curves for manganese as well as nickel in different kinds of base alloys.

Chemical interferences, such as the classical interference of phosphorus and aluminum on calcium, cannot be eliminated in the DC plasma arc but only decreased compared to the effect in conventional chemical flames. Although the temperature on the arc axis may be high enough to break the interfering chemical bonds with the analyte atom, the radial temperature gradient towards room temperature is always responsible for temperature zones promoting such bonds. Thus, the effect can only be weakened since the effective mean temperature of the volume under measurement usually is higher than flame temperatures. This viewpoint is corroborated by experimental results.[56]

Some analytical applications of the plasma jet are summarized in Table 15.

E. Inductively Coupled Plasmas

1. Description

In an inductively coupled plasma, radio frequency power is transferred from a coil carrying an oscillating current to the electrodeless plasma contained in a quartz tube within the coil as shown in Figure 14. The operating principle is similar to that of a transformer, where the coil may be regarded as the primary winding and the plasma the short-circuited secondary winding or load. Since the plasma is an ionized gas and therefore electrically conductive, oscillatory electric currents are induced into it by the electromagnetic field created in the coil. These eddy currents encounter resistance resulting in Joule heating as they flow in closed paths in the plasma perpendicular to the coil axis in the region known as the skin depth. The skin depth is the penetration depth of the em field into the plasma. It follows that for effective coupling, the skin depth must be of the same order or smaller than the plasma radius. From this basic relationship, the approximate operating frequency can be calculated for a given setup since the skin depth s is given by the well-known formula

$$s\ (\text{cm}) = \frac{5.03}{\sqrt{\mu\sigma\nu}} \tag{1}$$

TABLE 15
Selection of the Fields of Application of DC Plasma Jets

Ref.	Application
14	Oils: trace metals
44, 45	Oil field brines
46, 47	Boron in gasoline powders
48	Boron tribromide
49	Scandium in bauxite and zircon
50	Calcium and magnesium in cast iron and iron ores
51, 52	Oils: oxygen, hydrogen, sulfur, and nitrogen
53	Rare earths
64	Several major and minor elements in ash
54, 55, 58, 59	As atomic absorption atom reservoir for refractory oxide elements

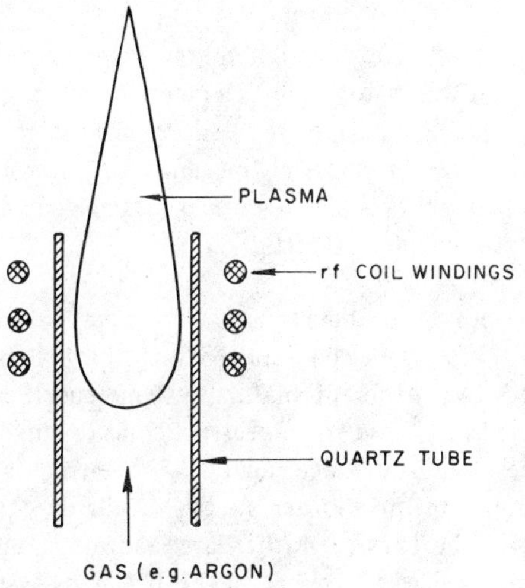

FIGURE 14. Schematic diagram of inductively coupled plasma system.

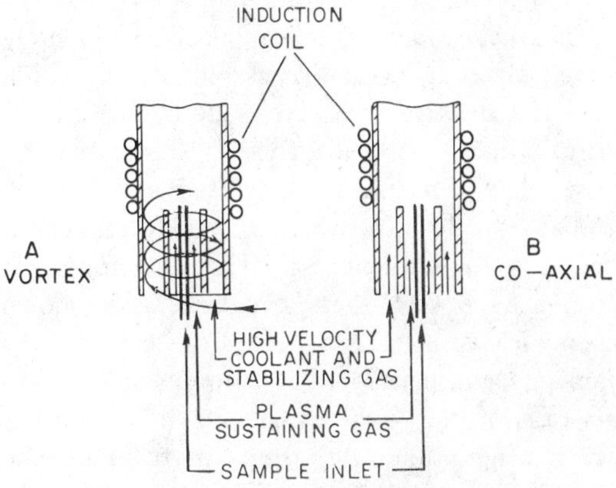

FIGURE 15. Various techniques used to stabilize and thermally isolate an inductively coupled plasma.

where μ is the relative permeability (taken as unity for gases), σ the specific electrical conductivity (Ω^{-1} cm^{-1}) of the absorbing medium, and ν the frequency of the electromagnetic field (MHz); ν is generally chosen to be in the 3 to 100 MHz range since this results in practical plasma dimensions (4- to 1-cm diameter).

Some form of thermal isolation of the plasma from the wall of the supporting quartz tube is necessary to prevent the wall from melting since the plasma temperature can be anything from 5,000 K to 10,000 K, depending on factors such as the available rf power, coupling efficiency, gas composition, and flow characteristics. Two techniques to isolate the plasma are shown in Figure 15. (A) is the commonly used vortex stabilization technique where the coolant and stabilizing gas is introduced tangentially at a high velocity. The vortex flow in the region inside the induction coil cools the wall of the tube and cushions the plasma which is sustained in the reduced pressure zone in the center of the vortex. A plasma-sustaining gas may be introduced through a second concentric tube as shown in Figure 15, although this is not necessary if the coolant is capable of sustaining the plasma as when argon is used. The second technique (B) is based on the use of a high velocity laminar flow of coolant gas which creates a thermally isolating sheath between the plasma and the tube wall. In both (A) and (B) the sample is introduced, either in the form of an aerosol or powder, through the central injection tube.

2. Development

Although inductively coupled plasmas were

observed in air by Babat[66] as early as 1947 using very high power levels (100 kW), no effort was made to flow gases through the discharge to form a plasma torch. This was achieved by Reed,[67-69] who successfully generated a stable argon plasma at atmospheric pressure using a commercial rf heating unit with a maximum power output of 10 kW. The frequency of operation was 4 MHz. Reed initiated the plasma by heating a graphite rod inductively coupled within the rf field and then withdrawing it. The heating by conduction of the gases in the vicinity of the rod was sufficient to initiate the plasma. Reed used the vortex stabilization method shown in Figure 15(A). This method is probably the most successful presently in use for stabilizing the plasma.

The first studies of the application of purely inductively coupled plasmas as emission sources in analytical spectroscopy were made by Greenfield, Jones, and Berry[70] and by Wendt and Fassel.[71,72] Greenfield et al. used a 2.5 kW rf generator at 36 MHz, whereas Wendt and Fassel used a 5 kW unit at 3.4 MHz. The important difference between these two systems is shown schematically in Figure 16. For similar tube diameters, the plasma is more annular in form in the case of the higher frequency operation. A greater penetration of the sample particles into the plasma can be attained in this case since they can be injected into the lower temperature region in the center of the plasma. When the plasma is operated at lower frequencies, sample injection becomes increasingly more difficult because the expansion of the plasma gas in a direction perpendicular to the exterior surface of the plasma and the high temperature gradients near the surface develop an aerodynamic barrier to the injection of the sample aerosol. Consequently, the particles tend to circumvent the plasma and do not all experience the high plasma temperature.

The merits of the annular (doughnut) shaped plasma as compared with the lower frequency teardrop-shaped plasma became more obvious after a study of the latter plasma type by Veillon and Margoshes[73] in which it was established that although this plasma type gave useful emission signals for several elements which are difficult to excite in chemical flames (elements such as Ba, Ta, and Ti), pronounced interelement effects were found to be present. Dickinson and Fassel,[74] in the meanwhile, had realized the advantages of the

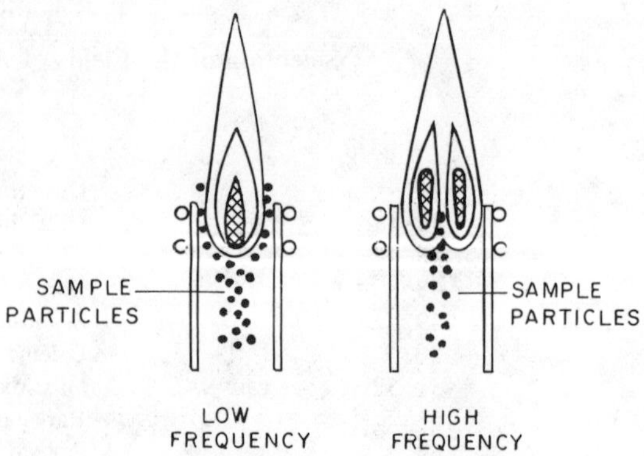

FIGURE 16. Schematic diagram to illustrate the formation of an inductively coupled plasma at higher frequencies and the entry of aerosol particles into the plasma.

annular plasma and were able to achieve improved detection limits for many elements in solution as well as a high degree of freedom from chemical interferences on spectral line emission intensities and absorbances using an annular plasma generated by a frequency of 30 MHz.

Recently, Boumans and De Boer[75-77] and Scott, Fassel, Kniseley, and Nixon[78] have demonstrated two different plasma systems specifically designed for use as spectrochemical emission sources for the trace analysis of elements in solutions. In most other studies, available equipment in the form of rather large radio frequency heating devices was used. In the Boumans system (described in Reference 77), the rf power fed into the plasma is stabilized by allowing the operating frequency to vary as the coupling efficiency varies. In this system, the frequency is allowed to swing between 51.8 and 52.3 MHz as the load changes in order to keep the dissipated power constant within 0.5%. The plasma in part determines the frequency and is to be regarded as an "active" circuit element. In the system described by Scott et al.,[78] the frequency of operation is crystal controlled (27.12 MHz), and the plasma therefore acts as a "passive" circuit element. The relative merits of these two systems with regard, for instance, to the power transfer stability and the resulting nature and magnitude of interferences (particularly excitation interferences) have yet to be determined. Thus, the method of plasma generation and the plasma configuration are important parameters in the analytical application of inductively coupled plasmas.

F. Various Plasma Systems for the Analysis of Solutions: Operating Parameters and Performance

A comparison of the various plasma systems and operating parameters when used as emission sources for the analysis of solutions is given in Table 16 (see Figures 17 to 24). The analytical performance in terms of detection limits obtained by the various systems is given in Table 17. It is noted that use of the annular plasma combined with an ultrasonic nebulization technique[75] produced the lowest detection limits. For comparison, the best of the detection limits reported in the literature for flame emission, atomic absorption, and fluorescence are listed (from References 85 and 86).

Inductively coupled plasmas have been shown to be less sensitive to chemical interferences than flames.[70,73,79,88] In Figure 25, the results obtained by Greenfield[70] for the well-known phosphate and aluminum interferences on calcium are shown. It is noted that in the case of the inductively coupled plasma, little or no depression of the calcium signal occurred with increasing phosphate or aluminum concentration. The corresponding interferences in the case of the air-acetylene flame are shown for comparison.

The inductively coupled plasma does suffer from ionization interferences due to the large amount of thermal energy available. Because of the high temperature of these plasmas compared to ordinary combustion flames, a higher degree of ionization exists in the case of elements with low ionization potential. Thus, the ionization

TABLE 16

Various Plasma Systems

Authors	Ref.	Torch Design	Frequency. MHz	Power kW	Coolant Gas	Coolant Gas Flow Rate l/min	Plasma Gas
Greenfield et al.	70	Fig.17	36	1.5	Ar	17	Ar
Wendt and Fassel	71	Fig. 18	3.4	5	Ar	22	Ar
Hoare and Mostyn	79	Fig. 19	36	2.5	Ar	18	Ar
Fassel and Dickinson	74	Similar to Fig. 17 except inverted	30	2.5	Ar	17	Ar
Veillon and Margoshes	73	Fig. 20	4.8	5 (max)	Ar	30	Ar
Mermet and Robin	80	–	1.6	5	Ar	20	No flow
Greenfield et al.	81	Same as Fig. 17 except inverted	7	5.5	N_2	64	Ar
Souilliart and Robin	82	Fig. 21	5.4	6.6 (max)	Ar	20	Ar
Boumans and De Boer	75–77, 89	Fig. 22	52	2 (max)	Ar	15	No flow
Scott et al.	78	Fig. 23	27.12	1	Ar	10	No flow
Kleinmann and Svoboda	93	Fig. 24	40	0.2	Ar	3.5	No flow

*Temperature was calculated from measured degree of ionization of test element.
**Temperature was calculated by two line method using Abel inversion technique.
[1] These values are considered erroneously high (Ref. 87).

equilibrium is more sensitive to the electron concentration, and, consequently, the presence of easily ionizable concomitants will shift this equilibrium. The above effect can be removed or considerably reduced by the addition of an ionization buffer to the solution.

G. Use of Inductively Coupled Plasmas for the Direct Analysis of Powders

Although the introduction of powders directly into the plasma has been the subject of study in other fields,[68] the application as a spectrochemical source has received relatively little attention. Hoare and Mostyn[79] and Dagnall et al.[83] have studied this application. A schematic diagram of the plasma torch and powder injection assembly used by Hoare and Mostyn is shown in Figure 19. Dagnall et al. studied the use of a swirl cup as well as a fluidized bed chamber to produce the powder cloud. Schematic diagrams of these two systems are shown in Figure 26.

The problem in direct powder analysis is twofold. Firstly a representative cloud of particles has to be produced, and secondly this cloud has to be carried by a flow of gas into the plasma for atomization and excitation. A representative cloud is not easy to obtain since particle segregation by size and mass may occur in the various systems used. These segregation effects have not been studied in any detail using the plasma as excitation source. On the second point, it has been clearly ascertained that the excitation of solids is a less efficient process than the excitation of an aerosol

TABLE 16 (Continued)

Plasma Gas Flow Rate l/min	Method of Aerosol Production	Carrier Gas	Carrier Gas Flow Rate l/min	Solution Uptake Rate ml/min	Measured Plasma Tailflame Temperature (K)	Measured Max. Temp. (K)
5	Pneumatic	Ar	–	2.5	8,000*	12,000–15,000*[1]
0.4	Ultrasonic	Ar	0.5	0.12	–	–
3	Ultrasonic	Ar	0.5	–	–	–
0.75	Ultrasonic	Ar	1.7	0.6	–	–
1.7	Pneumatic (with desolvation)	(Plasma gas used as carrier gas)		0.8	–	–
–	Pneumatic and ultrasonic	Ar	1–3	0.1 (ultrasonic)	–	–
15	Pneumatic (into heated chamber)	Ar	2–3.5	μl sampling technique	–	–
7	Ultrasonic (with desolvation)	Ar	2	–	–	–
–	Ultrasonic (with desolvation)	Ar	1–2	1.2–1.5	4,500 (from Ref. 89)	6,000 (from (Ref. 89
–	Pneumatic	Ar	1.4	3	5,000**	6,500**
–	Independent vaporization from ohmic heated graphite disc	No flow	–	μl sampling technique	–	–

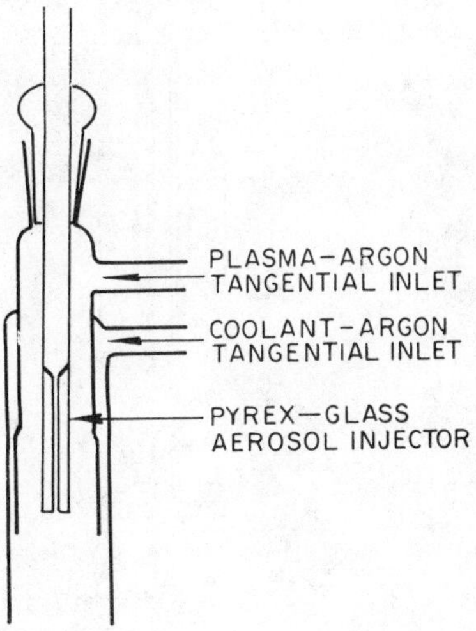

FIGURE 17. The plasma torch used by Greenfield et al.

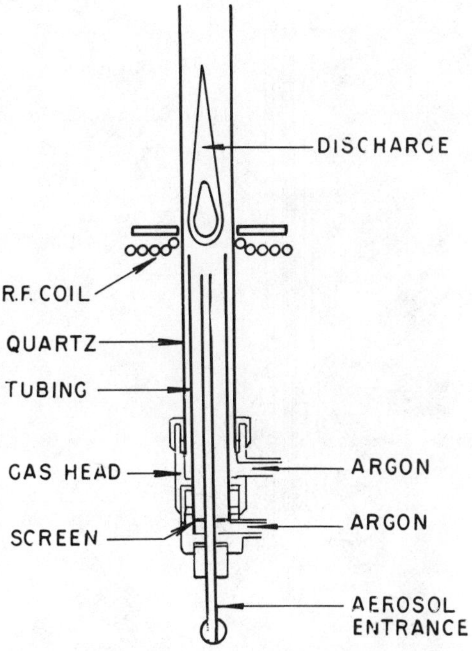

FIGURE 18. The plasma torch used by Wendt and Fassel.

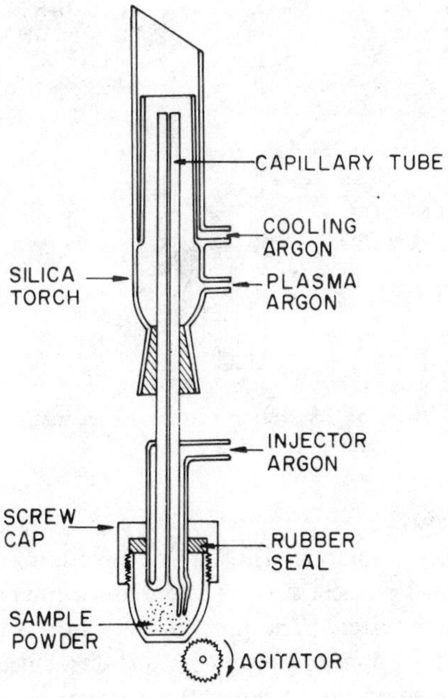

FIGURE 19. The plasma torch used by Hoare and Mostyn. The swirl cup attachment for the direct analysis of powders is also shown.

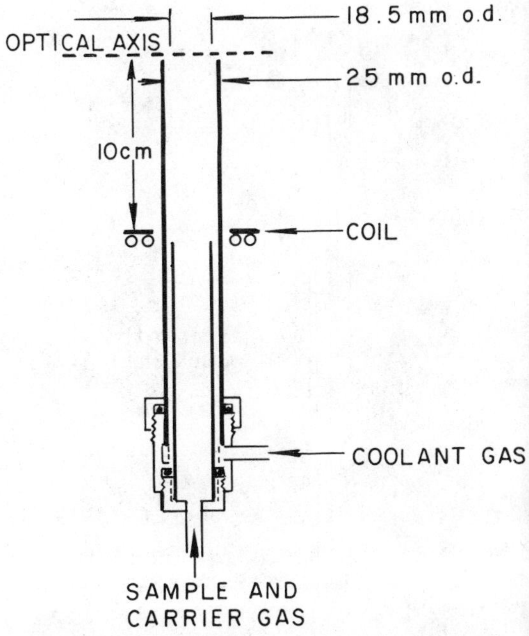

FIGURE 20. The plasma torch used by Veillon and Margoshes.

formed from nebulizing a solution (if the quantity of material consumed is related to the sensitivity of detection). This was attributed to the large difference in particle sizes between the injected powders and the dried aerosol droplets of nebulized solutions.[79] The energy transfer from

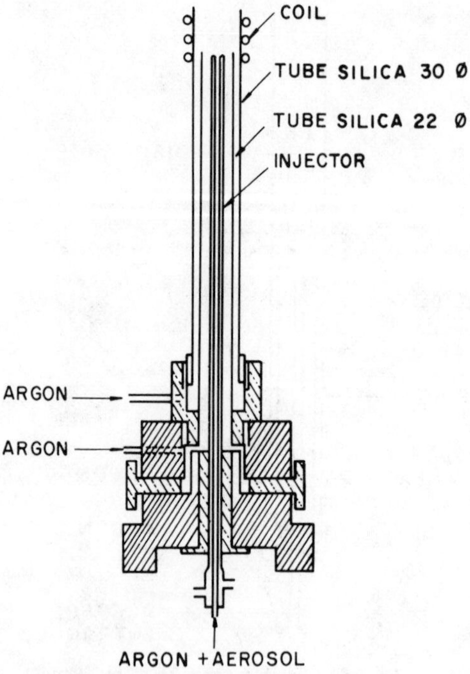

FIGURE 21. The plasma torch used by Souilliart and Robin.

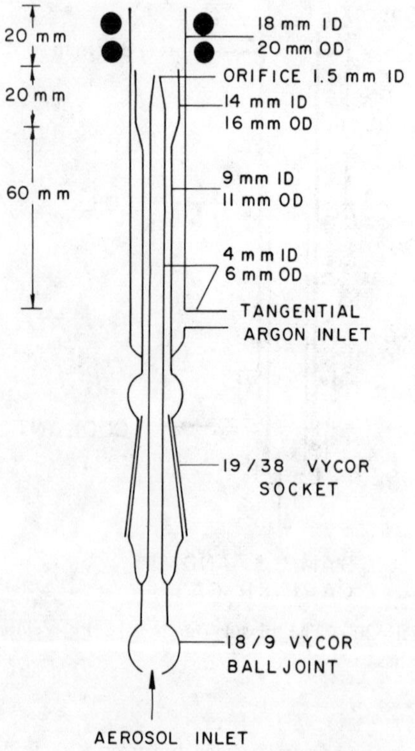

FIGURE 23. The plasma torch used by Scott et al.

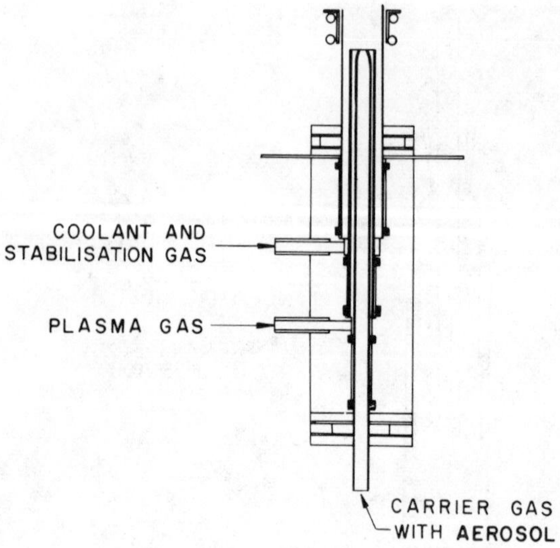

FIGURE 22. The plasma torch used by Boumans and de Boer.

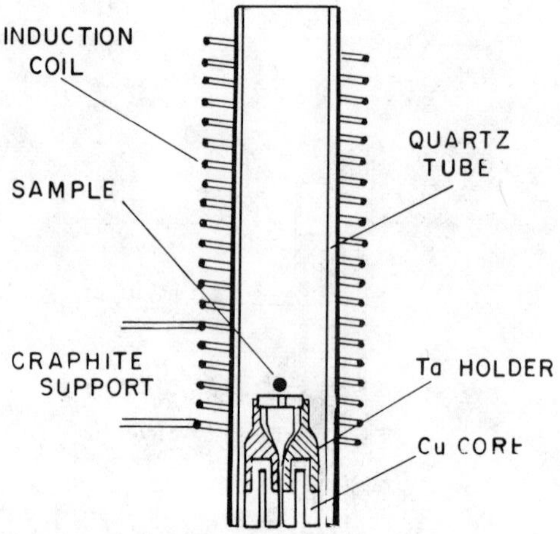

FIGURE 24. A section of the plasma torch used by Kleinmann and Svoboda.

the plasma is very low when the particles are large and nonconducting. Thus, a low injection velocity and small particle size are essential for the powder injection system. The limit of detection is of the order of 1 ppm or better for most elements and is dependent on the nature of the material.[79]

H. Advantages and Disadvantages of Inductively Coupled Plasmas as Spectroscopic Emission Sources

Advantages

1. The method is ideally suited for simultaneous multielement trace analyses.

TABLE 17
Detection Limits* ppm

Inductively Coupled Plasmas

Element	(Ref.) 70	71	73	74	75	78	79	82	93	Best of flame methods (85, 86)
Al	50	3	1	0.002	0.0002	0.001	0.02	0.03	–	0.1
As	–	25	–	0.1	0.36	–	–	–	–	0.1
B	–	–	0.5	0.03	0.08	–	–	0.03	0.5	0.05
Ba	–	–	–	0.0001	0.00002	0.0001	0.002	–	0.003	0.001
Be	–	–	–	–	0.0004	–	–	–	–	–
Ca	1	0.2	0.5	0.00002	0.0005	–	–	–	–	0.002
Cd	–	20	–	0.003	0.003	–	–	–	–	0.000001
Co	100	–	–	0.003	–	0.004	0.1	–	0.01	0.005
Cr	20	0.3	–	0.001	0.0003	0.001	0.03	–	0.0003	0.004
Cu	10	0.2	1.7	–	0.0001	–	0.01	–	–	0.001
Fe	–	3	–	0.005	0.0003	–	0.1	–	–	0.005
La	–	50	–	0.003	0.0004	–	–	–	–	0.01
Mg	5	2	–	–	0.00005	–	0.005	0.00005	–	0.0003
Mn	10	1	–	–	0.00006	–	0.05	–	0.001	0.008
Mo	–	–	0.8	–	0.0002	–	0.05	–	–	0.03
Ni	5	1	–	0.006	0.0004	0.003	0.05	–	0.003	0.003
P	–	10	–	0.1	0.07	–	–	–	–	–
Pb	–	–	–	0.008	0.002	0.01	0.3	–	–	0.01
Se	–	–	–	–	–	0.1	–	–	–	0.1
Si	–	3	–	–	–	–	–	–	–	0.1
Sn	–	50	–	–	0.03	–	1	–	–	0.03
Ta	–	16	2	0.07	–	–	–	0.03	–	4
Ti	–	–	0.4	0.003	0.0002	0.005	0.03	–	–	0.1
V	–	–	1.3	0.006	0.0002	0.002	0.5	0.001	–	0.01
Y	–	–	–	0.006	0.00006	0.0006	–	–	–	0.03
Zn	–	30	–	0.009	0.016	0.01	1	0.05	0.16	0.00004

*In aqueous solution.

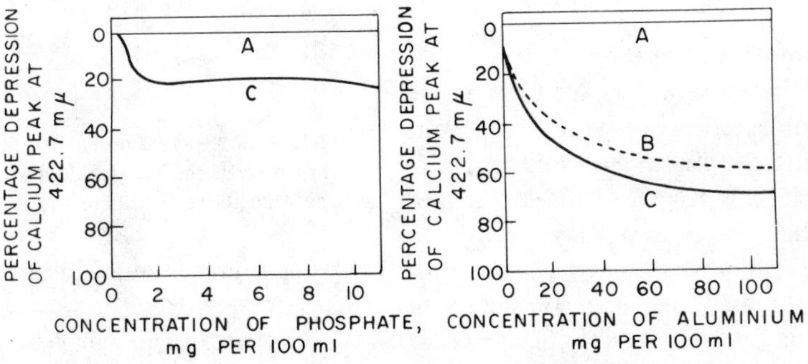

FIGURE 25. Results obtained by Greenfield et al. for phosphate and aluminum interferences on 12 ppm calcium and 30 ppm calcium respectively. Curve A, inductively coupled plasma; curve B, oxygen-rich air-acetylene flame; curve C, air-acetylene flame.

2. Choice of background spectrum. The plasma can be operated using a number of coolant gases, such as nitrogen, argon, or oxygen.[84]
3. High stability. Precisions reported for the plasma source are normally very good (generally <1%), and the use of internal standards is not necessary.[76,78,84]
4. High sensitivity. Detection limits are equal or better than other emission sources and absorption and fluorescence techniques for most elements.[88]
5. Chemical interference effects are minimal.

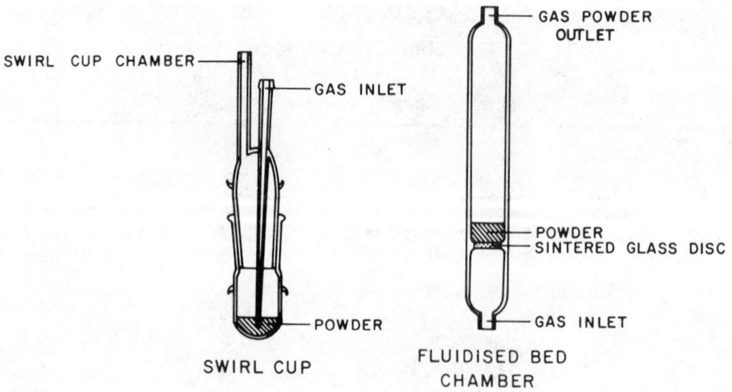

FIGURE 26. Schematic diagrams of the swirl cup and fluidized bed system for the production of powder clouds used by Dagnall et al.

6. The introduction of powders directly into the plasma is possible.
7. Cost of a plasma generator is about the same as that of a conventional arc or spark source.
8. Electrodeless operation. Therefore, there is no electrode contamination as in the case of arcs or sparks.

Disadvantages.

1. Ionization interference effects are present. These can be reduced by the addition of a buffering agent to the sample solutions.
2. Spectral background may constitute a problem.
3. The best detection limits were obtained using an ultrasonic nebulizer. Use of this device increases the complexity of the technique.

I. Atomic Absorption Investigations

The use of inductively coupled plasmas in atomic absorption spectroscopy as atom reservoirs has been investigated by a few authors.[72,73,90-92] A multiple pass system[72] and a T-shaped plasma cell[91] have been used in endeavors to increase the absorption path length. The plasma torch has also been used as an emission source for atomic absorption spectroscopy.[91] Elements for which hollow cathode lamps are difficult or impossible to construct can be excited in the plasma. Furthermore, one plasma torch is required for all the elements, whereas a separate hollow cathode lamp is normally required for each element.[91]

The advantage of using the inductively coupled plasma in atomic absorption spectroscopy is questionable since the plasma in its simplest form, as an emission source for emission spectroscopic analysis, is highly satisfactory.

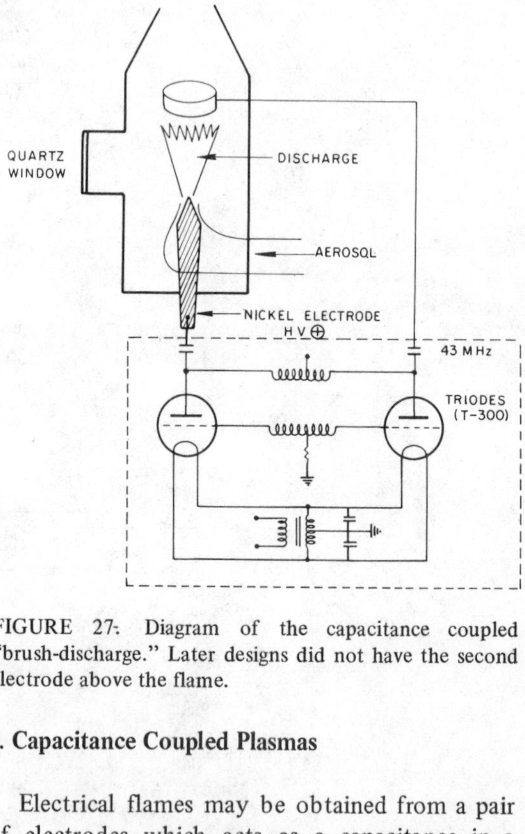

FIGURE 27. Diagram of the capacitance coupled "brush-discharge." Later designs did not have the second electrode above the flame.

J. Capacitance Coupled Plasmas

Electrical flames may be obtained from a pair of electrodes which acts as a capacitance in a tuned circuit. A typical example of this is illustrated in Figure 27.

In this design the air gap into which the aerosol is aspirated acts as the dielectric. A breakdown occurs between the two electrodes. By shaping the sample electrode to a point, a high field is created, thus enhancing the discharge from the electrode.

Two electrodes are not really necessary for this type of discharge as the ambient air is at a low enough potential in relation to the pointed electrode to enable the brush-type of discharge to take place. A typical example of this type of discharge is the Tesla coil. (They are particularly well suited to the excitation of gases at low pressures.)

Early examples of the use of the brush discharge are found in the work of Gerlach and Schweitzer,[94] Potapenko,[95] Asami and Hori,[96] and others.[97-99] Descriptions of the electrical driving circuits are also found in the early literature.[100,101] Most of these authors used vacuum-tube-driven, freely resonating oscillators operating at between 20 and 100 MHz with powers (measured as input power to the supply) of up to 500 W.

Bădărău et al.,[102] Mavrodineanu,[103-105] and West and Hume[106] have studied this type of source for analytical applications.

In the design suggested by Mavrodineanu[104] (Figure 28), the sample aerosol is introduced into the plasma via a molybdenum discharge tip, having negotiated the copper coil wound around the central electrode. Bădărău et al.[102] were among the first to apply this source to the analysis of solutions. They noted that the source gave better sensitivity for several elements than an air-acetylene flame in emission. The values obtained for the elements they investigated are given in Table 18. It would appear that these early workers did not attempt to obtain the lowest figures, as their figures compare poorly with those of West and Hume.

1. Temperature

It is clear that in this type of source thermal equilibrium conditions do not prevail.[88,104] This is seen by the difficulties experienced in atomizing samples (low gas temperature) and the high degree of excitation that exists once the atoms enter the plasma (high electron temperature). When these plasmas operate in air or with diatomic gases such as nitrogen, they come closer to thermal equilibrium. This is due to the inelastic collisions absorbing energy and this being distributed through the vibrational and rotational states of the molecules. Energy is released not only through collisional processes but also through recombination of dissociated gas species, resulting in flames with higher gas temperatures. Mavrodineanu[104] noted the difficulty of volatilizing substances with this flame, even with diatomic gases present.

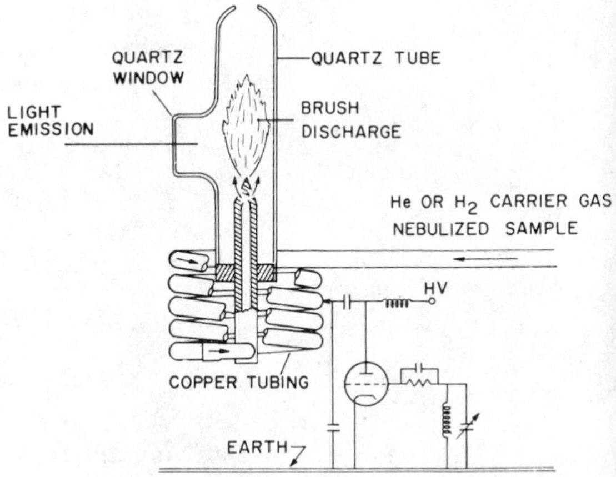

FIGURE 28. The brush discharge torch of Mavrodineanu and Hughes, with axial sample introduction.

K. Microwave Flames

Microwave sources may also be used to induce gases at atmospheric or reduced pressures to radiate light. Electrodeless discharge lamps (EDLs) are well-known as sources for atomic absorption and atomic fluorescence spectroscopy. Also as emission light sources they have been used for the determination of deuterium in hydrogen,[107] sulphur,[108] mercury,[109] and N^{15} in nitrogen and nitrous oxide.[110,111]

As sources for emission analysis at atmospheric pressure, microwave flames have been used for many different purposes even in routine analytical laboratories. The apparatus used by most authors stems from the early design of Cobine and Wilbur[112,113] and Tappe and van Calker[114] and is shown schematically in Figure 29.

A magnetron-driven microwave generator operating at a frequency of 2,450 MHz provides the power. This is one of the frequencies made available in nearly all developed countries for industrial and medical usage. A coaxial wave guide conducts the energy from the magnetron to the wave guide cavity, where it is induced into the discharge tube. The plasma discharge appears at the tip of the burner. A small tungsten electrode for initiating the discharge may be placed here. The tuning stub (wave guide tuner) is adjusted to achieve maximum power at the discharge tip and minimum reflected power on the reflected power meter, although some early workers did not measure reflected power. From the difference between input power and reflected power, it is

TABLE 18
Capacitance Coupled Electrical Flames
(a) Operating Conditions

Author	Ref.	Frequency mHz	Power W	Nebulizer	Gas	Applications
Bădărău et al.	102	43	?	Pneumatic	Ar	
Mavrodineanu	104	30		Pneumatic	He or H_2	Spectra of 75 elements recorded
West and Hume	106	27	500	Ultrasonic	N_2	Zn solution

(b) Detection Limits (As Given by the Authors) in ppm

Element	Badarau et al. (102)	West and Hume (106)
Al	90	0.02
Au	–	0.02
B	7.2	–
Ba	8.9	0.08
Be	2.3	–
Bi	–	2
Ca	–	0.005
Cd	–	0.1
Ce	930	–
Co	–	0.01
Cs	665	–
Cu	–	0.001
Fe	18.6	0.015
Hg	–	0.02
K	391	–
Li	–	0.02
Mg	–	0.005
Mn	–	0.004
Ni	–	0.01
Pb	13	0.08
Pt	–	0.1
Sn	1,187	0.2
Sr	–	0.05
Tl	–	0.07
V	204	0.015
Zn	3,268	0.1

possible to obtain a quantitative estimate of the power dissipated in the flame.

1. Sample Introduction

The sample may be introduced in various ways. An aerosol entering along the hollow (sometimes water-cooled) discharge tube enters the plasma via a molybdenum, aluminum, or tungsten tip. By using relatively low streaming velocities, it is possible to obtain relatively good mixing with the hot plasma, with no contamination from the tip. Some authors[115-117] prefer introducing the aerosol tangentially at the base of the burner tube.

As with the other plasma sources, some authors have used ultrasonic nebulization.[120] In several instances the aerosol was dried.[118,120,121] Gebhard and Horn[122] and Runnels and Gibson[123] have successfully introduced powdered samples, and Aldous et al.[119] have used a heater platinum wire loop to evaporate the samples into the tube carrying gas to the discharge.

The degree of atomization is very dependent on the power from the source reaching the flame.

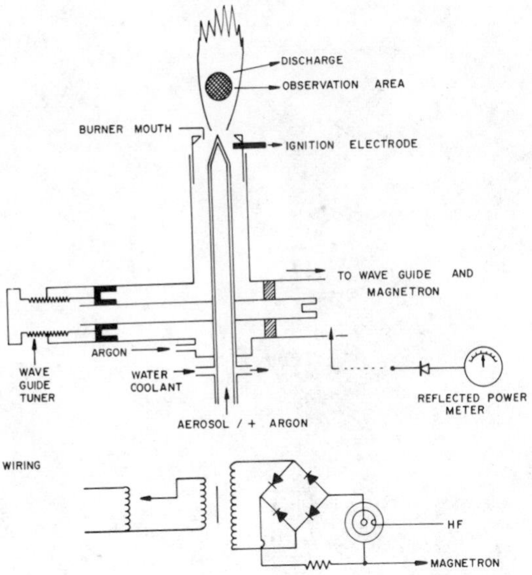

FIGURE 29. Schematic diagram of the microwave plasma torch. Sample may be introduced axially through the electrode tip or by means of the tangential gas at the base of the center electrode.

Mavrodineanu and Hughes[104] were able to melt various metals placed in a hollowed electrode tip. In this way they were able to estimate the available gas temperature. Using this source they were able to analyze some lead-tin solders quantitatively.

2. Temperature and Detection

There is some controversy in the literature about the state of thermal equilibrium and the temperatures of these flames. As with capacitive coupled plasmas, much depends on the gas. Kessler[125-127] states that his plasma is in thermal equilibrium but that 1 kW of power is the minimum. His circuit design is given in Figure 29. At lower powers (50 to 400 W), there appears to be deviation from thermal equilibrium.[117]

In Table 19 are given some of the main parameters of various authors.

In a most incisive paper, Busch and Vickers[128] discuss the fundamental properties of microwave plasmas as spectrochemical light sources. Unfortunately, these authors used only a 100 W source at reduced pressure. However, they showed the existence of both low and high energy electron groups. The low energy electrons are responsible for the radiative temperatures.

Detection limits obtained by some authors are given in Table 20.

L. Conclusion

The impact that electrical flames have made in the field of emission spectroscopy is considerable. In general, they have greater stability than other classical light sources such as the DC arc and the spark. They also have relatively higher temperatures and operate in inert atmospheres. This makes them especially suited for the measurement in emission of those elements which form refractory species in conventional sources.

Nearly all electrical flames require the sample to be presented in an aerosol form, which may be seen as a limitation because of solution and dilution requirements. However, in instances where samples are already solutions, this is an advantage.

The power of detection for nearly all elements is at least as good as for other sources such as arcs and chemical flames. This is due partly to the control which may be exercised over all the parameters giving stable emission and partly to the low backgrounds.

Many electrical flames, especially the high frequency types, are in their infancy. It is expected that considerable development will take place within the next few years in the production of less expensive and more easily operated units.

TABLE 19
Some Parameters of Microwave Discharges Used by Various Authors

Author	Ref.	Power W	Carrier Gas	Nebulizer*	Supply to Flame**	Temp. K	Applications
Mavrodineanu and Hughes	104	2,000	H_2	Pn and solid	Axial	2,300	Solder analysis
			He			1,400	
Goto et al.	115	~800	N_2	Pn	Tan.	N.D.	Detection limits
Yamamato and Murayama	116	200(520 MHz)	Ar	Pn	Tan.	8,130	Detection limits
Murayama et al.	117	400	Ar	Pn	Tan.	6,400	Detection limits
Hingle et al.	118	200	Ar	Pn (heated)	Axial	N.D.	Detection limits
Aldous et al.	119	35	Ar	solid	Axial	N.D.	Detection of small quantities
Kawaguchi et al.	120	50	Ar	Ul dry	Axial	2,150 (OH)	Detection limits
			Ar			5,650 (Cu)	
Fallgatter et al.	121	200–400	Ar	Pn dry	90°	1,440 (rot.)	
						6,560 (Ar)	
Kessler	127	→1,000	N_2	Pn	Axial	8,000(OH)	Detection limit and dolomite anal.
Busch and Vickers	128	→ 100	Ar	Pn	N.S.	3,300 (Ar)	
			He	Pn	N.S.	5,200 (He)	

*Pn – Pneumatic
Ul – Ultrasonic
dry – Aerosol heated and dried
N.D. – Not determined
N.S. – Not stated

**Axial – Where the sample is introduced in the center electrode or in the center of the discharge.
Tan. – Where the sample is introduced with a tangential gas supply into the outer tube.
90° – Where the sample is introduced at right angles to the discharge.

TABLE 20
Best Detection Limits (As Given by the Authors) in ppm for Microwave Flames

Element	References: 115	116	117	118	119	120	127	127 (+ 1,000 ppm Na)
Ag						0.005		
Al		0.5	0.025			1	0.2	0.1
As			4	1	0.35			
Au			0.07					
B			0.03		1		0.1	0.1
Ba			1					
Be					1			
Bi	250		5			1		
C							100	120
Ca	0.7	0.005	0.003	0.02		0.01	0.2	0.01
Cd			0.5	0.04	0.002			
Ce							46	1.5
Co						1	1	0.5
Cr							0.4	0.1
Cu				0.4	1	0.1		
Fe				1	2.5	1	0.3	0.2
Ga			0.15					
Ge			1.5					
Hg			0.04	0.001	0.13			
I					10			
In			0.3			0.1		
Li								
Mg				0.1		0.5	0.2	0.04
Mn		0.5	0.15					
Mo			0.45				1.5	1
Na				0.02			0.1	
Ni		0.5	0.3				0.7	0.3
Pb	30				1	0.1		
Pd			0.4					
Pt			0.3					
Rh			0.05					
Sb			0.6	0.1	4.6	0.1		
Se				10	3.2			
Si			0.2					
Sn	250			4		1		
Te			1	0.2				
Th								
Ti						0.1		
V		0.8	0.1				0.3	0.1
W			1.5					
Zn	15	0.2	0.1	0.05	0.67	0.01		
Zr			15				2	1

REFERENCES

1. Gerdien, H. and Lotz, A., *Z. Tech. Physik,* 4, 157, 1923.
2. Weiss, R., *Z. Physik,* 138, 170, 1954.
3. Peters, R., *Naturwissenschaften,* 41, 571, 1954.
4. Giannini, G. M., *Sci. Am.,* 197, 80, 1957.
5. Greenfield, S., *Metron,* 3, 224, 1971.
6. Gegus, E., *Proc. XIV Coll. Spectrosc. Int.,* p. 269, 1967.

7. Fassel, V. A., *Proc. XIV Coll. Spectrosc. Int.*, p. 63, 1971.
8. Margoshes, M. and Scribner, B. F., *Spectrochim. Acta*, 15, 138, 1959.
9. Korolev, V. V. and Vainshtein, E. E., *Zh. Anal. Chim.*, 14, 658, 1959.
10. Korolev, V. V. and Vainshtein, E. E., *Zh. Anal. Chim.*, 15, 686, 1960.
11. Owen, L. E., *Appl. Spectrosc.*, 15, 150, 1961.
12. Osborn, A. B., *J. Sci. Instrum.*, 36, 317, 1959.
13. Scribner, B. F. and Margoshes, M., *Proc. IX Coll. Spectrosc. Int.*, p. 309, 1961.
14. Mitteldorf, A. J. and Landon, D. O., *Spex Speaker*, Vol. 8, No. 1, 1963.
15. Yamamoto, M., *Jap. J. Appl. Phys.*, 2, 410, 1963.
16. Goto, H. and Atsuya, I., *Fres. Z. Anal. Chem.*, 225, 121, 1967.
17. Kranz, E., *Proc. XIV Coll. Spectrosc. Int.*, p. 697, 1967.
18. Kranz, E., *Emissionspektroskopie*, Ritschl, R. and Holdt, G., Eds., Akademie-Verlag, Berlin, 1964, 160.
19. Valente, S. E. and Schrenk, W. G., *Appl. Spectrosc.*, 24, 197, 1970.
20. Elliot, W. G., *Am. Lab.*, 3, 45, 1971.
21. Sirois, E. H., *Anal. Chem.*, 36, 2389, 1964.
22. Sirois, E. H., *Anal. Chem.*, 36, 2394, 1964.
23. Serin, P. A. and Ashton, K. H., *Appl. Spectrosc.*, 18, 166, 1964.
24. Owen, L. E., *Dev. Appl. Spectrosc.*, 1, 143, 1962.
25. Lerner, R., *Spectrochim. Acta*, 20, 1619, 1964.
26. Boyd, I. H., M.Sc. thesis, University of Cape Town, 1970.
27. Hoffmann, E. and Holdt, G., *Can. Spectrosc.*, 12, 10, 1967.
28. Veillon, C. and Margoshes, M., *Spectrochim. Acta*, 23B, 553, 1968.
29. Uny, G., N'Guea, J., Tardif, J. P., and Spitz, J., *Spectrochim. Acta*, 26B, 151, 1971.
30. Kleinmann, I. and Svoboda, V., *Proc. XVII CSI*, p. 118, 1973.
31. Boumans, P. W. J. M., *Theory of Spectrochemical Excitation*, Hilger and Watts, London, 1966.
32. Korolev, F. A. and Kvaratskheli, Iu. K., *Opt. Spectrosc.*, 10, 200, 1961.
33. Frisch, M. S. and Startsev, G. P., *Opt. Spectrosc.*, 16, 396, 1964.
34. Yudelevich, I. G. and Cherevko, A. S., *Zh. Prikl. Spektrosk.*, 14, 597, 1971.
35. Mermet, J. M. and Robin, J. P., *Rev. Int. Htes Temp. Refract.*, 10, 133, 1973.
36. Golubovskaya, S. M., Golubovskii, Yu.B., and Kagan, Yu.M., *Opt. Spectrosc.*, 28, 122, 1970.
37. Bykhovskii, D. G., Golubovskaya, S. M., Golubovskii, Yu.B., and Kagan, Yu.M., *Opt. Spectrosc.*, 30, 450, 1971.
38. Schirrmeister, H., *Spectrochim. Acta*, 23B, 709, 1968.
39. Schirrmeister, H., *Spectrochim. Acta*, 24B, 1, 1969.
40. Bögershausen, W. and Consée, O., *Spectrochim. Acta*, 25B, 289, 1970.
41. Kaiser, H., Laqua, K., and Schrirrmeister, H., *Proc. XII CSI*, p. 31, 1965.
42. Schirrmeister, H., *Proc. XIV CSI*, p. 729, 1967.
43. Muntz, J. H., *Appl. Spectrosc.*, 21, 300, 1967.
44. Collins, A. G., *Appl. Spectrosc.*, 21, 16, 1967.
45. Collins, A. G. and Pearson, C. A., *Anal. Chem.*, 36, 787, 1964.
46. Vigler, M. S. and Failoni, J. K., *Appl. Spectrosc.*, 19, 57, 1965.
47. Drutskaya, L. V. and Shtipelman, Z. V., *Zh. Prikl. Spectrosk.*, 2, 267, 1965.
48. Fagan, A. W. and Klein, H. M., *Anal. Chem.*, 40, 2041, 1968.
49. Granovskii, E., *Zavodsk. Lab.*, 31, 962, 1965.
50. Atsuya, I. and Goto, H., *Spectrochim. Acta*, 26B, 359, 1971.
51. Heemstra, R. J., *Dev. Appl. Spectrosc.*, 9, 199, 1971.
52. Heemstra, R. J., *Appl. Spectrosc.*, 24, 568, 1970.
53. Laqua, K., Massmann, H., and Schirrmeister, H., *Proc. XIV CSI*, p. 725, 1967.
54. Malinek, M. and Massmann, H., *Can. J. Spectrosc.*, 15, 77, 1970.
55. Friend, K. E. and Diefendorfer, A. J., *Anal. Chem.*, 38, 1763, 1966.
56. Marinkovic, M. and Dimitrijevic, B., *Spectrochim. Acta*, 23B, 257, 1968.
57. Kliska, M. and Marinkovic, M., *Spectrochim. Acta*, 25B, 545, 1970.
58. Marinkovic, M., Bojovic, V., and Pesic, D., *Proc. XIV CSI*, p. 1181, 1967.
59. Marinkovic, M. and Vickers, T. J., *Appl. Spectrosc.*, 25, 319, 1971.
60. Riemann, M., *Proc. XII CSI*, p. 199, 1965.
61. Riemann, M., *Fres. Z. Anal. Chem.*, 215, 407, 1966.
62. Chapman, J. F., Dale, L. S., and Whittem, R. N., *Analyst*, 98, 529, 1973.
63. Holdt, G. and Hoffmann, E., *Fres. Z. Anal. Chem.*, 225, 114, 1967.
64. Karacki, S. S. and Corcoran, F. L., *Appl. Spectrosc.*, 27, 41, 1973.
65. Karjakin, A. V., Sawinova, E. M., Andreeva, T. P., and Vnukovskaja, G. L., *Proc. XVI CSI*, p. 307, 1971.
66. Babat, G. I., *J. Inst. Elec. Eng.* (Lond.), 94, 27, 1947.
67. Reed, T. B., *J. Appl. Phys.*, 32, 821, 1961.
68. Reed, T. B., *Intern. Sci. Technol.*, 6, 42, 1962.

69. Reed, T. B., *Proc. Natl. Electron. Conf.*, 19, 654, 1963.
70. Greenfield, S., Jones, I. L., and Berry, C. T., *Analyst*, 89, 713, 1964.
71. Wendt, R. H. and Fassel, V. A., *Anal. Chem.*, 37, 920, 1965.
72. Wendt, R. H. and Fassel, V. A., *Anal. Chem.*, 38, 337, 1966.
73. Veillon, C. and Margoshes, M., *Spectrochim. Acta*, 23B, 503, 1968.
74. Dickinson, G. W. and Fassel, V. A., *Anal. Chem.*, 41, 1021, 1969.
75. Boumans, P. W. J. M. and De Boer, F. J., *Spectrochim. Acta*, 27B, 391, 1972.
76. De Boer, F. J. and Boumans, P. W. J. M., *Florence CSI XVII*, p.107, 1972.
77. Boumans, P. W. J. M., De Boer, F. J., and De Ruiter, J. W., *Philips Tech. Rev.*, 33, 50, 1973.
78. Scott, R. H., Fassel, V. A., Kniseley, R. N., and Nixon, D. E., *Anal. Chem.*, 46, 75, 1974.
79. Hoare, H. C. and Mostyn, R. A., *Anal. Chem.*, 39, 1153, 1967.
80. Mermet, J. M. and Robin, J., *Proc. XIV Coll. Spectrosc. Int.*, Adam Hilger, London, 1968, 715.
81. Greenfield, S. and Smith, P. B., *Anal. Chim. Acta*, 59, 341, 1972.
82. Souilliart, J. C. and Robin, J. P., *Analusis*, 1, 427, 1972.
83. Dagnall, R. M., Smith, D. J., West, T. S., and Greenfield, S., *Anal. Chim. Acta*, 54, 397, 1971.
84. Greenfield, S., *Metron*, 3, 224, 1971.
85. Winefordner, J. D., Svoboda, V., and Cline, L. J., *Crit. Rev. Anal. Chem.*, p. 233, August 1970.
86. Christian, G. D. and Feldman, J. F., *Appl. Spectrosc.*, 25, 660, 1971.
87. Miller, R. C. and Ayen, R. J., *J. Appl. Phys.*, 40, 5260, 1969.
88. Fassel, V. A., Electrical flame spectroscopy, *XVI Coll. Spectrosc. Int.*, Adam Hilger, London, 1972, 63.
89. Boumans, P. W. J. M., Wagenaar, H., and De Boer, F. J., Measurements of some fundamental parameters in an HF inductively coupled argon plasma and a discussion of some matrix effects, *XVII Coll. Spectrosc. Int.*, Adam Hilger, London, 1973, 114.
90. Morrison, G. H. and Talma, Y., *Anal. Chem.*, 42, 809, 1970.
91. Greenfield, S., Smith, P. B., Breeze, A. E., and Chilton, N. M. D., *Anal. Chim. Acta*, 41, 385, 1968.
92. Bordonali, C. and Biancifiori, M. A., *Proc. XIV CSI*, p. 1153, 1968.
93. Kleinmann, I. and Svoboda, V., *Anal. Chem.*, 41, 1029, 1969.
94. Gerlach, W. and Schweitzer, E., *Z. Anorg. Allg. Chem.*, 195, 255, 1931.
95. Potapenko, G. Z., *Anorg. Allg. Chem.*, 215, 44, 1933.
96. Asami, Y. and Hori, T., *Nature*, 144, 981, 1939.
97. Korolev, F. A. and Zheenbaev, Z., *Izv. Vyssh. Uchebn. Zaved.*, 5, 134, 1959.
98. Cristescu, G. D. and Grigorovici, R., *Bull. Soc. Roum. Phys.*, 42, 3, 1941.
99. Grigorovici, R. and Cristescu, G., *Optik Spectrosk.*, 6, 85, 1959.
100. Heinrich, K., *Z. Elektrotech.*, 50, 1655, 1929.
101. Roddy, C. and Green, B., *Electron. World*, 65, 29, 1961.
102. Bădărău, E., Giurgea, M., Giurgea, G. H., and Trutia, A. T. H., *Spectrochim. Acta*, 11, 441, 1956.
103. Mavrodineanu, R. and Boiteux, H., *L'Analyse Spéctrale Quantitative par La Flamme*, Masson, Paris, 1954, 26.
104. Mavrodineanu, R. and Hughes, R. C., *Spectrochim. Acta*, 19, 1309, 1963.
105. Mavrodineanu, R. and Boiteux, H., *Flame Spectroscopy*, John Wiley & Sons, New York, 1965.
106. West, C. D. and Hume, D. N., *Anal. Chem.*, 36, 412, 1964.
107. Broida, H. P. and Moyer, J. W., *J. O. S. A.*, 42, 37, 1952.
108. Taylor, H. E., Gibson, J. H., and Skogerboe, R. K., *Anal. Chem.*, 42, 1569, 1970.
109. Lichte, F. E. and Skogerboe, R. K., *Anal. Chem.*, 44, 1321, 1972.
110. Broida, H. P. and Chapman, M. W., *Anal. Chem.*, 30, 2049, 1958.
111. Goleb, J. A. and Middleboe, V., *Anal. Chim. Acta*, 43, 229, 1968.
112. Cobine, J. D. and Wilbur, D. A., *Electronics*, p. 92, June 1951.
113. Cobine, J. D. and Wilbur, D. A., *J. Appl. Phys.*, 22, 835, 1951.
114. Tappe, W. and Van Calker, J., *Z. Anal. Chem.*, 198, 13, 1963.
115. Gotô, H., Hirokawa, K., and Suzuki, M., *Z. Anal. Chem.*, 225, 130, 1967.
116. Yamamoto, M. and Murayama, S., *Spectrochim. Acta*, 23A, 773, 1967.
117. Murayama, S., Matsuno, H., and Yamamoto, M., *Spectrochim. Acta*, 23B, 513, 1968.
118. Hingle, D. N., Kirkbright, G. F., and Baily, R. M., *Talanta*, 16, 1223, 1969.
119. Aldous, K. M., Dagnall, R. M., Sharp, B. L., and West, T. S., *Anal. Chim. Acta*, 54, 233, 1971.
120. Kawaguchi, H., Hasegawa, M., and Mizuike, A., *Spectrochim. Acta*, 27B, 205, 1972.
121. Fullgatter, K., Svoboda, V., and Winefordner, J. D., *Appl. Spectrosc.*, 25, 347, 1971.
122. Gebhard, F. and Horn, H., *XVI Coll. Spectrosc. Int.*, 2, 291, 1971.
123. Runnels, J. H. and Gibson, J. H., *Anal. Chem.*, 39, 1398, 1967.
124. Hagenah, W. D., Laqua, K., and Leiss, F., *C. S. I. XVII*, 2, 491, 1973.
125. Jecht, U. and Kessler, W., *Z. Anal. Chem.*, 198, 27, 1963.
126. Jecht, U. and Kessler, W., *Z. Phys.*, 178, 133, 1964. Publ. Adam Hilger, London.
127. Kessler, W., *Glastechs. Bericht.*, 44, 479, 1971.
128. Busch, K. W. and Vickers, T. J., *Spectrochim. Acta*, 28B, 85, 1973.

Section E

Emission Spectroscopy

Atomic Emission Spectroscopy

EMISSION SPECTROSCOPY

R. K. Skogerboe, Colorado State University

I. LIMITS OF DETECTION BY ARC AND SPARK EMISSION SPECTROMETRIC TECHNIQUES

Table 1 lists the amount of element in nanograms that must be present in the vaporization-excitation discharge indicated to produce a detectable atomic emission. The values represent limits which have been experimentally achieved under fairly idealized conditions in many instances. The limits have been presented in weight units because large differences exist in the actual amount of sample which may be utilized for the different discharges. Conversion to relative concentration units may be accomplished by dividing the weight limits given by the weight of sample generally utilized by the respective techniques. In general, the solution methods utilize 0.1 to 0.5 ml of sample, the solid spark and residue methods utilize 1 mg of sample or less, and the arc methods utilize 10 to 100 mg of sample. Each depends on the particular analytical circumstances.

The term "limit of detection" in analytical spectroscopy generally refers to the concentration or amount of an element required to produce an atomic emission signal equal to twice the magnitude of background fluctuation. In some instances, it is designated as the amount required to produce a line-to-background intensity ratio of 1:3 or 1:5. The use of the most sensitive interference-free emission wavelength for each element is implied. Obviously, there is a lack of consistency in definition and specification of the detection limit. The values given, however, should be good estimates to within an order of magnitude.

The limits designated in Table 1 for solution analysis generally refer to high voltage spark excitation using different means of presentation of the solution to the discharge. These include the porous cup, the rotating disk, and the vacuum or Teflon® cup methods. The mode of presentation producing the best limit is cited for a 0.1 ml sample volume in each case. The solid spark data also refer typically to a high voltage spark discharge involving a point-to-plane spark configuration and assuming a 1 mg sample. The residue methods primarily refer to excitation of micro deposits contained on some substrate of high purity material. These include the copper and graphite spark techniques and hollow-cathode-type discharges. The arc methods refer to continuous discharges of constant polarity and assume a 25 mg sample utilization. Finally, it should be noted that failure to include data for a particular element by any one of these techniques does not necessarily mean that the element cannot be determined by the said technique. Rather, it may imply that specialized modifications of the technique are required or that data are not readily available.

TABLE 1

Limits of Detection by Arc and Spark Emission Spectrometric Techniques

Element	Solution Methods	Solid Spark	Arc Methods	Residue Methods
Ag	2.0	3.0	0.03	0.03
Al	10.0	5.0	3.0	0.5
As	300.0	100.0	3.0	50.0
Au	2,000.0	100.0	8.0	20.0
B	5.0	2.0	0.2	0.3
Ba	5.0	20.0	25.0	10.0
Be	0.3	10.0	0.2	0.03
Bi	100.0	10.0	0.8	5.0
Ca	1.0	4.0	0.3	0.5
Cd	20.0	2.0	0.2	20.0
Ce	300.0	300.0	130.0	30.0
Co	50.0	4.0	0.1	0.3
Cr	10.0	10.0	15.0	1.0
Cs	1,500.0	–	50.0	50.0
Cu	5.0	1.0	3.0	0.03
Dy	200.0	1,000.0	20.0	20.0
Er	200.0	1,000.0	50.0	10.0
Eu	50.0	1,000.0	30.0	2.0
F	–	–	2,500.0	10.0
Fe	20.0	10.0	0.2	0.3
Ga	50.0	20.0	3.0	0.03
Gd	50.0	1,000.0	15.0	10.0
Ge	50.0	10.0	3.0	10.0
Hf	400.0	700.0	25.0	50.0
Hg	1,000.0	30.0	8.0	10.0
Ho	50.0	1,000.0	50.0	20.0
In	300.0	100.0	3.0	10.0
Ir	1,000.0	–	100.0	50.0
K	20,000.0	–	25.0	5.0
La	30.0	100.0	15.0	2.0
Li	10.0	–	15.0	0.1
Lu	50.0	1,000.0	3.0	1.0
Mg	3.0	4.0	0.3	0.03
Mn	2.0	1.0	0.8	0.03
Mo	30.0	30.0	25.0	2.0
Na	50.0	3.0	15.0	0.03
Nb	200.0	–	130.0	20.0
Nd	500.0	600.0	130.0	20.0
Ni	50.0	10.0	3.0	1.0

Element	Solution Methods	Solid Spark	Arc Methods	Residue Methods
Os	1,500.0	–	1,300.0	10.0
P	100.0	100.0	4.0	10.0
Pb	400.0	10.0	0.5	1.0
Pd	200.0	–	25.0	5.0
Pr	200.0	500.0	130.0	20.0
Pt	100.0	–	100.0	2.0
Rb	–	–	25.0	20.0
Re	500.0	–	250.0	200.0
Rh	70.0	200.0	15.0	30.0
Ru	200.0	–	10.0	10.0
S	–	100.0	8.0	–
Sb	200.0	100.0	3.0	2.0
Sc	5.0	–	15.0	0.5
Se	7,000.0	–	500.0	–
Si	100.0	8.0	10.0	1.0
Sm	300.0	500.0	75.0	20.0
Sn	200.0	10.0	3.0	5.0
Sr	6.0	40.0	25.0	5.0
Ta	200.0	–	750.0	10.0
Tb	300.0	1,000.0	50.0	100.0
Te	1,000.0	400.0	250.0	50.0
Th	1,000.0	500.0	2,500.0	20.0
Ti	10.0	30.0	25.0	2.0
Tl	300.0	10.0	0.2	20.0
Tm	200.0	100.0	15.0	5.0
U	10,000.0	–	2,500.0	100.0
V	20.0	20.0	25.0	1.0
W	300.0	500.0	250.0	10.0
Y	10.0	80.0	50.0	0.5
Yb	4.0	100.0	15.0	1.0
Zn	30.0	50.0	3.0	3.0
Zr	20.0	60.0	250.0	3.0

Based on Skogerboe, R. K. and Morrison, G. H., Trace analysis: essential aspects, in *Treatise on Analytical Chemistry*, Part 1, Vol. 9, Kolthoff, I. M. and Elving, P. J., Eds., John Wiley & Sons, New York, 1971. With permission.

II. REPORTED RELATIVE DETECTION LIMITS FOR ARC EXCITATION

While the absolute detection limits given in the previous table are indicative of what can be achieved in the general case, consideration of relative detection limits reported serves as useful supplementary information. The limits given in Table 2 are expressed in parts per million (μg/g) as determined by variations of DC arc excitation techniques. The open arc column lists data accumulated by operation of the arc in air under conditions deemed optimal for the sample type in question. The carrier distillation data refer to the technique of blending a sample with a carrier material and subsequent vaporization and excitation of the blend. Thus, selective volatilization may be combined with the use of the spectroscopic buffer to provide some degree of control over the vaporization-excitation process, thereby enhancing the sensitivity in many instances. Controlled atmospheres may be used to reduce background, change vaporization rates, and obtain a higher energy distribution in the arc column. A general indication of changes in the detection capabilities can be obtained by cross comparison of the columns. The cathode layer data refer to use of the sample electrode as the cathode rather than the anode and observation of the light emitted from the region closely adjacent to the cathode. Enhancement is typically greatest for the elements with the lowest ionization potentials. The sustaining arc data refer to the use of an AC arc. This column provides a general comparison between AC and DC arc capabilities. It should be emphasized that the results given were obtained from the general literature and reflect differences in sample types, technique, equipment, definition of detection limit, etc. The data should consequently be used only as a general indication of the relative merits of the different excitation approaches.

TABLE 2

Reported Relative Detection Limits for Arc Excitation

Element	Open Arc	Carrier Distillation	Controlled Atmospheres	Cathode Layer	Sustaining Arc
Ag	0.1	0.05	0.001	1.0	1.0
Al	0.5	1.0	0.1	–	1.0
As	10.0	10.0	0.1	3.0	–
Au	5.0	0.3	0.5	–	–
B	0.2	0.08	0.4	–	–
Ba	1.0	1.0	2.0	5.0	10.0
Be	0.1	0.1	0.005	10.0	–
Bi	0.4	0.5	0.03	0.2	–
Ca	1.0	1.0	0.01	–	2.0
Cd	0.2	0.3	0.08	–	–
Ce	10.0	300.0	5.0	–	–
Co	3.0	0.5	0.04	2.0	–
Cr	0.5	1.0	0.5	1.0	1.0
Cs	2.0	30.0	500.0*	–	–
Cu	0.1	0.3	0.1	–	–
Dy	5.0	–	2.0	–	0.8
Er	5.0	–	2.0	–	–
Eu	5.0	1.2	2.0	–	–
F	100.0	–	–	–	–
Fe	0.05	1.0	0.4	–	2
Ga	3.0	10.0	0.1	1.0	–
Gd	10.0	–	2.0	–	0.5
Ge	1.0	0.2	0.1	–	–
Hf	1.0	–	10.0	–	200.0
Hg	0.5	–	0.3	–	–

TABLE 2 (continued)

Element	Open Arc	Carrier Distillation	Controlled Atmospheres	Cathode Layer	Sustaining Arc
Ho	5.0	–	2.0	–	30.0
In	1.0	0.5	0.1	–	–
Ir	50.0	5.0	4.0	–	–
K	1.0	5.0	1,000.0*	–	3.0
La	0.5	100.0	2.0	30.0	–
Li	0.5	0.5	500.0*	–	1.0
Lu	5.0	–	2.0	–	0.1
Mg	0.01	0.5	0.1	–	1.0
Mn	0.05	0.5	0.03	–	1.0
Mo	3.0	1.0	10.0	1.0	–
Na	0.5	1.0	500.0*	–	3.0
Nb	10.0	10.0	5.0	–	30.0
Nd	20.0	–	5.0	–	–
Ni	1.0	1.0	0.1	2.0	3.0
Os	50.0	–	80.0	–	–
P	20.0	8.0	0.15	–	–
Pb	0.02	1.0	0.3	10.0	–
Pd	1.0	1.0	1.0	–	–
Pr	20.0	–	5.0	–	–
Pt	5.0	–	4.0	–	–
Rb	1.0	10.0	1,000.0*	–	–
Re	50.0	–	10.0	–	–
Rh	10.0	5.0	0.6	–	–
Ru	100.0	–	0.4	–	–
S	–	–	0.3	–	–
Sb	5.0	4.0	0.1	50.0	–
Sc	1.0	–	0.5	–	0.5
Se	20.0	–	500.0*	–	–
Si	0.5	2.0	0.4	–	10.0
Sm	20.0	3.0	5.0	–	–
Sn	1.0	0.5	0.1	5.0	–
Sr	5.0	1.0	5.0	–	–
Ta	30.0	–	–	–	60.0
Tb	50.0	–	10.0	–	2.0
Te	10.0	–	40.0	–	–
Th	100.0	–	500.0	–	–
Ti	1.0	2.0	1.0	–	–
Tl	0.05	0.3	0.3	50.0	–
Tm	5.0	–	2.0	–	0.5
U	100.0	–	500.0	–	–
V	5.0	1.0	5.0	5.0	–
W	20.0	10.0	100.0	–	–
Y	5.0	–	2.0	–	–
Yb	1.0	5.0	0.5	–	–
Zn	1.0	8.0	0.1	100.0	3.0
Zr	10.0	10.0	10.0		

*Most sensitive line not used.

From DeKalb, E. L., Kniseley, R. N., and Fassel, V. A., *Ann. N.Y. Acad. Sci.*, 137, 235, 1966. With permission.

III. RELATIVE DETECTION LIMITS FOR SPARK EXCITATION OF SOLIDS

Spark excitation refers to those excitation conditions in which the energy across the electrode gap varies regularly and rapidly, and typically, with a change in electrode polarity whenever the energy flow drops to zero. Spark excitation is reputed to be a precise technique with decreased sensitivity at least in relative terms. The sample electrodes, however, remain cooler and much less sample is consumed. Thus, heterogeneous distribution of the analytical species within the sample matrix may degrade the precision of the technique unless rotating sample techniques are used. The types of spark excitation for which detection limits are given in Table 3 have been somewhat arbitrarily grouped into three classifications. The AC arc here refers to a system using an open circuit potential of a few hundred volts which must be ignited by a high voltage spark on each half-cycle. The high voltage spark data are for those systems where the open circuit potentials are 10,000 to 20,000 V and are self-sustaining. The data for mixed discharges refer to some combination of spark and arc excitation. Generally, the data presented in this table are the reported determination limits. All limits are given in parts per million ($\mu g/g$).

TABLE 3

Relative Detection Limits for Spark Excitation of Solids

Element	AC Arc	HVAC Spark	Mixed Discharge
Ag	0.3	0.3	1.0
Al	0.5	10.0	10.0
As	30.0	10.0	10.0
Au	30.0	10.0	–
B	0.4	2.0[a]	0.2
Ba	3.0	2.0	10.0
Be	3.0	1.0[a]	1[a]
Bi	1.0	1.0	2[a]
Ca	0.5	0.4[a]	0.4[a]
Cd	1.0	1.0	0.2
Ce	100.0	30.0	40.0
Co	0.4	10.0[a]	1.0[a]
Cr	1.0	5.0[a]	2.0[a]
Cs	–	–	–
Cu	0.1	1	0.5[a]
Dy	100.0	–	–
Er	100.0	–	–
Eu	100.0	–	–
F	–	–	–
Fe	1.0	2.0	3.0[a]
Ga	–	10.0[a]	2.0[a]
Gd	100.0	–	–
Ge	–	–	1.0
Hf	–	–	70.0
Hg	3.0	50.0	–
Ho	100.0	–	–
In	10.0	–	–
Ir	–	–	–
K	–	–	–
La	10.0	100.0	–
Li	–	–	–
Lu	100.0	–	–
Mg	0.4	0.6[a]	0.5[a]
Mn	0.1	2.0[a]	0.5[a]
Mo	3.0	1,000.0	10.0
Na	50.0*	0.4[a]	0.3[a]
Nb	–	–	–
Nd	60.0	100.0	–
Ni	1.5	2.0	1.0[a]
Os	–	–	–
P	10.0	–	40.0
Pb	2.0	10.0[a]	1.0
Pd	–	–	–
Pr	100.0	50.0	–
Pt	–	–	–
Rb	–	–	–
Re	–	–	–
Rh	–	20.0	–
Ru	–	–	–
S	10.0	–	–
Sb	30.0	10.0	10.0
Sc	–	–	–
Se	–	–	–
Si	1.0	5.0[a]	0.8[a]
Sm	50.0	–	–
Sn	6.0	10.0[a]	1.0
Sr	4.0	–	–
Ta	–	–	–
Tb	100.0	–	–
Te	–	–	40.0
Th	–	50.0	–
Ti	6.0	3.0[a]	5.0[a]
Tl	10.0	10.0	1.0
Tm	10.0	–	–
U	–	–	–
V	2.0	10.0[a]	10.0[a]
W	–	–	50.0
Y	8.0	–	–
Yb	10.0	–	–
Zn	20.0	10.0[a]	5.0[a]
Zr	50.0	6.0[a]	10.0[a]

[a]Detection limit.
*Most sensitive line not used.

From DeKalb, E. L., Kniseley, R. N., and Fassel, V. A., *Ann. N.Y. Acad. Sci.*, 137, 235, 1966. With permission.

IV. DETECTION LIMITS FOR LIQUID SAMPLES(μg/ml)

Analysis of solution samples is often desirable because dissolution destroys the chemical and physical history of the material, which may be a source of matrix interference effects. Moreover, standards are readily prepared, and preconcentration of analytical species is possible. Several techniques have been developed for the excitation of solution samples, some of which may be used for solutions which are 10% dissolved solids. In the porous cup method, the solution is placed in the electrode and a spark discharge initiated to the bottom of the electrode. The electrode floor becomes porous, and the solution seeps through into the excitation column. A circular graphite disk, the bottom half of which is immersed in the analytical solution, may be rotated on a horizontal shaft to carry a film of solution into the spark column struck between a counter electrode and the rotating disk electrode. Other procedures such as the vacuum cup electrode may be used. Atomic emission and absorption measurements are usually made by nebulizing the solution into a flame. The same is true of the plasma jet system, where the excitation medium is a gas stabilized DC arc capable of reaching unusually high excitation temperatures. The limits given in Table 4 are in μg/ml.

TABLE 4

Detection Limits for Liquid Samples

Element	Porous Cup	Rotating Disk	Flame Emission	Atomic Absorption	Plasma Jet
Ag	0.02	0.1	0.3	0.02	–
Al	0.3	0.3	0.2	0.5	0.1
As	3.0	–	290.0	1.0	–
Au	20.0	–	15.0	0.1	–
B	0.1	–	250.0	–	0.05
Ba	0.1	0.05	0.03	0.9	–
Be	0.003	–	7.6	0.05	–
Bi	1.0	2.5	410.0	0.2	–
Ca	0.01	–	0.005	0.01	0.5
Cd	0.2	0.3	33.0	0.01	–
Ce	3.0	–	10.0	>10,000.0	–
Co	0.5	–	1.3	0.15	–
Cr	0.1	0.5	0.1	0.01	0.1
Cs	15.0	–	8.4	0.05	–
Cu	0.05	–	0.005	0.005	0.14
Dy	2.0	–	0.1	0.5	–
Er	2.0	–	0.3	1.0	–
Eu	0.5	–	0.0025	0.4	–
F	–	–	–	–	–
Fe	0.2	0.3	0.14	0.05	0.14
Ga	0.5	–	0.07	1.0	–
Gd	0.5	–	2.0	–	–
Ge	0.5	–	4.5	3.0	–
Hf	4.0	–	75.0	–	–
Hg	10.0	–	100.0	0.5	–
Ho	0.5	–	0.1	2.5	–
In	3.0	–	0.03	0.1	–
Ir	10.0	–	110.0	–	–
K	200.0	–	0.003	0.005	–
La	0.3	–	1.0	–	–
Li	0.1	–	0.000003	0.004	–
Lu	0.5	–	0.2	53.0	–

TABLE 4 (continued)

Element	Porous Cup	Rotating Disk	Flame Emission	Atomic Absorption	Plasma Jet
Mg	0.003	0.005	0.2	0.003	0.01
Mn	0.02	0.1	0.03	0.01	0.03
Mo	0.3	–	0.03	0.2	–
Na	35.0	–	0.0001	0.005	0.46
Nb	2.0	–	1.0	26.0	–
Nd	5.0	–	1.0	38.0	–
Ni	0.8	0.5	0.6	–	1.0
Os	15.0	–	10.0	–	–
P	5.0	–	–	–	1.1
Pb	4.0	5.0	3.3	0.15	–
Pd	2.0	–	1.1	1	–
Pr	2.0	–	2.0	64.0	–
Pt	1.0	–	190.0	0.5	–
Rb	–	–	0.1	0.2	–
Re	5.0	–	1.0	5.0	–
Rh	0.7	–	0.3	0.3	–
Ru	2.0	–	0.3	–	–
S	–	–	–	–	–
Sb	2.0	2.5	92.0	0.2	–
Sc	0.05	–	0.07	1.1	–
Se	70.0	–	–	–	–
Si	1.0	–	74.0	12.0	–
Sm	3.0	–	0.6	14.0	–
Sn	2.0	–	3.5	2.0	10.0
Sr	0.06	–	0.004	0.02	–
Ta	2.0	–	20.0	–	–
Tb	3.0	–	1.0	26.0	–
Te	10.0	–	1,400.0	0.5	–
Th	10.0	–	150.0	–	–
Ti	0.1	–	0.5	2.0	–
Tl	3.0	–	0.09	0.2	–
Tm	3.0	–	0.3	0.1	–
U	100.0	–	10.0	–	–
V	0.2	0.25	0.3	0.6	0.2
W	3.0	–	4.0	5.0	–
Y	0.1	–	0.3	13.0	–
Yb	0.04	–	0.05	0.2	–
Zn	4.0	5.0	1,500.0	0.005	0.3
Zr	0.2	0.25	50.0	–	–

From DeKalb, E. L., Kniseley, R. N., and Fassel, V. A., *Ann. N.Y. Acad. Sci.*, 137, 235, 1966. With permission.

V. DETECTION LIMITS FOR MICRO OR RESIDUE SAMPLES (ng)

The results presented in Table 5 refer to analysis of unusually small amounts of material. A residue obtained from a preconcentration or enrichment procedure may, for example, be deposited on the spectrographic electrode for analysis. Often, unique spectral techniques may be employed to maximize the total amount of radiation collected by the spectrometer. The methods listed below are those which have gained reasonably broad acceptance. The cathode layer method previously described utilizes a DC arc as does the reduced atmosphere excitation system. The latter takes place in an enclosed chamber-argon atmosphere system at intermediate pressure. A spectroscopic buffer is used in conjunction with cathode excitation. The copper or graphite spark data were accumulated with a high voltage spark discharge with the sample residue deposited on either copper or graphite electrode surfaces. The hollow cathode results were obtained by placement of the sample in a cathode of high purity from which it was vaporized and excited by a glow discharge in an inert atmosphere at low pressure. The discharge may be produced by a several hundred volt potential drop between the anode and the cathode.

TABLE 5

Detection Limits for Micro or Residue Samples

Element	Cathode Layer	Copper or Graphite Spark	Hollow Cathode	Reduced Argon Atmosphere
Ag	0.5	0.5	0.03	–
Al	0.5	2.5	10.0	1.5
As	50.0	100.0	–	–
Au	50.0	20.0	–	–
B	5.0	0.25	1.0	–
Ba	20.0	10.0	–	–
Be	0.5	0.2	0.03	0.12
Bi	50.0	5.0	–	–
Ca	0.5	10.0	–	–
Cd	200.0	20.0	30.0	20.0
Ce	3,000.0	30.0	–	–
Co	5.0	5.0	0.3	4.0
Cr	5.0	1.0	1.0	2.0
Cs	50.0	50.0	–	–
Cu	2.0	0.5	0.03	0.4
Dy	300.0	20.0	–	–
Er	80.0	10.0	–	–
Eu	200.0	2.0	–	–
F	–	10.0	–	–
Fe	2.0	2.5	3.0	0.3
Ga	5.0	100.0	0.03	10.0
Gd	300.0	10.0	–	–
Ge	10.0	–	–	–
Hf	50.0	50.0	–	–
Hg	100.0	10.0	–	–
Ho	90.0	20.0	–	–
In	10.0	10.0	–	–
Ir	50.0	500.0	–	–
K	5.0	10.0	10.0	20.0
La	400.0	2.0	–	–
Li	0.1	0.2	0.1	1.0
Lu	30.0	1.0	–	–

TABLE 5 (continued)

Element	Cathode Layer	Copper or Graphite Spark	Hollow Cathode	Reduced Argon Atmosphere
Mg	1.0	1.0	0.03	0.2
Mn	2.0	0.25	0.03	1.3
Mo	2.0	5.0	–	1.6
Na	1.0	10.0	0.03	7.0
Nb	50.0	20.0	–	–
Nd	2,000.0	20.0	–	–
Ni	10.0	1.0	1.0	3.0
Os	10.0	–	–	–
P	500.0	10.0	30.0	30.0
Pb	10.0	5.0	10.0	1.0
Pd	5.0	50.0	–	–
Pr	900.0	20.0	–	–
Pt	5.0	2.0	–	–
Rb	20.0	20.0	–	–
Re	500.0	200.0	–	–
Rh	30.0	–	–	–
Ru	10.0	–	–	–
S	–	–	–	–
Sb	20.0	10.0	100.0	2.0
Sc	10.0	0.5	–	–
Se	–	–	–	–
Si	5.0	10.0	1.0	3.0
Sm	2,000.0	20.0	–	–
Sn	5.0	–	10.0	7.0
Sr	5.0	50.0	–	–
Ta	400.0	10.0	–	–
Tb	300.0	100.0	–	–
Te	50.0	50.0	–	–
Th	2,000.0	20.0	–	–
Ti	5.0	2.5	–	2.0
Tl	20.0	50.0	–	–
Tm	30.0	5.0	–	–
U	400.0	100.0	–	–
V	5.0	1.0	–	–
W	500.0	10.0	–	–
Y	8.0	0.5	–	–
Yb	3.0	1.0	–	–
Zn	100.0	10.0	3.0	45.0
Zr	20.0	2.5	–	–

From DeKalb, E. L., Kniseley, R. N., and Fassel, V. A., *Ann. N.Y. Acad. Sci.*, 137, 235, 1966. With permission.

VI. DETECTION LIMITS WITH THE LASER MICROPROBE (μg/g)

The laser microprobe system introduced in 1962[1] was designed specifically for micro-sampling-microanalysis problems. A laser pulse is fired through a microscope focused on the sample surface to vaporize the microsection of the sample of interest. A high voltage spark, initiated by passage of the vapor plume through an electrode gap above the sample surface, is used to provide supplementary excitation of the constituents of the vapor plume. The system is capable of vaporizing sample from a surface with a spatial resolution of a few microns. Consequently, multielement emission spectrometric analyses are carried out on a sample which may be only a few micrograms in size. Even though high absolute sensitivities are realized by this method, relative concentration detectabilities are limited by the small amount of samples vaporized. The detection limits given in Table 6 were obtained by analysis of metal alloy standards using photographic recording of the spectra. A 3 μg sample was vaporized.

TABLE 6

Detection Limits with the Laser Microprobe

Element	Detection Limit* μg/g	Element	Detection Limit* μg/g
Ag	10.0	Mn	40.0
Al	200.0	Ni	210.0
B	40.0	Pb	250.0
Be	12.0	Sb	600.0
Bi	180.0	Si	270.0
Co	>700.0	Sn	450.0
Cr	60.0	Ti	280.0
Fe	240.0	V	830.0
Ga	80.0		

*Based on vaporization of 3 μg of sample by laser pulse.

From Snetsinger, K. G. and Keil, K., *Am. Mineralogist*, 52, 1842, 1967. With permission.

[1] Brech, F., *Appl. Spectrosc.*, 16, 59, 1962.

VII. PRECONCENTRATION-SEPARATION PROCEDURES USED FOR EMISSION SPECTROMETRIC ANALYSES

While a large variety of samples can be conveniently and reliably analyzed by direct emission spectrographic procedures, there is always a need for analyses at lower concentration levels and for analyses in which the matrix and/or some interfering sample constituents are removed. Thus, a variety of preconcentration and/or separation methods have been utilized as integral parts of emission spectrometric analysis methods. In addition to accomplishing the required preconcentration separation, primary consideration must be given to contamination of the sample or loss of the analytical constituents of interest. The following condensed list summarizes the procedures that have been used in a general classification. For further descriptions and references to specific reports on these methods, the reader is referred to Mizuike, A., in *Trace Analysis: Physical Methods,* Morrison, G.H., Ed., Interscience, New York 1965 and to the references given below. If contamination and loss of analytical species are suspected, the comprehensive treatment of this topical area by Gorsuch should be consulted.

TABLE 7

Preconcentration-Separation Procedures Used for Emission Spectrometric Analyses

Amalgamation
Ashing
  Wet
  Dry
Chromatography
  Ion exchange
  Miscellaneous

Distillation
  Evaporation
  Vaporization
    of matrix
    of impurities
Electrochemical
  Reduction
  Electrolysis

Extraction
  Liquid-liquid

Fire Assay
Magnetic Methods
Precipitation
  of matrix
  of impurities
  coprecipitation

Zone Refining

REFERENCES:

1. **Pinta, M.,** *Recherche et Dosage des Éléments Traces,* Dunod, Paris, 1962, chap. II-V.
2. Separation, principles, and technics, in *Treatise on Analytical Chemistry,* Kolthoff, I. M., Elving, P. J., and Sandell, E. B., Eds., Part I, Vols. 2 and 3, Interscience, New York, 1961, chap. 22-37.
3. **Thiers, R. E.,** *Methods Biochem. Anal.,* 5, 273, 1957.
4. **Sandell, E. B.,** *Colorimetric Determination of Traces of Metals,* 2nd ed., Interscience, New York, 1950.
5. **Morrison, G. H. and Frieser, H.,** *Solvent Extraction in Analytical Chemistry,* John Wiley & Sons, New York, 1957.
6. **Gorsuch, T. T.,** *The Destruction of Organic Matter,* Pergamon Press, New York, 1970.

Condensed from Mizuike, A., in Trace Analysis: Physical Methods, Morrison, G. H., Ed., Wiley Interscience, New York, 1965. With permission.

VIII. SENSITIVE LINES FOR USE IN ATOMIC EMISSION SPECTROMETRY

Table 8 gives the most sensitive lines of the elements with the line excitation potentials, the arc and spark intensities, and the origin of the line. The table is arranged in alphabetical order by chemical symbol.

The following symbols are used in the wavelength tables:

bh	band head
d	double line
h	hazy diffuse line
IS	international primary standard
l	shaded or displaced to longer wavelength
r	narrow self-reversal
R	Wide self reversal
s	shaded or displaced to shorter wavelength
S	international secondary standard
w	wide or complex
W	very wide or complex
[ ]	discharge tube intensity
I	line classified as emitted from neutral atom
II	line classified as emitted from singly ionized atom.

For the neutral atom, the most sensitive lines are indicated by U1, U2, U3, etc. in the order of decreasing sensitivity. For the singly ionized atom, the most sensitive lines are indicated by V1, V2, V3, etc. in the order of decreasing sensitivity. If U1, U2, etc. are not given, they lie outside the 2,000 to 10,000 Å range.

TABLE 8

Sensitive Lines for Use in Atomic Emission Spectrometry

Symbol	Element	Wavelength Å	Intensity Arc	Intensity Spark	Excitation Potential (eV)	Origin
Ar	Argon	8,115.311		5,000	13.0	U2
		7,503.867		700	13.4	U4
		7,067.217		400	13.2	U3
		6,965.430		400	13.3	U3
Ag	Silver	5,465.487	1,000 R	500 R	6.0	U4
		5,209.067	1,500 R	1,000 R	6.0	U3
		3,382.891	1,000 R	700 R	3.6	U2
		3,280.683	2,000 R	1,000 R	3.8	U1
Al	Aluminum	6,243.36		100	21.0	V3
		6,231.76		30	21.0	
		3,961.527	3,000	2,000	3.1	U1
		3,944.032	2,000	1,000	3.1	U2
		3,092.713	1,000	1,000	4.0	U3
		3,082.155	800	800	4.0	U4
		2,816.179	10	100	17.7	V2
		2,669.166	3	100	10.6	V1
As	Arsenic	2,898.71	25 r	40	6.7	
		2,860.452	50 r	50	6.6	
		2,780.197	75 R	75	6.7	U5
		2,456.53	100 r	8	6.5	U4
		2,370.77	50 r	3	6.7	
		2,369.67	40 r		6.7	
		2,349.84	250 R	18	6.6	U3
		2,288.12	250 R	5	6.7	U3

TABLE 8 (continued)

Symbol	Element	Wavelength Å	Intensity Arc	Intensity Spark	Excitation Potential (eV)	Origin
Au	Gold	2,802.19		200	>13.6	
		2,675.95	250 R	100	4.6	U2
		2,427.95	400 R	100	5.1	U1
B	Boron	3,451.41	5	30	20.9	V2
		2,497.733	500	400	4.9	U1
		2,496.778	300	300	4.9	U2
Ba	Barium	5,777.665	500 R	100 R	3.8	U2
		5,535.551	1,000 R	200 R	2.2	U1
		5,519.115	200 R	60 R	3.8	U3
		5,424.616	100 R	30 R	3.8	U4
		4,934.086	400 h	400 h	7.7	V2
		4,554.042	1,000 R	200	7.9	V1
		4,130.664	50 r	60 wh	10.9	V3
		3,891.785	18	25	10.9	V4
		3,071.591	100 R	50 R	4.0	U5
		2,335.269	60 R	100 R	11.2	
		2,304.235	60 R	80 R	11.2	
Be	Beryllium	3,321.343	1,000 r	30	6.4	U2
		3,321.086	100		6.4	U3
		3,321.013	50		6.4	U4
		3,131.072	200	150	13.2	V2
		3,130.416	200	200	13.2	V1
		2,650.781	25		7.4	U5
		2,348.610	2,000 R	50	5.4	U1
Bi	Bismuth	4,722.552	1,000	100	4.0	
		3,067.716	3,000 hR	2,000 wh	4.0	U1
		2,989.029	250 wh	100 wh	5.5	
		2,938.298	300 w	300 w	6.1	
		2,897.975	500 WR	500 WR	5.6	U2
		2,809.625	200 w	100	6.3	
		2,780.521	200 w	100	5.8	
		2,276.578	100 R	40	5.4	
		2,061.70	300 R	100	6.0	
Br	Bromine	4,816.71		300	14.4	V3
		4,785.50		400	14.4	V2
		4,704.86		250	14.4	V1
C	Carbon	4,267.27		500	32.1	V2
		4,267.02		350	32.1	V3
		2,837.602		40	27.5	V5
		2,836.710		200	27.5	V4
		2,478.573	400	400	7.7	U2
		2,296.89		200	53.5	
Ca	Calcium	4,454.781	200		4.7	U2
		4,434.960	150		4.7	U3
		4,425.441	100		4.7	U4
		4,226.728	500 R	50 W	2.9	U1

TABLE 8 (continued)

Symbol	Element	Wavelength Å	Intensity Arc	Intensity Spark	Excitation Potential (eV)	Origin
		3,968.468	500 R	500 R	9.2	V2
		3,933.666	600 R	600 R	9.2	V1
		3,179.332	100	400 w	13.1	V3
		3,158.869	100	300 w	13.1	V4
Cd	Cadmium	6,438.4696	2,000	1,000	7.3	
		3,610.510	1,000	500	7.3	
		3,466.201	1,000	500	7.3	
		3,403.653	800	500 h	7.3	
		3,261.057	300	300	3.8	
		2,748.58	5	200	19.2	
		2,573.09	3	150	19.2	
		2,312.84	1	200	20.1	
		2,288.018	1,500 R	300 R	5.4	U1
		2,265.017	25 d	300	14.4	V2
		2,144.382	50	200 R	14.7	V1
Ce	Cerium	4,186.599	80	25	>8.6	
		4,165.606	40	6	>8.6	
		4,040.762	70	5	>8.7	
		4,012.388	60	20	>8.7	
Cl	Chlorine	4,819.46		200	28.3	V4
		4,810.06		200	28.3	V3
		4,794.54		250	28.3	V2
Co	Cobalt	3,529.813	1,000 R	30	4.0	U3
		3,465.800	2,000 R	25	3.6	U2
		3,453.505	3,000 R	200	4.0	U1
		3,405.120	2,000 R	150	4.0	
		2,519.822	40	200	14.7	
		2,388.918	10	35	14.1	
		2,378.622	25	50 w	14.1	
		2,363.787	25	50	14.2	
		2,307.857	25	50 w	14.3	
		2,286.156	40	300 l	14.3	V1
Cr	Chromium	5,208.436	500 R	100	3.3	U4
		5,206.039	500 R	200	3.3	U5
		5,204.518	400 R	100	3.3	U6
		4,289.721	3,000 R	800 r	2.9	U3
		4,274.803	4,000 R	800 r	2.9	U2
		4,254.346	5,000 R	1,000	2.9	U1
		2,860.934	60	100	12.5	V5
		2,855.676	60	200 wh	12.5	V4
		2,849.838	80	150 r	12.6	V3
		2,843.252	125	400 r	12.6	V2
		2,835.633	100	400 r	12.6	V1
Cs	Cesium	8,943.50	2,000 R		1.4	U2
		8,521.10	5,000 R		1.4	U1
		4,593.177	1,000 R	50	2.7	U4
		4,555.355	2,000 R	100	2.7	U3

TABLE 8 (continued)

Symbol	Element	Wavelength Å	Intensity Arc	Intensity Spark	Excitation Potential (eV)	Origin
Cu	Copper	5,218.202	700		6.2	U3
		5,153.235	600		6.2	U4
		5,105.541	500		3.8	U5
		3,273.962	3,000 R	1,500 R	3.8	U2
		3,247.540	5,000 R	2,000 R	3.8	U1
		2,824.37	1,000	300		
		2,246.995	30	500	15.9	V3
		2,192.260	25	500 h	16.2	V2
		2,135.976	25	500 w	16.2	V1
Dy	Dysprosium	4,211.719	200	15	>2.9	
		4,167.966	50	12	>3.0	
		4,077.974	150 r	100	>3.0	
		4,045.983	150	12	>3.0	
		4,000.454	400	300	>3.1	
Er	Erbium	3,906.316	25	12	>3.2	
		3,692.652	20	12	>3.4	
		3,499.104	18	15	>3.5	
Eu	Europium	4,661.87	300 R	120		550
		4,627.22	400 R	150		650
		4,594.02	500 R	200		750
		4,205.046	200 R	50	8.6	
		4,129.737	150 R	50 R	8.6	
F	Fluorine	6,902.46		500	14.5	U3
		6,856.02		1,000	14.4	U2
		5,291.0	200 CaF			bh
Fe	Iron	3,748,264	500	200	3.4	U4
		3,745.903	150	100	3.4	U5
		3,745.564	500	500	3.4	U3
		3,737.133	1,000 r	600	3.4	U2
		3,719.935	1,000 R	700	3.3	U1
		3,581.20	1,000 R	600 R		600
		2,413.309	60	100 h	13.1	V5
		2,410.517	50	70 h	13.1	V4
		2,404.882	50	100 wh	13.0	V3
		2,395.625	50	100 wh	13.0	V2
		2,382.039	40 r	100 R	13.0	V1
Ga	Gallium	4,172.056	2,000 R	1,000 R	3.1	U1
		4,032.982	1,000 R	500 R	3.1	U2
		2,943.637	10	20 r	4.3	U3
		2,874.244	10	15 r	4.3	U4
Gd	Gadolinium	3,768.405	20	20	>3.3	
		3,646.196	200 w	150	>3.4	
Ge	Germanium	4,226.570	200	50	4.9	
		3,269.494	300	300	4.7	U3
		3,039.064	1,000	1,000	4.9	U2

TABLE 8 (continued)

Symbol	Element	Wavelength Å	Intensity Arc	Intensity Spark	Excitation Potential (eV)	Origin
		2,709.626	30	20	4.6	
		2,651.575	30	20	4.7	
		2,651.178	40	20	4.8	
H	Hydrogen	6,562.79		3,000	12.0	U2
		4,861.327		500	12.7	U3
He	Helium	5,875.618		1,000	23.0	U3
		4,685.75		300	75.3	
		3,888.646		1,000	22.9	U2
Hf	Hafnium	7,240.87	5,000	600		50
		7,237.10	8,000	1,000		80
		7,131.82	7,000	1,000		70
		7,063.82	3,000	400		20
		6,818.94	2,000	300		15
		6,789.28	1,000	100		8
		4,093.161	25	20	>7.8	
		3,134.718	80	125	>8.7	
		3,072.877	80	18	4.0	
		2,940.772	60	12	4.2	
		2,916.481	50	15	4.2	
		2,904.408	30	6	4.8	
		2,898.259	50	12	4.6	
		2,820.224	40	100	>9.2	
		2,773.357	25	60	>9.3	
		2,641.406	40	125	>9.5	
		2,516.881	35	100	>9.7	
		2,513.028	25	70	>9.7	
Hg	Mercury	5,460.753	2,000		7.7	320
		4,358.35	3,000 w	500	7.7	
		4,046.561	200	300	7.7	
		3,663.276	500	400	8.8	U5
		3,654.833		200	8.8	U4
		3,650.146	200	500	8.8	U3
		2,536.519	2,000 R	1,000 R	4.9	U2
Ho	Holmium	3,891.02	200	40	>3.2	
		3,748.17	60	40	>3.3	
		2,936.77		1,000 R	>7.4	
I	Iodine	5,464.61		900	22.7	
		5,161.188		300	22.8	
		2,062.38		900	>16.4	
In	Indium	4,511.323	5,000 R	4,000 R	3.0	U1
		4,101.773	2,000 R	1,000 R	3.0	U2
		3,258.564	500 R	300 R	4.1	U5
		3,256.090	1,500 R	600 R	4.1	U3
		3,039.356	1,000 R	500 R	4.1	U4
Ir	Iridium	3,513.645	100 h	100	3.5	U2
		3,437.015	20	15	4.4	

TABLE 8 (continued)

Symbol	Element	Wavelength Å	Intensity Arc	Intensity Spark	Excitation Potential (eV)	Origin
		3,220.780	100	30	4.2	U1
		2,924.792	25 wh	15	4.2	
		2,849.725	40 h	20 h	4.3	
		2,661.983	600 R	60		480
K	Potassium	7,698.979	5,000 R		1.6	U2
		7,664.907	9,000 R		1.6	U1
		4,047.201	400	200	3.0	U4
		4,044.140	800	400	3.1	U3
Kr	Krypton	5,870.9158		3,000	12.1	U2
		5,570.2895		2,000	12.1	U3
La	Lanthanum	6,249.929	300		2.5	U1
		5,930.648	250		2.2	U2
		5,455.146	200	1	2.4	U3
		4,123.228	500	500	8.9	V4
		4,077.340	600	400	8.9	V3
		3,949.106	1,000	800	9.1	V2
Li	Lithium	6,707.844	3,000 R	200	1.8	U1
		6,103.642	2,000 R	300	3.9	U3
		4,603.00	800		4.5	U4
		3,232.61	1,000 R	500	3.8	U2
Lu	Lutetium	4,518.57	300	40	>2.7	
		3,554.43	50	150	>6.2	
		3,472.48	50	150	>6.3	
		3,397.07	50	20 r	>6.3	
		2,911.39	100	300	>6.9	
		2,894.84	60	200	>7.0	
Mg	Magnesium	5,183.618	500 wh	300	5.1	
		5,172.699	200 wh	100 wh	5.1	
		5,167.343	100 wh	50	5.1	
		3,838.258	300	200	5.9	U2
		3,832.306	250	200	5.9	U3
		3,829.350	100 w	150	5.9	U4
		2,852.129	300 R	100 R	4.3	U1
		2,802.695	150	300	12.0	V2
		2,795.53	150	300	12.0	V1
Mn	Manganese	4,034.490	250 r	20	3.1	U3
		4,033.073	400 r	20	3.1	U2
		4,030.755	500 r	20	3.1	U1
		2,801.064	600 R	60		480
		2,798.271	800 R	80		650
		2,605.688	100 R	500 R	12.2	V3
		2,593.729	200 R	1,000 R	12.2	V2
		2,576.104	300 R	2,000 R	12.2	V1
Mo	Molybdenum	3,902.963	1,000 R	500 R	3.2	U3
		3,864.110	1,000 R	500 R	3.2	U2
		3,798.252	1,000 R	1,000 R	3.3	U1

TABLE 8 (continued)

Symbol	Element	Wavelength Å	Intensity Arc	Intensity Spark	Excitation Potential (eV)	Origin
		2,909.116	25	40 h	11.6	V5
		2,890.994	30	50 h	11.7	V4
		2,871.508	100	100 h	11.7	V3
		2,848.232	125	200 h	11.8	V2
		2,816.154	200	300 h	11.9	V1
N	Nitrogen	5,679.56		500	35.1	V2
		5,676.02		100	35.0	V4
		5,666.64		300	35.0	V3
		4,109.98		1,000	13.7	U2
		4,103.37		80	74.3	
		4,099.94		150	13.7	U3
		4,097.31		100	74.3	
Na	Sodium	5,895.923	5,000 R	500 R	2.1	U2
		5,889.953	9,000 R	1,000 R	2.1	U1
		5,688.224	300		4.3	
		5,682.657	80		4.3	
		3,302.988	300 R	150 R	3.7	U4
		3,302.323	600 R	300 R	3.7	U3
Nb	Niobium	4,137.095	100	60	3.0	U5
		4,123.810	200	125	3.0	U4
		4,100.923	300 w	200 w	3.1	U3
		4,079.729	500 w	200 w	3.1	U2
		4,058.938	1,000 w	400 w	3.2	U1
		3,225.479	150 w	800 wr	>7.6	
		3,194.977	30	300	>7.7	
		3,163.402	15	8	>7.8	
		3,130.786	100	100	>7.9	
		3,094.183	100	1,000	>8.0	V1
Nd	Neodymium	4,303.573	100	40	>2.9	
		4,177.321	15	25	>3.0	
		3,951.154	40	30	>3.1	
Ne	Neon	6,402.246		2,000	18.5	
		5,852.488		2,000	18.9	
		5,400.562		2,000	18.9	
Ni	Nickel	3,524.541	1,000 R	100 wh	3.5	
		3,515.054	1,000 R	50 h	3.6	
		3,492.956	1,000 R	100 h	3.6	U2
		3,414.765	1,000 R	50 wh	3.6	U1
		3,050.819	1,000 R			280
		2,287.084	100	500	14.8	V1
		2,270.213	100	400	14.2	V2
		2,264.457	150	400	14.3	V3
		2,253.86	100	300	14.4	V4
O	Oxygen	7,775.433		100	10.7	U4
		7,774.138		300	10.7	U3
		7,771.928		1,000	10.7	U2

TABLE 8 (continued)

Symbol	Element	Wavelength Å	Intensity Arc	Intensity Spark	Excitation Potential (eV)	Origin
Os	Osmium	4,420.468	400 R	100	2.8	
		3,267.945	400 R	30	3.8	
		3,262.290	500 R	50	4.3	
		3,058.66	500 R	500	4.0	
		2,909.061	500 R	400	4.2	U1
P	Phosphorus	2,554.93	60	20	7.1	
		2,553.28	80	20	7.1	U3
		2,535.65	100	30	7.2	U2
		2,534.01	50	20	7.2	
Pb	Lead	5,608.8		40	16.9	V2
		4,057.820	2,000 R	300 R	4.4	U1
		3,683.471	300	50	4.3	U2
		3,639.580	300	50 h	4.4	
		2,833.069	500 R	80 R	4.4	
		2,614.178	200 r	80	>4.7	
		2,203.505	50 W	5,000 R	14.7	V1
		2,169.994	1,000 R	1,000 R	5.7	
Pd	Palladium	3,634.695	2,000 R	1,000 R	4.2	U3
		3,609.548	1,000 R	700 R	4.4	
		3,516.943	1,000 R	500 R	4.5	
		3,421.24	2,000 R	1,000 R	4.6	U2
		3,404.580	2,000 R	1,000 R	4.4	U1
		2,854.581	4	500 h	16.6	
		2,658.722	20	300	16.9	
		2,505.739	3	30	17.5	
		2,498.784	4	150 h	17.2	
		2,488.921	10	30	16.3	
Pr	Praseodymium	4,225.327	50	40	>2.9	
		4,189.518	100	50	>2.9	
		4,179.422	200	40	>3.0	
		4,062.817	150	50	>3.0	
Pt	Platinum	3,064.712	2,000 R	300 R	4.0	U1
		2,997.967	1,000 R	200 r	4.2	
		2,929.794	800 R	200 w	4.2	
		2,830.295	1,000 R	600 r	4.4	
		2,659.454	2,000 R	500 R	4.6	U2
Ra	Radium	4,825.91		800	2.6	U1
		4,682.28		800	7.8	V2
		3,814.42		2,000	8.4	V1
Rb	Rubidium	7,947.60	5,000 R		1.6	U2
		7,800.227	9,000 R		1.6	U1
		4,215.556	1,000 R	300	2.9	U4
		4,201.851	2,000 R	500	2.9	U3
Re	Rhenium	4,889.17	2,000 w		2.5	U2
		3,460.47	1,000 W		3.6	U1

TABLE 8 (continued)

Symbol	Element	Wavelength Å	Intensity Arc	Spark	Excitation Potential (eV)	Origin
Rh	Rhodium	3,692.357	500 hd	150 wd	3.3	
		3,657.987	500 W	200 W	3.6	
		3,434.893	1,000 r	200 r	3.6	U1
		3,396.85	1,000 w	500	3.6	
		3,323.092	1,000	200	3.9	
Rn	Radon	7,450.00		600	8.5	U2
		7,055.42		400	8.4	U3
Ru	Ruthenium	3,596.179	30	100	3.7	U3
		3,498.942	500 R	200	3.5	U1
		3,436.737	300 R	150	3.7	U2
		2,976.586	60	200	>10.5	
		2,965.546	60	200	>10.6	
		2,945.668	60	300	>10.6	
		2,712.410	80	300	>11.0	
		2,692.065	8	200	>11.0	
		2,678.758	100	300	>11.0	
S	Sulphur	9,237.49		200	7.8	U6
		9,228.11		200	7.8	U5
		9,212.91		200	7.8	U4
		4,696.25		15	9.1	U9
		4,695.45		30	9.1	U8
		4,694.13		500	9.1	U7
Sb	Antimony	3,267.502	150	150 Wh	5.8	
		3,232.499	150	250 wh	6.1	
		2,877.915	250 W	150	5.3	
		2,598.062	200	100	5.8	
		2,528.535	300 R	200	6.1	
		2,311.469	150 R	50	5.3	
		2,175.890	300	40	5.7	U2
		2,068.38	300 R	3	6.0	U1
Sc	Scandium	4,023.688	100	25	3.1	U3
		4,020.399	50	20	3.1	U4
		3,911.810	150	30	3.2	U1
		3,907.476	125	25	3.2	U2
		3,642.785	60	50	10.0	V3
		3,630.740	50	70	10.1	V2
		3,613.836	40	70	10.1	V1
Se	Selenium	4,742.25		500	>2.6	U6
		4,739.03		800	>2.6	U5
		4,730.78		1,000	>2.6	U4
		2,062.788		800	6.3	U3
		2,039.851		1,000	6.3	U2
Si	Silicon	3,905.528	20	15 W	5.1	
		2,881.578	500	400	5.1	U1
		2,528.516	400	500	4.9	U2
		2,516.123	500	500	4.9	U3
		2,506.899	300	200	4.9	U4

TABLE 8 (continued)

Symbol	Element	Wavelength Å	Intensity Arc	Intensity Spark	Excitation Potential (eV)	Origin
Sm	Samarium	4,434.321	200	200	8.8	V2
		4,424.342	300	300	8.9	V1
		4,390.865	150	150	8.6	
Sn	Tin	4,524.741	500 wh	50	4.8	
		3,262.328	400 h	300 h	4.8	U3
		3,175.019	500 h	400 hr	4.3	
		3,034.121	200 wh	150 wh	4.3	
		3,009.147	300 h	200 h	4.3	
		2,863.327	300 R	300 R	4.3	U2
		2,839.989	300 R	300 R	4.8	U1
Sr	Strontium	4,962.263	40		4.3	U4
		4,872.493	25		4.3	U3
		4,832.075	200	8	4.3	U2
		4,607.331	1,000 R	50 R	2.7	U1
		4,305.447	40		11.6	
		4,215.524	300 r	400 W	8.6	V2
		4,077.714	400 r	500 W	8.7	V1
		3,474.887	80	50	12.2	
		3,464.57	200	200	12.2	
		3,380.711	150	200	12.2	
Ta	Tantalum	3,406.664	70 w	18 s	>3.6	
		3,318.840	125	35	>3.7	
		3,311.162	300 w	70 w	>3.7	U1
Tb	Terbium	3,874.18	200	200	>3.2	
		3,848.75	100	200	>3.2	
		3,561.74	200	200	>3.5	
		3,509.17	200	200	>3.5	
Te	Tellurium	2,769.67		30	5.8	
		2,530.70		30	5.5	
		2,385.76	600	300	5.8	U2
		2,383.25	500	300	5.8	U3
		2,142.75	600		5.8	55
Th	Thorium	4,019.137	8	8	>3.1	
		3,601.040	8	10	>3.4	
		3,538.75		50	>3.5	
		3,290.59		40 h	>7.3	
Ti	Titanium	5,007.213	200	40	3.3	
		4,999.510	200	80	3.3	
		4,991.066	200	100	3.3	
		4,981.733	300	125	3.3	U1
		3;653.496	500	200	3.4	U2
		3,642.675	300	125	3.4	
		3,635.463	200	100	3.4	
		3,383.761	70	300 R	10.4	
		3,372.800	80	400 R	10.5	V3
		3,361.213	100	600 R	10.5	V2
		3,349.035	125	800 R	11.1	V1

TABLE 8 (continued)

Symbol	Element	Wavelength Å	Intensity Arc	Intensity Spark	Excitation Potential (eV)	Origin
Tl	Thallium	5,350.46	5,000 R	2,000 R	3.3	U1
		3,775.72	3,000 R	1,000 R	3.3	U2
		3,519.24	2,000 R	1,000 R	4.5	U3
		3,229.75	2,000	800	4.8	
		2,918.32	400 R	200 R	5.2	
		2,767.87	400 R	300 R	4.5	
Tm	Thulium	3,761.917	200	120	>3.3	
		3,761.333	250	150	>3.3	
		3,462.21	200	100	>3.6	
U	Uranium	4,241.669	40	50	>2.9	
		3,672.579	8	15	>3.4	
		3,552.172	8	12	>3.5	
V	Vanadium	4,389.974	80 R	60 R	3.1	
		4,384.722	125 R	125 R	3.1	
		4,379.238	200 R	200 R	3.1	U1
		3,185.396	500 R	400 R	3.9	
		3,183.982	500 R	400 R	3.9	
		3,183.406	200 R	100 R	3.9	
		3,125.284	80	200 R	11.0	
		3,118.383	70	200 R	11.1	V4
		3,110.706	70	300 R	11.1	V3
		3,102.299	70	300 R	11.1	V2
		3,093.108	100 R	400 R	11.2	V1
W	Tungsten	4,302.108	60	60	3.2	U1
		4,294.614	50	50	3.2	U2
		4,008.753	45	45	3.4	U3
		3,613.790	10	30	>9.2	
		3,215.560	10	9	5.3	
		2,589.167	15 d	25	>10.6	
		2,397.091	18	30	>10.9	
Xe	Xenon	4,671.226		2,000	10.9	U2
		4,624.276		1,000	10.9	U3
		4,500.977		500	11.0	U4
Yb	Ytterbium	3,987.994	1,000 R	500 R	>3.1	1,900
		3,694.203	500 R	1,000 R	>3.3	3,200
		3,289.37	500 R	1,000 R	>3.8	2,600
Y	Yttrium	4,674.848	80	100	2.7	U1
		4,643.695	50	100	2.7	U2
		3,788.697	30	30	9.9	
		3,774.332	12	100	9.9	
		3,710.290	80	150	10.0	V1
		3,633.123	50	100	9.9	
		3,600.734	100	300	10.1	
		3,242.280	60	100	10.5	

TABLE 8 (continued)

Symbol	Element	Wavelength Å	Intensity Arc	Spark	Excitation Potential (eV)	Origin
Zn	Zinc	6,362.347	1,000 Wh	500	7.7	
		4,810.534	400 w	300 h	6.6	
		4,722.159	400 w	300 h	6.6	
		4,680.138	300 w	200 h	6.6	
		3,345.020	800	300	7.8	U2
		3,302.588	800	300	7.8	U3
		3,282.333	500 R	300	7.8	U4
		2,557.958	10	300	15.3	V3
		2,502.001	20	400 w	15.3	V4
		2,138.56	800 R	500	5.8	U1
		2,061.91	100	100	15.4	V2
		2,025.51	200	200	15.5	V1
Zr	Zirconium	4,772.312	100		3.2	
		4,739.478	100		3.2	
		4,710.075	60		3.3	
		4,687.803	125		3.4	U4
		3,601.193	400	15	3.6	U1
		3,572.473	60	80	10.4	V4
		3,547.682	200	12	3.5	U2
		3,519.605	100	10	3.5	U3
		3,496.210	100	100	10.5	V3
		3,438.230	250	200	10.6	V2
		3,391.975	300	400	10.7	V1

From the *M.I.T. Wavelength Tables,* The M.I.T. Press, Cambridge, Massachusetts, 1969. With permission.

IX. SENSITIVE LINES OF THE ELEMENTS ARRANGED IN ORDER OF WAVELENGTH

The wavelengths given in Table 9 are presented in order of wavelength to permit cross checking for the most obvious spectral interference problems. The symbols used are the same as those used previously.

TABLE 9

Sensitive Lines of the Elements Arranged in Order of Wavelength

Wavelength	Element		Intensity Arc	Intensity Spark	Sensitivity	Wavelength	Element		Intensity Arc	Intensity Spark	Sensitivity
9,237.49	S	I	–	[200]	U6	6,362.347	Zn	I	1,000 Wh	500	–
9,228.11	S	I	–	[200]	U5	6,249.929	La	I	300	–	U1
9,212.91	S	I	–	[200]	U4	6,243.36	Al	II	–	100	V3
8,943.50	Cs	I	2,000 R	–	U2	6,231.76	Al	II	–	30	–
8,521.10	Cs	I	5,000 R	–	U1	6,103.642	Li	I	2,000 R	800	U3
8,115.311	Ar	I	–	[5,000]	U2	5,930.648	La	I	250	–	U2
7,947.60	Rb	I	5,000 R	–	U2	5,895.923	Na	I	5,000 R	500 R	U2
7,800.227	Rb	I	9,000 R	–	U1	5,889.953	Na	I	9,000 R	1,000 R	U1
7,775.433	O	I	–	[100]	U4	5,875.618	He	I	–	[1,000]	U3
7,774.138	O	I	–	[300]	U3	5,870.9158	Kr	I	–	[3,000]	U2
7,771.928	O	I	–	[1,000]	U2	5,852.488	Ne	I	–	[2,000]	–
7,698.979	K	I	5,000 R	–	U2	5,777.665	Ba	I	500 R	100 R	U2
7,664.907	K	I	9,000 R	–	U1	5,688.224	Na	I	300	–	–
7,503.867	Ar	I	–	[700]	U4	5,682.657	Na	I	80	–	–
7,450.00	Rn	I	–	[600]	U2	5,679.56	N	II	–	[500]	V2
7,240.87	Hf	I	5,000	600	50	5,676.02	N	II	–	[100]	V4
7,237.10	Hf	I	8,000	1,000	80	5,666.64	N	II	–	[300]	V3
7,131.82	Hf	I	7,000	1,000	40	5,608.8	Pb	II	–	[40]	V2
7,067.217	Ar	I	–	[400]	U3	5,570.2895	Kr	I	–	[2,000]	U3
7,063.82	Hf	I	3,000	400	20	5,535.551	Ba	I	1,000 R	200 R	U1
7,055.42	Rn	I	–	[400]	U3	5,519.115	Ba	I	200 R	60 R	U3
6,965.430	Ar	I	–	[400]	U3	5,465.487	Ag	I	1,000 R	500 R	U4
6,902.46	F	I	–	[500]	U3	5,464.61	I	II	–	[900]	–
6,856.02	F	I	–	[1,000]	U2	5,460.753	Hg	I	2,000	–	320
6,818.94	Hf	I	2,000	300	15	5,455.146	La	I	200	1	U3
6,789.28	Hf	I	1,000	100	5	5,424.616	Ba	I	100 R	30 R	U4
6,707.844	Li	I	3,000 R	200	U1	5,400.562	Ne	I	–	[2,000]	–
6,562.79	H	I	–	[3,000]	U2	5,350.46	Tl	I	5,000 R	2,000 R	U1
6,438.4696	Cd	I	2,000	1,000	–	5,291.0	CaF	bh	200	–	–
6,402.246	Ne	I	–	[2,000]	–	5,218.202	Cu	I	700	–	U3

TABLE 9 (continued)

Wavelength	Element		Intensity Arc	Intensity Spark	Sensitivity	Wavelength	Element		Intensity Arc	Intensity Spark	Sensitivity
5,209.067	Ag	I	1,500 R	1,000 R	U3	4,739.03	Se	I	–	[800]	U5
5,208.436	Cr	I	500 R	100	U4	4,730.78	Se	I	–	[1,000]	U4
5,206.039	Cr	I	500 R	200	U5	4,722.552	Bi	I	1,000	100	–
5,204.518	Cr	I	400 R	100	U6	4,722.159	Zn	I	400 w	300 h	–
5,183.618	Mg	I	500 wh	300	–	4,710.075	Zr	I	60	–	–
5,172.699	Mg	I	200 wh	100 wh	–	4,704.86	Br	II	–	[250]	V1
5,167.343	Mg	I	100 wh	50	–	4,696.25	S	I	–	[15]	U9
5,161.188	I	II	–	[300]	–	4,695.45	S	I	–	[30]	U8
5,153.235	Cu	I	600	–	U4	4,694.13	S	I	–	[500]	U7
5,105.541	Cu	I	500	–	U5	4,687.803	Zr	I	125	–	U4
5,007.213	Ti	I	200	40	–	4,685.75	He	II	–	[300]	–
4,999.510	Ti	I	200	80	–	4,682.28	Ra	II	–	[800]	V2
4,991.066	Ti	I	200	100	–	4,680.138	Zn	I	300 w	200 h	–
4,981.733	Ti	I	300	125	U1	4,674.848	Y	I	80	100	U1
4,962.263	Sr	I	40	–	U4	4,671.226	Xe	I	–	[2,000]	U2
4,934.086	Ba	II	400 h	400 h	V2	4,661.87	Eu	I	300 R	120	550
4,889.17	Re	I	2,000 w	–	U2	4,643.695	Y	I	50	100	U2
4,872.493	Sr	I	25	–	U3	4,627.22	Eu	I	400 R	150	650
4,861.327	H	I	–	[500]	U3	4,624.276	Xe	I	–	[1,000]	U3
4,832.075	Sr	I	200	8	U2	4,607.331	Sr	I	1,000 R	50 R	U1
4,825.91	Ra	I	–	[800]	U1	4,603.00	Li	I	800	–	U4
4,819.46	Cl	II	–	[200]	V4	4,594.02	Eu	I	500	200	750
4,816.71	Br	II	–	[300]	V3	4,593.177	Cs	I	1,000 R	50	U4
4,810.534	Zn	I	400 w	300 h	–	4,555.355	Cs	I	2,000 R	100	U3
4,810.06	Cl	II	–	[200]	V3	4,554.042	Ba	II	1,000 R	200	V1
4,794.54	Cl	II	–	[250]	V2	4,524.741	Sn		500 wh	50	–
4,785.50	Br	II	–	[400]	V2	4,518.57	Lu		300	40	–
4,772.312	Zr	I	100	–	–	4,511.323	In	I	5,000 R	4,000 R	U1
4,742.25	Se	I	–	[500]	U6	4,500.977	Xe	I	–	[500]	U4
4,739.478	Zr	I	100	–	–	4,454.781	Ca	I	200	–	U2

TABLE 9 (continued)

Wavelength	Element		Intensity Arc	Intensity Spark	Sensitivity
4,434.960	Ca	I	150	–	U3
4,434.321	Sm	II	200	200	V2
4,425.441	Ca	I	100	–	U4
4,424.342	Sm	II	300	300	V1
4,420.468	Os	I	400 R	100	–
4,390.865	Sm	II	150	150	–
4,389.974	V	I	80 R	60 R	–
4,384.722	V	I	125 R	125 R	–
4,379.238	V	I	200 R	200 R	U1
4,358.35	Hg	I	3,000 w	500	–
4,305.447	Sr	II	40	–	–
4,303.573	Nd		100	40	–
4,302.108	W	I	60	60	U1
4,294.614	W	I	50	50	U2
4,289.721	Cr	I	3,000 R	800 r	U3
4,274.803	Cr	I	4,000 R	800 r	U2
4,267.27	C	II	–	500	V2
4,267.02	C	II	–	350	V3
4,254.346	Cr	I	5,000 R	1,000	U1
4,241.669	U		40	50	–
4,226.728	Ca	I	500 R	50 W	U1
4,226.570	Ge	I	200	50	–
4,225.327	Pr		50	40	–
4,215.556	Rb	I	1,000 R	300	U4
4,215.524	Sr	II	300 r	400 W	V2
4,211.719	Dy		200	15	–
4,205.046	Eu	II	200 R	50	–
4,201.851	Rb	I	2,000 R	500	U3
4,189.518	Pr		100	50	–
4,186.599	Ce	II	80	25	–

Wavelength	Element		Intensity Arc	Intensity Spark	Sensitivity
4,179.422	Pr		200	40	–
4,177.321	Nd		15	25	–
4,172.056	Ga	I	2,000 R	1,000 R	U1
4,167.966	Dy		50	12	–
4,165.606	Ce	II	40	6	–
4,137.095	Nb	I	100	60	U5
4,130.664	Ba	II	50 r	60 Wh	V3
4,129.737	Eu	II	150 R	50 R	–
4,123.810	Nb	I	200	125	U4
4,123.228	La	II	500	500	V4
4,109.98	N	I	–	[1,000]	U2
4,103.37	N	III	–	[80]	–
4,101.773	In	I	2,000 R	1,000 R	U2
4,100.923	Nb	I	300 w	200 w	U3
4,099.94	N	I	–	[150]	U3
4,097.31	N	III	–	[100]	–
4,093.161	Hf	II	25	20	–
4,079.729	Nb	I	500 w	200 w	U2
4,077.974	Dy		150 r	100	–
4,077.714	Sr	II	400 r	500 W	V1
4,077.340	La	II	600	400	V3
4,062.817	Pr		150	50	–
4,058.938	Nb	I	1,000 w	400 w	U1
4,057.820	Pb	I	2,000 R	300 R	U1
4,047.201	K	I	400	200	U4
4,046.561	Hg	I	200	300	–
4,045.983	Dy		150	12	–
4,044.140	K	I	800	400	U3
4,040.762	Ce	II	70	5	–
4,034.490	Mn	I	250 r	20	U3

TABLE 9 (continued)

Wavelength	Element		Intensity Arc	Intensity Spark	Sensitivity	Wavelength	Element		Intensity Arc	Intensity Spark	Sensitivity
4,033.073	Mn	I	400 r	20	U2	3,814.42	Ra	II	–	[2,000]	V1
4,032.982	Ga	I	1,000 R	500 R	U2	3,798.252	Mo	I	1,000 R	1,000 R	U1
4,030.755	Mn	I	500 r	20	U1	3,788.697	Y	II	30	30	–
4,023.688	Sc	I	100	25	U3	3,775.72	Tl	I	3,000 R	1,000 R	U2
4,020.399	Sc	I	50	20	U4	3,774.332	Y	II	12	100	–
4,019.137	Th		8	8	–	3,768.405	Gd		20	20	–
4,012.388	Ce	I, II	60	20	–	3,761.917	Tm		200	120	–
4,008.753	W	I	45	45	U3	3,761.333	Tm		250	150	–
4,000.454	Dy		400	300	–	3,748.264	Fe	I	500	200	U4
3,987.994	Yb		1,000 R	500 R	1,900	3,748.17	Ho		60	40	–
3,968.468	Ca	II	500 R	500 R	V2	3,745.903	Fe	I	150	100	U5
3,961.527	Al	I	3,000	2,000	U1	3,745.564	Fe	I	500	500	U3
3,951.154	Nd		40	30	–	3,737.133	Fe	I	1,000 r	600	U2
3,949.106	La	II	1,000	800	V2	3,719.935	Fe	I	1,000 R	700	U1
3,944.032	Al	I	2,000	1,000	U2	3,710.290	Y	II	80	150	V1
3,933.666	Ca	II	600 R	600 R	V1	3,694.203	Yb		500 R	1,000 R	3,200
3,911.810	Sc	I	150	30	U1	3,692.652	Er		20	12	–
3,907.476	Sc	I	125	25	U2	3,692.357	Rh	I	500 hd	150 wd	–
3,906.316	Er		25	12	–	3,683.471	Pb	I	300	50	U2
3,905.528	Si	I	20	15 W	–	3,672.579	U		8	15	–
3,902.963	Mo	I	1,000 R	500 R	U3	3,663.276	Hg	I	500	400	U5
3,891.785	Ba	II	18	25	V4	3,657.987	Rh	I	500 W	200 W	–
3,891.02	Ho		200	40	–	3,654.833	Hg	I	–	[200]	U4
3,888.646	He	I	–	[1,000]	U2	3,653.496	Ti	I	500	200	U2
3,874.18	Tb		200	200	–	3,650.146	Hg	I	200	500	U3
3,864.110	Mo	I	1,000 R	500 R	U2	3,646.196	Gd		200 w	150	–
3,848.75	Tb		100	200	–	3,642.785	Sc	II	60	50	V3
3,838.258	Mg	I	300	200	U2	3,642.675	Ti	I	300	125	–
3,832.306	Mg	I	250	200	U3	3,639.580	Pb	I	300	50 h	–
3,829.350	Mg	I	100 w	150	U4	3,635.463	Ti	I	200	100	–

TABLE 9 (continued)

Wavelength	Element		Intensity Arc	Intensity Spark	Sensitivity	Wavelength	Element		Intensity Arc	Intensity Spark	Sensitivity
3,634.695	Pd		2,000 R	1,000 R	U3	3,474.887	Sr	II	80	50	–
3,633.123	Y	II	50	100	–	3,472.48	Lu		50	150	–
3,630.740	Sc	II	50	70	V2	3,466.201	Cd	I	1,000	500	–
3,613.836	Sc	II	40	70	V1	3,465.800	Co	I	2,000 R	25	U2
3,613.790	W	II	10	30	–	3,464.57	Sr	II	200	200	–
3,610.510	Cd	I	1,000	500	–	3,462.21	Tm		200	100	–
3,609.548	Pd	I	1,000 R	700 R	–	3,460.47	Re	I	1,000 W	–	U1
3,601.193	Zr	I	400	15	U1	3,453.505	Co	I	3,000 R	200	U1
3,601.040	Th		8	10	–	3,451.41	B	II	5	30	V2
3,600.734	Y	II	100	300	–	3,438.230	Zr	II	250	200	V2
3,596.179	Ru	I	30	100	U3	3,437.015	Ir	I	20	15	–
3,581.20	Fe	I	1,000 R	600 r	600	3,436.737	Ru	I	300 R	150	U2
3,572.473	Zr	II	60	80	V4	3,434.893	Rh		1,000 R	200 r	U1
3,561.74	Tb		200	200	–	3,421.24	Pd	I	2,000 R	1,000 R	U2
3,554.43	Lu		50	150	–	3,414.765	Ni	I	1,000 R	50 wh	U1
3,552.172	U		8	12	–	3,406.664	Ta		70 w	18 s	–
3,547.682	Zr	I	200	12	U2	3,405.120	Co	I	2,000 R	150	–
3,538.75	Th		–	50	–	3,404.580	Pd	I	2,000 R	1,000 R	U1
3,529.813	Co	I	1,000 R	30	U3	3,403.653	Cd	I	800	500 h	–
3,524.541	Ni	I	1,000 R	100 wh	–	3,397.07	Lu		50	20 r	–
3,519.605	Zr	I	100	10	U3	3,396.85	Rh	I	1,000 w	500	–
3,519.24	Tl	I	2,000 R	1,000 R	U3	3,391.975	Zr	II	300	400	V1
3,516.943	Pd	I	1,000 R	500 R	–	3,383.761	Ti	II	70	300 R	–
3,515.054	Ni	I	1,000 R	50 h	–	3,382.891	Ag	I	1,000 R	700 R	U2
3,513.645	Ir	I	100 h	100	U2	3,380.711	Sr	II	150	200	–
3,509.17	Tb		200	200	–	3,372.800	Ti	II	80	400 R	V3
3,499.104	Er		18	15	–	3,361.213	Ti	II	100	600 R	V2
3,498.942	Ru	I	500 R	200	U1	3,349.035	Ti	II	125	800 R	V1
3,496.210	Zr	II	100	100	V3	3,345.020	Zn	I	800	300	U2
3,492.956	Ni	I	1,000 R	100 h	U2	3,323.092	Rh	I	1,000	200	–

TABLE 9 (continued)

Wavelength	Element	Intensity Arc	Intensity Spark	Sensitivity	Wavelength	Element	Intensity Arc	Intensity Spark	Sensitivity
3,321.343	Be I	1,000 r	30	U2	3,185.396	V I	500 R	400 R	U2
3,321.086	Be I	100	–	U3	3,183.982	V I	500 R	400 R	–
3,321.013	Be I	50	–	U4	3,183.406	V I	200 R	100 R	–
3,318.840	Ta	125	35	–	3,179.332	Ca II	100	400 w	V3
3,311.162	Ta	300 w	70 w	U1	3,175.019	Sn I	500 h	400 hr	–
3,302.988	Na I	300 R	150 R	U4	3,163.402	Nb II	15	8	–
3,302.588	Zn I	800	300	U3	3,158.869	Ca II	100	300 w	V4
3,302.323	Na I	600 R	300 R	U3	3,134.718	Hf II	80	125	–
3,290.59	Th	–	40 h	–	3,131.072	Be II	200	150	V2
3,289.37	Yb II	500 R	1,000 R	2,600	3,130.786	Cb II	100	100	–
3,282.333	Zn I	500 R	300	U4	3,130.416	Be II	200	200	V1
3,280.683	Ag I	2,000 R	1,000 R	U1	3,125.284	V II	80	200 R	–
3,273.962	Cu I	3,000 R	1,500 R	U2	3,118.383	V II	70	200 R	V4
3,269.494	Ge I	300	300	U3	3,110.706	V II	70	300 R	V3
3,267.945	Os I	400 R	30	–	3,102.299	V II	70	300 R	V2
3,267.502	Sb I	150	150 Wh	–	3,094.183	Nb II	100	1,000	V1
3,262.328	Sn I	400 h	300 h	U3	3,093.108	V II	100 R	400 R	V1
3,262.290	Os I	500 R	50	–	3,092.713	Al I	1,000	1,000	U3
3,261.057	Cd I	300	300	–	3,082.155	Al I	800	800	U4
3,258.564	In I	500 R	300 R	U5	3,072.877	Hf I	80	18	–
3,256.090	In I	1,500 R	600 R	U3	3,071.591	Ba I	100 R	50 R	U5
3,247.540	Cu I	5,000 R	2,000 R	U1	3,067.716	Bi I	3,000 hR	2,000 wh	U1
3,242.280	Y II	60	100	–	3,064.712	Pt I	2,000 R	300 R	U1
3,232.61	Li I	1,000 R	500	U2	3,058.66	Os I	500 R	500	–
3,232.499	Sb I	150	250 wh	–	3,050.819	Ni I	1,000 R	–	280
3,229.75	Tl I	2,000	800	–	3,039.356	In I	1,000 R	500 R	U4
3,225.479	Nb II	150 w	800 wr	–	3,039.064	Ge I	1,000	1,000	U2
3,220.780	Ir I	100	30	U1	3,034.121	Sn I	200 wh	150 wh	–
3,215.560	W I	10	9	–	3,009.147	Sn I	300 h	200 h	–
3,194.977	Nb II	30	300	–	2,997.967	Pt I	1,000 R	200 r	–

TABLE 9 (continued)

Wavelength	Element		Intensity		Sensitivity	Wavelength	Element		Intensity		Sensitivity
			Arc	Spark					Arc	Spark	
2,989.029	Bi	I	250 wh	100 wh	–	2,852.129	Mg	I	300 R	100 R	U1
2,976.586	Ru		60	200	–	2,849.838	Cr	II	80	150 r	V3
2,965.546	Ru		60	200	–	2,849.725	Ir	I	40 h	20 h	–
2,945.668	Ru		60	300	–	2,848.232	Mo	II	125	200 h	V2
2,943.637	Ga	I	10	20 r	U3	2,843.252	Cr	II	125	400 r	V2
2,940.772	Hf	I	60	12	–	2,839.989	Sn	I	300 R	300 R	U1
2,938.298	Bi	I	300 w	300 w	–	2,837.602	C	II	–	40	V5
2,936.77	Ho		–	1,000 R	–	2,836.710	C	II	–	200	V4
2,929.794	Pt	I	800 R	200 w	–	2,835.633	Cr	II	100	400 r	V1
2,924.792	Ir	I	25 wh	15	–	2,833.069	Pb	I	500 R	80 R	–
2,918.32	Tl	I	400 R	200 R	–	2,830.295	Pt	I	1,000 R	600 r	–
2,916.481	Hf	I	50	15	–	2,824.37	Cu	I	1,000	300	50
2,911.39	Lu		100	300	–	2,820.224	Hf	II	40	100	–
2,909.116	Mo	II	25	40 h	V5	2,816.179	Al	II	10	100	V2
2,909.061	Os	I	500 R	400	U1	2,816.154	Mo	II	200	300 h	V1
2,904.408	Hf	I	30	6	–	2,809.625	Bi	I	200 w	100	–
2,898.71	As	I	25 r	40	–	2,802.695	Mg	II	150	300	V2
2.898.259	Hf	I	50	12	–	2,802.19	Au		–	200	–
2,897.975	Bi	I	500 WR	500 WR	U2	2,801.064	Mn	I	600 R	60	480
2,894.84	Lu		60	200	–	2,798.271	Mn	I	800 R	80	650
2.890.994	Mo	II	30	50 h	V4	2,795.53	Mg	II	150	300	V1
2.881.578	Si	I	500	400	U1	2,780.521	Bi	I	200 w	100	–
2.877.915	Sb	I	250 W	150	–	2,780.197	As	I	75 R	75	U5
2.874.244	Ga	I	10	15 r	U4	2,773.357	Hf	II	25	60	–
2.871.580	Mo	II	100	100 h	V3	2,769.67	Te	I	–	[30]	–
2.863.327	Sn	I	300 R	300 R	U2	2,767.87	Tl	I	400 R	300 R	–
2.860.934	Cr	II	60	100	V5	2,748.58	Cd	II	5	200	–
2.860.452	As	I	50 r	50	–	2,712.410	Ru		80	300	–
2,855.676	Cr	II	60	200 Wh	V4	2,709.626	Ge	I	30	20	–
2,854.581	Pd	II	4	500 h	–	2,692.065	Ru		8	200	–

TABLE 9 (continued)

Wavelength	Element		Intensity Arc	Intensity Spark	Sensitivity	Wavelength	Element		Intensity Arc	Intensity Spark	Sensitivity
2,678.758	Ru		100	300	–	2,513.028	Hf	II	25	70	–
2,675.95	Au	I	250 R	100	U2	2,506.899	Si	I	300	200	U4
2,669.166	Al	II	3	100	V1	2,505.739	Pd	II	3	30	–
2,661.983	Ir	I	150	15	130	2,502.001	Zn	II	20	400 w	V4
2,659.454	Pt	I	2,000 R	500 R	U2	2,498.784	Pd	II	4	150 h	–
2,658.722	Pd	II	20	300	–	2,497.733	B	I	500	400	U1
˙2,651.575	Ge	I	30	20	–	2,496.778	B	I	300	300	U2
2,651.178	Ge	I	40	20	–	2,488.921	Pd	II	10	30	–
2,650.781	Be	I	25	–	U5	2,478.573	C	I	400	[400]	U2
2,641.406	Hf	II	40	125	–	2,456.53	As	I	100 r	8	U4
2,631.553	Al	II	–	40	–	2,437.791	Ag	II	60	500 wh	V2
2,614.178	Pb		200 r	80	–	2,427.95	Au	I	400 R	100	U1
2,605.688	Mn	II	100 R	500 R	V3	2,413.309	Fe	II	60	100 h	V5
2,598.062	Sb	I	200	100	–	2,410.517	Fe	II	50	70 h	V4
2,593.729	Mn	II	200 R	1,000 R	V2	2,404.882	Fe	II	50	100 wh	V3
2,589.167	W	II	15 d	25	–	2,397.091	W	II	18	30	–
2,576.104	Mn	II	300 R	2,000 R	V1	2,395.625	Fe	II	50	100 wh	V2
2,573.09	Cd	II	3	150	–	2,388.918	Co	II	10	35	–
2,557.958	Zn	II	10	300	V3	2,385.76	Te	I	600	[300]	U2
2,554.93	P	I	60	[20]	–	2,383.25	Te	I	500	[300]	U3
2,553.28	P	I	80	[20]	U3	2,382.039	Fe	II	40 r	100 R	V1
2,536.519	Hg	I	2,000 R	1,000 R	U2	2,378.622	Co	II	25	50 w	–
2,535.65	P	I	100	[30]	U2	2,370.77	As	I	50 r	3	–
2,534.01	P	I	50	[20]	–	2,369.67	As	I	40 r	–	–
2,530.70	Te	I	–	[30]	–	2,363.787	Co	II	25	50	–
2,528.535	Sb	I	300 R	200	–	2,349.84	As	I	250 R	18	U3
2,528.516	Si	I	400	500	U2	2,348.610	Be	I	2,000 R	50	U1
2,519.822	Co	II	40	200	–	2,335.269	Ba	II	60 R	100 R	–
2,516.881	Hf	II	35	100	–	2,312.84	Cd	II	1	200	–
2,516.123	Si	I	500	500	U3	2,311.469	Sb	I	150 R	50	–

TABLE 9 (continued)

Wavelength	Element		Intensity Arc	Intensity Spark	Sensitivity	Wavelength	Element		Intensity Arc	Intensity Spark	Sensitivity
2,307.857	Co	II	25	50 w	–	2,192.260	Cu	II	25	500 h	V2
2,304.235	Ba	II	60 R	80 R	–	2,175.890	Sb	I	300	40	U2
2,296.89	C	III	–	200	–	2,169.994	Pb	I	1,000 R	1,000 R	–
2,288.12	As	I	250 R	5	U3	2,144.382	Cd	II	50	200 R	V1
2,288.018	Cd	I	1,500 R	300 R	U1	2,142.75	Te	I	600	–	55
2,287.084	Ni	II	100	500	V1						
2,286.156	Co	II	40	300 l	V1	2,138.56	Zn	I	800 R	500	U1
2,276.578	Bi	I	100 R	40	–	2,135.976	Cu	II	25	500 w	V1
2,270.213	Ni	II	100	400	V2	2,068.38	Sb	I	300 R	3	U1
2,265.017	Cd	II	25 d	300	V2	2,062.788	Se	I	–	[800]	U3
						2,062.38	I		–	[900]	–
2,264.457	Ni	II	150	400	V3						
2,253.86	Ni	II	100	300	V4	2,061.91	Zn	II	100	100	V2
2,246.995	Cu	II	30	500	V3	2,061.70	Bi	I	300 R	100	–
2,246.412	Ag	II	25	300 hs	V3	2,039.851	Se	I	–	[1,000]	U2
2,203.505	Pd	II	50 W	5,000 R	V1	2,025.51	Zn	II	200	200	V1

From the *M.I.T. Wavelength Tables,* The M.I.T. Press, Cambridge, Massachusetts, 1969. With permission.

INTRODUCTION TO THE INDEX

Compiled by Paul T. Gilbert

Authors and subjects are indexed together. Where an author's name in a bibliography is not easy to locate by page alone, the reference numbers are given in parentheses preceded by R. Thus,

Allan, C. J. 513f, 750f (R19, 38, 69)

means that citations occur on pp. 513 and 514 and references are listed on pp. 750 and 751 under numbers 19, 38, and 69. When citations in a table are by reference number only, as on pp. 513 and 514 for Allan, the R numbers in the index will help to identify the citations at a glance. The citations in Table 3 of Section B have not been indexed.

Most compounds are named according to the system of the CRC *Handbook of Chemistry and Physics*, 54th edition, but there is a liberal inclusion of familiar synonyms.

To save space, certain commonly recurring subentries are abbreviated and, for the elements, the subentries are run together in a solid paragraph. The following are some subentries that might be sought but are listed under other names:

absorption cross section = xr. abs. coef.
detection limit = lim. detec.
electric flame, *see* capac. coup. plasma, induct. coup. plasma, microwave fl., plasma fl.
infrared spectrum = vs *or* vibr. sp. *or* vibrational spectrum
jump factor = xr. jump fac.
mass attenuation coefficient = xr. abs. coef.
optical spectral wavelengths, *see* arc sp., emis. sp., spark sp., *etc.*
photoelectron spectrum, *see* core bind. en., ip *or* ioniz. pot., vs *or* vibr. sp.
plasma, *cf.* electric flame (*above*)
sensitivity, *see* char. conc., int. emis. lines, lim. detec.
transition probability, *see* Coster-Kronig, osc. str., xr. jump fac.
wavelengths: *implicit in many subentries*

Abbreviations

arc sp. = arc spectrum, arc spectroscopy
at. abs. sp. = atomic absorption spectroscopy
at. fluor. sp. = atomic fluorescence spectroscopy
atomiz. effic. = atomization efficiency in flames
capac. coup. plasma = capacitance coupled plasma
carbon rod = carbon rod atomizer (*cf.* L'vov, Massmann)
char. conc. = characteristic concentration
core bind. en. = core binding energy, core photoelectron spectra
Coster-Kronig = Coster-Kronig transition probability
cryst. lat. = crystal lattice
detn. = determination
disch. tube = discharge tube spectrum
elec. range = electron mass range, electron stopping power
emis. sp. = emission spectral lines (wavelengths in optical region)
excit. pot. = excitation potential
fl. emis. sp. = flame emission spectroscopy
fl. sp. = flame spectrum
hol. cath. = hollow cathode spectrum
induct. coup. plasma = inductively coupled plasma
int. emis. lines = intensities of optical emission lines
intf. = interference by
ioniz. fl. = ionization in flames
ioniz. pot. = ionization potential, x-ray ionization energy
ip = ionization potential (for compounds)
laser = laser microprobe
lim. detec. = limit of detection
L'vov = L'vov furnace
Massmann = Massmann furnace
microwave fl. = microwave flame

molec. sp. = molecular spectrum
osc. str. = oscillator strength
plasma fl. = plasma flame
spark sp. = spark spectrum, spark spectroscopy
spectr. intf. = spectral interference
vibr. sp. = vibrational spectrum
vs = vibrational spectrum (for compounds)
xr. abs. coef. = x-ray absorption coefficient
xr. abs. edge = x-ray absorption edge
xr. analyzer = for use as x-ray crystal analyzer
xr. contin. = x-ray continuum intensity
xr. emis. = x-ray emission lines (wavelengths)
xr. emis. int. = intensities of x-ray emission lines
xr. fluor. yield = x-ray fluorescence yield
xr. jump fac. = x-ray jump factor

INDEX

A

B

C

D

E

F

G

H

J

K

L

M

N

O

P

Q

R

T

U

Y

Z